HEALTH, ILLNESS, AND HEALTH CARE IN CANADA

HEALTH, ILLNESS, AND HEALTH CARE IN CANADA

SECOND EDITION

B. Singh Bolaria • Harley D. Dickinson

UNIVERSITY OF SASKATCHEWAN

HARCOURT
BRACE
CANADA

Harcourt Brace & Company, Canada
Toronto Montreal Fort Worth New York Orlando
Philadelphia San Diego London Sydney Tokyo

Canadian Cataloguing in Publication Data
Main entry under title:
Health, illness, and health care in Canada

2nd ed.
Previously published under title: Sociology of health care in Canada.
Includes bibliographical references and index.
ISBN 0–7747–3198–2

1. Medical care – Canada.   I. Bolaria, B. Singh, 1936–   .
II. Dickinson, Harley D., 1951–   .
III. Title: Sociology of health care in Canada.

RA395.C3S62 1994   362.1'0971   C94–930240–6

Publisher: Heather McWhinney
Editor and Marketing Manager: Daniel J. Brooks
Developmental Editor: Joanne Close
Director of Publishing Services: Jean Davies
Editorial Manager: Marcel Chiera
Production Manager: Sue-Ann Becker
Manufacturing Co-ordinator: Denise Wake
Copy Editor: Joanne Close
Cover Design: Brett Miller
Interior Design: boyes and connolly
Composition: Ibex Graphic Communications Inc.
Printing and Binding: Best Gagné Book Manufacturers

⊖ This book was printed in Canada on acid-free paper.

1 2 3 4 5 98 97 96 95 94

Preface

Health, illness, injury, and death, and the ways we as a society experience, understand, and respond to these realities of human existence affect us all. It is not surprising, therefore, that these issues are receiving an increasing amount of sociological attention in the form of new research, journals, books, and university courses. The publication of the second edition of *Health, Illness, and Health Care in Canada* in a small way serves to confirm the coming of age of both the sociology of health and illness and the sociology of medicine and health care in Canada.

In doing this revised and enlarged second edition, we have tried to be responsive to the comments and observations of those who have used the book, both instructors and students, as well as those of reviewers. We hope we have succeeded.

Many of the chapters for this edition are new; others are revised and updated versions of chapters from the first edition. All chapters are the result of original research and analysis written for this book by leading experts in the field. In addition to comprising original articles, this edition also contains study questions and recommended readings intended to facilitate its use as a textbook and to direct readers to key readings in each area covered.

For this, the second edition, we have expanded five sections: Health Status, Health Policy, and Delivery of Health Care; Inequality and Health Care; Women, Family, and Health; Health-Care Professions and the Division of Labour; and Nurses' Education and Work. Other sections contain new chapters to reflect recent developments in medical sociology.

With this second edition we hope that we have succeeded in bringing to instructors, students, and policy makers alike an accessible and timely collection of articles on key issues facing Canadians in the areas of health, illness, and health care. We could not have done it alone. Bringing this book together depended on the kind co-operation and consideration of a multitude of people. Of course, the authors who agreed to contribute their expertise to this endeavour must be acknowledged for their hard work—we would like to thank them for their efforts. We would also like to thank the many instructors and students who have used the first edition and thereby made this second edition both possible and necessary. We are grateful to Michael Owen, Ph. D., Director of Research

Services for his support, including a grant from the University of Saskatchewan Publication Fund to help defray the costs of manuscript preparation.

We must thank several people at Harcourt Brace and Company Canada Limited, particularly Heather McWhinney, Dan Brooks, and Marcel Chiera, who, with their colleagues, bore the responsibility to see this book through to its completion. We are grateful to them for their professional guidance, enthusiasm, and support for this project. We must also thank Joanne Close for the professional manner and approach taken to editing the various chapters and bringing them to a stage where they were ready for publication. Finally, we would like to thank our families yet again for their continued support.

Saskatoon
September 1993

A Note From the Publisher

Thank you for selecting *Health, Illness, and Health Care in Canada*, by B. Singh Bolaria and Harley D. Dickinson. The authors and publisher have devoted considerable time to the careful development of this book. We appreciate your recognition of this effort and accomplishment.

We want to hear what you think about *Health, Illness, and Health Care in Canada*. Please take a few minutes to fill in the stamped reply card at the back of the book. Your comments and suggestions will be valuable to us as we prepare new editions and other books.

Contents

Part Three

Inequality and Health care

Part Four

Women, Family, and Health

Part Eight

Nurses' Education and Work

Part Nine

Environment, Work, and Illness

Chapter 1

Sociology, Medicine, Health, and Illness: An Overview

B. Singh Bolaria, University of Saskatchewan

Introduction

Medical sociology covers a wide range of substantive areas and encompasses a diversity of issues pertaining to health and illness, medical institutions, the structure and organization of the health-care sector, and the political, economic, and social determinants of the nature and composition of the health-care delivery systems. Medical sociologists and others interested in this area approach and examine these essential topics and issues from various theoretical perspectives and paradigms and use varying levels of analyses and methodologies. Despite this diversity, certain paradigms and orientations are still dominant in the field of medical sociology. The purpose of this chapter is, by way of introduction, to outline these paradigms and discuss their policy implications. Specifically, the following topics are examined: Evolution and the dominant paradigm of scientific medicine, the definition and etiology of health and illness, and the focus and levels of analyses. In conclusion, the policy implications of dominant paradigms and levels of analyses are considered in the context of current fiscal constraints and the health-care "crisis."

Evolution and the Dominant Paradigm of Scientific Medicine

The knowledge of modern scientific medicine is founded on the work of Koch, Pasteur, and other bacteriologists. The germ theory of disease, which gained prominence in the late nineteenth century, had a profound impact on the practice of medicine. As Waitzkin

(1979:684) states: "The isolation of specific bacteria as the etiologic agents in several infectious diseases created a profound change in medicine's diagnostic and therapeutic assumptions. A unifactorial model of disease emerged. Medical scientists searched for organisms causing infections and single lesions in non-infectious disorders." Renaud (1977:139) emphasizes the same point:

> Contemporary medical knowledge is rooted in the paradigm of the "specific etiology" of disease, that is, diseases are assumed to have a specific cause to be analyzed in the body's cellular and biochemical systems. This paradigm developed out of the germ theory of disease of Pasteur and Koch.

While the germ theory helped to develop the prevention of infectious diseases and improved medical practice, this paradigm

> gave support to the idea of specific therapies, from which rose the essentially curative orientation of current medical technologies toward specific illness rather than the sick person as a whole, and the belief that people can be made healthy by means of technological fixes; i.e., the engineering approach. (Renaud, 1977:139)

This paradigm basically adopted a "mechanistic model" of the human body. This approach has a long history. Philosophers like Descartes (1596-1650) established the philosophical base for a machine model of the human body; that is, that the human body is assumed to work in the same way as a machine. As McKeown (1965:38) states:

> The approach to biology and medicine established during the seventeenth century was an engineering one, based on a physical model. Nature was perceived in mechanistic terms, which led in biology to the idea that a living organism could be regarded as a machine which might be taken apart and reassembled if its structure and function were fully understood. In medicine, the same concept led further to the belief that an understanding of disease processes and of the body's response to them would make it possible to intervene therapeutically, mainly by physical (surgery), chemical, or electrical methods.

Disease, then, is an alteration, a pathological change in the body machinery that must be "fixed" (Navarro, 1986:166). Many diseases are viewed as mere technical defects; treatments are oriented toward restoring the "normal" functioning of the human machine. This approach basically ignores social causes of much ill health. The mechanistic-individualistic paradigm narrows and limits the medical task. As Doyal and Pennell (1979:30) state:

> The adoption of a mechanistic paradigm of this kind did limit the nature and boundaries of what is conceived as the medical task. Thus, scientific medicine ultimately became curative, individualistic and interventionist, objectifying patients and denying their status as social beings.

This mechanistic conception brought about a shift from the consideration of illness as a breakdown of the total system to the notion that ill health could be caused by malfunctioning of one particular part of the body machinery — in other words, localized pathology (Doyal and Pennell, 1979). This idea led to the medical fragmentation of the delivery of health care. Again, it is based on the premise that the human body is like a machine, and can, like any mechanical system, be broken down into different parts for repair (Rossdale, 1965). Many instruments were developed (thermometer, stethoscope) to examine the interior of the body machinery. This shift toward localized pathology had a profound impact on the division of labour (specialization) in medicine.

The specialization in medical knowledge and practice tends to focus on specific parts of the body machine, such as the nervous system, the cardio-vascular system, the gastro-intestinal system, and so forth (Navarro, 1986:167).

The work of bacteriologists and other scientists undeniably had a positive impact on the control of infectious diseases and led to improvements in medical practice. However, recent studies tend to cast doubt on the historical importance of these discoveries (Powles, 1973; Carlson, 1975). It is argued that the major decline in mortality and morbidity was due to better nutrition and sanitation and other environmental improvements, and that the decline in mortality and morbidity patterns, rather than following significant diagnostic and therapeutic discoveries, in fact preceded them (Waitzkin, 1979). Whatever the sequence of events, laboratory medicine with its emphasis on an individualistic, scientific, machine model of the human body achieved ascendancy. It should be noted that the dominant scientific paradigm is not mere linear evolution of scientific discoveries. As Navarro (1986:167) and others have argued, the form and nature of medicine is determined by class and power relations in the society and not by scientific imperatives. The ascendancy of scientific laboratory-based medicine and the dominant position of allopathic medicine in North America in the beginning of this century is attributed by some writers to the publication of the Flexner Report (Brown, 1979; Berliner, 1977; Kunitz, 1974; Waitzkin, 1979; Kelman, 1977).

Abraham Flexner visited medical schools both in the United States and Canada in 1904-1905. The Flexner Report (1910) was critical of the medical schools that did not have the facilities to teach laboratory-based scientific medicine. It called for the reorganization or, failing that, closure of such institutions. Ninety-two medical schools were closed (mainly in the United States) or reorganized between 1904 and 1915 (Waitzkin, 1979). Some of these institutions taught alternative forms of healing, such as homeopathy, midwifery, and herbalism. This report was highly critical of these alternative practices and helped to relegate them to subordinate status vis-à-vis the allopathic practice of medicine (Kelman, 1977; Berliner, 1975; Kunitz, 1974). The norm for medical education and practice became the laboratory-based scientific medicine. The Flexner report was hailed "as the document that helped change modern medicine from quackery to responsible practice" (Waitzkin, 1979:685).

Before the report's recommendations were implemented, the allopathic physicians had faced stiff competition, which affected their incomes, from practitioners trained in a variety of alternative healing traditions. The costs of delivering premedical education, as well as the necessity for expensive laboratory facilities, led to high tuition fees in medical schools, making medical education all but inaccessible to working-class students. As Waitzkin (1979:686) notes:

> The American Medical Association strongly supported and subsequently helped enforce the Flexner Report's recommendations. The closure of many medical schools not based in laboratory science led to fundamental changes in the class composition of the profession, changes that went hand in hand with reduced competition and higher individual incomes for doctors.

The Carnegie Foundation also helped support Flexner's tour and subsequent publication of the report. In addition, the General Education Board of the Rockefeller Foundation provided financial support to medical schools which implemented the report's recommendations (Nielsen, 1972). The philanthropic support of the Foundations was, according to Waitzkin (1979:686-87), based upon a number of considerations:

> The humanitarian image of this philanthropic work helped justify the exploitation of workers and the environment by which the parent industries accumulated high profits. . . . Secondly, the development of laboratory based medical science diverted attention away from the illness-generating condition of capitalist production and class structure. . . . A third reason for support of scientific medicine by the capitalist class was the need for a work force healthy enough to participate in the production process.

The Flexner Report, supported by the medical profession and by philanthropic foundations, helped to consolidate the dominance of the allopathic practitioners and to establish laboratory-based scientific medicine as the norm for medical education and practice. This mechanistic-individualistic conception is currently pervasive in medical practice and research. As Rodberg and Stevenson (1977:113) point out: "Modern medicine operates according to an individualistic, scientistic, machine model. Humans receive medical treatment outside of, and abstracted from, their normal social and environmental context."

Health and Illness

The mechanistic view of the human organism has dictated a similar vision of health and illness. For instance, Dorland's medical Dictionary defines health as "a normal condition of body and mind, i.e., with all the parts functioning normally"; and disease is defined as "a definite morbid process having a characteristic strain of symptoms — it may affect the whole body or any of its parts, and its etiology, pathology, and prognosis may be known or unknown" (Inglefinger, 1982).

This mechanistic view of health and illness is of particular significance with regard to the etiology of health and illness as well as the treatment. As Doyal and Pennell (1979:34) note: "Ill health is now defined primarily in terms of the malfunctioning of a mechanical system, and treatment consists of surgical, chemical or even electrical intervention to restore the machine to normal working order." Medical experts' advanced training permits them to recognize a "malfunction" and prescribe appropriate treatment to correct it and thus make the body "functional." In functional terms, health means "the state of optimum capacity of an individual for the effective performance of the roles and tasks for which he has been socialized" (Parsons, 1972:117). In Parsons' definition, this "capacity to perform" appears to be the sole criterion of health. The experience of ill health in itself does not constitute illnesses.

Others have argued that health in capitalist society is tied to production and capital accumulation process. As Kelman (1977:12) comments:

> At any point in time functional "health" is that organismic condition of the population most consistent with, or least disruptive of, the process of capital accumulation. At the individual level, this means the capacity to effectively do productive (contributing to accumulation) work.

Health viewed in this way has important implications in terms of the level of health-care services. Employers want to keep workers in good working order. As Rodberg and Stevenson (1977:112) indicate: "From the point of view of capital, the health-care system does not have to satisfy workers and it is not important that they feel well, as long as they are able to work hard." The definition of health and illness in relation to the accumulation process is an important aspect of the capitalist value system, which regards workers primarily as producers —"they are machines, one dimensional contributors to the accumulation process" (Rodberg and Stevenson, 1977:112). This view is well illustrated in the following passage in an occupational medicine text:

> Chickens, race-horses, and circus monkeys are fed, housed, trained, and kept up to the highest physical pitch in order to secure a full return from them as producers in their respective functions. The same principle applies to human beings; increased production cannot be expected from workers unless some attention is paid to their physical environment and needs.
>
> The object of this book is to show those who manage plants and are, therefore, responsible for the management of medical departments, how the workers' health may be maintained and improved as means of increasing production. (Hacket, 1925:11) quoted in Kelman, 1977:17)

Viewed in this context the investments to maintain healthy and productive workers are considered the same way as investments in other factors of production, and have to be balanced against returns. If workers are hard to replace or reproduction costs are high, employers are greatly concerned about the health of the workers and are interested in prolonging their productive life span. Conversely, if workers are easily replaceable, employers are less concerned about their health. Workers are kept healthy so long as the cost of health care is less than the cost of replacing them.

If workers are "owned" by the employers, such as slave labour, the employers are deeply interested in protecting their property. For instance, slaves in the United States had more systematic access to health care and enjoyed somewhat better health status than the freed slaves and poor whites (Postell, 1961; Stampp, 1956). However, health expenditures were tempered with return on this investment. Slaves were kept healthy so long as the cost of health care was less than the cost of replacing them. This is illustrated in the following passage:

> Physicians provided prepaid contracts to slaveholders to cover the cost of caring for the slaves, and an entire holding of slaves would often be moved to a more healthy location in times of epidemic, even at the cost of a whole year's production. Irish labourers were sometimes hired in order to save the slaves from working in malaria-infested areas. However, medical care was withheld from slaves when the anticipated cost (times the probability of failure) did not seem justified in the eyes of the slaveholder. (Kelman, 1977:16-17)

In addition to this instrumental view of health and fitness of the workers, "under capitalism, health is also defined in an individualistic way. It is always individuals who become sick, rather than social, economic or environmental factors which cause them to be so" (Doyal and Pennell, 1979:35). As Stark (1977:V) has commented:

> Disease is understood as a failure in and of the individual, an isolatable "thing" that attacks the physical machine more or less arbitrarily from "outside" preventing it from fulfilling its essential "responsibilities." Both bourgeois epidemiology and "medical ecology" consider "society" only as a relatively passive medium through which "germs" pass en route to the individual.

This individualistic and functional definition of health provides the basis for the essentially curative focus of medicine itself, which has important social and economic significance (Doyal and Pennell, 1979). For instance, the expansion of technologically curative medicine provides the base for a profitable health-care industry.

This type of analysis would suggest the termination of health resources to the elderly and infirm who no longer work and contribute little to the accumulation process because investment in their health will produce few, if any, returns (Kelman, 1977;

Rodberg and Stevenson, 1977; Dreitzel, 1971). To be sure, such policies, strictly speaking, have not been politically and culturally feasible. Even in the United States, where there is no universal health-care programme as in Canada, the elderly, chronically unemployed, and poor receive certain health services, however limited, under the medicare and medicaid programmes. A strictly functional definition of health and sickness purely in terms of the worker's ability to perform cannot always be operationalized because of political and cultural considerations. It is of no less significance to note that nursing homes and other health-care institutions which provide services to the aged population also provide opportunities for capital investments and profits, particularly those nursing homes that are privately owned and operated but subsidized by public funds.

Reductionism in Medicine

The mechanistic-individualistic conception of disease, which attributes disease to "malfunctioning" of the human body, absolves the economic and political environment from responsibility for disease. Waitzkin (1979:686) points out the reductionist tendencies of this understanding:

> Scientific medicine, fostered by the Flexner Report and the great philanthropies, tended toward reductionism.
> It shifted the focus of research and action from societal problems — a topic that implied potential threats to
> the organization of capitalist production and class structure — to pathophysiological disturbance at the level
> of the individual patient — much less threatening subject matter.

A similar reductionist approach has emerged which emphasizes individual lifestyle. In Canada in 1974, the publication of Lalonde's paper "A New Perspective on the Health of Canadians," gave prominent attention to health risks associated with individual lifestyles and consumption patterns. Lifestyle was also one of the foci of a recent health policy, "Achieving Health For All: A Framework For Health Promotion" (Epp, 1986). While the clinical model attributes disease to the "malfunctioning" of the human body, the new reductionism introduces the idea that the causes of disease lie in individual lifestyles and behaviours. In the former case the normal functioning of the body can be restored through "technological fixes," while in the latter the solution lies primarily in changing individual behaviours and patterns of consumption. It is argued that since the major risk factors causing much of mortality are under the personal discretion of the individuals, there would be considerable reduction in mortality if individuals would focus their attention on changing those aspects of their lifestyles which are injurious to their health. This focus on individual etiology and individual solutions is being promoted also in other countries (Doyal and Pennell, 1979; Waitzkin, 1983). Both approaches obscure the social nature of disease and fail to recognize the important relationships between social and work environments and health and sickness.

Recent studies from the historical materialistic epidemiological perspective have focussed on illness generating conditions.

Social Origins of Illness

Social medicine is primarily concerned with the conditions in the society that produce illness and mortality. While "traditional epidemiology has searched for causes of morbidity and mortality that are amenable to medical intervention historical materialistic epidemiology [has] found causes of disease and death that derive from social conditions" (Waitzkin, 1983:64). Social epidemiology and the environmental approach to health are in conflict with the biological and individual orientation of the predominant paradigm. Several social conditions that generate illness are the focus of this approach. These include social class, economic cycles, socially produced stress, production process, and work and profit (Waitzkin, 1983; Navarro, 1986). For instance, cancer and other chronic diseases are substantially related to environmental factors and the workplace. There is also evidence that links incidence of illness to economic cycles and levels of employment. Disruptions of stable community relations have consistently led to an increase in hypertension rates. Rather than focussing on the individual life cycle and its relation to stress, "historical materialist epidemiology shifts the level of analysis to stressful forms of social organization connected to capitalist production and industrialization" (Waitzkin, 1983:63). Studies in the area of occupational health and safety provide persuasive evidence that links work environment and the labour process to illness and disease and points to basic contradictions between profit and safety. Differential mortality rates and life expectancy of men and women and among racial groups is related to their varying work experience and social environment.

Types of Analysis

A plethora of sociological and behavioural studies is devoted to analyzing the "medical behaviour" of individuals. These studies have produced a large body of theoretical and empirical literature. Much of this literature concerns the study of differential attitudes toward health and illness, differential health practices, variability of reactions to symptoms and illnesses, and variability in the use of health services.

Another kind of analysis focuses on the behaviour of the provider of services and health-care institutions. The health sector, however, is integrally related to the larger society. It is therefore argued that to study the health-care system without attention to its linkages to broad political, economic, and social forces is misleading. These studies try to transcend the individual level of analysis to find how these linkages determine the nature, composition, and function of the health-care sector and the very definition of health and illness.

A significant portion of past research in medical sociology has been about the "medical behaviour" of consumers of health-care services and the social process which influence the decisions of individuals to use medical services (Albrecht et al., 1979; Cockerham, 1978; Coe, 1970; Krause, 1977; Tuckett, 1976). A number of authors have identified socio-psychological, socio-demographic, and socio-economic variables to account for variability in health behaviour and illness behaviour. According to Kasl and Cobb (1966:246): "health behaviour is any activity undertaken by a person believing himself to be healthy for the purpose of preventing disease or detecting it in an asymptomatic stage" and "illness behaviour is an activity undertaken by a person who feels ill, to define the state of his health and to discover a suitable remedy." Kasl and Cobb state that the likelihood of one's engaging in any particular behaviour is a function of the perceived amount of threat (perceived susceptibility and perceived seriousness) and the attractiveness of the behaviour (perceived probability of amelioration). Social class status, education, occupation, and income levels are important variables in influencing these perceptions.

King (1962) also emphasizes the importance, in any health related action, of the way one "sees or perceives the situation of disease and all of the social ramifications that accompany it." Mechanic's (1962, 1963) concept of illness behaviour has a similar basis, and is concerned with "the ways in which given symptoms may be differentially perceived, evaluated and acted (or not acted) upon by different kinds of persons."

Rosenstock (1966) as well suggests that preventive health behaviour is determined by one's perception of the seriousness of and susceptibility to the problem, perceived benefits of taking action, barriers to taking action, and cues to action. Rosenstock's (1966:98) health behaviour model is based on individual motivation and beliefs and includes two classes of variables: the individual's readiness (psychological) to act and the belief that a particular course of action will, on the whole, be beneficial in reducing the threat of illness. Rosenstock (1966:119) states that an individual's decision to participate in preventive health behaviour will not be made unless the individual is psychologically ready to take action concerning a particular health condition, believes that the action is feasible and appropriate, and encounters a stimulus that triggers the response.

Zola (1964), approaching the problem from a somewhat different perspective, presents a sequential model consisting of "five triggers" in an individual's decision to seek medical care. These are:

1. interpersonal crisis (whereby attention is called to the symptom);
2. social interference (the symptom threatens the individual's social activity);
3. the presence of sanctioning (some other person telling him or her to seek help);
4. perceived threat of the symptom (cognitive response); and
5. the nature and quality of the symptom (involves comparison of symptoms to previous ones, or to those of his or her friends and relatives in order to decide whether to seek help).

Zola also reports that these triggers are viewed differently in importance by various social strata and ethnic groups. Among the Italians the predominant triggers were "interpersonal crisis" and "social interference"; "sanctioning" was the predominant Irish trigger, and "nature and quality of the symptom" was the most significant trigger for Anglo-Saxons.

Suchman (1965b) presents stages of illness and medical care, discerning five stages "demarcating critical transition and decision making points in medical care and behaviour." These stages are symptom experience, sick-role, medical-care contact, dependent-patient role, and rehabilitation. Mechanic (1968) has identified a list of socio-psychological and socio-economic factors which affect individual coping response to illness.

Andersen's (1968:14) "behaviour model of families' use of health services" is composed of predisposition, ability, and need. The model suggests that a sequence of conditions contribute to the volume of health services used. Use of health services is dependent on: "the predisposition of the family to use health services, their ability to secure services, and their need for such services."

Other writers have emphasized the role of cultural, ethnic and social class differences in health and illness behaviour. These writers primarily view health and illness behaviour as a socially learned response. Thus Koos (1967:160) observed that "the health attitudes and behaviour of a family are related to its position in the social class hierarchy of the community, and are significantly affected by the prescriptions and proscriptions regarding health shared by those who are members of the same social class." Koos underlines the variation of health related activities from one social stratum to another based on differential perception of health and illness. For instance, upper-class persons were more likely than lower-class persons to view themselves as ill when they had particular symptoms and were more likely to seek medical advice. In brief, Koos (1967) emphasized two factors: (1) social class differences in opinions, attitudes, and behaviour and (2) perceptions of illness and health which are dictated by culture and environment. These factors also influence what the individual "will or will not, can or cannot, expect or accept from those who make his health their professional concern" (Koos, 1967: 156-157).

Saunders (1954) notes the differences between Spanish-speaking Americans and Anglos in their attitudes and response to illness and in their use of health facilities. The Anglos preferred modern medicine for many illnesses while Spanish-speaking people were more likely to use home remedies or folk medicine and family care. Similar observations have been made concerning other groups in various cultural contexts (Clark, 1959; Paul, 1955; Leighton and Leighton, 1945; Mead, 1953; Joseph, 1964; Adair et al., 1957; Stone, 1962; Rubel, 1960; Hartly, Straus, and Mead, 1961).

The role of cultural and ethnic differences in illness behaviour is described by Zborowski (1952) in his study of Jewish, Italian, Irish, and "old Americans." Both the Jewish and the Italian patients respond emotionally to pain and tend to exaggerate the pain experience, the Irish tend to deny pain, and "old Americans" tend to be stoical and "objective." Zborowski views these behavioural differences in light of the familial response to children's health and illness among the Jewish and Italian families.

Ethnic differences in illness behaviour have been described in a variety of other studies (Croog, 1961; Mechanic, 1963; Suchman, 1964, 1965b). These studies show a considerable variation in illness behaviour according to ethnicity.

The response to illness may also take the form of self-help or self-medication and consultation with relatives, friends, and neighbours (Phillips, 1965). Some writers also relate the delay in seeking medical help to particular medical orientations and to socio-economic factors (Polgar, 1959; King, 1962; Suchman, 1965a; Goldsen, 1957, 1963; Kutner et al., 1958; MacGregor, 1961).

However, the socio-psychological models with their emphasis on characteristics of individuals, their value systems, perceptions, health beliefs, and orientations are of limited use because they tend to overlook the importance of class inequalities (except indirectly as they affect perceptions and values), availability of and accessibility to medical services, organization and delivery of health-care services, and other structural factors. These inequalities continue to exist even in Canada, where the principle of universality was a major impetus to the introduction of medical care in the sixties (See for example, Wilkins and Adams, 1983; Shah and Farkas, 1985). While a number of studies in this book attest to these inequalities, it is worth quoting at length from a statement by Jake Epp, Minister of Health and Welfare, in a recent policy paper entitled "Achieving Health For All: A Framework For Health Promotion." Epp (1986:398) states:

> The first challenge we face is to find ways of reducing inequities in the health of low-versus high-income groups in Canada.
>
> There is disturbing evidence which shows that despite Canada's superior system, people's health remains directly related to their economic status. For example, it has been reported that men in the upper income group live six years longer than men with a low income. The difference is a few years less for women. With

respect to disabilities, the evidence is even more startling. Men in upper income groups can expect 14 more disability-free years than men with a low income; in the case of women, the difference is eight years.

Among low-income groups, people are more likely to die as a result of accidental falls, chronic respiratory disease, pneumonia, tuberculosis and cirrhosis of the liver. Also, certain conditions are more prevalent among Canadians in low-income groups; they include mental health disorders, high blood pressure and disorders of the joints and limbs.

Within the low-income bracket, certain groups have a higher chance of experiencing poor health than others. Older people, the unemployed, welfare recipients, single women supporting children and minorities such as natives and immigrants all fall into this category. More than one million children in Canada are poor. Poverty affects over half of single-parent families, the overwhelming majority of them headed by women. These are the groups for whom "longer life but worsening health" is a stark reality.

Rather than studying the behaviour of the consumers, others have analyzed the behaviour of the providers of health services and the interaction among different interest groups within the health sector. Focus is primarily on what "goes on" within the health sector without reference to the linkages between the health sector and the broader society. Studies in this area have focussed on such topics as organization and distribution of health-care services, medical education, health-care institutions (e.g., hospitals and nursing homes), professional domination and medical division of labour, and racial inequality in the health sector (See for example, Freidson, 1970a, 1970b; Fee, 1983).

Other analysts question the clinical effectiveness and technical claims of modern scientific medicine. Illich's work, *Medical Nemesis*, has received considerable attention in mass media and in professional circles. Illich (1976) provides considerable evidence of the ineffectiveness of modern medicine in reducing morbidity and mortality and in improving the health of the population. He portrays medicine as a coercive institution and has taken the view that current medical practices are generally doing more harm than good. Illich's analysis centres around three categories (clinical, social, and structural) of iatrogenesis (disease caused or induced by a physician or medical treatment). He feels that iatrogenesis is clinical when "pain, sickness, and death result from the provision of medical care"; social when "health policies reinforce an industrial organization which generates dependency and ill health"; and structural when "medically sponsored behavior and delusions restrict the vital autonomy of people by undermining their competency in growing up, caring for each other and aging" (Illich, 1976:165).

According to Illich, clinical iatrogenesis includes "all clinical entities for which remedies, physicians or hospitals are the pathogens or 'sickening' agents." Medical domination has led to loss of autonomy and creation of dependency for patients. The responsibility for health is expropriated from individuals by the medical profession.

Illich attributes these iatrogenic effects to the industrialization, bureaucratization and monopoly power of the medical profession, and the over-medicalization of life which perpetuates the addictive dependency of the populace on medicine and medical institutions. The solution, therefore, lies in de-bureaucratization, de-industrialization, and de-monopolization. He proposes de-medicalization, and the return of more autonomy and responsibility to individuals for their health and self-care (For a critique, see Starr, 1981; Navarro, 1977:38-58; Waitzkin, 1976). He confines the solutions to the health-care system itself without reference to the structural tendencies and political, social, economic, and class forces in the broader society which perpetuate this system. As Waitzkin (1983:5) notes: "Without attention to these connections, the health system falsely takes on the appearance of an autonomous, free-floating entity, whose defects purportedly can be corrected by limited reforms in the medical sphere."

In recent years, a considerable volume of literature has in fact emerged which does focus on the linkages between the political, economic, and social systems and the health-care sector. (See for example, Navarro, 1986; Waitzkin, 1983; Doyal and Pennell, 1979). This approach is predicated on the fact that the contradictions in medicine reflect the contradictions in society; that is, the health sector is so integral to the broader society that the attempt to study the one without attention to the other will be misleading. As Waitzkin (1983:5) comments: "Difficulties in health and medical care emerged from social contradictions and rarely can be separated from those contradictions." For instance, one of the contradictions in this society is between profit and safety. If it interferes with profits, an improvement in occupational health and safety is not very likely to be implemented. Gender and other inequalities in the health sector are reflections of these inequalities in the society. While in the discussion of escalating health-care costs the focus is generally on consumers and the health-sector labour force, little attention is given to the corporate invasion of the medical sector, usually referred to as the "medical-industrial complex." A high-technology mentality has encouraged costly and expensive medicine. To fully understand the escalating costs in medicine, one must consider the nexus of societal contradictions. As Waitzkin (1983:37) states:

> While physicians' earnings are important, it is an error to overrate them. Professional fees have their impact within a nexus of social contradictions that encourage practices, inappropriate technology, uncritical acceptance of innovations, corporate exploitation of illness, and the public subsidization of private medicine.

Others have noted the role of the capitalist state, class contradictions, ideology of medicine, medicalization, and illness related to the capitalist production process (For example, see Berliner, 1977; Fee, 1983; Salmon, 1977; Swartz, 1977; Walters, 1982;

Kelman, 1971, 1975, 1977; Navarro, 1986, 1977, 1976; Turkshew, 1977; McKinley, 1984; Waitzkin, 1983; Waitzkin and Waitzkin, 1974; Minkler, 1983; Crawford, 1980).

It is increasingly being recognized that the socio-psychological models of consumer behaviour and studies with exclusive focus on the health sector and its contradictions do not provide an adequate and comprehensive analysis of the current health crisis which is characterized by escalating costs and diminishing returns. By focussing on individuals and the health sector, these analyses tend to portray individuals and the health sector as though they existed in a vacuum. They tend to decontextualize the individuals and the health sector. The health-care policies which flow from these analyses would further increase the disparities in health status and health-care utilization in the populace. For instance, those who depend upon public sponsored health services would be adversely affected by any rationing of services or promotion of self-care. As Waitzkin comments:

> . . . the medicalization of social problems has many damaging effects, but the demedicalization of medical problems promises even worse repercussions. Self-care is fine, but it does not substitute for health services when needed. Nor can self-care offset the necessity of struggle against illness generating conditions in the workplace, environment, and organization of society.

It is argued that because of the close linkages between medicine and the social, economic, political, and class forces in the broader society, attempts to reform and transform medicine must be tied to wider strategies of change in the societal structure. The contradictions in medicine reflect contradictions of larger society and they cannot be resolved by focussing on the health sector alone or on individual clinicians. As Waitzkin (1983:8) notes:

> It is the structure of the system, rather than decision making by individual entrepreneurs and clinicians, that is the appropriate level of analysis. This distinction makes all the difference for policy and social action.

Summary and Conclusions

It was noted that the mechanistic view of human organism is still the prevalent and dominant paradigm in scientific medicine. This is of significance with regard to the etiology of health and illness as well as the treatment. Ill health in this context means the breakdown and malfunctioning of the machine (human body) and the treatment consists of surgical or chemical interventions to restore normal functioning. In functional terms, the sole criterion of health is the capacity of the individual to perform as he or she has been socialized to perform. The experience of ill health in itself does not constitute illness.

Others have argued that health in capitalist society is tied to production and the capital accumulation process. Health viewed in this way has important implications in terms of the levels of health services. Employers want to keep workers in good working order and "it is not important that they feel well as long as they are able to work hard." Viewed in this context, the investments to maintain healthy and productive workers are considered the same way as investments in other factors of production, and have to be balanced against returns.

While the clinical model attributes disease to "malfunctioning" of the human body, the new reductionism introduces the idea that disease lies in individual lifestyle and behaviour. In the former case, the normal functioning of the body can be restored through "technological fixes," while in the latter, the solution lies primarily in changing individual behaviour and patterns of consumption. Both approaches obscure the social nature of disease, which is the subject matter of historical materialistic epidemiology, which identifies social conditions in society that produce illness, disease, and mortality.

This chapter also discussed the various socio-psychological, socio-demographic, and socio-economic factors that influence the medical behaviour of consumers. Other studies have focussed upon the health sector and its contradictions, and recently a body of literature has emerged that focusses on the linkages between the political, economic, social, and class forces in the broader society and in the health-care system.

The collection of essays in this book examines the essential topics in medical sociology from a variety of theoretical perspectives and at varying levels of analysis. Their common intention is to provide an understanding of medicine, health, illness, and the health-care system.

References

Adair, John, et al. (1957) Patterns of Health and Disease Among the Navajos. *Annals of the American Academy of Political Science* 311 (May) 8-94.

Albrecht, Gary L., and Paul C. Higgins, eds. (1979) *Health, Illness, and Medicine.* Chicago: Rand McNally.

Anderson, Ronald. (1968). *A Behavioral Model of Families' Use of Health Services.* Center for Health Administration Studies Chicago: University of Chicago Press.

Berliner, Howard S. Emerging Ideologies in Medicine. *Review of Radical Political Economics* 9, (1) (1977): 116-24.

———. A Larger Perspective on the Flexner Report. *International Journal of Health Services* 5 (1975): 573-92.

Brown, E.R. (1979). *Rockefeller Medicine Men: Medicine and Capitalism in The Progressive Era.* Berkeley, California: University of California Press.

Carlson, Rick. (1975). *The End of Medicine.* New York: Wiley Interscience.

Clark, M. (1959). *Health in the Mexican-American Culture.* Berkeley: University of California Press.

Cockerham, William C. (1978). *Medical Sociology.* Englewood Cliffs, New Jersey: Prentice-Hall.

Coe, Rodney M. (1970). *Sociology of Medicine.* New York: McGraw-Hill.

Croog, S.H. Ethnic Origins, Educational Level, and Responses to a Health Questionnaire. *Human Organization* 20 (1961); 65-69.

Crawford, R. Healthism and the Medicalization of Everyday Life. *International Journal of Health Services* 10, (3) (1980): 365-88.

Doyal, Lesley, with Imogen Pennell. (1979). *The Political Economy of Health*. London: Pluto Press.

Dreitzel, H.P. (Ed.). (1971). *The Social Organization of Health*. New York: Macmillan Company.

Epp, Jake. Achieving Health For All: A Framework For Health Promotion. *Canadian Journal of Public Health* 77, (6), (November-December 1986): 393-407.

Eyer, Joe. (1984). Capitalism, Health, and Illness. In J.B. McKinlay (Ed.), *Issues in the Political Economy of Health Care*, (pp. 23-59). New York: Tavistock Publications.

Fee, Elizabeth, (Ed.). (1983). *Women and Health: The Politics of Sex in Medicine*. Farmingdale, New York: Baywood Publishing Co.

Flexner, A. (1910). *Medical Education in the United States and Canada*. New York: Carnegie Foundation.

Freidson, E. (1970a). *Professional Dominance*. New York: Atherton Press.

———. (1970b). *Profession of Medicine*. New York: Dodd Mead and Company.

Goldsen, R. Patient Delay in Seeking Cancer Diagnosis: Behavioral Aspects. *Journal of Chronic Diseases* 16 (1963): 427-36.

———. Some Factors Related to Patient Delay in Seeking Diagnosis for Cancer Symptoms. *Cancer* 10 (1957): 1-7.

Hackett, J.D. (1925). *Health Maintenance in Industry*. Chicago: Shaw.

Hartly, E., R. Straus, and M. Mead. Determinants of Health Beliefs and Behavior. *American Journal of Public Health* 51 (October 1961): 1541-54.

Illich, Ivan. (1976). *Medical Nemesis: The Expropriation of Health*. New York: Pantheon.

Inglefinger, F.J., (Ed.). (1982). *Dorland Medical Dictionary*. New York: Holt, Rinehart and Winston.

Joseph, Alice. Physicians and Patients, Some Aspects of Interpersonal Relationships between Physicians and Patients with Special Regard to the Relationship between White Physicians and Indian Patients. *Applied Anthropology* 1 (July-August-September 1964): 1-6.

Kasl, Stanislav V., and Sidney Cobb. Health Behavior, Illness Behavior, and Sick-Role Behavior. *Archives of Environmental Health* 12 (February 1966): 246-66; and 12 (April 1966): 531-41.

Kelman, Sander. Toward the Political Economy of Medical Care. *Inquiry* 8, (3), (1971): 30-38.

———. (1977). The Social Nature of the Definition of Health. In V. Navarro (Ed.), *Health and Medical Care in the U.S.: A Critical Analysis*, (pp. 3-20). Farmingdale, New York: Baywood Publishing Co.

———. The Social Nature of the Definition Problem in Health. *International Journal of Health Services* 5, (4), (1975): 625-42.

King, Stanley H. (1962). *Perceptions of Illness and Medical Practice*. New York: Russell Sage Foundation.

Koos, Earl L. (1967). *The Health of Regionville*. New York: Hafner Publishing Company.

Krause, Elliott A. (1977). *Power and Illness: The Political Sociology of Health and Medical Care*. New York: Elsevier.

Kunitz, S.J. Professionalism and Social Control in the Progressive Era: The Case of Flexner Report. *Social Problems* 22 (1974): 16-27.

Kutner, B., et al. Delay in the Diagnosis and Treatment of Cancer: A Critical Analysis of the Literature. *Journal of Chronic Diseases* 7 (1958): 95-120.

Lalonde, Marc. (1974). *A New Perspective on the Health of Canadians*. Ottawa: Information Canada.

Leighton, A., and D. Leighton. (1945). *The Navaho Door*. Cambridge: Harvard University Press.

MacGregor, G. Social Determinants of Health Practices. *American Journal of Public Health* 51 (November 1961): 1709-14.

McKeown, T. (1965). *Medicine in Modern Society*. London: Allen and Unwin.

McKinlay, John B., (Ed.). (1984). *Issues In The Political Economy of Health Care*. London: Tavistock Publications.

Mead, Margaret. (1953). *Cultural Patterns and Technical Change*. UNESCO, World Federation for Mental Health.

Mechanic, David. The Concept of Illness Behavior. *Journal of Chronic Diseases* 15 (February 1962): 189-94.

———. (1968). *Medical Sociology*. New York: The Free Press.

———. Religion, Religiosity, and Illness Behavior: The Special Case of The Jews. *Human Organization* 22 (1963): 202-8.

Minkler, Meredith. Blaming the Aged Victim: The Politics of Scapegoating in Times of Fiscal Conservatism. *International Journal of Health Services* 13, (1), (1983): 155-68.

Navarro, Vicente. (1986). *Crisis, Health, and Medicine*. New York: Tavistock Publications.

———, (Ed.). (1977). *Health and Medical Care in the U.S.: A Critical Analysis*. Farmingdale, New York: Baywood Publishing Co.

———. (1977). The Industrialization of Fetishism or the Fetishism of Industrialization. In V. Navarro (Ed.), *Health and Medical Care in the U.S.: A Critical Analysis*, (pp. 38-58). Farmingdale, New York: Baywood Publishing Co.

———. (1976). *Medicine Under Capitalism*. New York: Prodist.

Nielsen, W.A. (1972). *The Big Foundations*. New York: Columbia University Press.

Parsons, Talcott. (1972). Definitions of Health and Illness in the Light of the American Values and Social Structure. In E. Gartly Jaco (Ed.), *Patients, Physicians, and Illness*, (2nd ed.), (pp. 107-27). New York: Free Press.

Paul, B., (Ed.). (1955). *Health, Culture and Community*. New York: Russell Sage Foundation.

Phillips, D.L. Self-Reliance and the Inclination to Adopt the Sick Role. *Social Forces* 43 (May 1965): 555-63.

Polgar, S. Health and Human Behavior. *Current Anthropology* 3 (April 1959): 159-205.

Postell, W.D. (1961). *The Health of Slaves on Southern Plantations*. Baton Rouge, Louisiana: The Louisiana State University Press.

Powles, John. On the Limitation of Modem Medicine. In *Science, Medicine and Man*, London: Pergamon, Vol. 1, no. 1 (1973): 1-30

Renaud, Marc. (1977). On the Structural Constraints to State Intervention in Health. In V. Navarro (Ed.), *Health and Medical Care in the U.S.: A Critical Analysis*, (pp. 135-6). Farmingdale, New York: Baywood Publishing Co.

Rodberg, Leonard, and Gelvin Stevenson. The Health Care Industry in Advanced Capitalism. *Review of Radical Political Economics* 9, (1), (1977): 104-15.

Rosenstock, Irwin M. Why People Use Health Services. *Milbank Memorial Fund Quarterly* 44, (July 1966): 94-127.

Rossdale, M. Health in a Sick Society. *New Left Review* 34 (November-December 1965): 82-90.

Rubel, A.J. Concept of Disease in Mexican-American Culture. *American Anthropologist* 62 (October 1960): 795-814.

Salmon, J. Warren. Monopoly Capital and the Reorganization of the Health Sector. *Review of Radical Political Economics* 9, (1), (1977): 125-33.

Saunders, L. (1954). *Cultural Differences and Medical Care*. New York: Russell Sage Foundation.

Shah, C.P., and C. P. Farkas. The Health of Indians in Canadian Cities: A Challenge to the Health Care System. *Canadian Medical Association Journal* 133 (1985): 859-63.

Stampp, K.M. (1956). *The Peculiar Institution*. New York: Knopf.

Stark, Evan. Introduction to the Special Issue on Health. *Review of Radical Political Economics* 9, (1), (Spring 1977).

Starr, P. (1981). The Politics of Therapeutic Nihilism. In P. Conrad and R. Kern (Eds.), *The Sociology of Health and Illness: Critical Perspectives*, (pp. 434-48). New York: St. Martin's Press.

Stone, Eric. (1962). *Medicine Among the American Indians*. New York: Hafner Publishing Company.

Suchman, E. A. Health Orientations and Medical Care. *American Journal of Public Health* 56 (November 1965a): 97-105.

———. Sociomedical Variations Among Ethnic Groups. *American Journal of Sociology* 70 (1964): 319-31.

———. Stages of Illness and Medical Care. *Journal of Health and Human Behavior* 6 (Fall 1965b): 114-28.

Swartz, D. (1977). The Politics of Reform: Conflict and Accommodation in Canadian Health Policy. In L. Panitch (Ed.), *The Canadian State: Political Economy and Political Power*. Toronto: University of Toronto Press.

Tuckett, David, (Ed.). (1976). *An Introduction to Medical Sociology*. Tavistock Publications.

Turshen, Meredith. The Political Ecology of Disease. *The Review of Radical Political Economics* 9, (1), (1977): 45-60.

Waitzkin, Howard. Recent Studies in Medical Sociology: The New Reductionism. *Contemporary Sociology* 5 (1976): 401-5.

———. (1983). *The Second Sickness*. New York: Free Press.

———. The Marxist Paradigm in Medicine. *International Journal of Health Services* 9, (4), (1979): 683-98.

Waitzkin, Howard, and B. Waterman. (1974). *The Exploitation of Illness in Capitalist Society*. Indianapolis: Bobbs-Merrill.

Walters, V. State, Capital and Labour: The Introduction of Federal-Provincial Insurance for Physician Care in Canada. *Canadian Review of Sociology and Anthropology* 19 (1982): 157-72.

Wilkins, R. and O. Adams. (1983). *Healthfulness of Life*. Montreal: Institute For Research on Public Policy.

Zborowski, M. Cultural Components in Responses to Pain. *Journal of Social Issues* 8 (1952): 16-30.

Zola, I. (1964). Illness Behavior of the Working Class: Implications and Recommendations. In A. Shostak and W. Gomberg (Eds.), *Blue Collar World: Studies of the American Worker*, (pp. 350-61). Englewood Cliffs, New Jersey: Prentice-Hall.

Part One

Health Status, Health Policy, and Delivery of Health Care

Part One

Introduction

There are currently a number of questions being raised about the national health insurance program and the health-care system in Canada. Because of the country's current economic crisis, the problems of overall health-care costs and the financing of health-care services tend to dominate the discussion. Issues relevant to financing include: federal-provincial cost-sharing arrangements, extra-billing, income and wages of health personnel, user fees, and other institutional costs. Also under debate is the inequality of health status between various socio-economic groups. It is argued that some of the cost-reduction proposals currently being advanced are, if implemented, likely to adversely affect the sick and the poor, and further increase the disparity of health status between high and low socio-economic groups. These concerns are addressed by readings in this section, which provide an overview of the health status of the Canadian population, the development of the health-insurance program, utilization of health-care resources, and the structure and cost of health care.

Trovato, in Chapter 2, analyzes mortality trends in Canada from the early 1920s and 1930s through the late 1980s. Data from Statistics Canada and Dhruva Nangur show that Canada has witnessed, in accordance with the epidemiologic transition theory, a shift in its cause of death structure, from one characterized by a predominance of infectious and parasitic diseases to one characterized by a predominance of man-made causes and degenerative diseases as the leading cause of death. Dramatic improvements in survival possibilities that began in the 1950s denote the importance of improved standards of living and the positive effects of universal health care. Despite this, however, wide disparities in survivorship exist, not only on the basis of age and sex, but also in relation to income and ethnicity, suggesting that universal health care cannot eradicate all differences in health status among Canada's various populations.

Trovato suggests that further gains in longevity and health status could be made if we shift our focus from one of a curative nature to one of prevention since many of the leading killers in today's society are preventable. Such an emphasis, while logical and positive, carries with it the possibility that governments could place unrealistic responsibility on the shoulders of the individual in order to tackle health-care budgets.

Northcott, in Chapter 3, briefly reviews the development of Canada's health insurance program and the five principles on which it rests: universality, accessibility, comprehensiveness, portability, and public administration. He goes on to examine issues associated with the financing of the health-care system, with particular emphasis on extra-billing and user fees. Northcott points out that user fees will affect primarily the poor, the sick, and the elderly, who will be deterred from seeking needed care. Furthermore, total costs are not reduced by deterrent fees, because under a fee-for-services system, the providers of health care tend to compensate for lost income by generating extra demand.

Although there is a degree of conformity among the health-care plans of Canada's ten provincial governments, Quebec's system has realized some of the more radical aspects of the federal government's health policy makers with its proliferation of community health centres and the integration of social and medical dimensions of health. White, in Chapter 4, details the formation of the province's health-care system, its uniqueness, its advantages and disadvantages, and its future directions. With increasing pressure to curb health-care costs, all provinces must decide how they will spend their monies — on increasingly high-tech equipment and specialization or on initiatives that will bring equity to all, regardless of class or ethnicity. In Quebec, this decision parallels to a degree the province's division of health-care services: small community medical centres that tend to focus on the needs — social, emotional, physical — of their particular population in contrast to regional health centres that practise a more traditional health-care approach.

Total health-care expenditures in Canada rose from 2.14 billion in 1960 to an estimated 61.7 billion in 1990. Concern about these rising costs has become commonplace. Canadians place a high value on universal health care; necessary changes will have to be implemented that curb costs while at the same time maintaining as much as possible of the current system.

At present, there are two aspects of current health policy: cost-containment efforts stemming from the medically dominated, hospital-based illness care system and an emergent health-promotion and illness-and injury-prevention policy. Dickinson outlines these aspects in Chapter 5 and illustrates how the two are not as divergent as they appear initially. Both would curb health-care expenditures — cost-containment in the immediate future and health promotion in the longer term — and both are not without problems. Cost-containment strategies are viewed with scepticism on the part of most Canadians and health-promotion policies may be difficult to promote and maintain.

Chapter 2

Mortality Trends in Canada

Frank Trovato, University of Alberta

Introduction

Mortality is often the end result of trauma, such as in accidents and violence, or as a consequence of sickness. Therefore, a population's overall health status can be monitored by observing changes in mortality rates by cause of death. Disparities in overall health status in the population may be studied by examining mortality differentials on the basis of social and economic discrepancies. However, to the extent that persons with disabilities and diseases are able to postpone death due to medical intervention and therapies, mortality rates will reflect only a portion of overall sickness in the population (Bergner, 1987; Johansson, 1991; Myers, 1989; Patrick & Bergner, 1990; Riley, 1989). As argued by Frenk and colleagues (1991, p. 30), "health status manifests itself in various degrees that range from positive health, a concept including bio-psychic development and well-being, to the irreversible extreme of death. In between are various states that include uncomplicated disease and temporary or permanent disability."

In this chapter, statistics pertaining to mortality by cause of death will be examined in order to provide an indication of change in health status as reflected in mortality trends in Canada from the early 1920s and 1930s to the mid to late 1980s. The data presented in this overview were taken from official Vital Statistics publications by Statistics Canada (or Dominion Bureau of Statistics) and from the work of Dhruva Nagnur (1986) on mortality by cause of death for Canada from 1921 to 1981. Some of his tabulations have been expanded to include more causes of death, and have also been updated to 1986.

Since the focus of this chapter is on causes of death, it is worth emphasizing that not only have there been changes in the classification of diseases over time, making strict comparisons over the decades somewhat problematic, but in describing cause of death, one is merely dealing with the medically stated (or immediate cause) of death, which fails to give away any direct indication of the behavioural, environmental, and/or biological conditions leading to death.

The Epidemiologic Transition

The processes of modernization and demographic evolution engender significant shifts in morbidity and mortality conditions (Omran, 1971). The most fundamental premise of the epidemiologic transition theory is that with modernization the cause of death structure shifts from one where infectious and parasitic diseases predominate as the major causes of morbidity and death, to one where the leading causes of illness and death become human-made and degenerative chronic conditions.

The mechanisms responsible for epidemiologic transition are partly demographic, of which fertility decline is a critical component. With modernization, societies develop a small family ideal that ultimately results in prolonged large-scale fertility reductions. As a consequence of this process, societies experience a fundamental change in their age structures, from a predominantly young age composition to one in which adults and senior citizens represent a growing segment of the population.

According to Frenk and colleagues (1991), a second important mechanism in this transition is associated with a change in risk factors that predispose people to injury, disease, and death. As the process of modernization intensifies and there is a shift in the modes of production from a predominantly agrarian system to an urban industrial economic order, significant improvements in the standards of living evolve that contribute to lowering the risk of infectious and parasitic disease in the population (McKeown, 1976).

However, not all aspects of the modernization process engender a reduction in the probability of sickness. Industrial work and an urban lifestyle produce an increased incidence of injuries, violence, and illnesses from non-communicable diseases leading to premature death. For example, in most industrialized countries, lung cancer, which is largely associated with tobacco use, is a leading killer (Ravenholt, 1990). Motor-vehicle accidents, suicide, and other forms of violence represent a significant proportion of all deaths in modern societies (Lopez & Ruzicka, 1983; Ruzicka & Kane, 1990). A predominantly sedentary lifestyle, coupled with rising stress levels and overconsumption of animal fats, have also been linked to modern man's increased risk of cardiovascular complications (Smil, 1989).

A third source of epidemiologic transition is an improvement in case-fatality rates. In general terms, this refers to the ability of society, primarily through the health-care system and medical technology, to treat and cure disease such that people with serious ailments live longer than during previous eras of societal development. According to Gruenberg (1977), modern societies are now faced with the paradoxical situation of increasing the absolute levels of morbidity in their populations by extending the average duration of disease and disability through the successful application of medical intervention. Johansson (1991) has added that when mortality rates fall in society, morbidity levels rise, not only due to better health care and other aspects of the social system that serve to prolong life among the sick, but also as a consequence of the "cultural inflation of morbidity." As expectations rise concerning what constitutes good health, the demand for health care also increases, which means that more people are likely to be defined ill by the health-care system.

The epidemiologic transition is part of an overall process referred to by Caldwell (1986, 1990) and others as the health transition (Frenk et al., 1991; Johansson, 1991; Ruzicka & Kane, 1990). While the epidemiologic transition theory concerns itself mainly with shifts in the patterns of disease, sickness, and death, the health-care transition of society corresponds to the social system's organized response to epidemiologic change by way of health-care infrastructures, better medical technology, and the institution of social-security systems.

The industrialized nations have recently entered a new phase of epidemiologic transition. While Omran (1971) spoke of three stages — the era of pestilence and famine, the era of receding pandemics, and the era of human-made and degenerative diseases — Olshansky and Ault (1986) have argued that we have entered a fourth stage, the "era of delayed degenerative diseases." Their thesis is consistent with the view that modern society experiences significant improvements in case-fatality rates because people with chronic disabilities now live longer due to the availability of better medical and therapeutic technologies (Frenk et al., 1991; Gruenberg, 1977; Riley, 1989). A significant corollary of this phenomenon is the tendency for persons in old age to experience declines in mortality risk, which means that they are living longer in comparison to older people in the past. However, in connection with this development, some researchers have raised the question as to whether a longer life for the elderly may not be accompanied by worsening health (Verbrugge, 1984; Manton, 1982, 1989).

A more optimistic picture of future epidemiologic development is proposed by James Fries (1980, 1983, 1989). He has argued that rising life expectancy is accompanied by a process of "compression of morbidity," a state in which average life span is fixed at 85 and individuals postpone the onset of major infirmity to a few years before this limit. He places great faith in the ability of modern science, medicine, and on improved individual lifestyles to ensure optimum health throughout most of a person's life, until close to the point of natural death. Some support has been given for Fries's position on the average human life span being fixed at about 85 years (Olshansky et al., 1990; Nagnur, 1986). But there is less agreement with his views of the "compression of morbidity and mortality." Manton (1982) has argued against this proposition on the basis that life-table survival curves do not show convergence at age 85, but rather indicate a general movement toward further improvements in old age survivorship. Olshansky and associates (1990) refer to this tendency as the phenomenon of "mortality expansion." Nagnur (1986) shows a similar pattern for Canada from 1921 to 1981, where survival curves have become increasingly "rectangular" over time, and are also characterized by successive "expansion" beyond age 85.

The evolution of morbidity and mortality patterns as described by the epidemiologic transition will have significant implications for our future health-care system, health policy, and economic burden of health-care provision. As society continues to age demographically, and as life expectation continues to rise among the aged, and persons with major disabilities are able to postpone death, health-care costs will most certainly increase. Also, the predominance of chronic ailments in an aging population will place increasing pressures on the need for more complex health services, and more elaborate medical technologies and human resources (Frenk et al., 1991).

Mortality Change in Canada

Overall Death Rates

Canada's mortality rate of 11.6 per 1 000 population in 1921 was lower than the crude death rate prevailing in many of today's developing nations. For example, 55 countries in 1990 (mostly developing ones) had a crude death rate above 12 per 1 000 population (United Nations Population Data Sheet, 1990). This comparison suggests that our nation's mortality levels have been relatively low for quite some time.

As demonstrated in Table 1, the largest declines in overall mortality in Canada occurred between 1941 and 1951. From 1921 to 1931, the overall age-standardized death rate declined by only 1 percent, from 12.9 per 1 000 population to 12.8. By 1941, the death rate had declined by almost 13 percent, to 11.2 per 1 000 population. The decade of 1941 to 1951 witnessed a reduction of overall mortality by approximately 20 percent, from 11.2 to 9.0 per 1 000. A further decline of about 16 percent occurred between 1951 and 1961; and by 1971, the standardized death rate had reached a low of 6.7. In 1988, we experienced the lowest level of overall mortality since the turn of the century (5.1 per 1 000 population).

The change in overall mortality level between 1921 and 1988 is substantial,

Table I   Crude and Standardized Death Rates, by Sex and Period, Canada, 1921–1988

	Crude Death Rate			Age-Standardized Death Rate			% Change from Previous Period Standardized Death Rate		
Period	(1) Male	(2) Female	(3) Total	(4) Male	(5) Female	(6) Total	Male	Female	Total
1921	11.9	11.1	11.6	13.3	12.4	12.9	—	—	—
1931	10.5	9.6	10.2	12.7	11.7	12.8	– 4.5	– 5.6	– 1.0
1941	10.8	9.1	10.1	12.0	10.2	11.2	– 5.5	–12.8	–12.5
1951	10.1	7.8	9.0	10.0	8.0	9.0	–16.7	–21.6	–19.6
1961	9.0	6.5	7.7	9.0	6.3	7.6	–10.0	–21.3	–15.6
1971	8.5	6.1	7.3	8.4	5.2	6.7	– 6.7	–17.5	–11.8
1981	8.0	6.0	7.2	7.2	4.3	5.8	–14.3	–17.3	–13.4
1986	8.1	6.5	7.3	6.8	4.1	5.4	– 5.6	– 4.7	– 6.9
1987	8.0	6.4	7.2	6.6	4.0	5.1	– 2.9	– 2.4	– 5.6
1988	8.1	6.5	7.3	6.6	3.9	5.1	0.0	– 2.5	0.0
% Change 1921-1988	– 31.9	– 41.4	– 37.1	– 50.4	– 68.5	– 60.5			

Sources: Adapted from the following sources: Peron Y. & Strohmenger, C. (1985). *Demographic and Health Indicators: Presentation and Interpretation*. Ottawa: Minister of Supply and Services, Catalogue 82-543E, p. 109; Nagnur, D., Nagrodski, M. (1990). Epidemiologic Transition in the Context of Demographic Change: The Evolution of Canadian Mortality Patterns. In *Canadian Studies in Population*, 17(1), p. 5; Statistics Canada (1988). Vital Statistics. (1986). *Mortality Summary List of Causes*, pp. 35-37; Statistics Canada (1990). *Health Reports, Deaths 1987-1988* (Supplement No. 15, Vol. 2, No. 1).

Note: Crude and standardized death rates are expressed per 1 000 population. Standardized rates are based on the population of Canada in 1956 as the standard.

representing approximately a 60 percent decline. Given the modest declines in the age-standardized death rate since the early 1960s, and the tendency for mortality reductions to be smaller during each succeeding period, it seems unlikely that in the future our society will experience further major declines in overall death rates.

Females have enjoyed lower death rates than men, and their mortality declines over time appear to have been more precipitous. Large improvements in survival were attained by both sexes between 1931 and 1951. Men's age-standardized death rates declined by 5.5 and 16.7 percent respectively, between 1931-1941 and 1941-1951. The combined percent decline in female death rates over this twenty-year period was 34.4 percent. The sex differential in death rates widened considerably between 1951 and 1971 in favour of females. However, since 1976 males have shown larger proportionate declines in death rates than females.

Life Expectancy Trends

A useful method to summarize mortality conditions in a population is to examine life expectancy by age. Analysts have relied on this measure to draw conclusions concerning the health status of the population (Wilkins & Adams, 1983a, 1983b).

Table 2 shows life expectancy at selected ages, from 1921 to 1986. Longevity has improved significantly over the decades for all age groups and for both sexes. In 1921, males at birth could expect to live 58.84 years on average, while female babies had an average of 60.60 years left to live. In 1986, male and female newborns could expect to live 73.04 and 79.73 years, respectively. These changes in longevity between 1921 and 1986 represent increases over time of 24 and 31 percent for males and females, respectively.

In 1921, life expectancy at age one was 63.71 for males and 64.33 for females. It is interesting to note that until 1976, life expectancy for one-year-olds exceeded life expectancy at age zero. This phenomenon is a result of mortality probabilities in infancy having been much higher in earlier decades, such that life expectancy for infants improved once the first year of life had passed. The significant declines in infant mortality over the decades has reversed this trend. Currently, life expectation in infancy exceeds life expectancy at age one for both sexes.

Since the early part of this century, survivorship has improved anywhere from a low of 3 percent for males aged 40, to almost 49 percent for females 85 years of age. Among men, the largest gains have occurred in infancy (by 24 percent) and at ages 75 and 85 (by 19.5 and 25.8 percent, respectively). Increases in female longevity exceed those of men, irrespective of age class. The most substantial improvements have occurred in elderly women beyond age 40.

For both sexes, it is evident that the most substantial improvements among infants and children took place between 1921 and 1951, the improvements having been larger for females. For the remaining age categories in the table, the largest gains materialized between 1951 and 1971 for females, particularly those in the older age groups. For men, important improvements in their average length of life are also noticeable during the same period, particularly in connection with the age groups 75 and 85, and between 1971 and 1976 for men aged 40 and 65. The gains over subsequent periods of observation tend to follow a decelerating trend for all age groups. In fact, between 1981 and 1986, Canadian men and women aged 85 show a slight decrease in life expectancy in relation to 1981.

Another important feature in Table 2 corresponds to the sex differential in the degree of gain in life expectancy over time. It is an established fact that modernization is associated with a widening sex differential in mortality in favour of women (Preston, 1977; Lopez & Ruzicka, 1983; Nathanson, 1984; Waldron, 1986). Although not shown

Table 2   Life Expectancy at Selected Ages, by Sex and Period, Canada, 1921–1986

Age and Sex	Period						% Change from Previous Period					
	1921	1951	1971	1976	1981	1986*	1921-51	1951-71	1971-76	1976-81	1981-86	1921-86
Males												
0	58.84	66.40	69.40	70.26	71.88	73.04	+12.8	+ 4.5	+ 3.6	+ 1.2	+ 1.6	+24.1
1	63.71	68.31	69.78	70.26	71.65	72.67	+ 7.2	+ 2.2	+ 2.7	+ 2.7	+ 1.4	+14.1
5	61.65	64.87	66.04	66.48	67.82	68.81	+ 5.2	+ 1.8	+ 2.7	+ 2.0	+ 1.5	+11.6
20	48.90	50.77	51.75	52.16	53.40	54.27	+ 3.8	+ 1.9	+ 0.8	+ 2.4	+ 1.6	+11.0
40	32.12	32.45	33.26	33.67	34.74	35.52	+ 1.0	+ 2.5	+ 4.5	+ 3.2	+ 2.3	+ 3.4
65	13.04	13.31	13.77	14.04	14.57	14.90	+ 2.1	+ 3.5	+ 5.8	+ 3.8	+ 2.3	+14.3
75	7.64	7.87	8.54	8.69	9.01	9.13	+ 3.0	+ 8.5	+ 5.5	+ 3.7	+ 1.3	+19.5
85	4.07	4.25	4.97	5.11	5.18	5.12	+ 4.4	+16.9	+ 4.2	+ 1.4	– 1.2	+25.8
Females												
0	60.60	70.90	76.45	77.70	79.06	79.73	+17.0	+ 7.8	+ 3.4	+ 1.8	+ 0.9	+31.4
1	64.33	72.36	76.63	77.59	78.72	79.27	+12.5	+ 5.9	+ 1.4	+ 1.5	+ 0.7	+23.2
5	62.05	68.85	72.86	73.78	74.86	75.40	+11.0	+ 5.8	+ 1.3	+ 1.5	+ 0.7	+21.5
20	51.75	54.45	58.26	59.14	60.16	60.65	+ 5.2	+ 7.0	+ 1.5	+ 1.7	+ 0.8	+17.2
40	32.68	35.67	39.06	39.87	40.80	41.20	+ 9.2	+ 9.5	+ 2.1	+ 2.3	+ 1.0	+40.8
65	13.55	15.00	17.55	18.22	18.93	19.12	+10.7	+17.0	+ 3.8	+ 3.9	+ 1.0	+41.1
75	8.04	8.76	10.72	11.30	11.88	11.92	+ 9.0	+22.4	+ 5.4	+ 5.1	+ 0.3	+48.3
85	4.33	4.68	5.86	6.30	6.61	6.44	+ 8.1	+25.2	+ 7.5	+ 4.9	– 2.6	+48.7

Sources: Adapted from Nagnur, D. (1986). *Longevity and Historical Life Tables 1921-1981 (Abridged): Canada and the Provinces*. Ottawa: Minister of Supply and Services, pp. 70-71; Statistics Canada (1989). Health Division Vital Statistics and Disease Registries Section. *Life Tables, Canada and Provinces, 1985-1987*, pp. 16-19.

* Based on single years of Life Table.

explicitly in the table, the gender gap in life expectation at age zero has widened from an average of only 1.76 years in favour of women in 1921, to 6.69 years in 1986.

Recently, this differential has been narrowing slightly. In 1976, women showed an advantage of 7.44 years in life expectancy at age zero; this differential declined to 7.18 in 1981, and narrowed to 6.69 in 1986. These small decrements between 1976 and 1986 can be attributed to males' greater proportionate gains in survival in comparison to women across virtually all age groups. For example, the male gain in life expectancy in infancy was 1.6 percent during this period, while it was only 0.9 percent for females. A similar pattern is noticed for subsequent age groups in the table. Thus, while there has been a general slow-down in life expectancy gains for both sexes in recent decades, the male experience in this trend is less intense, which explains why the gender gap in survival has narrowed slightly in recent years. This phenomenon suggests that female life expectancy has come close to reaching a plateau in terms of further gains of the average length of life. Men, on the other hand, can expect further improvements by virtue of their significantly lower life expectancy in comparison to females.

Improvements in life expectancy over time have been accompanied by a significant shift in the age distribution of deaths. During the early stages of Canadian history, a large proportion of deaths were concentrated in infancy and in old age. This pattern has gradually shifted to the contemporary distribution, where the majority of deaths are concentrated in the older age classes. Table 3 displays this general pattern from 1931 to 1986, along with the corresponding number of deaths and the period-specific average age at death.

While the absolute number of deaths in Canada has risen, from 104 500 in 1931 to 184 200 in 1986, the average age at death has increased from 48.5 in 1931 to 70.1 in 1986. This is an expected progression since, as we observed earlier, life expectancy in Canada has been improving over time. Thus, while there are more people dying in Canada today, on average people die at an older age, explaining the tendency for an increasing concentration of deaths into the older age groups. A large part of this phenomenon is attributed to the historical declines in infant and childhood mortality. As survival probabilities improve, an increasing number of deaths will occur at ages beyond infancy and childhood (King, Gartrell, & Trovato, 1991).

Mortality Trends by Age Group and Cause of Death

Infancy

Table 4 concerns itself with the distribution of deaths and corresponding rates by age component during the first year of life, from 1921 to 1988. The decline in the absolute number of infant deaths is dramatic. In 1921, death claimed 27 051 babies prior to their

Table 3　Percent Distribution of all Deaths by Age Group, and Average Age at Death, Canada, 1921–1986

Age Group	Period					% Change from Previous Period				
	1931	1951	1971	1981	1986	1931-51	1951-71	1971-81	1981-86	1931-86
0	19.5	11.7	4.0	2.1	1.6	− 7.8	− 7.7	− 3.8	− 0.5	− 17.9
1-4	5.1	2.0	0.8	0.4	0.4	− 3.1	− 1.2	− 0.4	− 0.0	− 4.7
5-14	3.7	1.5	1.3	0.7	0.4	− 2.2	− 0.2	− 0.6	− 0.3	− 3.3
15-24	5.2	2.2	2.8	2.7	1.9	− 3.0	+ 0.6	− 0.1	− 0.8	− 3.3
25-44	11.5	7.0	5.8	5.5	5.2	− 4.5	+ 1.2	− 0.3	− 0.3	− 6.3
45-64	19.7	22.2	23.0	21.6	19.4	+ 2.3	+ 1.0	− 1.4	− 2.2	− 0.3
65+	35.3	53.6	62.3	67.0	71.2	+18.3	+ 8.7	+ 9.2	+ 4.2	+35.9
Total Deaths in Thousands	104.5	125.8	157.3	171.0	184.2	+ 21.3	+ 31.5	+ 13.7	+ 13.0	+ 76.3
Average Age at Death	(48.5)	56.8*	65.3**	68.0***	70.1	(+17.1)	+ 8.5	+ 2.7	+ 2.1	+ 44.5

Sources: Adapted from Hay, D.H. (1988). Mortality and Health Status Trends in Canada. In B.S. Bolaria and H.D. Dickinson (Eds.). *Sociology of Health Care in Canada*, p. 21, Toronto: Harcourt Brace Jovanovich; Statistics Canada (1988). Vital Statistics, 1986. *Mortality Summary List of Causes*, pp. 17, 76. Dominion Bureau of Statistics. (1933). Vital Statistics, 1931. *Mortality*, pp. 240-241.

*, **, *** Averages of male and female average age at death for 1950-52, 1970-72, and 1985-87.

( ) Estimated by interpolation between 1920-22 average and 1950-52 average.

Table 4 Infant Deaths and Rates by Age Component, Canada, 1921-86 (Both Sexes)

Year	Infant Mortality*		Age Component: < 28 Days		Age Component: 28 Days - 1 Year		% Change from Previous Period			% Death
	Number	(1) Rate	Number	(2) Rate	Number	(3) Rate	(1)	(2)	(3)	< 28 Days
1921	27 051	88.1**	7 333***	43.4	7 560***	44.7	—	—	—	27.1
1931	21 269	86.0	10 262	41.5	10 988	44.5	- 2.4	- 4.4	- 0.5	48.2
1951	14 673	38.5	8 619	22.6	6 054	15.9	-55.2	-45.5	-64.3	58.7
1971	6 356	17.6	4 485	12.4	1 871	5.2	-54.3	-45.1	-67.3	70.6
1981	3 562	9.6	2 359	6.4	1 203	3.2	-45.5	-48.4	-38.5	66.2
1986	2 938	7.9	1 909	5.1	1 029	2.8	-17.7	-20.3	-12.5	65.0
1988	2 705	7.2	1 719	4.6	986	2.6	- 8.9	- 9.8	- 7.1	63.5
% Change 1921-1988	-90.0	-91.8	-76.6	-89.4	-87.0	-94.2				

Sources: Adapted from Nagnur, D. (1986). *Longevity and Historical Life Tables, 1921-1981 (Abridged): Canada and Provinces*, Ottawa: Ministry of Supply and Services, pp. 50-59; Statistics Canada (1988). Vital Statistics, 1986, p. 14; Statistics Canada (1990). Vital Statistics, 1988. *Health Reports*, pp. 102, 108.

* Rates per 1 000 live births

** Excludes Quebec

*** The figures for neonatal and post-neonatal deaths do not add up to the total infant deaths for 1921 since Quebec and Newfoundland did not report such data.

first birthday. In 1988, the number of infant deaths was 2 705. The fall in infant deaths between these two time points represents a change of 90 percent. The infant mortality rate has declined from 88.1 per 1 000 live births in 1921 to 7.2 in 1988, reflecting a reduction in risk of 92 percent.

The most significant improvements in infant survival occurred between 1931 and 1951 (by 55.2 percent), followed by the thirty-year period of 1951 through 1981. In recent years there has been a deceleration in this general process. The rate of decline has been reduced from well over 40 percent during the decades following 1951 through 1981, to 18 and 10 percent between 1981-1986 and 1986-1988, respectively. Since mortality levels in the first year of life represent a significant barometer of social-economic conditions in society, including the extent and quality of health care, the overall pattern of infant mortality decline over time must be viewed as a Canadian success story.

The French demographer Bourgeois-Pichat (1951) proposed that deaths during the first month of life, and particularly those that occur in the first seven days from birth, are largely a reflection of congenital ("endogenous") complications and anomalies. Deaths to infants beyond the first month of life are predominantly associated with what he called "exogenous" causes that result from poor environmental conditions (such as accidents, neglect, poverty, and exposure to infectious and parasitic diseases).

The overall pattern of change in neonatal (deaths between birth and the first 28 days of life) and postneonatal mortality rates (deaths between 28 days and the first 12 months of life) is generally similar to that observed for infant mortality. The neonatal death rate declined from 43.4 per 1 000 births in 1921 to 4.6 in 1988, which corresponds to 7 333 and 1 719 neonates succumbing to premature death in these two time points, respectively. Historical improvements in neonatal survival probabilities have been significant from the early 1930s through the mid 1980s, but the most intense periods in this development were between 1931 and 1971, and then from 1971 to the early 1980s. In recent years, the intensity of reduction in risk has waned somewhat, largely because the most dramatic achievements in stemming the number of deaths early in life have been actualized in previous decades, leaving less room for further major improvements. Undoubtedly, this development reflects the introduction of hospitals and medical facilities directed at neonatal complications, the growth of public health, and better prenatal and postnatal care by mothers.

In 1921, out of 1 000 births, almost 45 infants died in the postnatal period. Today, only about 3 in 1 000 births are claimed by death during this period in infancy. The most pronounced improvements took place between the early 1930s and the early 1970s. Though subsequent gains in survivorship are significant, they have occurred at a lower degree of intensity in comparison to earlier decades.

These developments have been accompanied by a gradual shift in the preponderance of deaths from the postneonatal period to the neonatal phase in infancy. While approximately 27 percent of all infant deaths in 1921 were neonatal, this proportion increased to 70.6 in 1971, and declined to 63.5 percent in 1986. Social, economic, and environmental conditions have improved to such an extent that many "killers" of infants in the postneonatal period have either been controlled or removed altogether. Immunization programs, better safety consciousness, and surveillance by parents have all served to reduce many potential hazards in the environment of infants. Our society has introduced regulations and standards to maximize infant survival through such regulations as mandatory car seats for infants, and the development of better and more secure methods of storing medicines and other substances in the home that are potentially harmful to infants and young children.

With regard to causes of death in infancy, King, Gartrell, and Trovato (1991, p. 8) mention that in the past, tuberculosis and influenza epidemics played a significant part in infant mortality, and in the incidence of other diseases, such as measles, mumps, chicken pox, whooping cough, and scarlet fever. However, mortality rates from all communicable diseases and from many parasitic diseases have dropped considerably since the early 1920s, and today are responsible for very few infant and childhood deaths.

Table 5 shows the distribution of deaths by cause for infants in Canada during 1988. Infectious and parasitic diseases account for less than 1 percent of all infant deaths; and while male infants show a larger number of deaths than female infants, the levels for this category of death are quite low. Respiratory illnesses account for 2.2 percent of all deaths, while gastrointestinal diseases contribute 0.6 percent to the overall number of deaths in the first year of life. By far the most important cause of death are congenital anomalies, representing 33 percent of all deaths. Out of 1 000 births, 234 would succumb to death as a consequence of congenital complications. This is in sharp contrast to the situation that prevailed during the early 1920s and 1930s in Canada. King, Gartrell, and Trovato (1991, p. 10) show that during 1926-1930, congenital anomalies accounted for only 8.9 percent of neonatal and 4.0 percent of postneonatal mortality, respectively.

Other important sources of infant death in contemporary Canada include disorders associated with short gestation and low birth weight, maternal complications during pregnancy, and complications involving the placenta, cord, and membranes. These problems accounted for 14.2 percent of all infant deaths in 1988. Sudden infant death syndrome (SIDS) (14.4 percent), respiratory distress syndrome (9.2 percent), and other respiratory conditions (7.2 percent) combine to account for an additional 30.8 percent of deaths. Clearly, future improvements in infant survival will depend on our success in controlling these causes of infant mortality.

Table 5　Distribution of Infant Deaths and Rates for Leading Causes of Death in Infancy, Canada, 1988

Cause of Death	Rates per 100 000 Live Births			Number of Deaths	%
	Males	Females	Total		
Infectious and parasitic diseases	6.2	4.4	5.3	20	0.7
Respiratory diseases	16.1	15.2	15.7	59	2.2
Gastro-intestinal diseases	6.2	2.2	4.2	16	0.6
Congenital anomalies	250.3	217.1	234.1	882	32.6
Disorders: short gestation/low birth weight	42.0	39.7	40.9	154	5.7
Material complications of pregnancy	26.4	25.0	25.7	133	4.9
Complications: placenta/cord/membranes	26.9	25.0	26.0	98	3.6
Respiratory distress syndrome	78.8	52.2	65.8	248	9.2
Other respiratory conditions of newborn	61.7	40.8	51.5	194	7.2
Sudden infant death syndrome	125.9	79.4	103.2	389	14.4
Meningitis	4.7	2.7	3.7	14	0.5
Accidents and violence	15.5	19.1	19.3	75	2.8
All other causes	140.9	107.2	122.5	423	15.6
Total	801.6	630.0	717.9	2 705	100.0

Sources: Statistics Canada (1990). Vital Statistics, 1988. *Health Reports*, pp. 98-109.

Age Group 1-4

Table 6 shows death rates by selected causes for persons 1-4 years of age for selected years from 1931 to 1986. The distribution of deaths in 1986 is also given. Around the turn of the century, until the early 1950s, infectious diseases were the leading causes of death among young boys and girls. Ailments, such as influenza, bronchitis, pneumonia, tuber-culosis, diarrhea, diphtheria, whooping cough, and meningitis claimed many lives. In 1931, a major killer of young boys was diarrhea and enteritis, with a death rate of 92 per 100 000 male children. For young girls, influenza, bronchitis, and pneumonia (one category) claimed 190 out of every 100 000 female children in this age group.

The second most influential cause of death for young boys in 1931 were accidents, poisonings, and violence (one category), with a death rate of 81. For girls during this period, diarrhea and enteritis was the second leading killer out of the various causes listed in the table. For both boys and girls, measles, polio, and appendicitis were relatively minor causes of death.

As can be seen from the total death rates at the bottom of the table, mortality to 1-4 year olds has declined considerably over the years, from 679 and 612 per 100 000 for

Table 6   Death Rates for the Age Group 1–4 by Leading Cause, Canada, 1931, 1951, 1971, 1981 and 1986

Cause of Death	1931		1951		1971		1981		1986		Distribution of Deaths in 1986	
	Male	Female	Male	Female	Male	Female	Male	Female	Male	Female	Male	Female
Influenza, bronchitis and pneumonia	59	160	98	40	8	10	2	2	1	2	6	11
Diarrhea and enteritis	92	70	41	9	1	1	—	—	—	—	0	0
Accidents, poisonings and violence	81	50	48	61	41	28	28	19	23	14	167	99
Tuberculosis	51	45	31	14	—	—	—	—	—	—	0	0
Diphtheria	36	34	11	1	—	—	—	—	—	—	0	0
Whooping cough	21	32	16	3	—	—	—	—	—	—	0	0
Meningitis	22	22	15	8	2	—	1	—	2	1	11	9
Appendicitis	15	9	8	3	—	—	—	—	—	—	1	2
Poliomyelitis	14	8	1	1	—	—	—	—	—	—	0	0
Measles	8	12	12	5	—	—	—	—	—	—	0	0
All Causes	679	612	399	205	91	78	59	46	49	41	(185)	(121)

Sources: Adapted from Nagnur, D. (1986). *Longevity and Historical Life Tables, 1921-1981 (Abridged): Canada and the Provinces*. Ottawa: Minister of Supply and Services, pp. 62-67. Statistics Canada (1988). Vital Statistics, 1986. *Mortality Summary List of Causes.*

Note: Death rates are expressed per 100 000 population. Rates are rounded to whole numbers. Residual causes are included in the overall death rate for all causes.

boys and girls in 1931, to 49 and 41 respectively in 1986. This drop in death rates represents a 93 percent improvement for both sexes.

The largest mortality reductions for boys took place between 1951 and 1971 (77 percent), while for girls the largest improvements are noted for the interval from 1931 to 1951 (66 percent reduction in the death rate). As would be expected, given these early improvements in childhood survivorship, the pace of mortality decline in recent years has slowed somewhat. For example, between 1981 and 1986, the percentage decline in death rates was only 17 percent for boys and 11 percent for girls.

Since the early 1950s, the major diseases of earlier decades have receded to a considerable degree. Influenza, bronchitis, and pneumonia have been reduced from 59 and 160 per 100 000 in 1931, to only 1 and 2 per 100 000 in 1986, for boys and girls respectively. Diarrhea and enteritis have disappeared altogether, as well as most of the remaining causes listed in the table. In fact, out of all the conditions listed, accidents, poisonings, and violence continue to be leading causes of death of young children today. In 1986, 167 boys lost their lives as a consequence of either accidents, violence inflicted on them, or by poisonings. The number of girls who died of these causes is 99. These figures are disturbing since they represent 90 percent of all deaths to 1-4 year-old boys, and 82 percent of all deaths to girls in this age class.

Age Group 5-14

As is true for very young children, Table 7 shows that for 5-14 year olds, deaths due to infectious and parasitic diseases have also fallen dramatically since the early part of this century. Also, while death rates associated with accidents, poisonings, and violence have decreased considerably since the early 1930s, they still claim a significant number of young lives. In 1986, out of 320 total male deaths in this age category, 279 (87 percent) were due to these sources of premature death; and out of 178 total female deaths, 149 (84 percent) could be attributed to these preventable causes.

The temporal pattern of overall mortality reduction shows large gains in survivorship for 5-14 year olds between 1931 and 1951. During this period, the male death rate declined from 185 per 100 000 to 89, respectively. The female death rate declined by 64 percent, from 162 to 59 per 100 000. Reductions since 1951 continue to be significant, but have been occurring at a more modest pace.

Age Group 15-24

Young men and women between the ages of 15 and 24 are particularly prone to accidental and violent death. As can be seen in Table 8, motor-vehicle accidents have figured prominently as a leading cause of premature death among young people throughout the time periods under observation. While the homicide death rate is not

Table 7 Death Rates for the Age Group 5–14 by Leading Cause, Canada, 1931, 1951, 1971, 1981 and 1986

Cause of Death	1931 Male	1931 Female	1951 Male	1951 Female	1971 Male	1971 Female	1981 Male	1981 Female	1986 Male	1986 Female	Distribution of Deaths in 1986 Male	Distribution of Deaths in 1986 Female
Accidents, poisonings and violence	46	15	45	16	34	17	24	12	15	9	279	149
Tuberculosis	23	28	6	8	—	—	—	—	—	—	0	0
Appendicitis	17	16	2	2	2	2	—	—	—	—	0	0
Influenza, bronchitis and pneumonia	14	16	5	5	—	—	—	—	1	1	23	14
Diphtheria	11	12	1	1	—	1	—	—	—	—	0	0
Cardiovascular disease	8	11	2	2	—	—	1	—	1	1	17	15
Meningitis	5	6	1	1	—	—	—	—	—	—	0	0
Rheumatic fever	5	4	2	2	—	—	—	—	—	—	0	0
Poliomyelitis	4	4	2	1	—	—	—	—	—	—	0	0
Nephritis and nephrosis	4	3	2	2	—	—	—	—	—	—	1	0
All Causes	185	162	89	59	53	35	37	24	27	18	(320)	(178)

Sources: Adapted from Nagnur, D. (1986). *Longevity and Historical Life Tables, 1921–1981 (Abridged): Canada and the Provinces.* Ottawa: Minister of Supply and Services, pp. 62-67. Statistics Canada (1988). *Vital Statistics, 1986. Mortality Summary List of Causes.*

Note: Death rates are expressed per 100 000 population. Rates are rounded to whole numbers. Residual causes are included in the overall death rate for all causes.

Table 8   Death Rates for the Age Group 15–24 by Leading Cause, Canada, 1931, 1951, 1971, 1981 and 1986

Cause of Death	1931 Male	1931 Female	1951 Male	1951 Female	1971 Male	1971 Female	1981 Male	1981 Female	1986 Male	1986 Female	Dist. Male	%	Dist. Female	%
Tuberculosis	71	118	18	24	—	—	—	—	—	—	0	0.0	0	0.0
Motor vehicle accidents	22	5	37	10	73	23	66	18	48	14	1 103	47.6	301	44.3
Other accidents	67	9	41	5	40	9	35	8	20	4	345	14.9	88	12.9
Homicide	1	1	1	—	4	2	3	2	3	2	64	2.8	37	5.4
Suicide	6	4	6	2	18	4	28	5	27	5	570	24.6	101	14.9
Cancers	7	5	10	6	9	6	6	4	6	4	134	5.8	86	12.6
Influenza, bronchitis and pneumonia	19	13	5	4	2	2	1	1	1	1	31	1.3	21	3.1
Cardiovascular disease	14	16	8	7	4	3	3	2	3	2	70	3.0	46	6.8
All Causes	284	269	161	92	158	57	150	46	122	41	(2 317)	100.0	(680)	100.0

Sources: Adapted from Nagnur, D. (1986). *Longevity and Historical Life Tables, 1921-1981 (Abridged): Canada and the Provinces*. Ottawa: Minister of Supply and Services, pp. 62-67; Statistics Canada (1988). *Vital Statistics, 1986. Mortality Summary List of Causes*; Dominion Bureau of Statistics (1933). *Vital Statistics, 1931. Mortality by Cause*.

Note: Death rates are expressed per 1 000 population. Rates are rounded to whole numbers. Residual causes are included in the overall death rate for all causes; therefore, the percentages for deaths in 1986 will not add to 100. Rates for motor vehicle accidents, other accidents, homicide and suicide for 1931-1986 were computed using corresponding Vital Statistics data for these years.

particularly high, it has been increasing over time. Suicide rates have also been rising generally, and have always been considerably higher than the homicide rate.

In comparison to young women, male death rates from violence and accidents tend to be approximately three to five times higher, depending on the specific cause. As an indication of this, in 1986 out of 2 317 total deaths to young men, 1 103 were the result of motor-vehicle accidents (48 percent); other accidents represent 345 additional deaths, homicide claimed 64 lives, and suicide was responsible for 570 deaths (25 percent). In contrast, only 301 women died in motor-vehicle accidents, representing a male excess in risk by a ratio of 3.66:1. Other accidents claimed 88 females, 37 died due to homicide, and 101 perished as a result of suicide (male/female ratio is 5.64:1).

An encouraging trend in these data is that motor-vehicle fatalities have been declining since the early 1970s. The use of seat belts, better vehicle construction, and greater safety consciousness have undoubtedly contributed to this welcomed trend. However, there is considerable room for further improvements, not only in connection with this cause of death, but other accidents and suicide, especially among males.

Although chronic diseases in this age group are not major causes of premature death, there has been a general improvement in cardiovascular disease mortality. Over the decades under observation, cancer has not changed much, but the death rate from cardiovascular diseases has declined considerably for both genders. In 1986, the death rate for cancer was 6 and 4 per 100 000 for men and women respectively; and the corresponding cardiovascular death rates were 3 and 2.

Substantial declines in general mortality took place between 1931 and 1951 for both sexes (43 percent for men, 66 percent for women). A large part of this trend can be attributed to the drop in tuberculosis as a cause of death during this same period, from 71 and 118 per 100 000 in 1931, to 18 and 24 in 1951, for men and women respectively. Since 1951, the death rate for this ailment has been zero or negligible.

If we were to identify an area for further mortality improvements among 15-24 year olds, it would have to be accidents and violence. In total, motor-vehicle accidents, other accidents, homicide, and suicide accounted for 87 percent of all deaths to this age group in 1986.

Age Group 25-44

Since 1931, overall death rates for young adults aged 25-44 have shown a 61 and 82 percent drop for men and women respectively. In 1931, the overall death rate for men was 410 per 100 000, while it was 440 for females. In 1986, these rates had declined to 158 and 77 for men and women, respectively. Women's higher overall mortality in 1931 was largely a function of their higher rates of tuberculosis, cancers, cardiovascular disease, and nephritis, and perhaps a high incidence of maternal mortality. By 1951, however, male rates from all these causes, except cancer, were higher than the corresponding female rates; and by 1971, men's rates for all the causes listed in Table 9 surpassed those of females.

Some of the most lethal diseases in the earlier decades became insignificant causes of mortality by the early 1950s and 1970s. For example, tuberculosis, appendicitis, ulcers of the stomach and duodenum, hernia, and intestinal obstruction do not play much of a role in present mortality conditions. Unfortunately, the same cannot be said of cancer, motor-vehicle accidents, suicide, and cardiovascular disease.

Age Group 45-64

Mortality trends for adults aged 45-64 in Canada are shown in Table 10. Men in 1931 had an overall death rate of 1 249 per 100 000, while women showed a death rate of 1 118. In 1986, both sexes showed overall death rates of 928 and 529 per 100 000 respectively. These changes represent mortality declines of 26 and 53 percent for men and women, respectively, from their corresponding levels in 1931.

The pace of overall mortality decline between 1931 and 1951 up until the early 1970s has been more rapid for females. After 1971, the death rate for men has been declining faster, although the magnitude of change for both genders has been small since then. The largest improvements for both sexes occurred between 1951 and 1971, with a 31 percent decline in the female rate, and a 10 percent decrease for men.

Certain causes of death have been important in accounting for these overall trends in death rates. For example, cardiovascular disease mortality increased for men between 1931 and 1951, from 352 to 687 per 100 000, and declined from 597 to 368 per 100 000 over the subsequent three periods. However, in relation to 1931, the 1986 rate for this cause of death is higher. The situation for females is generally similar, but differs from that of men in that the degree of change since 1951 is more precipitous for women. For example, female death rates from cardiovascular disease increased from 319 to 376 between 1931 and 1951, but declined to 199 in 1971, to 160 in 1981, and to 102 in 1986. Moreover, the overall decline since 1971 in this cause of death is 68 percent for females, whereas men's risk actually increased by 5 percent.

Cancer mortality has followed an increasing trend over time for both sexes. In 1931 men's death rate from cancer was 202 per 100 000, while in 1986 it was 327, representing an overall increase of 38 percent. The corresponding female death rate in the earlier period was above that of men at 267 per 100 000; in 1986 females showed a rate of 269, denoting a small overall increase in risk since 1931.

Death rates associated with motor-vehicle accidents peaked in 1951 for men and in 1971 for females. The trend since the early 1970s is one of decline for both sexes. This

Table 9 Death Rates for the Age Group 25–44 by Leading Cause, Canada, 1931, 1951, 1971, 1981 and 1986

Cause of Death	1931 Male	1931 Female	1951 Male	1951 Female	1971 Male	1971 Female	1981 Male	1981 Female	1986 Male	1986 Female	Distribution of Deaths in 1986 Male	%	Female	%
Tuberculosis	86	110	28	26	1	1	—	—	—	—	5	0.0	1	0.0
Motor vehicle accidents	27	5	41	6	39	12	39	10	27	8	1 102	17.0	330	10.5
Other accidents	54	7	120	20	59	10	24	7	19	5	778	12.0	193	6.2
Homicide	2	1	1	1	5	2	4	2	4	2	153	2.4	74	2.4
Suicide	19	7	12	4	24	9	26	9	30	8	1 239	19.1	334	10.7
Cancers	25	53	25	45	29	37	23	28	24	30	979	15.1	1 235	39.4
Cardiovascular disease	43	48	59	34	46	18	32	12	25	9	1 036	16.0	355	11.3
Influenza, bronchitis and pneumonia	31	26	6	5	4	3	1	1	2	1	92	1.4	56	1.8
Nephritis and nephrosis	15	21	7	6	2	1	1	—	—	—	3	0.0	1	0.0
Appendicitis	15	7	2	—	—	—	—	—	—	—	3	0.0	0	0.0
Ulcer of stomach and duodenum	9	2	3	1	1	—	—	—	—	—	10	0.2	9	0.3
Hernia and intestinal obstruction	5	5	1	1	1	—	—	—	—	—	3	0.0	9	0.3
All Causes	410	440	252	183	218	118	174	87	158	77	(6 472)	100.0	(3 135)	100.0

Sources: Adapted from Nagnur, D. (1986). *Longevity and Historical Life Tables, 1921-1981 (Abridged): Canada and the Provinces.* Ottawa: Minister of Supply and Services, pp. 62-67; Statistics Canada (1988). *Vital Statistics,* 1986. *Mortality Summary List of Causes;* Dominion Bureau of Statistics (1933). *Vital Statistics,* 1931. *Mortality by Cause.*

Note: Death rates are expressed per 1 000 population. Rates are rounded to whole numbers. Residual causes are included in the overall death rate for all causes; therefore, the percentages for deaths in 1986 will not add to 100. Rates for motor vehicle accidents, other accidents, homicide and suicide for 1931-1986 were computed using corresponding Vital Statistics data for these years.

Table 10   Death Rates for the Age Group 45–64 by Leading Cause, Canada, 1931, 1951, 1971, 1981 and 1986

Cause of Death	1931 Male	1931 Female	1951 Male	1951 Female	1971 Male	1971 Female	1981 Male	1981 Female	1986 Male	1986 Female	1986 Dist. Male	%	Female	%
Cardiovascular disease	352	319	687	376	597	199	454	160	368	102	9 110	39.7	2 455	19.3
Cancer	202	267	243	266	286	238	309	250	327	269	8 076	35.2	6 451	50.8
Motor vehicle accidents	39	12	44	10	35	14	32	11	20	9	503	2.2	223	1.8
Other accidents	58	13	49	10	52	17	37	13	27	11	680	3.0	258	2.0
Homicide	2	1	1	1	4	1	3	1	2	1	60	0.3	28	0.2
Suicide	37	8	25	9	32	14	29	12	27	10	669	3.9	252	2.0
Nephritis and nephrosis	86	89	30	27	5	4	5	4	—	—	14	0.5	15	0.1
Influenza, bronchitis and pneumonia	89	71	35	25	34	14	17	8	20	12	495	2.2	277	2.2
Tuberculosis	90	61	48	21	6	3	2	1	—	—	13	0.1	6	0.0
Diabetes mellitus	20	35	16	20	18	15	14	9	14	11	354	1.5	256	2.0
Hernia and intestinal obstruction	17	16	7	6	4	3	1	2	1	1	25	0.8	31	0.2
Ulcer of stomach and duodenum	24	6	17	3	10	3	5	2	3	2	70	0.3	53	0.4
Syphilis	23	6	10	3	—	—	—	—	—	—	1	0.0	2	0.0
All Causes	1 249	1 118	1 336	868	1 208	599	1 044	552	928	529	(22 964)	100.0	(12 702)	100.0

Sources: Adapted from Nagnur, D. (1986). *Longevity and Historical Life Tables, 1921–1981 (Abridged): Canada and the Provinces.* Ottawa: Minister of Supply and Services, pp. 62–67; Statistics Canada (1988). *Vital Statistics, 1986. Mortality Summary List of Causes;* Dominion Bureau of Statistics (1933). *Vital Statistics, 1931. Mortality by Cause.*

Note: Death rates are expressed per 1 000 population. Rates are rounded to whole numbers. Residual causes are included in the overall death rate for all causes; therefore, the percentages for deaths in 1986 will not add to 100. Rates for motor vehicle accidents, other accidents, homicide and suicide for 1931–1986 were computed using corresponding Vital Statistics data for these years.

development reflects the introduction of better safety measures, increased awareness of safety, better car quality, and seat-belt legislation.

Suicide among men is a leading cause of death. In 1931 males showed a rate of 37 per 100 000 population, while in 1986 this rate reduced to 27 per 100 000, for a 27 percent drop in risk. Female suicide rates have always been relatively low. In 1931, women committed suicide by a rate of 8 per 100 000, while in 1986, their rate of self-death was 10 per 100 000. Suicide risk for both sexes peaked in 1971 and has shown a continued decline since then. This is a positive development, but there is need for further improvements.

Although notable reductions in the incidence of influenza, bronchitis, pneumonia (one category), and diabetes mellitus have occurred, they continue to be important causes of death. Although nephritis and nephrosis were major killers in 1931, by 1986 the death rate from these ailments became negligible. A similar pattern is evident for tuberculosis, syphilis, hernia, and stomach ulcers.

Age Group 65-74

Since the early 1930s, the pace of mortality decline among persons aged 65-74 has been more rapid for females. Between 1931 and 1986, female rates declined by 52 percent, while death rates for Canadian men diminished by only 19 percent. The largest improvement in mortality conditions for women occurred between 1951 and 1971, with a 31 percent reduction in risk. In contrast, the largest improvement in male overall death rates took place between 1971 and 1981, but at a modest 11 percent decline. However, since 1981 the male death rate has declined by 4 percent, while the rate for women has changed by 3 percent.

In 1931, cardiovascular disease, cancer, influenza, bronchitis, pneumonia, nephritis, accidents, and tuberculosis represented leading causes of death for both sexes. Today, cardiovascular disease and cancer are the major causes of death, claiming a total of 33 250 lives annually (or 77 percent of all deaths in 1986). Between 1931 and 1986, the male cardiovascular disease death rate declined from 1 754 to 1 606 per 100 000 (8 percent decline). Over this same period, the corresponding death rate for females changed from 1 532 to 764 (50 percent decline). This difference is a key factor explaining the greater gains in longevity women in this age group have experienced over past decades as compared to men. Also, cancer death rates have been higher among men, and their pattern of change over time reflects a greater degree of increase than is the case for females, explaining further the sex differential in survivorship over time.

Age Group 75+

With the increasing aging of the population, a great deal of attention is being devoted to the health conditions of elderly persons. Epidemiologists and demographers are

Table II   Death Rates for the Age Group 65–74 by Leading Cause, Canada, 1931, 1951, 1971, 1981 and 1986

Cause of Death	1931 Male	1931 Female	1951 Male	1951 Female	1971 Male	1971 Female	1981 Male	1981 Female	1986 Male	1986 Female	Distribution of Deaths in 1986 Male	%	Female	%
Cardiovascular disease	1 754	1 532	2 488	1 862	2 271	1 201	1 827	895	1 606	764	11 867	45.3	6 963	41.4
Cancer	763	696	783	618	1 034	566	1 073	610	1 147	652	8 477	32.4	5 943	35.3
Influenza, bronchitis and pneumonia	332	366	170	127	193	60	100	42	129	64	951	3.6	585	3.5
Nephritis, nephrosis (and renal failure*)	329	338	105	97	15	12	25	16	33	9	23	0.1	15	0.1
Suicide	35	5	27	8	24	9	18	10	28	9	210	0.8	84	0.5
Other accidents and violence	155	82	141	56	111	58	105	42	47	32	556	2.1	374	2.2
Diabetes mellitus	77	133	53	98	73	90	59	55	66	53	489	1.9	485	2.9
Tuberculosis	107	85	72	35	14	6	5	2	4	—	29	0.1	7	0.0
Senility	64	70	5	8	1	1	—	—	4	4	29	0.1	37	0.2
Anemia	52	65	17	18	5	4	4	3	5	2	35	0.1	21	0.1
All Causes	4 352	3 835	4 309	3 207	4 174	2 215	3 703	1 901	3 543	1 845	(26 183)	100.0	(16 814)	100.0

* Renal failure included in 1986 figures.

Sources: Adapted from Nagnur, D. (1986). *Longevity and Historical Life Tables, 1921-1981 (Abridged): Canada and the Provinces.* Ottawa: Minister of Supply and Services, pp. 62-67; Statistics Canada (1988). *Vital Statistics, 1986. Mortality Summary List of Causes;* Dominion Bureau of Statistics (1943). *Vital Statistics, 1931. Mortality by Cause.*

Note: Death rates are expressed per 1 000 population. Rates are rounded to whole numbers. Residual causes are included in the overall death rate for all causes; therefore, the percentages for deaths in 1986 will not add to 100. Suicide rates for 1931-1986 were computed using corresponding Vital Statistics data for these years.

devoting more attention to this age group than ever before for both analytical and policy purposes. As indicated earlier, senior citizens have been experiencing recent improvements in longevity. If mortality and morbidity follow a pattern of compression, as claimed by Fries (1980, 1983, 1989), the implications for health status and health care are not so pessimistic. However, if expansion of mortality in old age is actually occurring, as claimed by Manton (1982, 1989), Olshansky et al. (1990), and by Olshansky and Ault (1986), this will likely engender the possible scenario of older people "living longer" but "getting worse" in health (Verbrugge et al., 1990; Verbrugge, 1984). For example, Maclean and Oderkirk (1991) have reported that surgery has become far more common in recent years among Canadian elderly people. Between 1975 and 1986, surgical separations as a percentage of total hospital separations among elderly people increased from 29 to 37 percent. This trend may intensify over time.

The historical evidence in Table 12 indicates that the mortality rates of older Canadians aged 75 and older have been declining over time. In 1931, men in this age group had an overall death rate of 11 881 per 100 000 population, while in 1986 they showed a death rate of 10 206 per 100 000 (a 14 percent decline in risk). The corresponding death rates for Canadian women are 11 635 for 1931, and 7 330 for 1986 (a 37 percent drop in risk).

The pace of decline between each period has been more precipitous for females than for males. Between 1931 and 1951, the female death rate declined by 5 percent, while that of males was reduced by 2 percent. Between 1951 and 1971, women enjoyed a 25 percent reduction in risk, but men experienced only a 6 percent reduction. From 1971 to 1981, the reduction was 14 percent for women, and only 10 percent for men. But in the five-year interval between 1981 and 1986, males experienced a 2 percent decline in mortality, while females actually increased their death rate by 2 percent. This outcome may be a function of the fact that this is an open-age interval, and that since women have a higher life expectancy than men, there are more elderly women near the upper limit of this age class, hence more women will eventually die.

Cardiovascular diseases and cancers are the leading causes of death of elderly people. Both are chronic-degenerative in nature, associated with the aging process. Nevertheless, the cardiovascular death rate has declined from 5 247 and 5 302 for men and women respectively in 1931, to 4 997 and 4 097 respectively in 1986, which represents declines of 5 percent for males and 23 percent for females. The male and female rates of death from cardiovascular complications peaked in the early 1950s and have been on a downward trend since then.

The same cannot be said of cancer. Male rates have risen by 84 percent from 1 186 in 1931 to 2 185 in 1986. Females experienced increases in cancer mortality between 1931 and 1951, declines from 1951 through 1981, and then witnessed a recent ascendancy, bringing their death rate to 1 188 per 100 000 in 1986, as compared to 1 016 in 1931.

Table 12   Death Rates for the Age Group 75 + by Leading Cause of Death, Canada, 1931, 1951, 1971, 1981 and 1986

Cause of Death	Period 1931 Male	1931 Female	1951 Male	1951 Female	1971 Male	1971 Female	1981 Male	1981 Female	1986 Male	1986 Female	Distribution of Deaths in 1986 Male	%	Female	%
Cardiovascular disease	5 247	5 302	7 456	7 085	7 025	5 662	5 749	4 514	4 997	4 097	19 712	49.0	26 759	55.9
Cancer	1 186	1 016	1 446	1 137	1 880	1 088	2 074	1 084	2 185	1 188	8 620	21.4	7 759	16.2
Influenza, bronchitis and pneumonia	1 142	1 136	890	808	836	453	593	326	739	430	2 194	5.5	2 809	5.9
Senility	1 021	1 205	234	273	40	45	23	27	13	26	51	0.1	167	0.3
Nephritis, nephrosis (and renal failure*)	945	824	335	357	50	38	124	79	200	134	39	0.1	36	0.1
Diabetes mellitus	93	132	101	140	206	207	160	170	195	187	770	1.9	1 224	2.6
Hernia and intestinal obstruction	128	85	74	57	55	48	47	41	39	44	154	0.4	286	0.6
Diarrhea and enteritis	81	97	24	31	13	9	9	10	—	3	7	0.0	18	0.0
Suicide	35	5	31	6	27	4	32	12	36	6	144	0.4	36	0.1
Other accidents and violence	316	458	331	376	259	217	216	172	183	183	865	2.1	1 236	2.6
All Causes	11 881	11 635	12 169	11 059	11 446	8 329	10 410	7 190	10 206	7 330	(40 255)	100.0	(47 869)	100.0

*Renal failure included in 1986 figures.

Sources: Adapted from Nagnur, D. (1986). *Longevity and Historical Life Tables, 1921-1981 (Abridged): Canada and the Provinces.* Ottawa: Minister of Supply and Services, pp. 62-67; Statistics Canada (1988). *Vital Statistics, 1986. Mortality by Cause;* Dominion Bureau of Statistics (1933). *Vital Statistics, 1931. Mortality Summary List of Causes;* Dominion Bureau of Statistics (1933). *Vital Statistics, 1931. Mortality by Cause.*

Note: Death rates are expressed per 1 000 population. Rates are rounded to whole numbers. Residual causes are included in the overall death rate for all causes; therefore, the percentages for deaths in 1986 will not add to 100. Rates for suicide, accidents, and other violence for 1931 to 1986 were computed using appropriate Vital Statistics data for these years.

Between 1981 and 1986, the female cancer death rate has risen more than that of males (males increased their risk by 5 percent, women by 10 percent).

Since 1931, mortality from influenza, bronchitis, pneumonia (one category), senility, and nephritis (including renal failure), has declined significantly for both men and women. However, deaths from diabetes have been on the increase. In 1931, men had a death rate of 93 per 100 000; by 1986 this rate changed to 195 per 100 000. For women, the corresponding change was from 132 in 1931 to 187 in 1986. Hernia and intestinal obstructions, along with diarrhea and enteritis, represent declining trends overall.

Suicide for elderly men has followed two trends: a decline between 1931 and 1971, and a rise thereafter. For women, the highest risk of suicide occurred in 1981. Although accidents and violence show overall decline since 1931 for both sexes, the rates are quite high across all time periods observed.

All Age Groups

From an overall point of view, the population as a whole has followed similar trends in mortality as noted for the various age groups. Table 13 shows death rates per 100 000 population for leading causes of death in Canada during 1971 and 1988. The table also gives the distribution of all deaths by cause. Heart disease and cancer continue to be the leading causes of death in Canada. Lung cancer took the lives of 5 391 Canadians in 1971, and 13 104 in 1988, respectively. Other cancers were responsible for almost 26 000 deaths in 1971 and over 38 000 in 1988. In terms of potential years of life lost, Wilkins and Mark (1991) report that during 1987-88, lung cancer ranked fourth as a cause of premature death. Coronary heart disease ranked first as a cause of premature death among men, while it is second for women.

It is interesting to note that while cancer death rates have been on the increase, ischaemic heart-disease mortality (which is the leading cause of death overall) has declined since the early 1970s. The male death rate from ischaemic heart disease in 1971 was 279.4 per 100 000 and it was reduced to 208 per 100 000 in 1988. The corresponding rates for women declined from 174.6 in 1971 to 151.9 in 1988. The decline has been more precipitous for men (26 percent versus 13 percent for women), a fact that has contributed to the recent narrowing of the sex differential in overall life expectancy noted earlier.

This phenomenon has also occurred in the United States (Levy, 1981; Rothenberg & Koplan, 1990; Muir & Sasco, 1990) and in other parts of the industrialized world since the early 1970s (Breslow, 1985; Hatton et al., 1985). Important in the decline of heart disease has been a reduction in cigarette smoking and diet modification, accompanied by more participation in physical exercise, all of which contribute to a reduction in hypertensive complications.

However, in the case of cancer, the trends are not as optimistic. The data point to an increasing incidence over the years for both lung cancer and "all other cancers" combined (Gaudette, Makomoski, & Hill, 1991; Brancker, 1990). According to Wigle and associates (1986, p. 234), progress in the treatment of cancer has been rather modest. Muir and Sasco (1990, p. 144) refer to the prospect of a "demographic nightmare" regarding future trends in cancer since in many parts of the world the average age of the population has been rising for some time. As cancer is more common in older persons, the total number of deaths will increase in the years ahead. Muir and Sasco (1990) opine that prospects for reducing this scenario will rest to a large extent on how well society can promote primary prevention of the key known risk factors such as tobacco, alcohol, and high-fat diets.

Rothenberg and Koplan (1990, p. 292) suggest that a certain fatalism exists in our ability to deal with cancer and other forms of chronic disease. However, they indicate that if countries that have the lowest rates of chronic diseases are used as a gauge of potential future attainable reductions in death rates, coronary heart disease can be lowered by approximately 85 percent (to the current Japanese level), and cancer can be reduced by 37 percent (to the current Israeli level). Of course, the mechanisms and the length of time it would take to actualize such reductions is an open question.

Of the remaining causes of death in Table 13, respiratory disease accounts for a large number of deaths (over 10 000 in 1971, and almost 16 000 in 1988). Liver disease and cirrhosis led to just over 1 000 deaths in 1988. Congenital anomalies and causes of perinatal mortality take away fewer infants today than in 1971. In 1988, there were fewer people dying from suicide, motor-vehicle accidents, and violence as compared to 1971. This is an encouraging development because, as shown by Wilkins and Mark (1991), motor-vehicle traffic accidents and suicide rank second and third, respectively, in their effects on premature mortality among men. For women, motor-vehicle accidents rank third, while suicide ranks fifth behind lung cancer. Traffic accidents and suicide account for a large share of potential years of life lost, as such deaths tend to be concentrated among relatively young persons.

Regional Disparities

The degree of variation in death rates across provinces is not as marked as it was in earlier decades (Adams, 1990). Brancker (1991) has shown that the current difference in the age-adjusted death rate between the highest region (Yukon) and the lowest (Saskatchewan) is roughly 1.5 per 1 000. In 1987, death rates were above the national level in Quebec and Eastern Canada, and below the average in Ontario and Western Canada.

Table 13 Death Rates (Per 100 000) and Distribution of Deaths by Major Cause, Canada, 1971 and 1988

Cause of Death	Rates						Total Number of Deaths			
	1971			1988			1971		1988	
	Male	Female	Total	Male	Female	Total	Number	%	Number	%
Cancer of the lung, trachea and bronchus	42.5	7.4	25.1	72.3	29.4	50.6	5 391	3.4	13 104	6.9
All other cancers	119.8	120.8	120.3	147.7	143.1	147.1	25 947	16.5	38 115	20.1
Diabetes mellitus	12.8	15.7	14.2	13.7	15.7	14.7	3 073	2.0	3 819	2.0
Ischaemic heart disease	279.4	174.6	227.1	208.2	151.9	179.7	48 975	31.1	46 556	24.5
All other heart disease	60.1	57.9	58.9	41.9	45.2	68.5	12 714	8.1	17 758	9.3
Cerebrovascular disease	70.5	78.5	74.5	45.9	62.5	54.3	16 067	10.2	14 078	7.4
Atherosclerosis	13.3	16.2	14.8	7.5	11.5	9.6	3 186	2.0	2 477	1.3
Respiratory disease (excluding infectious and parasitic	61.3	34.1	47.7	73.4	49.6	61.4	10 286	6.5	15 919	8.4
Chronic liver disease and cirrhosis	11.9	6.0	9.1	10.9	5.1	3.9	1 937	1.2	1 014	0.5
Congenital anomalies and causes of perinatal mortality (excluding still-births	28.0	20.8	24.4	10.6	8.2	9.4	5 266	3.3	2 427	1.3
Motor vehicle accidents	37.3	14.7	26.0	23.4	8.7	17.2	5 616	3.6	4 445	2.3
Suicide	42.6	15.5	29.1	21.4	5.9	13.5	6 274	4.0	3 510	1.8
All other accidents and violence	40.3	20.1	30.2	29.7	16.7	21.9	6 518	4.1	5 673	3.0
All other causes	30.1	26.6	41.9	107.5	100.4	81.5	6 022	3.8	21 116	11.1
TotalCauses	849.9	608.0	729.2	814.8	654.0	733.3	157 272	100.0	190 011	100.0

Sources: Statistics Canada (1990). *Health Reports* (Supplement No. 12), Vol. 2, No. 1, *Mortality-Summary List of Causes*, 1988, pp. 10-56; Statistics Canada. (1974). Vital Statistics, 1971. Volume III, *Deaths*, pp. 112-157.

Analyses by Hay (1988) and by Adams (1990) indicate that with regard to life expectancy at age zero, the provinces have followed a trend toward convergence. In 1931, the difference between the lowest and highest regions was approximately seven to eight years. By 1986, the gap between the lowest (Quebec) and the highest province (British Columbia) had been reduced to approximately one year.

Undoubtedly, one of the most significant contributions to the convergence in life expectancy has been the extension of universal health care since the late 1950s and early 1960s. An implication of this trend is that region may be of lesser importance in explaining health status inequalities in comparison to age, sex, socio-economic status, and ethnicity (Hay, 1988, p. 29).

Socio-economic Inequality and Mortality

Disparities in death rates on the basis of socio-economic status have been observed in many investigations in different parts of the world (Antonovsky, 1967; Kitagawa & Hauser, 1973; Duleep, 1989; Kitagawa, 1977; Marmot, Kogevinas, & Elston, 1987; Wolfson et al., 1990). Unfortunately, mortality statistics in Canada are not cross-classified by socio-economic status. Analysts have therefore resorted to ecological-level investigations of the link between social inequality and mortality.

Wigle and Mao (1980) examined 1971 census tract data in urban Canada to assess the correlation between income class and life expectancy. They reported a strong positive association between income and survivorship. Men in the highest income quintile could expect to live to an average age of almost 73 years, while men in the lowest income quintile had a life expectancy of just over 66 years. The situation for females was shown to have been similar: the gap in life expectancy at age zero in favour of females in the highest income quintile as compared to women in the lower income group was almost three years.

Subsequent analyses by Wilkins and Adams (1983a, 1983b) and by Wilkins, Adams, and Brancker (1989) point to similar conclusions. Table 14 indicates that between 1971 and 1981, life expectancy in urban Canada rose for all income groups. Between 1971 and 1986, the difference in life expectancy at age zero between the top and lowest-income quintiles had narrowed from 4.6 to 3.7 respectively. Nevertheless, in 1986 there was a 5.6-year disadvantage among men with the lowest income in comparison to men with the highest income. For women, the differential is 1.8 years in favour of the upper-income quintile.

It would be important to ascertain why the association of income with life expectancy is not as strong among women as it is among men. While it is known that men generally possess higher mortality rates than do women, it is not clear why the effect of

Table 14   Life Expectancy at Birth by Income Quintile, by Sex, Urban Canada,
1971 and 1986

Income Quintile	Total			Males			Females		
	1971	1986	1986-71	1971	1986	1986-71	1971	1986	1986-71
First quintile	76.6	78.5	1.9	73.4	76.1	2.7	79.7	80.9	1.2
Second quintile	75.9	78.1	2.1	72.4	75.3	2.9	79.4	80.8	1.4
Third quintile	74.6	77.5	3.0	71.0	74.4	3.4	78.1	80.7	2.6
Fourth quintile	74.4	76.9	2.5	70.6	73.5	2.8	78.1	80.4	2.2
Fifth quintile	72.0	74.8	2.8	67.1	70.4	3.4	76.9	79.1	2.2
Total	74.5	77.1	2.6	70.6	73.8	3.2	78.4	80.4	2.0
Difference: $Q_1 - Q_5$	4.6	3.7	−0.9	6.3	5.6	−0.7	2.8	1.8	−1.0
Ratio: $Q_5 - Q_1 \times 100$	94.0	95.3	+1.3	91.4	92.6	+1.2	96.4	97.7	1.3

Source: Wilkins, R., Adams, O., & Brancker, A. (1989). Changes in Mortality by Income in Urban Canada from 1971 to 1986. *Health Reports* 1, (2), p. 146.

socio-economic status should be different for the sexes. These results suggest that
poverty is more devastating to men.

The quality of the social environment and lifestyle differences play important roles
in producing mortality discrepancies. According to Syme and Berkman (1976), the poor
are less resistant to disease and illness due to the disadvantaged conditions they face and
their relative lack of social supports. The poor share a high degree of fatalism, powerlessness, and isolation. Consequently, they tend to smoke and drink excessively, which over
time contribute to a lowering of resistance to illness. As a result, the poor are more likely
to die from infectious and chronic diseases in general, as well as from accidents and
violence (Marmot, Kogevinas, & Elston, 1987; Pamuk, 1985).

Occupational differences play a major role in the observed differences in death
probabilities across income groups (Moore & Hayward, 1990; Duleep, 1989; Hayward
et al., 1989; Behrman et al., 1990; Marmot, Kogevinas, & Elston, 1987). Many persons
in the lowest income class are actually working poor and are more likely to be exposed to
work-related injury and fatalities, in comparison to persons who are more skilled and
educationally qualified and enjoy a safer work environment. Also, occupation and
education are highly correlated; therefore, those in professional jobs are more likely to
seek prompt medical treatment in time of need, they smoke less, and are more inclined to
exercise. Thus, the social-class gradient in mortality reflects the interplay of poverty,
lifestyle differences, occupational hazards, variations in the quality of the social environment, and orientation to health and illness.

Table 15   Other Canadians' and Status Indians' Life Expectancy at Birth,
              1978–1981 and 1982–1985 Averages

Period	Other Canadians		Status Indians		Difference: Other Canadians – Status Indians	
	Male	Female	Male	Female	Male	Female
1978-1981	70.95	79.17	61.62	68.95	9.33	10.22
1982-1985	72.39	80.14	64.02	72.79	8.37	7.35
Difference between Periods	1.44	0.97	2.40	3.84	−.96	−2.87

Source: Adapted from Health and Welfare. (1988). Health Indicators Derived from *Vital Statistics for Status Indian and Canadian Populations, 1978-1986.*
        Ottawa, pp. 14, 15.

The gap in longevity by social class cannot be easily eliminated by sole reliance on universal health care since part of the problem is tied to health beliefs, response to illness, and general orientations to health-care utilization. While access to health care is a valuable privilege, it would appear that other aspects of the health/socio-economic relationship need to be manipulated in order to engender desirable improvements in longevity, namely, the social environment of the poor, lifestyle tendencies, health attitudes, and health behaviours.

Mortality Among Registered Native Peoples

To a large extent, the analysis of income and mortality also applies in describing the situation of the aboriginal population in Canada. Most Natives are poor and live in isolated and unhealthy social environments. Consequently, it is not surprising that they have high death rates and low life expectancies in relation to the general Canadian population (Siggner, 1986; Young, 1988a, 1988b; Postl & Moffat, 1988; Mao et al., 1986; Health & Welfare, 1988a, 1988b). For example, estimates for the period 1982–85 produced by Health and Welfare (1988a) show that Native men have a life expectancy of 64 years and women of 73 years. These levels represent a gap of eight years between non-Native and Native men, and a seven-year difference between non-Native and Native females (see Table 15).

Notwithstanding these large deficits in survivorship, Natives have made significant strides in improving their mortality conditions over recent decades (Health & Welfare, n.d., 1988a, 1988b; Frideres, 1993). Between the intervals 1978-81 and 1982-85, life expectancy at age zero increased by almost 2.5 years for Native men and by almost four years for Native women.

Infant mortality is a sensitive indicator of prevailing health levels and the quality of social conditions. To the extent that social, economic, and health conditions improve, infant mortality will fall. According to Hay (1988), the infant mortality of Natives fell between 1960 and 1981 from 79 per 1 000 live births to 15. During the same period, the corresponding infant mortality rate among non-Natives also declined, but at a slower pace, from 39 in 1960 to about 10 in 1981. Infant mortality declines have also been reported for the Inuit of the Northwest Territories, from 40 per 1 000 live births in 1976 to 28 in 1985 (Health & Welfare, 1988b). In time, the Inuit's rates should approximate the pattern established by Natives and non-Natives.

Table 16 contains cause-specific mortality data corresponding to Natives and non-Natives for the periods 1978-1980 to 1984-1986. There is a relatively high incidence of stillbirths among Natives as compared to non-Natives. In 1984-86, the stillbirth rate among Natives was 12.77 per 1 000 births, while it was 4.68 for non-Natives. This differential probably reflects differences in the quality and quantity of prenatal care between Natives and non-Natives. However, Native perinatal mortality rates in the most recent period are quite comparable, at just less than 5 per 1 000 births.

Besides the differences in the stillbirth rates, the most striking differences are noted in connection with postneonatal and overall infant mortality. Although Native rates have declined from almost 15 postneonatal deaths per 1 000 live births in 1978-1980 to 10.64 in 1984-1986, the latter represents a disadvantage for Natives of over 7 per 1 000 in relation to non-Natives. An analysis by Morrison and associates (1986) reveals that Native infants have above-average rates of mortality associated with accidents, violence, and infectious and parasitic diseases, which are causes largely associated with poverty, neglect, and isolation.

The mortality experience of aboriginal groups in Canada is similar to the experience of aboriginals in many developing nations undergoing demographic and epidemiologic transition (Broudy & May, 1983; Kunitz, 1990; Young, 1988a, 1988b). Infectious and parasitic disease mortality account for a large number of aboriginal deaths, even though the general societal context may be one of receding infectious and parasitic diseases.

According to Young (1988a, 1988b), Canada's aboriginals may be entering a precarious stage of modernization characterized by a double negative. With modernization comes fertility declines, which in turn lead to aging of the population; and an aging society will experience increased levels of chronic diseases. Within this general development, it is feared that the relative socio-economic disadvantages of the aboriginals are not likely to vanish, implying that the population will probably come to experience

Table 16   Infant Mortality Rates by Age Component, Status Indians and
Other Canadians, 1978-1980, 1981-1983 and 1984-1986 Average Rates
(Rates per 1 000 Births)

Status Indians	Stillbirth Rate	Other Perinatal Rate	Neonatal Rate	Post-Neonatal Rate	Infant Mortality Rate
1978-1981	11.54	9.65	11.37	14.72	26.09
1981-1983	11.72	5.23	8.08	10.84	18.92
1984-1986	12.77	4.82	7.33	10.64	17.97
Change, 1978-1986	+1.23	−4.83	−4.04	−4.08	−8.12
Other Canadians					
1978-1980	5.65	4.20	7.08	3.65	10.73
1984-1986	4.68	4.63	5.45	2.95	8.40
Change, 1978-1986	+0.97	−0.43	−1.63	−0.70	−2.33

Source: Adapted from Health and Welfare. (1988). Health Indicators Derived from *Vital Statistics for Status Indian and Canadian Populations, 1978-1986*. Ottawa, pp. 24-25; 28-29.

Note: The rates for other Canadians are for 1978-1981 and 1982-1985. Data for 1981-1983 corresponding to other Canadians not given.

unusually high rates of chronic and degenerative conditions, along with continued high rates of preventable causes of premature death, such as accidents, violence, and suicide.

Kunitz (1990, p. 665) adds that such a situation is problematic for other reasons. While improved health services have had a profound impact on the control of infectious diseases in society, it is doubtful that the health system can be as effective in the control of man-made and non-infectious causes of death. Circulatory diseases, cancers, and particularly accidents and violence are not preventable with vaccines or curable with anything analogous to antibiotics. Moreover, alcohol plays a predominant role in explaining the higher death rates of aboriginals, particularly deaths related to injury, accidents, and violence (Jarvis & Boldt, 1980; Levi & Kunitz, 1971; Siggner, 1986; Broudy & May, 1983).

Table 17 displays major causes of death for Natives and for non-Natives between 1978-1981 and 1982-1985. Deaths from complications of the circulatory system rank number one in both populations. The change over time has been minimal for Natives but it is noticeable for other Canadians, who experienced a reduction in this cause of death of almost 13 percent. Injuries and poisonings rank second among Natives but are fourth

Table 17 Other Canadians' and Status Indians' Age- and Sex-Adjusted Mortality Rates per 100 000 Population, 1978–1981 and 1982–1985 Averages

Cause of Death	1978-81			1982-85			Percentage Change Between Time Periods	
	Status Indians	Other Canadians	Ratio: Indians/Other Canadians	Status Indians	Other Canadians	Ratio: Indians/Other Canadians	Status Indians	Other Canadians
Circulatory system	313.8	344.3	0.91	315.0	301.2	1.05	+ 0.4	– 12.5
Injuries and poisonings	278.1	64.3	4.32	218.2	55.0	3.97	– 21.5	– 14.5
Neoplasms	118.5	168.0	0.71	120.5	171.1	0.70	– 1.7	– 1.8
Respiratory system	102.7	46.5	2.21	90.6	49.9	1.82	– 11.8	+ 7.3
Digestive system	70.8	28.9	2.45	49.2	26.1	1.89	– 30.6	– 9.7
All other	201.3	74.2	2.71	174.4	73.9	2.36	– 13.4	– 0.4
Total	1 085.2	726.1	1.49	967.9	677.2	1.43	– 10.8	– 6.7

Source: Health and Welfare. (1988). Health Indicators Derived from *Vital Statistics for Status Indian and Canadian populations, 1976-1986*. Ottawa, p. 5.

Notes: All age- and sex-adjusted rates are adjusted to the Canadian population distribution of 1981. The Status Indian mortality rate for 1985 does not include Pacific region.

among non-Natives. The gap between Natives and non-Natives has narrowed over time due to the former group's more precipitous declines in their death rate. In 1978, the Natives' rate from this cause of death was approximately five times greater than the rest of Canada; by 1988, this gap had narrowed to approximately four times.

Neoplasms are responsible for a large number of deaths in both populations, but the rate is lower for Natives in both time periods. Both groups have shared a small decline in risk over time. Respiratory and digestive system related mortality have also declined for Natives by almost 12 and 31 percent, respectively. In the general population, the rate for respiratory system mortality has actually increased over time; and for digestive system mortality the decline has been less dramatic (10 percent) than for Natives.

Overall, Natives showed a 43 percent greater death rate in 1982-1985 than non-Natives. As noted in the table, much of this excess risk is accounted for by the Natives' significantly greater risk of death as a consequence of injuries and poisonings, and to a lesser extent, respiratory and digestive system complications. Further improvements in Native health will depend largely on continued reductions in these major causes of death and on complications associated with infancy.

International Comparisons

Overall, the Canadian population shows a promising pattern of survivorship that has been improving since the early part of this century. The question addressed in this section is how well Canada's current mortality and survivorship levels compare with other major industrial nations.

Table 18 shows selected indicators of overall health status for Canada, the United States, Japan, Sweden, England-Wales, and France. As can be seen from the table, the differences in the overall age-standardized death rate across nations are not very large, but Japan has the lowest level followed by Sweden. France and Canada appear to be in an intermediate position, while England-Wales and the United States are highest in overall mortality level. However, the difference between Japan (lowest rate) and the United States (highest rate) is only 146 deaths per 100 000 population (or 1.46 per 1 000).

In 1990, the difference in life expectancy between Japan and both the United States and England-Wales is four years. Canada, Sweden, and France are tied, with a life expectancy of 77 years. The Japanese's current life expectancy of 79 (highest in the world) is largely a function of their significant declines in infant mortality since the early 1980s (from 8 per 1 000 live births to 4.8), and their relatively low rates of chronic disease mortality (cancer mortality is the lowest among the countries listed, and cardiovascular disease is second lowest, next to France). However, an assessment of this phenomenon by Masaki and Koizumi (1987) indicates that significant reductions in the probability of death have also been experienced by persons in middle and old age. These authors attribute these gains to the well-organized medical care and public services prevalent in Japan.

Canada compares favourably to Japan in regards to life expectancy (77 in 1990) and infant mortality (7.3 in 1990), but shows an intermediate position in connection with cardiovascular and cancer-related deaths. With respect to accidents and violence, Japan and Sweden demonstrate relatively low death rates, while our country ranks third highest, surpassed by the United States and France. England and Wales show the lowest rate of accidents and violence mortality (35.2 per 100 000), but demonstrate relatively high death rates from cardiovascular complications and cancer.

In a comparative sense, Canada's mortality levels are quite low. If Japan is used as a standard for setting goals for future mortality reductions, Canada could potentially experience further reductions in infant mortality and in cancer and cardiovascular disease.

The bottom panel of Table 18 indicates the extent of survivorship in the context of disability levels for Canada and the United States. Although the data are not strictly comparable due to their different dates of observation, an overall assessment may be attempted. These two countries differ in their health-care policies: Canada has universal health care, while the United States does not. Although on average the United States spends more than we do on health care, it appears that their returns on health-care spending are lower than in Canada (Evans, Berer, & Hertzman, 1991). Not only do Canadians enjoy a higher life expectancy, but on average we spend more years in good health than do men and women in the United States. Canadian men spend on average 61.1 years in good health as compared to 57.1 years for American men. Canadian women enjoy 66.1 years of good health on average, while women in the United States can expect 62.7 years in good health. These differences also imply that on average Canadians spend fewer years in restricted activity due to infirmity in comparison to men and women in the United States.

Conclusions

This chapter has outlined the Canadian experience with regard to its pattern of mortality change from the early part of this century to the late 1980s. Consistent with the postulates of the epidemiologic transition theory, Canada has witnessed a shift in its cause of death structure, from one exemplified by the predominance of infectious and parasitic diseases in the past, to one characterized by a predominance of human-made causes and degenerative diseases as the leading causes of death in contemporary society.

Significant improvements in survival probabilities were noted over all the time points studied. The period between 1931 and 1951 represents a significant interval in

Table 18　Some Population Level Health Status Indicators for Canada and Selected Industrialized Nations

Indicator	Country					
	Canada	United States	Japan	Sweden	England-Wales/U.K.	France
A. Standardized death rate per 100 000 (1987)	492.4	553.0	407.1	474.5	547.2*	484.8
B. Malignant neoplasms standardized death rate per 100 000 (1987)	135.5	131.8	108.5	110.2	149.0*	138.8
C. Cardiovascular disease standardized death rate per 100 000 (1987)	334.7	373.5	227.7	388.8	426.6*	222.6
D. Accidents and violence standardized death rate per 100 000 (1987)	63.2	71.6	47.1	50.1	35.2*	73.8
E. Life expectancy at birth (1990)	77	75	79	77	75 **	77
F. Life expectancy at birth (1980)	73	73	75	75	72 **	73
G. Infant mortality per 100 000 live births (1990)	7.3	9.7	4.8	5.8	9.5**	7.5
H. Infant mortality per 100 000 live births (1980)	12	13	8	8	14 ***	11

I. Life expectancy at birth

	Canada		United States	
	Male	Female	Male	Female
(1978 Canada, 1976 U.S.A.)	70.8	78.3	68.7	75.8
In good health	61.1	66.1	57.1	62.7
With restriction of activity	9.7	12.2	11.5	13.1

Sources:　A, B, C, D: Adapted from Adams, O. (1990). *Life Expectancy In Canada — An Overview.* Statistics Canada Health Reports 2 (4), p. 372.　E, F, G, H: United Nations. 1990 and 1980. *Population Data Sheets.*
I: Adapted from a table presented in Myers, G. (1989). Mortality and Health Dynamics at Older Ages, in L. Ruzicka, G. Wunsch & P. Kane (Eds.), *Differential Mortality: Methodological Issues and Biosocial Factors* (pp. 189-214). Oxford: Clarendon Press.

Notes:　For A, B, C, D, Standard Population is the World.
* England and Wales　　** United Kingdom

Canadian history in that the largest declines in overall death rates took place within these two decades. In connection with infant and childhood mortality, dramatic improvements in survival probabilities have continued beyond the early 1950s, denoting the important role of not only improved standards of living over the decades, but also of the positive effects of universal health care. Significant gains in longevity have also been recorded recently for persons beyond the age of 65, a phenomenon common to all Western nations in their final stages of demographic and epidemiological transitions.

Notwithstanding the institutionalization of universal health care in Canada, this overview of mortality trends shows that wide disparities in survivorship exist not only on the basis of age and sex, but also with respect to income and ethnicity (aboriginals versus non-aboriginals). These persisting differentials suggest that lifestyle, social environment (e.g., work, community, family), and health habits play important roles in the incidence and prevalence of disease and mortality. Therefore, improved access to health care by itself cannot eradicate these differences.

Further improvements in survival probabilities will depend on how well people in our society are willing to make the necessary lifestyle adjustments (e.g., diet, exercise, alcohol consumption, smoking, safety precautions, health habits) to promote good health, and on how well educational programs and public-health measures aimed at promoting aspects of good health and well-being are successful. Improvements in socio-economic conditions among the disadvantaged sectors of our society will also engender reductions in overall death rates, as many deaths to disadvantaged groups are largely due to avoidable causes.

Our society is now in the advanced stages of the health transition. We have succeeded in eliminating and controlling many sources of illness and premature death through medical intervention and social and economic improvements in the standards of living. In this context, an important issue facing the prospects for further improvements in health status pertains to affordability. Wigle and colleagues (1986, pg. 6) have estimated that in 1986 the grand total economic burden of illness to Canada was 97.2 billion dollars. Since 1960, health costs have increased from 5.5 percent of the GNP to 9.0 percent in 1980 (Beaujot, 1991). It is likely that these costs will continue to rise and that governments will feel compelled to introduce further cost containment measures in the future.

A detailed discussion of this issue is beyond the scope of this chapter, but it is instructive to consider some observations made by Evans and colleagues (1991) concerning the presumed relationship of health-care spending and health status in the population. In comparison to the United States, we spend a smaller portion of our national wealth on health care, and as shown earlier, we enjoy higher life expectancy; and our infant mortality rate is significantly lower. On the other hand, Japan devotes a lower portion of its GNP to health care than do Canada and the United States, and yet the Japanese enjoy a higher life expectation and also possess lower rates of infant mortality than both Canada and the United States. These observations underscore the difficulties inherent in making any direct connection between a nation's amount of health-care spending and overall health outcomes in the population, but if we compare ourselves to the United States, the argument could be made that less spending does not necessarily imply a relative deterioration in overall health status. If we gauge ourselves against the experience of Japan, however, it could be argued that we may be spending too much on health care, with a relatively lower return on the population's health status.

Perhaps further improvements in longevity and health status will necessitate that our society shift its conception of health by placing less emphasis on the traditional curative model of health and illness to one based on prevention. A number of authors have proposed such a shift as being essential (Lalonde, 1974; Health & Welfare and Statistics Canada, 1981; Health & Welfare, 1986; Statistics Canada, 1987, 1990; Angus & Manga, 1986; Evans & Stoddart, 1990). From the evidence presented in this chapter, this new orientation would seem appropriate as many of the leading "killers" in contemporary society are preventable and are strongly associated with unhealthy environments and lifestyles. However, the new perspective could pose a potential danger. If overemphasized, governments could place unrealistic responsibility on the individual for health, well-being and sickness, and hence use it to justify large-scale cuts in health-care budgets.

Acknowledgements: I am grateful to my colleague Herbert Northcott for some helpful comments on an earlier draft of this chapter, and to Louise Bohachyk for her secretarial assistance.

Study Questions

1. Outline the general pattern of mortality change in Canada since 1921. What factors are responsible for this pattern of change?
2. What are the implications of current mortality conditions for further gains in life expectancy?
3. What are the sociological and biological bases for the sex differential in mortality and life expectancy? What age groups show the most pronounced sex difference in survival?
4. In this chapter, it is shown that notwithstanding universal health care in Canada during the last 30 years or so, there are still significant discrepancies in death on the basis of socio-economic status and ethnicity. Discuss the factors responsible for these persisting differentials and how these factors could be minimized in their impact on producing mortality discrepancies.
5. Would further increases in health-care spending be effective in raising the overall health status of Canadians? Why? Why not?

Recommended Reading

Beaujot, R. (1991). Population change in Canada: The challenge of policy adaptation. In *Mortality, health, and health care*. Toronto: McClelland and Stewart.

Fries, J. (1980). Aging, natural death and the compression of morbidity. *The New England Journal of Medicine*, (303), 130-135.

Kunitz, S.J. (1990). Public policy and mortality among indigenous populations of North America and Australasia. *Population and Development Review*, 16, (4), 647-671.

Manton, K.G. (1982). Changing concept of morbidity and mortality in the elderly population. *Milbank Memorial Fund Quarterly/ Health and Society*, 69 (2), 183-244.

Marmot, M.G., Kogevinas, M., & Elston, M.A. (1987). Social/economic status and disease. *Annual Review of Public Health*, 8, 111-135.

Nagnur, D. (1986). *Longevity and historical life tables, 1921-1981 (abridged): Canada and the provinces*. Ottawa: Minister of Supply and Services.

Olshansky, S.J., & Ault, B.A. (1986). The fourth stage of the epidemiologic transition: The age of delayed degenerative diseases. *The Milbank Quarterly*, 64, (3), 355-391.

Omran, A. (1971). The epidemiologic transition. *Milbank Memorial Fund Quarterly*, 49, 509-538.

Peron, Y., & Strohmenger, C. (1985). *Demographic and health indicators: Presentation and interpretation*. Ottawa: Minister of Supply and Services.

References

Adams, O. (1990). Life expectancy in Canada — An overview. *Health Reports*, 2, (4), 361-376.

Angus, D.E., & Manga, P. (1986, March/April). National health strategies: Time for a new 'new perspective'. *Canadian Journal of Public Health*, 77, 81-85.

Antonovsky, A. (1967). Social class, life expectancy and overall mortality. *Milbank Memorial Fund Quarterly*, 41, 31-73.

Beaujot, R. (1991). Population change in Canada: The challenges of policy adaptation. In *Mortality health, and health care*. Toronto: McClelland and Stewart.

Bergner, M., & Rothman, M.L. (1987). Health status measures: An overview and guide for selection. *Annual Review of Public Health*, 8, 191-210.

Behrman, J.R., Sickles, R.C., & Taubman, P. (1990). Age-specific death rates with tobacco smoking and occupational activity: Sensitivity to sample length, functional form, and unobserved frailty. *Demography*, 27, (2), 267-284.

Bourgeois-Pichat, J. (1951). La mesure de la mortalite infantile. II: "Le causes de Deces." *Population*, 3, 381-394.

Brancker, A. (1990). Lung cancer and smoking prevalence in Canada. *Statistics Canada, Health Reports*, 2, 67-83.

Brancker, A. (1991). Causes of death 1989. *Statistics Canada, Health Reports*, 3, (2), 170-175.

Breslow, L. (1985). The case of cardiovascular diseases. In J. Vallin & A.D. Lopez (Eds.), *Health policy, social policy and mortality prospects* (pp. 197-215). Liege, Belgium: Ordina Editions.

Broudy, D., & May, P. (1983). Demographic and epidemiologic transition among the Navajo Indians. *Social Biology*, 30, (1), 1-16.

Caldwell, J.C. (1986). Routes to low mortality in poor countries. *Population and Development Review*, 12, 171-220.

Caldwell, J.C. (1990). Introductory thoughts on health transition. In J.C. Caldwell, et al. (Eds.), *What we know about health transition (Volume I)*, (pp. xi-xii). Canberra: The Australian National University.

Dominion Bureau of Statistics. (1933). Vital statistics, 1931. *Mortality by cause*. Ottawa.

Duleep, H.O. (1989). Measuring socioeconomic mortality differentials. *Demography*, 26, (2), 345-351.

Evans, R.G., Berer, M.L., & Hertzman, C. The 20-year experiment: Accounting for, explaining, and evaluating health care cost containment in Canada and the United States. *Annual Review of Public Health*, 12, 481-518.

Evans, R.G., & Stoddart, G.L. (1990). Producing health, consuming health care. *CIAR Population Health Working Paper No. 6*. Toronto: Canadian Institute for Advanced Research, Population Health Program.

Frenk, J., Bobadilla, J.L., Stern, C., Freijka, T., & Lozano, R. (1991). Elements for a theory of the health transition. *Health Transition Review*, 1, (1), 21-38.

Frideres, J.S. (1993). Racism and health: The case of the Native people. In B.S. Bolaria & H.D. Dickinson (Eds.), *Sociology of health care in Canada* (this volume). Toronto: Harcourt, Brace and Company.

Fries, J. (1980). Aging, natural death and the compression of morbidity. *The New England Journal of Medicine*, (303), 130-135.

Fries, J. (1983). The compression of morbidity. *Milbank Memorial Fund Quarterly/Health and Society*, 61, (3), 397-419.

Fries, J. (1989). The compression of morbidity. Near or far? *The Milbank Quarterly*, 67, (2), 208-231.

Gaudette, L.A., Makomoski Illing, E., & Hill, G. B. (1991). Canadian cancer statistics 1991. *Health Reports*, 3, (2), 107-135.

Gruenberg, E.M. (1977). The failures of success. *Milbank Memorial Fund Quarterly*, 55, (1), 3-24.

Hatton, F., Flamant. R., Bouvier-Colle, M.H., & Maujol, L. (1985). The fight against cancer. In J. Vallin & A.D. Lopez (Eds.), *Health policy, social policy and mortality prospects* (pp. 217-239). Liege: Ordina Edition.

Hay, D.A. (1988). Mortality and health status trends in Canada. In B.S. Bolaria & H.D. Dickinson (Eds.), *Sociology of health care in Canada* (pp. 18-37). Toronto: Harcourt Brace Jovanovich.

Hayward, M.D., Grady, W.R., Hardy, M.A., & Sommers, D. (1989). Occupational influences on retirement, disability, and death. *Demography*, 26, (3), 393-410.

Health and Welfare Canada. (undated). *Indian and Inuit health: Statistics show some improvement*. Ottawa: Author.

Health and Welfare Canada. (undated). *Indian and Inuit health: Accepting a health promotion challenge*. Ottawa: Author.

Health and Welfare Canada. (1986). *Achieving health for all: A framework for health promotion*. Ottawa: Author.

Health and Welfare Canada. (1988a). *Health indicators derived from vital statistics for status Indian and Canadian population: 1978-1986*. Ottawa: Author.

Health and Welfare Canada. (1988b). *Health*

status of Canadian Indians and Inuit: Update 1987. Ottawa: Indian and Northern Health Services Medical Services Branch.

Health and Welfare and Statistics Canada. (1981). *The health of Canadians: Report of the Canada health survey*. (Catalogue 82-538) Ottawa: Statistics Canada.

Jarvis, G.K., & Boldt, M. (1980). Death styles among Canada's Indians. Discussion Paper No. 24, Population Research Laboratory, Department of Sociology, University of Alberta.

Johansson, R.S. (1991). The health transition: The cultural inflation of morbidity during the decline of mortality. *Health Transition Review*, 1, (1), 39-68.

King, M., Gartrell, J., & Trovato, F. (1991, Summer). Early childhood mortality, 1926-1986. *Canadian Social Trends*, 21, 6-10.

Kitagawa, E. (1977). On mortality. *Demography*, 14, (4), 381-389.

Kitagawa, E., & Hauser, P.M. (1973). *Differential mortality in the United States*. Cambridge: Harvard University Press.

Kunitz, S.J. (1990). Public policy and mortality among indigenous populations of Northern America and Australia. *Population and Development Review*, 16, (4), 647-672.

Lalonde, M. (1974). *A new perspective on the health of Canadians*. Ottawa: Health and Welfare.

Levy, J.E., & Kunitz, S.J. (1971). Indian reservations, anomie and social pathologies. *Southeastern Journal of Anthropology*, 27, (2), 97-128.

Levy, R. (1981). The decline in cardiovascular disease mortality. *Annual Review of Public Health*, 2, 49-70.

Lopez, A.D., & Ruzicka, L. (Eds.). (1983). *The sex differential in mortality: Trends, determinance and consequences*. Canberra: Australian National University.

Mao, Y., Morrison, H., Semenciw, R., & Wigle, D. (1986). Mortality on Canadian Indian reserves, 1977-82. *Canadian Journal of Public Health*, 77, 263-268.

Manton, K.G. (1982). Changing concepts of morbidity and mortality in the elderly population. *Milbank Memorial Fund Quarterly/ Health and Society*, 60, (2), 183-244.

Manton, K.G. (1989). Epidemiological, demographic and social correlates of disability among the elderly. *The Milbank Quarterly*, 67, (Suppl. 2, Part 1), 13-58.

Manton, K.G., & Soldo, B.J. (1985). Dynamics of health changes in the oldest old: New perspectives and evidence. *Milbank Memorial Fund Quarterly/Health and Society*, 63 (2), 206-285.

Marmot, M.G., Kogevinas, M., & Elston, M.A. (1987). Social/economic status and disease. *Annual Review of Public Health*, 8, 111-135.

Masaki, M., & Koizumi, A. (1987). Increase in life expectancy at birth in Japan: Some implications for variable patterns of disease in mortality. *Health Policy*, 7, 41-48.

Maclean, M.B., & Oderkirk, J. (1991, Summer). Surgery among elderly people. *Canadian Social Trends*, 11-13.

McKeown, T. (1976). *The modern rise of population*. London: Arnold Publishers.

Moore, D.E., & Hayward, M.D. (1990). Occupational careers and mortality of elderly men. *Demography*, 27, (1), 31-54.

Morrison, H.I., Semenciw, R.M., Mao, Y., & Wigle, D.T. (1986). Infant mortality on Canadian Indian reserves, 1976-83. *Canadian Journal of Public Health*, 77, 269-273.

Muir, C.S., & Sasco, A.J. (1990). Prospects for cancer control in the 1990s. *Annual Review of Public Health*, 11, 143-163.

Myers, G.C. (1989). Mortality and health dynamics at older ages. In L. Ruzicka, G. Wunsch, & P. Kane (Eds.), *Differential mortality: Methodological issues and biosocial factors* (pp. 189-214). Oxford: Clarendon Press.

Nagnur, D. (1986). Rectangularization of the survival curve and entropy: The Canadian experience. *Canadian Studies in Population*, 13, (1), 83-102.

Nagnur, D. (1986). Longevity and historical life tables, 1921-1981 (abridged): Canada and the provinces. Ottawa: Minister of Supply and Services Canada.

Nagnur, D., & Nagrodski, M. (1990). Epidemiologic transition in the context of demographic change: The evolution of Canadian mortality patterns. *Canadian Studies in Population*, 17, (1), 1-24.

Nathanson, C. (1984). Sex differences in mortality. *Annual Review of Sociology*, 10, 191-213.

Olshansky, J.S., & Ault, B.A. (1986). The fourth stage of the epidemiologic transition: The age of delayed degenerative diseases. *The Milbank Quarterly*, 64, (3), 355-391.

Olshansky, J.S., Carnes, B.A., & Cassel, C. (1990). In search of Methuselah: Estimating the upper limits to human longevity. *Science* 250, 634-640.

Omran, A.R. (1971). Epidemiologic transition: A theory of the epidemiology of population change. *Milbank Memorial Fund Quarterly*, 49, 509-615.

Pamuk, E.R. (1985). Social class inequality in mortality from 1921 to 1972 in England and Wales. *Population Studies*, 39, 17-31.

Patrick, D.L., Bergner, M. (1990). Measurement of health status in the 1990s. *Annual Review of Public Health*, 11, 165-183.

Postl, B., & Moffat, M. (1988, November). The health of Canada's native people: An overview. *Canadian Family Physician*, 34, 2413-2419.

Peron, Y., & Strohmenger, C. (1985). *Demographic and health indicators: Presentation and interpretation*. Ottawa: Minister of Supply and Services Canada.

Preston, S.H. (1977). Mortality trends. *Annual Review of Sociology*, 3, 163-178.

Ravenholt, R.T. (1990). Tobacco's global death march. *Population and Development Review*, 16, (2), 213-240.

Rothenberg, R.B., & Koplan, J.P. (1990). Chronic disease in the 1990s. *Annual Review of Public Health*, 11, 267-296.

Riley, J.C. (1989). *Sickness, recovery and death: A history and forecast of ill health*. Iowa City: University of Iowa Press.

Ruzicka, L., & Kane, P. (1990). Health transition: The course of morbidity and mortality. In J.C. Caldwell et al. (Eds.), *What we know about health transition* (pp. 1-26). Canberra, Australia: Australian National University.

Siggner, A.J. (1986, Winter). The sociodemographic conditions of registered Indians. *Canadian Social Trends*, 2-9.

Smil, V. (1989). Coronary heart disease, diet and western mortality. *Population and Development Review*, 15, (3), 399-424.

Statistics Canada. (1974). *Vital statistics, 1971. Volume III, deaths*. Ottawa: Minister of Supply and Services.

Statistics Canada. (1987). *A review of national health surveys in Canada, 1978-1987*. Ottawa: Health Division, Statistics Canada Workup Group on Health Status Indicators.

Statistics Canada. (1987). *General social survey analyses series: Health and social support*. Ottawa: Minister of Supply and Services.

Statistics Canada. (1988). *Vital statistics, 1986. Mortality summary list of causes*. Ottawa: Minister of Supply and Services.

Statistics Canada. (1989). *Life tables, Canada and the provinces, 1985-1987*. Ottawa: Health Division, Vital Statistics and Disease Registry Section.

Statistics Canada. (1988, 1990). *Vital statistics, 1988. Health reports (Supplement No. 12), Vol. 2, No. 1. Mortality-summary list of causes*. Ottawa: Minister of Supply and Services.

Statistics Canada. (1990). *The health and activity limitation survey highlights: Disabled persons in Canada*. Ottawa: Minister of Regional and Industrial Expansion.

Syme, S.L., & Berkman, L.F. (1976). Social class, susceptibility and sickness. *American Journal of Epidemiology*, 104, (1), 1-8.

United Nations. (1990). *World Population Data Sheet*.

Verbrugge, L.M. (1984). Longer life but worsening health? Trends in health and mortality of middle-aged and older persons. *Milbank Fund Quarterly/Health and Society*, 62, (3), 475-519.

Verbrugge, L.M., Lepkowski, J.M., & Imanaka, Y. (1990). Comorbidity and its impact on disability. *The Milbank Quarterly*, 67, (3-4), 450-484.

Waldron, I. (1986). What do we know about causes of sex differences in mortality? A review of the literature. *Social Science and Medicine*, 10, 349-362.

Wigle, D.T., & Mao, Y. (1980). Mortality by income level in urban Canada. Ottawa: Department of National Health and Welfare, Non-Communicable Disease Division, Health Protection Branch.

Wigle, D.T., Mao, Y., Semenciw, R., & Morrison, H.I. (1986, February). Cancer patterns in Canada. *Canadian Medical Association Journal*, 134, 231-235.

Wigle, D.T., Mao, Y., Wong, T., & Lane, R. (1991, May-June). Economic burden of illness in Canada, 1986. *Chronic Diseases in Canada Supplement to Volume 12*, (3).

Wilkins, K., & Mark, E. (1991, March). Potential years of life lost, Canada, 1987-1988. *Chronic Disease in Canada*, 12, (2), 12-15.

Wilkins, R., & Adams, O.B. (1983a). *Healthfulness of life*. Montreal: The Institute for Research on Public Policy.

Wilkins, R., & Adams, O.B. (1983b). Health expectancy in Canada. Late 1970s: Demographic, regional and social dimensions. *American Journal of Public Health*, 73, (9), 1073-1080.

Wilkins, R., Adams, O.B., & Brancker, A. (1989). Changes in mortality by income in urban Canada from 1971-1986. *Health Reports*, 1, (2), 137-174.

Wolfson, M., Rowe, G., Gentleman, J.F., & Tomiak, M. (1990). *Earnings and death-effects over a quarter century*. Social and Economic Studies Division Analytical Studies Branch, Statistics Canada.

Young, K.T. (1988a). *Health care and cultural change: The Indian experience in the central subarctic*. Toronto: University of Toronto Press.

Young, K.T. (1988b). Are subarctic Indians undergoing the epidemiologic transition? *Social Science and Medicine*, 26, (6), 659-671.

Chapter 3

Threats to Medicare:
The Financing, Allocation,
and Utilization of
Health Care in Canada

Herbert A. Northcott, University of Alberta

Introduction

This chapter begins with a brief review of the development of health insurance in Canada and the principles guiding Canada's medicare program. A discussion follows on the various means of financing health care and on selected funding issues. Next, certain debates regarding the allocation and utilization of health care are examined. Finally, the extra-billing issue is explored and the implications of both cuts in federal funding and the phenomenon of population aging are examined.

The Development of Health-Care Insurance in Canada

Residents of Canada currently enjoy a universal health-care insurance plan that covers a wide range of hospital and medical-care expenses (for a discussion of the development of Canada's health policy, see Weller & Manga, 1983a; Taylor, 1978). Before medicare, health care was financed primarily on a user-pay basis: when a person required hospitalization or the services of a physician, that person was billed accordingly. While most users paid their bills, some did not, often because they lacked sufficient financial resources (Taylor, 1978). The poor, the elderly, and the chronically ill were often unable to meet their health-care expenses, and indeed, treating major illness could threaten to reduce even the reasonably well-off to poverty and a dependence on "charity." Not only did the consumers of health care, (i.e., the sick) face financial difficulties, but so also did the providers of health care.

Hospitals and physicians had to absorb losses from unpaid accounts and often offered their services on a charity basis, knowing that the user could not meet expenses. Thus, by the end of the first third of this century, there was a widespread sentiment, shared by both users and providers of health care, favouring the concept of public health insurance (National Council of Welfare, 1982, pp. 5-7; Taylor et al., 1984, pp. 2-3).

Following World War II, a wide variety of private and public insurance programs for hospital and medical care came into being. However, many Canadians remained uninsured, and many of the insured had only limited and inadequate coverage (National Council of Welfare, 1982, p. 7; Taylor et al., 1984, pp. 3-5). In 1946 (1947),[1] Saskatchewan became the first province to institute a public hospital insurance plan (Taylor, 1978). In 1957, the federal government passed the Hospital Insurance and Diagnostic Services Act, which provided for the federal-provincial cost-sharing of provincial hospital programs. This act was implemented in 1958, and by 1961 all provinces were enrolled (Taylor, 1978).

Medical-care insurance developed separately from and later than hospital insurance. Again, Saskatchewan led the way, establishing in 1961 (1962) the first provincial medical-care insurance program in Canada — and precipitating the 1962 Saskatchewan doctors' strike (Badgley & Wolfe, 1967; Soderstrom, 1978, p. 159; Taylor, 1978). In 1961, the federal government established the Royal Commission on Health Services, with Mr. Justice Emmett M. Hall as Chair. The Royal Commission's report was released in 1964 and laid the groundwork for the federal government's 1966 (1968) Medical Care Act, which provided for the federal-provincial cost-sharing of provincial medical-care programs. By 1971, all ten provinces and the Northwest Territories had joined the plan; the Yukon followed finally in 1972 (Taylor, 1978).

Canada's medicare program was established on several principles: some sources identify four (Taylor, 1978, pp. 364-365; Soderstrom, 1978, pp. 132-133), while other sources list five (Hall, 1980, pp. 39-46; National Council of Welfare, 1982, p. 15; Taylor et al., 1984, p. 5). The four principles common to all sources are: (1) universality — coverage of all Canadians; (2) comprehensiveness — a broad range of insured services; (3) portability — coverage could be carried from one province to another; and (4) public administration — the program was to be publicly administered on a nonprofit basis without the involvement of the private sector. A fifth principle — accessibility — is often also listed, although accessibility (i.e., reasonable access to services) can be subsumed under the concept of universality. It would not make sense to make all Canadians eligible for benefits, and then to allow barriers such as excessive cost or distance to disenfranchise certain segments of the population. In short, universal coverage implies equal access to services. These five principles were reaffirmed in Mr. Justice Emmett Hall's federally commissioned review (1980) of the state of health services in Canada.

Costs: The Financing of Health Care

The intent of the hospital and medical-care insurance programs was to provide comprehensive health-care coverage to all Canadians by removing financial barriers and by reducing the financial risks of illness. In other words, the individualistic user-pay concept — payment for services when and only when obtained — was judged to be incompatible with the concept of "insurance" and the collective sharing of risks and costs.

While health care in Canada is a provincial jurisdiction, the two federal health-insurance acts oblige the federal government to share the costs of provincial hospital and medical services and to dictate certain guidelines, including the five principles listed previously. Canada's health-care insurance system has been financed by a variety of mechanisms that have varied from province to province and from time to time (Soderstrom, 1978, pp. 131-142). Funding for this public insurance plan is derived at the federal level from general tax revenues (and, increasingly, from deficit financing, i.e., borrowing). Provincial funding is based upon some combination of general tax revenues, premiums (usually in the form of a fixed monthly charge paid by persons enrolled in the provincial medicare plan — certain groups such as seniors may be exempted), and user fees. User fees have been charged by hospitals and/or by physicians. Premiums, and especially user fees, have generated fierce debate and are discussed in more detail later in this chapter.

Hospitals generally provide services according to the budgets provided them by government. From time to time, various provinces have allowed hospitals to charge user fees. Physicians, on the other hand, generally bill the provincial health-care agency on a fee-for-service basis, according to a fee schedule negotiated by the provincial government and the provincial medical association representing the province's physicians. Again, variations on this theme have existed. The National Council of Welfare (1982, pp. 25-26) found in the early 1980s that: (1) certain provinces, for example, Alberta, allowed doctors to bill both the patient and the provincial health-care agency — a practice known as 'extra-billing'; (2) certain other provinces, for example, Ontario and Manitoba, allowed doctors to 'opt out' of medicare and to bill patients directly, with the patient seeking (often only partial) reimbursement from the provincial health-care agency — that is, reimbursement was according to the negotiated fee schedule and doctors often billed 'extra'; and (3) Quebec allowed doctors to opt out and directly bill patients but allowed for no reimbursement at all. In the early 1980s, the federal government waged a campaign against extra-billing, finally implementing legislation discouraging the practice in the form of the 1984 Canada Health Act (Brown, 1986, p. 111). By 1986, extra-billing by physicians had virtually come to an end. The Ontario and Alberta experiences with extra-billing are discussed in more detail shortly.

While the founders of Canada's medicare system did not want cost to be a barrier to services, the cost of health insurance has nonetheless been a continuing concern. Before medicare, fears were expressed that without financial deterrents, people would overuse the system and costs would therefore rise exorbitantly. In retrospect, these fears of frivolous and excessive overuse have proved to be unfounded (Enterline et al., 1973; Barer et al., 1979, pp. 30-35). Costs did rise, nevertheless, following the initial introduction of medicare, though not from demonstrably frivolous utilization. Rather, the costs of service, and, therefore, the incomes of the providers of health care rose initially, although the growth of these costs has subsequently been relatively constrained (Evans, 1984, p. 100; Soderstrom, 1978, p. 248; Naylor, 1982, p. 14; Barer et al., 1979, p. 4; Evans, Lomas, et al., 1989; Evans, 1990; Fuchs & Hahn, 1990; Barer et al., 1988; for a different opinion see Coyte, 1990).

Various models have been used to suggest mechanisms by which the costs of health care might be contained. In the classical laissez-faire free-enterprise model, consumers are said to "demand" services, and providers to compete with one another to "supply" the services demanded. In this model, it is argued that when demand is high, relative to supply, costs will tend to rise, and vice versa — when supply exceeds demand, costs will decline. In order to restrain costs, then, this model suggests that increasing the supply of physicians, hospital beds, etc. reduce the unit cost of services. Of course, ideally, this model also implies increased competition among providers of services, i.e., the demonopolization of medicine, and also implies reprivatization, i.e., the termination of the state's role in the provision of health care (for a discussion of the "push for reprivatization," see Weller & Manga, 1983b). Evans (1984, pp. 23-24) calls this model "the naive economic model" because it is, as he says, "not particularly realistic." The problem is basically that demand for health care is not the same as demand for automobiles or television sets. While advertising and "keeping up with the Joneses" influence my perceptions of need, in the end, I decide if I need a new car or not, and whether I can afford it. Health care is different. When I am sick, I go to the doctor and it is the doctor who decides what care I need. When faced with a choice between life or death, sickness or health, cost, while not irrelevant, tends to play only a peripheral role.

These criticisms of the naive economic model suggest that, alternatively, cost can be viewed as a function of the public's real need for health care, which, in turn, is accurately assessed and adequately serviced by the various providers of medical care. Evans (1984, pp. 21-23) calls this "the naive medico-technical model" and notes that it too is "not particularly realistic." This model fails for the same reason that the economic model fails; that is, the definition of "need" is not solely a function of the patient's real or even perceived state of health. The providers of health-care services tend to have the ability to generate as much "need" as they can service (Evans, 1984, pp. 88, 97, 99). To this point,

Evans (1984, pp. 85, 87) discusses Roemer's Law — "A built [hospital] bed is a filled bed" — and its parallel extension to physician services. In short, a more realistic model of the relationship among health-care supply, demand, and cost takes into account that the providers of health care themselves play a critical role in the determination of both demand and cost. I will refer to this model as the "professional control model."

A fourth model might be labelled the socialized medicine model. Under this model, the state controls the health-care system, determining the level of services and therefore utilization and cost. While Canada's current health-care system is occasionally described as socialized medicine, Weller and Manga (1983b, p. 495) argue that it is, in fact, a "mixed system, where demand [is] socialized via publicly funded health-insurance schemes, but where the supply side [consists] of an essentially private delivery system." Such a mixed system contains tensions that motivate various proponents to argue for movement either back towards a private enterprise system or further in the direction of the social medicine model.

Various solutions to the problem of costs are proposed. Those who adopt the rhetoric of the naive economic model identify consumer demand as the problem and argue for user fees to raise revenues and to reduce "unnecessary" demand. Critics of this proposal argue that user fees deter precisely those who most need services — the poor, sick, and elderly. Alternatively, those who adopt the rhetoric of the professional control model identify the power and monopoly of the medical profession as the problem, and argue for increased intervention against the suppliers of services. For example, some argue that hospital beds should be closed, that geographic quotas should be instituted to control the number and distribution of physicians, and that government payments in the form of hospital budgets and physician fee schedules, or even better, salaries, should be carefully rationed. Such intervention by the state, of course, follows the socialized medicine model. However, critics of this model argue that such restrictions will result in an insufficient level of services, such that legitimate medical needs will go untended. It is claimed that quality of care will suffer, that people will die in the streets awaiting services. This last criticism reflects the basic assumption of the naive medico-technical model, which assumes that medical practitioners identify and service only real medical needs and play no other role in the generation of demand for services. And so, round and round the debate goes with various proponents crying: "Control demand and thereby control costs!" or "Control supply and thereby control costs!" or "Control costs and thereby control both supply and demand!" Two things are certain: (1) supply, demand, and cost are intimately intertwined, and (2) the problem goes far beyond economics and lands squarely in the realm of politics and conflicting ideologies (Weller & Manga, 1983b, p. 514; Evans, Lomas, et al., 1989, p. 576; Evans, 1990). In other words, the problem may be economic; the solution, however, is political.

As a final note, as governments attempt to limit health-care costs, allegations of underfunding become widespread. Physicians claim that their real incomes are being diminished by inflation, or that they are losing ground relative to other professions. Accordingly, physicians argue that the fee schedule must be altered substantially and/or that they must be allowed the right to charge patients directly in addition to the fee paid to them by the government. Hospitals also often argue that they are inadequately funded and consequently have to cut valuable services and/or increase waiting times, with compromised patient care the result. Again, solutions are sought either through increased government financing and/or through the implementation of user fees. User fees, however, tend to be viewed as a violation of the basic principles of Canada's health-care program (equitable access, portability — see Hall, 1980, p. 32) and, consequently, have generated heated discussion.

Supply: The Allocation of Health-Care Resources

While the medical profession at one time endorsed the concept of national health insurance (National Council of Welfare, 1982, p. 1; Taylor et al., 1984, pp. 2-3), and while Mr. Justice Emmett Hall in his 1980 review of medicare "found no one," not even the medical profession, arguing for the termination of medicare (Hall, 1980, p. 2), the medical lobby has, just the same, frequently voiced its opposition to the idea of, or to various aspects of, government-sponsored insurance programs (see for example, Badgley & Wolfe, 1967; Blishen, 1969; Taylor et al., 1984; Stevenson & Williams, 1985). Underlying this resistance is the issue of professional autonomy and the model of the physician as a private entrepreneur.

Ultimately, the state controls medicine. It is the state that creates legislation that defines and regulates the medical profession. Further, the state funds the university medical schools, the hospitals, and the health-care insurance system. However, the state delegates its authority to the medical profession itself. In this fashion, the medical profession gains control over admissions to professional schools and over membership in the profession through licensing and disciplinary mechanisms. This delegation of authority from the state to the profession allows for professional "autonomy"; further, most physicians engage in "private practice" and bill the health-insurance commission on a "fee-for-service" basis. All of these practices support the notion of the physician as a private entrepreneur in a free-enterprise marketplace. Of course, this model ignores the fact that the medical profession enjoys a state-endorsed monopoly with severely curtailed competition and price-fixing in the form of negotiated fee schedules. Nevertheless, the free-enterprise rhetoric is regularly employed in order to protect the notion and image of professional autonomy.

In certain other respects, the physician fits the model of the "civil servant." For example, some doctors are paid salaries by hospitals or health units, and virtually all physicians, whether paid by salary or on a negotiated fee-for-service basis, are reimbursed ultimately by government funds. Further, major physical facilities used by health-care providers, such as hospitals and their support staff, are provided and funded by the state. Note that the doctor or nurse, who is employed by a hospital, is paid a salary, and can be terminated from employment by the hospital, more clearly fits the model of the civil servant than that of the private entrepreneur. While many physicians are not employed by the hospital per se, nevertheless, fee-for-service physicians working in the hospital must have hospital privileges that can be revoked.

Of course, the medical profession finds the civil servant model distasteful and threatening. The typical medical professional has little interest in becoming a salaried employee of the state, who is told when and where to practise or how much to charge for services rendered. Nevertheless, there are those who believe that "rational" allocation of health-care resources requires severe restrictions on the autonomous professional's freedom to practise where, when, and how she or he chooses (see, for example, Weller & Manga, 1983b, p. 515). There are those who have little faith that the forces of the free marketplace or of the medical profession will solve the problems of underservicing in rural areas or of overservicing in urban areas. Such persons argue that the adequate allocation of health-care resources depends on the intervention of the state, an intervention that threatens, increasingly, to transform the physician from a private entrepreneur into a civil servant. Not that this scenario is all bad! After all, the civil servant enjoys relatively high levels of job security, remuneration, and benefits such as a pension plan, paid holidays, predictable hours, and paid overtime — perks that the private practitioner often complains she or he lacks.

Demand: The Utilization of Health Care

Just as both the private entrepreneur and civil servant models can be applied, to certain degrees, to the physician, so also can the private consumer and civil service client models be applied, to certain degrees, to the patient. The patient is a free-market consumer in that she or he usually decides when services are required and generally has a relatively free choice of practitioner or service agency. The consumer model views demand for services as a personal choice, but recognizes that personal choices may be frivolous or unwise. Consumers may make personal decisions that result in the overuse or underuse of the health-care system. On the other side of the coin, consumers may be persuaded by health-care providers to make excessive use, or by means of deterrents such as user fees, to lower utilization.

On the other hand, there is a sense in which the patient becomes the client of a state-funded civil-service bureaucracy. Being a "client" implies entitlement to services offered or funded by the state. In short, the client has a "right" to health care, and health-care providers have an obligation of sorts to provide services to the client. Given that the client model sees services as a right, it ideally allows no barriers to services. Some argue that such undeterred 'clients' will tend to abuse/overutilize the health-care system, or, on the other side of the coin, that the health-care system might seek out clients and provide them with 'appropriate' care whether they want it or not.

It is, however, hardly clear what constitutes overuse or underuse. Similarly, it is difficult to define "need" in black-and-white terms. When a person falls and breaks a leg, it is clear to both the victim and the health-care provider that there is a legitimate need. But does a person need, for instance, a regular checkup? The answer will vary from person to person and from practitioner to practitioner. In other words, the definition of need is often subjective in nature. This means that the definitions of overutilization and underutilization are also often subjective in nature, and that what one considers legitimate use, another might consider overuse or even underuse.

Despite the difficulties of defining legitimate need, appropriate use, overuse, underuse, and abuse, it is often argued that user fees will deter people from seeking unnecessary health care. There is evidence that if user fees are high enough, utilization will go down (Badgley & Smith, 1979, p. 7), although there tends to be a "rebound effect" as physicians shift their patients to more expensive categories (Badgley & Smith, 1979, p. 7) or otherwise generate more demand (Barer et al., 1979, p. 34; Manga, 1981, pp. 672, 675; National Council of Welfare, 1982, p. 33). There is evidence that medical needs differ by social class, tending to be greatest among the poor (Manga, 1987; National Council of Welfare, 1982, pp. 9-11, 16-20; Canadian Sickness Survey, 1960, p. 150; Barer et al., 1982, pp. 19-20, 62-66; Soderstrom, 1978, p. 184). There is also evidence that the deterrent effect of user fees varies by social class, again being greatest among the poor (Badgley & Smith, 1979, p. 7; Naylor, 1982; National Council of Welfare, 1982; Hall, 1980; Evans, 1984, pp. 91, 334; Barer et al., 1979, pp. 33-34). In short, those who need services most are most deterred from seeking them. Before medicare, while the poor were more likely to be sick, they were less likely to see a doctor. After medicare, the level of service obtained by the poor rose (Enterline et al., 1973; Greenhill & Haythorne, 1972; Beck, 1973; McDonald, 1974; Boulet & Henderson, 1979; Soderstrom, 1978, pp. 179-182; Manga, 1981). These studies suggest that the wealthier classes are not as likely to be affected by deterrent fees, while user fees do deter (often necessary) utilization among the poor, resulting in underutilization.

Barer et al., (1979, p. 116) examined the use of a variety of charges directed to patients in order to control health-care costs, and concluded that "the scope for deployment of direct charges as a strategy for cost containment . . . is extremely limited." These authors went on to note that "most proposals for 'patient participation in health care financing' reduce to misguided or cynical efforts to tax the ill and/or to drive up the total cost of health care while shifting some of the burden out of government budgets."

In short, user fees (synonyms include extra-billing, balance billing, authorized patient charges, patient participation fees, deductibles, deterrent fees, utilization fees, co-payment, co-insurance, and so on — see Barer et al., 1979, p. 4; Badgley & Smith, 1979, p. 32; Hall, 1980, p. 4) are ineffective in discouraging unnecessary use, and indeed, tend to deter necessary utilization by the poor, sick, and elderly. Such deterrence violates the principle of equal access to health care. In rebuttal, some argue that the poor, sick, and elderly should be exempt from direct charges. The counter-rebuttal states that this proposal would create a two-tiered health-care system, with a public social-welfare tier for the poor and a private free-enterprise user-pay tier for the wealthy, who could purchase (more and better) services (Hall, 1980, p. 27; National Council of Welfare, 1982, p. 37).

The Issue of Extra-Billing

In spite of the establishment of a universal health-care insurance program, Canada's physicians have preserved the right to directly bill their patients, although certain provinces require that the physician "opt out" of medicare to do so. Further, physicians have preserved the right to charge whatever fee the market will bear, although the majority of physicians in Canada have remained in medicare and charged according to negotiated fee schedules (see Brown, 1986, pp. 123-125).

With the high inflation of the 1970s and the recession of the early 1980s, and with the 1977 Established Programs Financing Act, which extricated the federal government from the inflationary cost spiral and shifted more of the responsibility for health-care decisions to the provinces (Brown, 1980, pp. 525-526; 1986, p. 112), allegations that the health-care system was underfunded became widespread. Inasmuch as the 1977 act placed fewer conditions on the transfer of funds for health care from the federal to the provincial governments, Brown argues that one consequence of this change was an increase in extra-billing by doctors, especially in the provinces of Ontario and Alberta (1980, pp. 522-530; 1986, p. 112; for a contrary opinion, see Weller & Manga, 1983a, p. 237 and 1983b, p. 507). As extra-billing became more widespread, it began to attract more and more attention. It was argued increasingly that extra-billing deterred precisely those who needed medical services — the poor, sick, and elderly — from seeking care and thereby violated one of the basic principles of Canada's health-care program, that is, the principle of accessibility. Several studies examining this allegation will be reviewed here.

For the 1980 review of medicare, Mr. Justice Emmett Hall commissioned Professors Stoddart and Woodward to conduct a study of extra-billing in Ontario (Hall, 1980, pp. 24-25). A sample was drawn from the residents of four Ontario counties. These counties were chosen because they had high percentages of opted-out general practitioners and because they varied along the rural-urban dimension. Interviews were conducted by telephone and several thousand households were contacted. The findings, as reported by Hall (1980, pp. 24-25), include the following: (1) about one-third of households in the areas surveyed had been extra-billed; (2) physicians practising among high-income populations were more likely to opt out and extra-bill; (3) both poor and non-poor alike indicated reluctance to negotiate fees with physicians; (4) of those persons who had been extra-billed, the poor were more likely to indicate that they had "reduced utilization and/or delayed in seeking medical care because of cost" (p. 25); (5) further, the poor were twice as likely as the non-poor to say that doctors' fees presented a financial problem for them; (6) satisfaction with the quality of medical care was lower for those who had been extra-billed, especially for the poor; and finally (7) more than one-quarter of the poor expressed difficulty in finding a doctor whose services they could afford. Hall (1980, p. 25) concluded that extra-billing violates the principle of accessibility in that it deters people, in particular the poor, from obtaining medical care.

About the time that the Stoddart and Woodward survey was done in Ontario, a related study was conducted in Alberta. It should be remembered that extra-billing had become especially visible in the provinces of Ontario and Alberta (Brown, 1980, p. 522), although Ontario physicians had to opt out to extra-bill while Alberta physicians could extra-bill without having to opt out.

The Alberta study (Northcott, 1982) was conducted early in 1980 as part of the annual Edmonton Area Survey and involved face-to-face interviews with a representative sample of 428 adult residents of the city of Edmonton. This study found that: (1) the great majority of respondents had seen a doctor at least once in the past year and, of these, 46 percent had been extra-billed at least once; (2) two-thirds of all respondents were opposed to extra-billing, with one-third registering "strong" disagreement with the practice (only 19 percent were supportive of extra-billing; another 14 percent were neutral on the subject); (3) there was some evidence that those persons opposed to extra-billing tended to either avoid seeking medical care or sought out non-billing doctors; and finally, (4) the poor were most opposed to extra-billing.

In addition to the extra-billing issue, this study explored the public's perceptions of and attitudes towards physicians' incomes. The public exhibited a fairly accurate perception of the level of net income reported by physicians generally and was supportive of income increases approaching the high levels of inflation prevalent at the time. In other words, there was no evidence of public hostility directed towards physicians on account of their high incomes or income increases.

In summary, the findings of the 1980 Edmonton study indicated strong opposition to the practice of extra-billing as a means of raising physician incomes; nevertheless, perhaps paradoxically, the public was supportive of the high levels of income enjoyed by physicians. These findings lend public opinion support to Hall's (1980, p. 27) two recommendations that extra-billing be banned and that physicians be "adequately compensated."

A second study (Northcott & Snider, 1983) was conducted in Alberta in 1982, again as part of the annual Edmonton Area Survey. This 1982 survey involved face-to-face interviews with 507 adult residents of the city of Edmonton. The study found that: (1) the great majority of respondents had visited a doctor at least once in the past year, and of these, 37 percent had been extra-billed at least once; (2) there was evidence that the elderly were less likely to be extra-billed than the non-elderly; (3) those persons who reported that their health was poor made more visits to the doctor; (4) the elderly, in comparison to the non-elderly, made more visits to the doctor; (5) the poor, however, who were more likely to report health problems and who were expected therefore to make more visits to the doctor, did not; (6) while two-thirds of all respondents disagreed with the practice of extra-billing (44 percent strongly disagreed, only 18 percent were supportive, 17 percent were neutral on the subject), the elderly and the poor were even more likely to be opposed to extra-billing; (7) one-third of respondents felt that their own health care suffered as a result of extra-billing and 40 percent of these cited financial deterrence as the reason; (8) those who had actually been extra-billed, especially the poor, sick, and elderly, were more likely to perceive a deterioration in medical care than were those who had not experienced extra-billing; (9) conversely, the experience of being extra-billed had little impact on perceived quality of care for the non-poor, non-sick, and non-elderly; and finally, (10) the greater majority of respondents felt that the health care of Albertans generally suffered as a result of extra-billing, primarily due to the financial barrier to seeking care. In short, this study in Alberta in 1982 found strong opposition to the practice of extra-billing. Respondents, especially the poor, sick, and elderly, considered extra-billing to be a threat both to accessibility to and to the quality of health care.

As the evidence increased in support of the allegation that extra-billing or user fees deterred needy persons from seeking necessary medical care, thereby violating the basic health-care insurance principle of equal accessibility, the federal government increasingly pressured the offending provinces to ban extra-billing and user fees. This pressure culminated in the April 1, 1984 Canada Health Act which, starting on July 1, 1984, imposed a dollar-for-dollar penalty. That is, the federal government would withhold from its transfers to the provinces the equivalent of the amounts raised by extra billing and other user fees (Brown, 1986, p. 111). The federal government promised to refund these withheld payments provided the provinces ban extra-billing and user fees before April 1, 1987. Given that the funds withheld by the federal government amounted to millions of dollars a month, this placed the provinces under considerable pressure. Nova Scotia acted first, outlawing extra-billing in June of 1984. Manitoba and Saskatchewan followed suit in August of 1985. By January of 1986, only Ontario, Alberta, and New Brunswick were continuing to allow extra-billing.

Following months of heated debate between the government of Ontario and Ontario physicians, represented by the Ontario Medical Association, the Ontario Health Care Accessibility Act was passed on June 20, 1986, legislating an end to extra-billing. Ontario's physicians responded with a walkout that began on June 12, 1986 and lasted 25 days, ending officially on July 7, 1986 — the longest doctors' strike in Canadian history.[2] Nevertheless, not all doctors participated and physician support for the strike declined as time passed, with many returning to work before the walkout's official conclusion. By the end of 1986, relations between the Ontario Medical Association and the Ontario government had more or less returned to normal.

By the fall of 1986, only New Brunswick and Alberta continued to allow extra-billing, with the practice being in fact relatively inconsequential in New Brunswick. Extra-billing in Alberta, however, amounted to millions of dollars yearly, and while the Alberta government had opposed the federal government's attempts to end extra-billing, under the pressure of federal withholding of funds, the Alberta government began to campaign for an end to extra-billing. Alberta physicians argued strongly in favour of their right to extra-bill; nevertheless, the Alberta government and the Alberta Medical Association eventually, and in fact relatively peacefully, worked out an agreement ending extra-billing. This agreement was endorsed by a vote of the AMA membership and came into effect on October 1, 1986. And so the extra-billing issue, which many thought a threat to the entire medicare program, was resolved. However, since 1986, federal funding for medicare has eroded and as a result the issue of extra-billing and user fees may have to be debated yet again.

The Decline in Federal Funding

Initially, the federal and provincial governments shared the costs of the hospital and medical insurance programs on a 50-50 basis. Because of concerns about rising costs and the federal government's ability to pay, the 1977 Federal-Provincial Fiscal Arrangements and Established Programs Financing Act (EPF Act) redefined the federal government's obligation as an annual per capita contribution adjusted from year to year on the basis of increases in the gross national product. Furthermore, the federal contribution to the provinces was to take the form of both transfer of cash and transfer of powers of taxation (National Council of Welfare, 1991, pp. 10-15).

The federal government's ability to pay has been compromised by large budgetary deficits. The federal government has been running a deficit (i.e., spending more money than it takes in) each year since 1970 and, as a consequence, the total federal debt reached $400 billion in 1991 (Department of Finance Canada, 1991). Facing huge annual deficits and a rapidly mounting cumulative debt, the federal government in 1986 restricted the annual growth in EPF payments to the annual percentage increase in the gross national product minus two percentage points. In 1989, the formula was changed to growth minus three percentage points. In 1990, a freeze in EPF payment levels was implemented and in 1991 it was announced that the freeze would continue through 1994-95, reverting after that date to the 1989 formula of growth minus 3 percent (National Council of Welfare, 1991, pp. 16-17). Over time, these financial cutbacks have eroded and will continue to erode the federal transfers of cash to the provinces, ultimately leaving the provinces to finance medicare through the powers of taxation relinquished to them by the federal government. The National Council of Welfare (1991, p. 21) estimated that under the 1991 formula federal cash payments would disappear starting with Quebec in 1996-97 and ending with the Yukon in 2008-09.

Despite the federal government's reassurance that it will continue to require the provinces to conform to medicare's founding principles, the National Council of Welfare (1991) argues that the erosion of federal cash payments to the provinces will result in the demise of the national medicare program and its replacement with twelve different provincial and territorial programs. Further, it is argued that the poorer provinces and territories will tend to evolve inferior health-care services and may be tempted to deinsure presently covered services and/or implement hospital user fees and extra-billing by health-care practitioners. In other words, in this dismal scenario, the fundamental principles of universal and equal access, comprehensive coverage, and portability will be compromised. In short, the extra-billing debate which was accompanied by such rancor during the late 1970s and early-to mid-1980s may once again resurface as a contentious issue resulting from the erosion of the federal government's ability and willingness to fund the medicare program.

The Aging of the Population

The phenomenon of population aging, that is, the increase in the proportion of the population that is made up of persons 65 years of age and older, has raised questions about the viability of medicare (Evans, 1987). Because seniors are disproportionate users of the health-care system (Evans, 1987, pp. 165-166), and because the proportion of seniors in the population will most likely continue to increase well into the next century (McDaniel, 1986, pp. 33-34, 106), fears have been expressed that Canada's already costly health-care system will become unaffordable. However, most analysts agree that the "crisis scenario" places far too much emphasis on population aging, per se, and over-looks other perhaps more important trends (Denton, Feaver, & Spencer, 1986, 1987; Denton, Li, & Spencer, 1987; Denton & Spencer, 1983; Messinger & Powell, 1987; Barer et al., 1987; Evans, 1989; Evans, Barer, et al., 1989; Barer, et al., 1989; Hertzman et al., 1990). For example, studies done in British Columbia show that the aging of the population per se accounts for only a portion of the increases in the utilization of both physician and hospital services (Anderson et al., 1990; Hertzman et al., 1990; Barer et al., 1989; Evans et al., 1989; Barer et al., 1987). These studies show that a far more important trend than population aging is the trend towards increasing per capita rates of utilization. That is, seniors, on the average, are receiving increasingly more services than in the past.

There are a number of possible explanations for increased age-specific per capita utilization. It may be that while seniors on the average are living longer, they may also be on the average sick longer. Perhaps modern technological medical innovations are effective in prolonging both life and sickness. Indeed, there is evidence that patients who die are receiving increasing amounts of health-care services prior to their deaths (Evans et al., 1989). Alternatively, patients may be demanding more health care and/or health-care providers themselves may be generating increased rates of utilization. Whatever the explanation, upward trends in health-care utilization appear to be more a function of increasingly intensive servicing rather than population aging, per se.

Conclusion

Canada's health-care insurance program was founded on the five principles of universality, accessibility, comprehensiveness, portability, and public administration. Health care is expensive (although Canada's medicare system is apparently less expensive than America's free-enterprise system) and financial issues have led to numerous struggles between various levels of government, in particular the federal and provincial governments, and to many struggles between provincial governments and the providers of services, in particular, hospitals, doctors, and nurses. Allegations of underfunding have become widespread, and in the past have led to the imposition or escalation of user fees. Among the most controversial of user fees were those charged by physicians in the form of extra-billing. Many felt that user fees in general, and extra-billing in particular, violated the basic principles of accessibility and portability and threatened to destroy medicare. While few want to dismantle medicare entirely, there are many who advocate a return to a more free-enterprise system of medicine, with less intervention from the state, more professional autonomy, and more emphasis on the user-pay concept (although with a public insurance "safety net" provided by the government for the poor, sick and elderly). Proponents of this model (often referred to as the "two-tiered model") advocate "reprivatization" and argue that the problem of costs should be resolved in a free marketplace (free, that is, from government intervention, although not free in the sense of free competition), where providers of services charge according to demand for services. There are many others, however, who oppose these demand-side adjustments, and instead emphasize supply-side reforms. First of all, proponents of supply-side change argue that the providers of services must not impose user fees, which violate the principle of equitable access. Further, in their attempts to shore up medicare, arguments are made against any movement towards reprivatization or emphasis on free-market mechanisms. Instead, it is argued that there must be greater constraints on the providers of health care. Many of the supply-side suggestions (for example, salary or capitation rather than fee-for-service, or quotas on the number of practitioners who can practise in a given area) imply the transformation of health care into a civil service, a direction that is opposed by the medical profession.

And so the debates continue. Canada's health-care program is currently neither free-enterprise medicine nor socialized medicine. Rather, it is something in between. The practice of extra-billing, which threatened to undermine medicare and move the health-care system back toward the free-enterprise marketplace, has been banned. For now, the principles on which medicare were founded remain in place. However, Canada's mountainous debt, declines in federal funding, the aging of the population, and increasing rates of health-care servicing continue to challenge Canada's medicare program.

Acknowledgements: I am grateful to Earle Snider for suggestions regarding the outline/conceptualization of this chapter, to Jan Storch for her comments, to Caterina Pizanias and Lynn Skillen for research assistance, and to Judy Mitchell and Shirley Stawnychy for transforming my handwriting into readable copy.

Notes

1. The reader will note apparent discrepancies in the dates reported for various insurance programs. Some sources report the date that the legislation was passed; other sources report the date that the legislation came into effect. Both dates are reported with the date of implementation in parentheses.

2. The 1962 doctors' strike in Saskatchewan lasted 23 days. A 1970 strike in Quebec lasted ten days and involved specialists only. For surveys of physicians' attitudes following the 1986 Ontario strike, see Stevenson et al., 1988 and Globerman, 1990.

Study Questions

1. What were the circumstances and events that led to the implementation of Canada's national health-insurance program? Be sure to distinguish between hospital insurance and medical-care insurance. Why do you suppose these two related programs developed separately?
2. Discuss the five principles on which Canada's health-care insurance program is based. Assess the relevance of these principles for a national-health insurance program.
3. Discuss the relationship between social class, health status, utilization of health services, and user fees. Discuss the tension between extra-billing and the principles of accessibility and portability.
4. Compare and contrast the free-enterprise economic model, the medico-technical model, the professional control model, and the socialized medicine model. How does each of these models view the demand for services, the supply of services, and the issue of cost?
5. Discuss the problems in defining terms such as need, overuse, underuse, abuse, necessary and unnecessary or frivolous demand, underservicing, and overservicing. In practice, what roles are played by the public, the media, and the providers of services in defining these terms?
6. Compare and contrast the perspectives of government, the providers of health care, and the general public with respect to allegations of underfunding.
7. Discuss the implications of high budgetary deficits, a large public debt, and population aging for the future of medicare in Canada.

Recommended Reading

Barer, M.L., Evans, R.G., & Stoddart, G.L. (1979). *Controlling health care costs by direct charges to patients: Snare or delusion?* Toronto: Ontario Economic Council.

Blishen, B.R. (1969). *Doctors and doctrines: The ideology of medical care in Canada.* Toronto: University of Toronto Press.

Evans, R.G. (1984). *Strained mercy: The economics of Canadian health care.* Toronto: Butterworths.

Hall, E.M. (1980). *Canada's national-provincial health program for the 1980s: A commitment for renewal.* Ottawa: Health and Welfare Canada.

National Council of Welfare. (1991). *Funding health and higher education: Danger looming.* Ottawa.

National Council of Welfare. (1982). *Medicare: The public good and the private practice.* Ottawa.

Taylor, M.G. (1978). *Health insurance and Canadian public policy: The seven decisions that created the Canadian health insurance system.* Montreal: McGill-Queen's University Press.

Taylor, M.G., Stevenson, H.M., & Williams, A.P. (1984). *Medical perspectives on Canadian medicare: Attitudes of Canadian physicians to policies and problems of the medical care insurance program.* Toronto: York University.

References

Anderson, G.M., Pulcins, I.R., Barer, M.L., Evans, R.G., & Hertzman, C. (1990). Acute care hospital utilization under Canadian national health insurance: The British Columbia experience from 1969 to 1988. *Inquiry*, 27, 352-58.

Badgley, R.F., & Smith, R.D. (1979). *User charges for health services.* Toronto: Ontario Council of Health.

Badgley, R.F., & Wolfe, S. (1967). *Doctors' strike: Medical care and conflict in Saskatchewan.* Toronto: Macmillan.

Barer, M.L., Evans, R.G., Hertzman, C., & Lomas, J. (1987). Aging and health care utilization: New evidence on old fallacies. *Social Science and Medicine*, 24, 851-862.

Barer, M.L., Evans, R.G., & Labelle, R.J. (1988). Fee controls as cost control: Tales from the frozen north. *Milbank Quarterly*, 66, 1-64.

Barer, M.L., Evans, R.G., & Stoddart, G.L. (1979). *Controlling health care costs by direct charges to patients: Snare or delusion?* Toronto: Ontario Economic Council.

Barer, M.L., Manga, P., Shillington, E.R., & Siegel, G.C. (1982). *Income class and hospital use in Ontario.* Toronto: Ontario Economic Council.

Barer, M.L., Pulcins, I.R., Evans, R.G., Hertzman, C., Lomas, J., & Anderson, G.M. (1989). Trends in use of medical services by the elderly in British Columbia. *Canadian Medical Association Journal*, 141, 39-45.

Beck, R.G. (1973). Economic class and access to physician services under public medical care insurance. *International Journal of Health Services*, 3, 341-355.

Blishen, B.R. (1969). *Doctors and doctrines: The ideology of medical care in Canada*. Toronto: University of Toronto Press.

Boulet, J., & Henderson, D.W. (1979). *Distributional and redistributional aspects of government health insurance programs in Canada*. Ottawa: Economic Council of Canada.

Brown, M.C. (1980). The implications of established program finance for national health insurance. *Canadian Public Policy*, 6, 521-532.

Brown, M.C. (1986). Health care financing and the Canada health act. *Journal of Canadian Studies*, 21, 111-132.

Canadian Sickness Survey. (1960). *Illness and health care in Canada*. Ottawa: Queen's Printer.

Coyte, P.C. (1990). Current trends in Canadian health care: Myths and misconceptions in health economics. *Journal of Public Health Policy*, 11, 169-188.

Denton, F.T., Feaver, C.H., & Spencer, B.Y. (1986). Prospective aging of the population and its implications for the labour force and government expenditures. *Canadian Journal on Aging*, 5, 75-98.

Denton, F.T., Feaver, C.H., & Spencer, B.Y. (1987). The Canadian population and labour force: Retrospect and prospect. In V.W. Marshall (Ed.), *Aging in Canada: Social perspectives* (2nd ed.). Markham: Fitzhenry & Whiteside.

Denton, F.T., Li, S.N., & Spencer, B.G. (1987). How will population aging affect the future costs of maintaining health-care standards? In V.W. Marshall (Ed.), *Aging in Canada: Social perspectives* (2nd ed.), (pp. 553-568). Markham: Fitzhenry & Whiteside.

Denton, F.T., & Spencer, B.G. (1983). Population aging and future health costs in Canada. *Canadian Public Policy*, 9, 155-163.

Department of Finance Canada. (1991). *The deficit and the public debt*. Ottawa.

Enterline, P.E., Salter, V., & McDonald A.D., et al. (1973). The distribution of medical services before and after 'free' medical care — the Quebec experience. *New England Journal of Medicine*, 289, 1174-1178.

Evans, R.G. (1984). *Strained mercy: The economics of Canadian health care*. Toronto: Butterworths.

Evans, R.G. (1987). Hang together, or hang separately: The viability of a universal health care system in an aging society. *Canadian Public Policy*, 13, 165-180.

Evans, R.G. (1989). Reading the menu with better glasses: Aging and health policy research. In S.J. Lewis (Ed.), *Aging and health: Linking research and public policy* (pp. 145-167). Chelsea: Lewis Publishers.

Evans, R.G. (1990). Tension, compulsion, and fear: Directions, stresses, and outcomes of health care cost control. *Journal of Health Politics, Policy and Law*, 15, 101-128.

Evans, R.G., Barer, M.L., Hertzman, C., Anderson, G.M., Pulcins, I.R., & Lomas, J. (1989). The long good-bye: The great transformation of the British Columbia hospital system. *Health Services Research*, 24, 435-459.

Evans, R.G., et al., (1989). Controlling health expenditures — The Canadian reality. *New England Journal of Medicine*, 320, 571-577.

Fuchs, V.R., & Hahn, J.S. (1990). How does Canada do it? A comparison of expenditures for physicians' services in the United States and Canada. *New England Journal of Medicine*, 323, 884-890.

Globerman, J. (1990). Free enterprise, professional ideology, and self-interest: An analysis of resistance by Canadian physicians to universal health insurance. *Journal of Health and Social Behavior*, 31, 11-27.

Greenhill, S., & Haythorne, D. (1972). *Alberta health care study: Health care utilization patterns of Albertans, 1968 and 1970*. Edmonton: University of Alberta.

Hall, E.M. (1980). *Canada's national-provincial health program for the 1980s: A commitment for renewal*. Ottawa: Health and Welfare Canada.

Hertzman, C., Pulcins, I.R., Barer, M.L., Evans, R.G., Anderson, G.M., & Lomas, L. (1990). Flat on your back or back to your flat? Sources of increased hospital services utilization among the elderly in British

Columbia. *Social Science and Medicine, 30,* 819-828.

Manga, P. (1980). Arbitration and the medical profession: A comment on the Hall Report. *Canadian Public Policy, 6,* 670-677.

Manga, P. (1981). Income and access to medical care in Canada. In D. Coburn et al. (Eds.), *Health and Canadian society* (pp. 325-342). Markham: Fitzhenry & Whiteside.

Manga, P. (1987). Equality of access and inequalities in health status: Policy implications of a paradox. In D. Coburn, et al. (Eds.), *Health and Canadian society* (pp. 637-648). Markham: Fitzhenry & Whiteside.

McDaniel, S.A. (1986). *Canada's aging population.* Toronto: Butterworths.

McDonald, A. (1974). Effects of Quebec medicare on physician consultation for selected symptoms. *New England Journal of Medicine, 291,* 649-652.

Messinger, H., & Powell, B.J. (1987). The implications of Canada's aging society on social expenditures. In V.W. Marshall (Ed.), *Aging in Canada: Social perspectives* (2nd ed.), (569-585). Markham: Fitzhenry & Whiteside.

National Council of Welfare. (1982). *Medicare: The public good and the private practice.* Ottawa.

National Council of Welfare. (1991). *Funding health and higher education: Danger looming.* Ottawa.

Naylor, C.D. (1982, April). In defence of medicare. *Canadian Forum, 61,* 12-16.

Northcott, H.C. (1982). Extra-billing and physician remuneration: A paradox. *Canadian Public Policy, 8,* 200-206.

Northcott, H.C., & Snider, E.L. (1983). Deterring physician utilization: Medical care user fees in Canada. *Edmonton Area Series Report Number 26.* Edmonton: Population Research Laboratory, Department of Sociology, University of Alberta.

Soderstrom, L. (1978). *The Canadian health system.* London: Croom Helm.

Stevenson, H.M., & Williams, A.P. (1985). Physicians and medicare: Professional ideology and Canadian health care policy. *Canadian Public Policy, 11,* 504-521.

Stevenson, H.M., Williams, A.P., & Vayda, E. (1988). Medical politics and Canadian medicare: Professional response to the Canada health act. *Milbank Quarterly, 66,* 65-104.

Taylor, M.G. (1978). *Health insurance and Canadian public policy: The seven decisions that created the Canadian health insurance system.* Montreal: McGill-Queen's University Press.

Taylor, M.G., Stevenson, H.M., & Williams, A.P. (1984). *Medical perspectives on Canadian medicare: Attitudes of Canadian physicians to policies and problems of the medical care insurance program.* Toronto: York University.

Weller, G.R., & Manga, P. (1983a). The development of health policy in Canada. In M. Atkinson & M. Chandler (Eds.), *The politics of Canadian public policy* (pp. 223-246). Toronto: University of Toronto.

Chapter 4

The Rationalization of Health and Social-Service Delivery in Quebec

Deena White, University of Montreal

Introduction

When we refer to Quebec as a "distinct society," we are usually thinking in terms of language, religion, and culture. However, Quebec is also distinct with respect to institutions, such as the family, labour relations, education, politicics, and health care. While Quebec and the other Canadian provinces have faced many common challenges and dilemmas in the area of health care, particularly since the early 1960s, Quebec's means of handling them have been quite distinct.

Quebec, for example, is the only province to have systematically integrated all health and social services into a tightly co-ordinated network, extending from the community to the ministry; or to have imposed ceilings on payments to doctors, achieving a singular level of control over rising health costs. Furthermore, Quebec's health system conforms closely to the most radical visions of federal policy-makers with respect to the proliferation of community health centres (Hastings, 1972; Royal Commission, 1964) and the integration of the social and medical dimensions of health (Lalonde, 1974).

On the other hand, the Quebec health system has been self-diagnosed as suffering from paralyzing bureaucratization and sectorization, supposedly unable to initiate creative solutions to emerging health problems. The sweeping Castonguay Reform of 1971, which dramatically invented a health and social-service system as though from scratch, was a hallmark of the province's Quiet Revolution. Now, in the 1990s, the state has again taken the initiative and new reforms are underway that could once more bring about fundamental changes.

In this chapter, we shall address the following questions: How and why is Quebec's health-care system unique? Why was the rapid establishment of such an innovative, complete, and tightly co-ordinated system possible in Quebec, when other provinces' systems were changing more incrementally, and less comprehensively? What have been some of the advantages and disadvantages of Quebec's system? And, given the economic realities of the 1990s, what plans are currently being laid for the future?

Quebec was the last of Canada's provinces to adopt both hospital insurance (1961) and medicare (1971). This is because Quebec's institutional legacies from the period of British colonization and since Confederation were significantly different from those of English Canada; the process of shaping them to blend with federal initiatives had to take a unusual route. In the following section, we will focus on the special conditions that influenced Quebec's reforms in the health and social-service domain; examine the structure and dynamics of its health-care system; and, finally, explore the implications for the system of Quebec's evolution from welfare state to neo-liberal state.

The Historical Conditions of Change

To the extent that Quebec's cultural differences have been at the root of the province's historical development, these have had a significant, if indirect, effect on its social and political institutions. Without some reference to this history, it would not be possible to explain the preponderant role of the state in Quebec in developing, organizing, and regulating health care.

Under British colonial rule (1763-1867), the religious communities of Quebec took up a position of responsibility for the cultural survival and social welfare of the Catholic francophone population in the New World. This arrangement, which played a key role in keeping French Canada alive up to and beyond Confederation, gradually developed into an informal but powerful compact between the local francophone government, the Catholic Church, and the Anglo-Protestant economic elite of Quebec. Each of these "partners" was unofficially granted its own protected sphere of responsibility within the society. The twentieth-century legacies of this compact included, on the one hand, Church-dominated institutions in the educational, health, and welfare spheres (Rivard, 1970), and on the other hand, conspicuous ethno-linguistic inequality in the economic and occupational spheres (Royal Commission, 1967-70).

For close to two centuries, then, most health services in Quebec were owned and managed by religious communities and funded through the resources of the Catholic Church.[1] For the anglophone population, the situation was not altogether different:

Table 1   Life Expectancy at Birth, Quebec and Canada

Period	Quebec	Canada
1925-27	53.76	61.39
1930-32	59.96	61.00
1935-37	59.24	62.45
1940-42	61.73	64.50
1945-47	64.49	66.73
1950-52	66.54	68.51
1955-57	68.52	70.13
1960-62	70.00	71.14
1965-67	70.75	71.79
1970-72	71.64	72.74
1975-77	72.78	73.83
1980-82	74.84	75.39
1985-87*	75.67	76.39

Sources: Government of Canada (1986). *Longevity and Historical Life Tables 1921-1981, Canada and the Provinces.* Ottawa: Minister of Supply and Services.

* Statistics Canada

communities built and operated their own medical and social-service facilities. How-ever, following the British model, these were generally funded and run by secular phil-anthropic associations, rather than religious ones, and relied heavily on donations from the private, anglophone business sector, a source to which francophones had limited access. The Quebec government, like other provincial governments of the time, contrib-uted minimally to the maintenance of these services.

Social indicators suggest that throughout much of this period, the health status of Quebeckers was lower than the Canadian average. Differences in life expectancy and infant mortality rates were especially significant in the early twentieth century, and persisted up to the 1950s and beyond (Tables 1 and 2). Not only did death come sooner in Quebec, but the province also had nearly twice the national rate of disability (Boucher, 1963). This may have been partially attributable to the absence of health facilities in rural regions, where the majority of the population lived up to the 1930s, as well as to the harsh living conditions and occupational hazards faced by the farmers and loggers. But, throughout this period, most other provincial governments contributed no more to health care than did Quebec.

In the wake of the Second World War, some provincial governments — Saskatchewan and British Columbia in particular — began to intercede more systemati-cally in issues of health and welfare (Torrance, 1981). The Quebec government, however,

Table 2   Infant Death Rates per 1 000 Live Births, Quebec and Canada.

Period	Quebec	Canada
1921	128.3	88.2
1931	112.9	86.0
1941	75.9	61.1
1951	48.1	38.5
1961	31.5	27.2
1971	18.4	17.5
1981	8.5	9.6
1989*	6.9	7.2

Sources: Government of Canada (1986). *Longevity and Historical Life Tables 1921-1981, Canada and the Provinces.* Ottawa: Minister of Supply and Services.

* Statistics Canada

remained steadfastly non-interventionist, mainly because of the political tenacity of Maurice Duplessis, provincial premier almost continuously for 23 years (1936–39, and again from 1944 to his death in 1959). Duplessis's conservative, rural-nationalist government resisted federal initiatives in areas officially under provincial jurisdiction because it supported — and was to a large extent supported by — the traditional political, social, and economic compact between state, church, and economic elite. Yet Table 3 shows that throughout the 1950s, and even the 1960s, Quebec was not alone in resisting

Table 3   Percent of Gross General Expenditures Disbursed for Health, Selected Years, Selected Provinces and Canada.

Year	Que.	Ont.	Sask.	B.C.	N.B.	Canada
1952	13.9	13.3	31.2	21.2	10.6	16.0
1955	12.3	15.3	34.3	26.4	10.4	16.9
1959	12.3	12.9	28.6	19.2	10.5	14.8
1962	16.5	22.0	25.5	17.0	19.1	19.3
1965	17.6	20.1	31.1	16.5	19.6	19.3
1968	23.6	26.4	31.3	23.3	18.0	24.1
1979*	22.0	20.7	21.7	27.5	20.7	23.9
1985*	20.3	30.4	23.6	27.4	22.4	24.1

Sources: Government of Canada, Public Finance and Transportation Division. 1952-1968. *Percentage Distribution of Net General Expenditure. Financial Statistics of Provincial Governments: Revenue and Expenditure.* Ottawa: Dominion Bureau of Statistics. *Government of Canada. (1989). *Public Accounts of Canada: Summary Report of Financial Statements.* Ottawa: Minister of Supply and Services.

massive fiscal involvement in health: during these two decades of change, government contributions varied widely across provinces and over time.

Despite Duplessis, Quebec society was rapidly evolving during the postwar era. A new, educated, francophone middle class had been publicly and stridently calling for the fall of Duplessis and the modernization of Quebec institutions since the mid-1940s (Guindon, 1964; Lesemann, 1984). By the 1950s, the religious communities had become aware that their traditional institutions were lagging behind social and medical progress. They were confronted by deteriorating facilities, rapid population growth, an increasingly secularized public, and spiralling costs (Lesemann, 1984). To add to the crisis, in the following decade a plunge in the number of women choosing to join religious communities was to drastically reduce the Church's access to cheap professional labour in hospitals.

By the 1960s, significant developments began to occur within the health and social-service professions as well, despite the persistence of traditional institutions. A new generation of young physicians, captivated by the concept of social medicine, waged ideological warfare against the traditional medical elite (Lesemann, 1977); and the emerging "community organizations" challenged traditional social work in ways inspired by the American activist Saul Alinsky, as well as the American War Against Poverty (Godbout, 1983; Favreau, 1989). Parallel educational programs for health and social-service professionals were set up in some universities, competing with more traditional training programs (Lesemann, 1977). If the political and institutional modernization of Quebec society was stalled until the death of Duplessis in 1959, social progress was not.

The new government taking over from Duplessis, and representing the aspirations and values of the growing, educated middle class, quickly implemented universal hospital insurance (1961). But further progress would not have been possible without the establishment of a new institutional order. Although increasing sums of public money were being injected into health and social services during the 1960s (Table 3), the Church, still legal owner and manager of most health institutions, was no longer a socially legitimate, or even a willing trustee. Under these conditions, the Quebec government faced the task of inventing an entirely new health system.

This might explain why reforms in Quebec appeared to take the form of a "quiet revolution." John Hastings characterized the "revolutionary" aspect of this period (1960-75) by comparing the health-reform process in Quebec to that in Ontario.

The development of the Ontario health system has been evolutionary, incremental and sectoral rather than *system-wide* and *comprehensive* in nature. It has been pragmatic and responsive rather than *ideological* in motivation. . . . It has reflected short-term rather than *strategic planning* approaches. It has led to adjustments in the system rather than to *radical innovation* and changes in direction. It has been cautiously reformist rather than *visionary and sweeping*.

(Hastings, 1987, p. 37, author's italics)

Two factors in particular account for the capacity of the Quebec government of the 1960s and 1970s to enact and implement such a "radical" and "visionary" health reform, so swiftly and unilaterally that some have suggested it was somewhat authoritarian (Lesemann, 1977; Renaud, 1989). The first is the extent to which existing health institutions had lost all legitimacy in the context of an otherwise modern, industrialized, and urban society. The second is that these comprehensive reforms corresponded to the values of the expanding middle class, and even more importantly, met the economic aspirations of this class by opening up a profusion of professional jobs in the rapidly swelling para-public health and social-service sphere (Guindon, 1964; Renaud, 1978).

The Castonguay Reforms

One of the distinctive aspects of health and other major reforms in Quebec during the Quiet Revolution is that, rather than simply regulating existing organizational operations and activities, a wholesale institutional restructuring was undertaken. In 1966, Claude Castonguay, an actuary by profession, was appointed to head a Commission of Enquiry into Health and Social Welfare. The vast mandate of the Castonguay Commission included the definition of basic principles for social development in Quebec, recommendations for the organization and regulation of health, social services, welfare and professional structures, and plans for the design and management of medicare. Castonguay soon after entered politics and headed the Ministry of Social Affairs. In 1971, he had the unusual privilege of implementing the comprehensive systems he and his commissioners had conceived as government consultants.

The first two guiding principles of the Castonguay refoms were equity and efficiency: equity in the sense of reducing the substantial gap in health status between the small, wealthy minority and the massive *classe populaire*, or working class, as well as between urban and rural dwellers; and efficiency in the sense of ensuring the greatest possible gains without losing control over costs. Within these reforms, issues related to the production of health services and the organization of the service delivery system have tended to take precedence over issues related directly to the state of health of the population. This is not to suggest that the health status of Quebeckers has stagnated since the reforms were instituted. On the contrary, gains have been impressive. These improvements, however, had begun long before the adoption of the 1971 reform (see

Tables 1 and 2), and corresponded to similar trends throughout Canada and the industrialized West.

While advances in both curative and preventive medicine in the West have undoubtedly played a leading role in enhancing the population's health, it is tempting to believe that the particular socio-health orientation of Quebec's system, and the province-wide provision of a range of statutory health and social services has had a special impact. However, since it is difficult to isolate the impact of the Castonguay Reform itself on the health of the nation, in the remaining sections of this chapter, we shall focus on service delivery and its relation to the global objective of the reform: to establish an efficient and equitable health-care system that could answer to the full range of health and social-service needs of the Quebec population.

An Integrated Network of Public Establishments

The 1971 Castonguay reforms instituted a universal public medicare system in Quebec. Along with it, Quebec's first Health and Social Services Act was adopted to manage the provision of publicly funded services. This act imposed the integration of almost all Church-and community-run health and social-service organizations in the province into a single, coherent network of public establishments, tightly co-ordinated and fully financed by the newly created Ministry of Social Affairs. The network included all general and specialized hospitals, most convalescent and rehabilitation facilities, and all major social-service agencies.

Two entirely new institutions were introduced: CLSCs (local community service centres) mandated to provide both primary and preventive health and social services in a multidisciplinary, non-bureaucratic, participatory environment; and Regional Health and Social Services Councils to act as intermediaries between the public network establishments in each region and the central ministry. Furthermore, all municipal public-health units were replaced by the DSCs, or departments of community health, which were established in 32 regional hospitals covering the province.

The constituent facilities of the network remained autonomous to the extent that each had its own board of directors to decide on issues related to internal functioning. But, in an effort to democratize the system, the composition of the boards of all hospitals, agencies, CLSCs, and regional councils was determined by the Act Respecting Health and Social Services. Local communities were assured some measure of input into the management of their institutions through their presence on these boards, as were the professionals who worked in the establishments. On the other hand, the act restricted the powers of the boards of directors by stipulating the mission and mandates of each type of establishment, and by assigning to the ministry the responsibility of co-ordinating the network as a whole.

The principle for network co-ordination was complementarity: each type of estab-lishment in the network had its own carefully circumscribed mandate so that its services did not overlap with those offered by other establishments. This was one of the chief rationalizing strategies adopted to ensure efficiency. It permitted a clear distinction between those establishments and professionals that provided primary and less costly services, and those that provided highly specialized and expensive services. Hospitals and social-service centres, for example, were to be reserved for specialized services, while consultation for less serious health and social problems were to be made available in CLSCs at considerably lower cost to the government.

This rationalization through complementarity was supposed to reduce the inappro-priate use of costly hospital emergency wards and outpatient clinics. It was also intended to protect the autonomy of organizations and professionals in a context of multidisci-plinary intervention — particularly social organizations and professionals against medi-cal dominance. For example, it was not in a hospital's mandate to administer social services; therefore, all social workers were employed by, and operated under, the func-tional authority of social-service centres, which in turn provided social services in hospital and other settings.

But co-ordination-by-complementarity has not had the intended results. For exam-ple, hospital emergency rooms are still being used as providers of primary care, with the attendant problems of overcrowding. Complementarity has also had a somewhat per-verse effect on the internal functioning of the health and social-service network. During the early years of system expansion and consolidation in particular, when tight finances imposed zero-sum strategies, the different types of establishments found themselves in competition with each other for mandates and the resources associated with them. For example, which health and social services were to be considered "primary" and which "specialized"? Which, therefore, were to be offered in newly created CLSCs versus well-established hospitals or social-service centres? The answers determined which of these establishments would lose human and material resources, or gain them at the expense of the other. Indeed, CLSCs have been founded mainly on the basis of transfers of person-nel from municipal public-health units, hospitals and DSCs, and social-service centres, a situation that has not been conducive to co-operative relations between organizations.

Some of the contradictory aspects of the socio-health approach, particularly as it was manifested in the development of CLSCs, will be examined here.

The CLSC: Contradictions of the Socio-Health Approach

Although CLSCs were originally designated the corner-stone of the 1971 Caston-guay reform of socio-health policy, it was to take at least fifteen years of stop and go development before they were finally established in over 160 communities through-out Quebec.

The CLSC concept had grown out of the citizens' committees and popular clinics that had mushroomed in Montreal and other parts of the province during the 1960s. Ideally, the concept was to combine both health and social services in small, local organizations that would be sensitive to the collective needs of the community, emi-nently accessible to the local population, and open to citizen involvement. In CLSCs, community organizers work side by side with nurses, social workers, and other profes-sionals committed to a community approach in health care.

Ultimately, the systematic creation of CLSCs by the Quebec government was to annihilate the very grass-roots organizations that originally had inspired them. CLSCs rapidly came to be mistrusted by community activists, and citizen participation was rendered ineffective as CLSC health, social, and community service professionals unionized and asserted their professional power. These efforts to professionalize, how-ever, did not earn CLSCs the respect of health workers in traditional medical environ-ments. To many, the socio-health mandate of the CLSCs remains somewhat obscure and suspect. First, its community approach, including health education, prevention and community programs, is not always taken seriously by traditional clinical or scientifi-cally oriented professionals. Second, its internal organization is relatively non-hierarchic, leading some to see it as inefficient and ineffective. Third, many other institutions were losing personnel to the CLSCs, causing the latter to be viewed as the "favourite child" of the ministry. In other words, the CLSCs came to be looked upon by community organizations as "public establishments" that had appropriated their domain of activity, and by many in the public network as rather unprofessional "com-munity organizations."

One of the gravest threats to the CLSC concept has been the lack of physician participation. Not surprisingly, while most professionals had a great deal to gain from the development of Quebec's comprehensive health and social-service system, the majority of doctors responded defensively to such massive state intervention. As in other provinces, they were also wary of medicare because it ostensibly cast the government in the role of intermediary between doctor and patient. This represented an important loss of professional autonomy that doctors in the United States have continued to resist (Starr, 1984). In Quebec, the CLSC in particular has been perceived as a bureaucratic instrument to wrest the control of health services from the hands of the medical profes-sion. This is because in CLSCs, all full-time professional staff — including physicians — are salaried and work under the supervision of a non-medical co-ordinator.

The physicians' strategic opposition to the CLSCs has had a permanent impact on the functioning of the health network. Not only did doctors collectively boycott the

CLSCs by refusing to work in them, but they organized a concerted effort to annihilate them, by setting up strong competition in the form of group medical practices. More traditional in their approach, these "polyclinics" incorporate under one roof both general and specialized medical services, as well as technical services such as X-ray laboratories. The polyclinics do not, however, embrace the community development orientation of the CLSCs, nor their socio-health perspective.

Between the doctors' boycott, the competition presented by polyclinics, sporadic development (depending on the availability of public funds), and limited co-operation from other network establishments, the CLSCs have had to struggle for survival. Today, many are still unable to recruit doctors. This means they have never served their intended role as the gateway into the health-care system. They have, however, proved extremely effective for implementing community health programs such as home care, perinatal care, and school and workplace health services, and for providing valuable assistance to local self-help groups and independent community organizations. Thus, despite the fact that each new government in Quebec has questioned their usefulness, repeated evaluations have concluded with recommendations to maintain CLSCs, and even to reinforce their role in the network (Champoux et al., 1975; Ministère, 1981; Brunet, 1987; Ministère, 1990).

The hoped-for integration of social and medical concerns in the public network has met with other obstacles. The principle of complementarity between professions and between the establishments of the network, which has led to the identification and defence of particular professional and organizational interests, has also pitted social concerns against medical and community-oriented organizations and professionals against traditional, treatment-oriented institutions. Despite these problems, Quebec's health system has served as a model for many developing countries, where system-building must begin from scratch.

Still, if the original goal of equity has advanced somewhat, in Quebec as elsewhere important inequalities between regions, social groups, and classes persist (Pompalon, 1990; Paquet, 1989). The goal of efficiency has had mixed results as well: systemic rigidity on the one hand, but exceptional cost control on the other. Quebec compares very favourably with other provinces with respect to the variety and number of services covered under medicare (Ministère, 1991), while still maintaining the second lowest annual increase in health-care costs in Canada, after British Columbia (Figure 1). Despite these successes, the limitations and conflicts discussed above gave rise in the altered political economic environment of the 1980s to a renewed reform initiative.

A new set of reforms undertaken in the 1990s seeks to adapt the system to new and tougher fiscal conditions, while increasing its flexibility and instituting a rational plan for the attainment of significant improvements in the health of the population. In the

Figure I   Provincial per Capita Public Health Costs Average Annual Growth, 1981-1987

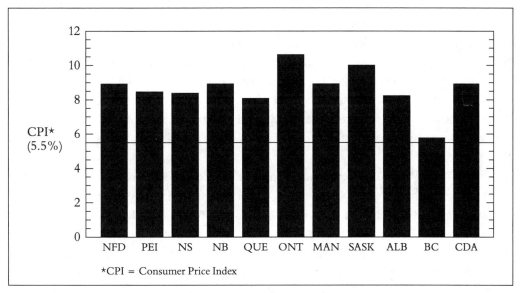

Source: Ministère de la santé et des services sociaux. (1991). *Un financement équitable à la mesure de nos moyens.* Québec: Gouvernement du Québec.

next section, we examine the context and process of this second major reform and the means envisaged for improving the system.

Current Issues: From Rochon to Côté

The Rochon Commission, mandated in 1985 to carry out an assessment of the functioning of Quebec's health and social-service system, was initiated in the face of a number of factors. Among these was the dramatic change in the economic and political climate of the 1980s; the level of dissatisfaction apparent among system professionals; and the inability of the rigidly structured system to adapt to new socio-health realities such as increasing chronicity, growing numbers of dependent elderly, and the deinstitutionalization and non-institutionalization of the mentally ill. In addition, the lack of progress in more strictly social areas, such as domestic violence of all types, was glaring.

Many of these situations are known in other provinces, but may have been exacerbated in Quebec by the comprehensive ambitions of the institutional structure. The establishment of the public-health and social-service network very nearly wiped out all other forms of service, both community-run and private (with the exception of doctors in private practice and polyclinics); but now the public network monopoly could not handle problems that had never been envisioned at its birth in 1971.

Moreover, health costs were rising at an average rate of 10 percent per year. If better-than-average cost control had been possible up to the mid-1980s, continuous, deep cuts in federal transfer payments were rapidly creating an uncontrollable fiscal crisis for the province (Figure 2). Under the guidance of Marc-Yvan Côté, Minister of Health and Social Services, this crisis was defined as the principal challenge to health care, since a bankrupt system would never be able to meet even minimal objectives. The Quiet Revolution was long over in Quebec. The ideological consensus of the 1970s, shared by most health and social-service professionals and government, according to which public services could respond to the full range of needs of the population, had been shattered by the 1980s.

In 1987, the Rochon Report made a number of recommendations for readjusting the delivery of health and social services in Quebec. But it steadfastly rejected any form of privatization of the network, as well as any form of user fees. Instead, it called for a decentralization of planning and co-ordination, the legitimization and strengthening of the role of community-run resources for service delivery, a reorganization of mandates to focus on type of clientele rather than type of service, and the establishment of health objectives. The recommendations of the Rochon Report were auspicious, without calling for radical change. But the government of Quebec in 1990 was seeking a more decisive departure from the status quo, one better reflecting the neo-liberal economic and political climate of the decade.

The Quebec government was a staunch supporter of free trade, and promptly joined the federal government in instituting its own goods and services tax (GST). Since the mid-1980s, it has also totally revamped its welfare policy to include modified "workfare" requirements, raised the price of higher education, and dropped its marginal income tax rates, which used to force the wealthiest Quebeckers to pay higher taxes than their counterparts in other provinces. While other provinces have reacted to the economic and political trends of the 1980s by electing social democratic governments in the 1990s, the socio-economic platform of the major opposition party in Quebec (the Parti Québécois) is almost identical to that of the incumbent Liberal party.

This political context provided the framework for the introduction in 1991 of Côté's first package of reforms, contained in a new Health and Social Services Act. The stated aim of Bill 120 was to increase the flexibility of public establishments, thereby encouraging them to develop innovative services with respect to target clients. Following the recommendations of the Rochon Commission, the network monopoly over health and social services was to be cracked with a new, official recognition and legitimization of independent, nonprofit community organizations, injecting a new source of creativity and alternative strategies into Quebec's health-care system.

While Bill 120 may alleviate some of the conflict and rigidity of the health system, the general tenor of the Côté reforms, which go beyond Bill 120, is very different from that of both the Castonguay and the Rochon reports. For example, the recognition of community organizations as legitimate service providers is contrived in such a way as to force them to respond to needs identified by government in order to qualify for funding. In this way, the government can shift the burden of certain cost-intensive services — particularly social services for youth, the elderly, women, and the mentally ill — from the high-cost, unionized public system to low-cost, relatively impoverished community groups (White & Mercier, 1991).

In fact, the Côté reforms entail a whole series of plans aimed directly at managing costs, which may be classified under four general strategies: (1) the elimination of obstacles to systemic efficiency; (2) the rationing and rationalization of supply and demand in services; (3) the regionalization and decentralization of budgetary and organizational planning; and (4) the creation of new sources of financing. The first of these has already been implemented in the guise of Bill 120 and through the gradual integration of community organizations into the official health-care system. In the following sections, we discuss the remaining three strategies.

Rationing Supply and Demand

The Côté reforms are based on the premise that the constant rise of health costs is attributable in part to the behaviour of health-care consumers. For example, too many still choose to use expensive emergency-room facilities for problems that could more efficiently be handled in a CLSC, polyclinic, or general practitioner's office. Thus, among the reform strategies suggested is a nominal, $5 orientation fee to be levied against those who use emergency services when CLSC services would be both adequate and easily available, for a flu or cough, for example. The objective is to create incentives or disincentives to modify consumer habits — a strategy evident in other aspects of the reform as well.

But abuses of the medicare system, often laid at the feet of consumers, lie more with physicians, who are paid according to the number and type of medical acts they perform and who normally make the decisions regarding their patients' consumption of medical services and medication. The management of service supply — again through incentives and disincentives, this time directed at physicians — is therefore a priority for the Quebec government in its efforts to contain health-care costs. Although Quebec already pays its physicians less per medical act than do other provinces, the cost of medicare is just as high. This is attributed to the fact that, first, Quebec has a higher percentage of specialists in relation to general practitioners (Ministère, 1991), and second, doctors will deliver as many services as necessary to achieve a desired income level (Barer et al., 1979; Evans, 1984).

Initial reform announcements, therefore, came down hard on Quebec doctors. The objective appears to be the "rehabilitation" of physicians, pressuring them to become more socially responsible participants in the health-care system as a whole. For example, doctors tend to use hospital facilities as "free" testing, consulting, and surgical resources for treating their private patients, with little regard for the cost. Quebec's reforms would not directly ration their use of such facilities, as some insurance schemes in the United States do, but may exact a price for hospital privileges in the form of services, such as a number of hours of clinical work for the hospital or for a CLSC — with pay, of course. The purpose is to mobilize the medical profession to contribute to the functioning of a health-care system which serves them well by providing extensive and expensive support services for their private practice.

Up to the present, premiums to entice doctors to spend several years in outlying regions where medical facilities are scarce or absent have had little impact, and significant geographical inequities in health status persist. In face of the failure of incentives for physicians to leave urban areas, Côté has proposed a system of disincentives for young doctors to set up practice in over-serviced metropolitan areas. According to the proposals, a maximum number of medicare billing accounts would be determined for each region of the province, according to population and other factors, such as the concentration of sophisticated medical technology and expertise. Access to an account number would be tied to the acquisition of a permit to practise in the region. Those doctors unable to obtain a permit for their region of choice would have two options: either to practise in under-serviced areas, where premiums would still apply, or to "privatize," that is, to opt out of medicare altogether. But of course, having to opt out of medicare is a powerful disincentive since these doctors would have to recruit patients willing to pay fees themselves, in a society where socialized medicine has long been the norm.

The ideology behind this proposal and others is that the health system ought to be seen as a market in public goods. This assumes that physicians should not be allowed to create a market for their services wherever they wish, but should be expected to answer to consumers' needs wherever they exist. But faced with physician opposition, including strike threats, media propaganda, and appeals directly through their patients, certain of these measures to control the supply of medical services have been indefinitely delayed. Instead, the government is concentrating on incremental limits to demand by chipping away at the list of items covered by medicare, and on other reforms that may pave the way for greater control over the medical profession in the future.

Regionalization and Decentralization

While Quebec is not the only province to be considering policies for increasing control over the cost of health services, it has been implementing fiscal controls since 1977, including capping the general health and social-service budget and indexing it to the gross domestic product (GDP). Now, under the Côté reforms, similar ceilings will be applied at the regional level and will eventually include the medicare budget from which physicians are remunerated. New regional health and social-service authorities, or Régies, will be granted the mandate to plan and co-ordinate health and social-service establishments in their territories, a mandate backed by control over the distribution of regional health-care budgets. The Régies will eventually be responsible for determining the missions and budgets of all publicly funded health and social-service organizations in their territory.

The system would in some ways be democratized through this decentralization process. For example, regional advisory boards would involve elected representation from all sectors of society. But decentralization also has the effect of bringing the controllers closer to the object of their control. In fact, major transfers of personnel from the central ministry to the regional Régies are expected in the future. This will constitute not only a much more immediate form of regulation of network establishments, but also more comprehensive control, since the jurisdiction of the regional Régies will extend not only over the resources of the public health and social-service network, but also over community-based health and social-service organizations that seek government support.

This reform would end the negotiation of establishments' budgets directly with the ministry, on an individual basis. Instead, budgets would be awarded to the Régies, and each Régie would be called upon to remit a comprehensive service plan to the ministry, in which the mandates of all funded organizations, public and community-run, would be identified, as well as the manner of their co-ordination. If, previously, organizations negotiated for their budgets on the basis of the specific merits of their programs and needs of their clientele, now, they would in essence be competing directly with every other organization seeking to gain, maintain, or enhance its role within the regional system. The Côté reform would thus put in place the means for an even more tightly rationalized health system than existed previously.

Seeking New Sources of Health-Care Funding

Finally, a refinancing of the health system appears to have become a Quebec government priority. Quebec does spend a slightly greater proportion of its GDP on health care than

Figure 2   Evolution of Federal Contributions to Quebec's Health and Social Service
Expenses

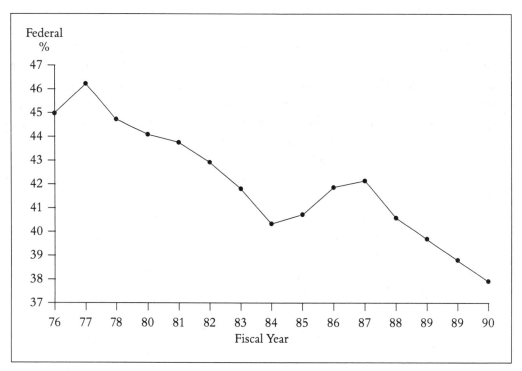

Source: Commission d'enquête sur les services de santé et les services sociaux. (1988). Rapport de la commission d'enquête sur les services de santé et les
services sociaux. Québec: Les publications du Québec.

the Canadian average (9 percent versus 8.7 percent). But health-care expenditures have
faithfully moved up or down in tandem with the GDP, meaning that Quebec has
controlled the rise of health expenditures better than most other provinces (Figure 2;
also see Table 3). Why then the obsession with controlling costs?

Quebec is hardly alone in this obsession, especially in the context of the continuous reduction of federal contributions to health care — while the federal government
used to finance about 50 percent of provincial health-care costs, it now finances a
little over 30 percent (Ministère, 1991). Furthermore, the demand for health and social
services seems to have no limit, and in fact rises as economic conditions deteriorate.
Finally, since the economic recession of the early 1980s, when the Quebec government made deep cuts into the health and social-service budget, the system has been
functioning under permanent and critical financial stress (Renaud, 1989). Quebec
seems prepared to attack this problem with more sweeping and radical changes than
any other province to date.

Unlike many other Canadians, Quebeckers do not pay medicare premiums and have never been subject to extra-billing. Instead, health care is financed from four sources: general provincial tax revenues (38 percent), federal contributions (33.1 percent), employers' payroll contributions (22.2 percent), and other sources (6.7 percent), such as the Occupational Health and Safety Commission (also financed by employers). In the context of the Côté reforms, the government appears to be seeking to contain, and even reduce that part of the health budget now eating up almost one-third of general provincial tax revenues. It is hoped that this may eventually permit income tax cuts (Gazette, 1992a), or the freeing up of a portion of the general fund to reduce the public debt. Most important, the treasury department does not want to see an even greater portion of the general fund attributed to health care each year.

Several options under consideration for creating new sources of health-care financing have been made public. One proposal has been to finance health care from provincial GST revenue, which is about one and one-half times the entire health and social budget. But this source of funds is likely to be captured by other policies and objectives, which has led Côté to announce clearly that the Quebec government favours the introduction of user fees (Gazette, 1992a). This would effectively, if regressively, ration the demand for services, discouraging overuse, but also discouraging many from using any services at all.

User fees are currently forbidden by the Canada Health Act (1984), but Côté is campaigning fiercely to have this act revised on the grounds that with the reduction of federal transfer payments, the Canadian government can no longer dictate uncompromising standards to the provinces. The possible forms of user fees being contemplated in Quebec include: (1) a $5 charge for each visit to a doctor, with welfare recipients and certain other sectors of the population exempted; (2) charges for hospital room and board; and/or (3) an "income" tax on the value of health services used, with a given deductible and ceiling per person (Ministère, 1991). Although all these options would ostensibly exempt the very poorest Quebeckers from user fees, they could well act as a deterrent to seeking needed consultation, hospitalization, tests, and treatment for the working classes, which are reeling under job losses and uncertainty, frozen, or even retreating salaries, ever-increasing taxes, and little hope of financial security in their old age.

Public reaction to the threat of deteriorating medicare standards is divided. The Quebec Hospital Association, several physicians' associations, and the major employers' lobby in Quebec (Conseil du Patronat) support one form or another of user fees — typically, the form that would work in their favour. On the other hand, patients' rights groups, lobby groups for the elderly, and unions are firmly opposed to any form of user fee, arguing that they will have the greatest negative effect on the poor, the elderly and, of course, the sick. A plan to impose taxes immediately on the value of "free" medication used by the elderly was withdrawn in the face of public opposition, but has been replaced since with a $2 fee for every prescription for the elderly currently covered under medicare.

Setting Health Objectives

The Côté reforms have the potential of introducing more than a systemic and fiscal restructuring. In a second phase of the reform announced in June 1992, the setting of health objectives, first suggested in the Rochon Report, has become the cornerstone of an official, interministerial health policy. This policy claims to mount a direct attack on the significant correlation between poverty and ill health. The ministries of Education, Employment, Income Security, and Vocational Training, among others, are "partners" of the Ministry of Health and Social Services in this policy, insofar as their own programs ostensibly contribute to reducing the gap between the rich and the poor.

Health objectives refer to a strategy whereby health and social problems are prioritized and targeted for concerted, multidisciplinary, province-wide clinical, scientific, and social attention, with a view to reducing their incidence by a given percentage, or even eliminating them by a specified date. The strategy is being presented in Quebec as the counterpart to simultaneous cuts being made in certain service areas. For example, on the one hand, the government has suggested that a woman under 50 should be be limited to one mammogram every two years. On the other hand, the new health policy pledges to reduce the incidence of breast cancer by 15 percent by the year 2002. Other types include heart disease, premature births, accidents, and respiratory diseases, as well as socio-health problems such as homelessness, violence against women, and child abuse and neglect.

"Management by objectives" is clearly a strategy imported from the world of commerce and industry. It reflects the political culture of the current government, as plainly as does the willingness to introduce user fees. But the setting of health and social objectives, combined with a highly rationalized and fiscally reliable health and social-service system, holds the promise of remarkable progress in the health-care sector in Quebec. The unique ability to orchestrate a multilevelled, multidisciplinary campaign to reduce the rate of chronic back pain or high blood pressure in the population, for example, could eventually have a significant impact on quality of life and longevity, as well as on the collective cost of treatment and lost labour time.

But the health policy is disappointing in some ways. Despite a clear recognition of the close correlation between poverty and ill health, and a pledge to gear programs towards the needs of the poor and other vulnerable groups, policy objectives appear to focus more on controlling "deviant" behaviours among the poor that ultimately cost the ministry money. For example, there is a tendency towards "blaming the victim," by referring to the notion that poverty breeds child abuse, neglect, and delinquency, and to statistics reporting that the poor smoke more, exercise less, and use more medication. Stated objectives such as cutting tranquillizer use by welfare recipients may appear wholesome and progressive, but are likely to be accomplished by reducing these groups' access to subsidized drugs, not by alleviating the problems at the root of their use. In short, the policy at this stage remains well ensconced in the cost-cutting orientation of the Quebec government.

Furthermore, the social objectives announced in the policy are vague and suggest little more than familiar rhetoric about the need to attack homelessness and domestic violence. Unlike the medical objectives, these are not tagged with clear, specific percentage reductions. Obviously, there is far less certainty about our ability to control these problems compared to those medical conditions for which well-funded scientific research has been underway for years. Still, the inclusion of social objectives augers well for a shift in the lopsided spending on high-tech medical treatment versus prevention and health promotion. As might be expected, then, the health policy has been welcomed by the Federation of CLSCs and derided by the head of the Corporation of Physicians. The question remains whether systemic and fiscal rationalization will take precedence over the effort to tackle socio-health problems with the solid research and pilot projects that they require.

Perhaps the most valuable aspect of the health policy is its appreciation that access to health services is not equivalent to access to health. The Castonguay reforms, in the exhilaration of implementing expansive welfare state policies, did not take this consideration into account. In this respect, a socially conscious — as opposed to cost-conscious — version of management by health and social objectives could prove valuable, and could possibly succeed under the comprehensive and co-ordinated conditions embodied in Quebec's health network.

Conclusion

In the 1990s, health issues have taken centre stage in the arena of public debate in Quebec. In the wake of more then five years of official enquiries, white papers, bills, legislated reforms, policy documents, and announced intentions, opposing views of the future of health care are regularly aired on television and in the press. On the editorial pages of the *Le Devoir* (e.g., Renaud, 1989; Gélineau & Renaud, 1990; Renaud et al., 1991), the dilemma that plagues health policy-makers everywhere is presented to the public: do we as a society choose to continue to invest ever-greater amounts of public money in an increasingly high-tech and specialized medical system that knows no bounds in terms of demand or supply? Or do we begin to shift our investment more towards policies that would improve the health of the population as a whole, particularly those groups that, for social and economic reasons, are currently benefiting least from the existing service system? Should future investments be mainly for the bio-medical side of the health and social-service system, which focusses on cure, or should investments be rebalanced in favour of social objectives which may, in the long run, be the only way to bring about significant improvement in the health status of the population (Renaud, 1991)?

Quebec's socio-health network is uncommonly suited to attack the social conditions of ill health. The main obstacle now lies in the extent to which the government is prepared to trade off equity for increased efficiency, and global health gains for fiscal gains. Those characteristics that make Quebec's health system distinct — its central planning, tight integration, and co-ordination, coupled with its socio-health ideology and "visionary" ambitions — may place it in a uniquely advantageous position to implement an innovative approach to health care. If political will rallies to the cause, a concerted effort to attack both the bio-medical and socio-economic conditions at the root of key health problems could show the way to the next significant advancement in improving the health status of populations everywhere.

Notes

1. The Catholic Church in Quebec paid no taxes up until the 1960s. Thus, it managed to accumulate significant wealth in the form of property, often bequeathed in people's wills. This property allowed them to build and maintain institutions such as hospitals, orphanages, and schools, which they could then operate relatively cheaply with the professional labour of religious sisters and brothers, who had taken a vow of poverty. For an excellent study of religious administration and labour in the educational sphere (which functioned very similarly to the health sphere), see Laurin et al., 1991.

2. Permits will be distributed by a committee on which doctors themselves will have a determining role — a right gained by physicians only after intensive lobbying. This could make life more difficult for young doctors, while protecting the acquired rights of others.

Study Questions

1. We have said that the health status of Quebeckers is about equal to the health status of other Canadians. On what grounds, then, could we try to evaluate the health-care system? What factors other than national health status determine whether a health-care system is better, worse, or equal to another?

2. Compared to the rest of Canada, the state in Quebec has tended to play a more active role in initiating, implementing, and monitoring broad reforms in the health domain. Why was this unusually massive intervention possible in Quebec during the Quiet Revolution (1960-75)? Do you think Quebec has changed to become more similar to the other provinces in terms of the extent of state intervention in health?

3. Quebec has been able to efficiently control the evolution of medical costs, mainly by limiting the rates paid to doctors. It now

contemplates implementing even stricter controls affecting doctors' income and place of practice. What does this say about the structural relationship between the medical profession and the state in Quebec? Is the relationship symbiotic, or is it one of the state actively undercutting medical dominance?

4. CLSCs were designed to be sensitive to community needs and the culture of local populations, to be easily accessible, and to encourage citizen participation. Why, then, would their health promotion, education, and prevention programs generally fail to bring about significant changes in health-related behaviour within the *classe populaire*?

5. Quebec's health network was designed as a socio-health system. But the evidence suggests that the social dimensions of health receive considerably less funding and less regard than do the medical dimensions. Why is this the case? To what extent does this suggest that the systematic effort to integrate the social and medical aspects of health has been a failure?

6. The term *technocratic* is often used to describe Quebec's health and social-service network, due to the preponderant influence of planners, co-ordinators, and public administrators. In your opinion, would a stronger orientation towards the definition and attainment of health objectives for the population reduce or reinforce such technocratic tendencies?

7. The Quebec government has recently suggested that it may have to introduce user fees to avoid a serious deterioration of its health-care system. Do you believe that there may be ways of imposing limited user fees that do *not* discriminate against certain sectors of the population with respect to access to quality care?

Recommended Reading

Boudreau, F. (1981). Insurance and invasion: Thresholds of change in the delivery of psychiatric care in Quebec. In D. Coburn, C. D'Arcy, P. New, & G. Torrance (Eds.), *Health and Canadian society* (393-406). Markham: Fitzhenry & Whiteside.

Bozzini, L. (1987). Local community service centres (CLSCs) in Quebec: Description, evaluation, perspectives. *Journal of Public Health Policy*, 9, (3), 346-375.

Champagne, F., Contandriopoulos, A-P., Fournier, M.A., & Laurier, C. (1984). Pursuit of equity, pursuit of liberties and control of health care cost in Quebec. *Journal of Health and Human Resources Administrations*, 7, 4-31.

Lesemann, F. (1984). *Services and circuses: Community and the welfare state*. Montreal: Black Rose Books.

Palley. H. (1987). Canadian federalism and the Canadian health care program: A comparison of Ontario and Quebec. *International Journal of Health Services*, 17, (4), 595-615

Renaud, M. (1978). Quebec's new middle class in search of hegemony. *International Review of Community Action*, 39-40, 1-36.

Renaud, M. (1981). Reform or illusion? An analysis of the Quebec state's intervention in health. In D. Coburn, C. D'Arcy, P. New, & G. Torrance (Eds.), *Health and Canadian society* (pp. 369-392). Markham: Fitzhenry & Whiteside.

References

Barer, M.L., Evans, R.G., & Stoddart, G.L. (1979). *Controlling health care costs by direct charges to patients: Snare or delusion?* Toronto: Ontario Economic Council.

Brunet, J., et al. (1987). *Rapport du comité de réflexion et d'analyse sur les services dispensés par les CLSC*. Québec: Ministère de la santé et des services sociaux.

Champoux, L., et al. (1975). *Opération Bilan: Rapport du groupe d'étude sur le fonctionnement des centres locaux de services communautaires au Québec*, (Rapport majoritaire). Québec: Ministère des affaires sociales.

Commission d'enquête sur les services de santé et les services sociaux. (1988). *Rapport de la commission d'enquête sur les services de santé et les services sociaux* (Rochon Report). Québec: Les publications du Québec.

Evans, R.G. (1984). *Strained mercy: The economics of Canadian health care*. Toronto: Butterworths.

Favreau, L. (1989). *Mouvements populaires et inter-vention communautaire de 1960 à nos jours: conti-nuité et ruptures*. Montréal: Editions du Fleuve.

Gélineau, G.R.M. (1991, June 7). Le chantage des médecins: La fausse prétention d'un groupe professionnel au monopole de la vérité. *Le Devoir*, p. B-8.

Godbout, J. (1983). *La participation contre la démo-cratie*. Montréal: Editions coopératives Albert Saint-Martin.

Government of Canada, Public Finance and Transportation Division. (1952-1968). *Per-centage distribution of net general expenditure. Financial statistics of provincial governments: Rev-enue and expenditure*. Ottawa: Dominion Bureau of Statistics.

Government of Canada. (1986). *Longevity and historical life tables 1921-1981, Canada and the provinces*. Ottawa: Minister of Supply and Services.

Government of Canada. (1989). *Public accounts of Canada: Summary report of financial statements*. Ottawa: Minister of Supply and Services.

Guindon, H. (1964). Social unrest, social class and Quebec's bureaucratic revolution. *Queen's Quarterly*, 71, 150-162.

Hastings, J.E.F. (1972). *The community health centre in Canada: Report of the community health care project* (3 vol.). Ottawa: Health and Welfare Canada.

Hastings, J.E.F. (1987). The Ontario health sys-tem: An overview. In G. Desrosiers, (Ed.), *Le système de santé de l'Ontario: enseignements pour le Québec, actes du 8e colloque Jean-Yves Rivard* (23-40). Université de Montréal: Les Editions Administration de la Santé.

Lalonde, M. (1974). *A new perspective on the health of Canadians*. Ottawa: Information Canada.

Laurin, N., Juteau, D., & Duchesne, L. (1991). *A la récherche d'un monde oublié: Les communautés religieuses de femmes au Québec de 1900 à 1970*. Montreal: Le Jour, Editeur.

Lesemann, F. (1984). *Services and circuses: Commu-nity and the welfare state*. Montreal: Black Rose Books.

Ministère des affaires sociales. (1981). *Le réseau des CLSC au Québec: Un parachèvement qui s'impose*. Québec: Gouvernement du Québec.

Ministère de la santé et des services sociaux. (1987). *Et la santé, ÿa va? Rapport de l'enquête santé Québec*. Québec: Les Publications du Québec.

Ministère de la santé et des services sociaux. (1990). *Une réforme axée sur le citoyen*. Québec: Gouvernement du Québec.

Ministère de la santé et des services sociaux. (1991). *Un financement équitable à la mesure de nos moyens*. Quebec: Gouvernement du Québec.

New strategies for health care. (1992b, January 30). *Gazette*, p. B2.

Paquet, G. (1989). *Santé et inégalités sociales, un problème de distance culturelle*. Québec: Institut québécois de recherche sur la culture.

Pompalon, R., Gauthier, D., Guy, R., & Beau-dry, D. (1990). *La santé à la carte: Une explora-tion géographique de l'enquête santé Québec*. Québec: Les publications du Québec.

PQ vows to fight medical user fees but hospitals, doctors view charges as positive step. (1992c, February 4). *Gazette*, p. A5.

Quebec sales tax could cover medicare cost, Côté suggests. (1992a, January 30). *Gazette*, p. A5.

Renaud, M. (1978). Quebec's new middle class in search of hegemony. *International Review of Community Action* (39, 40), 1-36.

Renaud, M. (1981). Reform or illusion? An anal-ysis of the Quebec state's intervention in health. In D. Coburn, C. D'Arcy, P. New, & G. Torrance (Eds.), *Health and Canadian society* (pp. 369-392). Markham: Fitzhenry & Whiteside.

Renaud, M. (1989, March 10). Guérir ou bien prévenir? *Le Devoir*, p. 9 (Section Libre Opin-ion).

Renaud, M. (1989). Le Québec en débat: enjeux et perspectives dans le domaine socio-sanitaire. *Sciences sociales et santé, VII*, (4), 12-38.

Renaud, M. (1991). *The future: Hygeia vs Pana-keia. Internal document No. 29D, population-health programme*. Toronto: Canadian Institute for Advanced Research.

Renaud, M., Doré, S., & White, D. (1989). Soci-ology and social policy: From a love-hate relationship with the state to cynicism and pragmatism. *Canadian Review of Sociology and Anthropology, State of the Art Edition: Franco-phone Québécois Sociology*, 26, (3), 426-456.

Renaud, M., Contandriopoulos, A.P., Corin, E., Pless, B. (1990, February 1). Au delà des politiques de soins: La santé est d'abord liée à l'environnement social, économique et culturel. *Le Devoir*, p. 9 (Section Libre Opin-ion).

Rivard, J-Y. (1970). *L'évolution des services de santé et des modes de distribution des soins au Québec.* Commission of Inquiry into Health and Social Welfare, Annex 2. Quebec: Government of Quebec.

Royal Commission of Enquiry on Bilingualism and Biculturalism. (1967–1970). *Report of the royal commission of enquiry on bilingualism and biculturalism.* Ottawa: Queen's Printer.

Royal Commission on Health Services. (1964). *Report of the royal commission on health services* (Hall Report). Ottawa: Queen's Printer.

Starr, P. (1984). *The social transformation of American medicine.* New York: Basic Books.

Study Committee on Public Assistance. (1963). *Report of the study committee on public assistance,* (Boucher Report). Quebec: Government of Quebec.

Torrance, G.M. (1981). The development of the Canadian health system. In D. Coburn, C. D'Arcy, P. New, & G. Torrance (Eds.), *Health and Canadian society* (pp. 9–28). Markham: Fitzhenry & Whiteside.

White, D., & Mercier, C. (1991). Reorienting mental health systems: The dynamics of policy and planning. *International Journal of Mental Health,* 19, (4), 3–24.

Chapter 5

The Changing Health-Care System: Controlling Costs and Promoting Health

Harley D. Dickinson, University of Saskatchewan

Introduction

Access to necessary medical care without any direct out-of-pocket costs at the point of service delivery is taken for granted by Canadians. The system of universal, comprehensive and portable health-care insurance, publicly administered on a nonprofit basis, commonly known as medicare, is consistently identified as one of the most popular government programs. Consequently, politicians and policy-makers traditionally have been hesitant to publicly advocate changes to it.

In recent years, however, concern about the growing crisis in health care has become common. The two main dimensions of this crisis are rising costs and the increasing gap between the health needs of the population and the capacity of the existing health-care system to satisfy them.

Efforts to control the crisis of rising costs generally have been of three types: (1) attempts to reduce number/duration of contacts with the health-care system during illness; (2) attempts to reduce the costs per contact; and more recently (3) reduction of the amount budgeted to health care.

In addition to these direct cost-containment strategies there also have been attempts to reduce the episodes of illness/injury requiring medical or hospital care (Minister of National Health and Welfare, Vol. 3, 1970). In recent years, this strategy has taken the form of a major health-policy initiative referred to as health promotion. In addition to being a cost-containment strategy, however, health promotion has two other dimensions. Firstly, it is an attempt to modify health and illness behaviours among the population in order to prevent illness and injury and promote health and secondly, it is an effort to modify the nature and organization of health-care services in order to make them more appropriate to current and projected health-care needs.

In the first, major part of this paper I shall examine selected aspects of the cost-containment strategies used in the illness-care system. In the second section I shall outline the main dimensions of current health-promotion initiatives. The paper ends with a few brief comments.

Health-Care Costs: Crisis and Control

Rising costs appear to be a permanent feature of our health-care system. Between 1960 and 1990, for example, total health expenditures in Canada rose from $2.14 billion to an estimated $61.7 billion. Total health expenditures include both private-and public-sector expenditures. Since the introduction of state hospitalization insurance in 1958, and physician-care insurance in 1966, public-sector health expenditures have increased, from approximately 43 percent of total health expenditures in 1960 to about 74 percent in 1987 (Health and Welfare, 1990, p. 22). What is interesting to note about these figures is that even in Canada, where there is supposedly a universal, comprehensive and compulsory health-care insurance system, 25 percent of health-care expenditures are still privately paid for. This compares favourably to the United States, where there is no universal health-care insurance system and where only 41 percent of health-care expenditures in 1987 were covered by various types of state insurance (Health and Welfare, 1990, p. 22).

Since at least the mid-1970s, about 87 or 88 percent of the total amount expended has been for personal health care. Personal health care is defined as "all health expenditures related to the care of the individual" (Health and Welfare, 1990, p. 170). It consists of various services organized under the headings "institutional and related services," "professional services," "drugs and appliances," and a number of services provided as entitlements under the terms of various government programs such as welfare, workers' compensation, and veterans' service programs.

The remaining 12 or 13 percent of health expenditures are generally reported under the heading "other health costs." This category "covers all health expenditures not primarily related to the care of individuals" (Health and Welfare, 1990, p. 184). It consists of five categories of expenditure: "prepayment administration," "public health," "capital expenditure," "health research," and "miscellaneous health costs."

Table 1 shows the actual dollar figures expended on personal health care in selected years between 1971 and 1987. The estimated percentage distribution of those

Table I   Total Health Expenditures, Canada, Selected Years 1971, 1976, and 1987

| | (millions of dollars) | | | |
Category	1971	1976	1982	1987
Total Health Expenditures	7 118.7	14 119.9	31 150.2	47 934.8
Personal Health Care	6 206.2	12 360.9	27 044.0	42 136.2
Institutions	3 674.6	7 893.8	16 974.1	24 547.4
Hospitals	3 149.9	6 349.8	13 036.4	18 808.8
Other institutions	516.0	1 424.5	3 535.7	4 945.6
Home care	—	51.5	183.5	377.5
Ambulances	8.7	67.9	218.5	415.4
Professional Services	1 666.7	3 019.1	6 731.9	10 933.3
Physicians	1 250.4	2 165.7	4 649.8	7 678.8
Dentists	311.5	699.8	1 702.4	2 609.6
Chiropractors	39.3	77.4	209.9	356.7
Optometrists	49.1	39.0	83.5	141.8
Podiatrists	4.2	14.6	27.6	36.3
Osteopaths	2.1	1.4	1.6	1.4
Private-duty nurses	10.1	13.5	16.9	26.0
Physiotherapists	—	7.8	40.3	82.8
Drugs and Appliances	865.0	1 447.9	3 338.0	6 655.5
Other Health Care Costs	912.4	1 759.0	4 106.2	5 798.7
Prepayment administration	122.6	209.1	403.0	578.3
Public health	214.7	631.3	1 325.8	2 130.8
Capital expenditures	420.2	649.6	1 712.6	2 132.6
Health research	78.3	113.3	273.6	411.3
Miscellaneous health costs	76.7	155.7	391.2	545.7

Sources: National Health Expenditures in Canada Databank, Health Information Division, Health and Welfare Canada. September 1992.

expenditures for 1987 is as follows: institutional and related services, 51.2 percent; professional services, 22.8 percent; drugs and appliances, 13.9 percent; and other health expenses, 12.1 percent.

In the following section, I shall describe the development and transformation of federal-provincial cost-sharing arrangements in the health-care sector, and shall examine selected attempts to reduce the number of contacts between medical professionals during an episode of illness and various efforts to reduce the costs per contact in the medical-care and hospital-services sectors.

Financing and Cost Containment

Because medicare is considered by many to be a right of citizenship, it is often assumed that it will continue to exist, more or less in its present form, indefinitely. This need not be the case. Our existing illness-care system is of relatively recent origin, being established in stages in the post–World War II period.

The first stage corresponded to the introduction of the hospital construction grants by the federal government in 1948. The second step was marked by the introduction of the Hospitalization Insurance and Diagnostic Services Act by the federal government in 1958. This piece of legislation established a national system of hospitalization insurance on a cost-shared basis between the federal and provincial/territorial governments. The next step occurred with the passage of the 1966 Medical Care Services Act by the federal government. The passage of the Canada Health Act in 1984 consolidated the provisions and principles of the two previous health-insurance acts (Vance 1988, revised 1991).

Under the Canadian constitution, health is a provincial responsibility. Consequently the federal government is able to act in this area only with the consent and co-operation of the provinces. This necessary consent and co-operation is generally achieved through financial incentives or disincentives. In the case of hospitalization and medical-care insurance, for example, the federal government was able to persuade recalcitrant provinces to institute health-care insurance programs by equally sharing the costs.

Under the terms of the first cost-sharing arrangement, federal contributions were tied directly to, and determined by, provincial government expenditures. As a result, the federal government had no control over its own health-care expenditures. Naturally this was an undesirable situation. The provincial governments too came to be dissatisfied with this arrangement because it discouraged innovation and experimentation with alternative forms of health-care service delivery. Nonphysician and nonhospital forms of care and treatment were ineligible for federal funds. In addition to discouraging institutional innovation, the original cost-sharing agreement also discouraged attempts to increase the efficiency of hospital and medical-care services, insofar as every reduction by the provinces in the costs of those services resulted in a corresponding reduction in the amount of federal money transferred to them. Thus, both federal and provincial governments were interested in changing the terms and conditions of the original cost-sharing arrangement (Soderstrom, 1978).

The Federal-Provincial Arrangements and Established Programs Financing Act (EPF) of 1977 was the first substantial revision of health-insurance cost-sharing arrangements. The EPF reduced federal contributions to health care from approximately 50 to 25 percent, it uncoupled them from provincial expenditures, and limited future direct federal increases to the rate of growth in the gross national product (GNP). Any provincial expenditures above that did not receive matching federal funds. The intent was to provide the provinces with an incentive to contain costs (Vayda et al., 1979). These changes were made attractive to the provinces by the transfer of federal "tax points," which enabled them to increase their levels of income taxation to make up for reduced federal cash transfer payments.

Further cost-control incentives were provided to the provinces by the federal government in the mid-1980s. Revisions to the cost-sharing arrangements at that time limited federal transfers to the provinces to an annual rate 2 percentage points below the rate of increase in the GNP. More recently, the federal government has further reduced the level of transfer payments to the provinces. The new formula froze federal transfers to the provinces for two years at the 1989-90 levels. In 1992-93, federal transfers were allowed to increase at the rate of growth in GNP *less* 3 percent.

By shifting an increasing proportion of the financial burden for health-care services to the provinces, tremendous pressure has been created to reduce and redirect health-care spending. The range of possible responses of provincial governments to their intensified fiscal crisis is limited. They can attempt to develop new forms of revenue, they can cut back or ration the number and types of services provided, or they can reduce the costs of the services provided. Not surprisingly, there is a growing concern that these efforts will erode the principles upon which our health-care insurance system rests.

Alternative Sources of Financing

The cutback of federal cash transfers has been accompanied by a transfer of tax points to the provinces to enable them to increase taxes to pay for health care and other services. In practice, increasing taxes may be a difficult course of action to pursue insofar as many Canadians feel that they are already being unfairly taxed and may not, therefore, support any government or party that imposes additional tax burdens.

User fees (sometimes referred to as deterrent fees) are another possible source of revenue. User fees can take several forms, including direct out-of-pocket charges to patients for each visit to the doctor, or for a range of medical and hospital services considered nonessential. In the hospital, these include semi-private and private rooms, some drugs, and prostheses. With regard to medical services, various services have been deinsured or are being considered for exclusion. In Saskatchewan, for example, optometrists' services were recently deinsured, and there is considerable support all across the country for deinsuring other services and even for making certain categories of individuals ineligible for selected health-care services.

Another form of user fee that has been used in the past and that is being considered again is an annual premium. These would be charged to individuals or families, but would not constitute a direct out-of-pocket charge at the time of service use.

Extra-billing, or the practice of allowing doctors to charge patients a fee in addition to the amount they receive from the health-care insurance system, is another means developed to shift some of the cost of medical-care services to the public. Doctors were willing to negotiate lower fee schedules with governments when extra-billing was allowed. Despite this cost-controlling effect, it was seen to create a financial barrier to health care for those with low incomes and, therefore, antithetical to the principles upon which medicare was founded. Consequently, in 1984, extra-billing was eliminated when the federal government imposed a dollar-for-dollar reduction in transfers to those provinces/territories for every dollar they allowed physicians to extra-bill. Although there was considerable resistance on the part of the medical profession, it was ineffective and may well have had negative public-relations consequences for them.

In an attempt to minimize the political liability of imposed tax increases or various user fees, governments are increasingly turning to different types of voluntary taxation in the form of lotteries and, in Manitoba, the opening of a full-time casino in Winnipeg. As the recipient of an estimated $10 million of the expected annual profits, the Manitoba Department of Health was identified as a major beneficiary of this undertaking.

Critics of these developments point out that gambling revenues are an unreliable basis from which to finance essential services such as health care. Another criticism relates to the fact that gambling is often associated with social problems and increased crime rates. Additionally, it is suggested that gambling tends to be seen as an attractive option for the poor, who see the possibility of winning as a "quick fix" to their financial problems, but who frequently find themselves losing and intensifying their financial woes. In general terms, state-sponsored gambling is seen to be a tax on the poor that contributes to the perpetuation and intensification of the problems of poverty, including poor health.

Reduce the Number of Contacts with the Health-Care System

Generally there are three mechanisms for reducing the number of contacts with the health-care system: first, improvement of the health status of the population so that need is reduced; second, modification of illness and help-seeking behaviours; and third, modification of caregivers' behaviours. These last two strategies do not presuppose improvements in health status. We shall look at attempts to improve the health of the population in the section on health promotion. This section looks at selected efforts to modify illness and caregiver behaviours in order to reduce service utilization patterns.

An obvious way to reduce the number of contacts with the health-care system is to reduce the number and types of services that are eligible for coverage under the terms of medicare. This is, of course, a form of rationing. Clearly, one of the consequences of such a cost-containment strategy is that the comprehensiveness of medicare is eroded.

Despite that, this strategy has some important proponents. A recent survey of Canadian physicians,[1] for example, showed that 81 percent of those who responded supported rationing some services and treatments for those too old to benefit from them, or for those who "persist in unhealthy lifestyles or habits" (Kirkey, 1992, p. A14). A majority of the doctors who responded also supported ending medicare coverage for all cosmetic surgery, making reproductive technologies available only to those who could afford to pay for them, and charging $5 user fees to everybody who uses hospital emergency wards (Kirkey, 1992, p. A14).

These types of "solutions" are based on the premise that some categories of individuals in Canada are undeserving of health-care services, either because of their status or their behaviour. Such a position violates the principle of universality, namely that all Canadians regardless of age, sex, race, religion, income, or region of residence are eligible for necessary health-care services as a right of citizenship, and may be a form of "victim blaming."

Although most doctors responding to the survey supported rationing and deinsuring services in order to contain costs, they were opposed to controlling costs through the imposition of caps on doctors' incomes. Despite medical opposition, however, a number of provincial governments have imposed caps on the amount budgeted for physician services and/or restructured the fee-setting procedures. Doctors, of course, resist any such attempts to limit their incomes or otherwise undermine their interests (Badgley & Wolfe, 1967). Over the past few years, doctors in a number of provinces have taken various forms of job action in protest of threats to their earnings. In the summer of 1992, for example, doctors in British Columbia responded to provincial government attempts to cap their incomes and alter the fee-bargaining process with a series of walkouts, which resulted in the cancellation of appointments, lab tests, and elective surgery (*Star Phoenix*, 1992, p. A12).

Withdrawal of medical services is always an undesirable event, therefore, the medical profession and policy makers have agreed that reductions in the number of physicians is one way to control rising costs. This marks a reversal of opinion. Traditionally, a shortage of physicians was seen as one of the main problems of the health-care system. As a result, vigorous and successful efforts were made to increase their numbers. Between 1968 and 1984, for example, the number of physicians increased from approximately 22 965 to 41 440 (Blishen, 1991, p. 45). By 1984, the number had increased to 49 916 (Health Manpower Directorate, 1985).

Reductions in the number of physicians will reduce costs by imposing an absolute limit on the number of medical services that can be provided. Because of the maldistribution of physicians, this form of rationing will not affect all Canadians equally. It seems inevitable that unless other changes to the nature and organization of health-care services also take place, those who live in rural, remote, and other underserviced areas will find their situation worsened.

Elimination of the fee-for-service system of remuneration for physician services is an often discussed cost-control reform (Wright, 1991). In a 1992 government policy document, the Saskatchewan government pointed out that:

> Under the current payment structure, some health care providers are rewarded (receive larger incomes) for high use of their services. This may encourage user dependency and is inconsistent with the goal of people taking more responsibility for their own health and relying less on the service system (Simard, 1992, p. 9).

These comments are in reference to the existing fee-for-service physician payment system.

Two alternatives generally considered are a capitation payment system and a salaried payment system. Capitation payment schemes can assume a number of different forms, but generally they involve establishing health districts with a certain population density. On the basis of an estimate of medical-care needs of the population, the physician is paid an agreed-upon amount per person in the district, regardless of whether the individuals actually use physician services. This remuneration system eliminates the structural pressure produced by the fee-for-service system of payment because the physician receives a predetermined income, regardless of the level of services provided. It is generally agreed that the capitation form of remuneration greatly reduces the tendency to overprescribe and overtreat patients. It is also agreed that there is a greater incentive for physicians to spend a greater proportion of their time in patient education and other health-promotion activities. Currently, in Saskatchewan, one health district is experimenting with a capitation payment scheme.

Traditionally, physicians, especially their professional organizations, have been opposed to the salary system of payment and have been strong advocates of the fee-for-service system. Their main concern was with the potential for loss of professional autonomy and income that a salaried system of remuneration entails. In a sense, it is precisely these potentials that make the salary system of remuneration an attractive policy alternative for those interested in reducing the costs and level of service utilization.

Successful physician resistance to working for salaries has had a profound influence of the nature and organization of health care throughout Canada. In the first place, it was one of the reasons that hospitalization insurance and medicare incorporated the fee-for-service payment system, despite the fact that its many limitations and inflationary effects were well known. It also accounts for, in part, the general failure to develop an integrated, co-ordinated and holistic approach to health and illness care.

The attenuated development of the community clinic and community health centre approach to providing a comprehensive range of co-ordinated health and social welfare services in this country is partly the result of physician resistance to the salaried system of remuneration. The recent cost crisis and efforts to respond to it in a constructive way, however, have resulted in increased interest in, and commitment to, the development of community health centres.

Increasingly throughout Canada, the community health centre concept (Hastings, 1972), or some variant of it, is being advocated as an alternative to the private practice fee-for-service doctor's office, and as a means of integrating the illness-care and health-promotion aspects of health care. Many envision salaried doctors working in these new settings as one of a team of health-care professionals. In this context, the role and autonomy of the physician is likely to be reduced, if not in absolute terms, at least relative to an expansion of the roles and functions of other health-care professionals, particularly primary-care nurses.

From the point of view of service recipients, these anticipated changes are hoped to have positive consequences. The fee-for-service physician payment system militates against doctors spending time with patients, providing health education, or counselling services, or basic human care and compassion. This, in turn, is thought to contribute to the alienation and frustration experienced by many patients, both in hospitals and in doctors' offices.

Increasing dissatisfaction with the nature of medical care is contributing to a burgeoning legitimation crisis. The legitimation crisis assumes many forms. Perhaps the most dramatic and disturbing are the increasing number of allegations of sexual abuse (Gray, 1992; Sears, 1992) and a growing number of malpractice suits, which suggest a growing problem, or at least a growing awareness of the issue of iatrogenic injury and illness caused by inappropriate forms of treatment and drug prescription (Illich, 1976).

Other issues that are forcing a re-examination of the nature and organization of medicine are related to the development of new knowledge about human genetics and the application of new reproductive and life-sustaining technologies. This knowledge and the associated technologies have created an unprecedented capacity for control over life and death. Associated with this potential power, however, are awesome ethical and legal responsibilities. Available knowledge and technology forces us as a society to confront questions about who is to live, who is to die, and who is to decide? Historical experience with the eugenics movement and the atrocities of Nazi Germany teaches us that we cannot assume that the answers to these questions will be benevolent, or even benign.

In combination with the intensifying fiscal crisis, this multidimensioned legitimation crisis is contributing to a growing interest in reorganizing the health-care system. This often assumes the form of patient rights and various self-help movements, as well as expanded responsibilities for non-physicians. These developments are related to and encouraged by the rise to dominance in the policy arena of the health-promotion initiative, which will be discussed in the following section.

Modifying Help Seeking and Illness Behaviour

The other main focus for reducing service utilization is the help-seeking and illness behaviour of service consumers (Barale, 1991; Webb, 1991). This basically involves efforts at public education intended to make people less reliant on the formal health-care system and concurrently more self-reliant in terms of health-care needs. As we shall see, these efforts are a major part of the new health-promotion policy initiative. As laudable as the goal of increasing self-reliance may be, in some cases it may also contradict other well-established health-promotion behaviour patterns. In particular, efforts to reduce service-utilization patterns may discourage people from having regular diagnostic checkups, or seeking medical assistance when symptoms first appear. As we are constantly told, for example, the best way to cure cancer is to prevent it through the choice of low-risk lifestyles and to have regular medical checkups and early treatment once symptoms are identified.

It is increasingly common to hear the argument that universal access to diagnostic services for early detection purposes is a wasteful and ineffective use of scarce resources. It is suggested that only those known to be at high risk and/or likely to benefit from early detection and treatment should be eligible for insured diagnostic testing. The current debate with regard to mammographic screening of women for breast cancer provides a good example. Some researchers maintain that only women 50 years and over should be screened on a regular basis because it is only women in this age group who benefit from early diagnosis and treatment. Others claim that all women, regardless of age, should regularly receive mammographic screening to aid in early detection and treatment. It has been suggested that those who support universality with regard to this issue tend to be those who have a direct, often economic, interest in expended service delivery. This includes the medical technology corporations who benefit from increased demand for mammography machines, those professionals who benefit from providing the service, and others who have an interest in sustaining a cancer hysteria for fund-raising purposes.

Proponents of selective screening maintain that universal mammographies are an irrational and ineffective waste of scarce health-care resources.

Cost Control in the Hospital Sector

Table 1 clearly shows that the largest category of health resources is expended on institutional care and, of the amount spent on the provision of institutional care, the largest proportion is spent on acute-care general hospitals. In 1990, for example, it is estimated that over $25 billion was spent on hospital services in Canada.

Cost control efforts in the hospital sector are of two general types: efforts to reduce hospital use, and efforts to reduce the duration and cost of each hospital service provided.

Reducing hospital use assumes several forms. Perhaps one of the most obvious, and at the same time least acceptable, is the common practice of leaving available hospital beds empty. In 1989-90, it is estimated that on average, one bed in five was not filled, even though long waiting lists are a fact of life throughout Canada.

Another strategy involves decreasing the number of hospital beds available. This strategy is usually associated with attempts to create more appropriate forms of residential and nonresidential care. An indication of this strategy is given by the fact that between 1982 and 1987 hospital expenditures rose by about 31 percent, and expenditures for other forms of institutional care increased by about 29 percent, while home care expenditures rose by approximately 51 percent (Health and Welfare, 1990).

Other efforts to reduce the number and duration of hospitalizations include early release and/or delayed admission programs. An increasingly common example is the early maternity discharge program. Under these types of programs, mothers who have had healthy pregnancies and who meet other standards may choose to go home from hospital with their newborn babies from a few hours to a few days after delivery. Expectant mothers are made aware of the program in Saskatchewan through their doctors and at prenatal classes. Once a woman has decided to participate, she is visited in the hospital by a community health nurse to provide information and to make final arrangements at home. The nurse visits the mother and baby at home within the first twenty-four hours, and then daily from between three and five days. During these visits, the nurse does complete examinations and assessments of mother and baby and provides additional information on infant care and feeding, as well as on self-care for the mother. As part of the home-based services, the community nurse will also collect lab specimens and remove sutures. The community nurse works in co-operation with both the mother and her doctor. Participating women also have twenty-four hour, seven-days-a-week access to nursing services through a special telephone number. They also have the option of contacting their physicians should an emergency arise (Staff of Saskatoon Community Health Unit, 1992, p. 34; the information for this discussion was taken from this source).

An extension of this early-discharge program is the extramural hospital developed in New Brunswick (Adams, 1987; Ferguson, 1987). The two main functions of the extramural hospital are to facilitate early discharge of a range of patients and to delay or prevent the need for hospitalization through the provision of a range of community-based services and treatments that enable people to remain in their homes. About half of the admissions to the extramural hospital are early-discharge patients and the other half are admitted directly from the community, thus delaying or preventing the need for their admission to the much more expensive acute-care hospitals.

Although the budget for the extramural hospital is additional to that of existing acute-care hospitals so that there are no immediate savings, it is thought that savings will be realized in the long run, especially if a more integrated and better co-ordinated social-welfare and health-care system can be established. Some believe that making the extramural hospital the master institution of a co-ordinated health-care and social-services system will result in the more effective and efficient use of health-care and social-services dollars, and that this will also result in increased health status among the population.

Attempts to rationalize the organization and delivery of health care and social-support services has assumed other forms in different jurisdictions. Despite differences, however, all efforts seem to be directed towards developing innovative organizational and administrative frameworks that will allow for more effective and efficient use of health-care resources. This entails, among other things, the elimination of service duplication and inefficiencies, while at the same time increasing the responsiveness of the health-care system to the needs of local populations.

In Saskatchewan, the plan for the future of health care involves what appears to be a contradictory process of increasing centralization-decentralization. Under the provincial government's "wellness" plan, for example, the current 400 local hospital boards will be reduced to between 20 and 30 district boards. Each district will consist of about 12 000 persons, and each board will be given a global budget by the provincial government. The regional boards will have the responsibility for deciding which facilities and services are to be provided within the district. It seems clear that within this new decision-making and administrative framework the total number of hospital beds will be reduced, and some small rural hospitals will be closed or converted to other functions.

Increased efficiency in the organization and delivery of health-care services and the anticipated savings realized as a result are expected to be redirected towards various health-promotion and injury and illness-prevention programs. Such programs include home care, family planning, and various programs intended to encourage people to choose healthy lifestyles and to forego high-risk behaviours. The latter includes smoking-cessation initiatives, anti-drug programs, efforts to encourage healthy eating habits, as well as campaigns aimed at reducing family violence and increasing positive capacities to cope with uncertainty and stress, which seems to be a permanent part of life in contemporary society.

These and various other efforts to reduce the utilization of medical and hospital services are related to efforts to reduce the costs of health-care services. A key element in reducing the costs of services is changing the nature of the services provided. We have touched on this topic; it will be further developed in the following section.

Reducing the Costs per Hospitalization

The largest proportion of hospital expenditures are for salaries and wages. Because of this, some of the most vigorous cost-containment efforts are directed towards increasing hospital worker productivity and reducing the costs per service provided.

Labour costs can be reduced in absolute or relative terms. Absolute reductions in labour costs can be achieved in two ways; by reducing wages and/or by reducing the number of workers or the number of hours worked without reducing the number of services provided. Relative cost reductions can be achieved through increasing the level of productivity at a rate higher than the increase in wages. Relative cost reductions are often accomplished through either organizational or technical means. Organizational strategies usually involve extensions to the occupational division of labour. Technical means of reducing costs entail the development and application of labour-replacing and productivity-enhancing technologies.

Various factors, including government policy, influence the capacity to use and the effectiveness of different managerial strategies. It is not possible to examine them in detail here. With reference to absolute wage reductions in the hospital sector, however, it is important to note that the imposition of wage controls in the mid-1970s, as part of a more general anti-inflation policy, had the effect of real wage reductions for nurses and other hospital workers (White, 1990). Government policy since that time has resulted in real income reductions for many categories of workers in both the private and public sectors of the economy (Myles, Picot, & Wannell, 1988). This is interesting insofar as it contributes to growing levels of poverty, which in turn are related to lower levels of health.

Besides simply reducing wages, absolute reductions have been achieved by trans- forming the nature and organization of hospital work processes. The most dramatic example of this is the replacement of full-time with part-time workers. Part-time workers are less expensive than those who work full-time for a number of reasons. First, part-time workers' wage rates tend to be lower than those of full-time employees. One of the reasons for this is that part-time workers tend not to be unionized and have not achieved the benefits of collective bargaining. Another reason that part-time workers are less expensive than full-time workers relates to the fact that part-time workers, in many cases, are not covered by the full range of employment-related benefits, such as pension and unemployment insurance. Employers are not required to make contributions to these on behalf of part-time employees. It is estimated that this saves employers about 10 percent of employment-related expenses.

The use of part-time workers can also reduce costs by increasing productivity. Because part-time workers are only called upon to work at times of peak demand — that is, when there is work to be done — they are only paid for time that they are actually working. The amount of slow time, that is time when there is little work to be performed, is reduced and consequently productivity is increased.

The intensity of work, and hence productivity, is also increased by the use of labour-replacing technologies. These technologies tend to be developed to replace workers who perform routine, standardized, and repetitive tasks. In the hospital setting, for example, robots are being developed and used to perform a growing array of tasks such as the pickup and delivery of linens, meals, lab specimens, and medical supplies (Robertson, 1985). Although this is more common in the United States where hospitals are generally run for profit, the Toronto Hospital for Sick Children uses a robot for lab-specimen preparation (Robertson, 1985).

Although labour-replacing technologies tend to replace living labour with machines, other forms of technology increase directly the intensity of the workers who remain on the job. A good example of this is the development of various kinds of monitoring equipment. Because patients are connected through these technologies to a central observation station, all patients on a ward, in principle, can be monitored by a single person (Brady & Dickinson, 1984). This means that fewer nurses are required to constantly observe and monitor patients. As a result, there are fewer nurses are on a ward during any given shift; consequently those who are on duty find their responsibilities both intensified and extensified. That is, each nurse is responsible for monitoring both more patients and for collecting and interpreting more information about each patient and his or her health-care needs.

In principle, more information is a good thing, at least insofar as it can result in more appropriate and effective care. In the context of cost-reduction strategies, however, it often has the opposite effect. There are two reasons for this. First, intensifying and extensifying nurses' work can contribute to information overload, fatigue, stress, and burnout, which in turn can be associated with reduced proficiency in judgement and decision-making abilities. Second, reduced staffing levels enabled by new technologies can result in the situation where patient requirements exceed the capacity of available nurses to satisfy them. For example, in an acute-care unit, if more than one patient at a time is in need of intensive care, there might not be an adequate number of nurses to provide care.

For many nurses, these and other cost-containment and productivity-enhancing management strategies result in a deterioration of working conditions and in their reduced capacity to provide the personal care that is generally considered to be the hallmark of good-quality nursing (Warburton & Carroll, 1988). From the patient's perspective, the rationalization of nursing work is often experienced as a lack of caring, compassion, or understanding of their experiences, concerns, and needs. These conditions are part of the current crisis in nursing (Hewa & Hetherington, 1990a). The crisis is manifested in a number of ways, many of which contribute to the deepening of the crisis itself. Central to the crisis is the problem of recruiting and retaining nurses, who often experience high levels of job dissatisfaction, job-created stress, frustration, and disappointment that often results from the gap between expectations generated in the professional socialization process and the realities of the alienating, oppressive, and exploitative conditions under which they work (Stroud, 1983; Armstrong, 1988; Campbell, 1988).

These problems are intensified in the general hospital setting to the extent that in many cases the nature of health problems has changed over the past few decades. Increasingly, major health problems are of a chronic long-term nature. This results in different care requirements, which in turn necessitate changes in the traditional caregiver-patient relationship away from one characterized by professional dominance of passive patients to one based upon a more egalitarian and collaborative relationship.

In Kirk's 1990 study of chronically ill patients' perceptions of nursing care, for example, she commented on the changing nature of the nurse-patient relationship necessitated by the management of chronicity. A dimension of this changing relationship "involves recognizing the patient as an expert who has already developed effective means of assessing and managing illness" (Kirk, 1990, pp. 138-9). Kirk goes on to note that relating to the "chronically ill patient as a collaborator in care rather than a [passive] recipient of care may be instrumental in bridging the gap between illness management at home and in the institution" (Kirk, 1990, p. 138).

This bridging function and the management of illness and disability at home, or more generally in the community rather than on an inpatient basis in hospital, is a central element of the new health-promotion initiative. It is to that that attention is now turned.

Health Promotion: Health as a Human Resource

In this section I shall outline the main dimensions of the framework for current health-promotion policy in Canada. This will include an overview of the concept of health underpinning health-promotion initiatives, along with a brief description of the main goals of health promotion and the strategies and mechanisms proposed for achieving them.

When the principle sources of morbidity were infectious diseases, health was defined in negative terms, that is, as the absence of disease. In the post-World War II period, however, as the primary forms of morbidity came to be chronic, degenerative, and largely uncurable, given the state of medical science and technology, the definition of health changed. Currently health is defined in positive terms as a resource. Maximum health is achieved when individuals are able to attain and sustain a state of complete physical, emotional, and social well-being. Health promotion, therefore, entails the creation of conditions which enable, or empower, individuals to cope with, or change, those factors that influence their health. Four general factors have been identified as important in this regard: the nature of human biology, lifestyles, the social and physical environments within which people live, and the nature and organization of the health-care system (Lalonde, 1974). Effective health-promotion policy and practice, therefore, must address each of these areas.

Given this conceptual framework, three main obstacles to the achievement of health have been identified: first, continued inequities in the distribution of health and illness among the Canadian population. This is related to the second impediment, namely, unhealthy lifestyles among those with poor health. The third impediment is seen to be the inability or unwillingness of people to cope with their illnesses and disabilities without undue reliance on expensive and, in many cases, unnecessary and ineffective modes of professional treatment and care. Overcoming these immediate barriers to health is seen as the main challenge to, and the primary means for achieving, health for all.

The health-promotion framework proposes three strategies and three mechanisms for meeting the challenges and achieving the goal. The three strategies are: (1) fostering public participation in the definition of health needs; (2) strengthening community health-services as the most appropriate means of achieving health; and (3) co-ordinating healthy public policy.

These three strategies are to be realized in the form of three health-promotion mechanisms, namely, self-care, mutual aid, and the creation of healthy environments. These mechanisms are not simply viewed as means to an end, rather the means are the end. Thus, self-care, mutual aid, and the capacity to achieve healthy environments are equivalent to the achievement of health, which is defined as "the ability to manage or even change [one's] surroundings" (Epp, 1986, p. 3).

We shall look at each of these three strategies before examining the three mechanisms, or means/ends, of self-care, mutual aid, and creation of healthy environments.

Strategy 1: Fostering Public Participation

At the general level, fostering public participation in health promotion is achieved by "helping people to assert control over the factors which affect their health" (Epp, 1986, p. 9). At a more concrete level, it is achieved through the two mechanisms of self-help and mutual aid. Fostering public participation also involves reorganizing various administrative structures in the health-care field in order to allow and encourage greater involvement on the part of those who traditionally have been excluded from or marginalized in the determination of health needs and the most appropriate means of satisfying them.

In Saskatchewan, for example, this involves the regionalization of health-care services and the integration of planning, administrative, and decision-making boards in order to put needs-determination and service-provision decisions in the hands of community members (Simard, 1992, p. 17). The regionalization of health care is often seen as a necessary aspect of the second health-promotion strategy, strengthening community health services.

Strategy 2: Strengthening Community Health Services

A commitment to strengthening community health services entails a commitment to reforming the existing health-care system, which as we have seen, is medically dominated and hospital oriented. Strengthening community health services then clearly implies enhancing their role and function in relation to the existing health-care system. This point is explicitly made in the Epp Report, which states that ". . . adjusting the present health care system in such a way as to assign more responsibility to community-based services means allocating a greater share of resources to such services" (Epp, 1986, p. 10). In this regard, the federal government has taken a number of initiatives in the areas of health promotion and education, including the allocation of "$30 million annually to improve the quality of life of the elderly through self-care projects and education" (Vance, 1988 [revised 1991], p. 14).

Within this commitment it is taken for granted that "communities will become more involved in planning their own services, and that the links between communities and their services and institutions will be strengthened" (Epp, 1986, p. 10). Of course, in principle, this commitment to increased participation and democratization of health needs definition, and provision seems both desirable and necessary. To fundamentally alter the structural framework within which health-care needs are defined and satisfied promises to be difficult.

Past experience with increasing public participation through altered budgeting procedures (in the Regina Community Clinic, for example), leads one to expect the medical profession to resist any changes that they see as detrimental to their professional autonomy and dominance (Young, 1975). Times and circumstances have changed, however, since the 1970s and the necessity and willingness of the medical profession to adapt constructively to a changed role in the health system may be greater. The health-promotion plan for the transformation of the Saskatchewan health-care system, for example, states that:

> The medical profession is receptive to innovation and to reviewing its role in the health system, including working as team members with other health professionals. Major consultation has begun and a new dialogue is emerging. Alternative methods of payment for physicians and the lack of physicians in rural areas will be explored. (Simard, 1992, p. 21)

Although the medical profession may be receptive to innovation, the outcomes of these consultations remain to be seen.

It seems inevitable that different structures of service delivery and modes of payment will emerge, depending on local conditions and factors. Indeed, the capacity to respond to the circumstances and needs of different communities is identified as one of the main advantages of the health-promotion initiatives. A potential problem associated with the decentralization of needs determination and service delivery is the erosion of standards and fragmentation of services. Cutbacks in the level of federal-government support for health-care services has led some to express concern over the continued capacity of the federal government to ensure the maintenance of uniform standards in terms of the quality and extent of health-care services across the country.

The decentralization of needs assessment and service delivery envisioned by health-promotion policy, of course, is consistent with the definition of health that underpins this policy initiative. It is also consistent with the relativistic definition of health upon which the entire health-promotion edifice rests. Referring to the view that health is a resource and that health promotion is the development and application of the knowledge and skills required to secure control over oneself and one's surroundings, the Epp Report goes on to state that "This view of health . . . emphasizes the role of individuals and communities in defining what health means to them" (Epp, 1986, p. 3). Thus, it is clear that health is neither absolute nor universal. Rather, it is relative to one's social, economic, political, and cultural roles and functions. Although this conceptualization is generally seen as a progressive advance over purely medical and reductionist conceptions of health and illness, it too is characterized by its own contradictions.

The contradictions emerge most clearly in relation to the main challenges identified by health-promotion policy and the concrete mechanisms proposed for meeting those challenges. For example, the first challenge identified is the reduction of inequities. The Epp Report states in this regard that health-promotion policy "assumes that there will be a greater emphasis on providing services to groups that are disadvantaged. It further takes for granted that communities will become more involved in planning their own services, and that the links between communities and their services and institutions will be strengthened" (Epp, 1986, p. 10).

At first glance, these assumptions do not seem problematic. The assumption that greater emphasis, presumably in the form of greater resources, will be put on providing services to the disadvantaged raises the possibility of fewer resources and emphasis being placed on providing necessary services to those groups that are not defined as disadvantaged. This suggests the possibility that those deemed not to be disadvantaged will be required either to do without services or to pay for them in one way or another. It also raises the spectre of further privatization of health-care delivery and the erosion of medicare. It suggests too the possibility of different rights and entitlements for different categories of the Canadian population, and in this way may contribute to the amplification of jealousies and hostilities between different segments of the nation or community.

It is a well-known fact of life in Canada that national unity is an elusive and, in some quarters, undesirable goal. The greater involvement of communities in needs-assessment and service-delivery decisions assumed and encouraged by health-promotion policy also may be Janus-faced. Increased participation in defining problems and solutions politicizes those processes. Politicized decision making, of course, can have either positive or negative consequences. Positive consequences ensue when previously marginalized and disempowered groups are empowered and integrated into all aspects of community life. Negative effects of politicization are related to the fact that power and other resources are not equally distributed throughout society or within communities. Existing inequities, then, may be further entrenched and exacerbated through the political process. If politicizing health-care policy and practice does not result in democratization, it may contribute to an entrenchment or extension of existing inequities. The form that this negative effect is most likely to take is the abandonment of the marginalized and disempowered to their own resources in the name of self-care and mutual aid.

Strategy 3: Co-ordinating Healthy Public Policy

This strategy is a direct extension of the broadened and context-sensitive definition of health underpinning health-promotion policy. It is essentially a recognition that a broad spectrum of policy decisions can and do affect people's behaviours, and hence affect health and illness. Some of those specifically identified in the Epp Report are income security, employment, education, housing, business, agriculture, transportation, justice, and technology (Epp, 1986, p. 10).

The problem is that health concerns in many cases are not priority items in other policy areas. Indeed, in some cases priority objectives in some policy areas may even be in direct opposition to health-promotion objectives. Economic development and business policies, for example, may create conditions that are detrimental to environmental, worker and/or consumer health and safety (Bolaria, 1991; Dickinson & Stobbe, 1988; Harding, 1988).

Reconciling contradictory policy objectives may not be possible, and in many cases, even if it is possible, it won't be easy. The health-promotion policy recognizes this difficulty, but has little to offer in the way of concrete suggestions on how to solve it. The only specific comment is the rather platitudinous observation that "we have to make health attractive to other sectors in much the same way that we try to make healthy choices attractive to people" (Epp, 1986, p. 10). How this is to be done remains a mystery.

The three health-promotion strategies are linked to three mechanisms for achieving health: self-care, mutual aid, and the creation of healthy environments.

Mechanism 1: Self-Care

Self-care is defined as "the decisions and actions individuals take in the interest of their own health" (Epp, 1986, p. 7). As conceptualized in health-promotion policy, it refers largely to individual lifestyle decisions and practices. Some examples of self-care are choosing a healthy diet, exercising regularly, limiting alcohol consumption, not smoking, and using a seat belt when driving.

For effective self-care, people must be both willing and able to make healthy choices. Consequently, individuals must possess the necessary information, abilities, and capacities required to make healthy lifestyle choices. A key means of providing these resources is through the mechanism of mutual aid.

Mechanism 2: Mutual Aid

Mutual aid is seen as a primary way to enable self-care: "It implies people helping each other, supporting each other emotionally, and sharing ideas, information and experiences" (Epp, 1986, p. 7). Ideally, from the health-promotion perspective it takes place in the family, the voluntary organization, and self-help groups.

Mutual aid is seen as an informal complement to professionally provided care and services available in the formal health-care system. It has been pointed out however that self-care and mutual aid as health-promotion mechanisms may also be seen as alternatives to professional services from the formal health-care system (Bolaria, 1984). Thus, both these health-promotion mechanisms have contradictory potential; they can enhance independence and control over the factors affecting one's health, and they can be seen as an inexpensive, and possibly less effective, alternative to professionally provided health-care services.

Conceived of in the most positive way, mutual aid refers to the enhancement of community interdependence in order to increase the capacity for individual independence. There are many examples of this form of mutual aid. Some mentioned in the Epp Report are Alcoholics Anonymous, One Voice for Seniors, Block Parents, the Coalition of Provincial Organizations of the Handicapped (COPOH), as well as rape crisis centres and other types of crisis counselling services (Epp 1986, p. 7). On the negative side, there is some concern that community-based caregivers, particularly women, potentially may be expected to carry an even greater burden of caring in the name of mutual aid. The third mechanism, the creation of healthy environments, is intended, among other things, to ensure that the potentially negative effects of health-promotion policy and practice are minimized or eliminated.

Mechanism 3: Creating Healthy Environments

The creation of healthy environments as a mechanism for the achievement of health is the most amorphous and ill-defined of the three. It is defined as "altering or adapting our social, economic, or physical surroundings in ways that will help not only to preserve but also to enhance our health" (Epp, 1986, p. 9). This is understood to entail "ensuring that policies and practices are in place to provide Canadians with a healthy environment at home, school, work or wherever else they may be" (Epp, 1986, p. 9). In many respects, it is little more than a restatement of the health-promotion strategy of co-ordinating healthy public policy.

The difficulties inherent in this health-promotion mechanism are clearly acknowledged. The practical definition and activation of this mechanism in many instances is being left to the initiative of specific special-needs groups and local communities.

Conclusion

In this chapter we have examined two aspects of current health policy: the cost-containment efforts characteristic of the medically dominated and hospital-based illness-care system, and the various dimensions of an emergent health-promotion and illness-and injury-prevention policy. Although analytically, and in many respects institutionally and functionally distinct, these two dimensions of health policy and practice are interrelated. Indeed, health-promotion policy as it is currently conceived is not only intended to facilitate the achievement and preservation of health, in the long run it is also seen as a way to reduce health costs, or at least to slow the rate of growth (Epp, 1986, p. 13).

Health-promotion policy is also seen as a means to integrate and more effectively co-ordinate the organization and delivery of health-and illness-care services. As such, it promises major changes to the distribution of resources and power within the health-care arena. Change in the nature and organization of health-care services has traditionally been a conflictual and often traumatic experience for Canadians. Despite an apparent consensus concerning the need for cost control and the principles of health promotion, there is likely to be much struggle over the specific ways in which current health-care goals and priorities are implemented.

Note

1. About 12 000 surveys were mailed to Canadian doctors in May 1992; approximately 3 400 replied. This is about a 28 percent response rate, therefore, caution must be exercised in interpreting the results (*Star Phoenix*, 23 October, p. A 14).

Study Questions

1. Outline and discuss the main forms of cost control currently being applied to the illness-care system in Canada.
2. What are the main mechanisms proposed for implementing health-promotion objectives.
3. The primary goal of health promotion is the achievement of health for all. What is the definition of health used in this policy initiative? What are the main impediments to the realization of that goal?
4. The achievement of health and the containment of costs cannot be achieved without first limiting the power and autonomy of the medical profession. Discuss.

Recommended Reading

Blishen, B.R. (1991). *Doctors in Canada: The changing world of medical practice.* Toronto: University of Toronto Press in association with Statistics Canada.

Clarke, J.N. (1990). *Health, illness, and medicine in Canada.* Toronto: McClelland & Stewart.

Edginton, B. (1989). *Health, disease and medicine in Canada.* Toronto: Butterworths.

Epp, J. (1986). *Achieving health for all: A framework for health promotion.* Ottawa: Health and Welfare Canada.

Northcott, H.C. (1991). Health status and health care in Canada: Contemporary issues. In B.S. Bolaria (Ed.), *Social issues and contradictions in Canadian society* (pp. 178-199). Toronto: Harcourt Brace Jovanovich.

Taylor, M.G. (1978). *Health insurance and Canadian public policy: The seven decisions that created the Canadian health insurance system.* Kingston and Montreal: McGill-Queen's University Press.

Vance, J. (1991). Health policy in Canada. *Current Issue Review, Library of Parliament, Research Branch,* 1-16.

References

Adams, O. (1987, April 15). Hospital without walls: Is New Brunswick's extra-mural hospital the way of the future? Interview with Gordon Ferguson. *Canadian Medical Association Journal*, 136, 861-864.

Armstrong, P. (1988, Summer). Where have all the nurses gone? *Healthsharing*, 17-19.

Badgley, R., & Wolfe, S. (1967). *Doctors' strike: Medical care and conflict in Saskatchewan.* Toronto: Macmillan.

Barale, A.E. (1991, September 16). Patients have unrealistic expectations of the system. *Saskatoon Star Phoenix*, p. A5.

Blishen, B.R. (1991). *Doctors in Canada: The changing world of medical practice.* Toronto: University of Toronto Press in association with Statistics Canada.

Bolaria, B.S. (1984). Self-care and lifestyles: ideological and policy implications. In J.A. Fry (Ed.), *Economy, class and social reality: Issues in contemporary Canadian society* (pp. 350-363). Toronto: Butterworths.

Bolaria, B.S. (1988). Profits and illness: exporting health hazards to the Third World. In B.S. Bolaria & H.D. Dickinson (Eds.), *Sociology of health care in Canada* (pp. 477-496). Toronto: Harcourt Brace Jovanovich.

Bolaria, B.S. (1991). Environment, work and illness. In B.S. Bolaria (Ed.), *Social issues and contradictions in Canadian society* (pp. 222-246). Toronto: Harcourt Brace Jovanovich.

B.C. doctors escalate dispute with government. (1992, July 3). *Saskatoon Star Phoenix*, p. A12.

Campbell, M.L. (1993). The structure of stress in nurse's work. In B.S. Bolaria & H.D. Dickinson (Eds.), *Sociology of health care in Canada* (this volume). Toronto: Harcourt Brace and Company.

Chappell, N.L., Strain, L.A., & Blandford, A.A. (1986). *Aging and health care: A social perspective.* Toronto: Holt Rinehart & Winston.

Dickinson, H.D. (1993). Health and health care in Canada. In M. Kanwar & S. Hewa (Eds.), *Issues in Canadian Society.* Dubuque: Kendall/Hunt.

Dickinson H.D., & Brady, P.D. (1984). The labour process and the transformation of health care delivery in Canada. In J.A. Fry (Ed.), *Contradictions in Canadian society* (pp. 194-206). Toronto: John Wiley & Sons.

Dickinson, H.D., & Stobbe, M. (1988). Occupational health and safety in Canada. In B.S. Bolaria & H.D. Dickinson (Eds.), *Sociology of health care in Canada* (pp. 426-438). Toronto: Harcourt Brace Jovanovich.

Epp, J. (1986). *Achieving health for all: A framework for health promotion.* Ottawa: Health and Welfare Canada.

Ferguson, G. (1987). The New Bruswick extra-mural hospital: A Canadian hospital at home. *Journal of Public Health Policy*, 8, (4), 561-70.

Gray, C. (1992). Ontario's task force on sexual abuse: McPhedran fights back. *Canadian Medical Association Journal*, 146, (4), 555-558.

Hastings, J.E.F. (1972). The community health centre in Canada. *Report of the community health centre project to the conference of health ministers.*

Harding. J. (1993). Environmental degradation and rising cancer rates: Exploring the links in Canada. In B.S. Bolaria & H.D. Dickinson (Eds.), *Sociology of health care in Canada* (this volume). Toronto: Harcourt Brace and Company.

Health and Welfare Canada. (1990). *National health expenditures in Canada, 1975-1987.* Ottawa: Author.

Hewa, S., & Hetherington, R.W. (1990). Specialists without spirit: Crisis in the nursing profession. *Journal of Medical Ethics*, 16, 179-84.

Illich, I. (1976). *Limits to medicine, medical nemesis: The expropriation of health.* Toronto and London: McClelland & Stewart in association with Marion Boyers.

Kirk, K. (1990). *Chronically ill patient's perceptions of nursing care.* Unpublished M. Sc. thesis. Saskatoon: College of Nursing, University of Saskatchewan.

Kirkey, S. (1992, October 23). MDs back rationing of care: Survey. *Saskatoon Star Phoenix*, p. A14.

Lalonde, M. (1974). *A new perspective on the health of Canadians: A working document.* Ottawa: Health and Welfare Canada.

Minister of National Health and Welfare. (1970). *Task force reports on the cost of health services in Canada, Vols. 1-3.* Ottawa: Information Canada. Minister of National Health and Welfare. (1985). *Health Manpower Directorate.* Ottawa: Author.

Myles, J., Picot, G., & Wannell, T. (1988, October). *The changing wages distribution of jobs,*

1981-1986. The labour force (pp. 85-129). Ottawa: Supply and Services Canada.

Naylor, D.C. (1986). *Private practice, public payment: Canadian medicine and the politics of health insurance, 1911-1966.* Kingston and Montreal: McGill-Queen's University Presses.

Northcott, H.C. (1988). Health care resources and extra-billing: financing allocation and utilization. In B.S. Bolaria & H.D. Dickinson (Eds.), *Sociology of health care in Canada* (pp. 38-50). Toronto: Harcourt Brace Jovanovich.

Robertson, S. (1985, November 25). Check-up. *Saskatoon Star Phoenix*, p. A11.

Sears, W.L. (1992). Alberta college latest to tackle issue of physician related sexual abuse. *Canadian Medical Association Journal*, 146, (4), 567-568.

Simard, L. (1992). *A Saskatchewan vision for health: Working together for change.* Regina: Saskatchewan Health.

Soderstrom, L. (1978). *The Canadian health system.* London: Croom Helm.

Staff of Saskatoon Community Health Unit. (1992, June 28). Early maternity discharge program begins Thursday. *Saskatoon Sun*, p. 34.

Stroud, C. (1983, March). Silent nightingale. *Quest*, 62-8.

Vance, J. (1991). Health policy in Canada. *Current Issue Review*, Library of Parliament, Research Branch, 1-16.

Vayda, E., Evans, R.G., & Mindell, W.R. (1979). Universal health insurance in Canada: History, problems, trends. *Journal of Community Health*, 4, 217-31.

Warburton, R., & Carroll, W.K. (1993). Class and gender in nursing. In B.S. Bolaria & H.D. Dickinson (Eds.), *Sociology of health care in Canada* (this volume). Toronto: Harcourt Brace and Company.

Webb, J. (1991, September 6). Education, not political interference will fix medicare. *Saskatoon Star Phoenix*, p. A5.

White, J.P. (1990). *Hospital strike: Women, unions and public sector conflict.* Toronto: Thompson Educational Publishing.

Wright, C.J. (1991). The fee-for-service system should be replaced. *Canadian Medical Association Journal*, 144, (7), 900-903.

Young, T. Kue. (1975). Lay-professional conflict in a Canadian community health centre: A case report. *Medical Care*, 13, 897-904.

Part Two

Doctors, Patients, and Health Care Delivery

Introduction

In earlier times, physicians did not possess the skills and knowledge to offer their patients the cures that are available today, nor did they occupy the relatively high position in society that today's physicians have come to enjoy. Improvement in the health of the general population resulted mainly from public health measures (nutrition, sanitation, pasteurization, regulation of working conditions, housing) rather than from medical practice. Scientific advances in the area of vaccination and drugs, however, made it possible for doctors to actually begin to cure disease. The physician thus came to be viewed as the ultimate authority in the health-care system, not only in the eyes of the patient, but also among other health-care professionals.

As government funding decreases, threatening working conditions and incomes, health-care provider groups have found themselves in greater conflict over patient responsibility. Technological change, the increasing decentralization of health care, and heightened consumer expectations have also influenced the educational systems and forms of practice of health-care professionals. In Chapter 6, Battershill examines the means by which those in the health occupations control, or seek to control, their work. Based on Abbott's model of professionalism (1988), he presents data on eight health-care professions, grouped according to autonomy, scope of practice, and knowledge base within the context of a shifting division of labour. The findings indicate that the dominant professionals — doctors and dentists — have the most autonomy and are involved in maintaining it. However, economic and political pressures are forcing them to become more patient-oriented in their work. The less autonomous providers — pharmacists, occupational therapists, and physiotherapists — have a narrower scope of practice and are seeking to clarify their duties and extend their responsibilities. The groups with the least education and autonomy — medical radiation therapists, laboratory technologists, and respiratory therapists — are upgrading their entrance qualifications and expanding basic and postgraduate training.

These health-care professionals are interdependent; all endorsing to some extent the concept of a health-care team. Their responses to social and economic change will dramatically affect the health-care division of labour in the future.

Kirk, in Chapter 7, uses a feminist approach to examine women in medical training programs. She begins with an exploration of latent patriarchal culture, arguing that this concept is central to the discussion since the institution of medicine exists within a patriarchal society and that the stereotypes, barriers, and discrimination experienced by women in medicine are the products of such a society used to oppress them. She points out that we have a limited understanding of the issues concerning women in medicine since the majority of research has tended to exclude them. Recently, however, with the ever-increasing enrollment of women in medical schools, there have been more studies aimed at understanding and describing their experiences. Kirk also notes that women enter medical school with qualifications equal to those of men and do as well as men throughout their training. The question of equality of women's experiences within their training programs is explored. Kirk points out that by grade 10, females enrol in fewer mathematics and science classes than do males, hence significantly limiting their career choices. Society, subtle sexism in schools, and sexist language also contribute to limited career options. Kirk reviews the current literature on women's experiences within medi-cal school and concludes that they face both overt and subtle forms of gender discrimi-nation; must deal with more complex role demands in terms of balancing professional and personal obligations; have limited female role models and mentors among medical school faculty members; are often excluded from male cliques; and experience difficul-ties in appearing credible.

Lastly, the author asks whether an increase in female physicians will ultimately result in more humane patient care, starting a trend away from scientific and technology-bound medicine. Citing various studies, Kirk reports that few gender differences have been found among medical school graduates. She points out that the socializing aspects of medical school are very powerful in shaping students' attitudes and priorities; that problem-solving skills and the humanistic aspects of health-care are excluded from the curriculum; that homogenization is the result of socialization, creating stronger "class loyalties" than gender loyalties among women in medicine.

Kirk concludes that greater numbers of women in medicine is not the answer as long as the framework remains the same.

The dynamics of the patient-physician relationship are the subject of Chapter 8. Frenkel presents a brief review of the history of interaction between patients and medical practitioners, and discusses structural-functionalist, conflict, and interaction models postulated by various theorists. Each of these perspectives provides some understanding of the dynamics of the doctor–patient relationship. It is then pointed out that the interaction between doctors and patients must be studied in the social framework within which it occurs; it cannot be seen as separate from that context. The author demonstrates this by her review of the modification of the traditional interaction between patients and health–care practitioners, brought about by third–party insurance and other legislative initiatives and by the consumer movement, which emphasizes individual patients' rights.

Chapter 6

Social Dimensions in the Production and Practice of Canadian Health Care Professionals

Charles Battershill, Ryerson Polytechnical Institute

Introduction

This chapter examines the social aspects of educational systems and forms of practice of principal health-care professionals. In the background lie major, ongoing changes in the organization and delivery of health care, from the international sphere to the community level (White & Connelly, 1991). These definitive influences, although discussed in other chapters in this book, must also be noted here. Foremost is the cost crisis and the rate and impact of technological change. Related issues are the increasing decentralization of health care through expanding non-hospital, community, and home-oriented health care. As governmental funding decreases, threatening working conditions and incomes, provider groups have found themselves in greater explicit and implicit conflict over patient responsibility. Moreover, the public is increasingly informed and critical of consumption of health-care services, especially with medicine, where conflict with patients and patients' groups is not uncommon.

The occupational responses to the social and economic climate in Canada are the underlying themes of this chapter. First, Canadians are becoming more participatory in their own health care. Second, provider groups are upgrading the standards of their curriculum and practice. Third, health-care services are increasingly politicized, with the government (as third party insurer) beginning to demand greater accountability for health-care dollars. Indeed, the "monopsony" power of governments as sole buyers of medical services in Canadian medicare increasingly confers power over service provision.

All provinces are increasingly regulating established and new health-care provider groups. For instance, Ontario's Health Professions Legislative Review (HPLR) has recently concluded its regulatory activities (Schwartz, 1989). In sociology, the gaining of respect and autonomy is known as "professionalization" (Goode, 1960; Torrance, 1987). The counter-trend, noted as "deprofessionalization," refers to the imposition of outsider perspectives on the established practice of a health-care provider group (Coburn, et al., 1983; Wahn, 1987).

However, the reality of crisis and negotiation permits the application of a new model of professionalism that is more flexible than the professionalization/ deprofessionalization model. In *The System of Professions*, Andrew Abbott (1988) advanced a theory of professions, applicable to Canada. His model deals with the reality of change in the Canadian health-care system while simultaneously involving a multidimensional comparison with other provider groups. Using Abbott's model, this chapter examines the means by which occupations control, or seek to control, the form and content of their work. As well, this model identifies occupational claims over jurisdiction and intraoccupational negotiation to occur in the workplace, in the public eye, and in the legislative arena. The system's cost crisis and the growing consumerism of the public are "disturbances" that have an impact on the health-care division of labour.

According to Abbott (1988), "professionalism" is a type of work applying abstract knowledge and esoteric skills to particular cases. Thus, we will examine each profession's knowledge base and education, their forms and scope of practice, and their relationship to other providers and to the public. Contemporary social, political, and economic forces, as well as technological advancements, are viewed as the key forces of change that affect various health-care professions' workplace interrelationships, their internal structure and knowledge base, and finally, their ties to the public and to legislators.

Eight health-care professions, grouped according to autonomy, scope of practice, and knowledge base are examined within the context of a shifting health-care division of labour. The findings are that those dominant professionals (physicians and dentists) have the most autonomy and are involved in maintaining it. Those with less autonomy and a narrower scope of practice (pharmacy, occupational therapy, and physiotherapy) seek to consolidate and extend their positions. Those with the narrowest scope of practice are the least autonomous professions (radiation technologists, laboratory technologists, and respiratory therapists). In order to garner more autonomy and respect, these occupations are upgrading their entrance qualifications and expanding their knowledge foundation and basic and postgraduate training. Although important in the overall health-care division of labour, these providers are most dependent on the actions of others, usually doctor's orders, to initiate their work.

The bulk of the data on provider groups was gathered from national bodies and agencies headquartered in Ottawa or Toronto. Thus, even though it has the greatest number of health professionals of each type, the provincial scene is disproportionately represented by the amount of data on Ontario. Readers should be aware of differences among the provinces, especially with respect to Quebec. All are medical science-oriented, with dentists and pharmacists least linked to hospitals as a workplace (see Table 1). The following sections are ordered to correspond to the most-to-least-autonomy model described above.

Medicine

Medicine remains the "dominant" health-care profession (Coburn, et al., 1983). It continues to be the highest paid profession and the one that makes the most decisions about health care. It defines the nature of Canadian health care more than any other provider group (Freidson, 1970). As it changes or is forced to change, the status and role of the other groups also change. Next to nurses, physicians are the most numerous provider group (see Table 1).

As the dominant profession in health care and the usual reference point for sociological discussion of professionalism, what is happening to physicians is a key to understanding the wider changes in the health-care system. The "managerial revolution" in medicine is bringing greater awareness of the alternative ways to train, fund, and practise medicine while considering expanding the role of other health-care professionals. While it is not politically astute for policy makers to talk about replacing physicians with lower-cost providers, medicine is now proactively seeking to direct the change in health care. In 1989, Rachlis and Kushner's *Second Opinion* made the public and ministries of health aware of various inefficiencies in medical practice. The title of the Ontario Ministry of Health's 1989-90 annual report heralds the future of Canadian health care and medical practice: "Managing for Quality."

What is medicine? Medicine prevents, relieves, and cures disease, which requires putting into practice knowledge about the body's normal and abnormal structures and processes. Medicine's ability to fulfil this mandate was founded by the Flexner Report of 1910. This study reformed medical training around a "scientific" model of knowledge production and clinical education, replacing the apprenticeship type of training common at the time. Under its guidance, medical practice became increasingly specialized as medical technology advanced and its overall knowledge base grew.

Acquiring medical knowledge begins with a highly competitive contest to enter medical school. Normal requirements are a science background, high academic achievement, and less well-defined personal qualities. The competition is tough, with more than

Table 1   Number of Selected Health Professionals, in Canada, by Province, 1989

Province	Dental	Medical Lab. Tech.*	Medical Rad. Tech.*	Occup. Therap.	Pharm.	Medical Doctor	Physio-Therap.	Resp. Therap.
Newfoundland	137	275	185	45	398	1 165	100	
Prince Edward Island	52	104	58	19	82	183	30	198
Nova Scotia	418	910	343	125	707	2 038	296	
New Brunswick	220	542	518	94	390	1 061	169	
Quebec	3 155	2 075	3 291	1 147	4 323	15 882	2 021	1 602
Ontario	5 679	7 674	3 806	983	6 259	22 755	3 486	913
Manitoba	524	1 058	597	223	773	2 239	366	154
Saskatoon	389	1 067	389	92	905	1 754	315	47
Alberta	1 347	2 503	1 258	435	2 228	4 869	1 166	350
British Columbia	2 204	2 688	1 185	284	2 284	6 913	1 608	186
Yukon	16†	39	—	—	14	38	—	1
North West Territories	36†		—	—	25	45	5	—
Canada	13 997	18 935	11 630	3 447	18 388	58 942	9 562	3 451

* Refers to "technologists"   † Estimated data   — denotes data missing

Sources: *Health Personnel in Canada 1989* (1989). Ottawa: Health and Welfare Canada, pp. 276-286.

twenty applications received for one place in some schools. In Canada medical students typically encounter a two-year, pre-clinical program of gross and microscopic anatomy, as well as physiology, biochemistry, pathology, embryology, and pharmacology. In the final two years of medical school, they apply this knowledge in clinical settings with actual patients, usually in hospitals, as the most junior member of a team of physicians. Students spend varying amounts of time associated with the various divisions within medicine. After the fourth year of medical school, they complete an internship. Interns have increased responsibility and further learn general medicine by "rotating" through the major areas of medicine within the hospital. They write the Medical Council of Canada Qualifying Exam during this internship year. A licence to practise medicine is then issued by any one of each province's medical licensing bodies. Medical education is conducted in "teaching hospitals" and their affiliates, which have special facilities oriented to providing both care and education; patients are examined by students at all levels.

The new M.D. can go on to specialized training as a resident, from one to five further years. The College of Family Physicians of Canada licenses family practitioners. The Royal College of Physicians and Surgeons licenses the other specialties. It recognizes (as of 1986) 42 specialties (24 clinical, 6 laboratory, 12 surgical). About half of Canada's doctors are specialists, including family practitioners, and half are general practitioners (White & Connelly, 1991). Evaluation is through standardized written exams and the clinical judgement of supervisors.

Most physicians now work in group practices, sharing the overhead costs of office space with a number of colleagues and usually treating patients in one hospital. Increasingly, group practice is also seen of a way of sharing responsibility for 24-hour patient care with a view to improving the quality of life of each partner physician. Physicians' services are fully covered by provincial health-insurance plans. Each provincial medical association negotiates a contract with the provincial government over the fee-schedule payment. Specialists' services are reimbursed at a higher rate than are those of general practitioners.

In terms of the scope of practice, physicians are the only health-care professional licensed by the state to perform surgery and to prescribe pharmaceutical drugs. They also order high-tech diagnostic tests and treatments, involving the work of many other health-care providers, including laboratory and X-ray technicians, social workers, psychologists, and occupational therapists. Overall, these are the tools physicians use to prevent, relieve, and cure disease.

Today, major changes in medical education affect student demographics and curriculum reform. Until recently, medicine was male-dominated; now women comprise a large proportion of medical students. In 1990-91, of the 7 110 Canadian medical students, 44 percent were women, varying by school, from McMaster at 66 percent to Saskatchewan at 33 percent (ACMC, 1991).

Another demographic feature of medical education is the recent slight reduction in the number of students graduated. Historically, in 1964-65, 842 students began their studies in twelve medical schools. Then, the 1964 Royal Commission on Health Services added another four medical schools. (It should be noted that these — Calgary, McMaster, Memorial, and Sherbrooke — sought to emphasize the importance of family practice and community-oriented medicine.) Today's oversupply of physicians began then, as the number of first-year students jumped to 1 452 in 1970-71 and peaked at 1 887 in 1980-81 and again in 1983-84. Amid discussion of physician oversupply (FPAC, 1985), entrance was reduced to below the 1 800 mark after 1987-88.

A significant benchmark in the evolution of medical education was the General Professional Education of the Physician and College Preparation for Medicine (GPEP) report, published by the Association of American Medical Colleges in 1984. The Canadian medical education community is interwoven with the American, themselves inside an international network. The report's purpose was to redress the alienation of patients and physicians caused by technological development and subsequent specialization. It was composed of a panel of experts from leading medical educators. They solicited input from a wide number of sources, including the public and provider groups.

The GPEP report concluded that a general professional education must underlie specialized medical training and must be the basis for a satisfying, solid relationship between the physician and the patient as a whole person. It sought to de-emphasize passive accumulation of facts as an inadequate educational strategy given the rapid advances in medical knowledge. It recommended that medical training incorporate humanistic values, social and humanistic knowledge, communication skills, and information science toward practising preventive, environmentally aware medicine; that the curriculum should be oriented towards self-directed, active learning and problem solving from a lecture-based system.

On the GPEP panel was Dr. Victor Neufeld, a founder of the McMaster University medical school in Hamilton. The McMaster model, notable for its progressiveness, is an actual instance of reform (Kendall & Reader, 1988). It has been in the forefront of educational reforms internationally and has had a direct impact on medical education in Canada. That this model resembles the GPEP's recommendations is not surprising since it has been reported that Dr. Neufeld, a major architect of the McMaster curriculum, was also a major presence on the GPEP panel.

The major features of the McMaster program are (1) a student-oriented, problem-solving curriculum reducing the importance of facts transmitted through lectures; (2) an emphasis on family or whole-person medicine through primary-care practice; (3)

integration of clinical and basic sciences learned in association with active, first-year involvement in patient care; (4) broadened admissions criteria beyond a natural science background (the display of leadership, teamwork, problem-solving abilities, and liberal arts education, selected primarily through interpersonal evaluation by faculty members, medical students, and community representatives); and (5) a program of three rather than four years.

McMaster revised its program in 1983 and today is in the process of further change. It introduced more learning/communication skills, more behavioural and population knowledge organized around the individual's community-based life cycle of experience, and critical appraisal of medical information skills. According to its founders it is successful (Neufeld, Woodward, & MacLeod, 1989), but others believe that a component of its success is the enthusiasm of students and faculty, sociologically known as the "Hawthorne Effect" (Kendall & Reader, 1988). Slowly, medical education in Canada is incorporating some of these new ideas. Medical educators are aware of the slow shift from a conventional to a problem-based curriculum, and are studying aspects of it (Patel, Groen, & Norman, 1991).

Broader and quicker change to Canadian medical education and practice has recently been proposed. The federal/provincial/territorial deputy ministers of health commissioned two of Canada's leading health-policy analysts to study physician resources (see Table 2). This report, entitled *Toward Integrated Medical Resource Policies for Canada*, was published in June of 1991 (Barer & Stoddart, 1991).

It partially links the system's problems of physician oversupply, maldistribution (rural-urban, interprovincial), and cost crisis to medical education. It may well finalize the 1980s' debates over physician resources policy (Lomas & Barer, 1986), but it also points to undergraduate medical training as a point where these over numerous doctors are ill trained for societal health-care needs.

The report's 53 recommendations deal with all aspects of health care, including a call for reducing the number of entering medical students to 1 600 per year from the present 1 700. Its recommendations regarding education are similar to those in the GPEP report, suggesting that problem-solving and interpersonal skills should be among the selection criteria for medical students. Moreover, it calls for an awareness of the "societal context" of medicine to be included in the undergraduate curriculum. For internship training, it recommends greater familiarization with primary health care, such as mental health and chronic care in urban and rural communities. Overall, it suggests that academic medical centres should be more responsive to societal needs. This study is the blueprint for a revamping of the health-care system. That such co-ordination among the provinces and territories has never before been achieved signifies a willingness to solve the crisis in medicare and medicine.

Table 2 Population per Active Civilian Physician, Including Interns and Residents, Canada, by Province, 1979–1989

Provinces	1979	1980	1981	1982	1983	1984	1985	1986	1987	1988	1989
Newfoundland	687	655	635	604	586	582	583	545	530	506	492
Prince Edward Island	801	805	790	800	831	796	766	716	696	686	714
Nova Scotia	537	533	531	522	499	505	483	478	461	449	436
New Brunswick	905	885	853	798	760	757	743	764	736	700	681
Quebec	531	527	510	494	485	472	454	447	433	424	424
Ontario	524	516	509	498	486	482	466	459	450	436	425
Manitoba	556	545	539	509	499	500	494	488	486	502	503
Saskatoon	667	669	659	641	635	640	629	620	595	580	571
Alberta	650	647	642	611	595	580	564	549	520	502	503
British Columbia	526	516	515	497	485	482	469	467	461	449	449
Yukon	837	811	843	793	763	755	839	831	775	731	679
North West Territories	1 197	1 125	1 110	1 386	1 227	1 350	1 303	1 117	1 120	1 226	1 189
Canada	554	547	538	521	510	503	487	479	467	455	449

Sources: *Health Personnel in Canada 1989* (1989). Ottawa: Health and Welfare Canada, p. 186.

However, change is also being advanced by forces within medical education itself. In 1990, Ontario's five medical schools began collaborating on developing a project named "Educating Future Physicians for Ontario" (EFPO), aimed at making medical education and subsequent practice responsive to the needs of Ontario society and less driven by the imperatives of growing medical technology (EFPO, 1990, 1991). It is consistent with GPEP, and McMaster faculty are prominent members of its steering committee. Seeking to reorient medical education as a response to public expectation, it attempts to measure them and to conceive of them as specifications for medical practice. On this foundation it hopes to foster problem-solving curricula in students by developing the faculty members' knowledge of contemporary techniques for clinical decision making, and by encouraging more of a team approach to health care with other providers.

This reform most embodies the broader societal imperative to improve the cost effectiveness of practice. EFPO will be an important advance in reforming medical education and so improve the quality of practice. It could pioneer accelerated national educational reform since Ontario medical students represent (at 1990-91 class sizes) 29 percent of Canada's 7 110 medical students.

Dentistry

Source: Canadian Dental Association (CDA)

Dentistry is a form of medical care focussing on oral and dental anatomy and physiology. In Canada it became recognized as a profession separate from medicine in the 1860s.

Dental education consists of four years of training, with core courses similar to medicine's: anatomy, physiology, biochemistry, microbiology, pharmacology, and pathology. Students also focus on mouth-specific courses in histology, microbiology, biochemistry, and neurology. The curriculum is organized into a two-year basic science block and a two-year clinical block. But curriculum reforms are being introduced to integrate both components around early patient exposure (Kenny, 1988). Specialized training is also taken in pediatric and geriatric dentistry, as well as prosthodontics, endodontics, and dental public health. In 1990, 302 students began dental study at eight English-language university-based dental schools; 113 entered the two French-language schools in Quebec. Postgraduate training is offered at nine of the ten dental schools. Nine specialties are recognized, including orthodontics, oral surgery, and periodontics. From CDA figures, in 1991, 1 638 specialists represented 12 percent of Canada's 13 918 total dentists. (Unlike other professional associations, the CDA does not record the sex of its members.) Research is also conducted in the university environment. Since the findings are published in many types of journals, according to where the investigator feels the information is most useful — dental, medical, surgical, speech, or psychology — dental research and practice are somewhat cross-disciplinary.

Dental licensure since 1952 requires passing the National Dental Examining Board exam (NDEB). It both assures a standard of quality and permits the interprovincial portability of credentials, recognized by each province's dental licensing agencies. The Canadian Dental Association accredits dental schools. Each province licenses generalists and specialists through dental colleges with legal recognition in provincial health-care legislation.

The vast majority of dentists work in a private, fee-for-service setting, although the number of group practices is growing. A very small minority of dentists work for a salary, usually with local, provincial, or federal governments. Three types of specialists are salaried: public-health specialists, oral pathologists, and oral radiologists. These specialists are centralized resources, supporting the practice of general dentistry as a referral "safety valve" for difficult cases.

Contemporary developments in dentistry include educating patients about the benefits of elective treatments beyond the obvious relief of pain by extraction. Thus dentistry has moved to rehabilitation and maintenance of teeth imperilled by decay or gum disease. Technological developments have led to the utilization of dental hygienists and assistants to deliver the simpler aspects of care. Another feature of dentistry today is an undersupply of patients, partly due to the simple, preventative health technology of fluoridating Canadians' drinking water.

Greater competition exists for patients than ever before, forcing expansion of the patient base downward into the lower social classes. Indeed, "the profession is trying to increase demand from the undertreated dentist-shy segment of the population" (Kenny, 1988, p. 9). For patients in the middle class, practices are shifting to prevention-oriented dental care. The relative oversupply of dentists has coincided with the appearance of extended-hours, retail (shopping mall) dentistry. This puts financial pressure on private practitioners whose overhead is about 60 percent (Kenny, 1988). Since dental services to the general public are not covered by medicare, dentists feel vulnerable to changes in the consumption of dentistry and attitudes toward dentists. Dentistry has been especially subject to increasing technological advances. Its clientele may not be aware of the value of these developments and must be brought up-to-date regarding dentistry as not merely "drill and fill."

Overall, medicine and dentistry are becoming more patient-oriented in their work in order to maintain their respective dominance. Medicine's wider scope of practice makes it both a bigger target for patient and insurer (ministries of health) discontent and more labile, more able to change to meet pressing external forces while retaining overall dominance. Changing technology is having a major effect on dental practice, both inventing new tasks and displacing old (Abbott, 1988, p. 92).

Pharmacy

Source: Canadian Pharmaceutical Association (CPhA) and the Canadian Foundation for Pharmacy

Pharmacy is the "provision of drug therapy" to achieve quality-of-life improving outcomes for the patient. Pharmacy as a health-care modality has long left behind the early days of this century when pharmacists made and sold their own potions and medicines. As health science matured, and political battles were fought, pharmacy and medicine separated (Torrance, 1987; Abbott, 1988). Historically, the industrialized manufacture of pharmaceuticals improved the quality of the goods produced. This technological change was another force narrowing the pharmacist's tasks. In today's division of health-care labour, the pharmacist is the drug expert on the care team. As guided by Abbott's model, pharmacy is a less autonomous profession, with a scope of practice narrower than dentistry or medicine.

According to the 1991 figures of CPhA, the distribution of pharmacists is 76 percent in the community, 19 percent in hospitals, 2 percent in the pharmaceutical industry, and the remaining 3 percent in government, academic, and administrative positions. It should be noted that pharmacy is increasingly becoming a female occupation; women will constitute an estimated 75 percent of pharmacists in the near future. Moreover, women are more "professional" and "idealistic" than males in their orientation to service ideals, but prefer non-community work settings such as a hospital or clinic. Research indicates that the absence of business competition facilitates family life (Hornosty & Coulas, 1988).

Community practice refers to the role of dispensing prescriptions to the public. More than three-quarters of pharmacists are community-based in drugstores or in extended-care facilities. These drugstores are independently owned, part of a chain, or are units within a department store, supermarket, or clinic. This type of career puts the pharmacist simultaneously into opposing roles: health-care professional, manager, and marketer. In the sociology of professions, such an orientation is contradictory because of the potential for economically exploiting the client who is in a trust relationship. Nonetheless, the pharmacist is often the first health professional the patient meets. Patients develop symptoms, then seek self-medication at the drugstore. The pharmacist's role is to direct customers in greatest potential health distress to a physician.

Hospital pharmacies position the pharmacist on the health-care team. They work with nurses and physicians in patient history taking, monitoring drug use and reactions, and in counselling. Additional responsibilities are the selection, purchase, and distribution of the hospital's drugs and the preparation of intravenous drugs.

Employment in the pharmaceutical industry largely means dealing with government, physicians, hospitals, and community pharmacists. They mostly disseminate information about drugs. The research and development of new drugs is undertaken by pharmacists with postgraduate training.

Pharmacists provide technical expertise to fulfil the federal government's responsibility for ensuring the safety of pharmaceuticals. They serve the federal government as integral members of the armed forces, and also administer local, provincial, and federal governmentally sponsored drug programs. Pharmacists work in the national and provincial organizations that represent pharmacy. In each province they are licensed to practise through regulations set out by a college of pharmacy and recognized by government legislation.

Pharmacy education is available at seven English-language and two French-language schools across Canada. The four-year programs are heavily weighted with basic and applied sciences, especially mathematics and chemistry. Important components in the curriculum are biology, physiology, anatomy, pathology, pharmacology, and biochemistry. On top of this foundation comes training in clinical aspects of pharmacy, including communication and informatics. Of the University of Toronto's 645 undergraduates, 60 percent are women.

Specialized training is available in residency programs in 35 teaching hospitals across Canada. Specialization occurs in the areas of geriatric pharmacology, poison control, nuclear pharmacy, intravenous additives, patient education, and drug information and administration. In industrial pharmacy, co-certification in residency training is offered between pharmaceutical companies and universities (mainly the University of Toronto and Toronto-area companies).

The major challenge to Canadian pharmacy is to expand pharmaceutical "care" into the community. Today's developments seek to reverse the minimal interaction between pharmacist and client as long-term effects of the industrialized manufacture of pharmaceuticals. Hence pharmacy training has increasingly included the goal of educating and communicating with the public, partly through requiring some humanities/social science courses. Pharmacists also see themselves as potentially crucial in reducing the problems of an overmedicated and toxified elderly population.

More generally, Canadian pharmacists are aware that the broader changes in the health-care system are leading to the redefinition of the role of pharmacy. Health care is becoming less physician-dominated and more patient-centred through the assembled, co-operative expertise of many groups. Pharmacy itself is becoming even more patient-centred and is seeking to expand its health-care role. Pharmacy is unlike dentistry in being affected by technological changes in the presentation of and treatment of patient problems. The same non-technological forces affecting medicine are also affecting pharmacy and adjusting their relationship.

Occupational Therapy

Source: Canadian Association of Occupational Therapy (CAOT)

Occupational therapy (OT) is a holistic form of client-oriented care. It was developed during World War I to provide wounded and handicapped soldiers with basic job-related skills during their hospital convalescence. In the next decade representative associations formed across Canada, and in 1926 a two-year diploma in OT was offered at the University of Toronto (Brintnell & Goldenberg, 1988).

Occupational therapy's self-appointed mandate is:

> Through assessment, interpretation, and intervention . . . to address problems impeding functional or adaptive behaviour in persons whose occupational performance is impaired by illness or injury, emotional disorder, developmental disorder, social disadvantage, or the aging process. The purpose is to prevent disability; and to promote, maintain or restore occupational performance, health and spiritual well-being. (CAOT, 1990, p. xvi)

It recognizes the "holistic contribution of the client's environment, motivation, and roles, as well as the performance components (physical, mental, socio-cultural, spiritual) required for a particular function" (CAOT, 1987, p. vi). In short, OT is the promotion of "optimal occupational performance."

The claim for OT's jurisdiction arose because of the absence of competitors, when a health-care need became apparent after the First World War. It subsequently produced and disseminated its knowledge through the *Canadian Journal of Occupational Therapy*. Moreover, its code of ethics has recently been formulated by the Canadian Association of Occupational Therapists (CAOT). In addition to stipulating professional behaviour toward clients, fellow OTs, and employers, the code requires members "maintain and improve" their professional abilities. At the time of writing, the CAOT was refining its model of the "environment" and the "spiritual component of the model" towards highlighting the uniqueness of OTs' knowledge base and practice.

Organizationally, occupational therapy is developing its educational and certification standards. The entrance requirements are comparable to general science programs, and are accredited by the CAOT and in Quebec by the College Professionnel des Ergotherapeutes du Quebec (CPEQ). Across Canada, only 574 students per year begin the study of OT in small classes at twelve universities: 165 in two French-language schools, plus the University of Ottawa's bilingual school, and 409 in nine English-language schools.

The curriculum reflects the profession's knowledge base in medical, clinical, behavioural, and sociological knowledge, as well as OT theory and practice-oriented training. Moreover, the programs are academically rigorous to foster the ability and desire for postgraduate training and research. McMaster's OT and physical therapy schools, which opened in 1989, are based on the medical school's problem-based learning model. Entrance to its two-year program requires a previous baccalaureate degree.

In 1985 a national certification examination was instituted, with each province having its own licensing body. A minimum of 1 200 hours of field training is required, carried out during academic years and in the summers. These training settings are the same as those where most OTs are employed: general and auxiliary hospitals, extended-care facilities, and community non-profit agencies. Accreditation of these training centres is optional at this point, although strongly recommended by CAOT to increase their credibility, visibility, and quality of posteducational practice. Graduate training is endorsed by the CAOT. Its 1990 "Position Statement on Graduate Education" views specialized training as necessary to create, transmit, and practise more advanced knowledge and skill. There are six graduate programs available in OT. Two small scholarships are offered by the CAOT to promote graduate study.

Since most OTs practise in the hospital sector, they work in positions formally subordinate to physicians, but usually on equal terms as part of the health-care team. Most of their clients are referred by physicians (Brintnell & Goldenberg, 1988) and they are paid out of the hospitals' global budgets. OTs also work in schools, for community-based agencies, and in industry. In addition to working with client types specific to places of employment, OTs specialize by psycho-social or physical disability or by developmental period in the human life cycle. Occupational therapy is mainly the work of young women: from the 1990 membership data, 95.5 percent of members are female; 77 percent are 25-44 years old. The "ultimate objective" guiding the OT at work is to "establish an appropriate balance between client's time at activities of self care, work and leisure" (Brintnell & Goldenberg, 1988, p. 46).

Demographic and other changes have increased the demand for OTs beyond the supply. A very flat career ladder related to a lack of graduate training forces OTs into other forms of training or employment. However, immigration is a source of OTs: 17 percent of the CAOT members (polled in 1990) graduated from foreign schools. Employment and Immigration Canada lists OT as a desired and therefore favoured occupation.

The OT profession's contemporary challenges are examples of what Abbott understood to be the typical professional struggle of controlling jurisdictions. A crucial challenge for OT today is to develop outcome measures for its interventions. This is "vital to the advancement of the profession" as it will "demonstrate the effectiveness" of occupational therapy to clients and other health-care providers. This will also "clarify the role of occupational therapy" (CAOT, 1987, p. 1). Conceptual development and incorporating new techniques are crucial to maintaining occupational jurisdiction. This would provide greater credibility for OT to expand its jurisdiction within its shared workplace.

OT practitioners wish to expand their power by becoming case managers of the interdisciplinary health-care team. Their claim is justified by their wide-ranging and holistic skills (Brintnell & Goldenberg, 1988, p. 52). Since this would encroach upon the physicians' jurisdiction, it is unlikely to happen. However, the CAOT is actively involved in clarifying the boundary separating it from the other sub-medical provider groups. It recognizes that some "role overlap" occurs and is tolerable for the sake of the client. But while supporting training in the concept of a health-care team, it believes that OT is unique and indispensable for the client's well-being. The CAOT views most "adjunctive" provider groups as lacking the medical training received by OTs, thus having a potentially adverse effect on the client.

Using Abbott's model, we see OT in a struggle for workplace control. It is challenging medical dominance, separating itself from competitors (essentially physiotherapy) within the group of providers subordinate to medicine by "de-legitimating" their knowledge bases. OT also argues that clients who have been discharged still require their care, hence extending the market for its own work. Ontario is the last province to regulate the practice of occupational therapy to those with credentials. This protects OT's jurisdictional boundaries by legally creating the distinction between qualified and unqualified. Overall, internal developments in its knowledge base, as well as the social and economic environment around health care, are providing opportunities for expanding the jurisdiction of occupational therapy.

Physiotherapy

Source: Canadian Physiotherapy Association

The most closely related profession to OT is physiotherapy (PT). Like OT it originated with caring for wounded World War I soldiers. Since then it has expanded into caring for the injured, rehabilitation, and providing postoperative care and services for the elderly. Its scope is narrower than OT in that it focusses on preventing and alleviating movement dysfunctions. Movement dysfunction is defined as abnormal body kinetics due to congenital problems, disease, aging, injury, or stress, both "psychological" and "social" (Canadian Physiotherapy Association, 1986).

Physiotherapy training is university-based, affiliated with medical/health-science schools. The curriculum standards are set by the Canadian Physiotherapy Association (CPA). Over four years of study students learn normal and basic human biology, physiology, and psychology. They then acquire knowledge of pathological movement and abnormal psychology, and learn physical examinations, evaluations, and treatment.

Treatments include exercise, mobilizations (akin to chiropractic), massage and heat, cold, sound, and electrical therapies. Students also learn counselling, communications, and research skills.

Each year 167 students enter the French-language PT programs at two Quebec universities (including 40 at the bilingual University of Ottawa). In the ten English-language university-based schools, 449 students begin each year (total enrollment is 616). The Quebec programs are three years in duration; the others are four. McMaster's innovative two-year program is designed around problem-centred learning and includes familiarization with northern health issues (in common with McMaster's OT and medical schools). Students acquire clinical experience in hospitals and clinics. Several master's programs in PT exist in Canada; related health-science programs draw master's and doctoral students. Continuing education is available.

Physiotherapy is primarily practised in health-care institutions: general hospitals, rehabilitation centres, extended-care hospitals, nursing homes, geriatric clinics, and sports clinics. PTs are also found in schools, industry, government, and in private practice. In these settings, the skills of co-ordination and consultation, initially acquired as a student, are an essential element of their work. PT practice is divided into the non-clinical activities of administration, research, education, and consultation; the medically derived clinical specialties of rheumatology, neurosciences, obstetrics, orthopedics, pediatrics, cardio-respiratory treatment, and sports physiotherapy. In the clinical/hospital setting, PTs plan and implement treatment; they counsel both acute and chronic patients. In community settings, physiotherapy is largely educational.

PT training provides for non-hospital employment. They are qualified to practise as primary health-care providers and do so depending upon provincial legislation. Like other physician-augmenting providers in hospitals, PT revolves first around the patient's well-being and second around the expertise of the "health-care team." A 1980 survey found, however, that three-quarters of Ontarian PTs wish for patient responsibility independent of the physician. The resolution of this situation was seen to lie in facilitating inter-team communication (Pickles, 1988).

PT is in more open conflict with chiropractors who are not members of the hospital-based health-care team. It considers unfair the chiropractic independence of hospital and physician and the partial coverage of their fee-for-service practice by provincial health-insurance plans (Pickles, 1988). Physiotherapy also shares some health-care labour with occupational therapy.

Today's major imperative is research. This is crucial since most of the tools used for patient evaluation were developed by physicians, kinesiologists, and exercise physiologists (Pickles, 1988). Hence, PT's knowledge base is not completely distinct from other providers, weakening its jurisdictional claim as noted by Abbott (1988, pp. 125-129).

Overall, physiotherapy seeks to make its claim to its work more credible and to prevent non-PTs from practising physiotherapy. The CPA believes that the growing demand for services reflects the movement of health care into the community, the aging population's needs, and the growth of health promotion, prevention, and education. This expansion could lead to further competition for clients.

Respiratory Therapy

Source: Canadian Society of Respiratory Technology (CSRT)

Respiratory therapy (RT) is one of the "auxiliary" health-care provider groups. Respiratory therapists work as part of a team in the treatment of cardio-pulmonary disorders. They are subordinate to the physician as team leader, but equal to the other members. The official definition of respiratory therapy is:

> An allied health discipline devoted to the scientific applications of therapy in order to assist the physician in the diagnosis, treatment, and promotion of the well-being of patients with respiratory and associated disorders. (CSRT, 1984)

Among their diagnostic capabilities are the analysis of blood gases, cardio-pulmonary testing and monitoring, and patient evaluation. In terms of treatment, RTs administer therapeutic gases, anesthetics and aerosols, provide mechanical ventilation, and can deliver (or assist) urgent cardio-pulmonary resuscitation. They also maintain and repair medical gas and respiratory equipment and are trained to provide "technical assistance" in related research.

The practice of RT is restricted to those who pass a registration examination set up by an adjunct agency, the Canadian Board of Respiratory Care. There are eleven community college-based training programs across Canada, including Quebec's one community college and five CEGEP-based programs in RT. These are accredited by the Canadian Society of Respiratory Therapists (CSRT), which has also developed continuing education programs and is in the process of developing advanced training courses in four specialty areas. Membership in the CSRT is 60 percent female. Ontario employs 49 percent of all RTs in Canada.

The socio-political tasks engaging RTs today are generally those of controlling the provision of respiratory therapy in the health-care division of labour. They are attempting to raise awareness, particularly among physicians, of the importance of RT to the patient's well-being. RTs are also sensitive to the duplication of some of their services by nurses, physiotherapists, and laboratory technologists. In Abbott's terms, then, RT is a profession encroached upon by others. It is notable that RT is in a very subordinate

position in the hierarchy of providers headed by physicians. However, the CSRT antici-
pates expansion of their scope of practice as cost-effective care providers to chronic
patients in their homes, and such a socio-economic development could strengthen its
jurisdictional claim.

Laboratory Technologists

Source: Canadian Society of Laboratory Technology (CSLT) and its affiliate, the Ontario Society of Medical Technologists (OSMT)

Medical laboratory technology (LT) is the broad term covering a number of laboratory-
based analyses, primarily oriented to diagnosing disease. These tasks are the testing of
body fluids, cells, and tissue cultures and blood typing. The CSLT's definition is the
"practice of all occupations or skills incumbent in carrying out laboratory investigations
relating to the diagnosis, treatment and prevention of disease." In general, physicians
order the tests performed by laboratory technologists. But, as laboratory data are
increasingly important to the provision of health care, LTs see themselves as integral
members of the health-care team.

Training courses of two or three years are offered in 31 Canadian community
colleges. The curriculum combines academic with clinical training. Theoretical knowledge and generic testing procedures are emphasized as the core skills of the profession,
permitting it to progress with the developing testing technology. Programs are accredited by a multidisciplinary national body.

The CSLT has been certifying members since 1937. Today initial certification is
offered in ten sub-areas, for example, clinical chemistry, clinical microbiology, hemato-
logy, cytology, and cytogenetics. According to a 1991 membership survey by the CSLT,
63 percent of members had basic-level certification and 7 percent held specialist-level
certification. Yet, although 70 percent of practitioners are specially trained in laboratory
technology, it is practised without certification or licensure. According to the CSLT, of
the other 30 percent of its membership, 16 percent had basic science degrees from
Canadian universities and 14 percent held other qualifications, such as foreign science
degrees, education degrees, and management degrees and diplomas. It should be noted
that government-sanctioned regulation is evolving across the provinces for this occupation, as it is for others.

After graduation an LT's career largely unfolds in large health-care institutions.
Hospital and private laboratory are the major employment sites for lab technology (70
percent and 20 percent respectively), while 4 percent work in public-health laboratories
or for the Canadian Red Cross. This is a female-dominated occupation, with just 12.5
percent males; its members are predominantly middle-aged, with 69.9 percent of LTs

between the ages of 30 and 49. After physicians, lab workers are the most numerous health-care worker in Canada (see Table 1).

The CSLT and provincial affiliates exist to promote the occupation, to establish standards, and generally to professionalize laboratory work. It recognizes that in the future LT education should become more principle-oriented to permit greater transferability of skills and to facilitate adaptation to changing testing technology. Baccalaureate training is also recommended for the professional purpose of expanding the managerial presence of LTs (Special Task Force, 1987). The CSLT is also promoting computer literacy and continuing education in management, as well as in laboratory sciences. Running tests ordered by others is a very weak jurisdictional position, as Abbott (1988) makes clear. The best laboratory technology can likely do is upgrade its educational credibility in preparation for the invention of new testing technology.

Medical Radiation Therapy

Source: Ontario Association of Medical Radiation Technologists (OAMRT) and the Canadian Association of Medical Radiation Technology (CAMRT)

The practice of medical radiation therapy (MRT) is hospital-based; the vast majority are radiographers who take and process X-ray pictures. This field also includes what is termed "nuclear medicine," the use of radioactive substances to test patients, and "radiation therapy," the radiation treatment of diseases such as cancer. Most MRT is practised under the direction of specialist physicians in hospitals.

A national representative organization, the Canadian Association of Medical Radiation Technologists (CAMRT), has set educational and practice standards since 1943. Two-year training programs are offered by 41 community colleges, clinics, and hospitals across Canada (no figures are available for Quebec). In 1989, 618 students were graduated. Training consists of basic science, medical science, and focussed clinical training. National and provincial registration is not yet mandatory. Registrants are subject to the national code of ethics which emphasizes safety, competence, patient respect, continuing education, and co-operation with health-care providers. Together with LT and RT, MRT is accredited by a multidisciplinary national agency. The CAMRT has affiliations with similar organizations in Europe, South Africa, Hong Kong, and the United States.

The career path of MRTs is flat, with little upward mobility. Practitioners can specialize in new forms of scanning beyond X-rays: CAT, NMR, and PET scanning, as well as in quality control. This is a largely female occupation; available figures indicate that in 1981, 86.4 percent of 494 graduates were female. By 1995 it is estimated that females will comprise 77 percent of 607 graduates (Minister of Supply and Services,

1990). The CAMRT acknowledges a nation-wide shortage of practitioners, with an increasing demand expected into the 1990s.

The major challenge for MRT is to raise its visibility and acceptance. While interacting with all other health-care workers, the CAMRT feels that they lack a full understanding of the unique contributions of MRT to health care. The 1992-94 goals of the CAMRT reveal the organization's conscious desire to professionalize. This includes controlling access to the profession, providing continuing education, raising public awareness of MRT, and broadening the scope of professional practice. MRT's jurisdictional claim is bolstered by the technical nature of the work, which discourages competitors. However, this technical specificity also minimizes its autonomy and power within the health-care division of labour.

Conclusion

Physicians lead the provision of health care. However, economic and political pressures are modifying their practice and education towards greater orientation to public need. The future will tell if this is deprofessionalization or a modified dominance. In accordance with Abbott's theory, future study should attend to (1) the loss of old and the production of new tasks; (2) the associated change in the knowledge base; and (3) the maintenance of control over what is defined as medical work. Despite the provincial governments acting like "corporate rationalizers" (Alford, 1975) by imposing (mostly economic) restraints on medical practice, medical jurisdiction is unchallenged. Hence, the American GPEP report and the subsequent Canadian changes in medical education, such as EFPO, can be viewed as strategies to stay on top of the changes in the social and cultural environment of medicine (Abbott, 1988). The other dominant profession, dentistry, is coping with changing client expectations as dental technology improves. Increased and more effective communication is their goal. Hence, the change in their technological base has led them into more direct management of client expectations in their social environment.

The less autonomous professions of pharmacy, occupational therapy, and physiotherapy are adjusting their internal division of labour, primarily because of external factors — the health-care system's social environment and its economic limitations. All are trying to achieve greater autonomy within the health-care team. Short of taking over medical tasks, they seek delegation of tasks from physicians, as well as respect and awareness: medicine's dominance determines the precise delegation of responsibilities over any particular patient. All endorse the concept of a health-care team. A unique development is McMaster University's attempt to partly co-educate physicians, occupational therapists, and physical therapists together to inculcate this sense of team work.

Much effort is being made to have other groups respect this group of less autonomous providers' scope of practice. Simultaneously these groups are clarifying their duties and seeking ways to extend their responsibilities. All have displayed many attributes of professionalism: research into theory and techniques, journals, codes of ethics, "upgraded" educational curricula, and the promulgation of national standards for practice. Licensure as a profession or regulation of practice through certification has been granted by provincial governments to each provider group.

The convergence of economic, social, and cultural factors is behind the trend to serve the aging population's need in the community. For these less autonomous provider groups, this is an opportunity for expansion and greater independence. Hence, although occupational therapy overlaps with physiotherapy, their capacities for primary care and holistic care put them into competitive relationships with medicine and each other.

At the lowest level of professional autonomy, respiratory therapy, medical radiation technology, and laboratory technology share the lack of university-based credentials. Their training occurs in community colleges and in hospitals. Their knowledge bases are weakest: RT's is not consensually distinct; as they lack a strong theoretical component, MRT's and LT's are mostly composed of specific testing procedures.

These Canadian health-care professionals are interdependent. Their relations are shifting as the health-care system attempts to remain economically viable and meet consumers' expectations. To differing degrees, all endorse the concept of a health-care team. Responses to these changes will more dramatically affect the health-care division of labour in the next ten years. This chapter supports Abbott's (1988) thesis that the study of professionalism is the study of how occupations make claim to, control, and lose jurisdiction over work activities.

Study Questions

1. Compare and contrast the education, practice forms, and contemporary concerns and issues of the eight professions studied.
2. What is professional "jurisdiction"? What are its features? Are independence, university education, and broad scope of practice the essential characteristics of professionalism?
3. This chapter has distinguished between three levels of professional autonomy within the hierarchy of health-care providers. What differentiates each level?
4. Why is the medical profession changing? Discuss the nature and likely effects of its educational reform for maintaining its pre-eminence.
5. What is a "health-care team"? Why do these professions endorse the concept? Do you think the substantive idea of "team" varies with the amount of autonomy each group enjoys?

Recommended Reading

Abbott, A. (1988). *The system of professions*. Chicago: University of Chicago Press.
Association of American Medical Colleges. (1984). Physicians for the twenty-first

century: *Report of the panel on the general professional education of the physician and college preparation for medicine (GPEP)*. Washington: Author.

Blishen, B. (1991). *Doctors in Canada*. Toronto: University of Toronto Press.

Crichton, A., Hsu, D., & Tsang, S. (1990). *Canada's health care system: Its funding and organization*. Ottawa: Canadian Hospital Association Press.

Torrance, G.M. (1984). The underside of the hospital: Recruitment and the meaning of work among non-professional hospital workers. In A. Wipper (Ed.), *The sociology of work: Papers in honour of Oswald Hall* (pp. 211–231). Ottawa: Carleton University Press.

References

Association of American Medical Colleges. (1984). *Physicians for the twenty-first century: Report of the panel on the general professional education of the physician and college preparation for medicine (GPEP)*. Washington: Author.

Association of Canadian Medical Colleges. (1991). *Canadian medical education statistics*, 13, Table 16. Ottawa: Author.

Alford, R.R. (1975). *Health care politics: Ideological and interest group barriers to reform*. Chicago: University of Chicago Press.

Barer, M.L., & Stoddart, G.L. (1991). *Toward integrated medical resource policies for Canada: Background document and appendices, Papers 91-7* (pp. 91–98). Hamilton: McMaster University, Centre for Health Economics and Policy Analysis.

Brintnell, S., & Goldenberg, K. (1988). Occupational therapy. In E. Boberg & E. Kassirer (Eds.), *Rehabilitation teams: Action and interaction* (pp. 43–53). Ottawa: Department of Supply and Services.

Canadian Association of Medical Radiation Technologists. (1991). *Annual report*. Ottawa: Author.

Canadian Association of Occupational Therapists. (1990a). *The health care system and its funding: A brief submitted to the House of Commons Standing Committee on Health and Welfare, Social Affairs, Seniors and the Status of Women*. Toronto: Author.

Canadian Association of Occupational Therapists. (1990b). *Annual report*. Toronto: Author.

Canadian Association of Occupational Therapists and Department of National Health and Welfare. (1983). *Guidelines for the client-centred practice of occupational therapy*. Ottawa: Minister of Supply and Services.

Canadian Association of Occupational Therapists and Department of National Health and Welfare. (1987). *Toward outcome measures in occupational therapy*. Ottawa: Department of Supply and Services.

Canadian Physiotherapy Association. (1986). *Physiotherapy scope of practice*. Toronto: Author.

Canadian Society of Respiratory Therapists. (1984). *The role of the respiratory therapists*. Ottawa: Author.

Coburn, D., Torrance, G.M., & Kaufert, J.M. (1983). Medical dominance in Canada in historical perspective: The rise and fall of medicine? *International Journal of Health Services*, 13, (3), 407–432.

Educating Future Physicians for Ontario (EFPO). (1990, November). *Annual report*. Hamilton: McMaster University, Faculty of Health Sciences.

Educating Future Physicians for Ontario (EFPO). (1991, January). *Demand-side medical education*. Hamilton: McMaster University, Faculty of Health Sciences.

Educating Future Physicians for Ontario (EFPO). (1991, June). *Progress report*. Hamilton: McMaster University, Faculty of Health Sciences.

Freidson, E. (1970). *The profession of medicine*. New York: Harper & Row.

Goode, W.J. (1960). Encroachment, charlatanism and the emerging profession: Psychology, sociology and medicine. *American Sociological Review*, 25, 902–914.

Hornosty, R., & Coulas, G.C. (1988, February). The feminization of pharmacy: Is the analysis right? *Canadian Pharmacy Journal*, 128, 92–98.

Kendall, P., & Reader, G.G. (1988). Innovations in medical education of the 1950s contrasted with those of the 1970s and 1980s. *Journal of Health and Social Behavior*, 29, (4), 279–293.

Kenny, D.J. (1988). Dentistry. In E. Boberg & E. Kassirer (Eds.), *Rehabilitation teams: Action and interaction* (pp. 1-11). Ottawa: Department of Supply and Services.

Lomas, J., & Barer, M.L. (1986). And who shall represent the public interest? The legacy of Canadian health manpower policy. In R.G. Evans & G.L. Stoddart (Eds.), *Medicare at maturity* (pp. 221-286). Calgary: University of Calgary Press.

Ministry of Supply and Services. (1990). *Job futures, experience of recent graduates: An occupational outlook to 1995, Vol. 2*. Toronto: Nelson.

Neufeld, V.R., Woodward, C.A., & MacLeod, S.M. (1989). The McMaster M.D. program: A case study of renewal in medical education. *Academic Medicine*, 64, (8), 423-432.

Ontario Ministry of Health. (1990). *Annual report, '89-90*. Toronto: Queen's Printer.

Patel, V., Groen, G.J., & Norman, G.R. (1991). Effects of conventional and problem-based medical curricula on problem solving. *Academic Medicine*, 66, (7), 380-389.

Pickles, B. (1988). Physiotherapy. In E. Boberg & E. Kassirer (Eds.), *Rehabilitation teams: Action and interaction* (pp. 55-66). Ottawa: Department of Supply and Services.

Rachlis, M., & Kushner, C. (1989). *Second opinion: What's wrong with Canada's health care system and how to fix it*. Toronto: Collins.

Schwartz, A.M. (1989). *Striking a new balance: A blueprint for the regulation of Ontario's health professions*. Toronto: Ministry of Health, Health Professions Legislation Review Commission.

Special Task Force on Future Trends in Medical Laboratory Services. (1987). Preliminary report presented to General Council. *Canadian Journal of Medical Technology*, 49, 76-83.

Torrance, G. (1987). Socio-historical overview: The development of the Canadian health system. In D. Coburn, C. D'Arcy, G. Torrance, & P. New (Eds.), *Health and Canadian society* (2nd ed.), (pp. 6-32). Markham: Fitzhenry & Whiteside.

Wahn, M. (1987). The decline of medical dominance. In D. Coburn, C. D'Arcy, G. Torrance, & P. New (Eds.), *Health and Canadian society* (2nd ed.), (pp. 422-440). Markham: Fitzhenry & Whiteside.

White, K.L., & Connelly, J.E. (1991). Redefining the mission of the medical school. *ACMC FORUM XXIV*, (2), 1-9.

Chapter 7

A Feminist Analysis of Women in Medical Schools

Jo-Ann Kirk, University of Victoria

Introduction

The medical profession and practice have both been criticized at length within socio-logical literature. The focus of much of this criticism has been on the structure of the organization and delivery of health care. In general, medicine has been criticized for its biomechanical and reductionist orientation. Within this framework, the human body is conceptualized, analyzed, and treated as a set of quasi-mechanical parts, operating almost exclusively according to the laws of biology, physics, and chemistry, rather than as an organically related whole (Benston, 1982, p. 73). This approach has, to a great degree, neglected and even ignored the influences of social, psychological, and environmental factors on health and illness. Consequently, an important result of this emphasis is that medicine has evolved in a scientific, technological, and hierarchical manner. Medical practice has become increasingly dependent on drugs and technology, and has emphasized specialization in reaction to disease rather than general, preventative health care. Medical education has also been singled out for its depersonalizing and dehumanizing aspects, which are all too often replicated within the context of patient care. The tendency to rely almost exclusively on scientific theory and methodology within medical training is evident later in the tendencies of medical researchers and practitioners to dehumanize others — people are treated as objects, not as participants in their own health.

Similarly, criticism of the orientation of the medical profession and practice has been further articulated within feminist literature. Feminist analysis concurs with much of previous criticism in pointing to "the need for fundamental restructuring of health care" (Pollock, 1988, p. 178). Feminism extends this critique by focussing on how the hierarchical organization of medicine has had a negative impact on women's health in particular. Fundamental to feminist analysis is the constant recognition of the connection between the social organization of medical research and practice, and its social products. It examines the social, political, and economic context within which medical knowledge is created and is used. More specifically, as Pollock asserts, "feminists are making the claim that the structure of medicine and health care has evolved historically according to political and economic interests outside of women's health" (Pollock, 1988, p. 178). Feminists point out how "health care" within the current medical model has resulted in medicalization of many of women's normal life events (i.e., the menstrual cycle, pregnancy and childbirth, menopause), and has served as a means of social control (for a more in-depth discussion, see Pollock in Bolaria & Dickinson, 1988). One need only be reminded of the litany of drugs, devices, and procedures — the rest cure; ovariectomies; hysterectomies; thalidomide; hormone replacement therapy; the Dalkon Shield; DES; Depo-Provera; the birth control pill; medicalized births, including the increase in Caesarean sections and fetal monitoring; and the new reproductive technologies (to name but a few) — which have been administered to women "for their own good" to realize that the impact of medical science on women has been, at best, negligent and, at worst, extremely violent — even fatal. Historically, sexist and paternalistic attitudes have been an integral part of the creation and dissemination of medical knowledge about women. Thus, a fundamental premise of the feminist analysis of the medical profession is that medicine does not exist in a vacuum, and that the values of society are critical in shaping and maintaining the orientation of the medical profession. More specifically, the underlying premise is that we live in a patriarchal society, and medicine mirrors the dominant values of such a culture.

In light of such criticism, it has been suggested that the increased numbers of women now entering medicine will ultimately be good for the profession as a whole. As more and more women are admitted into medicine, they will bring with them the traditional feminine qualities of sensitivity, compassion, and nurturance, which will be carried over into medical practice, resulting in a more humane medical profession. The discussion that follows explores this issue within a feminist analysis of the social and political context of today's medical education and practice. This will be combined with a discussion of how factors such as sexism within the profession, the medical-school socialization process, and increased female participation affect each other and the female recruits.

In this chapter, we attempt to answer the question of whether or not the presence of more women in the system can solve the perceived problem of women's health care, and more generally, make medical practice more humane. It is also, in part, an examination of the latent patriarchal culture of medical school.

An Exploration of Latent Patriarchal Culture

Since the concept of "latent patriarchal culture" is central to this discussion, it requires definition. The term "culture" is commonly defined as "a body of ideas and practices considered to support each other and expected of each other by members of the same group of people" (Becker et al., 1961, p. 435). Culture that is further distinguished as "latent" is described as having "its origin and social support in a group other than the one in which persons are now participating" (Becker et al., 1961, p. 143). In reference to medical school, the term "latent culture" refers to the patterns of meanings, behaviours, and beliefs that are intrinsic to the larger community within which the school is situated. It includes the deeply entrenched ways of perceiving, understanding, and controlling the reality of the situation (i.e., expectations of appropriate behaviour) that the majority of people in the medical school community share, based on their membership in the larger outside community (Grant, 1988, p. 109).

In their book *Boys in White*, Becker et al., (1961) argue that medical education is strongly influenced by a latent culture. Moreover, they contend that those who share the latent culture have a sense of belonging, while those who do not may feel alienated and marginal (Becker et al., 1961, p. 143). Similarly, Goode in his article entitled "Community within a Community: The Professions," states that the professions, including medicine, both exist within and are dependent upon the larger society (Goode, 1957, p. 200). Furthermore, Goode contends that medicine is one of the few professions that puts its recruits through a set of rigourous adult socialization processes, including punishment for inappropriate attitudes or behaviour as well as procedures for continuing social controls over the practising professional. However, he adds that "this socialization cannot be so complete as that of the child in the lay world, but that is not necessary, for the values of the professional community do not differ drastically from those of the larger society" (Goode, 1957, pp. 196-197). Thus, it is evident that the prevailing latent culture of medical-school students and faculty members in Canada corresponds with the prevailing cultural values of contemporary Canadian society.

A second concept that is equally important to this discussion is the concept of "patriarchy." This is not a precise or simple concept; it has many dimensions and embodies various meanings, all of which have been articulated and developed within feminist literature. At the most general level, the concept of patriarchy refers to the collective male dominance that permeates society "and to the power relationships by which men dominate women" (Millet in Beechey, 1979, p. 66). Patriarchal ideology is maintained by, and manifests itself within, the basic structures and institutions of society, including the family and the economy (Hunter College Women's Studies Collective, 1983, p. 186). Patriarchy has also been recognized as a significant concept politically because it identifies women's oppression as a distinct and real entity — a form of discrimination that is both the basis and the object of the politics of sex and gender. Indeed, as Fox (1988, p. 164) articulates:

> For feminist theory, use of the concept "patriarchy" has been a means of asserting that gender inequality is a pervasive feature of the society in which we live, that women's oppression is different from other kinds of oppression, and that gender inequality calls for specific explanation and analysis. In short the concept has been important because it problematizes gender and gender relations.

For the purpose of this discussion, the most relevant conceptualization of patriarchy explicitly links both social structure and gendered subjectivity as "two different but inseparable and constantly interacting levels of reality" that are responsible for the creation and maintenance of patriarchal ideology (Fox, 1988, p. 176). The focus is not merely the individual or society on its own, but rather, the process and products of interaction of both. Patriarchy is inherently linked to human cultural relations and, in particular, to the social relations and practices that organize human generational reproduction (Fox, 1988, p. 175). Thus, in general, "patriarchy is the system of practices, arrangements and social relations that ensure biological reproduction, child rearing, and the reproduction of gendered subjectivity" (Fox, 1988, p. 175). Moreover, characteristic of such relations of reproduction is a system of hierarchical ordering and control.

According to this conceptualization, the essence of women's oppression is the pervasive definition of woman as mother first and, in conjunction, the social and political institutions and structures that are in place to reinforce this "ideology of difference." The division of labour by sex, which serves to limit both women's and men's life options, is further entrenched in society through the division of social life into public and private spheres (Fox, 1988, p. 175). Historically, it was the establishment of the public realm and the corresponding necessity of the private domain that resulted in a pervasive division of labour between women and men (Muszynski, 1989, p. 68).

This dichotomy further necessitated social, cultural, political, and economic change, which resulted in the institutionalization and subsequent "naturalization" of gendered consciousness — that is, patriarchal ideology (Armstrong & Armstrong, 1990, p. 49; Muszynski, 1989, p. 71). What is particularly significant is that while the material composition of the public and private realms has been dynamic, the fundamental patriarchal ideology that underlies the need for such a division has remained intact. Although women are no longer relegated strictly to the private sphere, the "natural" connection between women and motherhood (with all of its associated functions and duties as the creator and sustainer of life) still remains ingrained in the collective consciousness of society. The result is that "labouring as necessity and, therefore, as non-human activity continues to be attached to the work of women whether in the private realm of the household or in the public realm of salaried employment" (Muszynski, 1989, p. 69).

This point is critical to understanding the pervasive discrimination women face in the public sphere. The identification of woman as mother is so much a part of our "natural consciousness" that not only is "traditional women's work" devalued as public labour (e.g., the service industry), but all women's work outside the household tends to be devalued or undervalued when compared to men's work. That is, women are often discriminated against simply for participating in the public realm. This discrimination is enforced, maintained and legitimized through social structures such as the family, the economy, and the state, and is ingrained in the generational reproduction of gendered subjectivity. Thus, the key to patriarchy is the creation and maintenance of difference — the transformation of biological sex into politicized gender, along with the social institutions that reflect and perpetuate this ideology of difference.

It is now necessary to bring these conceptualizations together in order to define "latent patriarchal culture" within the context of medical education. Simply stated, it is an expression that identifies the larger community from which medical students and faculty originate, as patriarchal. That is, medicine exists within and is dependent upon a society that is organized according to the general principle of differentiation and privilege based upon gender.

The question that now must be addressed is why this concept is important to the discussion. It is evident that beliefs about women and men and expectations of appropriate behaviour constitute an important part of the latent culture of medical school (Grant, 1988, p. 109). The implications of this statement are clear when it is juxtaposed with Goode's (1957) observation that the medical profession sanctions its recruits and practising members for violating the cultural norms of the profession. Since a fundamental principle of patriarchal ideology is the implicit definition of woman as mother in the private sphere, then women in medical school are indeed violating a norm of the latent patriarchal culture. While the actual activities that constitute the public and private domains have changed with time, the underlying patriarchal ideology that necessitates the concept of difference has remained intact.

In sum, the emphasis of this chapter is not merely on women in medicine, but rather on their experiences within the institution of medicine, which exists within and is dependent upon a patriarchal society. Consequently, the enduring and damaging stereotypes, the formal and informal barriers, and the collective and individual discrimination experienced by women in medicine must be recognized as products of a patriarchal society that are used to oppress women systematically. Furthermore, researchers have reported that students' adaptation to the medical-school environment is important as it directly relates to learning and professional performance (Vitaliano et al., 1989, p. 1327). It is critical therefore to discover how women medical students perceive their environment, how this perception is relevant to their overall experience, and ultimately, how this experience shapes their orientation in terms of the medical framework they internalize and promote.

Women in Medicine: An Overview

Today we have certain understandings about medicine as an institution — about the experience and climate of medical school, as well as the nature of medical practice. Yet we have only a limited understanding of many relevant issues because the majority of research has either excluded women in medicine as subjects of analysis, has discounted women's experiences as insignificant or irrelevant, and/or has assumed that women's experiences are identical to those of male medical students and practitioners. However, over the last twenty years, as the number of women in medicine has increased, so have the number of studies directed at understanding and describing their experiences.

Medical education has been described as the most gruelling and demanding form of professional training. It has been seen as a dehumanizing, psychologically stressful experience, often detrimental both to students' identities and to their interpersonal relationships, including that between patient and physician (Shapiro, 1978, pp. 27-28). Also, until relatively recently, medical-school recruits were selected almost exclusively from a narrow segment of the population — intelligent, well educated, and affluent white males — a social and cultural background shared by medical faculty and administrators (Grant, 1988, p. 109).

Recently, however, the profile of medical students in Canada has changed dramatically. The enrollment of women students and applicants seeking admission have consistently increased over the years. The enrollment and admissions numbers mirror the applicant trends. Table 1 shows applicants seeking admission to a Canadian faculty of medicine by gender, from 1965-66 to 1991-92.

As Table 2 indicates, in 1990-91, women comprised 44.4 percent of the total enrollment in Canadian faculties of medicine, compared with 7 percent in 1957-58 and a little under 18 percent in 1970-71.

There has also been a consistent increase in the number of M.D. degrees awarded to women. For instance, in the 1991 calendar year, women earned 44.8 percent of the M.D.

Table 1   Applicants Seeking Admission to a Canadian Faculty of Medicine by Sex
Compared with Population Aged 20 to 24 Years – 1965/66-1991/92

Year	Canadian Citizens and Landed Immigrants			Population Aged 20-24 (000's)		Applicants per 100,000 Population	
	Men	Women	Total	Men	Women	Men	Women
1965/66	*	*	976	690.0	693.3	*	*
1966/67	1 805	265	2 070	727.1	734.2	248	36
1967/68	1 893	275	2 168	779.6	780.2	243	35
1968/69	2 194	393	2 587	830.2	826.5	264	48
1969/70	2 647	562	3 209	874.5	868.6	303	65
1970/71	2 856	681	3 537	911.9	910.5	313	75
1971/72	3 688	914	4 602	941.8	947.6	392	96
1972/73	4 554	1 346	5 900	951.4	948.4	479	142
1973/74	5 457	1 815	7 272	969.7	966.7	563	188
1974/75	5 475	2 118	7 593	1 005.0	1 000.2	545	212
1975/76	5 139	2 237	7 423	1 039.6	1 039.0	494	215
1976/77	4 822	2 218	7 042	1 065.8	1 068.0	452	208
1977/78	4 874	2 282	7 156	1 096.5	1 097.0	445	208
1978/79	4 525	2 366	6 891	1 122.5	1 118.7	403	212
1979/80	4 452	2 535	6 987	1 139.4	1 133.4	391	224
1980/81	4 120	2 649	6 769	1 156.6	1 149.1	356	231
1981/82	4 292	2 779	7 071	1 174.2	1 169.4	366	238
1982/83	3 941	2 971	6 912	1 181.7	1 174.6	334	253
1983/84	4 249	3 168	7 417	1 187.0	1 177.5	358	269
1984/85	4 447	3 440	7 887	1 186.6	1 173.8	375	293
1985/86	4 301	3 527	7 828	1 170.7	1 158.9	367	304
1986/87	4 321	3 587	7 908	1 133.7	1 124.1	381	319
1987/88	4 151	3 573	7 724	1 104.5	1 087.9	376	328
1988/89	4 013	3 379	7 392	1 067.0	1 044.8	376	323
1989/90	3 892	3 268	7160	1 035.3	1 006.5	376	325
1990/91	3 883	3 416	7 299	1 016.6	981.6	382	348
1991/92	3 920	3 611	7 531	1 014.9	976.8	386	370

* Data not available

Notes: The methodology for conducting the applicant study changed in 1971. In earlier years some uncompetitive prospective applicants may not have been
counted because the initial goal of the applicant study was to find out how many *qualified* applicants were not gaining admission. Also up to 1970, some
students did not compete for admission but entered medicine directly from pre-medical programs. The figures were adjusted upwards to include
1 applicant for each person admitted directly. However, it is probable that more than 1 applicant would have competed for each available place had the
places been filled through open competition.

Source: Association of Canadian Medical Colleges, (1991). *Canadian Medical Education Statistics,* 1991. Ottawa.

Table 2   Enrolment in Canadian Faculties of Medicine by Sex 1957/58-1990/91

Year	Men	Women	Total	% Women
1957/58	3 424	259	3 683	7.0
1958/59	3 378	294	3 672	8.0
1959/60	3 243	306	3 549	8.6
1960/61	3 178	330	3 508	9.4
1961/62	3 165	360	3 525	10.2
1962/63	3 199	371	3 570	10.4
1963/64	3 279	419	3 698	11.3
1964/65	3 445	430	3 875	11.1
1965/66	3 564	459	4 023	11.4
1966/67	3 718	512	4 230	12.1
1967/68	3 863	553	4 416	12.5
1968/69	4 012	669	4 681	14.3
1969/70	4 259	795	5 054	15.7
1970/71	4 457	967	5 424	17.8
1971/72	4 690	1 162	5 852	19.9
1972/73	4 936	1 389	6 325	22.0
1973/74	5 127	1 632	6 759	24.1
1974/75	5 181	1 831	7 012	26.1
1975/76	5 167	2 042	7 209	28.3
1976/77	5 065	2 197	7 262	30.3
1977/78	5 002	2 306	7 308	31.6
1978/79	4 877	2 432	7 309	33.3
1979/80	4 810	2 537	7 347	34.5
1980/81	4 710	2 677	7 387	36.2
1981/82	4 649	2 787	7 436	37.5
1982/83	4 553	2 939	7 492	39.2
1983/84	4 433	3 051	7 484	40.8
1984/85	4 349	3 124	7 473	41.8
1985/86	4 219	3 131	7 350	42.6
1986/87	4 177	3 124	7 301	42.8
1987/88	4 059	3 147	7 206	43.7
1988/89	3 961	3 163	7 124	44.4
1989/90	3 960	3 112	7 072	44.0
1990/91	3 956	3 154	7 110	44.4

Source: Association of Canadian Medical Colleges, (1991). *Canadian Medical Education Statistics*, 1991. Ottawa.

Table 3   Number of M.D.s Awarded by Canadian Universities, 1940 to 1991, by Sex
of Degree Earners.

	Number of M.D. Degrees Earned by:					Number of M.D. Degrees Earned by:			
Year	Men	Women	Total	% Women	Year	Men	Women	Total	% Women
1940	584	25	609	4.1	1966	782	100	882	11.3
1941	515	26	541	4.8	1967	814	104	918	11.3
1942	510	27	537	5.0	1968	905	111	1 016	10.9
1943	842	47	889	5.3	1969	883	135	1 018	13.3
1944	478	26	504	5.2	1970	945	129	1 074	12.0
1945	555	45	600	7.5	1971	980	153	1 133	13.5
1946	400	26	426	6.1	1972	1 057	221	1 278	17.3
1947	373	33	406	8.1	1973	1 101	227	1 328	17.1
1948	589	55	644	8.5	1974	1 248	312	1 560	20.0
1949	653	62	715	8.7	1975	1 200	344	1 544	22.3
1950	708	44	752	5.9	1976	1 291	423	1 714	24.7
1951	799	62	861	7.2	1977	1 233	458	1 691	27.1
1952	749	36	785	4.6	1978	1 239	516	1 755	29.4
1953	783	46	829	5.5	1979	1 216	544	1 760	30.9
1954	831	58	889	6.5	1980	1 180	562	1 742	32.3
1955	874	59	933	6.3	1981	1 175	590	1 765	33.4
1956	766	51	817	6.2	1982	1 130	626	1 756	35.6
1957	830	68	898	7.6	1983	1 137	657	1 794	36.6
1958	786	44	830	5.3	1984	1 121	652	1 773	36.8
1959	838	50	888	5.6	1985	1 094	741	1 835	40.4
1960	805	66	871	7.6	1986	1 026	732	1 758	41.6
1961	773	66	839	7.9	1987	1 024	742	1 766	42.0
1962	768	86	854	10.1	1988	1 060	721	1 781	40.5
1963	752	65	817	8.0	1989	961	761	1 722	44.2
1964	707	80	787	10.2	1990	957	751	1 708	44.0
1965	934	98	1 032	9.5	1991	941	764	1 705	44.8

Source: Association of Canadian Medical Colleges, (1991). *Canadian Medical Education Statistics*, 1991. Ottawa.

degrees at all Canadian universities, compared with 4.1 percent in 1940 and 12.0 percent
in 1970. These data are reprinted in Table 3.

In 1990, the percentage of female graduates from the sixteen Canadian universities
with medical degree programs ranged from a low of 32.7 percent at the University of
Toronto to a high of 68.7 percent at McMaster University (Association of Canadian
Medical Colleges [ACMC], 1991, pp. 10, 35). While these statistics show that women

are better represented in medical school and in the profession than in the past, the question arises whether there has been a positive and progressive change in the medical profession's attitude towards women as students, as physicians and professionals, and ultimately, as patients.

The proportion of women enrolled in the first year of medical studies was 10.3 percent in 1960-61; 20.2 percent in 1970-71; 40.0 percent in 1980-81; and, in 1990-91, women comprised 45.5 percent of the entering classes in Canadian schools of medicine (ACMC, 1991, p. 11). In fact, according to statistics compiled by the Association of Canadian Medical Colleges, for the last fifteen years the proportion of women admitted into medicine has consistently been a function of the increasing number of women who applied to medical programs (ACMC, 1988, p. 6). While figures vary among each of the sixteen universities with medical degree programs, overall, women have fared slightly better than men in the admissions competition when the proportions of successful applicants are compared (ACMC, 1988, p. 6). To illustrate, in 1990-91, 22.99 women per 100 applications were admitted, compared with 22.52 men per 100 applications. This ratio represents 823 women to 943 men who were selected out of 4 188 male and 3 580 female applicants. A more apparent difference exists in the total number of applications submitted by men and women. Again, in the 1990-91 calendar year, women submitted 9 354 applications, while men submitted a total of 12 020 (ACMC, 1991, p. 119). Excluding foreign candidates, men submitted an average of 4.83 applications each, compared with an average of 4.09 by each woman (ACMC, 1991, p. 158). However, although men filed almost one-third more applications than did women in 1990-91, over the past two decades, the number of male applicants has steadily decreased, while the number of female applicants has steadily increased (Kinesis, 1988, p. 24). Furthermore, since the early 1980s, there continues to be an overall gradual reduction in the number of first-year spaces at Canadian faculties of medicine. Essentially, women appear to have an equal chance of being admitted to medical school, within the context of keener competition, because of reduced first-year spaces (ACMC, 1988, pp. 5-6).

Today, Canadian medical schools are overwhelmingly uniform in curricula and in standards of accomplishment (Kinesis, 1988, p. 23). Also, contrary to the notion that medical-school admission requirements have been lowered to accommodate women, women continue to enter with qualifications equal to those of men (ACMC, 1991, p. 135), and throughout training, do as well as men (Arnold et al., 1988, p. 730; Calkins et al., 1992, p. 58; Lorber, 1981, p. 329). Therefore, based on an overview of current literature on women in medicine, the question of the equality of women's experiences within their training programs will be explored.

To begin with, numerous factors discourage girls and women from even considering the medical profession long before application to medical school. That is, a sexual tracking system exists that serves to circumscribe the adult roles of women. Although young girls and boys statistically show no significant differences in abilities in mathematics and science, by approximately grade 10 females enrol in fewer mathematics and science courses (Hyde, 1985, p. 192). Consequently, most women not only have fewer math and science skills, but are also significantly more limited in their range of career choices.

Furthermore, our society is particularly discouraging to girls with an interest in and a talent for science and mathematics (Rose, 1986, p. 60). Throughout the socialization process, boys are instructed that they are "naturally" intelligent, objective, active, and independent, while girls are encouraged to be sensitive, emotional, obedient, and dependent. Since an aptitude for science and math implies traditional masculine traits, girls are often discouraged, both subtly and actively, from developing their interest in these subjects.

In a 1985 study undertaken for the Women's Bureau of Labour Canada, entitled *When I Grow Up . . . Career Expectations and Aspirations of Canadian Schoolchildren*, the findings were suggestive of pervasive sex-role stereotyping in Canadian society. A sample of just over 700 elementary-school pupils (approximately equal numbers of boys and girls) was studied to determine children's preferences for a selection of sex-stereotyped activities and their expectations of sex segregation in the labour force they will join as adults. The results showed that even among the youngest of the research subjects, girls and boys were significantly different in their responses. Both girls and boys believed that when they became adults, they would be engaged in many of the same occupations. However, girls expressed belief in the future participation of women in predominantly masculine professions was not always reflected in their individual career choices. As the authors state: "It was as though girls did not apply to themselves their general belief in the equality of the sexes. Many of them seemed to be saying, 'Yes, women can become doctors, but I expect to be a nurse,' 'Bank managers can be women as well as men, but I am going to be a teller,' or 'Dental assistant is my career goal, although I know that women can be dentists' " (Labour Canada, 1986, p. 55).

A recent study released in March 1992 by the American Association of University Women Education Foundation concluded that subtle sexism is still pervasive in schools. It revealed that teachers pay less attention to girls than boys; few teachers encourage girls to pursue male-dominated maths and sciences; tests are biased against girls; and school textbooks still ignore or stereotype women (Canadian Press, 1992, p. A2).

The identification of sexist language and the need for a change to non–sexist forms have long been topics of controversy. Language development and use, along with the socialization process, also further instills the notion that the "physician is male." The concept of doctor is routinely verbalized as "he." This again may contribute to limited career options among women, as well as support the patriarchal myth of appropriate and separate roles for women and men. In fact, a 1981 study of first-year medical students in the United States revealed that both female and male students (who tended to be very similar on the personality traits measured) attributed very different characteristics to hypothetical physicians who differed in gender only. Moreover, their ratings for "most physicians" (sex unspecified) tended to be most similar to their descriptions of the average male physician. The study concluded that, in general, the first-year medical student still sees the typical physician as male. The results also confirmed anecdotal reports that female medical students are more acutely aware of, and stressed by, traditional gender-based stereotypes (Dralle et al., 1987, p. 75-81). Anecdotal data from research in progress (Kirk, 1992) confirms that at one Canadian medical school there is still a distinct "maleness" to the medical-school environment. During in-depth interviews with 21 women at various stages of the four-year undergraduate medical-training program, women spoke of the "natural" use of the generic "he" in many contexts. While to some women this was seen as a non-issue, one particular example provided a sobering image:

> Things like when they wrote up cases for tutorials, the doctors were always male. Even now when I read a case history, if it's a female doctor, it blows my mind. . . . I think "that's impossible. We don't have women doctors." [But you're going to be one.] I know! It's contradictory, that's what I'm saying, but no matter how it happens, when someone refers to the doctor, I immediately bring out a male picture.

Several women agreed that the male body was often the norm in anatomy diagrams and texts and that women's health issues were often tacked on at the end, condensed into one token lecture slot, and often seen as non-core (Kirk, 1992).

It is apparent, therefore, that significant societal factors do influence women's (as well as men's) perceptions of the physician's role and contribute to discouraging women from considering the medical profession before and during application to medical school. Stereotypes and discrimination based on sexist ideology are important parts of the early sexual tracking system. Differences have been established between men's and women's opportunities for career choice and development in the professions in general, and in medicine in particular.

With the fairly recent increase in women entering medicine, there is a trend developing in the literature on medical education that implies that the educational process is psychologically more stressful for women than men. Some studies show that female medical students consult with mental-health services more frequently than do their male peers, and that females report a greater increase in depressive symptoms and a greater decrease in life satisfaction (Hammond, 1981, p. 162; Parkerson et al., 1990, p. 586;

Martin et al., 1988, p. 77). Women students also reported more role conflict and less support from their families (Martin et al., 1988, p. 77). Some studies have also suggested that conflicts with authorities may be more problematic for women medical students. Women have scored higher on measures reflecting stressful faculty-student relations and have reported more problems with administrators (who are often responsible for student promotions). Women were also more likely to report feeling hostility and discrimination from faculty members (Speigel et al., 1987, p. 19; Grant, 1988, pp. 109-110).

This literature can be quite damaging for women, especially when the information is interpreted without acknowledging the influence of patriarchy. To illustrate, other studies have emphasized that while female medical students are reporting higher levels of emotional distress, this is strongly linked to the higher levels of stress that women experience (Archer et al., 1991, p. 301; Coombs et al., 1988, p. 21). Several studies have suggested that women encounter unique obstacles, and consequently face unique stress during training that is not experienced to the same extent by males. To begin with, most women must deal with more complex role demands in terms of balancing professional and personal obligations (Elliot & Girard, 1986, p. 56). Women have limited female role models and mentors among medical-school faculty members (Cohen et al., 1988, p. 142; Nadelson, 1992, p. 95; Osborn et al., 1992, p. 59), and may often be excluded from informal cliques of male colleagues (Elliot & Girard, 1986, p. 55). There is also ample evidence that women's and men's performances, attributes, and tasks are valued differently in society. For example, studies have shown that female performances are often seen as less competent than identical male performances, and successful performances by women are attributed often to external or unstable causes, such as luck or temporary effort (Major, 1987, p. 3). Women medical students have also experienced difficulties in appearing credible, and many hold the perception that they have to work twice as hard, even appear superlative, just to qualify as average (Poirier, 1986, p. 83; Dralle et al., 1987, p. 80; Whiting & Bickel, 1990, p. 277). There seem to be unique pressures on women to perform well, as one woman interviewed explained: "Women must look competent, men just look incompetent for themselves, but when women fumble, they sort of give all other female students a bad name." (Kirk, 1992). Therefore, in analyzing the problems and discrimination that women face in the medical system, it is vital that attention not be focussed primarily on "women's special problems," but rather that the nature of the institutional structures and the organization of work be recognized as significant factors in circumscribing women's opportunities and experiences within the profession of medicine.

Role models are also extremely important in terms of professional learning and development. The problem is significant for female students since women still comprise a relatively small percentage of medical-school faculty members (Whiting & Bickel,

1990, p. 277). There are not enough women to serve as role models for the increasing number of female students, particularly in the specialties where women have been traditionally underrepresented (Hapchyn & Gold, 1990, p. 46). For example, the percentage of women physicians in surgery departments is almost the lowest of all specialties (Burnley & Burkett, 1986, p. 146). Furthermore, women are not only underrepresented as full-time faculty in medical schools, but the percentage of women faculty holding the M.D. degree is even lower (Burnley & Burkett, 1986, p. 145).

In a recent study (Kirk, 1992), women stated that there were not enough women teaching in medical school. Most women reported that only between 5 and 20 percent of their instructors had been female. All respondents were extremely enthusiastic about having more women occupy positions within the medical-school hierarchy — from lecturers and preceptors to department heads and deans. Women were seen as being important role models who provided females with a sense of belonging and comradeship. The women reported that female professors were very approachable, and served as much-needed sources of information regarding what it was like to be a woman in medicine. Women lauded the benefits of having more women visible in the medical college, and also described the effects of the lack of female role models. The message that several women conveyed was that, by and large, the physician is still seen as male, even in their own eyes. One woman reported that it was "strange to see a woman come in the room, to tell the truth," and another stated that "[I] find I just assume that the preceptor is going to be male generally because most are." Yet another woman stated that "often when a woman comes to the front of the class, people make the assumption — oh, she must be a dietician or a physiotherapist, or whatever else." One woman expressed concern that her male colleagues might not learn to value and respect women, or feel comfortable taking orders from female interns, because of the lack of female authority figures. Moreover, she wondered whether she and her female peers would garner the same respect as males once they got into the system. Another admitted that "a strange thing happened when I actually did get a female lecturer in medicine — once in a blue moon — I didn't take them as seriously as I took men. It was kind of disappointing when I realized . . . how much that influenced me" (Kirk, 1992).

Finally, some women also made the connection between the lack of female academics and the dearth of women in positions of authority within medical school. The message was clear: if there are few women in the power structure, the likelihood of change is a lot less promising.

Within medicine, women are still being encouraged to go into traditional "female specialties," such as pediatrics, family medicine, and obstetrics and gynecology. Women are also underrepresented in the upper echelons of the medical profession. The conventional explanations given for these patterns most often focus on women's strong commitment to (or relegation) of family responsibilities, or women's lesser motivation to achieve higher status, which again, is perceived to be the result of an early choice to consider family over career as a life-long commitment. However, these explanations ignore the reality that, in patriarchal societies, the institution of motherhood prescribes that mothering should exist at the centre of women's lives and that all else should remain secondary (Hunter College Women's Studies Collective, 1983, p. 288). This bias is evident even within the medical-school admission interview. One U.S. study revealed that the interview panel asked women more frequently about their plans regarding marriage and children, while men were more often asked about their motivations for entering medicine and their future career plans within the profession (Marquart et al., 1990, p. 411). Similarly, all women who participated in a recent Canadian study revealed that they had been asked themselves and/or had heard about other women who were asked about their intentions to have a family, and their ensuing ability to balance domestic demands with a career in medicine. Not one woman had ever heard of a man being asked a similar question during the admission interview. Indeed, many found the very prospect to be amusing (Kirk, 1992).

Although people now argue that traditional family patterns are disappearing, recent studies show that beneath the apparently egalitarian coping strategies of many dual-career couples with children, there still remains a traditional division of responsibility (Hyde, 1985, p. 176; Cartwright, 1987, p. 143). Interestingly, previous research regarding career decision making, marriage and family, and the practice of women physicians also confirms that women have legitimate concerns about being successful and satisfied in their roles. A number of studies show that women physicians were often confronted with a disparity between their expectations and their experiences regarding pregnancy, parenting, and family life, when they were compared with male physicians. Female medical students and residents expected to share child care, household chores, and financial responsibilities equally with their husbands. Their male peers expected to participate much less in child care and household chores and to contribute more financially. Since many physicians tend to marry one another (Shermerhorn et al., 1986, p. 74), it is obvious that some of these expectations will not be realized (Altekruse & McDermott, 1988, p. 80). Further, female medical students, residents, and practitioners all reported greater role stress than their male colleagues. When surveyed, between 30 and 60 percent of female physicians felt that family-career conflicts were important influences on their lives (Martin et al., 1988, p. 337). Another survey that asked men and women whether they had changed their career plans because of family influences found that none of the men said they had done so, whereas 44 percent of the women surveyed stated that they had (Martin et al., 1988, p. 337). A study of dual-doctor marriages also reported that 19 of 21 women interviewed (as compared with only 1 of 21 men) thought that they had made significant career compromises because of their marriage. Furthermore, the couples revealed that the husband's career was given priority over the wife's in all of the marriages (Johnson et al., 1991, p. 156).

Yet, in light of the above research, and despite a growing body of evidence to the contrary (for example, see Harris & Conley-Muth, 1981; Harward et al, 1981; Brown & Klein, 1982; Altekruse & McDermott, 1988; Kettner, 1988; Martin et al., 1988; Eisenberg, 1989; Wheeler et al., 1990; Dickstein, 1990; Phelan, 1991), the notion still persists that women's career commitment in medicine is weaker than that of men's. Studies now reveal that the gap between the number of hours worked by women and men is steadily diminishing, because, for the most part, the number of hours worked by male physicians has decreased (Ramos & Feiner, 1989, p. 24). Moreover, as one study concluded: "Women physicians spent 90 percent as much time in medical work as did the men, despite the fact that most of the women had full responsibility for homes and families" (Heins et al., 1977, p. 2514).

Still, women's motivation and career development have been explained by how different women are from men rather than in terms of the difference in the structure of opportunities available for women and men. As previously stated, women are often urged to enter specialties with high interaction with patients because these are felt to be compatible with women's interest in people. Women are also steered to low interaction specialties because the practice hours are seen to be compatible with family responsibilities. Women have stated that at one time or another they heard comments suggesting that "women don't make good doctors because they have kids and work part-time and are not in tune" (Kirk, 1992). Women are often assumed to have traditional feminine qualities that are more suitable for some specialties (e.g., family medicine, pediatrics, obstetrics, and gynecology), whereas other specialties are perceived as unsuitable because stereotypically masculine traits such as physical vigor and competitiveness are required (e.g., surgery, orthopedics, urology) (Burnley & Burkett, 1986, pp. 144-151). Research has revealed that faculty members recommended different specialties to women and men students based on the belief that some fields are suited to women. Women have also reported that surgeons raised questions, directly and indirectly, about their physical stamina, their emotional stability, their motives for being interested in surgery, and their perceived lack of aggression, a trait that faculty considered essential for successful surgeons (Osborne, 1983, p. 23; Opinion, 1986, p. 58; Grant, 1988, p. 115). Women in medical school have spoken about the reputation that surgery has for being a male-dominated and paternalistic "boys' club." Reports abound that still describe surgery as a hostile environment for women. Women still recount tales about the bad hours and inflexible time commitments; the lack of maternity leave and the lack of female change rooms; the lack of respect for, and poor treatment of, female patients; as well as the lack of female residents and surgeons to serve as role models (Kirk, 1992).

Consequently, most women are still "choosing" to go into traditional female fields. Women report that the demand for female family practitioners, as well as perceived benefits such as more flexible residencies and work opportunities, maternity leave and on-site day care, and an overall less hostile environment, are definite assets that these specialties have to offer. However, for many women, the perceived curtailment of their career options is not taken lightly, but with regret and disappointment, even frustration and anger (Kirk, 1992). It appears that women face a Catch-22 situation: while they recognize the need to make inroads into male-dominated specialties, they also recognize the need to learn and work in a tolerable environment, and many are not willing to endure the pitfalls of being token women.

Research shows little evidence that female physicians prefer primary-care specialties more than male physicians do. When specialty choices of male and female medical students were examined, it was found that the men who specialized in family practice preferred it, but that women who specialized in family medicine, did not always prefer it even when they chose it, suggesting strongly that women are making career compromises, or being tracked into this type of specialty (Burnley & Burkett, 1986, p. 145). Another study reported that even when they prefer it, proportionately fewer female medical students choose surgery residencies (Ramos & Feiner, 1989, p. 24).

It is apparent that gender inequalities in medicine are pervasive because they are built into social institutions and maintained by everyday assumptions about appropriate work and roles for women and men in and out of the home. Interestingly, it has also been shown that female physicians often structure their own analyses of the medical system in terms of being women in medical school, while men more often contextualize their experiences in terms of being students in medicine (Poirier, 1986, p. 83). Again, this suggest the importance that gender plays within the medical-school environment.

Not surprisingly, as reported in one U.S. study, female students encountered overt and covert forms of sexism from faculty, peers, and sometimes even patients. Overall, 34 percent of the women said they had personally experienced gender discrimination, while 62 percent had observed gender discrimination toward classmates. Thus, while the majority of women did not perceive themselves as being victims of gender discrimination, they perceived that it existed in the medical school (Grant, 1988, pp. 109, 110). The researcher further revealed that: "Faculty and hospital physicians were identified most often as the sources of gender discrimination. More than 80 percent of women's reports of discrimination toward themselves involved faculty or other physicians, and more than 75 percent of discrimination toward others emanated from physicians" (Grant, 1988, p. 110).

In a recent Canadian study (Kirk, 1992), women also described many ways that they were made to feel marginal and less or differently valued. Women were called "girls" or mistaken for nurses; they pointed out that even senior nurses in their fifties were called "girls" by male clerks and residents in their twenties. Some women reported feeling invisible or being ignored by male professors and preceptors, or conversely, felt that they were judged more harshly than their male peers. Women articulated a variety of ways in which they were treated differently and inappropriately by male professors and clinicians. These included being called "a skirt," witnessing and experiencing inappropriate touching and sexual advances, as well as more subtle incidents, such as:

> Subliminal messaging . . . just in terms of, say there are 8 people working with a physician, when it comes to doing things like putting the robe back on the patient, usually it's a woman singled out to do things like that . . . just kind of a different treatment. (Kirk, 1992)

Many women mentioned crude, misogynous, pornographic, and offensive humour that surfaced in many places, including lectures given by established professors and medicine's traditional night out — beer and skits.

Just as important as the examples of sexism that women spoke about were the reactions they got from those within the medical school. Women spoke of male peers and professors who were supportive and understanding. But as many women pointed out, this was not always the case. In one instance, complaints against offensive jokes and inappropriate terminology were trivialized by faculty, administration, and students alike. Reactions to the complaints were described as defensive and dismissive. Several women said that they wouldn't feel comfortable objecting publicly to blatant sexism or harassment because they didn't want to be labelled as troublemakers. Others mentioned that due to work overload, they didn't have the time to notice or to make an issue over the subtle and not-so-subtle inequities that existed. One woman voiced another frequently stated opinion: "I'm so used to laughing along with jokes like that, I didn't find it insulting" (Kirk, 1992).

What appears to be most disquieting is that several women admitted that they would be reluctant to make a formal complaint because they were afraid of the ramifications. Even among their peers, many women stated that when they spoke out against sexism they were told that they were overreacting, were too sensitive, or they couldn't take a joke. Some began to question whether indeed they had overreacted, and others admitted that they had simply given up speaking out against perceived discrimination. Several women stated that the most painful part was seeing their female colleagues not support each other (Kirk, 1992).

Clearly, women still encounter both overt and subtle forms of gender discrimination within the medical school environment. Not only does gender discrimination create stress for women students, but it also reinforces "the view that sexism is still an accepted and integral part of medicine in the real world, even if it is disavowed in formal policies of the medical school" (Grant, 1988, p. 118).

Having reviewed the current literature on women's experiences within medical school, we can return to the issue of whether an increase in female physicians will ultimately result in more humane patient care — initiating a trend away from scientific and technology-bound medicine.

Will More Women M.D.s Improve the Profession?

Even though it is apparent that medicine is still a male-oriented profession on many levels and that women are still discriminated against and/or treated differently through-out training and practice, research still shows that "women physicians more nearly resemble men physicians in professional attributes than they do other women in the population" (Eisenberg, 1983, p. 534; Dornbush et al., 1991, p. 150; Osborne, 1983, p. 25). While some studies report that female physicians are perceived more favourably by patients and seem better able to communicate sensitivity and caring to patients (Linn et al., 1984, p. 966; Arnold et al., 1988, p. 729), research also confirms that female and male M.D.s have comparable diagnostic and therapeutic skills, as well as comparable knowl-edge bases (Arnold et al., 1988, p. 729). Furthermore, while studies have shown that women start medical school with more humanistic views, "the conservative effect of medical socialization on both male and female students attenuates these differences" (Arnold et al., 1988, p. 729). For example, an American study of 773 first-and third-year students and recent medical graduates revealed that while female first-year students tended to give more importance to the human, social, and preventative dimensions of patient care than did their male counterparts, few, if any, gender differences were found among medical school graduates (Maheux et al., 1988, p. 73-75).

When the medical-school environment is examined from yet another angle, these results are not at all surprising. First of all, as stated previously, the socializing aspects of medical school are extremely powerful in shaping students' attitudes and priorities over the three-four-year undergraduate medical program. Medical-school curriculum still focusses on short-term memorization and regurgitation of "facts" originating almost exclusively from within the basic and medical sciences. Moreover, the emphasis in this learning process is on "what," rather than on "how" or "why," and as a result, what is blatantly excluded is general problem-solving skills and the humanistic aspects of general and preventative health care (Clawson, 1990, p. 86). Medical training takes place in a highly competitive and individualistic environment: a unique atmosphere that is further "associated with a lack of support for activities or behaviours that might threaten the authority, independence and financial potential of the physician" (Dornbush et al., 1991, p. 151). Without a doubt, one of the overriding factors is that professional socialization is a homogenizing process: students become more alike as they progress through medical school. Consequently, "class loyalties" become stronger than gender loyalties with regard to social issues within health care and medical practice (Dornbush et al., 1991, p. 152). Because of the hierarchical, competitive, and overwhelming nature of the medical-school educational experience, most students do not think to, or want to, question what they are taught. Therefore, most students (both female and male), tend to incorporate the same sexist and paternalistic theories about women's health into medical practice, whatever their style.

In addition, as stated previously, the "fine mesh of the admissions sieve" (Eisenberg, 1989, p. 1544) ensures that women enter medicine with qualifications and characteristics equal to those of men. The group of women (and men) who are admitted to medicine, are a very select group of intelligent and high-achieving individuals. Yet much of the current criticism of the medical-school process highlights that "the selection and education process has encouraged only science and high technology-oriented individuals to enter medicine, even though social and behavioural factors are the basis of a majority of today's medical problems" (Clawson, 1990, p. 85). Most medical schools require several years of premedical education, the rationale being that the individual should be broadly educated in arts and sciences before embarking upon medical studies. However, the reality of the situation is that in Canada, fifteen out of sixteen medical schools require one or more second-or third-year university-level science courses, while only eight schools require one entry-level course in the humanities or the social sciences. Furthermore, eleven out of the sixteen schools require the Medical College Admission Test (MCAT), which is composed of six sections, five of which are math and science-oriented, while the sixth focusses on reading skills (ACMC, 1991, p. 135). Such scientifically focussed admission requirements, in the context of today's keen competition for diminishing spaces, does not encourage a broad educational and theoretical base. Therefore, the vast majority of women entering medicine are trained in the same scientific assumptions, and as a result, hold similar values.

It has also been shown that professions are closed, self-regulating communities and, consequently, they have implicit and sometimes explicit expectations about the appropriate characteristics of their members. The purpose of these expectations is to ensure that all members of the profession are similar and hold common values and beliefs, which allows the profession to control the behaviour of its members and preserve its integrity (Goode, 1957, pp. 195-200). Within professions, an image of the appropriate candidate still exists. Today, while formal university policies prevent overt discrimination on the basis of gender, race, ethnicity, and religion, interestingly, most medical students continue to come from middle to upper socio-economic back-grounds. Clearly, the long-term, rigorous training schedule still prevents many students from considering medicine. A recent American study revealed that "financial concerns" were among the top three reasons listed by students who considered medicine, but decided against it (Colquitt & Killian, 1991, p. 273). A study of Canadian adolescent girls also indicates that the socio-economic background of the family is still an important factor in mediating future career aspirations. Girls from wealthier, better-educated families were more likely to consider non-traditional professions, especially medicine and law (Baker, 1985, pp. 101, 105). This is an important consideration, since people from the same socio-economic status tend to hold similar values to begin with, which will be further homogenized during medical training. This subtle aspect of the admissions process also works to ensure that all medical students resemble each other. Consequently, even though sexism is prevalent at every stage of the medical-education process, women are not immune to the overriding influences of professionalization. Again, for women in medicine, "class loyalties" prevail.

Conclusion

Obviously, greater numbers of women in medicine is not the answer if they are trained to think about medicine and medical practice in the same authoritarian, hierarchical, paternalistic, sexist, and destructive framework that exists today. Indeed, adding more women to medicine may strengthen an institution that should be weakened. On the other hand, suggesting that women remain outside of the medical profession is neither a viable nor reasonable solution. As Eisenberg, a female physician and a critic of the system writes:

> If medicine is to become more humane, admitting more women into the profession will not be enough. The task will be to cultivate the humane qualities in all health professionals by making career paths, and the reward structure that reinforces them, consonant with that goal. . . . Women, in themselves, are not likely to alter the perceived shortcomings of medical practice. For that to take place, it will be necessary to modify admission criteria, to broaden the narrow focus of medical education, and to change the reward systems which govern medical practice for both women and men. (Eisenberg, 1983, p. 534; 1989, p. 1544)

As research shows, women are not powerful within the medical profession, and therefore it is both unrealistic and ironic that we should look to women to be the initiators of fundamental philosophical and material change. Clearly then, there is no simple solution to this issue. The crux of the predicament is that medicine can be a very destructive enterprise, especially to women, but it is also a very powerful, and seemingly permanent institution within society. However, as many have stated, that is not to say that it must remain in its present form. The challenge is to continue the feminist critique of the medical profession and current medical practice, and in so doing, to create the political awareness, will, and climate for change from within and from outside of medicine.

Study Questions

1. Based on information from this chapter, give evidence to support the argument that women's health care will not improve solely as a direct result of the increased number of women in medicine.
2. This chapter uses a feminist theoretical approach to examine women within medical-training programs. What do you think are the most important aspects of the theoretical concept of "latent patriarchal culture"?
3. Using mainstream "gender-neutral" medical journals (e.g., not the *Journal of the American Medical Women's Association*), examine how women are represented within the articles on medical students. What themes do you note? Compared to ten and/or twenty years ago, how have these depictions changed?
4. In part, this chapter examines the experiences of women during medical training. Investigate the position women hold as consumers of health care.

Recommended Reading

Acterberg, J. (1991). *Woman as healer*. Boston: Shambhala.

American Medical Women's Association. *The Journal of the American Medical Women's Association* [a journal devoted to women's health issues].

Dreifus, C. (Ed.). (1978). *Seizing our bodies: The politics of women's health*. New York: Vintage Books.

Ehrenreich, B., & English, D. (1973a). *Complaints and disorders: The sexual politics of sickness*. New York: The Feminist Press.

Ehrenreich, B., & English, D. (1973b). *Witches, midwives and nurses: A history of women healers*. New York: The Feminist Press.

Lorber, J. (1984). *Women physicians*. New York: Tavistock Publications.

McDonnell, K. (Ed.). (1986). *Adverse effects: Women and the pharmaceutical industry*. Toronto: Women's Educational Press.

Rosser, S.V. (Ed.). (1988). *Feminism within the science and health care professions: Overcoming resistance*. New York: Permagon Press.

Shapiro, M. (1978). *Getting doctored*. Kitchener: Between the Lines.

Women's Healthsharing Inc. *Healthsharing: A Canadian women's health quarterly*. Toronto: Author

References

Altekruse, J., & McDermott, S. (1988). Contemporary concerns of women in medicine. In S.V. Rosser (Ed.), *Feminism within the science and health care professions: Overcoming resistance* (pp. 65-88). New York: Permagon Press.

Archer, L., Keever, R., Gordon, R., & Archer, R. (1991). The relationship between residents' characteristics, their stress experiences, and their psychosocial adjustment at one medical school. *Academic Medicine, 66*, (5), 301-303.

Armstrong, P., & Armstrong, H. (1990). *Theorizing women's work*. Toronto: Garamond Press.

Arnold, R., Martin, S., & Parker, R. (1988). Taking care of patients — Does it matter whether the physician is a woman? *The West-ern Journal of Medicine*, 149, (6), 729-733.

Association of Canadian Medical Colleges. (1988). *Admission requirements to Canadian faculties of medicine and their selection policies.* Ottawa: Author.

Association of Canadian Medical Colleges. (1991). *Canadian medical education statistics, Vol. 13.* Ottawa: Author.

Baker, M. (1985). *What will tomorrow bring? A study of the aspirations of adolescent women.* Ottawa: Canadian Advisory Council on the Status of Women.

Becker, H.S., Geer, B., Hughes, E.C., & Strauss, A.L. (1961). *Boys in white.* Chicago: University of Chicago Press.

Beechey, V. (1979). On patriarchy. *Feminist Review*, 3, 66-83.

Benston, M. (1982). Feminism and the critique of scientific method. In *Feminism in Canada: From pressure to politics.* Montreal: Black Rose Books.

Brown, S., & Klein, R. (1982). Woman power in the medical hierarchy. *The Journal of the American Medical Association*, 37, (3), 155-164.

Burnley, C., & Burkett, G. (1986). Specialization: Are women in surgery different? *The Journal of the American Medical Association*, 41, (5), 144-151.

Calkins, E., Willoughby, L., & Arnold, L. (1987). Gender and psychosocial factors associated with specialty choice. *The Journal of the American Medical Association*, 42, (6), 170-172.

Calkins, E., Willoughby, L., & Arnold, L. (1992). Women medical students' ratings of the required surgery clerkship: Implications for career choice. *The Journal of the American Medical Association*, 47, (2), 58-60.

Canadian Press. (1992, April 12). School sexism upsets educator: Separate classes suggested. *Winnipeg Free Press*, p. A2.

Cartwright, L. (1987). Role montage: Life patterns of professional women. *The Journal of the American Medical Association*, 42, (5), 142-148.

Clawson, D. (1990). The education of the physician. *Academic Medicine*, 65, (2), 84-88.

Cohen, M., Woodward, C., & Ferrier, B. (1988). Factors influencing career development: Do men and women differ? *The Journal*

of the American Medical Association, 43, (5), 142-154.

Colquitt, W., & Killian, C. (1991). Students who consider medicine but decide against it. *Academic Medicine*, 66, (5), 273-278.

Coombs, R., & Hovanessian, H. (1988). Stress in the role constellation of female resident physicians. *The Journal of the American Medical Association*, 43, (1), 21-27.

Dickstein, L. (1990). Female physicians in the 1980s: Personal and family attitudes and values. *The Journal of the American Medical Association*, 45, (4), 122-126.

Dornbush, R., Richman, S., Singer, P., & Brownstein, E. (1991). Medical school, psychosocial attitudes, and gender. *The Journal of the American Medical Association*, 46, (5), 150-152.

Dralle, P., Daum, D., Hein, D., & Elston, R. (1987). Sex role stereotypes in freshman medical students' perceptions of self and physicians. *The Journal of the American Medical Association*, 42, (3), 75-80.

Eisenberg, C. (1983). Women as physicians. *Journal of Medical Education*, 58, 534-541.

Eisenberg, C. (1989). Medicine is no longer a man's profession. *The New England Journal of Medicine*, 321, (22), 1542-1544.

Elliot, D., & Girard, D. (1986). Gender and the emotional impact of internship. *The Journal of the American Medical Association*, 41, (2), 54-56.

Fox, B. (1988). Conceptualizing patriarchy. *Canadian Review of Sociology and Anthropology*, 25, (2), 163-182.

Goode, W.J. (1957). Community within a community: The professions. *American Sociological Review*, 22, 195-200.

Grant, L, (1988). The gender climate of medical school: Perspectives of women and men students. *The Journal of the American Medical Association*, 43, (4), 109-119.

Hammond, J. (1981). Social support groups, women's programs, and research on gender differences: The bad press for women in medical education literature. *The Journal of the American Medical Association*, 36, (5), 162-165.

Hapchyn, C., & Gold, I. (1990). Training issues for a female psychiatric residency. *The Journal of the American Medical Association*, 32, (2), 43-46.

Harris, M., & Conley-Muth, M. (1981). Sex role stereotypes and medical specialty choice. *The Journal of the American Medical Association, 36*, (8), 245-252.

Harrison, M. (1990). Woman as other: The premise of medicine. *The Journal of the American Medical Association, 45*, (6), 225-226.

Harward, D., Lyons, C., Porter, C., & Hunter, R. (1981). A comparison of the performance of male and female medical students and residents. *Journal of Medical Education, 56*, 853-855.

Heins, M., Smock, S., Martindale, L., Jacobs, J., & Stein, M. (1977). Comparison of the productivity of women and men physicians. *The Journal of the American Medical Association, 237*, (23), 2514-2517.

Hunter College Women's Studies Collective. (1983). *Women's realities, women's choices*. New York: Oxford University Press.

Hyde, J. (1985). *Half the human experience*. Lexington: D.C. Heath.

Johnson, C., Johnson, B., & Liese, B. (1991). Dual-doctor marriages: *The British experience. The Journal of the American Medical Association, 46*, (5), 155-163.

Kettner, A.S. (1988). Female family-practice graduates at the University of Manitoba: Career patterns and perceptions. *Canadian Family Physician, 34*, 831-837.

Kirk, J. (1992). *Women in medicine: An experiential account of the persistence of sexism and its consequences*. Unpublished M.A. thesis. Winnipeg: University of Manitoba.

Labour Canada. (1986). *When I grow up ... Career expectations and aspirations of Canadian schoolchildren*. Ottawa: Minister of Supply and Services.

Linn, L., Cope, D., & Leake, B. (1984). The effect of gender and training of residents on satisfaction ratings by patients. *Journal of Medical Education, 59*, 964-966.

Lorber, J. (1981). The limits of sponsorship for women physicians. *The Journal of the American Medical Association, 36*, (11), 329-338.

Lorber, J. (1984). *Women physicians*. New York: Tavistock Publications.

Maheux, B., Dufort, F., & Beland, F. (1988). Professional and sociopolitical attitudes of medical students: Gender differences reconsidered. *The Journal of the American Medical Association, 43*, (3), 73-75.

Major, B. (1987). Women and entitlement. *Women and Therapy, 6*, (3), 3-19.

Marquart, J., Franco, K., & Carroll, B. (1990). The influence of applicants' gender on medical school interviews. *Academic Medicine, 65*, (6), 410-411.

Martin, C., Jones, J., & Bird, M. (1988). Support systems for women in medicine. *Journal of the American Medical Women's Association, 43*, (3), 77-83.

Martin, S., Arnold, R., & Parker, R. (1988). Gender and medical socialization. *Journal of Health and Social Behaviour, 29*, (4), 333-343.

McDonough, R., & Harrison, R. (1978). Patriarchy and relations of production. In A. Kuhn & A. Wolpe (Eds.), *Feminism and materialism: Women and modes of production* (pp. 11-42). London: Routledge and Kegan Paul.

Muszynski, A. (1989). What is patriarchy? *Socialist Studies, 5*, 65-86.

Nadelson, C. (1992). Advancing through the medical hierarchy. *The Journal of the American Medical Association, 46*, (3), 95-99.

Opinion (Anonymous). (1986). Why would a girl go into surgery? *The Journal of the American Medical Association, 41*, (2), 58-60.

Osborn, E., Ernster, V., & Martin, J. (1992). Women's attitudes towards careers in academic medicine at the University of California, San Francisco. *Academic Medicine, 67*, (1), 59-60.

Osborne, D. (1983, January). My wife, the doctor. *Mother Jones*, 18-44.

Parkerson, G., Broadhead, W., & Tse, C. (1990). The health status and life satisfaction of first-year medical students. *Academic Medicine, 65*, (9), 586-588.

Phelan, E. (1991). A survey of maternity leave policies in Boston area hospitals. *The Journal of the American Medical Association, 46*, (2), 55-58.

Poirier, S. (1986). Role stress in medical education: A literary perspective. *The Journal of the American Medical Association, 41*, (3) 82-86.

Pollock, S. (1988). Feminism and reproduction. In B.S. Bolaria & H.D. Dickinson (Eds.), *Sociology of health care in Canada* (pp. 168-182). Toronto: Harcourt Brace Jovanovich.

Ramos, S., & Feiner, C. (1989). Women surgeons: A national survey. *The Journal of the American Medical Association, 44*, (1), 21-25.

Rose, H. (1986). Beyond masculinist realities: A feminist epistemology for the sciences. In R. Bleirer (Ed.), *Feminist approaches to science* (pp. 57-76). New York: Permagon Press.

Schermerhorn, G., Colliver, J., Verhulst, S., & Schmidt, E. (1986). Factors that influence career patterns of women physicians. *The Journal of the American Medical Association*, 41, (3), 74-78.

Shapiro, M. (1978). *Getting doctored*. Kitchener: Between the Lines.

Spiegel, D., Smolen, R., & Hopfensperger, K. (1987). Interpersonal stress in medical education: Correlates for men and women students. *The Journal of the American Medical Association*, 42, (1), 19-21.

Vancouver Status of Women. (1988, June). Kinesis: News about women that's not in the dailies. *Notes* (pp. 10-25). Vancouver: Author.

Vitaliano, P., Maiuro, R., Mitchell, E., & Russo, J. (1989). Perceived stress in medical school: Resistors, persistors, adaptors and maladaptors. *Social Science and Medicine*, 28, (12), 1321-1329.

Wheeler, R., Candib, L., & Martin, M. (1990). Part-time doctors: Reduced working hours for primary care physicians. *The Journal of the American Medical Association*, 45, (2), 47-54.

Whiting, B., & Bickel, J. (1990). AAMC data report: Women on faculties of U.S. medical schools, 1979-1989. *Academic Medicine*, 65, (24), 277-278.

Chapter 8

Patient-Physician Relationships: Changing Modes of Interaction

B. Gail Frankel, University of Western Ontario

Introduction

The most fundamental interaction in the health-care system is that between patient and physician. In earlier times, physicians did not possess the technical skills and knowledge to offer their patients the cures that are available to us today, nor did they occupy the relatively high position in the social hierarchy enjoyed by their contemporary counterparts (Shorter, 1985; Starr, 1982). Major progress toward improving the health of the general population tended to be the result of public-health measures (nutrition, sanitation, pasteurization, regulation of working conditions, housing, etc.) rather than of medical practice per se (McKeown, 1976). However, scientific advances in the area of vaccination for the prevention of the spread of some diseases, and drugs for the treatment of others, made it possible for doctors to actually begin to cure disease. Because of this phenomenon, it was the physician, not the public-health advocate or the general scientist, who eventually came to be viewed as the ultimate authority in the health-care system. The physician became the figure of power, not only relative to the patient, but also among other health-care professionals.

The purpose of this chapter is to review some of the major theoretical approaches to the dynamics of the patient-physician relationship. It will show how power came to be invested in the role of the physician and how the traditional power relationship with the patient seems to be changing, albeit slowly. The review begins with the work of Talcott Parsons, and proceeds through other major theoretical perspectives on the patient-practitioner relationship. We then address changing roles of both physicians and patients in modern medical practice, and consider the impact of financial arrangements (the involvement of third-party insurers particularly) on the patient-physician relationship. Finally, we offer some speculations about the future of the interaction between patients and practitioners in the health-care system.

Talcott Parsons and the Sick Role

Writing from the functionalist perspective, Parsons (1951) outlines a series of expectations that govern the relationship between physician and patient and prescribe behaviour for both parties in that relationship. Caring for the sick is "not an incidental activity of other roles — but has become functionally specialized as a full-time 'job' " (Parsons, 1951, p. 434). Physicians are seen as the professionals who possess the high levels of technical competence necessary to perform this primary function in society. Because they (the physicians) are the only people who are recognized as possessing this essential technical competence, they are accorded higher status than the patients in the social structure, resulting in an asymmetric relationship between these functionaries in the health-care system.

According to Parsons (1951), the high level of technical competence required of the physician necessitates "specificity of function." He argues that the time and effort required to become expert in the field of health preclude comparable expertise in other fields. Thus one ought not to expect the physician to be more knowledgeable about issues outside of medicine than "any other comparably intelligent and well-educated citizen" (Parsons, 1951, p. 435).

One problem arising from such specific and focussed training is that physicians lack exposure to education in dealing with a variety of life experiences. The illnesses that patients present to their physicians are rooted in the contexts of their lives, and the diagnoses and treatment they receive will necessarily have an impact on those lives. To the extent that physicians are centred on medical rather than social and more general problems, they will attempt to deflect attention away from the context, or "lifeworld" as Waitzkin (1991) calls it. In doing so, "doctors subtly reinforce the ideas that pattern the lifeworld and help win acquiescence to those features of the lifeworld that patients find most disconcerting" (Waitzkin, 1991, p. 25). Even within medicine, there are subspecialties that require the physician to become expert in one specific area, often precluding functioning in other subspecialties.

Physicians are expected to behave in a universalistic fashion, treating all patients who present themselves for care in the same manner regardless of age, sex, social class, or other characteristics. The personal likes and dislikes of a physician vis-à-vis a specific patient should not interfere with the delivery of service to that patient. As an objective scientist, the physician must function from an affectively neutral stance. Parsons sees the physician as an individual who treats objective problems in objective terms, who maintains social distance from patients, and who does not become emotionally involved with patients. Realistically, one must recognize that scientists have as much difficulty as others in separating their beliefs, values, and biases from their professional activities. For example, research suggests that patients of higher social class receive more information and communication, as well as higher-quality care from physicians. At the same time, physicians report that they have less interest and patience with lower-class patients (Hall et al., 1988).

Finally, the physician's role is seen as having a strong "collectivity-orientation." In Parsons's words, the physician is obligated "to put the 'welfare of the patient' above his personal interests, and [to regard] 'commercialism' as the most serious and insidious evil . . . " (Parsons, 1951, p. 435). Thus, the profit motive ought not to be part of the medical professional's thinking.

From the point of view of the patient, Parsons believes that "being sick" constitutes a social role, not merely a state or condition. He identifies a set of four "institutionalized expectations," composed of two rights and two obligations, that govern this "sick role." First, the individual who is sick is seen to be exempt from the usual responsibilities and demands of social roles, relative to the nature and severity of the illness involved. This exemption requires legitimacy, which often comes from the physician, but which may also come from others, especially when the sick individual attempts to deny the sickness.

Second, Parsons argues that the individual who is sick cannot be expected to get well simply by deciding to do so, or by willing the illness to go away. Sick individuals are thus exempted from direct responsibility for their cures; it is up to others to take care of them. Thus, not only the attitude, but the "condition" of the sick individual must be altered (Parsons, 1951). It is this "right" of non-responsibility for the cure of the illness that leads to consideration of the obligations inherent in the sick role.

The third "institutionalized expectation" is based on the assumption that the state of being ill is undesirable and carries with it the obligation to want to get well. Only when this obligation is accepted are the first two elements, the rights of the sick person, legitimated. Finally, there is the obligation to seek "technically competent" help and to co-operate with the helper in the process of getting well (Parsons, 1951, p. 437). For Parsons, the physician is the most appropriate source of help necessary for the patient to get well. Once the patient has called on the physician for help, the patient "has assumed the obligation to cooperate with that physician in what may be regarded as a common task" (Parsons, 1951, p. 438).

In summary, then, the Parsonian model of patient-physician interaction is based on two basic beliefs. The first is that the patient is in an undesirable role — the so-called sick role — that requires him or her to co-operate with others in order to leave that role. The undesirable nature of the sick role places the patient in a powerless position, relative to the physician.

Zola (1991), in an attempt to shed understanding on the sick-role formulation, notes the context in which Parsons developed the model, a period during which most physicians were male and most patients were female. He indicates that seeing the patient in a powerless position relative to the physician reflects "the way in which society through much of its history, has thought of female-male relationships" (Zola, 1991, p. 7).

The second basic belief is that, although the physician's behaviour is dictated by certain expectations, the physician is always in a more powerful position than the patient, and this power is legitimated by the sick-role model. Generally, this legitimated dominant position of physicians has the potential to translate into social control. The hierarchical rank enjoyed by physicians empowers them to enforce social norms through their advice and diagnoses, whether they are conscious of this effect or not (Waitzkin, 1991).

The Parsonian formulation has been criticized on a number of other grounds as well. These criticisms have been summarized by Gallagher (1976), among others. It should be kept in mind that the value of a theoretical formulation lies, at least in part, in the extent to which it conforms to reality, and to which it can be generalized. Gallagher notes three of the major limitations of the sick-role theory, all of which indicate that gaps exist between theory and reality, and that the sick role cannot be widely generalized.

First, the theory fails to account for the circumstance of individuals with chronic physical illness, or some types of mental illness. Individuals with chronic arthritis, for example, may never "get well," despite their acceptance of its undesirability and their diligent co-operation with physicians' advice. Individuals who have developed lung cancer may, in many instances, actually be held responsible for their illness; after all, to hold that a heavy smoker is not responsible for his or her lung cancer flies in the face of scientific evidence. Mental illnesses are still not always amenable to treatment that leads to cure. Thus, at best, the sick-role paradigm is limited to cases of acute physical illness.

Parsons's formulation also fails to account for preventive health care, or to use Gallagher's term (1976, p. 209), health maintenance. Much of health "care" today involves practices designed to maintain health and to preclude adverse health phenomena. Such practices have become normative, yet appear to have no place in the Parsonian model, which really only deals with individuals who are "sick." This failure to account for a major health practice limits the usefulness of the sick-role model.

The third major criticism outlined by Gallagher (1976, p. 209) is that the model "presents a relatively undifferentiated picture of the social structure of health care." The role of the physician is seen as invariable, and no consideration is given to the potential effect of variations to the organization of medical practice. Freidson (1961) also notes that the definition of the sick role is seen entirely from the physician's perspective. As noted earlier, the physician's role is seen as limited to the treatment of illness, and not in the broader context of total health behaviour. As well, little attention is paid to variations in patient roles and expectations. Cultural values are not considered at all, and we must be cognizant of the fact that health and illness are not universally interpreted as they are in modern Western societies (see also Freidson, 1970b).

Yet Parsons's approach to the relationship between patients and their physicians remains the cornerstone of work in this area. It provides valuable insight and has also generated considerable effort to further our knowledge about the interaction between functionaries in the health-care system.

A Psychoanalytic/Interactionist Perspective

Szasz and Hollender (1956) consider the relationship between patients and physicians to be an abstraction rather than a "function" or a "thing." They believe that this abstraction is "appropriate for the description and handling of certain observational facts . . . [and] presupposes concepts of both structure and function" (Szasz & Hollender, 1956, p. 585). The relationship involves the encounter of two persons or roles in which there is joint participation. Such an interaction is conditioned by the attitudes, beliefs, and needs of both participants, and varies according to the particular circumstances.

Szasz and Hollender describe three basic models of patient-physician interaction that, they believe, are analogous to certain relationships among individuals in general. The first is the model of "activity-passivity," in which the physician actively does something to the patient, who is essentially passive. It is an interaction that takes place "irrespective of the patient's contribution and regardless of the outcome" (Szasz & Hollender, 1956). Such an approach to treatment is seen as entirely appropriate for certain medical situations, such as emergency care for the severely injured or comatose patient. The authors liken this model to the interaction between parents and helpless infants.

The second model, "guidance-co-operation," is what characterizes much of general medical practice. In such a model, the patient recognizes that she or he has symptoms of illness that require intervention, and that the physician is the most appropriate agent of this intervention. By seeking help, the patient to some extent places the physician in a position of power, because the physician has knowledge and skills that the patient does not possess. In order to maintain control over patients, physicians can choose to withhold information from them. Although there may be many reasons for such action, including releasing patients from difficult decision making, protecting them from traumatic news, or hiding their own lack of knowledge, when physicians choose to use the power of withholding information, they ultimately ensure that they maintain their dominant position over patients. The physician offers advice or guidance and the patient is expected to follow that advice, and neither to question nor to disagree with it. Szasz and Hollender (1956) believe that such interaction corresponds to that between parents and adolescent children.

The third model, called "mutual participation," is based on the philosophical belief in equality among human beings. Szasz and Hollender (1956) argue that the participants in such interactions have approximately equal power, that they need one another in some way, and that the interaction is satisfying to both of them. It is a model that seems apt for the care of individuals with chronic illnesses, since the patients' experiences provide valuable input into the kinds of treatment that work. These patients often know more about how their illnesses respond to various interventions than do their physicians (equal "power"), although they still need the physicians' assistance to obtain appropriate therapy. The relationship is mutually satisfying to the extent that both parties seek the best possible outcome for the patient. It is a relationship that most resembles adult–adult interactions in the general sense.

It seems that in all three models, however, the power or authority rests in the hands of the physician. While this observation is especially clear in the first two models, some clarifying comment is warranted regarding the third. Clearly, when both parties take an active role in the relationship, the distribution of authority is more equal. Yet, in contemporary medical care, the physician still retains the power to prescribe medication, to make referrals to many ancillary services, and to control admissions to hospital. Thus, even in the model of mutual participation, to the extent that the patient requires services other than those provided by the physician, the power in the relationship rests in the hands of the physician.

Theoretical Views of Professional Dominance: Conflict Perspectives

There is no single definitive "conflict" perspective on the patient–physician relationship. In fact, some of the work that appears to be conflict-oriented may be more appropriately treated in the interactionist perspective (especially the work of Freidson). Nonetheless, because of a common emphasis on professional dominance, power, and authority among theoretical points of view, we have chosen to examine a number of them under the general rubric of conflict perspectives.

Eliot Freidson (1961, 1970a, 1970b) has written extensively on the issue of medical dominance. He argues that the physician and patient are always potentially in conflict, not because they differ in their understanding of the goal of their interaction (i.e., solving the patient's problem), but because the means at their disposal to solve the problem are very different, and because their perceptions and definitions of the problem may vary considerably. On the basis of experience, the physician may see the problem as rather more routine than will the patient (Freidson, 1970b). What for the patient is a new and disturbing circumstance of pain and suffering is likely to be a situation that the physician has encountered and dealt with successfully in the past.

Freidson (1970b) also argues that it is not merely technical competence and knowledge that legitimate the physician's power and authority over the patient. The gap in knowledge between the patient and physician also contributes to the differential distribution of power in the relationship. Moreover, he suggests that medicine possesses the authority to determine when illness exists; in fact, he states, "medicine may be said to be engaged in the creation of illness as a social state which a human being may assume" (Freidson, 1970a, p. 205). Thus, while Parsons (1951) argues that medicine has the power to legitimate illness in patients, Freidson goes further to suggest that medicine has a monopoly on defining what illness really is, thus creating "illness as an official social role" (Freidson, 1970a, p. 206). Further, it must be remembered that defining and labelling illness is not a neutral activity, but is intertwined with creating and reinforcing the social norms held by society and medical professionals (mostly higher-class males). Defining behaviours or conditions as pathological, Riessman (1983, p. 5) argues is "related to the structure of power at any given historical period . . . note that structurally dependent populations — like children, old people, racial minorities and women — are subject disproportionately to medical labelling."

Increasingly in North America, human behaviour is becoming the context of definitions of health and illness, in part because of the social value placed on individual health. Medicine appears to intervene in more and more disruptions in human behaviour and more and more of these disruptions thus become labelled health problems or illnesses (Freidson, 1970a). Physicians are assuming control over a greater range of human behaviour that may previously have been in the domain of the church or the law. As the social value of health rises, so inevitably does a profession to claim jurisdiction over the maintenance of that value. The medical profession, then, may be viewed as creating its own ideas of illness, and the social values attached to those ideas. The patient comes to see that not only does the physician define what illness is, she or he also controls the "cure," and thus is the agent of the return to health, which society argues is paramount (Freidson, 1970a). Nowhere is this intervention in daily life more evident than with women. More and more stages of women's lives have come to be labelled pathological

— menstruation, premenstrual syndrome, pregnancy, fetal and maternal health, fertility, menopause, woman abuse, etc. Some positive consequences of such identification and labelling are obvious, including greater humanitarianism and tolerance because physicians have legitimated important experiences in the lives of women. The negative consequences of the medicalization reinforces the notion that women are controlled by their biology, specifically by their reproductive systems (Riessman, 1983). Inherent in this notion is the implication that women are emotional and unstable because of their body cycles, legitimating the exclusion of women from higher positions and greater social power.

Feminists argue that the increasing medicalization of women's lives is a result of the larger social phenomenon of "hegemonic masculinity" (Liddle, 1989), referring to the historical masculine normative tradition that confers a deviant or undesirable status on anything feminine. The masculine tradition in science (and medicine) perpetuates stereotypical views of female biology because the internal thought processes of medical students are being moulded, albeit unintentionally for the most part, by traditional science perspectives. Thus, medical professionals find it difficult to "take seriously phenomena that fall outside of their habitual patterns of observation, thought, and expectations" (Fox, 1989, p. 183). In addition, the descriptions and explanations of women's experiences that they have learned from textbooks frequently vary from the actual experiences of women (Riessman, 1983).

Medicalization has taken women out of familiar surroundings and subjected them to alienating procedures, placing control over their bodies in the hands of physicians. The real importance of medicalization lies in its emphasis on the biological rather than the social etiology of illness. Riessman (1983) argues that the medicalization of women's lives is not the product of a conspiracy among male physicians, but rather that women of higher-class backgrounds have invited and participated actively with physicians in the process. She predicts that with the growth of the medical arena and the increasing number of physicians, medicalization can be expected to increase. On the other hand, recent indications of increasing numbers of female applicants to medical school and increasing numbers of graduating female physicians (Fox, 1989), combined with an increasing awareness of feminist issues, may produce changes in the medical sector that may lead to a change in the trend toward ever-increasing medicalization of women's problems.

Twaddle and Gill (1978) discuss the concept of alienation within the interaction between patients and physicians. They note that Freidson (1970a) suggests that physicians' autonomy was achieved through a variety of circumstances, before a reasonable case for medical effectiveness could be made. They argue that technical competence ought not to justify autonomy and that the sources of physician autonomy may be found in patient alienation.

According to Twaddle and Gill (1978), autonomy is a function of the power and control that one social group exerts over another. Increases in autonomy in one group are associated with increases in alienation in the other. Thus they see that growing autonomy of physicians in the control and distribution of medical services has resulted in growing alienation among patients in the patient-physician encounter. This alienation has four dimensions: clinical, organizational, economic, and lifestyle.

Clinical alienation is described as being at least partially irreducible because it stems from the fact that medicine possesses a body of knowledge not immediately available to, and rarely shared by, patients. There is an assumption of inequality between patients and physicians with respect to medical knowledge. "Physicians know more and are better trained in important skills which are (a) not shared by other occupations or the lay public and (b) are thought to be effective in prolonging life and minimizing incapacity" (Twaddle & Gill, 1978, p. 45). In such a situation, the alienation of the patient is clear.

Organizational alienation for the patient is a direct result of the changing nature of medical practice. Modern medicine tends to be based in clinics and hospitals, settings that are largely controlled by the providers of medical care. In the past, much of the delivery of health care was centred in the home, in surroundings familiar to the patient. Contrast that circumstance with the situation today, where patients are subjected to a variety of complex tests and examinations, organized often for the convenience of the practitioner rather than that of the patient. These tests are not easily understood by the patient, and many times the results are not communicated to the patient in understandable terms; quite frequently, they are not communicated at all. "In short, the patient is more organizationally alienated than was the case in the earlier times" (Twaddle & Gill, 1978, p. 47).

In the United States (and to a lesser extent in Canada), the medical profession sets the terms of the financial arrangements between patients and the health-care system. Costs of all aspects of health-care delivery are escalating and are rendering health services unavailable to many. This is especially true where the fee-for-service system of payment prevails. Most importantly, no matter what the payment system, the public has little control over the economics of health care, and patients become increasingly alienated in an economic sense.

The final dimension of alienation discussed by Twaddle and Gill (1978) is termed lifestyle alienation. Essentially, what the authors refer to here is the widening gap in social class between physicians and most of their patients. Physicians' incomes have grown substantially over recent decades, especially relative to the incomes of others in the general population. Accordingly, there seems little likelihood that patients and physicians will understand or appreciate each others' lifestyles. It is also probable that they will have difficulty in communicating with one another, since they are unlikely to have a common language.

As Twaddle and Gill (1978, p. 47) state:

the patient must not only bridge the gap in knowledge, deal with organizations and settings that are strange and threatening, and accept the financial terms dictated by the medical profession, he must also bridge a widening gulf of social class as well.

It is little wonder then that the relationship between patients and physicians is not harmonious; rather, it is an interaction that is characterized by an increasing dissatisfaction growing out of the alienation of the patient.

A final theoretical formulation in terms of conflict is provided by Howard Waitzkin (1984), who focusses on the issue of medicalization and the use of social control as a means of maintaining the dominant ideology of society. Medicalization refers to the tendency among physicians to convert the personal suffering of patients into medical problems, largely ignoring the social roots of such suffering. Those who criticize medicalization argue that medicine, by depoliticizing health, has become an agent of social control in many societies. As Waitzkin (1984, p. 340) states, "medicalization of social problems involves the expansion of health professionals' activities to include control over wide areas of social and personal life." It is primarily in the patient-physician relationship that this activity occurs.

The principal mechanism with which medicine reinforces the dominant ideology in Western society is by its definition of health as the ability to work (Waitzkin, 1984). There are others, including government, who promote this definition of health, emphasizing the importance of economic forces and the ideology that is "crucial in sustaining and reproducing the social relations of production, and especially the patterns of domination" (Waitzkin, 1984, p. 340). On a macro level, public-health policies, government agencies, and the media emphasize the importance of a healthy work force in capitalist society, and a definition emerges of the healthy person as one who maintains maximum capacity to work and produce.

Waitzkin (1984) argues that interactions between doctors and patients may reinforce this definition of health as the ability to work. Frequently, when people become sick, they stop working, and it is the doctor who certifies that the patient is too ill to work, and later that the patient is fit to return to work. The physician, rather than attempting to investigate the social causes (and "cures") of the problem, may cast the patient's complaints or problems in terms of whether or not they interfere with work. Over time, patients too begin to see their problems in relation to their capacity to perform productive work, and thus the medicalization of social problems is complete. This, coupled, with the kind of alienation described by Twaddle and Gill (1978), clearly shows that the interaction between patients and physicians is one characterized by considerable distance (intellectual, motivational, lifestyle), with consequent dissatisfaction and distrust on the part of the patient.

Changing Physician Roles and the Rise of Consumerism

The practice of medicine has changed radically in the latter part of the twentieth century (Freidson, 1986; Waitzkin, 1984). Modern medical practice is increasingly fragmented, with the growth of numerous specialties and subspecialties. In many cases, scientific knowledge and technology have rendered these subspecialties incomprehensible to one another. There is a widening gap between patients and practitioners in this "high-tech" environment. At the same time, however, there is evidence, especially in the United States, that health-care consumers are not satisfied with the situation. Part of this evidence is the radical increase in malpractice suits over the past decade, especially against physicians who are involved in the delivery of highly specialized care (Twaddle, 1981).

Other evidence is the rapid growth of anti-authority trends in the public at large. Haug and Lavin (1983) argue that public willingness to question the authority of medicine may in part be due to increased levels of education in the general public. As well, there has been a proliferation of health magazines, health information on television and in the print media, and general public-awareness programs with respect to health issues. At the same time, the number of individuals reporting white-collar occupations exceeds those in blue-collar occupations. Haug and Lavin (1983) suggest that this change contributes to the growing willingness of the public to question the physician because of a narrowing of the social distance between physicians and their white-collar patients. Such patients are less likely to be intimidated and deterred from asking questions.

Consumers of health care are beginning to act like consumers of other products; they question the assertions of authority figures, request second opinions, and require that they be given information about the risks and benefits of their choices (Haug & Lavin, 1983).

The rise of consumerism in health care has resulted in other changes in the health-care system. Not only are patients questioning their doctors, they are involved to a much greater extent in self-care activities, and are turning more often to paraprofessionals for more of their basic health-care needs. The traditional relationship between patients and doctors is changing because of the challenge to physician authority. This challenge is likely to continue and may have the effect of increasing physician accountability.

When patients question medical authority several outcomes are possible, some positive and some negative. Clearly it will be incumbent upon physicians to inform their patients completely with respect to the diagnosis they give and the treatment they recommend. The increase in the seeking of second opinions may lead to "doctor-shopping," to inefficiency in the health-care system, to increased costs, and possibly to confusion for the patient, who is bombarded with conflicting information. On the other hand, it could result in greater sensitivity of physicians to patients' needs, to reductions in unnecessary surgery and tests, and to more knowledgeable, better-informed, and more satisfied patients.

The Effect of Third Parties on the Patient-Physician Relationship: Health Insurance in Canada

Many physicians believe that their relationship with their patients are sacrosanct, that there is no place in that relationship for a third party. Yet as Blishen (1969) notes, some third-party intervention has occurred throughout history, typified by the legal prescription of rewards and penalties described in the ancient code of Hammurabi some 4 300 years ago. What seems to be at issue for physicians today is not the media reports of malpractice suits or the legal requirements that physicians violate patient confidentiality in certain well-defined circumstances (Blishen, 1969), but the entry of third parties into the financial arrangements between doctors and their patients. Nowhere is this more apparent than in the history of government health insurance in Canada.

Since the focus of this discussion is on the patient-physician relationship, we cannot here discuss health insurance in great detail. However, since the funding of health care has a considerable impact on that relationship, we will examine briefly the historical background of the Canada Health Act of 1984, the ensuing legislation in Ontario (Bill 94: The Health Care Accessibility Act of 1986) and the effect of physicians' responses to the government's interference in patient-physician interaction.

The funding of health care in Canada is a matter of provincial jurisdiction. Initial federal funding involved a cost-sharing arrangement with the provincial governments for the planning and construction of hospitals (Vayda & Deber, 1984). By 1961, all provinces had adopted universal hospital insurance, which made them eligible to receive from the federal government half of the costs of all hospital-based health services under the terms of the Hospital Insurance and Diagnostic Services Act. The federal government moved into insurance for physician services with the Medical Care Act in 1968 (Vayda & Deber, 1984). Because of the jurisdictional boundary, participation in the plans was voluntary. However, in order to qualify for federal-provincial cost sharing, the provincial programs had to meet four criteria:

1. Universal coverage on uniform terms and conditions that does not impede, or preclude, either directly or indirectly, whether by changes made to insured persons or otherwise, reasonable access to insured services by insured persons;
2. portability of benefits from province to province;
3. insurance for all medically necessary services; and
4. a publicly administered non-profit program. (Vayda & Deber, 1984, p. 193)

The formula for determining the extent of federal contributions is complex and need not be discussed here. It amounts to an approximate 50-50 split between the two levels of government.

Over time, some erosion of the criteria occurred, particularly the first. A small but significant proportion of physicians began to charge fees above the rate set by government plans ("extra-billing"), especially in Ontario, New Brunswick, and Alberta. Many of these physicians were specialists, in some areas, all specialists were charging extra fees for their services. In addition, hospitals in some provinces charged "user fees" to hospital patients. These actions prompted new federal action in the form of the 1984 Canada Health Act, which provided fiscal penalties for provinces that continued to allow extra-billing and user fees. For each dollar collected above the rates set by provincial plans, the federal government was to withhold one dollar in transfer payments. Legislation to ban extra-billing in Ontario followed with the Health Care Accessibility Act of 1986.

The first provincial health insurance plan in Canada was introduced in Saskatchewan in 1962. The Saskatchewan College of Physicians and Surgeons opposed the plan, arguing that such government involvement would destroy the mutual trust of the doctor-patient relationship, and erode physicians' professional autonomy (Blishen, 1969). To make their point, the physicians withdrew their services, calling Canada's first doctors' strike. The strike lasted 23 days, and at the end, the legislation remained in place, although physicians did retain the right to bill their patients directly.

History repeated itself in Ontario following the introduction of Bill 94 to the provincial legislature. The physicians began attempting to solicit the support of their patients in fighting the proposed legislation. This action was seen as coercive, an abuse of power, inappropriate, and unethical. Further, the Ontario Medical Association threatened strike action if the bill became law (*London Free Press*, May 30, 1986). As the final reading progressed in Parliament, the physicians withdrew their services on June 12, 1986. The bill passed on June 20, 1986.

It was never clear how extensive the strike was; its short duration (about two weeks) may be a reflection of fairly limited support. Many physicians did not close their offices or withdraw hospital services. Perhaps this lack of consensus among physicians contributed to the failure of the strike. However, an important factor in ending the strike was the attitude of the public towards it. Before the beginning of the strike, when the physicians were arguing against the bill, a poll indicated that about half the population surveyed believed that the physicians were fighting for important principles and the other half felt that the primary focus of objections to the bill was financial. After the strike began, however, public support dropped drastically, with only 29 percent of the population surveyed supporting the strike action (*London Free Press*, June 27, 1986). A larger proportion of the general public came to see the doctors' opposition to the bill as motivated by greed.

The impact that this collective action on the part of physicians has had on their relationships with patients has not yet been investigated. Nevertheless, one can speculate that the view of doctors held by Parsons as collectivity-oriented and universalistic must be challenged. Patients who found their physicians unavailable during the strike may have had their faith in the medical profession severely shaken. Those who had to wait for treatment in understaffed emergency rooms may begin to question more seriously the authority of physicians and the meaning of professionalism among them.

Conclusion

We have reviewed some of the major theories on the relationship between patients and physicians. We have seen that each of these perspectives provides some assistance in understanding the dynamics of that relationship. Finally, we have attempted to show how social movements such as consumerism and political events such as government interventions have had an impact on the relationship. What we can conclude from our review is that the interaction between doctors and patients must be studied in the social context within which it occurs, that it cannot be seen as separate from that context. The simplest, and yet the most complex overall conclusion, is that this basic relationship in the health-care system is in a state of flux, and will likely continue to change in response to socio-political events in the future.

Study Questions

1. Using as a basis the criticisms of the sick-role paradigm that have been discussed, critically evaluate Parsons's description of the expectations of physicians in the context of modern medical practice.

2. Do you see any way that patient alienation, as described by Twaddle and Gill, can be reduced in today's health-care system?

3. What do you see as the positive and negative effects of the consumer movement in health care? Consider this question from the perspective of the patient, the physician, and the health-care system as a whole.

4. How can we apply Max Weber's concepts of traditional, charismatic, and legal-rational authority to explain physician dominance in the patient-practitioner relationship?

5. Why to you think doctors are so strongly opposed to government health-insurance plans?

6. How do you see the future of the relationship between doctors and patients?

Recommended Reading

Badgley, R.F., & Wolfe, S. (1967). *Doctors' strike.* Toronto: Macmillan.

Illich, I. (1976). *Limits to medicine: Medical nemesis, the expropriation of health.* Toronto: McClelland & Stewart.

McKinlay, J.B. (1982). Toward the proletarianization of physicians. In C. Derber (Ed.), *Professionals as workers: Mental labor in advanced capitalism* (pp. 37-62). Boston: G.K. Hall.

Navarro, V. (1976). *Medicine under capitalism.* New York: Prodist.

Soderstrom, L. (1978). *The Canadian health system.* London: Croom Helm.

Waitzkin, H. (1983). *The second sickness: Contradictions of capitalist health care.* New York: Free Press.

Waitzkin, H. (1985, June). Information-giving in medical care. *Journal of Health and Social Behavior, 26,* 81-101.

References

Badgley, R.F., & Wolfe, S. (1967). *Doctors' strike.* Toronto: Macmillan.

Blishen, B.R. (1969). *Doctors and doctrines: The ideology of medical care in Canada.* Toronto: University of Toronto Press.

Doctors warn of indefinite second strike. (1986, May 30) *London Free Press,* p. A1, A6.

Fox, R.C. (1989). *The sociology of medicine: A participant observer's view.* Englewood Cliffs: Prentice-Hall.

Freidson, E. (1961). *Patients' views of medical practice.* Philadelphia: Russell Sage Foundation.

Freidson, E. (1970a). *Profession of medicine.* New York: Harper & Row.

Freidson, E. (1970b). *Professional dominance.* New York: Atherton Press.

Freidson, E. (1986). The medical profession in transition. In L. Aiken & D. Mechanic (Eds.), *Applications of social science to clinical medicine and health policy* (pp. 63-79). New Brunswick: Rutgers University Press.

Gallagher, E.B. (1976). Lines of reconstruction and extension in the Parsonian sociology of illness. *Social Science and Medicine, 10,* 207-218.

Hall, J.A., Roter, D.L., & Katz, N.R. (1988). Meta-analysis of correlates of provider behaviour in medical encounters. *Medical Care, 26,* 657-683.

Haug, M., & Lavin, B. (1983). *Consumerism in medicine: Challenging physician authority.* Beverly Hills: Sage Publications.

Illich, I. (1976). *Limits to medicine: Medical nemesis, the expropriation of health.* Toronto: McClelland & Stewart.

Liddle, M.A. (1989). Feminist contributions to an understanding of violence against women — three steps forward, two steps back! *The Canadian Review of Sociology and Anthropology, 26,* 759-775.

McKeown, T. (1976). *The role of medicine: Dream, mirage or nemesis?* London: Nuffield Provincial Hospitals Trust.

McKinlay, J.B. (1982). Toward the proletarianization of physicians. In C. Derber (Ed.), *Professionals as workers: Mental labour in advanced capitalism* (pp. 37-62). Boston: G.K. Hall.

Navarro, V. (1976). *Medicine under capitalism.* New York: Prodist.

Parsons, T. (1951). *The social system.* New York: Free Press.

Public opposes strike but extra-billing gains. (1986, June 27). *London Free Press,* p. A1, A2.

Riessman, C.K. (1983). Women and medicalization: a new perspective. *Social Policy, 14,* 3-18.

Shorter, E. (1985). *The troubled history of doctors and patients.* New York: Simon & Schuster.

Soderstrom, L. (1978). *The Canadian health system.* London: Croom Helm.

Starr, P. (1982). *The social transformation of American medicine.* New York: Basic Books.

Szasz, T.S., & Hollender, M.H. (1956). The basic models of the doctor-patient relationship. *Archives in Internal Medicine, 97,* 585-592.

Twaddle, A.C. (1981). Sickness and the sickness career: some implications. In L. Eisenberg & A. Kleinman (Eds.), *The relevance of social science for medicine* (pp. 111-113) Dordrecht: Reidel.

Twaddle, A.C., & Gill, D.G. (1978, Summer). The concept of alienation. *Sociological Symposium, 23,* 41-60.

Vayda, E., & Deber, R. (1984). The Canadian health care system: An overview. *Social Science and Medicine, 18,* 191-197.

Waitzkin, H. (1983). *The second sickness: Contradictions of capitalist health care*. New York: Free Press.

Waitzkin, H. (1984). The micropolitics of medicine: A contextual analysis. *International Journal of Health Services*, 4, 339-378.

Waitzkin, H. (1985). Information-giving in medical care. *Journal of Health and Social Behaviour*, 26, 81-101.

Waitzkin, H. (1991). *The politics of medical encounters*. New Haven: Yale University Press.

Zola, I.K. (1991). Bringing our bodies and ourselves back in: reflections on a past, present, and future medical sociology. *Journal of Health and Social Behaviour*, 32, 1-16.

Inequality
and
Health Care

Part Three

Introduction

In the period following the Second World War, several countries developed national health insurance programs that were manifestly concerned with equalizing access to health services and assuring that minimum levels of medical care were available to all citizens on the basis of demonstrated medical need, rather than the ability to pay. In formulating such a policy, it was believed that the removal of financial barriers to medical care would equalize access to medical services, and that ultimately, this would go a long way to equalizing health status among the country's population.

Although such programs were well-intentioned, they have not accomplished what they set out to achieve, that is, the distribution of health and illness in Canada has not been significantly altered by medicare. Many of those groups with a history of heightened susceptibility to disease, disability, and death before medicare was instituted remain in a highly vulnerable position today. In addition, the availability of medical services varies from region to region, and even in areas where medical care is easily available, equalizing health status remains an elusive goal.

While disparities in health status continue to persist among different socio-economic groups, these disparities are even more pronounced between Native and non-Native populations. The health status of the Native population is the subject of Chapter 9 by Frideres.

High infant mortality rates, premature adult deaths, low life expectancy, and excessive acute respiratory and chronic disease provide a grim picture of the health status of the Native population. Frideres attributes this low health status to a number of factors that include colonial and racist practices, destruction of the indigenous health system and imposition of Western high-technology curative medicine, emphasis on individual etiology of disease, low socio-economic status, and the divergent cultural ethos of Native people.

Diseases of poverty, overcrowding, poor housing, and unsanitary living conditions continue to take a heavy toll among Native people. Yet because government health programs tend to focus on individual etiology of disease, failing to acknowledge social, economic, and political causes, health policies and practices have not significantly improved the health status (to achieve parity at least with the rest of the population) of the Native people.

In an effort to combat this problem, the Anishnawbe Health Toronto centre was established in 1989. Canada's only urban Native community health centre, AHT is a culturally consistent organization that combines conventional and traditional ways of dealing with ill health. King Hooper and Hagey, in Chapter 10, trace the development of the centre. Among issues they discuss are the importance of the circle as a means of balancing Western and traditional healing arts, the desire to achieve autonomy within the medical system, the role of women in rebuilding cultural order, and an exploration of Native health problems.

It is essential that Western and traditional healing arts be balanced. Native autonomy and control of health services are a fundamental prerequisite for this balance principle to work — only when a framework of community interest and grass-roots processes is established will the centre, and Native health care in general, be truly autonomous.

Canada, then, despite its national health initiatives, remains a highly stratified society with widespread disparities in wealth, income, power, and prestige. Bolaria explores some of the links between income inequality, poverty, and life opportunities with an emphasis on food banks in Chapter 11.

In 1990, more than 3.8 million Canadians were living at or below the level of poverty, a figure which represented 14.6 percent of the country's population. Many of those living in poverty were single-parent families headed by women; 1.1 million of the total number were children below the age of eighteen. Given the cost of essentials — housing, food, clothing — it is no surprise that those forced to rely on social assistance turn to food banks for help. The first food bank opened in Edmonton in 1981; today there are almost 300 food banks operating across the country. Once thought of as an emergency measure, food banks have become established institutions that service people on a regular basis.

For those who are reliant on food banks, malnutrition, psycho-motor and growth retardation, emotional disturbances, and shorter life spans are only some factors that they may face. Dependency on food banks only furthers these disadvantages. Although conclusive Canadian studies have not been done in this area, evidence from other countries suggests that the provision of food cannot be equated with nutritional and dietary adequacy. In addition, there is the social stigma that is attached to the use of food banks, leading to potentially disruptive social relationships both in and out of the family. Food banks, then, can be viewed as a form of temporary relief from hunger, but they cannot, and should not, serve as a long-term solution to meeting the needs of those Canadians living at or below the level of poverty.

Chapter 9

Racism and Health:
Case of the Native People

J.S. Frideres, University of Calgary

Introduction

The present chapter will demonstrate how colonialism and racism destroyed most Native institutions, in particular their traditional health-care system and health practices. We will also show that the health-care policies of the government contain a fundamental bias that reinforces the belief that sickness is located in the individual's body. This, in turn, reinforces the tendency for Canadians to view health care and health risks in terms of the individual, rather than in the context of society or of the actions taken by vested interest groups such as the Canadian Medical Association or large multinational corporations (Turshen, 1977). As Bolaria (1979) points out, this individual-centred conceptualization has led to a curative orientation, where technical medical solutions are offered to solve the individual's problems, and the social, economic, and political causes of ill health are ignored. He goes on to point out that this position obscures the extent to which health and illness depend upon socially determined ways of life.

According to recent data, well over one-half million people were identified as being at least partially of Native origin. Table 1 identifies the different categories of Native people.

Demographically speaking, there are many respects in which Native people are quite different from the remainder of the population. First of all, nearly half of the Native population is found in rural or rural non-agricultural areas; have on average more children than non-Natives; live shorter lives; and show a high dependency ratio. (This is

Table I   Population by Aboriginal Origins, Showing Single and Multiple Origins, On
and Off Indian Reserves and Settlements, 1986[1] (based on 20% sample data)

Aboriginal Origins[2]	Atlantic	Quebec	Ontario	Prairies	North	Canada
Total population[3]	2 255 100	6 454 490	9 001 170	7 205 870	75 380	25 022 010
Total aboriginal origins (single and multiple)[4]	34 440	80 940	167 375	393 440	35 525	711 725
Single origins: Total aboriginal	14 085	49 320	55 560	223 850	35 525	373 260
North American Indian	11 375	37 150	51 165	175 790	30 455	286 230
Metis	750	5 700	3 715	47 300	2 285	59 745
Inuit	1 955	6 470	675	760	17 420	27 290
Multiple origins: Total aboriginal	20 360	31 625	111 820	169 580	5 070	338 460

[1] All 1986 figures exclude the population estimated at about 45 000 on 136 incompletely enumerated Indian reserves and settlements.

[2] Aboriginal origins are derived from the ethnic origin question which asks whether respondents are North American, Metis, or Inuit.

[3] Total population refers to the total population of Canada, the provinces, and the territories, excluding the institutional population.

[4] Total aboriginal origins include persons who reported a single aboriginal origin (e.g., Inuit) and multiple origins, that is: (a) at least one aboriginal origin with any other non-aboriginal origin (e.g., Metis and French); (b) two or more aboriginal origins only.

the number of people who are either too young or too old to work relative to the number of people of working age — usually defined as ages 15-65). Nearly 40 percent of Native people (22 percent of non-Native) are under 15 years of age and only 3 percent are over 65 (9 percent of non-Native). Almost 70 percent of the Native population is under 30, compared to less than 50 percent of non-Native people. For the Native population, the average age is about 23, while for the non-Native population, it is 33 (Frideres, 1983).

Native people as a group can be considered to occupy the lower-status positions in Canadian society. For those over 15 years of age and not attending school full-time, nearly half have less than a Grade 9 education, with only 6 percent having received a high-school diploma. Comparable figures for the non-Native population are 22 and 14 percent, respectively (Government of Canada, 1985). Labour force participation is affected by the lack of education. Native people show high rates of unemployment (averaging 60 percent) everywhere in Canada, with rates as high as 90 percent in some areas of northern Saskatchewan and the Atlantic provinces. They are also disproportionately represented in the job market. Only about half of those working were employed for more than 40 weeks per year, and they were twice as likely as other Canadians to have worked less than 13 weeks. The educational and occupational status of Native people are reflected in their annual income. On average, Native incomes are less than two-thirds of non-Native incomes. In addition, nearly one-fourth of all Native people have no income. However, for those reporting an income, nearly 20 percent of this income was not earned; that is, it was a result of government transfers — family allowance, old-age pension, or welfare. At the other end of the income scale, we find about 15 percent of Native people making over $20 000 per year and 4 percent making over $30 000 (Abella, 1984). Comparable figures for non–Natives are 35 and 23 percent, respectively. The high unemployment and lower incomes are also evident in the quality of housing among the Native people: one house in every six is considered crowded (more than one person per room) compared to one in 43 among the non–Native population. In addition, one-quarter of Native homes require major repairs, over one-half lack central heating, and nearly one-third lack an indoor bathroom (Government of Canada, 1985; Indian and Northern Affairs Canada, 1988).

In summary, our statistics show that Native people have a low participation rate in the labour force, low educational attainments, low job status, and low incomes. They are further restricted by geographic concentration in rural and isolated areas. Native people are, for the most part, concentrated at the bottom of the class hierarchy of Canadian society. This position is primarily a result of government policies that have created and maintained a relationship of perpetual dependency (Dunning, 1959; Carstens, 1971). Paine (1977) has referred to this relationship as one of "welfare colonialism." As Tanner (1983) points out, the colonial structure emerged over an extended period, first with the French, then the British, and more recently with a rapidly expanding industrial state. The central goal of the federal government in dealing with Native people has always been to maintain close control over them in almost all aspects of their lives.

Native Health Care

The involvement of government in health care is a relatively recent phenomenon. As Meilicke and Storch (1980) point out, prior to Confederation there was limited government involvement with health-care issues. The government's position was that health and social needs of Canadians were family concerns and were to be dealt with by families and voluntary or religious organizations. As Heagerty (1934, 1943) pointed out, there is no reference to any measure taken by the provincial or federal governments to prevent the spread of smallpox, typhus, and other diseases that frequently decimated the Indian population. Only when various epidemics threatened the local non–Native population would the provinces and/or cities become involved in health care (Hastings & Mosley, 1964).

Traditional Native Health Care

For many Natives, the traditional understanding of illness was embedded in the system of religious beliefs. Illness was the result of some kind of action taken by an individual, for example, breaking of taboos and allowing an evil spirit to enter the body. Native people traditionally identified three kinds of illness. First, there were visible injuries that were a result of physical causes, such as bone fractures and lacerations. Secondly, there were diseases caused by some invisible external event, confirmed indirectly by the behaviour of the sick person, for example, smallpox, influenza, or cancer. Finally, there was a residual category, which included mental illness.

The traditional Native health-care practitioner generally applied routine medicines at the outset of his or her curative regimen. The assumption was that there was some biological basis for the illness and that the medicines administered would have a curative power. There were many different medicines developed to treat a variety of illnesses. However, if the illness did not pass, shamanistic methods — prayers and chants — would be employed (Sealey & McDonald, no date). Because Native people viewed illness as a result of some foreign object or spirit having entered the body, the task of the medicine man or woman or shaman was to remove the foreign object or spirit.

As the colonialization of Native people inexorably continued, it eroded the Native health-care system. This demise began slowly, and under seemingly benign conditions, during the Treaty Period (1850-1920) when some health-care benefits were included in the terms of the treaties with the colonizers. Traditional health-care activities were increasingly discouraged and discontinued as various government agencies defined them as inappropriate or sometimes illegal. The period after World War II found Natives still living in isolated rural communities with local subsistence economies, for example, hunting, fishing, and trapping, supplemented by seasonal labour in the dominant technological society. During this time, the government Indian Affairs department was the sole provider of educational and medical activities on the reserves. The major problem confronting Native people was the precipitous intrusion of white society on their way of life; high rates of neurosis and alcoholism resulted as they attempted to deal with the rapid changes imposed upon them. As Eyer and Sterling (1977) point out, the economic and cultural forces imposed on Native people by the government and its agencies created a great deal of stress by disrupting communal ties and by trying to mould competitive, striving individuals.

Current Health-Care Responsibility

Discussions between First Nations and the federal government over health-care issues begin with a belief by the federal government that, with certain exceptions, they do not have any legal or fiduciary obligations. First Nations disagree and claim the right to special treatment. Disputes between First Nations and the federal government revolve around three issues. The first conflict centres on definitions of health. The second issue is the difference in the way health policy is implemented for Native people. The third issue is the funding of First Nations health services, including the statutory, constitutional, or fiduciary obligations of the federal government regarding the provision of health services to Natives (Speck, 1989). The most recent policy — the transfer policy — is reflective of the above concern. While there is an agreement to disagree, the federal government has accepted some responsibility with regard to Native health. Under Health and Welfare Canada, approximately $500 million are spent on six major health programs: Community Health Services, Environmental Health and Surveillance, Non-insured Health Benefits, National Native Alcohol and Drug Abuse Program, Hospital Services, and Capital Construction. While there is no direct federal government legislation for the provision of these services, custom and historical commitment provide the basis and rationale for covering their cost. There are some exceptions, such as the references to the provision of a "Medicine Chest" in Treaty 6.

Until 1945, the Department of Indian Affairs solely provided health-care services to Natives on the reserve. However, at that time, these services were transferred to the Department of Health and Welfare, where they have remained. In 1962, Indian Health Services (a division of Health and Welfare) was merged with six other federal health programs to form the Medical Services Branch. In 1964, Treaty Indians were defined as insured persons under provincial medicare. The contemporary phase of health-care issues emerges from the 1969 "White Paper" policy that suggested elimination of distinct, separate services for Natives and that they receive health-care services from provincial governments (Weaver, 1981). Although this policy was officially withdrawn, the government has, on occasion, tried to gradually and covertly implement some of the recommendations. By 1970, the present structure of Indian Health Services was in place, although the 1974 Lalonde Report for the federal government first set the stage for the transfer of health care away from the federal government. The report argued that the federal government should cut back its social and health services by transferring responsibility for health and health care from the state to individuals and groups in the country.

In 1980, Justice T. Berger was commissioned by the federal government to study and make recommendations as to how the federal government and First Nations could consult with each other in a meaningful manner. As Young (1984) points out, he recommended intensive, regular consultations that would lead to greater Native involvement in the design, management, and control of health-care services in their communities. By 1981, a proposal to transfer responsibility for health-care services to Native communities was approved. In 1982, Indian Health Services standards were developed and introduced as a way of measuring the extent to which Native health needs were being met. The "Nielsen Report" was leaked in 1985 and focussed on duplication of services, as well as determining the legal basis of federal government involvement with Natives.

In 1986, Health and Welfare (Medical Services Branch) announced a new policy initiative: The "Indian Health Transfer Policy." This new policy was to facilitate a developmental approach to health care and services to Native communities and was centred on the concept of self-determination. It was hoped that it would lead to First Nations autonomy and community control of health-care services (Speck, 1989). The Transfer Policy in health care is a continuation of the "devolution policy" developed by Indian and Northern Affairs Canada a decade earlier in that it proposes that a larger share of the responsibility now allocated to the federal government be taken on by First Nations.

There is considerable conflict between the two parties with regard to this transfer. Speck (1989) points out that First Nations are denied self-determination, which in turn denies them the opportunity to create conditions whereby Native health could be improved. For example, she notes that the federal government continues to administer health services as an isolated "thing" that is separate from the political, social, and economic dimensions of life — a fact that Natives and others have consistently identified as one of the major problems in Native health care.

Today, in all but three of the provinces, insurance premiums are paid for everyone by provincial governments, who take payments from tax revenue. A variety of arrangements exist in these provinces for payment of premiums by registered Natives, ranging from bulk payments to general means tests. As Speck (1989) points out, the specific features that differentiate Native from non-Native health services are the payment of medical and hospital insurance premiums by the federal government for three provinces, the provision of public-health services by the federal government rather than the provincial government, and the federal funding of additional non-insured services for Natives (p. 193). Nonetheless, full medical services to Natives are provided, although these vary from one province to another, depending upon the standards set by each.

Programs of Medical Services

The federal government has assumed jurisdiction over the health of Natives throughout Canada. While the Indian Act says little about the specifics [see section 73 (1)] and its main focus is on the prevention of the spread of infectious diseases, there remains strong financial commitment to Native health care through a variety of programs (Woodward, 1989). The major program operated by Health and Welfare Canada is Community Health Services, which focusses on communicable disease control, health education, mental health, nursing, and the provision of medical advice and assistance.

The second is the Non-insured Health Benefits program. Through this program, Native people are provided general health care by having access to the provincial medicare systems and supplemental programs. It also covers the provincial health-insurance premium and user fees. In addition, the program includes the transportation of patients, dental services, and other medical appliances and services. This program was established to achieve equity, that is, all Natives will be treated alike in all provinces. Prior to 1978, Health and Welfare provided these benefits on the basis of need. The guidelines drawn up by cabinet in 1979 were met with stiff opposition and one year later they were withdrawn. These guidelines were replaced with a new health policy one year later, which established professional medical and dental judgement as the criteria for health-service delivery. The third major program is the Community Health activities where funding is provided to train and employ local health-care workers. In 1983, the National Native Alcohol and Drug Abuse Program was put in place. This experimental program still exists and has expanded its role as it deals with treatment, rehabilitation, and education.

The provision of services for Native people is carried out through all three levels of government. Services provided by provincial and municipal agencies are generally fully reimbursed by the federal government. At the federal level, Medical Services has over 200 doctors (less than 1 percent are Native) and over 1000 nurses (about 10 percent are Native). Over 500 community health workers are also contracted by Medical Services to provide health care for Native people. Nearly all the community health workers are Natives. On a per capita basis, Medical Services Branch spends about $400 per year per Native, approximately the same as is spent on non–Native people (Grescoe, 1981).

Health services are also provided through contributions and contract arrangements with Native organizations, bands, and postsecondary educational institutions. They carry out this program under four main activities: (1) health care and treatment services, (2) public health services, (3) involvement of Natives in the health-care system, and (4) the provision of physical facilities (DIAND, 1984).

The overall structure for providing medical and health services to Native people is complex. At the national level, several government agencies interact to set policies, determine programs, and establish funding levels, for example, Deputy Minister of Health and Welfare, Director General: Policy and Evaluation, Treasury Board, and the Directors of Indian/Inuit Policy, Planning and Evaluation. At the provincial level, the regional director oversees implementation of the programs for each health zone, which involves doctors, nurses, and environmental-health officers. At the local level, for those bands involved in health-care delivery, band councils make decisions regarding training programs and determining who will be admitted to various health programs.

In addition to the Medical Services Branch, The Department of Indian Affairs and

Northern Development (DIAND) operates three related programs that provide funds and services to Native people to assist them in maintaining health, safety, dignity, and family unity. These three subprograms are Social Assistance, Welfare Services, and Capital Facilities and Community Services. The Social Assistance program makes up $390 million (16 percent of the total DIAND budget), providing services to well over 130 000 people. Welfare Services make up an additional 7 percent, or $278 million, and Capital Facilities and Community Services make up an additional $450 million. Individuals faced with a deficit between needs and resources are eligible for assistance under the above programs. Adult care services for elderly and disabled Natives cost over $23 million in 1989. Today, nearly 60 percent of the reserve population is receiving some form of social assistance. Finally, in addition to the above programs, DIAND has created several joint health-care programs with other federal and provincial departments. One of the best known is the National Native Alcohol and Drug Abuse Program (with Medical Services Branch). This program provides Native communities with both financial and technical resources. At present, it funds nearly 300 community projects.

Health Conditions of Native People

Many of the statistics about disease and illness among Native people have been published and are well known (see Graham-Cumming, 1966). Diseases of poverty, overcrowding, and poor housing have led to chronic and acute respiratory diseases that take a heavy toll among Native people. The standardized death rate for the Native population is more than double that of the general Canadian population — 15.9 compared to 6.6 deaths per 1000 population, (Nuttal, 1982; Brady, 1983; INAC, 1988), with an average age of death more than 20 years below that of the average non-Native Canadian.

The overall trend in Native mortality shows that it has improved substantially over the past decade. Nevertheless, there is still a considerable gap between Natives and the general Canadian population (see Figure 1).

The data reveal that the overall death rate among Native people has decreased by nearly one-third since 1978. However, it is still about 1.5 times the national rate. The gap between Natives and the general Canadian population is particularly wide for ages 15–44. Natives in this age group are more than three times as likely to die as non-Natives.

Infant mortality has tremendous impact on the population of all societies since they will (if they live) contribute to the growth of the population when they reach childbearing age. Over the years (see Figure 2), there has been a substantial decrease in infant mortality rates.

The data show that the infant mortality rate for non-Natives is 7.9 per 1000 while the rate for Natives is 17.5 per 1000. A closer look at the infant mortality rate shows that

Figure 1   Death Rates 1978–1988, Indian and Canadian Populations

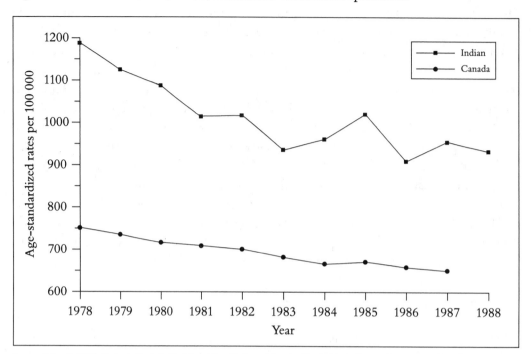

Source: Bobet, E. (1990). *The Inequalities in Health: A Comparison of Indian and Canadian Mortality Trends.* Ottawa: Health and Welfare Canada.

Native perinatal (still births and under one week) deaths are twice as high as they are in the general population. On the other hand, neonatal (birth to one month) death rates for the two groups are very similar. Post-neonatal (one month to one year) death rates are more than three times higher for Natives. These rates reflect poor housing and other adverse environmental conditions Native children are born into.

The effectiveness of the Native health–care system is related as much to the environmental conditions in which Natives live as to the treatment and facilities provided. When health care is provided it is sometimes countered by social and economic problems, such as overcrowding, poor nutrition, chronic unemployment, and community and family violence. Thus, a Native, after receiving effective medical treatment, finds himself or herself returning to the social conditions that created the problem in the first place. In short, the worst causes of poor mental and physical health are not dealt with.

What are the specific causes of death? For the past decade, over one-third of all Native deaths (compared to 8 percent in the general population) are due to accidents and violence. For all age groups up to 63, Native people are four times as likely as non-Natives to die from these causes. The most frequent are motor vehicles, drowning, and

Figure 2   Infant Mortality, Indian and Canada, 1960–1988

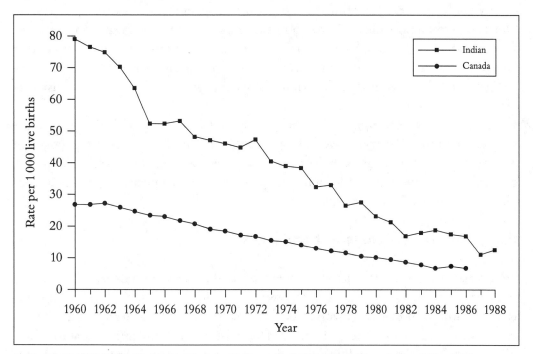

Source: Bobet, E. (1990). *The Inequalities in Health: A Comparison of Indian and Canadian Mortality Trends*. Ottawa: Health and Welfare Canada.

fire. Although these rates are extremely high, they have been reduced by over 40 percent since 1980.

The other major causes of death (in order) are diseases of the circulatory system, respiratory system, cancer, suicide, and chronic conditions, for example, tuberculosis and diabetes. A comparison of life tables (length of life) between the Native and non-Native populations over the past twenty years shows that there has been little improvement for Native people, and even a deterioration in the past decade (Nuttall, 1982). Today, the life expectancy of a Native person is 30 years less than that of a non-Native.

Bobet (1990) shows that in Native society, compared to the rest of the population, suicide and self-inflicted injuries are three times higher (six times higher for the 15–24 age group), homicide rates are twice as high, congenital anomalies are 1.5 times higher, tuberculosis is over nine times higher, and pneumonia is over three times higher. Native people have five times the rate of child welfare, four times the death rate, three times the violent death, juvenile delinquency, and suicide rates, and twice the rate of hospital admissions of Canada's non-Native population. Native people are also exposed to severe environmental hazards: industrial and resource development have polluted water and disrupted fish and game stock for many reserve communities, seriously affecting their quality of life. For example, residents of the White Dog and Grassy Narrows reserves in Ontario were found to have 40 to 150 times more mercury in their blood than the average Canadian (Bolaria, 1979). Various environmental disturbances have upset other Native communities such as Cluff Lake (uranium pollution), Serpent River (acid discharge), and St. Regis (fluoride pollution). Obviously, Native lifestyles vary considerably from those of the non-Natives.

In summary, statistics show that the quality of life experienced by Native people is far inferior to that of non-Natives. How have they found themselves in this position? These conditions have come about as a result of the cultural imperialism of the Canadian government and the racist philosophy that promoted the dominant society's insistence on the inferiority of Native people.

Perspectives on Native Health and Illness

Traditional health care, as practised by Native societies, was not only a way of dealing with private troubles and uncertainties, it was an integral part of social relationships and cultural patterns of belief. It involved both a practitioner and a patient, and the actions taken by the medical practitioner reinforced the existing social order (Birenbaum, 1981). Native people used their traditional health-care system as a form of social control. Like others, it aimed at producing a healthy person who could work and produce goods for domestic consumption and economic surplus.

Over the years, traditional Native health-care practices have been ridiculed by the practitioners of the dominant society. Non-natives, unfamiliar with the substances and methods used in Native medicine, saw its practices as primitive, irrational, and ignorant. From their ethnocentric and racist perspective, the use of shamans was evidence of paganism and heathenism; they persistently argued that shamans were evil and that Christian prayers were more efficacious in curing illness (Sealey & McDonald, no date). These moral entrepreneurs, who carried out their destruction of Native health-care practices with relentless zeal, were aided by the government's willingness to accept the medical profession's definition of what was appropriate and acceptable in health-care methods. To secure the primacy of this definition, laws were introduced that would ensure that traditional Native ways would be phased out and new ways legitimized. As a result, the Western medical model became the dominant accepted model. Over the years, then, many traditional medicinal practices and products have been forced underground. In certain communities, much of this knowledge has disappeared completely. The dominant society's medical system may be utilized by Native people, but their traditional health care provides them with a sense of security not obtainable through modern practices. Thus, they tend to retain and utilize some of the traditional approaches — under specific conditions, along with the more modern health-care practices. On many of the reserves, traditional health care remains viable, if not universally used. To the extent that Native people are isolated and institutionally complete, use of such traditional techniques is reinforced.

The basic elements upon which Canadian medical thinking, and hence the health-care system, rest are the acceptance of germ theory and the ability of people to diagnose and take steps to cure an illness. Both these presuppose that health is the concern of the individual. Most members of the population accept the first condition with little reservation; the second also does not seem to be problematic for many people. However, there are certain sectors of the population, for example, Native people, who do not accept the first assumption and find the second difficult to implement. Obviously, those who reject or are unable to accept or implement both these assumptions are at a distinct disadvantage in maintaining good health, and consequently in quality of life. The most serious consequence is a mortality rate considerably greater than among those people who accept germ theory and practise preventive medicine, and who are, in any case, already in a position of low risk with regard to life-threatening illnesses.

The health of an individual is influenced by four factors: lifestyle, environment, organizational structures of health care, and biological (genetic) makeup (LaFramboise, 1980). Lifestyle is comprised of decisions made by an individual that have an impact on overall health, for example, use of alcohol and tobacco, occupation, and physical fitness. There is a tendency to define this component in terms of only "voluntary" decisions. However, it must be pointed out that many of these seemingly voluntary decisions are actually involuntary or at least severely circumscribed. For example, smoking is a means to reduce hunger pangs, unskilled labourers are forced to take jobs with a high risk of accidents, and the nutritional value of one's diet may be determined by financial resources. The environmental element is the individual's physical and social environment, which includes factors such as air quality, potable water, place of residence, and housing. Health-care organization refers to the quality, arrangement, nature, and relationships of people and resources within society to health-care services. This component, usually referred to as the "health-care delivery system," includes such factors as medical practices, the existence and availability of hospitals and extended care facilities, and the availability and use of antibiotics and other drugs. The final component — human biological makeup — refers to the individual's physical and genetic makeup. There is a tendency to view this component as a constant, and to consider all people biologically the same.

Health problems experienced by the individual are, theoretically, the result of a "crack" in any one of the above four components. However, we will quickly come to see that each of these components can contribute differentially to illness for different groups of people. As noted, there is a tendency to assume that all Canadians have access to the same health-care system and have the same biological makeup, so that these two components are constant. To a certain extent, environment is also viewed as a constant. As a result, there is a tendency for researchers to focus on the individual's lifestyle as determining the quality of health, since it is considered the only variable in the formula (Wirick, 1966).

In other words, politicians, health-care practitioners, and the employment system view the Canadian population as homogeneous, or soon to become so. There is a continued insistence that one health-care model (the individual technical curative model) is correct and no others are to be recognized. Policy decisions and programs established by the government reflect this fundamental bias. However, it is clear that many social classes and cultural groups aside from middle-class whites have fundamental problems in adapting to the health-care model propounded by the medical profession. Native people are in double jeopardy — they tend to be shunted into a lower social class, and they are culturally separate from the dominant society. We will examine below how socio-economic and cultural factors influence Native people's access to health-care services and affect their health.

Etiology in Society

The definition of disease and illness or health has a social as well as pathological component. The physical condition of an individual must be defined as one of illness before the individual can perceive that she or he is ill (Berliner, 1977). If the group, neighbourhood, or community defines the condition as an illness, then certain steps are necessary to correct the condition. On the other hand, if it is not so defined by the individual's reference group, it would be inappropriate for the individual to assume a sick role and so the individual would not seek treatment (Kane, Kasteler, & Gray, 1976). If we accept this proposition, then the definition of illness for a community will determine the norm of health or state of health considered normal for its members. A Native individual living in a Native community thus interprets his or her own health status as do others in the community. What constitutes illness or sickness will be determined by the definition of the group and the group's reaction to people who exhibit certain symptoms or behaviour. As Kane et al., (1976) argue, the Native definition of reality means living with other Native people who share the same perspective, values, and beliefs. These beliefs and values are passed from one generation to the next.

There is also a middle-class mentality prevalent among professional health-care practitioners. Any patient not sharing these values is at a distinct disadvantage. First, the practitioners do not understand the attitudes and lifestyle of lower-class patients. Health-care professionals, socialized in a middle-class milieu with the modern medical ethic, are ill-prepared to deal with patients whose behaviour does not conform to middle-class values. They assume that Native patients share their perspective on illness and health care, and that they have the same resources (or access to the same resources) as the middle-class patient or the medical professional. In reality, however, Native people are usually poor and can manage only the barest of material necessities: heat, food, and clothing. Thus their desires are for material improvements — health is not a high priority nor is it considered in a specific sense. The day-to-day experience of medical practitioners clearly reinforces the notion that Native patients do not follow their orders and heal themselves. As a result, Native people are stereotyped as irresponsible, dirty, and incapable of carrying out orders or taking responsibility for themselves. Negative attitudes are expressed more or less openly, making encounters with health-care providers unpleasant for Native people. Every time they return to the health-care facility, they must suffer through this experience. The alternative strategy, usually chosen, is to avoid the unpleasant situation by not coming back.

Culture creates rules of behaviour for its members, dictating what is expected, encouraged, or allowed. Among various subcultures, there may be different rules. The extent to which a group is institutionally complete, or isolated from other cultural influences, will determine the extent to which the norms will differ from those of the dominant society and the extent to which they are enforced. Cross-cultural influences or memberships will reduce the influence and redefine the situation. Native people, since they retain residence in rural areas, remain an isolated group with a high frequency of contact within the group. All of this has created tight social networks that reinforce their collective definition of reality. Thus, Native people's attitude and behaviour toward illness and their strategy for dealing with it are a response to how their culture (and the community) defines it and to the types of social support or pressure they receive (Knowlton, 1971).

Because of their poverty and cultural ethos, Native people have a very tolerant attitude toward what middle-class culture defines as illness. However, when it becomes clear that there is little they can do to prevent an illness or to heal it, they learn to define certain conditions as not illness and not worthy of requiring health-care services. In other words, poor people learn to live with certain "illnesses" as long as they are not physically incapacitated. Since all people in the community take this perspective and share these attitudes, all members of the community learn to view certain debilitating physical conditions as normal.

Native people, with both lower-class status and a culture different from the dominant society, do not respond well to professional health-care workers. They prefer to deal with others from a more holistic perspective — taking note of all the aspects of the person with whom they are interacting. In the health-care system of the dominant society, there is an elaborate division of labour: nurses are only interested in one aspect of the patient, the X-ray technician in another, the orthopedic surgeon in still another. Native people find this a foreign experience, both confusing and frustrating (Suchman, 1963). They also perceive the rational, objective, and unemotional manner of health-care professionals, inculcated at medical school, as the mark not of a good professional but rather of a cold, heartless person, unsympathetic to the patient (Knowlton, 1971).

In addition, Native patients tend to resent and resist professional health-care workers' extracting private and personal information from them. It also sometimes seems irrelevant. They do not want health-care workers to have access to private information without any reciprocity and without being able to control how this information is used — both in the present context and in the future (Baca, 1969). Native women also find that they prefer to deal with women physicians rather than men, so that, unless they are experiencing an acute illness, they tend not to visit male doctors. One other factor that affects the overall health of Native people is the perception of health-care facilities. Because a pattern of health service provided to them has been well established over the years, Native people have learned to gauge their state of health very differently from non-Natives. Until recently, medical services were provided to Native people by the federal government on a nine-to-five, five-days-a-week basis. There were no home visits and no referrals, nor were any preventive services carried out. If a Native person got sick at night or on a weekend, she or he would have to define the illness as not serious and wait until morning or, in the case of a weekend, Monday. However, if it were in fact life-threatening, she or he would be forced to seek attention from medical personnel at the nearest hospital. For this reason, hospitals, not day clinics or doctors' offices, have become defined as the most appropriate place to seek health care (Ryan, 1987).

Native people do not utilize health-care services in part because of their perception of "health" and "illness." They operate from a different mentality than non-Natives. For example, many Native people do not believe in immunization of their children. They view the injection of a foreign substance into the body as harmful or potentially harmful. The major utilization of health-care services for Native people generally occurs when a person experiences acute pain or finds himself or herself in a life-threatening situation. Native people, because of their particular economic and cultural attitudes, adopt a sick role under different conditions than do middle-class, non-Native people. This is particularly true when the sick role is defined as a manifestation of weakness, or when it means that the individual would have to be removed from the community and isolated in health-care facilities far from friends and kin (Dutton, 1986).

Conclusion

Successful adaptation of Native people to the dominant society requires the denial, or at least repression, of traditional models of health care in favour of those of the dominant society. In this process, there is a fundamental inequity and dehumanization (Weidman, 1980). The dominant group has taken the position that its patterns of behaviour and institutions are not only the best, but morally superior. Behaviours that do not match the dominant group norms are viewed as undesirable. As a result, while Native people publicly utilize the dominant society's medical service, it is not uncommon for individuals to seek help simultaneously from the traditional health-care system. While Native people use the dominant health-care systems, they continue to regard their own understanding of the natural world as antecedent and superior knowledge (Press, 1978). Unfortunately, modern orthodox practitioners ignore the existence of a traditional health-care culture in Native communities. They are not trained to be aware of it, nor do they have any ability to evaluate it; they deny its existence, or if they acknowledge it, discount its significance to the medical world or to those people using it (Lam, 1980).

Because middle-class white Canadians have accepted germ theory as a legitimate causal explanation for illness, the Canadian lifestyle is organized in such a way as to minimize the adverse impact of germs; for example, sanitation and refrigeration. However, those who do not accept this perspective, or who are unable to implement the preventive strategies based on such assumptions, cannot avoid certain diseases or illnesses. Native people, because of cultural differences and poverty, find themselves unable to implement the preventive strategies.

The dominant society, and in particular our health-care practitioners, dismiss medicine men or women or shamanism among Native people as meaningless, though there are many prescribed medicines used in the modern world that are pharmacologically inert (Sealy & McDonald, no date). Despite this, the dominant medical profession still relies upon these medicines and, what is perhaps more startling, the patients using them get well. This suggests that medicine is not just a function of its pharmacological ingredients, but also of suggestion and social support.

We also find health services tend to be concentrated in urban areas, yet most Native people live in rural areas. When health professionals enter the rural areas, the "drop-in" mentality is seldom conducive to delivery of adequate service. Medical specialists have little understanding of Native culture, and language also poses a barrier to communication. When Native people have to travel to distant urban centres to obtain health services, disruptions are even more acute.

Most service and delivery systems are centralized and insensitive to input from local communities, operating on the assumption that Native patients are passive recipients with little or no say in what services are offered, by whom, or where. The bureaucracy of the Medical Services Branch (see Figure 1) shows that policies emanate from Ottawa and are then implemented by regional administrators and on-site health-care workers. There is little in which the bureaucracy can be responsive to local concerns or medical issues. In addition, professional autonomy in medical issues at the local level inhibits involvement of Native clients. Those services that are offered undermine Native culture by explicitly or implicitly providing incentives for Native people to abandon their heritage and be assimilated into the larger, non-Native society. The dominant society perpetuates this situation despite the obvious fact that one of the most effective ways of improving a people's health lies in individual maintenance. This is more important than having more doctors per capita or improving environmental conditions. An individual's quality of life is highest when she or he functions at a high level, is free from morbidity or impairment, and when his or her vitality and emotional health are high (Lerner, 1973). Rather than denigrating traditional medicine, the dominant society should spend more time learning about Native health care and how to utilize and integrate it with modern health-care practices.

Intergovernmental and interdepartmental divisions of responsibility generate debate and delay when dealing with issues that are health-related but not traditionally defined as such, for example, mercury pollution, where DIAND and Health and Welfare are jointly responsible (Castellano, 1982). The effectiveness of the entire health-care system is related as much to the environmental conditions of Native communities as to the treatment and facilities provided. Too often, the need for care is engendered by problems associated with overcrowded living conditions leading to contagion and/or infection, by generally poor nutrition associated with chronic unemployment, by family and community violence, and by the re-emergence of medical problems after effective treatment, when the patient returns to the conditions from which the problems arose. Nevertheless, the Medical Services Branch treats the symptoms and little is done to address the basic causes of poor health conditions in areas of housing, economic development, employment opportunities, and sanitation — all of which lie within the mandate of DIAND (Government of Canada, 1985).

Study Questions

1. What are some of the reasons that Native people do not use modern health practices?
2. How has the federal government tried to provide Natives with health-care services?
3. What are the health conditions of Natives compared to non-Natives?
4. How does the dominant health-care system fail Native people?
5. How is modern health care similar to traditional health-care practices used by Native people?
6. Why is it valuable for a health-care professional to have an understanding of traditional Native approaches to health care?

Recommended Reading

Boldt, M., Long, J., & Littlebear, L. (Eds.). (1985). *The quest for justice*. Toronto: University of Toronto Press.

Driben, P. (1985). *We are Métis*. New York: AMS Press.

Frideres, J. (1983). *Native people in Canada*. Scarborough: Prentice-Hall.

Li, P., & Bolaria, B.S. (Eds.). (1983). *Racial minorities in multicultural Canada*. Toronto: Garamond Press.

Morse, B. (Ed.). (1985). *Aboriginal peoples and the law*. Ottawa: Carleton University Press.

Ponting, J.R. (Ed.). (1986). *Arduous journey: Canadian Indians and decolonization*. Toronto: McClelland & Stewart.

Recommended Reading

Abella, R. (1984, October). *Report of the commission on equality in employment*. Ottawa: Government of Canada.

Baca, J. (1969). Some health beliefs of the Spanish-speaking. *American Journal of Nursing*, 69, 2172-76.

Berliner, H. (1977). Emerging ideologies in medicine. *Review of Radical Political Economics*, 9, (1), 189-218.

Birenbaum, A. (1981). *Health care and society*. Allanheld: Osmund.

Bobet, E. (1990). *The inequalities in health: A comparison of Indian and Canadian mortality trends*. Ottawa: Health and Welfare Canada.

Bolaria, B.S. (1979). Self-care and lifestyles: ideological and policy implications. In J.A. Fry (Ed.), *Economy, class and social reality* (pp. 350-363). Toronto: Butterworths.

Brady, P. (1983). The underdevelopment of the health status of treaty Indians. In P. Li & B.S. Bolaria (Eds.), *Racial minorities* (pp. 39-55). Toronto: Garamond Press.

Carstens, P. (1971). Coercion and change. In R. Ossenberg (Ed.), *Canadian society, pluralism, change and conflict* (pp. 126-148). Scarborough: Prentice-Hall.

Castellano, M. (1982). Indian participation in health policy development: implications for adult education. *Canadian Journal of Native Studies*, 2, (1), 113-128.

Department of Indian and Northern Development. (1984). *Annual report 1983-84*. Ottawa: Ministry of Supply and Services.

Dunning, R. (1959). Ethnic relations and the marginal man in Canada. *Human Organization*, 18, (3), 117-122.

Dutton, P. (1986). Financial organizational and professional factors affecting health care utilization. *Social Science and Medicine* 23, (7), 721-735.

Eyer, J., & Sterling, P. (1977). Stress-related mortality and social organization. *Review of Radical Political Economics*, 9, (1),1-44.

Frideres, J. (1983). *Native people in Canada*. Scarborough: Prentice-Hall.

Graham-Cumming, G. (1966). *The influence of Canadian Indians on Canadian vital statistics*. Ottawa: Medical Services Department of National Health and Welfare.

Grescoe, P. (1981). A nation's disgrace. In D. Coburn, C.D'Arcy, P. New, and G. Torrance (Eds.), *Health and Canadian society* (pp. 127-140). Markham: Fitzhenry & Whiteside.

Government of Canada. (1985). *Indians and native programs, A study team report to the task force on program review*. Ottawa: Supply and Services.

Hasting, J., & Mosley, W. (1964). *Introduction: the evolution of organized community health services in Canada*. Royal Commission on Health Services. Ottawa: Supply and Services.

Heagerty, J. (1934). The development of public health in Canada. *Canadian Journal of Public Health*, 25, 53-59.

Indian and Northern Affairs Canada. (1988). *Basic departmental data*. Ottawa: Minister of Supply and Services.

Kane, R., Kasteler, J., & Gray, R. (1976). *The health gap: Medical services and the poor*. New York: Springer Publishing Company.

Knowlton, C. (1971). Cultural factors in the non-delivery of medical services to southwestern Mexican Americans. In M. Riedesel (Ed.), *Health-related problems in arid lands* (pp. 118-113). Tempe: Arizona State University Press.

LaFramboise, H. (1980). Health policy: breaking the problem down into more manageable segments. In C. Meilicke & J. Storch

(Eds.), *Perspectives on Canadian health and social services policy: History and emerging trends* (pp. 269-279). Ann Arbor: Health Administrative Press.

Lam, A. (1980). Traditional Chinese medicine and western medical practice: personal observations. In M. Staum & D. Larsen (Eds.), *Doctors, patients and society* (pp. 147-151). Waterloo: Wilfrid Laurier University Press.

Lerner, M. (1973). Conceptualization of health and social well-being. In R.L. Berg (Ed.), *Health status indexes* (pp. 1-72). Chicago: Hospital Research and Educational Trust.

Meilicke, C., & Storch, J. (1980). *Perspectives on Canadian health and social services policy: History and emerging trends*. Ann Arbor: Health Administration Press.

Nuttall, R. (1982). The development of Indian boards of health in Alberta. *Canadian Journal of Public Health, 73*, 300-303.

Paine, R. (Ed) (1977). *The white arctic: Anthropological essays on tutelage and ethnicity*. St. John's: Memorial University of Newfoundland, Institute of Social and Economic Research.

Ponting, J.R., & Gibbins, R. (1980). *Out of irrelevance: A socio-political introduction to Indian affairs*. Toronto: Butterworths.

Press, I. (1978). Urban folk medicine: a functional overview. *American Anthropologist, 80*, 71-84.

Ryan, J. (1987). personal correspondence with author. Calgary: Department of Anthropology, University of Calgary.

Sealy, B., & MacDonald, N. (no date). *The health care professional in a Native community*. Ottawa: Department of National Health and Welfare.

Speck, D.C. (1989). The Indian health transfer policy: a step in the right direction, a revenge of the hidden policy? *Native Studies Review, 5*, (1), 187-214.

Suchman, E. (1963). *Social patterns of health and medical care*. New York: New York City Department of Health.

Tanner, A. (Ed.). (1983). *The politics of Indianness*. St. John's: Memorial University of Newfoundland, Institute of Social and Economic Research.

Turshen, M. (1977). The political ecology of disease. *Review of Radical Political Economies, 10*, (1), 250-267.

Weaver, S. (1981). *Making Canadian Indian policy. The hidden agenda 1968-1970*. Toronto: University of Toronto Press.

Weidman, H. (1980). Dominance and domination in health care: a transcultural perspective. In M. Staum & D. Larsen (Eds.), *Doctors, patients, and society* (pp. 133-145). Waterloo: Wilfrid Laurier University Press.

Wirick, G. (1966, Winter). A multiple equation model of demand for health care. *Health Services Research*, 301-346.

Woodward, J. (1989). *Native law*. Toronto: Carswell.

Young, K. (1984). Indian health services in Canada: a sociohistorical perspective. *Social Science and Medicine, 18*, (3), 257-264.

Chapter 10

Control Issues in Native Health Care: Perspectives of an Urban Community Health Centre

Barbara J. King Hooper, Health Education Consultant,
Vancouver and Rebecca Hagey, University of Toronto

We are not a political organization, like the treaty agencies. It is our responsibility to re-establish a way of life.
We do not have to legitimize our medicine wheel to anyone . . . its principles are laws of nature.
The late Joe Sylvester, elder, spiritual leader, and founder of Anishnawbe Health Toronto.

Introduction

In this chapter, we review issues of Native control over both conventional biomedical and Native traditional services as these are emerging in Anishnawbe Health Toronto (AHT), Canada's only urban Native community health centre. The chapter begins with a brief sketch of the health centre's early development. We discuss the circle conceptualization as expressed by AHT elders and healers as being a continuing balance and governance principle. This principle nullifies the opposition between non-Native and Native healers, and between conventional and traditional healing practices. It brings these two ways into a circle of development of Native healing capabilities and realization of Native holistic principles of health care, healing, and sharing. Native autonomy and control are fundamental prerequisites for that balance principle to work. The associated issues affecting health and health-care needs are further explored at a grass-roots level, and at the broader socio-economic and political levels.

Anishnawbe Health Toronto: Historical Overview

In the mid-1970s, a volunteer clinic was set up in the basement of the Toronto Native Canadian Centre on Spadina Road. The volunteer nutritionist and interning physician agreed with counsellors at the centre that health education should be the focus of this endeavour. However, some clients came for treatment of lacerations and physical wounds, indicating a perception of health service as providing band-aids and dressings. There was also an interest in diabetes, with growing numbers coming for medical treatment until the physician intern moved to residency status and could no longer afford the time to volunteer. After a lapse of a few years, the space was reopened in 1981 as a diabetes education and research project funded by the Donner Canadian Foundation. Rather than emphasize the technical management and physical control of diabetes, the program addressed cultural meanings and responses associated with the growing prevalence of diabetes among Native peoples.[1] As part of the Native Diabetes Project, workshops were developed and held around the province and on reserves across Canada. The program focussed upon honouring Native styles of communication etiquette, storytelling, ceremony, and cultural awareness, promoting the view that experts who do not know the language and culture should not be authorized and paid to do health education. When the research funding ran out, Natives on small-work contracts (funded via section 18 of CEIC) carried issues of Native control over health care out to the grass roots.

In 1984, Anishnawbe Health Resources incorporated as a nonprofit organization to analyze urban Native health concerns, provide information, and establish a network for health services by holding public hearings at selected Native agencies and in neighbourhoods where Natives were concentrated. Native people, compared to the general population, were found to suffer more from chronic health conditions. Unfamiliarity with the health-care system, cultural differences, discrimination, and poverty remain as reasons for chronically poor and inadequate Native health care.

Following a January 1986 conference/three-day vision workshop, which was attended by 70 Natives and allied health workers, a consensus was reached to establish a Native health centre in downtown Toronto. AHT was reorganized to work towards this goal. It was incorporated as a nonprofit, charitable, Native health organization whose sole purpose was to advocate and provide culturally appropriate health programs and services for Native people in Toronto.

AHT approached Health and Welfare Canada for development funds. Since its proposal was urban-based and therefore not under the control and authority of a chief and council, it was deemed ineligible for federal government funding. Health and Welfare Canada recommended that AHT approach the Metropolitan Toronto District Health Council, which in turn recommended development funds. The provincial ministry encouraged the Native group to join with other ethnic groups to form a multicultural health centre, but AHT maintained "we are already multicultural as we have so many tribal affiliations here in the city." In March 1988, the Ontario Ministry of Health granted funding for the establishment of the AHT Native community health centre under the Community Health Centre Program.

In August 1989, the community health centre began to see clients, and seven satellite clinics in the local Native community were developed. Other community and social-service activities were established. Pre-operational financial support was provided primarily by the Ontario Ministry of Health, with separate funding supporting an AIDS prevention worker and the creation of a street patrol (Street Workers of Anishnawbe Toronto, or SWAT) for the assistance of the homeless in the downtown west side. In April 1990, the first annual operational budget was initiated, and the Joe Sylvester Health Clinic was officially opened in June 1991.

Conceptualizing Options for Culturally Specific Health Care

Traditional healers exist worldwide in rural and urban settings and are involved in various combinations of a dual system of modern biomedical and Native traditional practices. The duality is often considered to be an opposition set, whereby the practitioners and practices of one way are politically sanctioned and more prominent than the other (Kaufert & Koolage, 1984; Green, 1988). Conceptually, this duality is problematic because in many cases "the two groups embrace distinct and perhaps intrinsically incompatible world-views or paradigms of illness" (Green, 1988, p. 1126). In Canada, the predominant and conventional health-care system is biomedical and Westernized. Native traditional knowledge has only recently become visible and deemed valuable by conventional professionals, some of whom may feel a threat of encroachment on their domain of expertise (Green, 1988).

Traditional health-care systems exist in Native cultures, parallelling the dominant conventional health-care system (Young, 1988, p. 5). The Native traditional healers "are resurfacing and are willing to share what they know with non-Natives who show a sincere interest in their art" (Gregory & Stewart, 1987, p. 25).

It is clear that the relationship between the two health-care systems is changing rapidly in Canada, but it is not clear exactly where the relationship is headed (Young, 1988, p. 7). Among the options possible is Native control over a conventional community health centre that also incorporates traditional knowledge and practices. This appears to be a new idea; to provide Natives with tools to address problems identified by Natives, and to allow them to develop culturally appropriate health-care services. Such a venture would have to avoid difficulties related to differences in paradigms, and possible control issues.

Figure I The Organizational Structure of the Proposed Centre (AHT, 1988)

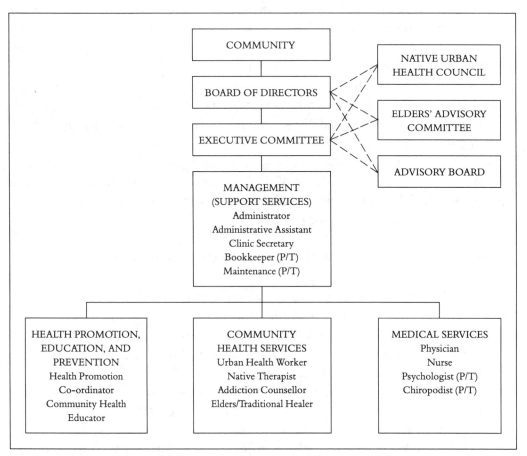

Figure used with permission from Anishnawbe Health Toronto

The Co-existence of Conventional and Traditional Approaches

In its development phase, AHT saw differences in the two approaches but envisioned them as being compatible. The proposed organizational chart (see Figure 1), which was included in the proposal to the Ontario Ministry of Health for community health-centre funding, contains boxes stacked on top of one another connected by lines. Similar organizational structures with the inherent linear hierarchical relationships are not uncommon in conventional health-care systems. AHT proposed an alternative structure, whereby the same organizational entities are placed within the model of the traditional, holistic, circular concept (see Figure 2). The organizational entities and the circles were optimistically adjoined to provide a plan for a culturally consistent Native

Figure 2   The Organizational Structure Incorporating the Traditional Holistic Circular
Concept, (AHT, 1988)

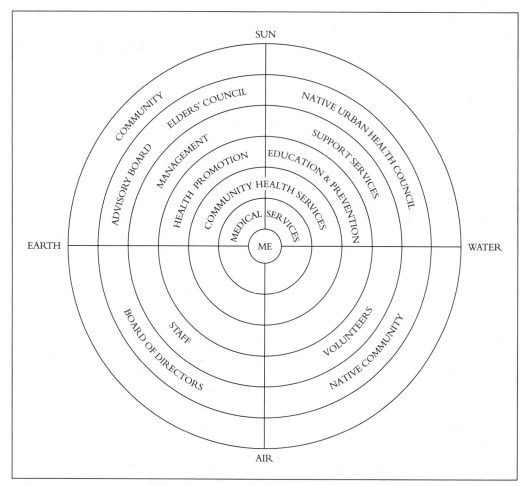

Figure used with permission from Anishnawbe Health Toronto.

community health centre. This blending reflects a different underlying philosophy; one
that is an ideal synthesis of conventional and traditional ways (AHT, 1988).

Evidence of Potential Conflict

The potential conflict between paradigms has been reported in other Canadian efforts at
cross-cultural health-related communications (Kaufert, Koolage, Kaufert, & O'Neil,
1984; Ryan & Larsen, 1981). A lack of input from involved Native people has often been

a weakness (Hirschfelder, Byler, & Dorris, 1983, p. 178). The AHT context is different from these related experiences. The conflict in the latter is between Natives and the medical establishment, while with AHT, the conflict concerns how to balance conventional and traditional knowledge and practices. The process of soliciting input from various members of the Native community, and particularly of asking traditional healers for guidance, is seen as the Native way.

Joe Sylvester and others at AHT have been sensitive to the link between political and economic realities and the deleterious manifestations of health breakdown: mentally, socially, physically, and spiritually. The rebuilding of a Native cultural order is at the centre of a collective vision for the Native community to have some control over the provision of Native health care. It is perceived by Native people that their health deteriorated "with the breakdown of the clan system." So the goal is not just to provide "culturally sensitive health care" as is the stated mandate, but also to influence the social, economic, and political variables that affect the health of Native people and communities.

Self-Determination, Self-Government, and the Urban Context

The urban Native population is growing, yet is mobile between urban and reserve communities (King, 1988, p. 3). The movement to urban areas is predicted to increase until the year 2000, with economic and educational opportunities presently being the two primary reasons for migration (Maidman, 1981). It is difficult to obtain an accurate census count and demographic profile of Natives residing in Toronto. However, in the late 1980s, the population was considered to be approximately 40 000 (King, 1988). Some estimates in the early 1990s are as high as 65 000.

Phil Fontaine, Grand Chief, Assembly of Manitoba Chiefs, believes that there is no self-government on the reserves — only self-administration. Native people are searching for self-determination, which can be based only on self-government. Fontaine, speaking at the University of Toronto, Faculty of Medicine in an October 1991 program sponsored in part by AHT, described the concept of self-government as Natives having the freedom to assist individuals without the constraints of status, non-status, or Métis labels, not as token Natives administering their own underfunded agencies and having to deal with conflicting federal and provincial definitions of a Native person. AHT can provide service and then assist individuals to apply for a provincial health card if they do not have one. They also undertake special administration of status Native people coming from a reserve to the city specifically for health services.

Native people in Toronto are aware that they have poor health status and that they need an urban Native community health centre because of the difficulties they experience with the existing health-care system, the lack of appropriate services, societal and system discrimination, and a strengthening desire and action for Native self-determination (AHT, 1987; AHT, 1988).

The Circle as a Control Principle through Balance

We have discussed the concept of balance between conventional and traditional community health care as being an opposing dualism, with the associated opposition sets not so much non-Native and Native as bureaucratic and personalistic, as exemplified in the contrasting organizational structures (see Figures 1 and 2).

However, there is another organizing principle, the principle of the circle. The circle or medicine wheel "is an ancient symbol used by almost all of the Native people of North and South America" (Bopp, Bopp, Brown, & Lane, 1984, p. 9). Everything in the natural world is seen as being intertwined, circularly connected, and continuous. The circle's roundness indicates life. Its never-endingness symbolizes the wholeness or oneness of the universe. One speaker at the 1990 Elders and Traditional Peoples Conference at Trent University spoke about the circle concept:

> Go outside and read. Read nature. There are lessons in every rock and leaf. There aren't many square things seen in nature. Everything is in a circle. Things are round. Life is round. It is a cycle with no beginning and no end, and there are circles within circles. This is the creation sign. For example, our eyes. Inside our round eye is another circle and this gives us vision. This is how we see life.
>
> Take this classroom, it should be in a circle, not in rows and rows with me here at the front. No front and no back, so we all have an equal place. No start and no end.

The centre of the circle is the symbolic centre of creation. Other symbols that occupy this central position include: the Creator or Mother Earth, the giver of life; the sacred fire of life; one's volition; and individual and/or collective visions.

In this conceptualization, the circle consists of four aspects: the physical, the spiritual, the mental, and the emotional. For a complete or balanced cycle, all four aspects have to be involved in the process (see Figure 3). All aspects of life are viewed in a holistic manner. Native traditional knowledge recognizes the power within the circle and the healing power in the use of the circle. The symbol of the circle is a central concept in the Native view of the world and the inter-relationships among the four directions provide understanding and explanations of the Native reality and way of life.

Rather than viewing sets of opposition as either/or dualities, which is the tendency of Westernized, positivist thinking (McKee, 1988, p. 776), both the conventional Western and traditional Native ways of conceptualizing health and healing can be viewed as aspects within one circle that have a balanced relationship through their circular

Figure 3   Mental, Emotional, Physical, and Spiritual Circle of the Four Directions and Colours

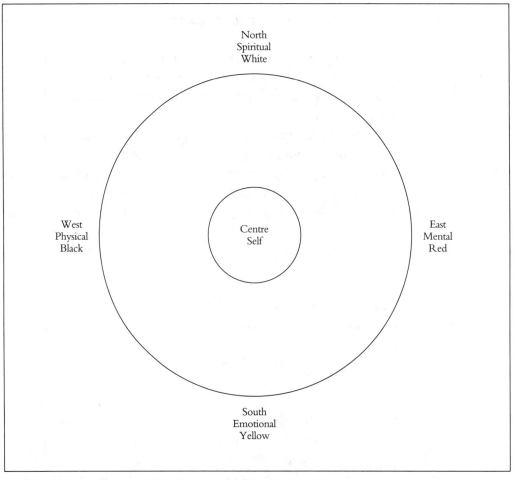

North
Spiritual
White

West
Physical
Black

Centre
Self

East
Mental
Red

South
Emotional
Yellow

Figure used with permission from Anishnawbe Health Toronto.

connection. Or they may indeed have imbalance, which gives rise to differences or problems. However, imbalanced relationships are still considered connected via the circle symbol. The aforementioned speaker said: "In the circle there are four directions. There are different names to the directions. We know that there is another side. It may be different on the other side, but there is another side. There always is."

Circle conceptualizations appear to be a consistent theme in a variety of Native discourses: spoken and written language; artwork and organizational logos; furniture arrangements; meeting and workshop structure; Native community input for the design of AHT's building renovations; healing (the circle is the basis of the sweat lodge structure and process); and as a cultural teaching tool. The circle serves as a structure of how things can be organized. Numerous rich metaphoric associations are entrenched in the symbol, and it is at the root of many Native cultural teachings. The circle and the four directions give rise to a vast symbolic and cultural web of meanings, and it is within this web that social relations are transacted: "Seeking truth and coming to knowledge necessitates studying the cycles, relationships and connections between things" (Colorado, 1988, p. 51).

Antiracism in the Circle's Healing Power

The organizing principle of the circle is embedded in talk about healers and healing knowledge. The uninitiated might think of healers as being a distinct Native category, as opposed to a non-Native category. This is not the case, however, because in Native conceptualization "all healers are on a level playing field" and within the same circle. At the health centre, for example, all of the healers' office doors have been enjoined by a healing circle symbol on the floor. One of the AHT staff said:

> Let's get everybody down. Let's all talk about it [organizing a healing workshop] and healers, I would include our doctors and nurses in that group 'cause they are healers. And if we have counsellors they're healers too, and let's all sit down and talk and not try to establish one over the other, but let's talk about healing, and let's talk about the centre, and let's talk about how, what's the best way that we at the health centre can bring healing forces to bear on the needs of clients.

To be a healer is not seen to be a racially exclusive category. However, cultural differences exists. One traditional healer openly recognized that "our [Native] community has a cultural heritage that is different than the dominant society's." From a traditional Native perspective, healing is symbolically the circle's power in action and the circle encompasses healing, including all races and colours of people (see Figure 3).

Sharing as a Resolution of Differences in Healing Traditions

Early in the health centre's development, the staff and board were concerned about the philosophical dilemma of balance in the organizational structure. Was a Native traditional cultural component to be grafted onto an otherwise conventional community health-care system, or was it to be a Native traditional system? This dilemma was labelled "the dragon." After considerable agonizing, a traditional healer calmly told us:

It is okay to share others' technology. Our people have always shared. Sharing is one of the greatest assets of
Native cultures. We have always done this. We take from them what is good and share with them, and they
take and share with us. And this will happen here also.

Conventional biomedical and Native traditional ways are not in absolute either/or
opposition. Sharing, the social activation of the circle principle, makes connections, not
oppositions.

Placing the Conventional and Traditional Duality within the Circle

At AHT, there is a polarity in the circle between conventional Western and traditional
Native health care. The supportive and challenging forces can be placed and described
within the circle symbol. The conventional system has been dominant and sometimes
the only available way for Natives, without regard to accessibility and/or acceptability
issues. The poor health status of urban Natives is well known, and lack of culturally
sensitive health care may be added to the list of accessibility barriers, which includes
good nutrition, housing, education, employment, and protection from police. Those
involved with the AHT community health centre believe that Native control and self-
determination of urban Native health care will help to rectify this situation. There are
two main issues affecting the community health centre. The first issue concerns the
strong belief that Native people should deliver Native health care. The second involves
the system of care to be delivered at the community health centre.

Nativizing Conventional Biomedical Facilities

It has been stated that Native people "believe strongly that Native health care should be
delivered by Native personnel for a successful program. Empowering Native people to
design and deliver their own health-care system is the point of it all" (Belleau & Watters,
1990). However, there is a lack of trained Native health-care workers. It is estimated, for
example, that currently there are about seventeen Native doctors in Canada, although it is
difficult to determine numbers (Gilmore, 1990, p. 52). A rough estimate of Native nurses
in the country is three hundred. There are no accredited health-care administrators; other
Native professionals such as physiotherapists, dietitians, and dentists are rare. One former
AHT board member who is in medical school has jokingly suggested that if AHT can wait
four years, she will be ready for a job as a Native doctor at the health centre.

An AHT staff member states that the lack of Native health-care workers from
whom AHT can draw "reflects many other things, one of which is Canada's commitment to aboriginal people." The reserve system, which is similar to the homeland system

of apartheid South Africa, has not provided equal access to opportunities for professional education (Frideres, 1988; Adams, 1985; Bourgeault, 1988).

A Native professional can function within the conventional health-care domain and have little knowledge of, or rootedness in, traditional knowledge. This may be due in part to the intensity of training and reorientation of health professionals, who themselves constitute a unique subculture. If Native professionals have not had exposure to, or interest in, traditional healing, then their methods of practice may rely upon their socialization and training. This concern has been expressed by the AHT Native nurses.

Combined with these issues is AHT's desire for greater traditional Native input. AHT leadership acknowledges that time is required to orient and retrain staff to work in the way they would like. AHT staff are involved in orientation programs in hospitals and professional schools that provide services to Native people in an effort to improve race relations. Any plans for professional education in the future must include traditional values and practices.

Removing Barriers to Holism

The vision for the system of care to be delivered at the community health centre is to have both conventional and traditional ways available. The intention is to emphasize the provision of traditional components, in part or in whole, in the services and programs. The difficulty associated with the lack of Native human resources is compounded by the biomedical training that Native nurses and doctors receive. During the early stages, the reality of the centre's operation assumed a focus on the physical aspects of the circle. Yet the idea of a greater traditional focus remains key, and the staff and board have engaged in many organizational activities aimed at achieving this goal, with Native and non-Native staff and board members alike.

It is not the centre's aim to revive Native health and healing traditions in lieu of, or at the expense of, the benefits of conventional primary health care. Nor is it the desire of the centre to impose traditional ways upon the entire Native community. By acknowledging and including traditional ways of life, it is believed that the circle is kept strong. A traditional healer said:

> The mind is powerful. Spirituality is the power of the mind. We need to reconnect this power with the other elements and we need to reconnect our minds with our dreams. One and a half generations ago we began to lose holistic healing and lose the language when we grew up in academic settings. Experience is learning. All life is built on experience. Now we need to provide experiences that Indians can relate to, for example, songs and dances. This is holistic education. That was the way of life.

Using the Native circle conceptualization, conventional medical practitioners are recognized as healers who enter the circle through the Western door (see Figure 3). They focus on the physical aspects of health and their knowledge is valuable "to help with illness" and "deal with symptoms." Traditional healers have a holistic perspective, with spirituality functioning as the core in traditional knowledge. Both ways are of value. One isn't better than the other; they are just different from each other. During the early development phase of the health centre there was an emphasis on the physical. Perhaps this was partly because some of the staff had received biomedical training. Numerous learning opportunities are provided by elders and traditional healers to augment the learning and provision of traditional ways.

Perspectives differ between and within the two paradigms of conventional health care, which emphasizes allopathic treatment of disease by someone else, and the traditional ways of life and healing, which emphasize personal responsibility for holistic balance to maintain health and prevent sickness.

> Traditional Indian medicine is more enabling than Western medicine, with a holistic view. A doctor fixes something specific. In traditional medicine, you must be an active participant in your own health. There are ceremonies, special teas that you drink in preparation for winter and summer, and twice a year you fast. Every season is with a colour and with certain obligations. To be totally healthy, you do all these things. You can't run to a healer for "a fix." (King Hooper & Lee, personal communication).

In a sense, the conventional and traditional categories are circumscribed. The distinction is maintained at AHT to acknowledge the two distinct cultural categories. No one expressed any conceptualization of collapsing the dual system into a single, blended union. In order to maintain balance between the two discrete categories, they are placed within the same circle, "on the same playing field." In this way, it is believed that conventional and traditional healers can be together because both are involved with healing. AHT is creating a circle of healing and balance. It can be seen as a metaphor for governance of self, family, and the community. It should not be seen as a recipe for public or private bureaucrats to impose "self-administration."

Grass-Roots Control Issues

Culturally Sensitive versus Culturally Based Health Care

In her article entitled "Praxis and Rhetorical Process," Hagey (1989) outlines early efforts, by what later became the AHT, to develop culturally sensitive diabetes education programs. It was not possible in that early phase to have truly culturally based programming, and much of the article describes conflicts with professionals and agencies influ-encing control over the project. It is felt now that the AHT community health centre is a legitimate provincially funded centre, and that there is a real basis for culturally based systemic change to take place. Yet there is an acute awareness of the enormous amount of strategizing and "bending the rules but not breaking them" that has to go on to develop what Native people might desire. There is a growing pride in the numbers of Native people in key agencies, including AHT, with whom plans can be generated, programs developed, and problems solved. The fun of working with other Natives who know of the culturally based, unspoken assumptions is energizing, even though there are ever-present differences in perceptions. This is common in any organization, although Native organizations perhaps tolerate more open disagreement than others.

Honouring and Acknowledging Traditional Knowledge

The Native value of elders as keepers of knowledge and respect for individuals with life experience overrides confidence in higher education as some sort of authorization to sanction or exercise accountability. Administrators and board directors are honoured for their sanctioning privilege. This privilege is believed to come from the "grass roots," which is why such emphasis is placed on ground-up development, feedback, and broad community participation. Even individuals with questionable backgrounds are hon-oured as knowledgeable if they have vindicated their past and are now epitomes of responsibility and trust. Some former board members in the past may not have com-pleted high school or even elementary school, but that did not interfere with their judgement and the respect granted by others on what was deemed best for the organiza-tion.

Many Natives make a distinction between book knowledge and practical knowl-edge, which is akin to the distinction made in sociology between cognitive knowledge and social-practice knowledge. Dorothy Smith (1990) has elaborated on how the knowledge contained in documents, which requires an educated person to manipulate, differs from the more humane sort of practical knowledge that is involved when people take care of one another. Natives would agree that the management and marketing of documents, such as funding proposals or health-promotion plans, can be quite divorced from the art of human caring and healing that those documents are assumed to codify. Being in charge of the agency provides the latitude to develop job descriptions for a registered nursing assistant with relevant life experience to be a family support nurse receiving supervision and guidance from a nurse rather than from a physician; a spiritual leader to be paid as an addiction counsellor; and occasional healers who can be consulted when a particular individual knows and respects them and is not interested in seeing an unknown psychiatrist or psychologist. Future categories might be traditional midwives, herbalists, and other ceremonial specialists. Other considerations include undertaking research to salvage knowledge that is disappearing as elders pass on.

Autonomy and Dependency without Self-Government

The "grass-roots" ideals mentioned above, namely, control and the balance principle of governance that it should engender, means being at the centre of what is going on in decision making and priority setting. It means having the autonomy to use a Native consensus process as a means of arriving at decisions. And that means not having to comply with adversarial styles and proceedings for making agreements, except for outside matters such as lobbying, negotiating, or settling resource disputes. Although the board reviews matters brought before it in a conventional fixed-agenda format, internal agreements may be made through a diverse array of informal and consensual means. Commitment to consensual means of decision making and conflict resolution is one reason why it is so easy for individual Natives to be picked off by government, corporate, or other potentially competing interests detrimental to the larger whole (Means, 1991, p. 3).

While control is realized in some measure by having a board that reviews formal and informal documents, events, incidents, and practices, real power is held with the purse strings in the ministry. Professional governmental facilitators may perceive the Native community health centre differently than other community health centres. AHT is the only community health centre that has had to go through a formal audit from the provincial Ministry of Health. Admittedly there were cash-flow problems, but not unlike those that had been handled informally in other community health centres. Once again, some Natives feel that being Native means being susceptible to undue policing.

Two other Canadian cities have been attempting to establish urban Native community health centres. In one case, the government facilitators, that is, the potential funding source, bypassed the grass-roots development stage, which led to an abortive set-back. In the other case, non-Native facilitators pirated control after a successful grass-roots phase had lead to significant funding. The non-Native perspective or excuse for imping-ing on Native control is often that the Natives are fighting among themselves. It is true that one Native way of handling conflict is to form factions. This has been beneficial in the history of Native organizational development in that splinter groups with unique goals establish their own agencies, thus expanding the array of functions and services. However, the potential to abuse this tendency by aiding and abetting, dividing and conquering is a well-known tactic of colonialism (Means, 1991, p. 3). The shrinking of available bureaucratic positions lessens the opportunity for Natives to move into mainstream positions of power, so their best prospects are likely to be ghettoized in local, grass-roots control. For some, this is control over misery.

After reviewing five proposed staff positions, the AHT program manager reflected on experiences gained in ministering to the Native poor, sick, and indigent:

> Anishnawbe Health can increase its staff ten-fold and it will still be applying band aid treatments to social wounds that are endemic and deeply-rooted in Native communities. It's unfortunate that we have to rely on government funding for our existence because I'd sure like to bite the hand that feeds me. Will we ever feed ourselves? That's what 20 years of frustration will do to your brain. It'd be dreadful if I were alone in my thinking. I keep telling people we should be working ourselves out of a job and stop benefiting from the misery of others but usually get a look that either conveys pity or "ain't that a cute thought." (Holota, 1990, p. 4)

The proposed revisions to the Ontario Health Professions Regulation Act will grant 24 health professions the privilege of self-regulation. Draft legislation is outlined in *Striking a New Balance: A Blueprint for the Regulation of Ontario's Health Professions* (Schwartz, 1989). Traditional Native healers are not included on the list of sanctioned health professionals. They are not legally sanctioned and lie outside the control of the conventional health-care system and government. McKee (1988, p. 775) suggests that "one reason why holistic practices are not accepted by Western medicine may be the challenge they pose to the Western model and to the commodification of health needs promoted by this model." AHT has the perception that there is an associated "major issue of liability"; an issue of being susceptible; of being under obligation; at the mercy of what "outsiders" can do about how the centre functions. The autonomy of traditional healers' knowledge and skills are undermined. They and the health centre remain in a dependent position.

How Gender and Class Affect Control Issues

Vanderburgh (1979) discusses conflicts within the Toronto Native community related to gender. She found that it is the men who wield power and attempt to maintain culture. Contemporary sources of power stem from government-derived funds and associated jobs in Native organizational settings:

> Prestige derived from spiritual power, however, is still very important, both in urban and rural environments, as well as reserve and non-reserve communities. Those wielding spiritual power in Toronto, and in Ontario generally, are almost without exception men and these men are anxious to gain control of the funding/job allocation sources of power. The bulk of the operational positions in Toronto Native organizations, involving only minor decision making concerning the allocation of funds and jobs, are occupied by women. (Vanderburgh, 1979, p. 16)

A decade later, during AHT's first year of operation, these gender and class issues have shifted. At the 1989 Annual General Meeting, the AHT board recognized that women's perspectives as board members and other influential positions in the community had been lacking. Women's input was needed to create balance in the centre's development process.

At the present time, there are more women than men on the AHT board and staff, although the organization's leadership is primarily male. However, attempts have been implemented to seek broad organizational input and utilize a consensus model to deal with decisions and issues. One AHT board member said: "Many decisions are to be made, and women and men contribute equally." The decision making of hiring has been a shared process between members of the AHT staff and board, with the board deciding the executive director's position and a minimum of five people interviewing candidates for the nurses' and doctors' positions.

An approximately equal number of women and men in the Native community are traditional healers, that is, those with spiritual power. Great respect is accorded traditional healers and there appears to be an equal value and degree of power allocated to both female and male traditional healers. The significance of gender does not appear to influence designation of traditional healer status, however, cultural beliefs delineate what one does or does not do according to gender. Cultural beliefs concerning gender differ between Native and non-Native cultures, as well as within Native cultures.

A motivation for the development of the AHT community health centre is in response to the conventional health-care system, which inadequately meets the health-care needs of Native people. Particular opposition is held against hospitals that are "white, male, and sexist. They make the military look silly."

Class, culture as a male activity, and cultural maintenance have been linked to reveal conflicts among social classes within the Toronto Native community (Vanderburgh, 1979). These conflicts often arise in the form of male-female power confrontations, whereby middle-and upper-class Native men attempt to maintain culture through Native organization programs attended by, but not desired by or appropriate to, lower-class needs. Contrary to these findings, in the early phases of the health centre's development, the majority of clients were men who were from the lower class. There are few women among those who are homeless and live on the street. These people want medical, health, social, and supportive care from the health centre and they respond positively to the Native cultural aspects of health-care services.

Vanderburgh (1979) also found that contemporary sources of power stem from government-derived funds and associated jobs in Native organizational settings. The AHT staff are not all middle class. For example, the street workers' program (SWAT) is organized by people who have lived in circumstances similar to their clientele. The success of the SWAT program is largely credited to this fact. Attempts to find a suitable woman or women to join the program are being considered. For the most part, AHT health and social care and program delivery are now rendered by women.

A female traditional healer talked about a study that had been reported in the newspaper claiming that 80 percent of Native women had been abused. She said:

> It's a tragic situation. We need to remind Native people of the stories and the legends of the place of Native women and how very precious and special and sacred they are. A Native man said: "Natives have forgotten women's position." It is believed to be important to respect women. Balance is hoped for in the revival of the cultural value of the circle and associated traditional ceremonies, in which the power and position of both sexes are respected.

Women's Position for the Rebuilding of Cultural Order

Native women are encouraging other Native women to heal Native society (*Canadian Woman Studies*, 1989). This form of healing activity is in the area of cultural and social rebuilding and maintenance. It is to be accomplished by a return to and conformity with Native socially contextualized, gender role norms. Women are to defend the indigenous way of life; "women are Keepers of the Culture" (Brady, 1989, p. 3).

> Woman is the Earth, the centre of the circle of life; she is the caretaker of life. She nourishes and heals in the same way that the Earth does. Her reproductive power is sacred and she has great natural healing powers that derive from her spiritual connection to the Earth.
>
> Because he [man] is not born with the same relationship to the Earth and lifegiving powers as is a woman, he must strive throughout his life to develop that relationship. This he does through ceremonies, the sweat, fasting and serving the people. (Malloch, 1989, p. 106)

Their association with the Creator is believed to provide women with the internal strength to protect the indigenous way of life. Women's activities are coming more in focus to serve their interest in the family and the clan. Custody battles have occurred between male band councillors on the reserve and women in urban hostels. This may be the Native variant of the quest for gender equality through economic and political self-interest as seen in non-Native contexts (Adamson, Briskin, & McPhail, 1988). The Native perspective appears to provide women with a key responsibility for cultural reawakening, rebirth, and strengthening. The rebuilding of cultural order at the grass-roots level has significance for all Native people.

Dealing with Socio-Economic and Political Variables Affecting Health at the Grass-Roots Level

"The central goal of the federal government in dealing with Native people has always been to maintain close control over them in almost all aspects of their lives" (Frideres, 1988, p. 136). As a result, Native people suffer from socially and economically determined variables that affect their health. In comparison to the general Canadian population, Native people have lower levels of education, higher rates of unemployment, and lower incomes. Other examples include: poverty, inadequate and overcrowded housing, homelessness, inadequate nutrition, racial discrimination, police harassment and brutality, and an inability or unwillingness within conventional health-care agencies to understand and respond effectively to Native-specific needs. The outcomes are a myriad of acute and chronic physical, mental, and spiritual problems. There are "broken circles" related to physical diseases and illnesses; lowered life expectancies; drug, alcohol, sexual, and physical abuse; and weak family and social structures. An AHT health-centre goal is to assist in making the circles within the Native people, families, and the broad community complete and strong. AHT advocates empowerment to reawaken and retain Native pride and culture by enabling Native people to take, once again, greater control over their health (AHT, 1988). AHT wants the inclusion of traditional knowledge and cultural values as part of the health centre's operation. This is a difficult task in face of the "cultural imperialism of the Canadian government and the racist philosophy that promoted the dominant society's insistence on the inferiority of Native people" (Frideres, 1988, p. 140).

The following are examples of AHT's efforts at the grass-roots level to deal with the broader socio-economic and political problems.

AHT's Journey to Oka to Ease the Suffering under the Army's Control

The Oka crisis during the summer of 1990 concerned a land dispute between the townspeople and the Native people in the area. The army was summoned when the local police were unable to settle the dispute. Barricades were set up with the army on one side and the Native people on the other. Native people in Kahnawaka were kept hostage by the army inside the community treatment centre. These people were denied access to health care, medication, and treatment for their medical conditions. In response to their suffering, an AHT physician, a nurse, and another AHT worker drove to Oka to provide supplies, medication, and assistance. At the barricade, the army was reluctant to allow the passage of the AHT staff, but consent was finally granted. The army led them on an out-of-the-way route to the treatment centre and jammed their cellular phone line. The nurse later commented:

It was really scary . . . frightening. It was the first time that I felt totally helpless. And I thought, how do I get out of this? There doesn't seem to be a way out. These feelings of helplessness happened to me very quickly. It makes me wonder about the effects in the Native communities, when they have already experienced so much previous manipulation. The power of the army is only an example of the control that Native reserves undergo.

During their short visit to the centre, the AHT staff were unable to provide much in the way of mental and spiritual support to the Native hostages. Their suffering lingered long after the army moved out of the area.

Fetal Alcohol Syndrome (FAS) as a Symptom of Social Disease

The Toronto Board of Health recently took depositions on the issue of passing a by-law that would result in placing posters in bars to inform women about the risks of drinking while pregnant. Not surprisingly, representatives of the restaurant and brewing industries raised opposition to the idea. The deposition by an AHT nurse raised what might be called alternative remedies that would address the causal factors of FAS as symptoms of larger social issues. She suggested that the provision of friendly, safe environments to enable people to stop drinking were needed.

At the present time, there are no support systems available, not even a phone number for caregivers of children, adolescents, or adults who are FAS victims. There is little support for the guilt and suffering of mothers who have borne children with FAS, and there are few resources for the stimulation and special learning needs of these children and their families.

Native client and community physical problems are like the tip of an iceberg. Using the circle conceptualization, the health-care approach at AHT is holistic. In this view, the broader socio-economic and political contexts are considered. The AHT nurses state:

One of our concerns is the vicious cycle of alcoholism. In it we see unemployment, poverty, inadequate housing, family violence, physical and sexual abuse, incest, family breakdown, and suicides. All these things perpetuate feelings of hopelessness and helplessness that in turn contribute to alcoholism. To deal with these problems in a holistic manner, as is the Native concept of health, we need a multidisciplinary approach, as well as support programs. (Belleau & Watters, 1990)

Theatre and Video Production as Media Forms to Address Control Issues

To stimulate new thinking and understanding about Native culture as it relates to the fields of medicine and healing, AHT asked the Native Earth Performing Arts theatre company to present a special performance of John McLeod's play, *Diary of a Crazy Boy*, for AHT funders, conventional health and social-service administrators, and direct-care workers.

Diary of a Crazy Boy is about a teenaged Native boy caught in the conflict between modern psychiatric and traditional spiritual healing practices. Darrell is a victim of FAS, and is under the treatment of a Native psychiatrist:

> who has given up his roots in order to succeed in the white world and is himself haunted by his neglected family's totemic animal, the lynx. . . . The troubled teenager relies on the help of his Uncle Bob, the last of a long line of medicine men, and his guardian Ojibway ancestral spirits, who send him an energetic Spirit Boy to guide him. Darrell achieves healing without the help of his doctor, and the viewer is left with the question, "Who is really crazy?" (Petrone, 1990, p. 176)[2]

The play was followed by a discussion about Native cultural values and beliefs with the author, cast, crew, one of the directors, Tomson Highway, and the audience. The production had a profound impact on the audience and several people commented on the power of the experience.

Videotapes have been produced in conjunction with elders and traditional healers. *Soul Spirit* (1989) "poetically portrays life stories told by Ojibway Elder Joe Sylvester" (video jacket). *Our Foods Are Our Medicine: Understanding Diabetes* (1990) addresses the profound role that changes to Native culture and lifestyle have played in the alarming increase in the occurrence of diabetes and how it has affected Native communities. The value of traditional Native healing practices is discussed along with other treatment modalities. *Nibo Apinewin* (1991) discusses the threat of AIDS in the Native community. *Wigwams and Flophouses: Housing Rights and Native Peoples* (1990) addresses Native people's right to housing. In this video:

> community workers, street people, an elder and other members of the Native community talk about the need for affordable housing. They discuss some of the difficulties acquiring even adequate shelter and problems Native people encounter in exercising their right to housing, both on reserves and in urban centres. (video jacket)

Sharing and learning opportunities such as the *Diary of a Crazy Boy* play and presenting copies of the *Soul Spirit* video to influential health-care community members (e.g., the Medical Officer of Health) have been astute and effective communication means to establish rapport, trust, and support with the conventional system's power structures. As well, they have helped garner support from the government bureaucracy to allow traditional practitioners to continue their work. The media can create an environment where non-Native and Native peoples can be shown that Native cultures have traditions of healing, health promotion, and health care. The media can facilitate this insight instead of formal legitimization processes under the government Health Professions Act.

The Street Workers of Anishnawbe Toronto: Dealing with Homelessness

Concerns increased within the Toronto Native community with respect to those who are homeless or living in poverty, particularly after the deaths of four homeless Native men between July and October, 1989. These concerns were shared by the police, city councillors, and drop-in and social agencies. In response, the Street Workers of Anishnawbe Toronto (SWAT) program was developed. Municipally funded and managed by health-centre staff, SWAT's goals are to ensure the safety, warmth, and general well-being of individuals who are homeless in the downtown west side by providing assistance through a supervised street foot patrol. Former street people manage SWAT and over one hundred volunteers assist. The workers walk and drive the streets to talk with people, provide counselling, offer blankets, food, and hot drinks, and make referrals to community agencies (e.g., detoxificiation centres, hostels, hospitals) as necessary.

In the winter of 1990, AHT successfully lobbied City Hall to leave a change house in a city park open 24 hours a day during the winter months as a central, heated place with washroom facilities for the homeless to gather, sleep, and eat. This change house was already a popular place for people to congregate, although previously it had been locked each night. The health-centre staff periodically "home-visited" during the day and the street workers visited at night. This area became "home" for several people.

In this way, AHT increased control over some of the circumstances affecting the health of some Native people and the opportunity to deal with solutions to their problems. However, this Native empowerment was usurped when city park officials locked the change-house door, without prior consultation with the health-centre staff. This was done in response to two incidents that had occurred there, both of which SWAT were aware and were dealing with.

Summary

Anishnawbe Health Toronto (AHT) has developed an urban community health centre that advocates and facilitates Native control over both conventional biomedical and Native traditional health-care services. This is a new idea whose future path of culturally specific health care is evolving. The symbol of the circle, as expressed by AHT elders and traditional healers as being a continuing balance and governance principle, is an important Native perspective for dealing with Native health concerns. This principle assists in dealing with the associated control issues by nullifying the opposition between non-Native and Native healers, and between conventional Western and traditional Native health-care practices. It brings them into a circle of development of Native capabilities with the realization of Native holistic principles of health care, healing, and sharing. Native autonomy and control is a fundamental prerequisite for the balance principle to work. This message needs to be heard by would-be facilitators attempting to assist Natives to establish and control their own facilities. It is important to work within a framework of community interest and grass-roots processes, which Native people conceive to be the basis for contending with health issues and resources. Gender-based differences are important in the perception of control over health-related matters in the Native community. Socio-economic and political variables that affect Native health are broad in their scope and pervasive in promoting Native dependency upon the government. AHT is attempting to address the associated issues of control at a grass-roots level and some success is being realized.

Acknowledgement: We wish to thank the staff and board of Anishnawbe Health Toronto for their assistance in the preparation of this paper.

Notes

1. Joe Sylvester, an Ojibway elder, was involved with Dr. Rebecca Hagey and others in the Native Diabetes Project (Hagey, 1989; Hagey, 1984). Joe is credited with the vision for a Native health-care centre in Toronto: "Once a vision has been had, it is not our job to get off it. We must get on with it." We can't change Joe's vision. It is our job to follow through with the vision.
2. Petrone (1990) provides a footnote to her description of the *Diary of a Crazy Boy* with a newspaper quote from Kenneth Charlotte, who played the boy "This mythological world has almost been forgotten . . . and it's up to this generation that's helping the circle to come around again" (quoted in "Play Gives New Life to Ojibway Myths" by Jon Kaplan in *Now*, 8 – 14 February, 1990, p. 24).

Study Questions

1. What are some Native holistic principles of health care, healing, and sharing?
2. What are some reasons that Native people desire autonomy and control relating to Native health care? Suggest ways that allow or encourage Native control of health care. Surmise possible limiting factors in the socio-economic and political contexts for Native people to increase control in Native health care.
3. Discuss reasons why Native people may become resistant to services of the conventional health-care system?
4. Compare and contrast conventional bio-medical and Native traditional perspectives about health care, including circle conceptualizations.
5. How is gender related to control issues in Native health care?

6. Review the following checklist to identify your feelings as a facilitator attempting to develop Native community control over health needs or facilities.

How would you:
- work in a meeting without an agenda?
- determine all the participant's viewpoints?
- encourage sharing among non-Native and Native participants?
- respond and proceed if there were intangible meeting outcomes?

Recommended Reading

Bopp, J., Bopp, M., Brown, L., & Lane, P. (1984). *The sacred tree*. Lethbridge: Four Worlds Development Press.

Colorado, P. (1988). Bridging Native and western science. *Convergence*, 21, (2 & 3), 49-68.

Canadian woman studies/les cahiers de la femme: Native women, 10, (2 & 3) (1989).

Frideres, J.S. (1988). Racism and health: The case of the Native people. In B.S. Bolaria & H.D. Dickinson (Eds.), *Sociology of health care in Canada* (pp. 135-147). Toronto: Harcourt Brace Jovanovich.

Frideres, J.S. (1991). From the bottom up: Institutional structures and the Indian people. In B.S. Bolaria (Ed.), *Social issues and contradictions in Canadian society* (pp.108-132). Toronto: Harcourt Brace Jovanovich.

Gregory, D., & Stewart, P. (1987). Nurse and traditional healers: Now is the time to speak. *The Canadian Nurse*, 83, (8), 25-27.

Hagey, R. (1984). The phenomenon, the explanations and the responses: Metaphors surrounding diabetes in urban Canadian Indians. *Social Science and Medicine*, 18, (3), 265-272.

Hagey, R. (1989). The native diabetes program: Rhetorical process and praxis. *Medical Anthropology*, 11, 229-255.

References

Adams, H. (1985). The Métis. In B.S. Bolaria & P.S. Li (Eds.), *Racial oppression in Canada* (pp. 61-79). Toronto: Garamond Press.

Adamson, N., Briskin, L., & McPhail, M. (1988). *Feminist organizing for change: The contemporary women's movement in Canada*. Toronto: Oxford University Press.

Anishnawbe Health Toronto. (1988, March). *A proposal to establish a community health centre*. Unpublished document submitted to the Ontario Ministry of Health, Community Health Centre Program. Toronto: Author.

Anishnawbe Health Toronto. (1987, January 20). *Toronto Native health conference: Final report*. (Unpublished report.) Toronto: Anishnawbe Health Toronto, 20.

Anishnawbe Health Toronto. (1990). *Anishnawbe health Toronto . . . working towards culturally sensitive health care for Native people*. Toronto: Author (pamphlet).

Bourgeault, R. (1988). Canada Indians: The South African connection. *Canadian Dimension*, 12, (8), 6-10.

Belleau, D., & Watters, D. (1990, June 27). *Native community outreach nurses' report*. Unpublished report in the Anishnawbe Health Toronto Annual General Meeting Minutes.

Bopp, J., Bopp, M., Brown, L., & Lane, P. (1984). *The sacred tree*. Lethbridge: Four Worlds Development Press.

Brady, E. (1989). Dedication and editorial. *Canadian Woman Studies/les cahiers de la femme: Native women*, 10, (2 & 3), 3-5.

Canadian woman studies/les cahiers de la femme: Native women, 10, (2 & 3), (1989).

Colorado, P. (1988). Bridging Native and western science. *Convergence*, 21, (2 & 3), 49-68.

Frideres, J.S. (1988a). *Native peoples in Canada: Contemporary conflicts* (3rd ed.), (pp. 366-411). Toronto: Prentice Hall.

Frideres, J.S. (1988b). Racism and health: The case of the Native people. In B.S. Bolaria & H.D. Dickinson (Eds.), *Sociology of health care in Canada* (pp. 135-147). Toronto: Harcourt Brace Jovanovich.

Frideres, J.S. (1991). From the bottom up: Institutional structures and the Indian people. In B.S. Bolaria (Ed.), *Social issues and contradictions in Canadian society* (pp. 108-132). Toronto: Harcourt Brace Jovanovich.

Gilmore, A. (1990). Canada's native MDs: Small in number, big on helping their community. *Canadian Medical Association Journal*, 142, (1), 52-54.

Gregory, D., & Stewart, P. (1987). Nurses and traditional healers: Now is the time to speak. *The Canadian Nurse*, 83, (8), 25-27.

Green, E.C. (1988). Can collaborative programs between biomedical and African indigenous health practitioners succeed? *Social Science and Medicine*, 27, (11), 1125-1130.

Hagey, R. (1984). The phenomenon, the explanations and the responses: Metaphors surrounding diabetes in urban Canadian Indians. *Social Science and Medicine*, 18, (3), 265-272.

Hagey, R. (1989). The Native diabetes program: Rhetorical process and praxis. *Medical Anthropology*, 11, 229-255.

Hirschfelder, A.B., Byler, M.G., & Dorris, M.A. (1983). *Guide to research on North American Indians*. Chicago: American Library Association.

Holota, R. (1990, March 14). *Program planning committee report*. Unpublished report accompanying Anishnawbe Health Toronto Board minutes.

Kaufert, J.M., & Koolage, W.W. (1984). Role conflict among 'culture brokers': The experience of Native Canadian medical interpreters. *Social Science and Medicine*, 18, (3), 283-286.

Kaufert, J.M., Koolage, W.W., Kaufert, P.L., & O'Neil, J.D. (1984). The use of 'trouble case' examples in teaching the impact of sociocultural and political factors in clinical communication. *Medical Anthropology*, 8, (1), 36-45.

King, B.J. (1988, June). Metropolitan Toronto Native demographic characteristics; a review. Unpublished paper submitted to Anishnawbe Health Toronto.

King, B.J., & Lee, W. (1990, February). *Personal communication*.

Maidman, F. (1981). *Natives in the urban setting: Problems, needs and services: Report of the Ontario task force on Native people in urban settings*. Toronto: Ontario Government.

McKee, J. (1988). Holistic health and the critique of western medicine. *Social Science and Medicine*, 26, (8), 775-784.

Means, R. (1991). On selling out. *Beedaudjimowin*, 1, (4), 3.

Malloch, L. (1989). Indian medicine, Indian health. *Canadian Woman Studies/les cahiers de la femme: Native women*, 10, (2 & 3), 105-112.

Petrone, P. (1990). *Native literature in Canada: From the oral tradition to the present*. Toronto: Oxford University Press.

Ryan, J., & Larsen, D.E. (1981). Cultural barriers to the establishment of a Native health center and the role of anthropological evaluation. In M.F. Guédon & D.G. Hatt (Eds.), *Papers from the sixth annual congress, Canadian ethnology society*, 78 (pp. 33-39). Ottawa: National Museum of Canada.

Schwartz, A.M. (1989). *Striking a new balance: A blueprint for the regulation of Ontario's health professions*. Toronto: Ontario Ministry of Health.

Smith, D. (1990). *Conceptual practices of power*. Toronto: University of Toronto Press.

Vanderburgh, R.M. (1979). Women and the politics of culture: Class and gender conflicts in the Toronto native community. *Resources for Feminist Research*, 8, (3), 16-17.

Young, D.E. (Ed.). (1988). *Health care issues in the Canadian north*. Edmonton: Boreal Institute for Northern Studies.

Chapter 11

Income Inequality, Poverty, Food Banks, and Health

B. Singh Bolaria, University of Saskatchewan

Introduction

Poverty, malnutrition, hunger, and disease have come to be identified with underdeveloped Third World countries. While the significance and concentration of these problems in the Third World cannot be overstated, neither have the advanced capitalist countries eliminated economic inequalities and poverty. The inequalities of wealth and income produce differential life chances — that is, chances for material and social rewards. Poverty translates into dependency on food banks, malnutrition and hunger, ill health, short life expectancy, and homelessness, to mention only a few of its effects (Bolaria & Wotherspoon, 1991).

Canada is a highly stratified society. There are widespread disparities in wealth, income, power, and prestige. These inequalities have important implications for people's lives. This chapter explores the linkages between income inequality, poverty, and life chances with particular emphasis on food banks and health.

Income Inequality and Poverty

Income inequality is an important dimension of social stratification. An examination of income distribution data reveals wide income disparities among Canadians. These data also show that there has been very little change in the share of income held by Canadians in different income categories over time (National Council of Welfare, 1988; 1989;

1990a; 1992). For instance, families in the lowest quintile had only 6.1 percent of the total income in 1951 and 6.3 percent in 1986. The corresponding figures for the highest quintile were 41.1 percent and 39.4 percent — over six times the lowest quintile's share. The figures for unattached individuals reveal that in 1986 the lowest quintile had 5.3 percent of the total income. In contrast, the highest quintile had 44.7 percent of the total income — over eight times the bottom group's share. The income distribution for unattached individuals was even more skewed in 1951 (National Council of Welfare, 1988). Income inequalities continue to persist in Canada.

A significant number of Canadians live in poverty. The most common measure used to establish the poverty line is the low-income cut-offs used by Statistics Canada. These cut-offs are set at levels where, on average, 58.5 percent of income is spent on the necessities of life — food, clothing, and shelter (National Council of Welfare, 1989). There is no single cut-off line for all of Canada, because living costs vary by family size and place of residence. It should also be noted that "poverty lines only establish the upper limit of the low income population. Most poor Canadians live on incomes that are hundreds and more often thousands of dollars under the poverty line" (National Council of Welfare, 1989, p. 5).

Poverty figures have fluctuated with the economic conditions in this country. While poverty declined in the 1970s, it increased substantially during the first half of the 1980s as a result of the 1981-82 recession (National Council of Welfare, 1988). Despite some movement, by the late 1980s the poverty rates had not returned to pre-recession levels.

Table 1 shows national trends in poverty from 1980 to 1990. In 1980, the number of people living in poverty was little over 3.6 million and the poverty rate was just over 15 percent. Both the number of people who lived in poverty and the poverty rate fluctuated throughout the 1980s. These figures rose throughout 1982-84, declined in 1985-89, and rose again in 1990.

As Table 2 shows, child poverty figures followed the same general pattern as statistics for the general population. Child poverty increased in the early part of the 1980s, declined during the next few years and rose again in 1990. During the peak years of 1983 and 1984, well over 1.2 million children were living in poverty in 1983 and 19.6 percent in 1984. Almost one in every five children was poor.

Certain groups face a high risk of poverty. These include families headed by women, unattached or elderly women, unemployed, irregular participation in the labour force, and persons with low educational levels (National Council of Welfare, 1992). Women overall face a much higher risk of poverty than men, a phenomenon that has come to be known as the "feminization of poverty" (National Council of Welfare, 1990a).

Because a vast majority of Canadians earn their income from wage employment, labour market characteristics that determine which jobs are well paid are particularly

Table 1 Poverty Trends, All Persons, 1980–1990

Year	No. of persons living in poverty	Poverty rate (percent)
1980	3 624 000	15.3
1981	3 643 000	15.3
1982	3 951 000	16.4
1983	4 406 000	18.2
1984	4 397 000	18.1
1985	4 170 000	17.0
1986	3 976 000	16.0
1987	3 912 000	15.6
1988	3 744 000	14.8
1989	3 487 000	13.6
1990	3 821 000	14.6

Source: National Council of Welfare. (1992). *Poverty Profile, 1980-1990*. Ottawa: Supply Services, Canada, Table 2, p.7.

important in any discussion of poverty. For instance, those in managerial and professional occupations and their families are unlikely to live in poverty, as compared to those in the service industries. Occupations with an above-average risk of poverty include farming, fishing, forestry, and services (National Council of Welfare, 1992).

Table 2 Poverty Trends, Children Under 18, 1980–1990

Year	No. of children under 18 living in poverty	Poverty rate (percent)
1980	984 000	14.9
1981	998 000	15.2
1982	1 155 000	17.8
1983	1 221 000	19.0
1984	1 253 000	19.6
1985	1 165 000	18.3
1986	1 086 000	17.0
1987	1 057 000	16.6
1988	987 000	15.4
1989	934 000	14.5
1990	1 105 000	16.9

Source: National Council of Welfare. (1992). *Poverty Profile, 1980-1990*. Ottawa: Supply and Services Canada, Table 3, p. 8.

It is evident that wide income disparities and poverty continue to persist in Canada. Income inequality and poverty have an important influence on the lives of individuals. Max Weber saw class as closely linked to people's life chances; that is, their chance to acquire material goods and other amenities (Gerth & Mills, 1958). Economic and social inequalities produce inequality of opportunities and life chances which are reflected in such measures as education, living standards, housing, health, and consumption patterns.

Most relevant to the discussion in this chapter is the link between income inequalities and consumption patterns. Chossudovsky points to

> the dual and divided structure of social consumption and of consumer goods markets between necessary subsistence goods on the one hand and luxury and semi-luxury goods consumed by the privileged upper-income groups on the other hand. . . . This duality in the structure of social consumption, while more pronounced in peripheral social formulations, is also present in the advanced capitalist countries (1983, p. 76).

In addition to the differences in the goods they consume, persons with different income levels devote a different percentage of their money income to necessary subsistence goods. Families and unattached individuals in the lowest quintile spend 57.5 percent of their income on the necessities of life. The corresponding figure for the second lowest quintile is 45.6 percent. Family units in the highest quintile spend 33 percent of their income on the necessities of life (National Council of Welfare, 1989, p. 13).

Chossudovsky notes that "food is by far the most important component of necessary consumption." Adequate production and supply of food in themselves do not assure adequate levels of food consumption and nutrition. Consumption levels are influenced by the social distribution of food to different groups in the population (Chossodovsky, 1983), which itself is a function of income distribution.

Since the early 1980s, it has become increasingly evident that a large number of Canadians depend upon food banks. The very existence of food banks indicates that hunger and poverty have become permanent features of Canadian society.

Food Banks

Since the first food bank opened in Edmonton in 1981, food banks and similar organizations have been established in many towns and cities across Canada (Canadian Association of Food Banks, 1989; Riches, 1986; Oderkirk, 1992; Webber, 1992). As Table 3 indicates, by 1984 there were 75 food banks in Canada, mostly in the western provinces. The number of food banks continued to increase through the 1980s. By 1991, there were 292 food banks in various parts of Canada. This growth is likely to continue as the economy further experiences the effects of economic recession.

Table 3   Food Banks in Canada, 1981-1991

	1981	1984	1988	1989	1990	1991
Newfoundland	0	0	1	1	1	17
Prince Edward Island	0	0	2	2	2	3
Nova Scotia	0	2	8	14	14	27
New Brunswick	0	2	27	34	35	40
Quebec	0	2	5	5	5	11
Ontario	0	4	19	33	35	88
Manitoba	0	1	1	3	3	4
Saskatchewan	0	5	5	5	8	11
Alberta	1	12	16	26	24	40
British Columbia	0	47	42	36	34	51
Canada	1	75	126	159	161	292

Source: Oderkirk, J. (1992, Spring). *Food banks. Canadian Social Trends, 24,* 6-14. (Sources: Riches, G. (1986). *Food banks and the welfare crisis.* Ottawa: Canadian Council on Social Development; Canadian Association of Food Banks.) Estimates from 1988 to 1991 from the Canadian Association of Food Banks do not include Salvation Army Family Services Divisions food banks. Growth during this period can be attributed to the creation of new food banks and to the registration of existing food banks with the association.

It is estimated that two million Canadians used food banks in 1991. Children account for a large number of food-bank users. While 25 percent of the Canadian population was under age 18, nearly 40 percent of the food-bank beneficiaries in 1990 were in this age group (Canadian Association of the Food Banks, 1991, cited in Oderkirk, 1992). For over two-thirds (68 percent) of the food-bank users, welfare was the primary source of income. It is evident that many Canadians depend upon food banks and other charitable meal operations for their daily food.

Poverty, Food Banks, and Health

Social medicine is primarily concerned with the social, economic, and environmental conditions in society that produce illness and mortality. Epidemiological data clearly demonstrates the differential health status of the population by socio-economic status. The health gap between the rich and the poor continues to exist in Canada, where the principle of universality was a major impetus to the introduction of medical care in the sixties (National Council of Welfare, 1990b; Grant, 1988). Upper-income Canadians live longer, healthier, and disability-free lives on average than poor Canadians. This gap in health status is primarily due to the "debilitating conditions of life that poverty forces upon people" (National Council of Welfare, 1990b, p. 6). Social and material conditions of existence such as poor housing, poor nutrition, poor neighbourhoods, and poor environment all contribute to high mortality in the low income population. High mortality levels in poor neighbourhoods are well documented (Thomson, 1990; National Council of Welfare, 1990b). Evidence indicates that the poorer the area, the shorter the life expectancy of both men and women. Data also show that children of parents in the poorest neighbourhoods have twice the infant mortality rates of children in the richest neighbourhoods. High mortality, high disability, and low health status of Natives are associated with environmental, economic, social, and living condition of the population (Borsellino, 1990; Mao et al., 1992). Other studies lend support to the general conclusion that low-income poor people not only have high mortality and morbidity, but low utilization of health services (Driver, 1991; Shah et al., 1987; Wilkins et al., 1991; Grant, 1988).

A number of studies show the relationship between low incomes and inadequate diets (Nutrition Canada, 1975; Myers & Kroetsch, 1978; Reid & Miles, 1977). Poverty, nutrition, and hunger are also closely linked to health status (Epp, 1986; Statistics Canada and Health and Welfare Canada, 1981; Wilkins & Adams, 1983; Wigle & Mao, 1980). A report published by the Minister of Health revealed that "men in the upper income groups can expect 14 more disability-free years than men with a low income; in the case of women, the difference is eight years" (Epp, 1986, p. 398). Other evidence associates poverty with malnutrition, psychomotor, and growth retardation, emotional disturbances, and visual difficulties. These problems are even more acute among Native people (Shah & Farkas, 1985).

The adverse health affects of poverty for children start during pregnancy; they have significant impact on complications during pregnancy, low birth weight of children, handicaps, poor growth, and intellectual and emotional disorders (National Council of Welfare, 1975; Brown, 1978). Child mortality rates are higher for poor children than their wealthy peers (Fine, 1989).

The cumulative effect of poverty, malnutrition, hunger, and ill health is the extensive reproduction of poverty. All of these things influence poor children's learning ability and performance in school (Chu, 1989; National Council of Welfare, 1975), which subsequently affect job prospects, employment patterns, and earnings. As a report by the National Council of Welfare (1975, p. 1) states: "To be born poor in Canada does not make it a certainty that you will live poor and die poor — but it makes it very likely."

Low income and poverty forces upon people many debilitating conditions which produce poor health, shorter lives, high infant mortality, and other physical and mental health problems for the disadvantaged. Dependency on food banks furthers these disadvantages. In this context, one of the questions most frequently raised is whether the food banks meet the diet and nutritional needs of their clients. While Canadian studies that provide systemic evidence on this subject are lacking, the evidence from elsewhere suggests that the provision of food assistance in itself cannot be equated with nutritional and dietary adequacy (Rauschenbach et al., 1990; Emmons, 1987; Laven & Brown, 1985; Carrillo et al., 1990; Reuler, 1989; Wood & Valdez, 1991). Poverty and homelessness are also likely to increase as "disadvantages" accumulate for individuals and groups, and with differential social status and power relations and differential medical and nutritional needs of the individuals. For instance, even in the food-bank population, women and children are likely to be at a higher risk than men. Factors that need to be considered here include women's reproductive health (Martin, 1989; Pollock, 1988; Trypuc, 1988), nutritional health needs during pregnancy, and children's nutritional needs. Abuse and violence against women and children also puts them at a greater health risk.

The effects of malnutrition and vitamin deficiencies have begun to appear in some cases. Mo Ali, physician and hematologist, points out in this regard:

> We're seeing more patients who suffer from blood diseases by lack of vitamins. One of the vitamins is folic acid, and that's present in fresh vegetables and fresh fruit. People who are living on canned food from food banks are the people we are starting to see in age groups I have not seen before, people in their 20s and 30s. They become anemic. They become weak and tired. They have to walk and line up for food, jobs, clothing, shelter. It is really sad what is happening (*Globe and Mail*, December 22, 1992, p. A4).

Folic acid, for instance, also prevents neural tube defects (Laxdal, Habbick, & Bolaria, 1993).

Researchers have also ignored the "hidden injuries" of food-bank dependency and their association with health status. The negative social attributes, such as social stigma and shame, which are usually associated with poverty are likely to be exacerbated by dependency on food banks (Eales, 1989; Sennett & Cobb, 1973; Matza, 1966; Coleman & Cressey, 1984; Tarasuk & MacLean, 1990). Shame, degradation, stigma, disrepute, sense of failure, loss of self-respect, self-blame, and powerlessness are likely to be disruptive of social relationships, both in and out of the family, with negative consequences such as social isolation and unhealthy social environment within the household.

Conclusion

Data presented in this chapter indicate that wide income disparities and poverty continue to persist in Canada. Economic and social imbalances produce inequalities of opportunities, differential life chances, and different social consumption patterns. A duality of social consumption patterns is linked to income levels — while upper-income and rich Canadians have disposable income for luxury goods, at the other extreme, low-income and poor Canadians are often unable to buy even necessary subsistence goods, including food. Since the early eighties, it has become increasingly evident that a large number of Canadians depend upon food banks. The continuous existence of food banks indicates that poverty, malnutrition, and hunger have become permanent features of Canadian society.

Low income and poverty forces upon people many debilitating conditions that produce poor health, shorter lives, high infant mortality, and other physical and mental health problems for the disadvantaged. Dependency on food banks only exacerbates these conditions and further increases the health risks for the dependent populations.

Study Questions

1. Discuss the statement that the material conditions of existence and debilitating conditions of life that poverty forces upon people produce poor health and shorter lives for the disadvantaged.
2. Discuss the physical and psychological health consequences of dependency on food banks.
3. Canada is one of the richest countries in the world and certainly produces abundant food. How, then, can we explain hunger and malnutrition in this country?
4. Discuss the relationships among inequality, poverty, hunger and health.
5. The negative social attributes, such as social stigma, disrepute, and shame, which are usually associated with poverty are likely to be exacerbated by dependency on food banks. Discuss the linkages between negative social attributes and social, psychological, and physical wellness.

Recommended Reading

Bolaria, B.S., & Wotherspoon, T. (1991). Income inequality, poverty and hunger. In B.S. Bolaria (Ed.), *Social issues and contradictions in Canadian society* (pp. 464–480). Toronto: Harcourt Brace Jovanovich.

Oderkirk, J. (1992). Food banks. *Canadian Social Trends*, 24, 6–14.

Riches, G. (1986). *Food banks and the welfare crisis.* Ottawa: Canadian Council on Social Development.

Tarasuk, V.S., & MacLean, H. (1990). The institutionalization of food banks in Canada: A public health concern. *Canadian Journal of Public Health*, 81, 331–332.

Warnock, J.W. (1987). *The politics of hunger.* Toronto: Methuen.

Webber, M. (1972). *Food for thought.* Toronto: Coach House Press.

References

Bolaria, B.S., & Wotherspoon, T. (1991). Income inequality, poverty and hunger. In B.S. Bolaria (Ed.), *Social issues and contradictions in Canadian society* (pp. 464–480). Toronto: Harcourt Brace Jovanovich.

Borsellino, M. (1990, March). Poor health care housing blamed for Native's high disability rate. *Medical Post*, 27, 20.

Bradley, C.F., Ross, S.E., & Warnyea, J.M. (1978, November). *Parent's choice. A comprehensive perinatal programme.* Vancouver Perinatal Health Project.

Brown, J.L. (1989). When violence has a benevolent face: The paradox of hunger in the world's wealthiest democracy. *International Journal of Health Services*, 19, (2), 257–277.

Canadian Association of Food Banks. (1989). *Canadian hungercourt, 1989. Summary.* Toronto: Author.

Carillo, T., Gilbride, A., & Chan, M.M. (1990). Soup kitchen meals: An observation and nutrient analysis. *Journal of the American Diet Association*, 90, 989–991.

Chossudovsky, M. (1983). Underdevelopment and the political economy of malnutrition and ill health. *International Journal of Health Services*, 13, (1) 69–87.

Coleman, J., & Cressey, D. (1984). *Social Problems* (2nd ed.). New York: Harper & Row.

Driver, D. (1991, September 17). Poverty linked to higher risks of poor health, death. *The Medical Post*, 81.

Eales, M.J. (1989). Shame among unemployed men. *Social Science and Medicine*, 28, (8), 783-789.

Emmons, L. (1987). Relationship of participation in food assistance programs to the nutritional quality of diets. *American Journal of Public Health*, 77, 856-858.

Epp, S., & Zinn, M.B. (1986). Achieving health for all: A framework for health promotion. *Canadian Journal of Public Health*, 77, (6), 393-407.

Fine, S. (1989, July 25). Poor children more likely to die than wealthy peers, study finds. *Globe and Mail*, p. A5.

Gerth, H.H., & Wright Mills, C. (Eds.). (1958). *From Max Weber: Essays in sociology*. New York: Oxford University Press.

Grant, K.R. (1988). The inverse care law in Canada: Differential access under universal free health insurance. In B.S. Bolaria & H.D. Dickinson (Eds.), *Sociology of health care in Canada* (pp. 118-134). Toronto: Harcourt Brace Jovanovich.

Grant, K.R. (1993). Health and health care. In P.S. Li & B.S. Bolaria (Eds.), *Contemporary sociology* (pp. 394-409). Toronto: Copp Clark Pitman.

Laven, G.T., & Brown, K.C. (1985). Nutritional status of men attending a soup kitchen: A pilot study. *Amercian Journal of Public Health*, 75, 875-878.

Laxdal, O.E., Hubbick, B., & Bolaria, R. Folic acid prevents neural tube defects. *Saskatchewan Medical Journal*, 4, (1), 11-14.

Mao, Y., Moloughney, B., Semenciw, R.M., & Morrison, H. (1992). Indian reserves and registered Indian mortality in Canada. *Canadian Journal of Public Health*, 83, 350-353.

Martin, S.L. (1989). *Women's reproductive health*. Canadian Advisory Council on the Status of Women.

Matza, D. (1966). The disreputable poor. In R. Bendix & S.M. Lipset (Eds.), *Class, status and power*. New York: Free Press.

Myres, A.W., & Kroetsch, D. (1978). The influence of family income on food consumption patterns and nutrition intake in Canada. *Canadian Journal of Public Health*, 69, (3), 208-21.

National Council of Welfare. (1975). *Poor kids*. Ottawa: Ministry of Supply and Services.

National Council of Welfare. (1987). *Welfare: The tangled safety net*. Ottawa: Ministry of Supply and Services.

National Council of Welfare. (1988). *Poverty profile 1988*. Ottawa: Minister of Supply and Services.

National Council of Welfare. (1989). *Poverty lines*. Ottawa: Ministry of Supply and Services.

National Council of Welfare. (1990a, Summer). *Women and poverty revisited*. Ottawa: Supply and Services Canada.

National Council of Welfare. (1990b, Autumn). *Health, health care and medicare*. Ottawa: Supply and Services Canada.

National Council of Welfare. (1992, Autumn). *Poverty profile, 1980-1990*. Ottawa: Supply and Services Canada.

Nutrition Canada. (1975). *Survey report on Indians and Eskimos*. Ottawa: Information Canada.

Oderkirk, J. (1992, Spring). Food banks. *Canadian Social Trends*, 24, (6), 6-14.

Olson, K.W. (1992). *Food security in Edmonton — Organizing for action*. Edmonton: Edmonton Food Policy Council.

Perkins, S. (1974). *Malnutrition and mental development*. International Union of Child Welfare Conference.

Pollock, S. (1988). Feminism and reproduction. In B.S. Bolaria & H.D. Dickinson, *Sociology of health care in Canada* (pp. 167-182). Toronto: Harcourt Brace Jovanovich.

Rauschenbach, B.S., Frongillo, E.A., Thompson, F.E., Anderson, E.Y.J., & Spicer, D. (1990). Dependency on soup kitchens in urban areas of New York state. *Amercian Journal of Public Health*, 80, (1), 57-60.

Reid, D. L., & Miles, J.E. (1977). Food habits and nutrition intakes of non-institutionalized senior citizens. *Canadian Journal of Public Health*, 68, (2), 154-58.

Reuler, J.B. (1989). Health care for homeless in a national health program. *American Journal of Public Health*, 79, (8), 1003-1035.

Riches, G. (1986). *Food banks and the welfare crisis*. Ottawa: Canadian Council on Social Development.

Ross, S.E., & Rutter, A.C. (1978). *Healthiest babies possible: An outreach program*. Vancouver: Vancouver Perinatal Health Project.

Sennett, R., & Cobb, J. (1973). *The hidden injuries of class*. New York: Vintage Books.

Shah, C.P., & Farkas, C.S. (1985). The health of Indians in Canadian cities: A challenge to the health-care system. *Canadian Medical Association Journal*, 133, 859-63.

Shah, C.P., Kahan, M., & Krauser, J. (1987, September 15). The health of children of low income families. *Canadian Medical Association Journal*, 137, 485-490.

Tarasuk, V.S., & MacLean, H. (1990, July-August). The insititutionalization of food banks in Canada: A public health concern. *Canadian Journal of Public Health*, 81, 331-332.

Thomson, M., & Philion, J. (1991, May/June). Children's respiratory hospitalization and air pollution. *Canadian Journal of Public Health*, 82.

Thomson, M. (1990, August). Association between mortality and poverty. *B.C. Medical Journal*, 32, 8.

Trypuc, J.B. (1989). Health care for homeless in a national health program. *American Journal of Public Health*, 79, (8), 1033-1035.

Vernon, P.E. (1979). *Intelligence: heredity and environment*. San Francisco: W.H. Freeman.

Webber, M. (1992). *Food for thought*. Toronto: Coach House Press.

Wiecha, J.L., Dwyer, J.T., & Dunn-Strhecker, M. (1991, July-August). Nutrition and health services needs among the homeless. *Public Health Reports*, 106, (4), 364-374.

Wigle, D.T., & Mao, Y. (1980). *Mortality by income level in urban Canada*. Ottawa: Health and Welfare Canada.

Wilkins, R., Adams, O., & Brancker, A. (1990, May). Highlights from a new study of changes in mortality by income in urban Canada. *Chronic Diseases in Canada*.

Wilkins, R., & Adams, O. (1983). *Healthfulness of life*. Montreal: Institute on Public Policy.

Winkleby, M.A. (1990). Comparison of risk factors for ill health in a sample of homeless and nonhomeless poor. *Public Health Reports*, 105, (4), 404-409.

Wood, D., & Valdez, B. (1991). Barriers to medical care for homeless families compared with housed poor families. *American Journal of Diseases in Children*, 145, 1109-1115.

Woods, D., Burciaga, L.R., Hayashi, T., & Shew, A. (1990, December). Health of homeless children and housed, poor children. *Pediatrics*, 86, (6), 858-866.

Part Four

Women, Family, and Health

Part Four

Introduction

Readings in this section discuss a range of issues with respect to women as patients and consumers of health-care services. One common theme runs through these chapters; that is, gender inequality and women's subordinate position in society dictate the inequality of treatment that women receive in the health sector. There are several manifestations of this, including: medical definition of women's sexuality and fertility, male definition of women's sexuality and fertility, and the medicalization of social problems. It should be noted that practices within the health sector not only observe but reinforce gender inequality in society.

Chapter 12, by Trypuc, begins with the basic premise that women's position in society has consequences for their health, as well as for their experiences as consumers of health care. The author examines three areas. First, an analysis of sex differences in Canadian mortality and morbidity patterns indicates that in general, women have greatly benefited from health improvements and disease control. There is a decline in women's mortality and an increase in life expectancy; women live longer than men. Women also seem to use the health-care system more than men. The major cause of morbidity differs between the sexes, with men suffering from more chronic conditions and women suffering from more acute conditions.

Second, the author critically examines the various explanations that have been proposed to explain sex mortality differentials. These include: the "genetic superiority of women" hypothesis, male socialization (wherein males ostensibly are socialized to be more aggressive than females), and the "male lifestyle" hypothesis (which suggests males engage more frequently in life-endangering behaviour).

Third, the author further examines various explanations that shed light on women's morbidity patterns. These include: the negative effects of the social role of women, the hypothesis that women are actually "sicker," the hypothesis that women are made to believe they are sicker (due to medicalization of procedures), the notion that women have a greater knowledge and interest in health (and thereby take better care of themselves), and the hypothesis that the concept of the health ethic is masculine (making it easier for a woman to be sick).

The chapter concludes by noting that women are increasingly challenging the health-care system and the society that supports this system. As long as women remain a devalued group in society, their health will continue to suffer.

Findlay and Miller, in Chapter 13, trace the medicalization of women's health through an examination of three topics: the historical emergence of modern medical knowledge as a powerful and prestigious perspective on the world; how the central facets of women's lives — motherhood and childrearing, the abuse of women, and bodily appearance — when viewed as medical events, influence their outcome; and the effects on women's lives when and if they and others decide to view their lives through medical eyes.

Medicalization, the process whereby a condition or object comes to be regarded as an illness, is a relatively new phenomenon — for centuries, people blamed deformities, diseases, and illnesses as a sign of disfavour by a spiritual being. As medicine began to emerge as a profession, a powerful, male-dominated one at that, conditions that had once been regarded as non-medical came under a doctor's supervision, and subsequently, his control. Women, with their inferior social status, held little interest for members of this burgeoning profession until it was decided that they, as childbearers, had at least some value (at least as bearers of future populations). Women, as a consequence of this new status, found themselves to be medically treated for pregnancy and childbirth. Findlay and Miller document how this form of medicalization of women's health has continued through the years to influence our lives in terms of pregnancy, childbirth, mothering, relationships with others, and self-concept. The authors suggest that although women have been controlled by the medical profession, they also have a vested interest in some aspects of medicalizing their health and have learned how to use this medicalization to their advantage. Interaction between women and the medical profession will likely continue, not as a win or lose situation, but rather as an ongoing negotiation for control.

Walters, in Chapter 14, discusses research on women's perspectives and priorities regarding health and illness, and suggests that the relationship between medical and lay perspectives is more complex than supposed. The typical image of women who are passive and compliant in the face of medical dominance is misleading. The medical model forms only one element of women's concepts of health and illness, and physicians are only one of several resources women draw upon when they experience health problems. Women's perspectives and responses are rooted in the nature of their lives, and to this extent are resistant to medicalization. This resistance can assume different forms. It may be expressed through a strong sense of fatalism, or in a more assertive manner, it may involve women's refusal to submit to medical procedures or their efforts to change the very nature of medical practice itself.

After reviewing literature relevant to the thesis of medicalization, Walters goes on to consider women's main health concerns. Despite the emphasis in medicine and in feminist scholarship on women and health, there is evidence that reproductive issues are not among women's main concerns. Rather, problems associated with stress, as well as worries about body image may be among the most important, along with health issues such as arthritis, migraines, and chronic headaches. In juxtaposing definitions of women's most important health problems, Walters raises questions about the interpretation and validation of women's own priorities. To what extent should we accept these at face value, or is our task as sociologists to reinterpret them as examples of constrained choices, limited aspirations, or false consciousness? If we opt for the latter, do we run the risk of invalidating women's concerns and injecting a form of dominance akin to that of medicine? A related issue is that of how women's priorities might be integrated into the policy-making process. Insofar as policy making is a rational process founded on systematically derived indices of need, is there a basis for arguing that these indices should incorporate lay perceptions of need? But, if policy is also the outcome of struggles over definitions of need, how can women identify and give voice to their sense of priorities? Walters suggests that not enough attention has been paid to the concerns of "ordinary women," and that a challenge for the future is the discovery and articulation of the voices of women, so that they may be expressed more assertively in the political arena.

Hinch and DeKeseredy, in Chapter 15, review the limited Canadian sociological research available on the types of corporate violence women experience in both the home and industrial workplace. From the discovery of the dangers of exposure to lead for pregnant women in the 19th century, numerous other health hazards have been identified. This number pales, however, when one considers that more than 500 000 chemical substances are in use, 3 000 new substances are introduced annually, yet only 3 percent of the total number of these chemicals have been tested for potential carcinogenic effects.

The authors first look at some of the hazards women experience in the workplace. These range from repetitive strain injuries (RSI) and lack of adequate training through sexual harassment and the risk of assault. Domestic hazards include: prescription drugs commonly prescribed to women; toxic substances in the form of cleaning products, construction materials, food additives, packaging, hygiene products, and pesticides; unsafe consumer products such as appliances; and IUDs.

Hinch and DeKeseredy maintain that this form of corporate and domestic violence results from manufacturers' and industries' desire to reduce cost and make profit at the worker's expense. Further, although both men and women are exposed to this chemical arsenal, women's concerns about health and safety are not taken as seriously as their male counterparts — their number in industry is less so therefore their concerns have less weight.

The issue of sexual abuse of patients by physicians and therapists is not new. Williams, in Chapter 16, details findings of two recent Canadian initiatives that explore this problem. CHASTEN (Canadian Health Alliance to Stop Therapist Exploitation Now) is an organization comprising mental-health practitioners who assist victims of physician-therapist abuse and promote awareness through research, lobbying, and workshops. The second initiative stems from the professional level. In 1991, the College of Physicians and Surgeons of Ontario established an independent task force that used public hearings, written briefs, and a 24-hour toll-free telephone line to gather information from victims of abuse, their advocates and a number of professional organizations. Williams explores aspects of physician-therapist sexual abuse, its impact on victims, problems and outcomes of reporting abuse, and prevention strategies. Excerpts from the CPSO task force are reprinted throughout the paper; its recommendations are also included.

Finally, in Chapter 17, Grant documents one of the most important recent developments in reproductive medicine — the new reproductive technologies (NRT). Though not all of these innovations are new, nor even technological, what makes the NRT significant is that they provide infertile people with the possibility of a genetic link to a child and/or the possibility of bearing a child who might not otherwise have been born. No doubt the public's fascination with the NRT is enhanced when we hear of "miracle" babies being born.

Yet there are many individuals who have raised serious questions about the NRT, and the most strident of critics are drawn from the feminist community. Fearing that the NRT will only further enslave women to the reproductive role, and that these technologies may pose serious health risks to women, not to mention overwhelming social implications for us all, feminist critics have been quick to implore us to impose a moratorium on NRT. This, they contend, is essential to allow for these technologies to be adequately tested, and for an indepth social dialogue on the consequences of the NRT for women, men, children, and society at large to be undertaken. Grant questions whether the NRT are a boon to the infertile, or potentially the bane of women, who ultimately are most often affected by these technologies, and examines some of the health and social consequences of NRT in detail.

Chapter 12

Women's Health

Joann M. Trypuc, University of Toronto

Introduction

If illness were viewed only from a medical or biological point of view, questions of power, resources, beliefs, and attitudes would be unimportant. However, the fact that sociology views illness as socially defined, with the medical system incorporating social relationships, makes it necessary to examine health care within a broader social context.

Women's position in society has consequences for their health, as well as for their experiences as consumers of health care. Essentially, women wield less economic and political power than men. Women are also more likely to be socially and psychologically dependent and economically disadvantaged. In our society, certain institutions and practices, reinforced by socialization processes, favour men over women in the achievement of power and authority. This sexual inequality has led to concerns by feminists regarding women's health and the care women receive.

One Canadian critic has observed that women get inferior health care mainly because of their upbringing and conditioning. Girls are taught not to question, to be unaggressive, and to defer to men and to authority figures. Most doctors are both. Furthermore, women are faced with conflicting societal expectations, and thus feel guilty about participating in the paid labour force while trying to fulfil the traditional role expectations of mother and homemaker. Often stressed and overworked, women have difficulty controlling their lives. Demanding more control within the medical system, which is supposed to provide care, is a struggle (Carver, 1984, pp. 38-45).

Table I Major Causes of Death in Canada, 1989

	Women		Men	
	No.	%	No.	%
Diseases of the heart	25 642	29.5	31 369	30.1
Malignant neoplasms (cancer)	22 955	26.4	28 345	27.2
Cerebrovascular disease	8 261	9.5	6 122	5.9
Respiratory diseases	6 914	8.0	9 243	8.9
Accidents and adverse effects	4 296	5.0	9 518	9.1
Sub-total	68 068	78.4	84 597	81.3
Other causes	18 789	21.6	19 511	18.7
TOTAL	86 857		104 108	

Source: Statistics Canada *Health Reports* Catalogue 82-003S12.

There are a large number of important issues surrounding women as patients and consumers of health care. This chapter will begin by presenting Canadian mortality (death) and morbidity (illness) statistics, and will then explore in more detail the issues surrounding the mortality and morbidity experiences of Canadian women.

Sex Differences in Mortality and Morbidity

Women have greatly benefited from health improvements in disease control. Before the turn of the century, females faced higher risks of dying than males. Although this was a time of high overall death rates due to infectious disease (e.g., tuberculosis, influenza) for women, repeated pregnancies, lengthy breast-feeding, and prolonged childbearing made them even more susceptible to illness and death (Omran, 1977, p. 30). Better sanitation and medical technology gradually lowered infectious disease rate for both sexes. As well, women's health benefited from the declining birth rate, and the increase in degenerative diseases (e.g., cancer, heart disease) seemed to affect men at higher rates than women. A noticeable increase in sex mortality differential appeared. For example, in 1931, Canadian women's life expectancy was 62.1 years, compared to 60.0 for men. By 1987, the differential increased to seven years, with women expected to live to 80 years of age and men to 73 years of age (Life Tables, Statistics Canada Catalogue 84-515; Canada Year Book, 1992).

Today, the major causes of death for Canadian women are similar to those for men. As Table 1 shows, the two major causes of death are disease of the heart and malignant neoplasms (cancer). Accidents and adverse effects, which include motor-vehicle accidents, suicide, and homicides, and which are avoidable deaths, are the fifth major killer of Canadian women, and the third major killer of Canadian men.

Unlike mortality, the major causes of morbidity differ between males and females. Table 2 compares the twenty leading causes of hospitalization of women and men. Hospitalization due to pregnancy, childbirth, and diseases of the reproductive organs account for a large proportion of women's hospitalization rates. In contrast, heart disease, a chronic condition and a major cause of hospitalization for men, is only the seventh major cause for women.

Men are hospitalized for more chronic conditions than females, whereas females suffer from more acute causes of hospitalized illness. In other words, the diseases of females are less likely to lead to death (Nathanson, 1977; Verbrugge, 1976b).

One of the most notable morbidity differences between the sexes is the fact that females more commonly admit to symptoms of both mental and physical illness than do males (Clancy & Gove, 1974, p. 210; Nathanson, 1975, p. 57; Verbrugge, 1976a, p. 400; Nathanson, 1977, p. 15; D'Arcy & Schmitz, 1979, p. 19). In the 1978-79 Canada Health Survey, 54.3 percent of females reported at least one health problem, compared to 45.7 percent of men. In addition, women reported more major activity days lost because of illness than did men. Women reported losing 83 188 000 major activity days compared to 30 977 000 reported by men, a ratio of 2.7:1 (Health & Welfare Canada and Statistics Canada, Catalogue 82-538E).

Women also use doctors and hospitals more frequently than do men (Rosenstock, 1966, p. 96; Anderson & Anderson, 1967, pp. 40-41; Nathanson, 1975, p. 57; Nathanson, 1977, p. 15; Mechanic, 1978, p. 196; Verbrugge, 1979, p. 61). In Canada in 1988-89, for every day spent in the hospital by a male, females spent 1.3 days. This differential use of hospitals has been shown to persist even with the exclusion of hospitalization for pregnancy (Rosenstock, 1966, p. 96; Andersen & Anderson, 1967, pp. 36-37; Nathanson, 1975, p. 58).

Why Do Sex Differences in Death Exist?

Various explanations have been proposed to shed light on the sex mortality differential.

Genetic Superiority of Women

Genetics have often been used to explain the fact that males have higher mortality rates than females in many species (Waldron, 1976, p. 3). Although more males are conceived than females (Bentzen, 1963, p. 93; Taylor et al., 1972, p. 216; Williamson, 1978, p. 4;

Ortmeyer, 1979, p. 123), the death rate of male fetuses is higher (Fuchs, 1974, pp. 47-48; Ortmeyer, 1979, pp. 124-125; Waldron, 1976, p. 3). For example, research has shown that more male than female fetuses are spontaneously aborted (Rasmuson, 1971, p. 43). Similarly, the number of male still-births is higher than that for females (Yerushalmy, 1963, p. 151; Rasmuson, 1971, p. 43), and in the first year of life, the male death rate is higher than the female death rate.

All of the above findings seem to point to a female genetic advantage. It has been suggested that the chromosomal arrangement may be a major factor in this advantage: if a gene on a male's X chromosome is defective, there may be no countering gene on the Y chromosome, whereas a female may have a corresponding gene on the second X chromosome acting as protection (Ortmeyer, 1979, p. 124). This explanation may have some validity. One study showed that out of 187 neonatal abnormalities identified in a study of 15 000 patients, 71.8 percent occurred predominantly among males, 25.1 percent among females, and only 3.1 percent had an equal sex distribution (Singer et al., 1968, p. 109).

Although more than 50 pathological conditions do occur exclusively in males, most of these pathologies are not common, and those that are common are seldom lethal; in fact, deaths due to these causes are less than 2 percent of excess male deaths up to the end of the reproductive years (Waldron & Johnston, 1976, pp. 22-23).

Although higher male fetal death rates seem to point to a female genetic advantage, care must be taken not to overemphasize genetics as a major contributor to the longer life expectancy for women. Retherford has noted that the increases in the human sex mortality differential over the past 50 years could not have been due to biological differences, for genetic structures do not change that quickly (1975, p. 12).

Male Socialization

It has been suggested that males are socialized to be more aggressive than females. "Boys and men (more than girls and women), have been encouraged to consume alcohol, drive cars, use guns, be adventurous, act unafraid, be brave, and if need be, take risks" (Ortmeyer, 1979, p. 129). As mentioned, this type of socialization may have a major effect on death rates as measured by accident and suicide fatalities. As Table 1 indicates, 9.1 percent of all Canadian male deaths in 1989 were a result of accidents and adverse effects, in contrast to 5.0 percent of female deaths.

Gender differences in death rates due to motor-vehicle accidents in particular may be explained by the fact that men drive more, and less safely, than women (Waldron & Johnston, 1976, p. 19). Furthermore, men consume more alcohol than women. For example, in Canada in 1978-79, 75.2 percent of Canadian men were current drinkers compared to 55.7 percent of women. Of these men, 57.9 percent consumed seven or more drinks per week, as compared to 35.2 percent of women who consumed this much (Health & Welfare Canada and Statistics Canada, Catalogue 82-538E). Needless to say, this drinking has deadly consequences. Half of all fatal motor-vehicle accidents involve drunken drivers; other accidents, as well as suicides, are also associated with alcohol use (Waldron & Johnston, 1976, p. 20). One can hypothesize that males are victims of a socialization that stresses being aggressive and engaging in risky behaviour. Unfortunately, the deaths that do occur as a result of these actions are violent, and for the most part preventable.

The "Male Lifestyle"

Closely related to socialization is a traditional male lifestyle that more women are beginning to emulate. Table 1 shows that the two major causes of death today in Canada are diseases of the heart and malignant neoplasms (i.e., cancers). As mentioned previously, males tend to suffer from these "killer" diseases at higher rates than females. Excessive tobacco use by males, hazardous occupational conditions, and stress have increased death rates due to these lifestyle-related diseases. Increasingly, women's health is being affected by these conditions as well.

"Smoking trends have played an important role in the evolution of the sex mortality differential during this century" (Retherford, 1972, p. 105). This trend has exacerbated the incidence of coronary heart disease, lung cancer, and emphysema (Waldron, 1976, p. 10). Since middle-class women were discouraged from smoking, at least until the twentieth century, women were less vulnerable than men to smoking-related illnesses. This is rapidly changing, however. The average consumption of cigarettes by Canadian males 15 years of age and older in 1931 was 1113 cigarettes, compared to 78 for females of the same age. By 1975, however, these figures had risen to 4311 cigarettes for males and, much more dramatically, to 2592 cigarettes for females (Abelson et al., 1983, p. 30). Between 1979 and 1983, in Canada, male smoking declined 15 percent, while female smoking declined only 4 percent. Furthermore, in 1985, 25 percent of teenage girls smoked daily, compared to 21 percent of teenage boys. The results of this trend towards smoking can be seen in female disease trends: in the past ten years, Canadian women's lung cancer mortality increased by 45 percent; within the next five, it is estimated to exceed breast cancer as the leading cancer in women (Edwards, 1986, p. 9). In 1988, 20 percent of female cancer deaths were due to breast cancer compared to 17.3 percent due to lung cancer (Statistics Canada Catalogue 82-003S12).

Why are women smoking more? A number of reasons have been suggested: smoking may be viewed as a symbol of emancipation (as stated in one brand's slogan: "You've

Table 2 Twenty leading Causes of Hospitalization by Number of Separations for Women and Men, Canada, 1988–89

Women	%	Number
Complications in labour and delivery	7.2	152 293
Indication for care in pregnancy, labour, and delivery	5.6	119 060
Other complications related to pregnancy	4.9	103 654
Symptoms, signs, and other ill-defined conditions	4.9	102 919
Normal delivery	3.5	74 629
Other disease of female genital organs	3.0	62 213
Other forms of heart disease	2.4	50 151
Cholelithiasis	2.1	43 497
All other forms of ischaemic heart disease	1.8	38 430
Cataract	1.6	33 402
Asthma	1.5	32 027
Non-infective enteritis and colitis	1.5	30 878
Chronic diseases of tonsils and adenoids	1.5	30 731
Other arthropathies and related disorders	1.4	29 624
Pneumonia	1.4	28 604
Other reasons for contact with health services	1.3	28 078
Other diseases of intestine and peritoneum	1.3	26 397
Contact with health services for specific procedures and after care	1.2	25 730
Disorders of menstruation	1.2	24 238
Fractures of femur	1.0	20 193
Sub total	50.3%	1 056 748
Other causes	49.7%	1 055 508
TOTAL	100.0%	2 112 256

Source: *Health Reports: Hospital Morbidity 1988-89*, Statistics Canada, Catalogue 82-003S1.

come a long way, baby''); smoking may also be a way to cope with the increasing stresses that women face in trying to fulfil home and paid work responsibilities.

Along with cigarette smoking, industrial pollutants have contributed to higher lung cancer rates (Waldron, 1976, p. 10), and to increases in cancer and heart and lung disease in general (Ortmeyer, 197, p. 130). With greater numbers of women moving into non-traditional occupations, industrial pollutants may begin to have a greater impact on women's death rates. In addition, it has been suggested that the stress associated with women's greater upward mobility in the paid labour force will increase female lifestyle death rates. The findings of a recent study, however, do not support this hypothesis. Although further research is needed, the authors point to the notion that the effects of occupational stress that women undergo may be minimized as long as mobility is seen as positive development (Sorensen et al., 1985, p. 390). It must be pointed out, however, that women may also experience stress as a result of frustrated ambition due to limited upward mobility.

Suicides have also been regarded as the deadly consequence of a stressful lifestyle. In Canada today, more men than women die by their own hand. For example, in 1989 for every 100 000 Canadian men between 20 and 24 years of age, approximately 30 committed suicide compared to 6 Canadian women (Statistics Canada Catalogue 82-003S12).

It has been postulated that one cause of the higher suicide rate among men is the stress of competition for jobs (Waldron & Johnston, 1976, p. 20). Women presumably experience less stress in adopting the homemaker role. This assumption may not hold true, however, since females attempt suicide four times more often than males; on the other hand, males are three times more likely to complete the act (Garai, 1970, p. 138; Gove, 1972, p. 205; Furnass, 1977, p. 15; Ortmeyer, 1979, p. 129). A higher male "completed" suicide rate may be a result of methods used (men tend to use immediately fatal methods, such as guns, whereas women tend to use more "reversible" methods, such as poisons and drugs). Further more, women may use the suicide attempt as a cry for help rather than as an act to fulfil the need to kill themselves, whereas men, finding it more difficult to "cry for help," carry the suicidal act through to its conclusion (Waldron & Johnston, 1976, pp. 20-22).

Why Do Sex Differences in Morbidity Exist?

Numerous attempts have been made to explain women's illness patterns. There seems to be a contradiction in the fact that women live longer and are, therefore, presumably healthier, yet report more illness and use more medical services than men. Consequently the popular view exists that the high rates of morbidity among women are artifactual (Gove & Hughes, 1979, p. 129), with women using health services and spending health dollars needlessly. Several reasons have been proposed to explain women's illness behaviour. A number of these are explored below.

The Social Role of Women

It is often part of a woman's role as a parent to take children to the doctor; women become accustomed to being there, are more familiar with the doctor, and possibly become more dependent on him or her (D'Arcy, 1977, p. 216; Simkin, 1978, p. 11). Thus, the finding that women are more likely than men to seek medical help, even for minor

Table 2 (cont.) Twenty leading Causes of Hospitalization by Number of Separations for Women and Men, Canada, 1988–89

Men	%	Number
Symptoms, signs, and other ill-defined conditions	6.0	92 482
Other forms of ischaemic heart disease	4.3	66 628
Other forms of heart disease	3.6	55 406
Inguinal hernia	3.1	46 867
Acute myocardial infarction	2.3	34 923
Pneumonia	2.3	34 621
Hyperplasia of prostate	2.2	34 333
Asthma	2.1	32 635
Other arthropathies and related disorders	1.8	27 680
All other diseases of respiratory system	1.8	27 261
All other diseases of urinary system	1.7	26 311
Fractures of the skull and intracranial injury	1.7	26 242
Other reasons for contact with health services	1.7	25 439
Chronic disease of tonsils and adenoids	1.7	25 291
Non-infective enteritis and colitis	1.6	24 820
Contact with health services for specific procedures and aftercare	1.5	22 198
Acute upper respiratory infections	1.5	22 193
Other and late effects of cerebrovascular disease	1.4	22 159
Complications of medical and surgical care	1.4	21 681
Other diseases of intestine and peritoneum	1.4	21 225
Sub total	45.0%	690 395
Other causes	55.0%	844 869
TOTAL	100.0%	1 535 264

Source: *Health Reports: Hospital Morbidity 1988-89*, Statistics Canada, Catalogue 82-003SI.

illnesses, may be due to this acquired dependency on the doctor, as well as to the opportunity that their role as the primary care-giver creates.

Related to this analysis is the fairly widely held assumption that the social role of women entails fewer time constraints than that of men. This presumably allows women to seek medical attention and to restrict activity more readily than males (Mechanic, 1965, p. 256; Verbrugge, 1976b, p. 292; Verbrugge, 1979, p. 66). Although it may be easier for women who do not work fixed hours to schedule medical appointments, the premise that women have fewer obligations and therefore more free time to be sick is unfounded. In fact, on the average, women work longer hours than men. Married women working for pay also fulfil their domestic responsibilities; as Luxton (1980,

p. 11) has noted, women "take on a double day of work, labouring as both wage workers and domestic workers."

As domestic workers, women take on the major role of being health-care workers in the home. In her study of 240 British women, Roberts (1985) points out that women are not only consumers but are also producers of health care. As producers, women take the major responsibility for keeping other people healthy, yet there seems to be little recognition that fulfilling this duty might actually make women sick. The study notes that overworked, stressed women were encouraged to quit work and stay at home to "rest," even though other findings suggest that women's unpaid work is more stressful than their paid labour. Therefore, the prescription for these women to stay home actually had the potential to make them sick.

Women Are Sicker

In view of the social role of women discussed above, women may actually be sicker, displaying more symptoms of illness as a result of pressures associated with their role demands. Gove and Hughes (1979, pp. 127, 134) found that the apparent higher rates of morbidity among women were based almost exclusively on higher rates of mild transitory disorders, such as cold, headaches, and dysmenorrhea. These illnesses, it is postulated, are physical disorders that are a reaction to psychological distress. Assuming the female's role entails an obligation to care for others that may interfere with their ability to care for herself, and because she has more role obligations which require ongoing activity (i.e., with children, spouse, and others), Gove and Hughes (1979, pp. 132, 144) hypothesize that a woman's self-care will be interrupted, leading to a negative effect on her health. After control of the data for marital status, living arrangements, psychiatric symptoms, and nurturant role obligations, health differences between women and men disappeared. The authors conclude that sex differences in physical health are due to sex differences in nurturant role demands and mental health. Furthermore, these differences reflect real rather than artifactual differences in physical health (Gove & Hughes, 1979, pp. 126, 141-143).

Women may also experience more sickness due to their reproductive functions. Verbrugge (1985, p. 164) notes that reproduction gives women morbidity risks not experienced by men. Furthermore, women's reproductive systems are more complex than men's, which increases the risk of female-specific disorders.

It has been suggested that women's morbidity rates are higher because the symptoms of some of women's illnesses are more easily detectable (Mechanic, 1978, p. 187). For example, Omran (1977, p. 32) notes that certain female cancers (e.g., cervical, uterine, and breast) produce more noticeable symptoms than certain male cancers (e.g., colon, lung, and prostate), where the organ is concealed and not routinely examined and produces symptoms only in the advanced stages of malignancy. Women, noticing these overt symptoms, are able to respond much more quickly than if the symptoms were not easily detectable.

Women Are Made to Believe They Are Sicker

The nature of Canadian health-care delivery may make women believe that they are sicker than is actually the case. We live in a society where high rates of hospital use have been said to reflect partly social custom rather than necessary medical procedure (Allentuck, 1978, p. 8). For example, unnecessary drug prescription, procedures, and surgery do occur. Unfortunately, these actions carry the implicit message that the recipient is sick and in need of treatment.

Women are more likely than men to use painkillers, sleeping pills, and tranquillizers. The National Alcohol and Other Drugs Survey (NADS) found that in 1989, 5.7 percent of women reported taking codeine, demerol, or morphine in the month before the survey compared to 4.3 percent of men. The proportion of women who had used sleeping pills was 4.6 percent compared to 2.5 percent for men (Eliany, 1991, p. 23). Another study found that physicians were more likely to offer tranquillizers to women than to men presenting the same complaints (Cooperstock, 1979, p. 33). And in a third study, when Ontario general practitioners were questioned about the higher mood-modifying prescription rate for women, doctors' replies ranged from biological vulnerability, to differential life stress, to self-indulgence, to male reluctance to seek help (Cooperstock, 1971, pp. 239-240).

Drug advertising, especially in medical journals, presents a negative view of women. Some of the themes of these ads include the notions that women cannot cope, that women are "dumb," that women can be a real nuisance to others, and that a woman's biology is her destiny (Rochon Ford, 1986, pp. 14-17). Besides this, the overall message comes through that many of life's ills can be remedied with a drug (Chesher, 1977, p. 35). Thus, rather than trying to change the stressful circumstances of one's life, a person will use drugs to enable toleration of this life.

Taking drugs can actually make one feel physically, emotionally, and psychologically sicker. Many drugs are toxic with "physical side effects, interaction effects with other substances, as well as effects on the emotion and behaviour of individuals" (Owen, 1977, p. 45). Furthermore, although many drugs are on the market, "in only a few cases can it be said that we know how the drug is working . . . in some cases it is still uncertain if the drug therapy is any more effective than placebo" (Chesher, 1977, p. 34).

In addition to drug use, women can be made to feel sicker through unnecessary operations and the overmedicalization of particular functions. For example, uncomplicated delivery of a baby is not a sickness so much as a normal part of life. It can be argued that low-risk, normal pregnancies do not require extensive medical backup. In fact, one consequence of such backup is that it can further medicalize childbirth. For example, the Caesarean rate as a percentage of live births has been gradually rising in Canada. In 1970, 6 percent of live births were by Caesarean section. By 1988, the figure had risen to 19.5 percent (Nair, 1991, p. 209).

Another example of a female experience that is unnecessarily medicalized is abortion. There is one legally induced abortion for every ten babies normally delivered in a Canadian hospital (Statistics Canada Catalogue 82-003S12). It can be argued that an expensive, technological hospital setting is not necessary for performing abortions safely within the first 16 weeks of pregnancy.

A close examination of Table 2 shows that childbirth and sex-specific ailments are important factors in female hospitalization rates. It seems reproduction and related functions consistently introduce a bias into women's use of health services. It can be argued that women consume disproportionately more health resources and facilities largely as a result of needs associated with their reproductive systems. In fact, they have been socialized to depend on the system for these particular functions, with the view that these functions constitute illness.

Women Have a Greater Knowledge of and Interest in Health

Women may be more aware of disease and health issues because they have a greater knowledge of and interest in health (Mechanic, 1978, p. 187). Since women tend to be responsible for their families' health, they, as domestic health-care workers, may have a better understanding of medical problems than do men. In one study, female patients were more likely to ask questions after a physician's explanation than were male patients; those questions were also more likely to elicit informative answers (Wallen et al., 1979, p. 139). Another study found that twice as many men as women ignore newspaper and magazine health columns, as well as health programs on radio and television. Furthermore, women proved to be better informed about the symptoms of cancer, polio, and diabetes, leading the authors to conclude that the broad area of health and illness is more of a feminine concern (Feldman, 1966, pp. 112-113; Lewis & Lewis, 1977, p. 866).

The Concept of the Health Ethic Is Masculine

In contrast to the notion that health and illness are feminine concerns is the notion that healthiness is part of masculinity. It has been suggested that perhaps defining oneself as ill is more appropriate to the social role of the woman than to that of the man (Phillips,

1964, p. 687; Phillips & Segal, 1969, pp. 59, 69; Wilson, 1979, p. 77; Verbrugge, 1976a, p. 398; Gove & Hughes, 1979, p. 126; Verbrugge, 1979, pp. 63, 66). Because of socialization patterns, women are allowed to complain more readily and to appear less stoic (Cooperstock, 1971, p. 241; Mechanic, 1978, p. 197), whereas males "suffer in silence." Thus, supposedly, women more readily admit symptoms and distress (Mechanic, 1976, p. 30). They report more illness because it is culturally more acceptable for them to be ill; the norm of health is masculine (Nathanson, 1977, p. 25), with men feeling more inhibited about reporting certain symptoms (Mechanic, 1979, p. 33).

In studies that have examined reporting of symptoms, methodological problems confound the issue somewhat. Women may be more responsive in interviews, more likely to perceive symptoms, and more likely to report them (Verbrugge, 1976b, p. 295). Similarly, proxy reporting tends to underestimate the illness of the absent person (Verbrugge, 1976a, p. 398; Nathanson, 1977, p. 20). Women are more likely to respond to illness surveys, and thus they may underestimate the illness experience of both their spouses and their children (Mechanic, 1976, p. 33; Verbrugge, 1979, p. 65). It seems sex-based differences in illness either disappear or become smaller when objective measures of illness are used, when symptoms are more "tangible and visible," or when a large degree "of incapacity or impairment is evident" (Mechanic, 1978, p. 188). It has further been suggested that if women are regarded as more willing to express distress, then the definition of distress should include characteristically male behavioural dimensions of distress as well, such as expressions of anger, violence, and drinking (Mechanic, 1976, p. 33). This would serve to provide a more accurate measure of impairment, as defined by the existence of distress.

An argument could be made that the concept of the health ethic as masculine originates from the structure of our system rather than from the socialization process itself. There are greater economic costs associated with males being sick as compared to females not in the labour force or in very low-level positions. Thus, the emphasis on remaining healthy is directed toward the more economically productive group. By viewing health as congruent with the male social role and using this argument to explain differences in health-care use, blame is misplaced. Rather than blaming the system, we end up blaming the socialization of the individual. The appropriateness of illness to the social role of women, structurally speaking, points to the essentially devalued position of women in society.

Conclusion

Challenging the health-care system and the society that supports it is a difficult task. But for women as a group, the challenge is important, since their health and well-being depend on the outcome.

Women are increasingly analyzing both the physical and mental health–care systems from a feminist perspective. For example, many drugs, once taken without question, are being viewed as a way to individualize and make women's structural role strains "manageable." In a study by Cooperstock and Lennard (1981, p. 155) one woman says:

> In the early years when I was so obviously unhappy with what was happening in my life the solution to the doctors was so obviously a drug solution. And I had to push everybody I knew, including the doctors, except my psychiatrist who supported me all the way, that the solution for me was going to be really to quite radically change my life and not to make me comfortable with the life I was in.

This woman highlights some familiar themes: the medical model with the medical cure for any problem; the professionals whose "expert advice" should be followed unquestioningly; and the struggle of the patient to participate in determining his or her own treatment. Beyond these themes, however, is the added dimension of the patient as a female. Since women have less value and less power as a group in our society, they run a greater risk of being taken less seriously.

It has been difficult for women to have their mortality and morbidity experiences legitimized. The fact that Canadian women outlive men, yet use more health services, has been used to suggest that perhaps women are feigning illness. They are not really sick. They are pretending. This view can adversely affect the quality of health care a woman receives. One instance of such a consequence was a study of 498 female rheumatoid arthritis patients. All of them presented symptoms to their physicians, yet 87 percent went twelve years or longer without a diagnosis, with most of them being told they were neurotic (Simkin, 1978, p. 12).

It cannot be denied that health–care advances have greatly benefited women. However, there is a need for improvement, especially in the areas of consumer/patients' rights and regaining control over one's body. Inherent in the women's health movement, which emerged in the early 1970s, is this emphasis on knowledge and self-determination (McDonnell, 1985, pp. 18-21). Self-help groups, the natural childbirth movement, the fight to legalize midwifery, and viewing health beyond the constraints of the medical model are some of the issues that have either been initiated by or incorporated into the women's health movement.

Fighting for better health care and having their illness experiences legitimized are part of the larger issue that women face. This issue is women's struggle for equality. As long as women are not allowed equal participation in public life and in the financially empowered sector of the economy, they will continue to be devalued as a group, and their health will continue to suffer.

Study Questions

1. Based on the information from this chapter, what are your predictions for the mortality and morbidity profiles of men and women in the year 2010? Support your answer.
2. Using medical journals (e.g., *Canadian Medical Association Journal*), examine how women are depicted in drug advertisements. What themes do you note? Compared to ten years ago, have these depictions changed?
3. This chapter examines women as consumers of health care. Investigate the position women hold as health-care workers in hospitals and in the professions.
4. Give evidence to support the argument that women's health care will not improve until women's position in society improves.

Recommended Reading

Barrington, E. (1985). *Midwifery is catching*. Toronto: NC Press.

Boston Women's Health Book Collective. (1984). *The new our bodies, ourselves*. New York: Simon and Schuster.

Carver, C. (1984). *Patient beware: Dealing with doctors and other medical dilemmas*. Scarborough: Prentice-Hall.

Dreifus, C. (Ed.). (1978). *Seizing our bodies: The politics of women's health*. New York: Random House.

Ehrenreich, B., & English, D. (1979). *For her own good: 150 years of the experts' advice to women*. Garden City: Anchor Press/Doubleday.

Healthsharing: A Canadian Women's Health Quarterly. Toronto: Women Healthsharing, Inc.

Health and Welfare Canada. (1990, April). *Working together for women's health: A framework for the development of policies and programs*. Prepared by the Federal/Provincial/Territorial Working Group on Women's Health with assistance from Anne Rochon Ford. Ottawa: Author.

McDonnell, K., & Valverde, M. (Eds.). (1985). *The healthsharing book: Resources for Canadian women*. Toronto: Women's Press.

Penfold, P.S., & Walker, G.A. (1983). *Women and the psychiatric paradox*. Montreal: Eden Press.

Pirie, M. (1988, November). Women and the illness role: rethinking feminist theory. *The Canadian Review of Sociology and Anthropology*, 25, 628-648.

Ruzek, S.B. (1979). *The women's health movement: Feminist alternatives to medical control*. New York: Praeger.

References

Abelson, J., Paddon, P., & Strohmenger, C. (1983). *Perspectives on health*. Statistics Canada, Catalogue 82-540E. Ottawa: Minister of Supply and Services.

Allentuck, A. (1978). *Who speaks for the patient?* Don Mills: Burns & MacEachern.

Andersen, R., & Anderson, O.W. (1967). *A decade of health services*. Chicago: University of Chicago Press.

Bentzen, F. (1963, January). Sex ratios in learning behaviour disorders. *American Journal of Orthopsychiatry*, 33, 92-98.

Bermosk, L.S., & Porter, S.E. (1978). *Women's health and human wholeness*. New York: Appleton-Century-Crofts.

Bird, C.E., & Fremont, A.M. (1991, June). Gender, time use, and health. *Journal of Health and Social Behaviour*, 32, 114-129.

Carver, C. (1984). *Patient beware: Dealing with doctors and other medical dilemmas*. Scarborough: Prentice-Hall.

Chesher, G. (1977). The psychotropic drugs; Part I pharmacological aspects. In M. Diesendorf (Ed.), *The magic bullet* (pp. 33-43). Canberra: Society for Social Responsibility in Science.

Clancy, K., & Gove, W. (1974). Sex differences in mental illness: An analysis of response bias in self-reports. *American Journal of Sociology*, 80, (1), 205-216.

Cooperstock, R. (1971, September). Sex differences in the use of mood-modifying drugs: An explanatory model. *Journal of Health and Social Behaviour*, 12, 238-244.

Cooperstock, R. (1979, February). A review of women's psychotropic drug use. *Canadian Journal of Psychiatry*, 24, 29-34.

Cooperstock, R., & Lennard, H.L. (1981). Role strains and tranquilizer use. In D. Coburn, C. D'Arcy, P. New, & G. Torrance (Eds.), *Health and Canadian society: Sociological perspectives* (pp. 142-157). Markham: Fitzhenry & Whiteside.

D'Arcy, C. (1977, August). Patterns of delivery of psychiatric care in Saskatchewan 1971-1972: Part III: Patient socio-demographic and medical characteristics. *Canadian Psychiatric Association Journal*, 22, 19-27.

Edwards, P. (1986, Summer). Cigarettes: A feminist issue. *Healthsharing*, 7, (3), 8-12.

Eliany, M. (1991, Spring). Alcohol and drug use. *Canadian Social Trends*, 20, 19-26.

Feldman, J.J. (1966). *The dissemination of health information*. Chicago: Aldine.

Fuchs, V.R. (1974). *Who shall live?* New York: Basic Books.

Furnass, B. (1977). Changing patterns of health and disease. In M. Diesendorf (Ed.), *The magic bullet* (pp. 5-32). Canberra: Society for Social Responsibility in Science.

Garai, J.E. (1970, Jan./June). Sex difference in mental health. *Genetic Psychology Monographs*, 81, 123-142.

Gove, W.R. (1972, June). Sex, marital status and suicide. *Journal of Health and Social Behaviour*, 13, 204-213.

Gove, W.R., & Hughes, M. (1979, February). Possible causes of the apparent sex differences in physical health. *American Sociological Review*, 44, 126-146.

Health and Welfare Canada and Statistics Canada. (1981). *The health of Canadians: Report of the Canada health survey*, Catalogue 82-538E. Ottawa: Minister of Supply and Services.

Lewis, C.E., & Lewis, M.A. (1977, October). The potential impact of sexual equality on health. *New England Journal of Medicine*, 197, 863-869.

Luxton, M. (1980). *More than a labour of love*. Toronto: Women's Press.

McDonnell, K. (1985). The women's health movement. In K. McDonnell & M. Valverde (Eds.), *The healthsharing book: Resources for Canadian women* (pp. 18-21). Toronto: Women's Press.

Mechanic, D. (1965, Winter). Perception of parental responses to illness: A research note. *Journal of Health and Human Behaviour*, 6, 253-257.

Mechanic, D. (1976, December). Sex, illness, illness behaviour and the use of health services. *Journal of Human Stress*, 2, 29-40.

Mechanic, D. (1978). *Medical sociology*. New York: Free Pres.

Nair, C. (1991). Trends in caesarian section deliveries in Canada. *Health Reports*, 3, 203-219. Statistics Canada.

Nathanson, C.A. (1975, February). Illness and the feminine role: A theoretical review. *Social Science and Medicine*, 9, 57-62.

Nathanson, C.A. (1977, January). Sex, illness and medical care — A review of data, theory and method. *Social Science and Medicine*, 11, 13-25.

Omran, A.R. (1977). Epidemiologic transition in the U.S.: The health factor in population change. *Population Bulletin*, 32, (2), 42.

Ortmeyer, L.E. (1979, Summer). Female's natural advantage, or the unhealthy environment of males? The status of sex mortality differentials. *Women and Health*, 4, 121-133.

Owen, A. (1977). The psychotropic drugs; Part II: Psychosocial aspects. In M. Diesendorf (Ed.), *The magic bullet* (pp. 44-48). Canberra: Society for Social Responsibility in Science.

Phillips, D.L. (1964, October). Rejection of the mentally ill: The influence of behaviour and sex. *American Sociological Review*, 29, 679-687.

Phillips, D.L., & Segal, B.E. (1969, February). Sex status and psychiatric symptoms. *American Sociological Review*, 34, 58-72.

Rasmuson, M. (1971, Jan/March). Men, the weaker sex? *Impact of Science on Society*, 21, 43-54.

Retherford, R.D. (1972, May). Tobacco smoking and the sex mortality differential. *Demography*, 9, 203-216.

Retherford, R.D. (1975). *The changing sex differential in mortality*. Westport: Greenwood Press.

Roberts, H. (1985). *The patient patients: Women and their doctors*. London: Pandora Press.

Rochon Ford, A. (1986, Winter). In poor health. *Healthsharing*, 7, (2), 13-17.

Rosenstock, I.M. (1966, July). Why people use health services. *Milbank Memorial Fund Quarterly*, 44, (3), (part 2).

Simkin, R.J. (1978, June). *The inadequacy of health care of women*. Unpublished paper (pp. 1-16).

Singer, J.E., Westphal, M., & Niswander, K.R. (1968, June). Sex difference in the incidence of neonatal abnormalities and abnormal performance in early childhood. *Child Development*, 39, 103-112.

Sorensen, G., et al. (1985, December). Sex differences in the relationship between work and health: The Minnesota heart survey. *Journal of Health and Social Behaviour*, 26, 379-394.

Statistics Canada. (1947). *Life tables for Canada and regions, 1941 and 1931*, Catalogue 84-515. Ottawa: Minister of Supply and Services.

Statistics Canada. (1985). *Women in Canada: A statistical report*, Catalogue 89-503E. Ottawa: Minister of Supply and Services.

Statistics Canada. (1986). *Hospital morbidity*, Catalogue 82-206. Ottawa: Minister of Supply and Services.

Statistics Canada. (1992). *Canada year book*. Ottawa: Minister of Supply and Services.

Statistics Canada. (1991). *Health reports: Hospital morbidity 1988-89*. Supplement No. 1, (Vol. 3), (1), Catalogue 82-003S1. Ottawa: Minister of Supply and Services.

Statistics Canada. (1991). *Health reports: Mortality — Summary list of causes 1989*. Supplement No. 12, (Vol. 3), (1), Catalogue 82-003S12. Ottawa: Minister of Supply and Services.

Taylor, D.C., & Ounsted, C. (1972). The nature of gender differences explored through ontogenetic analyses of sex ratios in disease. In C. Ounsted & D.C. Taylor (Eds.), *Gender differences: Their ontogeny and significance* (pp. 215-240). London: Churchill Livingstone.

Verbrugge, L.M. (1976a, December). Females and illness: Recent trends in sex differences in the United States. *Journal of Health and Social Behaviour*, 17, 387-403.

Verbrugge, L.M. (1976b, Winter). Sex differentials in morbidity and mortality in the United States. *Social Biology*, 23, 275-296.

Verbrugge, L.M. (1979, Spring). Female illness rates and illness behaviour: Testing hypotheses about sex differences in health. *Women and Health*, 4, 61-79.

Verbrugge, L.M. (1985, September). Gender and health: An update on hypotheses and evidence. *Journal of Health and Social Behaviour*, 26, 156-182.

Verbrugge, L.M. (1989, September). The twain meet: Empirical explanations of sex differences in health and mortality. *Journal of Health and Social Behaviour*, 30, 282-304.

Waldron, I. (1976, March). Why do women live longer than men? Part I. *Journal of Human Stress*, 2, 2-13.

Waldron, I., & Johnston, S. (1976, June). Why do women live longer than men? Part II. *Journal of Human Stress*, 2, 19-30.

Wallen, J., Waitzkin, H., & Stoeckle, J.D. (1979, Summer). Physician stereotypes about female health and illness: A study of patient's sex and the informative process during medical interviews. *Women and Health*, 4, 135-146.

Williamson, N.E. (1978). Boys or girls? Parents' preferences and sex control. *Population Bulletin*, 33, (1), 35.

Wilson, R.N. (1970). *The sociology of health: An introduction*. New York: Random House.

Yerushalmy, J. (1963). Factors in human longevity. *American Journal of Public Health*, 53, (2), 148-162.

Chapter 13

Through Medical Eyes: The Medicalization of Women's Bodies and Women's Lives

Deborah A. Findlay & Leslie J. Miller
Dalhousie University, University of Calgary

Introduction

It has been said that the influence of professional medicine has transformed the body from "an arena of sacred forces to the mundane reality of diet, cosmetics, exercise, and preventative medicine" (Turner, 1984, p. 216). The writer's point is that the human body, once the concern of the priest, is now the business of the doctor. In this chapter we examine the medicalization of women's bodies and women's lives. We begin by considering the historical emergence of modern medical knowledge as a powerful and prestigious perspective on the world, and go on to ask why it is that women's lives, in particular, have become favoured territory for medical intervention. The second part of the chapter looks at three central facets of women's lives — motherhood and child rearing, the abuse of women, and bodily appearance — in order to assess the outcome when these activities and conditions are defined as medical problems. In the final section we ask whether women stand to gain as well as lose, when they and others come to see their lives through medical eyes.

The Rise of Medical Discourse and the Professionalization of Medicine

"Medicalization" refers to the process whereby an object or a condition becomes defined by society at large as an illness (either physical or psychological) and is thereby moved into the sphere of control of the medical profession. Habitual gambling, for example, has been regarded by a minority as a sin, and by most as a leisure pursuit — perhaps wasteful, but a pastime nevertheless. Lately, however, we have seen gambling described as a psychological illness — "compulsive gambling." It is in the process of being medicalized. The consequences of this shift in discourse (that is, in the way of thinking and talking) about gambling are considerable: for doctors, who now have in gamblers a new market for their services or "treatment"; perhaps for gambling halls, which may find themselves subject to new regulations, insofar as they are deemed to contribute to the "disease"; and not least, for gamblers themselves, who are no longer treated as sinners or wastrels, but as patients, with claims to our sympathy, and to our medical insurance plans as well.

Our concern in this chapter is medicalization of women's bodies and lives. In our modern world, we are so accustomed to seeing the body through medical eyes (that is, as a site of health and sickness) that it is hard for us to grasp that the traditional way of seeing and knowing the body was a religious one. The traditional world view regarded the body as the outward aspect of the soul, and on it appeared the marks of the unending struggle between Good and Evil. Thus, a whole range of problems we now take for granted as medical ones — bodily deformities (e.g., missing limbs, birthmarks), infertility, contagious diseases like the plague, and madness — were customarily regarded as signs of God's displeasure. Similarly, many of the things people did on and with their bodies (e.g., "mortification of the flesh") were done to obtain God's favour; and people dieted (fasted) not for the health of their bodies but for the health of their souls. As Durkheim pointed out, these conditions (and the social reactions they provoked) were visible to all, and thus stood as stark reminders of the moral order to which all members of the community were bound (Durkheim, 1964).

Reminders of the religious discourse are still around today — in the Bible, for example, where the mention of health refers to the spirit rather than the body ("There is no health in us"), and in conflicts that sometimes occur between the state and certain religious minorities, who resist the imposition of medical procedures (e.g., blood transfusions) on the grounds that God owns the body and controls what befalls it — not the doctor, or the "ungodly" powers of the state. Despite these lingering remnants of an older world view, the secular discourse of modern medicine has emerged as the dominant way of thinking and speaking about the body.

This development is of particular importance for women. As medicine began to emerge as a profession in its own right, the lives of ordinary women were of little concern to doctors and other powerful groups, a situation which reflected women's inferior status. Instead, their health needs and the major social events in their lives (notably pregnancy and childbirth) were left to other women in the community. But as the modern state emerged and began to take a proprietary interest in the health and well-being of its citizens, women, as the creators of those citizens, were gradually encompassed within the sphere of state and medical observation and control. Social historians tell us that it was at this point that events like childbirth were first defined as medical events (Rothman, 1989, p. 77).

But instead of working to improve the skills and training of traditional female healers and midwives, the young, overwhelmingly male medical profession moved to usurp their role in the management of women's health. After a long struggle — and despite the fact that midwives regularly achieved lower maternal mortality rates than physicians (Rothman, 1989, p. 78) — doctors succeeded in discrediting women's traditional expertise (as "ignorance," "superstition," and "incompetence") and by the early twentieth century, in driving them from the field. The result of this successful poaching operation is that male doctors are now society's accepted experts on the subject of women. It is this history that forms the backdrop for the feminist criticism of modern mainstream medicine: the woman's well-being, once the responsibility of other women, has been taken over by a powerful male profession whose concerns are not necessarily their own. We should bear in mind, however, that this has not occurred without women's compliance.

The great prestige doctors presently enjoy is a relatively recent phenomenon. Until the mid-nineteenth century, surgeons occupied the same low rung on the ladder as barbers — the low status of both owing to the undesirable association with blood. What accounted then, for the rapid rise in power and prestige of the medical perspective? The dominance of medical discourse is related to the professionalization of medical practice. Professionalization occurs when an occupational group attains a monopoly over a certain area of expertise. First, the emerging profession must lay claim to the area and establish a legitimate "right to treat" the group in question. When the emerging medical profession wrested control over important aspects of women's lives from the less powerful community of traditional female healers and midwives, this conferred on doctors the authority to speak on a range of issues concerning women, beginning with reproductive matters and expanding into larger "problems" of health, disease, and even lifestyle. Second, the profession must be able to create a clientele — a market for its services (Turner, 1987, p. 140). This was especially important in the nineteenth century, as some major infectious diseases dropped from view and maternal mortality declined; in response, obstetricians and pediatricians medicalized (that is, problematized) a widening array of conditions associated with childbirth and child care, in order to legitimate their intervention into these new areas. Third, the profession must maintain its power, in this case by keeping the status, income, and demand for doctors high. The modern professional association accomplishes this by controlling the training and the number of recruits to the profession, by regulating its own practices and standards, and by securing a legal monopoly over delivery of its services, so that licensed doctors are the only legitimate practitioners of medicine, and competition is reduced to a minimum (Torrance 1987, p. 15; Freidson, 1970).

Finally, the power of the medical profession was aided by medicine's crucially important alliance with science. It is interesting to note that before the twentieth century, doctors were not uniformly in favour of a close relation between "the healing arts" and science, but as the nineteenth century drew to a close, they recognized science as the wave of the future, and "there was no longer any doubt that the scientific subjects and the laboratory belonged in the medical curriculum" (Ludmerer, 1985, pp. 102-104). Doctors followed this through by affiliating themselves with "progressive" institutions of learning and technological expertise (universities and research facilities) (Ludmerer, 1985, pp. 107, 231). By defining itself as a scientific endeavour, then, medicine could claim privileged access to the truth about conditions and problems and argue that its approach alone was technical, objective, and bias-free. In short, medicine was able to share the prestige that contemporary society accorded to fields that presented themselves as rational, scientific enterprises.

There are many factors, then, that contributed to the dominance of the medical perspective, and some scholars argue persuasively that social and political ones rather than strictly medical achievements (e.g., the ability to "conquer disease") led to that position of prominence (Fisher, 1988, p. 134; Rothman, 1989). Whatever the case, the medical profession continues to struggle today to maintain its dominant position, by warding off competitors (e.g., naturopaths, nurses, midwives, paramedics) and by expanding its services into ever-new markets, most recently, the "beauty business" (Wolf, 1991; Fisher, 1988, p. 141). Once again, women's bodies form a lucrative new territory.

Women's "problems" are more frequently medicalized than others', and feminists have argued that such a development amounts to a real reduction in women's control over their own lives. As we shall see, such a loss has important practical implications for women. The medical profession may discover a problem with women's bodies when women themselves feel none exists, thus needlessly enmeshing them in the medical system. Or it may perceive interactional or structural problems as medical ones, prescribing pills and surgery where social and political change is called for. In short, who gets to define women's needs and problems is an important aspect of power, for that group also gets to determine the solutions.

We now turn to some concrete examples of how women's lives have been medicalized and how that development has influenced women's own understanding of these phenomena. First we examine the case of mothering, child rearing, and childbirth. Then we discuss the medicalization of woman abuse, and finally, the creation of a medical discourse on the appearance, diet, and fitness of women's bodies.

The Medicalization of Mothering, Child Rearing, and Childbirth

Child Rearing and the "Medical Deprivation" Thesis

For many decades, doctors have been regarded as the authority on the correct or ideal way to raise children. Medical advice on child rearing has gained ascendance as a "scientific" and technical approach, and because it is viewed as both objective and modern, the voice of the doctor on family matters is generally accepted by mothers and in "society" at large.

Because medical advice recommends some practices and family arrangements over others, it has functioned as a means of social control over women and their families, albeit in a benevolent form. The roots of this influence lie in the diligent efforts of early medical men, as well as the clergy, to shape the family form and mothering style that gradually emerged among the new bourgeoisie in the eighteenth and nineteenth centuries in Western Europe (Ariès, 1962; Davidoff & Hall, 1987; Shorter, 1975). This image of family life (sometimes termed "domestic" or "companionate") is the one most people today still regard as "normal" (despite the fact that fewer and fewer families resemble it): the patriarchal, heterosexual married pair linked through bonds of sentiment to each other and to their natural offspring.

At the heart of this ideal is the notion that the home is the woman's "natural" sphere (as the workplace is the man's), and it followed from this strictly gendered division of social life, that mothering and domestic life would be every woman's full-time occupation. Such a standard represented a departure from that of previous eras, in which mothers had invested considerably less time in their children, for child care was only one role among many for wives in the premodern world (Shorter, 1977; Hareven, 1989, pp. 44-45). To promote the new ideal of full-time motherhood, doctors actively worked to elevate nurturing to the level of women's "sacred calling," and to promote the middle-class hearthside as the only fit setting for proper child rearing. As this ideal took hold, the involvement of mothers in economic activities, whether around the household or outside it, became increasingly stigmatized, and for the first time women's work was described as a threat to the well-being of children.

Efforts to upgrade the status of the full-time mother have occurred in this century too, primarily through the "domestic science" movement, which depicted homemaking in appropriately modern terms as a scientifically based, efficient "profession" — the wife's worthy counterpart (though always unpaid) to her husband's role in the labour force (Hareven, 1989, p. 45). This conception of woman's familial work was institutionalized in the educational system in "home ec" studied by generations of schoolgirls (Gaffield, 1990, p. 37), and it carried much force since its alleged superiority was argued on the basis of scientific, technical, and medical knowledge.

The efforts of the medical profession to prescribe and enforce its version of the correct (i.e., healthy) way to mother have gone forward on a number of fronts. Doctors have medicalized labour and the prenatal period, and even childlessness. But the full weight of medical opinion in the nineteenth and twentieth centuries settled on child rearing itself and medical doctrine took the position that full-time mothering, and nothing less, was the prerequisite for the development of a normal, healthy child. Embodied in the saying "a woman's place is in the home," this view constructed the "working mother" (i.e., the employed mother) as a medical problem who would produce abnormalities in herself, her husband, and especially in her children.

The larger context for this doctrine was the Mental Hygiene movement of the early twentieth century, whose proponents held that "the scientific promotion of well-being in childhood could prevent adult dysfunctions" (Richardson, 1989, p. 2). And as the main child rearers, women were the prime target of the mental hygienists and their programs: it was women who were to have their child-care skills and roles scrutinized by psychiatric and other mental-health professionals concerned with childhood socialization. These experts acquired the power to create and purvey knowledge about mothering and child mental health to those depicted as less knowledgeable. Thus the views of health professionals came to define "the proper personal and collective behaviours to be followed by parents, teachers, social workers and counselors in order to conserve normality" (Richardson, 1989, p. 191).

It was against this background that the employed mother would come to be seen as the cause of the medical problem of "maternal deprivation." Deprivation theorists claimed that children needed their mothers on a full-time basis in order to form the emotional attachments believed to be essential for the development of positive mental health. Mother-child attachment was considered necessary to prevent juvenile delinquency, psychiatric disorders, mental "subnormality," and "acute distress and affectionless psychopathy" in the child (Miller, 1991, p. 70; Rutter, 1981, p. 15). Bowlby's work on maternal deprivation, in particular, has been interpreted as stipulating that mothers be with their children at all times, and thus not be employed in the labour force. Riley (1983, p. 100) has pointed out how the concept of "continuous mothering" was interpreted narrowly to mean 24-hour-a-day care by mother alone, in a manner that precluded any absence from the home. And by the 1950s, the medical view on child rearing had become entrenched as common sense, in the attitude that "we all know that children need their mothers at all moments" (Riley, 1983, p. 100).

How was the medical perspective on correct child rearing enforced? Occasionally health professionals physically removed "at risk" children from parents who were deemed unfit, as in the now notorious case of the Dionne "Quints" of Callander, Ontario. Shortly after their birth in the 1930s, the five Dionne daughters were taken from their poor, French-speaking parents, to be scientifically reared by physicians and psychiatrists in a morally and physically "hygienic" laboratory environment (Strong-Boag, 1982; Berton, 1977). As Canada's Native peoples have discovered, this kind of direct intervention is usually reserved for families belonging to low-status groups in the society, and in these kinds of actions the legal system gives "teeth" to medical opinion.

More often, however, the medical perspective on fit mothering is enforced indirectly, that is, through rhetoric and persuasion, rather than coercion. This kind of social control works through medical depictions of the "horrors" (including homosexuality, criminality, and madness) predicted to result in children of mothers who failed to heed the medical experts. In effect, doctors used the threat of illness to produce conformity in the same way that village priests used to use the threat of hellfire.

It is easy to paint the medical profession as victimizing generations of helpless mothers, who struggled vainly to resist their views, but the reality is not so simple. Social historians remind us that modern-minded women in the last century were themselves persuaded that science (and especially medical science) was the key to a better future and many eagerly seized upon these new concepts and attempted to put them into practice in their own homes.

They promoted these ideas, as well, in the homes of others, especially among families of the "ignorant" or "depraved" classes. The French sociologist Jacques Donzelot has described nineteenth-century French efforts to reform the working-class family along middle-class lines, and this campaign depended on an alliance between doctors and middle-class mothers (Donzelot, 1979). Similar efforts to reconstruct the British working-class family are described by British social historians; there, the intervention generally took the form of "health visitors" who tried to persuade and cajole working-class mothers to exercise greater control and surveillance over their unruly offspring primarily by ensuring their regular attendance at school (Lewis, 1986). And "respectable" ladies of the middle and upper classes engaged in similar campaigns in working-class, immigrant communities in North America (see for example, Ehrenreich & English, 1979).

Such efforts at family reform along the lines set out in medical doctrine created real conflicts for working-class women, for the advice promoted a standard of living and a style of mothering many could not hope to attain. These mothers, unlike their bourgeois counterparts, were forced to work for pay to make ends meet. These women had to work, and studies have only recently begun to shed light on the pressures they were under and the strategies they evolved to reconcile the new "progressive" ideals of child rearing with their families' economic needs. Historical evidence shows that mothers continued to work for pay, but under an increasing barrage of medical criticism.

The negative consequences of the maternal deprivation thesis are not restricted to women of an earlier era. Many women today must face the charge of "bad mothering" the concept carries with it, and must resolve conflicts between economic pressure to be in the labour force and social, including medical, admonitions against doing so (Gaskell, 1988). Sociological studies regularly fail to find support for the maternal deprivation thesis as it pertains to mothers who work outside the home (Etaugh, 1974; Kamerman & Hayes, 1982). Nevertheless, the view that the employed mother will rear the bad, or mad, child retains the secure status of taken-for-granted wisdom. Even *The Globe and Mail* reported the results of its own 1991 poll under the headline: "Working Parents Spark Concern: Canadians worry the well-being of the nation's children is being sacrificed" (*The Globe and Mail*, November 5, 1991, p. A4).

Thus the medical legacy of Bowlby's deprivation thesis continues to influence government policy on matters such as day-care funding and educational curriculum. And it continues to colour women's own views on their proper role in the family and on their careers (see Brannen & Wilson, 1987). It is safe to conclude that the medical discourse on "correct" mothering still produces confusion and ambivalence in women who choose to work for pay, and guilt in those who must.

Childbirth and the Prenatal Period

The medicalization of mothering has not been restricted to the child-rearing period, however; the processes of labour and childbirth have gradually come to be controlled and reconstructed as medical issues or problems. More recently, this has even been extended to the fetal period, in the form of prenatal care.

The history of the medicalization of childbirth is one of a gradual takeover of the responsibilities of female midwives by largely male obstetricians. This shift was also a struggle between a more holistic view of childbirth as a "natural" process and the obstetrician's reliance on a scientific model, in which childbirth was treated as a potentially pathological condition (Leavitt, 1986, p. 208; Ehrenreich & English, 1979, pp. 111, 140). Doctors were trained to intervene in the process and at first were called in to assist midwives only when there were complications. Obstetricians had exclusive access to some of the tools of the trade, such as forceps, which could help in cases of difficult birth. But obstetricians in the eighteenth century had relatively low status and power (Lewis, 1986). To a fair degree, they were controlled by the aristocratic women whom they served and hence they had little of the professional autonomy needed to impose their own definitions of how childbirth should be conducted (Lewis, 1986, pp. 3-4). For working-class women, the birthing process was still female-dominated and they were assisted by midwives who themselves were often working-class immigrants to North America.

Although the prestige of science was on the rise in this era, many obstetricians were at first ambivalent about adopting "scientific" medicine. Only when it was socially accepted (particularly by the nineteenth century) and hence, advantageous to the developing professional status of medicine, was scientific medicine fully adopted (Leavitt, 1986, p. 208; Morantz-Sanchez, 1985, p. 241).

Women's own demands played a part as well in the medicalization of childbirth. Considering the historically high risk of infant and maternal mortality in childbirth (in early twentieth-century Britain, childbirth was the third highest cause of death among women aged 15-45), it is not surprising that women demanded an approach that they saw — though not always correctly — as providing greater safety. Moreover, obstetricians were able to provide women with pharmaceutical means of pain relief, such as the early twentieth-century "twilight sleep" which combined scopolamine and morphine, and many women demanded such relief in labour (Sandelowski, 1984, p. 6). Although initiated by women themselves, these developments inevitably took the management of labour out of their hands. Moreover, the safe administration of anesthesia meant that childbirth was moved to the hospital environment, under medical control. Thus, women chose safety and pain relief, but at the same time relinquished control over a process that had been formerly "theirs" (Sandelowski, 1984, pp. 17-20; Leavitt, 1986, pp. 134, 140).

The extent to which women themselves have accepted this new medical definition and discourse on childbirth is debated. It has been suggested that women's own views of childbirth have been influenced by medical approaches (Currer & Stacey, 1986, p. 97). Yet research by Graham and Oakley indicates that women think less in terms of medicalized childbirth as a pathological condition, and more in terms of it as a natural process (Currer & Stacey, 1986, p. 97). They outline two quite different perspectives — the medical and the maternal — which arise out of the two frames of reference. These frames emerge from the different social positions of doctors and patients as these two groups interact (Graham & Oakley, 1986, pp. 114-115). Women tend to draw on their own bodily experiences and their lives as a whole in their contextualization of the processes of pregnancy and childbirth, while for obstetricians, the processes are physiological ones, embedded in medical knowledge (Graham & Oakley, 1986, pp. 100-101). But despite the existence of two perspectives, it is clear that the medical one carries greater formal authority.

The degree to which women differentiate their knowledge of and discourse on their bodily processes from the medicalized version may also depend upon their social class. Martin (1987, pp. 139-155), for example, suggests that the age, race, and social class of a woman influences how she struggles with and resists the dominant medical discourse on childbirth and pregnancy. She argues that there are more issues for a black working-class woman to contend with than for a white middle-class woman, and that the former is more likely to encounter medical mismanagement and inadequate information from professional on matters related to childbirth. On this basis Martin (1987, p. 155) suggests that black women are less likely to take on the medical perspective as their own.

The medicalization process has increasingly been extended to the period prior to childbirth as well — pregnancy and the prenatal period. Oakley (1986, p. 135) notes that:

> At first the medical surveillance covered childbirth and child health only, then a more sophisticated epidemiology of health and illness took the medical spotlight back to the prenatal period.

She describes this process as part of the development of preventive medicine generally. Medicine was also allied with the state in developing prenatal (antenatal) care as a way of controlling the health and fertility rates of the population (Oakley, 1986, p. 34). From the 1950s on, after maternal mortality had been substantially reduced, obstetric attention became more focussed on issues relating to the fetus; this meant that women were regarded as needing monitoring during the prenatal period (Oakley, 1986, pp. 213, 251-252). Prenatal care is also part of a wider medicalization and social control of women's bodies and women's lives; the term for prenatal care in Latin America, and in some European languages, includes the word "control" (Oakley, 1986, p. 2). Just as the professional focus on mothers' child-rearing practices involved a concern with producing healthy adults and "perfecting" society, prenatal care expressed a social concern for the fetus in its role as a future family member and citizen of a nation (Oakley, 1986, p. 252).

The development of ultrasound technology has been a key tool for obstetricians to be able to see and know the fetus; technical knowledge was essential to the profession's claim to expertise (Oakley, 1986, pp. 182-183). It meant, for example, that obstetricians could further differentiate their knowledge from the traditional knowledge of midwives. Prior to the development of technical intervention into the environment of the fetus, obstetricians (as midwives and women themselves) had to depend for a diagnosis of pregnancy upon "subjective" or "folk" signs of fetal activity, such as "quickening" (Oakley, 1986, p. 182). "Quickening" belonged to a repertoire of traditional (feminine) tools and expertise, which was rapidly discredited by professional medicine as "myth" and "superstition."

But prenatal care also meant the entrenchment of "the definition of all pregnancies as potentially pathological" and this gave medicine and the state "an unprecedented degree of licence over the bodies and approved life-styles of women" (Oakley, 1986, p. 2). For example, there has been a revival of the 1950s discourse on the need for mother-infant "bonding" during and immediately following childbirth. The medical and psychological rhetoric around bonding expresses concern for prevention of mental-health problems in the child and child abuse behaviours on the part of the mothers. But in describing "bonding" as an essential part of childbirth, there is also a prescription for the way in which women are to give birth (as naturally and drug-free as possible) and relate to the baby (e.g., breastfeeding is promoted and even glorified). Oakley (1986, p. 185) hypothesizes that this type of control over the behaviours of mothers is currently being extended into the prenatal period. She shows that some doctors believe ultrasound is useful for having the mother see her fetus, so that a "bond" will be created and she will become a "good" mother. Oakley (1986, p. 185) predicts that:

> Along with postnatal bonding, prenatal bonding will now in future be added to the repertoire of reproductive activities named and controlled by obstetricians.

Here we see how the union of psychological rhetoric and technology works to further medicalize women's bodies.

The question then arises as to how women respond, resist, or reproduce medical discourse on prenatal care. Rarely have women's attitudes to such prenatal techniques as ultrasound fetal monitoring been assessed, and the extent of maternal satisfaction with the experience of prenatal care can be considered questionable (Oakley, 1986, pp. 183, 184). One study has indicated that when pregnant women receive more detailed feedback regarding the test results from the person providing the prenatal care, they feel more positively about the care (Oakley, 1986, pp. 184-185). Another indicated that working-class mothers, in particular, felt their need for information was not satisfied (Oakley, 1986, p. 245). So it seems that while women may believe that prenatal visits are necessary to ensure their own health and that of their babies, they may be less than pleased with the whole experience.

But the appeal and influence of the medical perspective is pervasive, and many concepts have been popularized and taken over by mothers as their own. "Bonding," for example, is accepted by many mothers as a truism, and has been taken up by the alternative health movement as well. It is ironic that this movement, which claims to offer a more "natural" (i.e., demedicalized) childbirth experience, should include "better parent-child bonding" as one of its features, a concept with clear origins in the professional medical lexicon.

In sum, while obstetric and prenatal care is often desired by mothers, and can certainly provide advantages for them and their children, we must recognize that it is constructed and delivered in a "profoundly class — and gender — divided culture." Moreover, women buy that care at the cost of reduced control over their own lives. As Oakley (1986, p. 292) states:

In these circumstances the wombs of women — whether already pregnant or not — are containers to be captured by the ideologies and practices of those who, to put it most simply, do not believe that women are able to take care of themselves.

The Medicalization of Woman Abuse

The Invisible Problem

The abuse of women in the family is a practice with a long history, yet it has only recently come to light as a public problem. And to the extent that it is now treated as a problem, it appears as a medical issue, rather than a social or criminal one. The medical perspective understands the cause of woman abuse to lie in the sickness or abnormality of the individual abuser, rather than in, for example, the gender inequalities in the family, or in Western society at large. We propose to discuss the invisibility of woman abuse, its emergence as a medical issue, and the consequences of viewing it through medical eyes.

Like the "problem" of employed mothers, the invisibility of woman abuse must be seen against the background of our collective investment as a society in the ideal of the domestic, patriarchal family form. In fact, the most important reason for the long-standing historical indifference to violence against women is that it was considered a natural and normal part of patriarchal family relations. Prior to the nineteenth century, the husband's right to "chastise" his wife was sanctioned by major social institutions, including the Church. Wives and children were deemed the property of the male head of the household — and not especially valuable property at that, as we are reminded when we look at the content of popular sayings that were common across peasant communities in Northern Europe, e.g., *Mort de femme et vie de cheval font l'homme riche*, "Rich is the man whose wife is dead and horse alive" (a proverb from Brittany, cited in Shorter, 1977, p. 58).

It is clear that against such views, the abuse of wives was unlikely to stand out as a problem. And, on a broader scale, abusive practices reinforced the unequal power relations that were part of "normal" patriarchal family life. As Dobash and Dobash state, wife beating is

a form of behaviour which has existed for centuries as an acceptable, and, indeed a desirable part of a patriarchal society (cited in Schur, 1984, p. 158).

Hence, it is only since women's groups have raised the larger challenge to patriarchy itself — the system that takes for granted the greater authority of men — that we have seen public discourse on the abuse of women change from indifference to concern.

A second reason for the long invisibility of woman abuse is tied to the modernizing of Western society more generally, and to the gradual decline of the village as the centre of life. As modernization proceeded, an important institution responsible for the regulation of family behaviour (and indeed, for conduct more generally) gradually weakened. We refer here to the local community — one's neighbours — who in the preindustrial world put pressure on each other to conform to local standards of "proper conduct." These social pressures ranged from rumour and gossip to noisy public demonstrations (called shivarees) that were designed to humiliate the transgressor in the eyes of the whole village (Shorter, 1977, pp. 218-227). Social historians like Shorter note that such techniques ignored much of what we would today define as abusive conduct, but did serve to curb its worst excesses. However, industrialization weakened these informal regulatory mechanisms, and shifted social control to the state and the rule of formal law. At the same time, the family (especially in the middle class) began to withdraw from community life around it, and gradually took on the appearance of the private, inward-looking institution we know today.

With respect to violence against wives, the rise of formal state power over family conduct had contradictory results: on the one hand, it gave rise to new legislation protecting women and children from the most extreme forms of abuse; but on the other, it closed off family life behind a wall of privacy. If neighbours knew that husbands and fathers beat their wives and children, they now regarded such goings-on as none of their business, and became increasingly reluctant to intervene. Thus, the overall effect of modernization was to render family life — the good and the bad — ever more hidden.

The emergence of the family as a haven of privacy, with the right to be free of "interference" from outsiders — whether neighbours or the police — is, then, the historical backdrop for the extreme reluctance to intervene against family violence which is so apparent in the late nineteenth and twentieth centuries. Ahluwalia and MacLean (1988, p. 185) note, for example, that while legal reforms that restricted the husband's power arose in this same period, such new laws were not always enforced. Although responsibility for regulating family violence was formally assigned to the police and the criminal justice system in the late nineteenth century, assaults by husbands against their wives continued to be a low social priority, especially when compared with assaults between strangers (Ahluwalia & MacLean, 1988, p. 185; DeKeseredy & Hinch, 1991, p. 31). Once again, the reasons for the non-arrest policy that prevailed — the belief that home life is private, that abused wives are "legitimate victims (DeKeseredy & Hinch, 1991, p. 31), the belief held by police that wives will not follow through on charges (Propper, 1990, pp. 287-288), and indeed, the patriarchal structure of the police force itself (DeKeseredy & Hinch, p. 31) — all stem from and maintain the common-sense image of the family as a sentimental, private, male-dominated world unto itself. We are only now coming to grasp our degree of emotional entanglement in this conception of family life, yet we also see clearly that this concept must change, if we are to find a solution to woman abuse (Stark, 1990; Miller, 1990).

Medical, Legal, and Feminist Discourses of Woman Abuse

In recent years, women's groups have raised a renewed outcry over the persistent failure to intervene effectively against the abuse of wives; and indeed, the last several decades have seen the historical trend reversed, as the "private sphere" of the family has become increasingly open to state scrutiny and regulation. Two arms of the state have staked out professional claim to the problem of wife abuse: one is the legal system, the other, professional social-service agencies, including the Department of Health and Welfare (Walker, 1990, pp. 57, 86). Both systems problematize the issue of violence against women, but each interprets it according to its own lights: the legal system as a criminal matter, social services agencies as a medical one. These two are the dominant state approaches to woman abuse, and the approach of women's groups is a third, competing perspective.

It is important to remember that different perspectives or discourses do more than identify a problem, they actively construct it, and thus they contain their own distinct versions of the problem's causes and solutions. For example, feminists see the root cause of the problem in the systemic imbalance of power between men and women in a sexist society, but for medical professionals, woman abuse is a mental-health matter, a problem of sickness in the abusive individual. The feminist discourse is a political one (in the sense that it addresses power) and calls for changes to "society," while the medical discourse is presented as apolitical and calls for therapeutic changes in the perpetrator. The criminal justice (or legal) model, for its part, constructs the abuse as a violent act rather than a sick one, and is less concerned with causes than with punishment and deterrence.

The major criticism feminists level against the medical model is its tendency to depoliticize the phenomenon; from their point of view, the medical discourse of sickness obscures the "real" causes of wife abuse, which lie in the ways even "normal" families are organized. At the heart of the medical perspective is the division of families, and individuals, into "normal" and "abnormal" ones. This important distinction serves to deflect the problem onto unusual or abnormal others, and allows us to avoid recognizing the structural proclivities for violence present in all families in a patriarchal society, including "healthy" or "normal" ones. (Gelles & Cornell, 1990, pp. 14, 112; Miller, 1990; Lupri, 1990). And by linking violence to mental illness, medical discourse appears to deny that normal individuals may also be violent and dangerous, without taking leave of their senses. In fact, theories that rely on this linkage (i.e., that suggest that only sick people can harm their intimates) fly in the face of evidence that only a small minority of woman abusers suffer from mental health or personality problems (Gelles & Cornell, 1990, pp. 14, 111-112).

The relevance of factors that have nothing to do with mental illness has been widely demonstrated: studies have found, for instance, that wives who are not employed full-time, and who have less decision-making power in the marriage, are more likely to be beaten (Propper, 1990, p. 273). More recently, Stark (1990, p. 22) has pointed to the role in domestic homicides of "intense" marital events that threaten the power of the husband. These quarrels, he argues, usually concern "prevailing familial arrangements": "men are assaultive to manage [disagreements] around sex, housework, money, work outside the home, child care, and friendships, and 'lose it' (by becoming violent) in order to gain control."

Such studies support the contention of women's groups that abuse is not just a matter of "troubled" individuals or familial pathologies, and that the structural features of "normal" patriarchal families, especially the relative powerlessness of wives, must instead be addressed. Stark (1990, p. 20) summarizes this point well: "The sheer frequency of domestic violence . . . suggests that it is an exaggeration of widely accepted values and behaviours, not an aberration."

While its failure to address such factors is the main sticking point for its opponents, the medical model has been criticized on other grounds as well. Walker (1990, p. 49), for example, has focussed on the issue of treatment, and contends that the therapeutic relationship between doctor (or social worker) and client reproduces, rather than rectifies, the powerlessness and stigmatization to be found in the wife's relationship with her abusive husband. Therapy thus perpetuates an aspect of the problem in the guise of solving it. Further, that medical terms like "battered wife syndrome," which focus on the wife rather than on the abusive husband, implicitly suggest victim compliance in the abuse (Ahluwalia & MacLean, 1988, p. 191).

An alternative to the medical discourse of mental illness is the legal one, which defines abuse as "assault." Some women's groups prefer the legal discourse because it makes it clear that wife abuse is a criminal act that demands punishment, rather than an illness that demands sympathy (Propper, 1990, p. 277; Walker, 1990, p. 18). Legal terminology cuts both ways, however; the term "domestic dispute," which reflects the approach of the police, carries the assumption that family assaults and assaults between strangers are two different things, and that the first is less serious a crime than the second.

The medical model is not the only perspective on woman abuse, then, nor even the only professional perspective. But it is arguably the one that carries the greatest authority in professional circles. Indeed, it may also be the preferred popular way of thinking about family violence, even among violent family members themselves. Both abusers and abused parties tend to shy away from the legal perspective, and prefer to regard violent acts within the family as acts of madness rather than badness. How can we account for the popular appeal of the medical view? Some of the resistance to the legal perspective may lie in the heavy-handed approach to the whole matter adopted by the criminal justice system; according to MacLeod (1989, p. 8), wives often feel bullied into taking action against their husbands, as if laying charges were an obligation, not a right (MacLeod, 1989, p. 8). More important, perhaps, is that the medical perspective poses no serious challenge to the sentimental family ideal and to the belief in family harmony in which we have so high an emotional stake — instead of painting the husband as deliberately violent (according to the legal model), the medical perspective portrays him as an essentially good man who temporarily "flipped out." Moreover, the wife of a "bad" (criminal) man may also see herself as a failure, but the wife of a "sick" man need only wait until therapy restores him to the "normal," loving husband she knows him to be.

In short, families may prefer the medical to the legal account just because it does not dismantle our cherished assumptions about the "real" (that is, sentimental and loving) nature of family life. This means that our cultural assumptions about family life shape our understanding of family violence more powerfully than do the realities of bruises and broken bones. This conclusion is supported by research into the ways family members make sense of violent family events around them. These studies suggest that both the abusers and the abused will go to considerable effort to protect and sustain the general cultural ideal of the harmonious family (Miller, 1990; MacLeod, 1989). The medical view of woman abuse as sickness may be a more comfortable way of thinking about violence in the family, because it fits with (rather than undermines) our common-sense beliefs about the way family life ought to go around.

These studies remind us of the heavy investment we have, as a society, in the patriarchal domestic family ideal, even among those who are clearly its victims. More generally, they suggest that research into woman abuse should attend more closely to the ways members of violent families construct their social realities, if we expect our analysis of the problem to lead to effective remedies.

The Medicalization of Women's Bodies

In this section, we turn to a consideration of how the physical appearance and form of women's bodies have come under medical control. This development has been part of a broader socio-historical trend toward social control of all bodies and we outline this trend first. Then we turn to some of the forms that this control takes for women in particular and the part the medical perspective plays in that outcome. Throughout, it is important to keep in mind the question of how women themselves perceive and deal with this medicalization process.

There is a long and interesting history of ideas about the meaning of physical appearance and beauty of human bodies, and of the face. Specifically, appearance has been and still is an important influence in the development of a "self" and our assessment of the selves of others. Synnott (1989, p. 611) states that a "beauty mystique," in which beauty and goodness are equated, originated with the Greeks and Romans: body and soul were taken to mirror each other. The notion that beauty is the reflection of inner goodness still prevails. It can be heard in the advice of beauty experts, for example, who tell us that "beauty comes from within," and in the results of many studies that show that people attribute crimes more readily to "ugly" suspects than to "handsome" ones. Synnott (1989, p. 632) suggests that the causal order may be gradually reversing, however, so that physical beauty is increasingly treated as the first, essential step toward internal, psychological beauty.

Still, strong traces of past attitudes to the body persist, especially, as we shall see, in the eating disorders experienced by women. Historically, the need to develop a self, particularly a purified and spiritual self, has been achieved through religious asceticism, the denial of bodily needs (Bordo, 1990, p. 83). But in earlier eras, fasting and other denials of the flesh were practised by elite social groups, mainly aristocrats and priests. Bordo and others note that treatises on diet can be found in the fifteenth and sixteenth centuries in Western Europe, but were always embedded in a religious discourse about renunciation and the subjection of "animal passions" and "appetites" (Bordo, 1990, p. 83; Turner, 1984, pp. 165-170).

The early modern era brought an important change in this pattern: for the first time an interest was taken in the ordinary individual, who until then had been an undifferentiated part in a faceless "horde" or "rabble." Foucault argues persuasively that the source of this new interest was the modern state, which began, with emerging professional groups as its instruments, to observe and document the lives and bodies of the masses, in the interest of producing useful and productive citizens (Foucault, 1979; Donzelot, 1979). The most important of these professional groups were the medical doctors, and it has been suggested that an emerging and powerful alliance between general practitioners and mothers allowed the state an important point of entry into, and control over, the "private sphere" of the family, especially the bodily habits of its members, including the mother herself (Donzelot, 1979; Turner, 1984). (As an aside it is interesting to note that Foucault locates the beginnings of sociology not in the revolutionary writings of St. Simon and Comte, but here, as medical sociology, in the earliest state-sponsored programs for the enlightened regulation of the masses, a project which survey techniques made possible (Turner, 1984, pp. 49-50).

The emphasis on useful and productive bodies, and hence a productive labour force, was aided by the seventeenth-century Cartesian model of the body as a machine (Bordo,

1990, p. 86). This image contributed to the development of the medical rationalization and classification of the body, including diet regimens where input and output could be mathematically calculated and managed (Turner, 1982, pp. 258-259). In contrast to the earlier religious treatises on diet, nineteenth-and twentieth-century medical writings regarded a dietary regime as a condition of efficient labour, and hence they were intended for the working class (Turner, 1984, p. 170).

One important mark of the modern, secular discourse on diet is its relentless focus on body weight. As the modern "scientific" approach to diet and food intake slowly diffused down the social ladder, a large stomach — the old symbol of wealth — faded into history. In the early twentieth century, the modern concept of the calorie allowed the quantification of nutrition based on an economist's notion of physiological equilibrium (as energy flow in and out of the body), and this development — the scientific management of nutrition — was, like Taylorism, part of the larger trend toward rationalization in many spheres of life, including the school, the workplace, and the home. Following the emergence of calorie-counting, insurance companies and the medical profession constructed an association of overweight or "obesity" with death, an association based on studies of men, but automatically applied to women as well (Schwartz, 1986, pp. 154-156). These and later developments (the linkage of fat to heart disease, and the classification of bodies into types, like "mesomorph") united to focus on overweight as the major threat to the worker's productivity under capitalism; as a result, the medical profession, backed by the state and business interests, began to recommend a lifelong vigilance over body weight in the form of dieting and exercise (Schwartz, 1986, pp. 189, 223). This approach to diet, while still heavy with moral overtones, is a far cry from earlier religious conceptions. In the transition to modernity, concludes Turner, "The vocabulary of passions, desires and humours was replaced by the discourse of calories and proteins" (1984, p. 170).

In general, the monitoring of health and body weight, which originated "outside" the individual in the state and the medical profession, has been largely taken over by those individuals themselves, bearing out arguments for a shift in the form of social regulation from policing-by-others, to self-policing in twentieth-century Western society (Foucault, 1979; Elias, 1978). However, there are important gender and class exceptions to this rule. First, men are less inclined to "police" or monitor their own bodily appearance and state of health than are women, in line with the cultural script that makes women the custodians of health care for their family members as well as themselves. Second, working-class individuals in late twentieth-century society have taken up the new regime of fitness, thinness, and exercise with less enthusiasm than their middle-class counterparts. Indeed, some authors claim that class differences are now expressed indirectly as discourses on bodily appearance and health, and observe that overweight in the working class is read as reflecting flaws in the working-class character, including a poor attitude and a lack of discipline (Bordo, 1990, p. 95).

These beliefs express and enforce the dominant middle-class view that health is the basis for success and worldly achievement (Edgley & Brissett, 1990, p. 258), and that those in the society who will not regulate their own bodies ought to be monitored, if not coerced, by others. The Alberta government is considering a proposal allowing doctors to give patients an "annual report card (covering) . . . health indicators like blood pressure, weight, smoking and cholesterol levels." Stating that "businesses [sic] have been doing this for years" in Japan and Europe, the president of the Alberta Medical Association notes with approval that bosses say to their employees: "We notice you are 40 pounds overweight and smoking two packs of cigarettes. We would like that changed and we'll give you so many months to do that. And we'll check you out again" (*Calgary Herald*, December 6, 1991, p. B1).

It is interesting to note that the cultural fear of fat is now applied not only to adults but to children, and recently has led to the control of women's bodies out of medical concern for the fat of the fetus (Schwartz, 1986, p. 269). The idea that too many fat cells in fetal life and childhood will lead to adult obesity has led doctors and mothers to restrict the weight gain that occurs in pregnancy (Schwartz, 1986, pp. 296-297). To that end, it became necessary to monitor pregnant women's bodies more closely through prenatal care. Not surprisingly, the restriction on weight gain became widely accepted gospel, being advocated through a medical discourse. We can hear that concern with weight gain in conversations that women have with pregnant friends or relatives, as the topic frequently turns to the number of pounds the woman has "put on." While women have taken up this medical concern and discourse, they also have the potential for resisting it; that it is open as a topic for discussion among women indicates that medical gospel may be considered somewhat contentious. However, faced with the prospect of having our fitness and body weight monitored and graded from the womb to the workplace, and perhaps into old age, we begin to grasp the far-reaching authority we have granted, as a society, to the medical profession.

The Medicalization of Appearance: Is Beauty Healthy?

If the medical profession is concerned with regulating the bodies of all citizens, why do we focus especially on women? We touched on one reason earlier: women, especially mothers, are assigned cultural responsibility for the health and appearance of other family members, as part of the larger feminine role. Therefore, as a group, women become the crucial bridge between the medical profession and the rest of the family. It is frequently mothers who first take up medical discourse as their own, and who watch over and regulate the bodily practices of their husbands and children — from their personal hygiene to their calorie intake. This line of thinking recognizes that women themselves are agents of social control who, in effect, act on behalf of the medical profession and disseminate medical discourse into the "private sphere," on the assumption that this is in the best interests of the family (Donzelot, 1979; Frykman & Lofgren, 1987; Miller 1987).

However, women not only monitor the bodily practices of others, they monitor their own — and with a vengeance. This is the second reason to focus on women. Western society teaches women to attach extraordinary significance to appearance, and while we would agree that concern is a desirable thing, the obsession with appearance, especially in the form of predominantly female disorders like anorexia, is nothing short of disastrous. We suggest that certain socio-cultural forces invite an excessive concern for "feminine beauty," and that medical rhetoric itself acts to exacerbate the already powerful cultural demands on women to overemphasize their bodily appearance.

While all members of society must evince some concern for the "presentation of self," the concern for bodily appearance has a special place in the lives of women. The norm that charges women with maintaining the "respectable" appearance of the home and its members — their clothing, bodies, hygiene, and demeanor — emerged in the late eighteenth century. It is embedded in the larger Western conception of femininity, and was strongly tied to the ideal of bourgeois respectability. (For a summary of this argument see Miller & Penz, 1991, pp. 150-152; Davidoff & Hall, 1987, chap. 8). The hegemonic success of this norm today is reflected in the central place it occupies in the socialization of girls. As Haug and her colleagues have shown so well, girls learn at a very young age that their appearance is consequential for their membership in the large social community; they learn, in fact, that their willingness to control their bodies is the key to achieving a social identity. In their book *Female Sexualization*, Haug et al., (1987, p. 127) show, for example, how social recognition is bestowed on the girl who takes responsibility for her body by, say, holding her tummy in, and later by neatly braiding her hair. "Having a tummy," says Haug, "signifies to others an attitude of the body, and a personal attitude of mind." It becomes an immoral and antisocial act. Girls are told "that we can and must be active in tackling the problem of our attitude," for a girl "who is not even capable of pulling her tummy in and thus of exercising self-discipline, is likely to be the kind who doesn't do her homework, goes out of her way to avoid housework" (Haug et al., 1987, p. 127).

The legacy of these kinds of lessons is two-fold: (1) The way women manage their appearance is invested, by themselves and by others, with greater social significance than in the case of men; and (2) women tend to respond to social demands with body work throughout their lives (Miller & Penz, 1991, p. 151). This means, for example, that the slim, "well-groomed" woman will be deemed to be socially competent, while women who "let themselves go," especially to fat, are seen as socially irresponsible — even as a threat to the social order. Moreover, the linkage between social responsibility and body regulation that we have been describing here is reaffirmed and enforced medically; that is, the medical perspective tends to identify women who fail to "keep up appearances" as suffering from health (psychological) problems. The equation of appearance ("beauty") with health is becoming widespread, according to Wolf (1991, p. 227); it is supported by the American Medical Association, for example, which states that "pre-occupation with beauty [is] the same as pre-occupation with health" (see also Spitzack, 1990). And the concern for health itself is made more fashionable through its association with the liberation of women from the chains of domesticity (Spitzack, 1990). Thus beauty, health, and liberation are combined in contemporary society into a powerful package promoting the thin, controlled body, and this package has considerable appeal for women. As Wolf (1991, p. 27) remarks, "medical discourse tells women that beauty and body work is the prescription for health, and who can argue with health?"

It is worth remembering, however, that the connection between health and cultural standards of beauty is by no means a natural one. Feminine ideals of beauty in other eras and societies have demanded distinctly unhealthy practices, ranging from tight corseting and genital mutilation to foot-binding. In this connection we should also note that cosmetic surgery is today one of the medical profession's most lucrative specialties, and doctors are involved in the active marketing of such questionable procedures as lipo-suction and breast augmentation. Thus, while the medical profession sometimes presents itself as the moral guardian of our health and well-being, at other times it looks more like the amoral technician who will help women in the search for the designer body, wherever it leads.

The air of legitimacy which the medical rhetoric of health lends to contemporary beauty ideals has other undesirable results as well. These include the expectation that women will divert their life energies into beauty work (Wolf, 1991, pp. 14, 16), and the idea that it is the public duty of all good citizens, especially women, to monitor the "health achievements" of others (Edgley & Brissett, 1990, p. 259). Again, it is the prestigious medical rhetoric of health that puts these activities on the moral high ground, and stigmatizes those who do not comply, with the labels of "deviant" or "sick." Observers of contemporary life have remarked that medicine has replaced the Church as society's moral arbiter: disease is the contemporary sin, and health the new religious salvation.

In presenting these arguments, we do not suggest that we should never take care of our bodies or our appearance. Rather, the issue is one of "lack of choice" in women's lives (Wolf, 1991, p. 272). Women experience intense social pressure to conform to ideal body images. As de Swaan (1990, p. 1) comments, "Whatever becomes a possibility for many turns into a necessity for everyone." When the thin body ideal is so prevalent and is considered the epitome of health, it makes it difficult to choose not to struggle to attain that ideal. As Spitzack comments, this predicament leads women to a permanent state of health surveillance and continuous confessions of bodily flaws and "sins" are demanded of them (Spitzack, 1990, p. 3). For example, women confess to falling off their diets and binging on chocolate fudge torte, or that they are carrying around five pounds "too many." Then an attempt at "normalization" of the body through diets, exercise, surgery, and so forth is renewed, in which the "disease" of the normal woman's body is evident (Spitzack, 1990, pp. 4, 9). This whole process reveals women's deep insecurity regarding their bodies, an insecurity presented by medicine as normal and right (MacNevin, 1990, p. 25).

From the medical perspective, women's "problems" — their fat, their insecurity, and their "lack of will" — lie in women themselves, but feminist scholars disagree. Many women's groups attempt to persuade women that "the problem" is not in their bodies but in the cultural forces that create the demand to be thin. Such forces include the patriarchal image of feminine beauty as delicate and vulnerable, a prestigious medical discourse that always presents itself as acting in the woman's best interests, and a business community that profits from the search for slimness through the diet-aids industry it creates. Women's groups argue that the woman's body is the site, but not the source of her problems, and they attempt to support women who would challenge cultural demands for the one "right" body. But the escape from the narrow repressive body ideal has proved to be no easy matter. Too often, these efforts are played out on the body in a distorted form: in anorexia, for example, or in yet more body work (e.g., body building).

The Medicalization of Women's Disorders: Anorexia Nervosa As a "Disease"
We turn now to a brief discussion of "feminine disorders." Although there is some indication that men are under increasing pressure to be fit and thin, disorders like anorexia in this century, and "hysteria" and agoraphobia in the last, are overwhelmingly disorders of women. Next to their gendered character, their most notable feature is their historical dimension; leaving aside "holy anorexia," a form of religious self-starvation encountered in the Middle Ages, they all belong to the last half of the nineteenth century or to the twentieth — that is, they are disorders of the modern age.

This fact, among others, has suggested to feminist scholars that they are responses to historically specific conditions that put greater pressure on women than on men. It has been argued, for example, that agoraphobia — the phobic fear of crowds and public spaces — became prevalent at just that period in the last century when middle-class women experienced the lure of a safer and more accessible world outside the household, while at the same time bourgeois notions of feminine respectability required them to remain at home, cloistered with their children and dependent on their husbands (Turner, 1984, pp. 107-108; 1987, pp. 105-106).

In this interpretation, social factors operated to open up and close down women's lives simultaneously, and some women responded to this dilemma with the exaggerated flight from public life portrayed in agoraphobia (and in "hysteria" as well, a disorder of the same era in which women became emotionally unstrung and "took to their beds," sometimes for years) (Turner, 1984, pp. 107-108). These disorders expressed a kind of resistance-through-parody of the requirements of femininity in a patriarchal era: in effect, wives were saying to their husbands, "You want dependence? I'll give you dependence!" (Bordo, 1989, p. 17). Agoraphobia and hysteria, then, can be formulated as women's responses to the cultural dilemmas of the day.

The earliest clinical records of anorexia in its modern sense seem to be from the 1860s (Turner, 1987, p. 106; 1984, p. 183). The traditional psychoanalytic interpretation of the roots of anorexia is that it represents a rejection of femininity, for the woman's body becomes more boy-like and her menstrual periods eventually cease (Boskind-Lodahl, 1976, pp. 343-345). More recently, it has been suggested that anorexia, like agoraphobia and hysteria, is linked with women's position in a society that creates contradictory expectations (Turner, 1987, p. 106; Orbach, 1979, p. 167). One of those contradictions entails the expectation that women will be feminine and domestic at home while aggressively pursuing middle-class achievement in the public sphere (Turner, 1984, p. 196). It is very difficult for a young woman to satisfy demands to be demure and passive at home, but competitive and assertive in the workplace. Here again, these theories suggest that middle-class women, in particular, may be pressed by their parents to be "feminine" achievers — that is, dependent and independent at the same time (Turner, 1987, p. 107; Chernin, 1985).

According to other researchers, a second contradiction can be found in the ethos of consumer capitalism, which sends mixed messages to women around the subject of body management. These writers hold that late capitalism, in particular, sets up a contradiction around gratification: on the one hand, our "producer-selves" are expected to control our appetites and desires, while our "consumer-selves" are encouraged to indulge them (Turner, 1984; Bordo, 1990, p. 96). We can clearly see this tension when advertisements for tempting foods are followed by articles on instant diets (Bordo, 1990, p. 97). It is evident, too, in the pressure women experience to desire and consume beauty products in order to achieve "the natural look"; such campaigns simultaneously advocate consumption and denial. Bordo (1990, p. 97) contends that social contradictions of this sort are dealt with partly by the institutional schism between our rigid daytime lives, when we are in control and "in order," and our evenings and weekends, which are organized around the release of bodily desire through indulgence (in makeup, clothing, food, liquor, and leisure toys). The compartmentalization of the consumer and producer parts of our selves, she says, leads some women to favour one side or the other — in anorexia, or obesity, or in bulimia, the latter replaying the excesses of both indulgence and denial in its binges and purges. But none of these attempts to deal with the tensions are socially acceptable, as Bordo (1990, pp. 97, 99) points out: women who are anorexic may be admired at first, but eventually hide their skeletal bodies from public view, while the obese are rejected as disgusting, and are especially scorned for stomachs, "the symbol of consumption."

In addition to identifying the various contradictions and tensions placed upon modern women, most of these analyses share the view that anorexia represents the adolescent girl's effort to take control over her life in the face of these contradictory demands. The question they often fail to address, however, is this: why do girls respond to these dilemmas in the language of the body? Why are power and control not sought in the workplace, say, or in political marches, or in personal relationships?

For an answer we must return to our earlier point about the special importance attached to women's appearance in contemporary culture. The message of girls' earliest socialization is that body work will be the key to full social membership. This means that girls learn to see body work as the appropriate way to achieve their goals in the world and they carry this lesson with them throughout their lives. Women bodybuilders, for example, state that they expect their workouts to lead to improvements in many other aspects of their lives, from public speaking to making love (Miller & Penz, 1991; Spitzack, 1990), and never see it as odd that one should be expected to guarantee the other. Men do not voice the same expectations (*Calgary Herald*, November 17, 1991, p. B8).

It is no surprise then that women's dilemmas, as well as their aspirations, are worked out in the mother tongue of appearance. With respect to the anorexic girl, control over body weight, of which she so often speaks, appears to her as control over her life. In short, for girls, body work is the normal way to relate to the world. The body is their workplace. From this perspective, the anorexic girl is not a "deviant" who has violated the appearance norms of her society; she is, rather, its star pupil. These women share with other women the cultural conviction that the body is the proper forum for their views; in addition, they share the specific body ideal (thinness) with "normal" women of all social classes (Boskind-Lodahl, 1976, pp. 345-346; Orbach, 1979, p. 167; Székely, 1988, p. 18).

It is these kinds of cultural continuities that the medical approach to anorexia conceals. Medical discourse is premised on the gulf between "normal" non-anorexic and "abnormal" anorexic women; by classifying them as healthy or sick, it places the two groups on opposite sides of the fence and eclipses all that they share. Moreover, the medical perspective again seeks the causes of anorexia in individual biographies, an interpretation that fails to recognize the role that "normal" gender socialization and "normal" structural impasses play in that "disease." Accordingly, medical treatment of anorexia focusses on the individual and her family, pointing to the girl's abnormal rejection of femininity rather than to the larger social-structural dilemmas women experience in capitalist and patriarchal societies. Here, the medical explanation, as in all of the phenomena we have discussed, leaves these larger factors untouched.

Conclusion

In the final section, we weigh the consequences of medicalization on women's lives. First, we review the main negative effects, then consider whether there are positive outcomes as well. Finally, we ask whether recent "woman-centred" health movements are able to provide significant alternatives to mainstream professional medicine.

The Pros and Cons of Medicalization

Perhaps the most important negative result of the medical perspective on women's lives is its tendency to individualize and depoliticize their problems. In all of the examples discussed, women's problems are viewed as personal, psychological matters, and this diagnosis leads to an avoidance of essential social and institutional remedies. The medical model tells women, "The problem is with you, so you must do the changing." As sociologists and as feminists, we find this approach myopic: it treats the female, but leaves dominant patriarchal conceptions of femininity untouched.

The second negative result of medicalization concerns the manner in which the medical rhetoric of illness is deployed to produce conformity to social norms of femininity. The idea that sickness will befall women who deviate from their "natural" — that is, social — gender roles runs through the history of Western thought. One of the earliest examples occurs in Platonic writings from the fifth century B.C. According to Plato, and to Hippocrates, the famous Greek physician of the same era, women's failure to bear children, and thus to fulfil their "natural function," would cause the uterus to rebel and to attack the rest of the body. Plato wrote:

> . . . the animal [the uterus] within them is desirous of procreating children, and when remaining unfruitful long beyond its proper time, gets discontented and angry, and wandering in every direction through the body, closes up the passages of the breath, and, by obstructing respiration, drives them to extremity, causing all varieties of disease. . . . (cited in Greenglass, 1982, p. 209)

With the benefit of hindsight it is easy to dismiss such notions as merely bizarre, but similar efforts to produce social conformity by invoking the medical rhetoric of disease have persisted into our own time. In the last century, medical opinion held that women who had "too much" schooling would suffer an array of ailments, from depression to an atrophied uterus, and "no reading" was often the medical prescription for restoring them to health (Greenglass, 1982, p. 211). We saw in the previous section how the maternal deprivation thesis of Bowlby and others in the 1950s was used to pressure women to conform to the ideal of full-time child rearing, and how contemporary medical thinking pushes women to accept a punishingly narrow body ideal. The point of these examples is not to ridicule the medical knowledge of the past, but to show how medical discourse has been, and continues to be, deployed in ways that limit women's options — in behaviour, in appearance, and in relationships.

But while the negative effects of medicalization on women's lives are considerable, it would be a mistake to portray women as the inevitable victims of medical discourse. The medical rhetoric of health and illness originated with the medical profession, but is not wholly "owned" by doctors, and this means that it is available to be used by other groups, including women, to achieve their own ends. Women have discovered, for example, that the visibility of formerly "invisible" problems like woman abuse, or pre-menstrual syndrome, is increased substantially once they are labelled as "medical problems." As such, they are more likely to draw public attention and sympathy, to attract research funding, and to appear on the political agenda. Women at the turn of the century used the findings of medical science and the rhetoric of health to regulate the sexual activity of their husbands, for example, and in general, to acquire a greater say in marital relations (Morantz, 1984). Thus, even if women's groups are opposed to the medical view and its implications, they have recognized that certain advantages may flow from adopting it as a strategy. In these instances, women, like other relatively low-power groups in society, see that if they cannot change the system that favours the medical perspective, they can at least borrow some of its benefits for themselves.

Second, women may welcome a medical approach to some issues just because it releases them from stigma and moral responsibility for "the problem"; — one cannot be blamed (at least not explicitly) for a "disease" one did not choose to get. The stigma is reduced when alcoholism is medicalized as a chemical disorder, for example, or when obesity is not longer called "the sin of gluttony," but rather a "glandular disorder" or a psychological problem called "compulsive eating." As we noted in the first section of this chapter, the consequences of such discursive shifts are quite concrete: instead of shunning the guilty party, or locking them up, we extend them our sympathy and send them for treatment. Furthermore, medicalization not only lightens the burden of stigma, it also transfers responsibility for the treatment of the problem from the sufferer to the doctor; the behaviour is now the doctor's problem (Conrad & Schneider, 1980, p. 248). The relief and security such a transfer provides may serve a real therapeutic purpose.

In the preceding section we have suggested how women can resist the powerful discourse of medicine by turning it to their own advantage. Women, especially middle-class women, have also resisted medicalization in a more radical fashion, by trying to change mainstream medical practices, or by sidestepping them altogether. For example, they have tried to escape the control of the medical profession by supporting midwifery and natural childbirth movements, by challenging the power hierarchies within doctor-patient relationships, and by forming self-help groups that emphasize self-help care (Fox, 1990, p. 410). In addition, strong advocacy has emerged for the patient's "right to know" and to decide on matters of their own health. These developments all represent a move toward "client control" (de Swaan, 1990, p. 71; Fox, 1990, p. 410).

But, while these movements are sometimes touted as a demedicalization of women's lives, they do not represent a wholesale rejection of modern medicine, partly because of the respect accorded to doctors by "society" at large, and by women themselves (Fox, 1990, p. 412). Despite the new interest science is currently showing in traditional medicine, most of us can scarcely imagine, nor would we choose, a world without modern medical expertise. Even the midwife's opposition to the doctor is mainly occupational; her training and information is largely drawn from the same body of knowledge, and the gulf between her perspective and that of the traditional midwife in a peasant society is immense. To some degree, we in the industrialized "first world" are all held hostage to modern medicine. In part, this is the case because medical discourse often involves the assumption that social consensus exists regarding that discourse and this limits our ability to conceive of "alternative frameworks" and definitions of problems (Gusfield, 1989, p. 436).

It is far more likely, then, that women will achieve not a "demedicalization" of their bodies, but a greater voice in the ways they are treated by the medical profession, in short, a greater degree of power. Clients could gain greater influence over the conditions under which medical expertise is applied, for example (de Swaan, 1990, p. 71); women could determine where they give birth, how and when anesthesia is administered, and when an obstetrician or general practitioner is to be in attendance. Moreover, there are signs that mainstream medicine is permeable to a range of consumer demands. For example, the midwifery and natural childbirth movements have had some of their procedures brought into the hospital setting. These developments include "birthing rooms," "rooming-in" of the newborn with the mother, prenatal Lamaze classes, preparation for pain control in natural childbirth, and an emphasis on mother–child bonding. Certainly, many of the early concerns of the natural childbirth movement have been taken up by mainstream medicine because they serve other medical aims (such as the lowering of maternal and fetal mortality rates), and it can be argued therefore that mainstream medicine has merely co-opted the concerns of these earlier, antiprofessional movements. But on the other hand, it is clear that these developments also address mothers' concerns and demands, albeit primarily those of middle-class mothers.

What we see, then, is not a demedicalization but an ongoing negotiation between two power groups, a two-way relationship in which the underdogs (women and other clients of the medical profession) are gaining increased leverage and muscle. It would appear, however, that these gains must be constantly defended, for with each new development (the new reproductive technologies, for example), the medical profession seems to be ready to disempower women anew.

We conclude that women are not the passive victims of medical institutions. They have been controlled by mainstream professional medicine, but they have also influenced it on occasion (Findlay, 1990). Like other groups, they have turned the profession's prestigious rhetoric to their own advantage. In the end, the encounter between women and the medical profession is much like women's encounter with other institutions of social control — neither victory nor defeat, but an ongoing struggle.

Study Questions

1. Recently we have read of two new "diseases": SAD (seasonal affective disorder) and micromastia (small breasts). Assess the consequences for women and for doctors when these conditions are medicalized.

2. How can women's food consumption practices, including anorexia and obesity, be interpreted as rational practices, rather than as "disorders" or "diseases"? Consider this issue in light of the socio-cultural context in which women live and eat.

3. Do natural childbirth movements depart from the medicalized approach to pregnant and labouring women that Oakley says views women as "containers of fetuses"? Which aspects of natural childbirth might actually perpetuate that view of women? Consider, for example, what natural childbirth advocates assume to be "natural" for women.

4. How do we maintain traditional notions of family life and gender expectations in our own families? How does this permit the medicalization of woman abuse? Which of our notions about familial and gender relations would we have to change in order to approach woman abuse as a social issue, rather than as a medical problem?

5. Compare traditional or folk wisdom on pregnancy, childbirth and child rearing (e.g., "spare the rod and spoil the child") with modern medical and psychological opinion on the same topics (e.g., the books of Dr. Spock). Using your experience, assess the degree to which one form of knowledge has replaced the other. In any given situation, which form appears to carry more authority? Why?

Recommended Reading

Martin, E. (1987). *The woman in the body: A cultural analysis of reproduction.* Boston: Beacon Press.

Oakley, A. (1986). *The captured womb: A history of the medical care of pregnant women.* Oxford: Basil Blackwell.

Székely, E. (1988). *Never too thin.* Toronto: The Women's Press.

Turner, B.S. (1984). *The body and society*. Oxford: Basil Blackwell.

Wolf, N. (1991). *The beauty myth*. Toronto: Vintage Books.

References

Ahluwalia, S., & MacLean, B.D. (1988). The medicalization of domestic violence. In B.S. Bolaria & H.D. Dickinson (Eds.), *Sociology of health care in Canada* (pp. 183-197). Toronto: Harcourt Brace Jovanovich.

Ariès, P. (1962). *Centuries of childhood: A social history of family life*. New York: Vintage Books.

Berton, P. (1977). *The Dionne years*. Toronto: McClelland & Stewart.

Bordo, S.R. (1989). The body and reproduction of femininity: A feminist appropriation of Foucault. In A.M. Jagger & S.R. Bordo (Eds.), *Gender/body/knowledge* (pp. 13-33). New Brunswick: Rutgers University Press.

Bordo, S.R. (1990). Reading the slender body. In M. Jacobus, E. Fox Keller, & S. Shuttleworth (Eds.), *Body/politics: Women and the discourses of science* (pp. 83-112). New York: Routledge.

Boskind-Lodahl, M. (1976, Winter). Cinderella's stepsisters: A feminist perspective on anorexia nervosa and bulimia. *SIGNS*, 2, (2), 342-356.

Brannen, J., & Wilson, G. (Eds.). (1987). *Give and take in families. Studies in resource distribution*. London: Allen and Unwin.

Chernin, K. (1985). *The hungry self: Women, eating and identity*. New York: Harper & Row.

Conrad, P., & Schneider, J.W. (1980). *Deviance and medicalization. From badness to sickness*. St. Louis: C.V. Mosby.

Currer, C., & Stacey, M. (Eds.). (1986). *Concepts of health, illness and disease: A comparative perspective*. Leamington Spa: Berg Publishers.

Davidoff, L., & Hall, C. (1987). *Family fortunes: Men and women of the English middle class, 1780-1850*. London: Hutchinson.

DeKeseredy, W.S., & Hinch, R. (1991). *Woman abuse: Sociological perspectives*. Toronto: Thompson Educational Publishing.

de Swaan, A. (1990). *The management of normality: Critical essays in health and welfare*. London: Routledge.

Doctors give top marks to patient report cards. (1991, December 6). *Calgary Herald*, p. B1.

Donzelot, J. (1979). *The policing of families*. New York: Pantheon Books.

Durkheim, E. (1964). *The division of labour in society*. New York: The Free Press. Original publication 1933.

Edgley, C., & Brissett, D. (1990). Health Nazis and the cult of the perfect body: Some polemical observations. *Symbolic Interaction*, 13, (2), 257-279.

Ehrenreich, B., & English, D. (1979). *For her own good: 150 years of the experts' advice to women*. Garden City: Anchor Books.

Elias, N. (1978). *The history of manners*. New York: Urizen Books. Original publication 1939.

Etaugh, C. (1974). The effects of maternal employment on children: A review of the research. *Merrill-Palmer Quarterly*, 20, 71-98.

Fast tracks. (1991, November 17). *Calgary Herald*, p. B8.

Findlay, D.A. (1990). *Women and medical knowledge in the 1950s: A study of the process of social construction*. Hamilton: McMaster University, Ph.D. Dissertation.

Fisher, S. (1988). *In the patients' best interest. Women and the politics of medical decisions*. New Brunswick: Rutgers University Press.

Foucault, M. (1979). *Discipline and punish: The birth of the prison*. New York: Vintage.

Fox, R.C. (1990). The medicalization and demedicalization of American society. In P. Conrad & R. Kern (Eds.), *The sociology of health and illness: Critical perspectives* (3rd ed.), (pp. 390-394). New York: St. Martin's Press.

Freidson, E. (1970). *Professional dominance: The social structure of medical care*. New York: Aldine.

Frykman, J., & Lofgren, O. (1987). *Culture builders: A historical anthropology of middle-class life*. New Brunswick: Rutgers University Press.

Gaffield, C. (1990). The social and economic origins of contemporary families. In M. Baker (Ed.), *Families: Changing trends in Canada* (2nd ed.). Toronto: McGraw-Hill Ryerson.

Gaskell, J. (1988). The reproduction of family life: Perspectives of male and female adolescents. In A. Tigar McLaren (Ed.), *Gender and society* (pp. 146-168). Toronto: Copp Clark Pittman.

Gelles, R.J., & Cornell, C.P. (1990). *Intimate violence in families* (2nd ed.). Newbury Park: Sage.

Graham, H., & Oakley, A. (1986). Competing ideologies of reproduction: Medical and maternal perspectives on pregnancy. In C. Currer & M. Stacey (Eds.), *Concepts of health, illness and disease: A comparative perspective* (pp. 97-116). Leamington Spa: Berg Publishers.

Greenglass, E.R. (1982). *The world of difference: Gender roles in perspective.* Toronto: John Wiley & Sons.

Gusfield, J.R. (1989, December). Constructing the ownership of social problems: Fun and profit in the welfare state. *Social Problems,* 36, (5), 431-441.

Hareven, T.K. (1989). American families in transition: Historical perspectives on change. In A.S. Skolnick & J.H. Skolnick (Eds.), *Family in transition* (6th ed.), (pp. 39-57). Glenview: Scott, Foresman.

Haug, F., et al. (Eds.). (1987). *Female sexualization.* London: Verso.

Kamerman, S., & Hayes, C.D. (Eds.). (1982). *Families that work: Children in a changing world.* Washington: National Academy Press.

Leavitt, J.W. (1986). *Brought to bed: Childbearing in America, 1750-1950.* New York: Oxford University Press.

Lewis, J. (1986). The working class wife and mother and state intervention, 1870-1918. In J. Lewis (Ed.), *Labour and love: Women's experience of home and family, 1850-1940* (pp. 99-120). London: Basil Blackwell.

Ludmerer, K.M. (1985). *Learning to heal: The development of American medical education.* New York: Basic Books.

Lupri, E. (1990). Harmonie and aggression: Uber die dialektik ehelicher Gewalt. *Kolner Zeitschrift fur Soziologie und Sozialpsychologie,* 42,(3), 474-501.

MacLeod, L. (1989). *Preventing wife battering: Towards a new understanding.* Ottawa: Canadian Advisory Council on the Status of Women.

MacNevin, A.L. (1990). The socially constructed female body: Can we intervene? *Unpublished paper.* Halifax: Dalhousie University.

Martin, E. (1987). *The woman in the body. A cultural analysis of reproduction.* Boston: Beacon Press.

Miller, L. (1987, Winter). Uneasy alliance: Women as agents of social control. *The Canadian Journal of Sociology,* 12, (4), 345-361.

Miller, L. (1990, June). Violent families and the rhetoric of harmony. *The British Journal of Sociology,* 41, (2), 263-288.

Miller, L. (1991). Family problems and problem families. In B.S. Bolaria (Ed.), *Social issues and contradictions in Canadian society* (pp. 57-85). Toronto: Harcourt Brace Jovanovich.

Miller, L., & Penz, O. (1991, August). Talking bodies: Female body builders colonize a male preserve. *Quest,* 43, (2), 148-163.

Morantz, R.M. (1984). The perils of feminist history. In J.W. Leavitt (Ed.), *Women and health in America* (pp. 239-245). Oxford: Oxford University Press.

Morantz-Sanchez, R.M. (1985). *Sympathy with science: Women physicians in American medicine.* Oxford: Oxford University Press.

Oakley, A. (1986). *The captured womb: A history of the medical care of pregnant women.* Oxford: Basil Blackwell.

Orbach, S. (1979). *Fat is a feminist issue.* New York: Berkley Books.

Propper, A. (1990). The invisible reality: Patterns and power in family violence. In M. Baker (Ed.), *Families, changing trends in Canada* (2nd ed.), (pp. 104-128). Toronto: McGraw-Hill Ryerson.

Richardson, T.R. (1989). *The century of the child: The mental hygiene movement and social policy in the United States and Canada.* Albany: State University of New York Press.

Riley, D. (1983). *War in the nursery: Theories of the child and mother.* London: Virago.

Rothman, B.K. (1989). Women, health and medicine. In J. Freeman (Ed.), *Women: A feminist perspective* (pp. 77-86). Mountainview: Mayfield Publishing Company.

Rutter, M. (1981). *Maternal deprivation reassessed.* Harmondsworth: Penguin.

Sandelowski, M. (1984). *Pain, pleasure, and American childbirth: From the twilight sleep to the Read method, 1914-1960.* Westport: Greenwood Press.

Schur, E.M. (1984). *Labelling women deviant: Gender, stigma, and social control.* Philadelphia: Temple University Press.

Schwartz, H. (1986). *Never satisfied: A cultural history of diets, fantasies and fat.* New York: Anchor Books.

Shorter, E. (1977). *The making of the modern family*. New York: Basic Books.

Spitzack, C. (1990). *Confessing excess: Women and the politics of body reduction*. Albany: State University of New York Press.

Stark, E. (1990). Rethinking homicide: Violence, race and the politics of gender. *International Journal of Health Services*, 20, (1), 3-26.

Strong-Boag, V. (1982). Intruders in the nursery: Childcare professionals reshape the years one to five, 1920-40. In J. Parr (Ed.), *Childhood and family in Canadian history* (pp. 160-178). Toronto: McClelland & Stewart.

Synnott, A. (1989). Truth and goodness, mirrors and masks — part I: A sociology of beauty and the face. *The British Journal of Sociology*, 40, (4), 607-636.

Székely, E. (1988). *Never too thin*. Toronto: The Women's Press.

Torrance, G.M. (1987). Socio-historical overview. In D. Coburn, C. D'Arcy, G.M. Torrance, & P. New (Eds.), *Health and Canadian society*. (2nd ed.). Markham: Fitzhenry & Whiteside.

Turner, B.S. (1982, June). The government of the body: Medical regimens and the rationalization of diet. *The British Journal of Sociology*, 33, (2), 254-269.

Turner, B.S. (1984). *The body and society*. Oxford: Basil Blackwell.

Turner, B.S. (1987). *Medical power and social knowledge*. London: Sage Publications.

Walker, G.A. (1990). *Family violence and the women's movement: The conceptual politics of struggle*. Toronto: University of Toronto Press.

Wertz, R.W., & Wertz, D.C. (1977). *Lying-in: A history of childbirth in America*. New York: The Free Press.

Wolf, N. (1991). *The beauty myth*. Toronto: Vintage Books.

Working parents spark concern: Canadians worry the well-being of the nation's children is being sacrificed. (1991, November 5). *The Globe and Mail*, p. A4.

Chapter 14

Women's Perceptions Regarding Health and Illness

Vivienne Walters, McMaster University

Introduction

This chapter focusses on issues that have generally been neglected in feminist research on women and health — women's own perspectives and priorities with respect to health and illness. Researchers appear to have overlooked the vitality and resilience of what Cornwell (1984) has called "commonsense notions" of health and illness. Instead, our primary emphasis has been on medical dominance. This means that while we have been critical of the constructs imposed by physicians, we may also have imposed our own and not listened closely enough to the voices of "ordinary women," using these as a starting point in our research to determine the focus of enquiry. The discussion here is organized around two main themes: a reassessment of arguments concerning the medicalization of women, and women's main concerns regarding their health. The first section draws on literature on women's own perspectives, which suggests that women have not been medicalized to the extent that we often suppose. I will argue that we need to continue to explore the relationship between women and medicine, for it may be more complex than our original critiques have assumed. The second section presents data on women's own concerns; concerns that have received relatively little attention in the literature on women and health. Two other related issues are also discussed here — the problems of how we should interpret the data we collect on women's perspectives, and how women's priorities should be taken into account, insofar as they differ from those specified in existing policy statements and indices of need.

The Medicalization of Women: A Reassessment

The medicalization of women is a primary focus in the literature on women and health. Research has emphasized the social control aspects of medicine and shown how medicine has helped to reinforce the concept of women's place being in the home by defining women primarily in terms of their reproductive roles. The normal has been defined as pathological and women's symptoms have been understood in primarily biological or individualistic terms. The hierarchical nature of the doctor-patient relationship is obvious in medicine's portrayal of women as weak, fragile, and emotional creatures, and the physician as the expert with a monopoly of medical knowledge. Within this relationship, compliance is expected. In the earlier stages of the analysis and critique of the medicalization of women, women were seen as relatively passive victims of medicine (Ehrenreich & English, 1979). Now, it is more commonly acknowledged that women have also played a role in the process — seeking the benefits that medicine appeared to offer, yet losing autonomy and also being prey to the hazards of medical intervention (Riessman, 1983).

Various aspects of the process of medicalization have been identified. Conrad and Schneider (1980) have suggested that it occurs conceptually when problems are defined by a medical vocabulary; in an institutional form when physicians legitimate a problem or a program; and in an interactional form when problems are diagnosed and treated. Cornwell (1984, pp. 119-120) distinguishes between medicalization-from-above and medicalization-from-below. The former refers to "changes in the Western view of mind and body that have occurred with the development of scientific medicine," and the latter to "a readiness on the part of subcultures and individuals who belong to them to accept modern (in this case, medical) legitimations for health and illness." Such distinctions are important because they encourage us to think of ways in which the process of medicalization may be more or less complete, and they also highlight aspects of the process that have received relatively little attention. While we have a substantial literature tracing the social control aspects of medicine and the ways in which medicine has influenced concepts of health and illness at the societal level, much less attention has been directed towards the ways in which individual women conceptualize health and illness. Neither do we have a good understanding of the extent to which the process of diagnosis and treatment is medicalized. It is a considerable leap of logic to assume that medicalization-from-above is replicated at the individual level and that it permeates the ways in which women deal with health and illness. It also reinforces notions of women as passive subjects.

What if we look at women themselves, are they as medicalized as the thesis suggests? How do women view illness? Do they rely on the medical model? To what extent do they turn to physicians for help? To what extent do they listen to their physician's advice? Do their priorities coincide with those of physicians? These are the types of questions that seldom have been asked. The experiences of women have been largely ignored by epidemiologists (Kaufert, 1988) and despite the charge of medicalization, medical research has often neglected women, particularly their own accounts of their experiences (Cohen, 1991). Even within the social science literature there has been little emphasis on lay perspectives, and few researchers have focussed on the ways in which women themselves interpret and perceive their health and illness (Pirie, 1988; Walters, 1991). The gaps are even more glaring with respect to particular problems such as occupational health.

But, to argue that these issues have been neglected is not to say that there has been no related research. There are studies that help us to understand women's perspectives and lead us to question some aspects of the thesis of medicalization. Two bodies of literature in particular are helpful in this regard. First, there is a tradition of sociological research that looks at lay perspectives and that almost completely focusses on women, though the issue of gender is seldom emphasized (see for example, Blaxter, 1983; Calnan, 1988, 1987; Hunt, Jordan, & Irwin, 1989; Pill & Stott, 1986). Researchers justify their focus on the basis of women's responsibility for the health of others and on the need to reduce confounding variables, or else they focus on women because they are more willing than men to be interviewed and more interested in talking about health-related issues. What might be distinctive about women's experiences and how they might reflect the control and subordination of women is not an issue. Secondly, there is a growing body of research on women's experiences that directly addresses the issues of gender and of medicalization (see for example, Kaufert, 1987, 1988; Pirie, 1988; Martin, 1989). Often this work has focussed on specific health concerns, particularly on aspects of women's reproductive health. Together, these different bodies of literature suggest that medicalization is less complete than has been supposed, and that we need to devote more attention to the complex interaction between lay and medical perspectives.

Let us turn now to look at research on women's explanations of the causes of illness, the ways in which they deal with health problems, and specific women's health issues that have been studied. With respect to women's conceptualizations of the causes of illness, the thesis of medicalization predicts that women would pattern their thinking on the medical model, emphasizing germ theory and biologically based explanations of illness. With regard to the ways in which women deal with health problems, the thesis of medicalization leads us to expect that women would readily consult doctors, that doctors would be a primary source of information, and that patients would generally accept their doctor's diagnoses and comply with treatment regimens. To what extent are these expectations borne out when we look at the available data?

Causes of Ill Health

Do women interpret disease in terms of the medical model? The evidence is mixed, suggesting that this is but one of several influences on the ways in which women think about health and illness. In Blaxter's (1983) study of 46 working-class grandmothers, the primary categories of cause they identified were infection, heredity or familial tendencies, and agents in the environment. From the point of view of medical science, their models of causal processes were incorrect, notes Blaxter, yet they were sophisticated and complex models that mirrored germ theory. In this sense the women borrowed from medicine, but Blaxter also shows how their models had a strong social character, closely bound to their own history and experiences. The work of Pill and Stott (1986), a study of 41 mothers, 30-35 years of age, living with their husbands, also revealed a strong emphasis on germ theory, again reflecting the medical model. Yet they, too, recognized the social bases of illness and were intolerant of explanations that relied on individual blame or responsibility for health. Cornwell's (1984) study juxtaposes the "public" and "private" accounts of illness that her respondents offered. "Public" accounts borrowed from the medical model and her respondents were obviously less comfortable with this vocabulary and less sure of themselves. They presented their "private" accounts with much greater ease and spoke of their own or others' experiences, weaving together an understanding of health and illness that incorporated many social factors, commonsense notions, and their own interpretations of medical information. She argues that people switch between different ways of viewing health and illness, mixing medical concepts with other explanations. The former tend to predominate in public accounts, while the latter receive more emphasis in private accounts. Both types of accounts represent a partial rendering of concepts of health and illness. Each of these three studies, then, suggests complex models of health and illness that only partly borrow from the models of medicine.

Another important source of data is a major British survey of health and lifestyles, which included 3905 men and 5098 women (Blaxter, 1990). This helps to highlight gender differences in concepts of health (women, for example, were more likely to include social relationships in their definitions of health) and provides a fairly detailed analysis of ways in which people conceptualize health and illness. Women's views of the causes of disease varied, depending on the particular questions they were asked — whether they were speaking of society as a whole, themselves, or particular diseases (Blaxter, 1990, p. 159). In their opinion, the main causes of health and ill health for society at large were individual behaviour (e.g., diet, smoking, exercise, standard of living), and aspects of the external environment, such as pollution and quality of housing. Women from non-manual backgrounds also emphasized stress and psychological contentment. Responses were different when the respondent's own health was under consideration. Standard of living was less frequently mentioned, while family and social relationships were seen to be among the primary determinants of health and illness. And when women were asked about the causes of specific diseases, the two major categories of cause they mentioned were individual behaviour; and stress, contentment, and psychological factors. In each of these instances, then, women placed a strong emphasis on the social bases of health and illness. Uncomfortable with a false dichotomy between "medical" and "non-medical" ways of looking at health, Blaxter presents lay concepts as a complex, subtle, and sophisticated mix of more or less well-informed biomedical elements and subjective experiences that only the individuals themselves can describe and about which they may be better informed (Blaxter, 1990, pp. 13-14).

But medicine may be rejected, too. In her study of a working-class community in Philadelphia, where she talked mainly with women, Balshem (1991) addresses the community's unwillingness to embrace the messages of health educators who urged changes in lifestyles. She links their fatalism regarding cancer with low social control and presents it as a form of resistance. In their responses, she argues, they "refuse science the power to define the terms of the discourse."

> Community members are disinclined to accept their assigned position as "targets" of a health education campaign. They have seen themselves labeled sick, and they have turned this around to label their social and material environment sick. They have considered blaming themselves as victims, and they have rejected the notion. Scientific authority, clearly, does not consider their interpretations of experience valid. So they use rhetoric about fate as a shield, and charge the scientists with hubris. (Balshem, 1991, p. 165)

So then, looking at the ways in which women themselves conceptualize health and illness, we see only partial evidence of medicalization. There is a rich diversity in women's ways of understanding health and illness, and medicine represents only one element in their complex models of explanation.

Dealing with Health Problems

To whom do women talk when they have health problems? To what extent do they rely on physicians? Do they accept and incorporate physicians' diagnoses into their own understanding of their problems? Do they comply with their physician's advice and instructions? Again, at each of these stages, there is evidence that medicalization is far from complete and that its influence is more complex than has been previously acknowledged.

The importance of lay referral networks has long been recognized (Freidson, 1970).

When we are sick it is most typical that we turn to family and friends (Kandrack, Grant, & Segall, 1991). We turn to them for advice and information. Men are likely to turn to women and women to other women. Kaufert (1988) notes that tales of childbirth, menopause, and of assorted aches and pains are shared with other women. Roberts's (1985) account of her research on women and their doctors also emphasizes the sharing of information among women. In Pirie's (1988) study of 244 dental hygienists, few had learned of pre-menstrual syndrome from their doctor, most had heard of it from a magazine, other media, or friends and family members. Blaxter's (1983) study also notes this type of amalgam of knowledge garnered from various sources. Eyles and Donovan (1990) suggest that doctors are one of the last resources to which people turn. Canadian, British, and U.S. studies all suggest that women blend several different sources of information and advice, and that medicine may not be the most important of these. Gabe and Calnan's (1989) research has shown that women are suspicious of medical technology, particularly working-class women, though the degree of scepticism varies in relation to the severity of the health problem.

But what happens when women do consult their doctors? Is it at this point that they lose their sense of autonomy? Here again there is evidence to suggest the limits of the process of medicalization. Following Cornwell (1984), Kaufert and Gilbert (1987) have looked at medicalization-from-below (the extent to which patients seek medical intervention and the extent to which doctors intervene). In their study of women going through menopause, they found less medical intervention than is often assumed; there was evidence that physicians vary in the management of menopause and women, too, vary in the extent to which they turn to physicians for advice and treatment.

Other studies confirm these types of findings and suggest the limits of medicalization as well as the resilience of lay perspectives. Women borrow from medicine as appropriate, transform and integrate this information with their own understandings. They are engaged in a dynamic process of constructing and reconstructing their understanding of their experiences. This is the major theme in the research of Hunt, Jordan, and Irwin (1989), who have shown that when symptoms are chronic and can resist definition, medicine may play a relatively small role in women's constructions of explanations of their illness. They studied 23 women who were experiencing very common, but non-specific and indefinite symptoms. These women were interviewed before their first medical consultation, two weeks after diagnosis, and then several times up to approximately four months after the first interview. They found substantial fluctuations over time in the explanations the women gave for their symptoms.

SL was experiencing a variety of physical discomforts including abdominal pain, headache, and dizziness. The possible causes she considered in the course of our 4 months contact with her ranged from sinus problems, flu, and kidney infection to pregnancy and cancer. For a time she settled on the doctor's explanation of urinary tract infection and emotional stress. But by the 15-week interview, she began to attribute her symptoms to an ulcer and the flu, while also maintaining the urinary tract infection and stress as partial explanations. (Jordan, Hunt, & Irwin, 1989, p. 949)

Reformulations of explanations did not appear to be triggered just by medical consultations — three of the four women who did not keep their appointment with their doctor also dramatically changed their explanations. And physicians' diagnoses were not simply accepted but transformed and incorporated into their pre-existing constructs.

TJ was 64 years old and was going to the doctor "to catch up with all my little problems." She was primarily seeking relief for chest and esophagus pain which she interpreted as heartburn and indigestion. Prior to seeing the doctor she said she felt the underlying cause was simply "old age." Her attitude was that it was only to be expected that one have minor aches and pains as one ages. She said: "As you get older things are never one hundred percent. Half these things they tell you everyone has as they get older. . . . Naturally my heart's not as strong, but it's good for me at my age."

Two weeks post-diagnosis she said that the physician found she had IHSS (Idiopathic Hypertrophic Subaortic Stenosis). He told her that this is a serious, untreatable heart condition that could kill her at any time. He also recommended an over-the-counter medication for her indigestion. At this time she talked a good deal about the heart condition, saying, "I don't let the pains worry me." She still held that she didn't "have any bad health problems for a person my age. At my age no one is A-1." In the 15-week interview, however, she never mentioned the heart condition at all. Instead she was again preoccupied with her indigestion saying that was what had been causing her pain, and discussing at length the effectiveness of the medication. She had tried out the physician's diagnosis for a time, then reverted to her original idea. It would seem that, finding little use in the diagnosis of an untreatable heart condition, she adopted the part of the doctor's explanation which was consistent with her prior ideas and which included a useful course of action. (Hunt, Jordan, & Irwin, 1989, p. 950)

The authors argue that these patients do not come in as blank slates, but with quite elaborate prior constructions of their conditions and that these constructions fit with their daily lives; physicians' diagnoses were modified so as to fit with these. Most respondents returned to their original explanations, though these were elaborated with elements of biomedical language.

A similar theme exists in Blaxter's (1983) research. She notes, for example, that the grandmothers she interviewed were scornful of doctors who explained their problems in terms of "nerves." Even though they themselves recognized the importance of stress and strain as causes of disease, such diagnoses from doctors were only acceptable if they had detailed knowledge of the respondent. In her concluding comments,

Blaxter describes how women have developed a concept of their body that is founded on their experiences.

> People have to inhabit their bodies, and their physical identity is part of themselves. Particularly as they grow older, they have a need to account for this identity, to draw together all that they have experienced. This body is their inheritance, it is the result of the events of their life, and it is their constraint. (Blaxter, 1983, p. 69)

Information from doctors has to be consistent with this sense of identity; it will not be accepted if it does not make sense in terms of the patient's models.

These observations also help us to understand the issue of non-compliance. There is a considerable medical literature that addresses the fact that patients seldom follow doctors' instructions to the letter. But most of the compliance literature examines this from the point of view of the doctor. If we take the standpoint of the patient, we see her striving to fit diagnoses and treatment regimens into everyday routines; continuing a "normal" life appears to take precedence over treatments. The research of Hunt, Jordan, Irwin, and Browner (1989) suggests that non-compliance cannot be explained by lack of understanding of doctors' diagnoses or by patients espousing explanations quite different from those of their doctors. They describe cases in which treatments were not followed because, for example, a diet did not fit with a patient's intensive work schedule, or medication caused drowsiness when it was essential for a woman to be alert. Women often modified their doctor's advice; one common pattern being to follow treatments only when problems were severe, and then to stop. Miles (1988), on the other hand, describes how women turn to other women for advice on how to take their medications. She notes that in recent years a considerable body of lay experience on the use of tranquillizers has accumulated, so that physicians are not the only source of information.

In sum, there is a considerable body of evidence that suggests that women do not incorporate medicine into their understanding and management of illness to quite the extent that is assumed in the thesis of medicalization.

Specific Women's Health Issues

There are other studies that have focussed on specific health-related issues: Miles (1988) on mental illness; Clarke (1985) on breast cancer; Pirie (1988) on pre-menstrual syndrome; Graham and Oakley (1986) on pregnancy and childbirth; Kaufert and Gilbert (1987) on menopause; and Martin (1989) on each of these aspects of women's reproductive roles. Not all of these are concerned with medicalization, but they are a source of information about women's concerns and experiences. For example, Graham and Oakley show us how the meaning of pregnancy and childbirth is quite different for women and their physicians. "It is not simply a difference of opinion about approach and procedures — about whether a pregnancy is normal or pathological, or whether or not labour should be routinely induced" (Graham & Oakley, 1986, p. 99); their frames of reference are different and involve differences in the significance attached to the nature of childbirth, the context from which it derives meaning, the criteria of success, the expertise that each possesses. (Consultations even revealed differences of opinion between women and doctors as to how advanced she was in her pregnancy — twenty or 26.5 weeks — and how many children she already had!) There were fundamental differences between women and their doctors, yet women had few choices about the care they received. Communication tended to be in one direction and decisions were made on their behalf. But still, women view childbirth within a frame of reference quite different from that of doctors and rooted in their own experiences.

> A woman views reproduction not as an isolated episode of medical treatment but as an event which is integrated with other aspects of her life. Having a baby affects not only her medical status, it has implications for most of her other social roles. This is seen most clearly during first pregnancy and birth, when a woman becomes a mother; that is, she acquires a new social role. But even in subsequent births, her role can change as her pregnancy affects her occupational standing, her financial position, her housing situation, her marital status and her personal relationships. (Graham & Oakley, 1986, p. 101)

Graham and Oakley's work hints at the vitality of women's own attitudes towards childbirth, which persist despite their loss of autonomy.

Martin, too, conveys the limits of medicalization in her analysis of women's responses to pre-menstrual syndrome, menstruation, childbirth, and menopause. For example, women do not use medical metaphors of "failed production" to describe menstruation; most women are not intending to get pregnant and for many of those with male partners, menstruation is a welcome sign. Neither is medical intervention welcomed in childbirth — women may go to great lengths to control the nature of the birth and resist intervention. One woman who had already delivered a child by Caesarean section described her subsequent pregnancy:

> I made up my mind if I started labor I was going to keep it a secret, as much as possible, because they were talking about time limits, you know, you start labor and you go fourteen hours and if you haven't had that baby yet, you might just get a c-section.
>
> So that night we went to bed and I didn't tell my husband too much because if he knew he'd say "Awww, let's go to the hospital, quick, it's forty-five minutes away." I made up my mind I'm not going to let anybody know until it's really there and I've got a headstart on those doctors, and I'm not telling them until it's too late almost.

. . . Get there seventeen hours too early and they've got you. They've got you hooked up and you feel like a
guinea pig and your labour slows down and they're going. (Martin, 1989)

She concealed the breaking of her waters and transition, but couldn't stay quiet once
pushing started.

Martin illustrates the medical metaphors present in the ways in which women think
about their bodies. Yet at the same time she also shows us how women reject these, a
rejection that appeared to be more marked among her working-class and black respondents. She identifies several ways in which "women express consciousness of their position and opposition to oppression" (Martin, 1989, p. 183). One of these is non-action, a
passive resistance because women perceive an organization, a procedure, or certain
terminology to be contrary to their interests. Another is sabotage, whereby women do
not comply or else interfere with treatments, for example, removing monitors when they
are not being observed, or going for long walks so the monitor cannot be used.
"Resistance" is the term she uses for those instances when women actually refuse
treatments, refuse to do what they are told, or reject ways in which they are defined.
"Rebellion" is even more forceful and seeks to change organizational routines, policies,
and other practices that affect women.

What then can we conclude about the thesis of the medicalization of women? My
emphasis has been on studies that help to show the distinctiveness of women's own
perspectives: their understanding of disease is socially grounded, rooted in their own
experiences, and based on information from many different sources, medicine being
only one of several sources of advice and information, which in turn is blended with
existing constructs. Insofar as explanations are rooted in women's own experiences —
and this is a primary theme in many of the studies discussed here — then women will
continue to resist medicalization.[1]

Women's Priorities

Sociological research has generally focussed on what researchers define as important,
often because of its centrality within particular theoretical perspectives. The studies that
do focus on women's experiences and that do take gender into account — I have already
cited many of them — have concentrated primarily on issues related to reproduction.
Among the more common topics of enquiry have been childbirth, pre-menstrual syndrome, menstruation, and menopause (Graham & Oakley, 1986; Kaufert, 1987; Martin,
1989; Pirie, 1988). But are these the issues that concern women most? Are they what
women consider to be their main health problems? In Blaxter's British survey, the index
of good health that was most often cited by women was being psychologically fit. This

alone suggests that something more than reproductive issues are important for women. And, of course, women may also be bothered most by problems that are not gender specific.

It is only very recently that researchers have started to look at what health issues are important for women themselves. A survey of women in an Australian community by Redman, Hennrikus, Bowman, and Sanson-Fisher (1985) may be the first study to look at women's own priorities. The women were presented with a comprehensive list of health and social problems, and for each of these they were asked whether they had worried about it during the past six months and whether they had experienced it during the same period of time. The problems women were most likely to worry about were tiredness (52.3 percent), anxiety (46.5 percent), being overweight (50.4 percent), stress (47.3 percent), road–traffic accidents (45.0 percent), and money problems (41.1 percent). The problems they had experienced were similar. Tiredness was the main problem (reported by 70.3 percent) and this was followed by stress (56.6 percent), anxiety (53.1 percent), being overweight (50.4 percent), disturbed sleep (50.8 percent), and depression (45.0 percent).

Preliminary results from my own research in Hamilton, Ontario — based on the study by Redman et al., — show patterns that are only slightly different (Walters, 1992). A stratified random sample of 356 women was interviewed in late 1990 and early 1991. They were asked what worried them about their health and what health problems they had experienced. The main health problems the women had worried about during the previous six months were road accidents (57.9 percent), breast cancer (52.5 percent), being overweight (46.9 percent), stress (44.7 percent), and arthritis (42.4 percent). When they were asked to pick the two problems that had worried them most, the list was slightly different: breast cancer (25.8 percent), cancer in general (22.2 percent), heart disease (19.1 percent), road accidents (17.7 percent), and cancer of the womb or cervix (14.6 percent) were the problems that were most frequently cited. It is a selection of problems that shows women's awareness of some of the major causes of mortality, though it is worth noting that the smaller percentages indicate less consensus over priorities. While women share similar concerns, they vary in the emphasis that they place on these.

When the respondents were asked about the problems they had actually experienced, those that were most often mentioned were tiredness (68.0 percent), stress (60.4 percent), disturbed sleep (46.1 percent), lack of time for self (46.1 percent), and anxiety (44.4 percent). When they were asked to pick their two main problems — a better index of priorities — slightly different priorities were revealed and, again, there was less consensus over them: stress (20.5 percent), arthritis (18.8 percent), being overweight (16.6 percent), migraine/chronic headaches (11.0 percent), and tiredness (9.8 percent).

These results are interesting for several reasons. One of the most striking findings is that reproductive issues do not figure prominently. This means that medicine's focus on women's reproductive roles omits much that is important to women. So, too, the emphasis in feminist scholarship — maybe even the women's health movement — has not fully reflected some of the primary concerns of women. In the development of our research agendas we have paid scant attention to such problems as tiredness, arthritis, migraines and headaches, and road accidents. Even cancer, heart disease, and stress have received relatively little attention from social scientists interested in women's health. A second noteworthy pattern in these data is the frequent reporting of mental-health problems. Stress was one of the two themes that appeared in responses to most of the questions posed to women. And this is amplified by the substantial proportions of women who reported tiredness, anxiety, depression, lack of time for themselves, disturbed sleep, and lack of confidence. One other pattern also deserves emphasis — the relatively high proportions of women who think that they are overweight. Half of the Australian women sample considered themselves overweight and 45 percent of the Hamilton sample did also. Just as stress was mentioned throughout the interviews, so too were concerns with weight and body image. This confirms other studies that have noted women's preoccupation with body image and their dissatisfaction with their weight (Chernin, 1981; Lawrence, 1987).

But these are priorities with respect to illness alone. If we also consider the social problems that help to generate ill health, then the picture is more complex and it is difficult to say how women would phrase their priorities. In the Hamilton survey the respondents were asked what they consider to be the main social problems for women in Canada. The issues they mentioned most frequently were violence, discrimination in the labour force, the problems of single mothers, poverty or severe financial problems, and inadequate day care. What is not clear is how women would order these issues alongside health problems.

Such observations suggest that surveys could help to reveal women's priorities and concerns and the ways in which they differ from the emphasis in medicine and academic research. They also suggest the virtue of modifying our research agendas so as to incorporate such themes. But it is critical that, in addition to more structured quantitative research, we place more emphasis on ethnographic studies. These would allow women's concerns to emerge more fully, giving women "space" to define their central health issues, and then looking at how they define them, how they explain the source of the problems they experience, documenting the ways in which these problems affect their lives and the ways in which they cope with them. It would benefit us to listen more closely and carefully for women's own meanings so that we might articulate women's "unarticulated experience" (Devault, 1990).

To argue for much greater attention to women's own concerns — research agendas that are not just directed by our own theoretical and conceptual frameworks — raises other issues in turn. I address two of these here: issues of interpretation of data and the related problem of how women's concerns might be taken into account in the development of health policy.

Issues of Interpretation

My primary argument in this chapter has been that we must attend to women's own concerns regarding health and illness. Certainly, feminist methodology has emphasized the importance of representing the world from the point of view of women. Yet there are dilemmas of interpretation that we confront in doing such research. One, in particular, merits attention in the context of this discussion: are we to view women's concerns as authentic, accepting them at face value? Or should they be re-interpreted, treated as examples of "false consciousness" or the influence of dominant ideologies? Is it the case that "women's perceptions of reality are distorted both by male-dominant ideology and by the male-dominated structure of everyday life" (Jaggar, 1983, p. 371)? How should we interpret our data? It is not a dilemma that is restricted to feminist research, but it may be particularly problematic here insofar as a primary goal of feminist scholarship is to articulate the voices of women.

Some examples of how these different positions can influence research may be helpful. One arises in my own research on women's perspectives and priorities. As we have seen, there were two consistent themes in the interviews — stress and weight problems. Intuitively, each calls for a different type of analysis, yet this represents an inconsistency in approach and a reluctance to treat women's concerns as authentic. Reports of stress can be accepted readily at face value and we would generally approve of subsequent analysis of the social production of stress — what it is about women's lives that generates stress? But what of women's concerns about their weight? Feminist analysis would probably be more reluctant to see overweight being placed on a public-health agenda. The voice of women is less likely to be seen as authentic and more likely to be analyzed as a social construction — as evidence of an "unhealthy" culture that overemphasizes women's bodies and encourages them to conform to unreal standards.[2]

Recent work by Aronson (1991) also provides an example of the choices that must be made. She describes the official discourse of social policy that poses the dual options for old women of "independent" living in the community and the less desirable option of institutional living, with its attendant loss of autonomy. Her interviews with older women show how some phrase their needs in terms of the official discourse, but others question it, and in so doing, question the very concepts of dependence and autonomy on which it is based. The right types of institutional settings may even help to promote autonomy; they can release women from the mundane tasks of housekeeping and cooking, leaving them time for other pursuits and providing them with companionship. And living at home alone need not necessarily signify independence. For many women it can mean loneliness and dependence on female kin or paid services for help.[3]

These alternative definitions were most likely to come from women who still lived at home, who spoke from anticipation and an awareness of their own priorities. Implicit in Aronson's analysis is the argument that we should not just attend to the definitions of need of those who already are enmeshed in the social-service network; experience may have taught them to narrow their sense of options. Those positioned outside may bring important insights and help us to envisage alternatives. Responses shaped by experience may be less valuable because they have become restricted.

Another instance is to be found in Gordon's (1988) work on childbirth. She interviewed women about childbirth long after the event — the respondents had at least one child between one and ten years of age. Most of the women defined the births as easy, even though there was a high rate of medical intervention. In this she sees evidence of successful medicalization, for the women accepted intervention as the norm. However, she is uncomfortable with this "facile" analysis and argues that because women had few chances to talk about their experiences, they had been unable to develop a critical perspective. She concludes that "Women have not been given the perspective or framework within which to judge their childbirth experiences . . . and do not have knowledge of other definitions or standards by which to evaluate their experiences" (Gordon, 1988, p. 47).

Often, the pull is to reinterpret the voice of women because it is important to understand the ways in which it reflects women's subordination, their poverty, economic dependence, fear of violence, low self-esteem, and so on; the conditions of women's lives. But the danger is that women's concerns are not then validated and women's consciousness is reduced to something "false." Certainly, women's concerns are shaped by many forces, and it is just such a perspective that I have developed in my chapter on nurses' responses to hazards in their work (see p. 627-643). But, insofar as we reinterpret what women have to say, then we run the risk of duplicating the dominance of medicine; we, too, are regretting the fact that "if only women knew better, they would think differently."

Policy Issues

As we move towards a more thorough documentation of women's health-related concerns, we confront the problem of how to take these into account in the formulation of policy strategies for change. This too, in part, is an issue of interpretation, based on the legitimacy we assign to women's concerns. But before addressing the problem of interpretation, let us look at the different indices used to assess women's needs regarding health and health care.

One traditional index is mortality rates. These identify the major causes of death and, because they provide relatively little information about the health of the living, they are frequently used in conjunction with morbidity data. Morbidity rates may often rely on the records of hospitals and physicians (though neither of these would document health problems for which women do not seek help from the health-care system). Another approach involves health surveys in which people record the various problems they experience and the extent to which their activity is limited. These capture a range of different types of problems and, depending on the questions asked, can help to portray problems from the point of view of patients' experience rather than in terms of the professional categories of medicine. More recently, lay input has been encouraged and needs assessments have more frequently relied on key informants, though these are very often non-medical service providers or representatives of special-interest groups. They do not necessarily reflect the concerns of "ordinary women" in all their diversity. Community-based surveys can provide some balance, but they do not provide a more textured understanding of women's definitions of need. In other words, each of these approaches has both strengths and limits.[4]

What are the varying definitions of need using these different indices? Mortality data show the following major causes of death: heart disease, cancer (breast, lung, colo-rectal, uterine, ovarian), strokes, respiratory disease, and accidents (Statistics Canada, 1990, pp. 133-134). Among the leading causes of hospitalization among women are pregnancy and delivery, diseases of the digestive system, genito-urinary system, circulatory system, and respiratory system. However, the greatest proportion of days of stay are for mental disease and diseases of the circulatory system (Statistics Canada, 1990, p. 142). A somewhat different set of issues is highlighted in a key informant survey that identified the following main health issues for women: mental health, violence against women, reproductive health, reproductive disorders, occupational and environmental health, nutrition and fitness, and chronic medical conditions such as osteoporosis, breast cancer, and arthritis (Health & Welfare Canada, 1988). And, as the reader will recall, in my survey in Hamilton discussed earlier, the problems most frequently mentioned as being the respondents' two main health worries were breast cancer, cancer in general, heart disease, road accidents, and cancer of the womb or cervix. When respondents picked the two main health problems they had experienced in the previous six months, the issues they mentioned most frequently were stress, arthritis, being overweight, migraine and/ or chronic headaches, and tiredness. They also itemized important social problems facing women in Canada: violence, discrimination in the labour force, the problems of single mothers, poverty or severe financial problems, and inadequate day care. Clearly, while there are consistent themes, there are also differences in emphasis in these possible indices of health needs.

How then are these to be integrated? What weight should be given to each? When decisions about the distribution of scarce resources must be made, on what basis can this be done? For example, if mortality data show that certain problems kill women, yet women speak of other priorities, what are the most appropriate indices? Redman, Hennrikus, Bowman, and Sanson-Fisher (1988, p. 127) argue that the "best method of needs assessment is that which identifies priorities which, in the long term, result in the greatest over-all improvement to the quality and quantity of life." But, as yet, there is no consensus on what best predicts quality of life. In such a situation, Redman et al., argue, it is best to take into account a wide range of data. Moreover, "it could be argued that the opinions of women themselves ought to have the greatest predictive validity since only they can describe and assess the priority of factors which affect their quality of life accurately" (Redman, Hennrikus, Bowman, & Sanson-Fisher, 1988, p. 127). In the absence of indices that provide a blueprint for decision making, and given the current emphasis on well-being, then, it is timely to explore women's own definitions and to incorporate them in the policy-making process.

However, to pose issues in this way is to focus on policy-making as a rational process guided by clearly specified criteria for decision making. Such an approach neglects the ways in which needs are constructed and social policy is the outcome of conflicts over definitions of problems and appropriate solutions. If policy is to reflect women's priorities, it is critical that women collectively assert their concerns and establish structures for their discovery and articulation, involving a broad spectrum of women in the creation of an oppositional discourse.[5] Feminists scholarship might also contribute to this through the documentation of women's health-related concerns. As I have suggested in this chapter, we have too long neglected the voices of "ordinary women."

Closer attention to women's priorities and perspectives would not only inform the policy-making process and influence the social construction of women's health. It could also lead us to a fuller understanding of the nature of the process of medicalization and the relationships between medical and lay perspectives. At the same time it could help us to generate research that no longer preserves medicine as a central reference point, and instead places women at the centre of the analysis.

Acknowledgements: My research on women's perspectives and priorities is funded by a grant from the Social Sciences and Humanities Research Council. Jane Vock was my research assistant in the early phases of the project, and she also helped with the review of the literature discussed in the section on medicalization.

Notes

1. Yet at the same time we must not lose sight of the influence of medicine. There are many examples, even in the references cited in this chapter, of the powerful effects of medicalization. One such instance is pre-menstrual syndrome. Both Pirie (1988) and Martin (1989) develop fascinating analyses of the contextual nature of pre-menstrual syndrome. They view it as an expression of anger which, according to Pirie, tends to be vented at home rather than at work. It may also represent a time of heightened creativity, increased consciousness, and rejection of discipline. But, unable to accept their rage as legitimate, women express it in another guise, claiming medical legitimation by explaining it in biological terms. Martin comments that if the root causes of the anger "could be named and known, maybe a cleaner, more productive anger would arise from within women, tying them together as a common oppressed group instead of sending them individually to the doctor as patients to be fixed" (Martin, 1989, p. 135). Here is but one example of the many ways in which medicine helps to individualize and diffuse problems that are social in nature.

2. Sometimes the problem can be resolved by going beneath the surface answers we receive to look at the reasoning underlying women's responses (one of the reasons why qualitative research is so important). In my survey in Hamilton, several interviews were tape-recorded and subsequently transcribed. In the structured section of the questionnaire, when the respondents were asked whether they worried about violence, many responded "no." What the tape-recorder picked up were their additional comments: "no, I never go out at night," "no, I don't go out alone," "no, I wait for my son to pick me up." In other words, they are saying "yes, I do worry about violence, but I have ways of coping with this that remove my fears; I modify the way I would otherwise live." These are the types of problems that can be eliminated if we use a variety of techniques of data collection. The more difficult problem is whether, in putting women's view in context, we might invalidate them, rather than helping to articulate them.

3. Those who like mystery novels might like to read *Sheep's Clothing* by Celia Dale (1988) for an account of the vulnerability of old women.

4. See Redman, Hennrikus, Bowman, and Sanson-Fisher (1988) for a fuller discussion of the limits of traditional measures of women's health needs.

5. In discussing the importance of oppositional discourses, the politicization of needs from below, Fraser (1989, p. 181) raises the question of how we might distinguish better from worse interpretations of women's needs. She rejects a relativist position in which all articulations of need are equal or equally compromised, emanating from specific interests (those based on class, race, sexual orientation, or age, for example). Rather, she argues that an important criterion is the process by which interpretations of need are generated; that it be inclusive, egalitarian, and fair.

Study Questions

1. How would you assess the thesis of medicalization? What information would you need?
2. Is there reason to suppose that women's and men's perspectives regarding health and illness are different?
3. In what ways are women's conceptualizations of health and illness shaped by the structure of their lives?
4. In what respects does the subordination of women help to generate their health problems?
5. In constructing indices of need, what weight would you give to lay concerns regarding health? If there are competing definitions of need, how would you choose between them?

Recommended Reading

Blaxter, M. (1983). The causes of disease: Women talking. *Social Science Medicine*, 17, 59-69.

Devault, M. (1990). Talking and listening from women's standpoint: Feminist strategies for interviewing and analysis. *Social Problems, 37,* 96-116.

Federal/Provincial/Territorial Working Group on Women's Health. (1990). *Working together for women's health: A framework for development of policies and programs.* Ottawa: Author.

Hunt, L., Jordan, B., & Irwin, S. (1989). Views of what's wrong: Diagnosis and patients' concepts of illness. *Social Science and Medicine, 28,* 945-955.

Kaufert, P.A., & Gilbert, P. (1987). Medicalization and the menopause. In D. Coburn, C. D'Arcy, G. Torrance, & P. New (Eds.), *Health and Canadian society* (2nd ed.), (pp. 172-184). Markham: Fitzhenry & Whiteside.

Martin, E. (1987). *The woman in the body: A cultural analysis of reproduction.* Boston: Beacon.

Pirie, M. (1988). Women and the illness role: Rethinking feminist theory. *Canadian Review of Sociology and Anthropology, 25,* 628-648.

References

Aronson, J. (1991). Are we really listening? Beyond the official discourse on needs of old people. *Canadian Social Work Review, 19,* (1), 73-87.

Balshem, M. (1991). Cancer, control, and causality: Talking about cancer in a working class community. *American Ethnologist, 18,* 152-172.

Blaxter, M. (1983). The causes of disease: Women talking. *Social Science and Medicine, 17,* 59-69.

Blaxter, M. (1990). *Health and lifestyles.* London: Routledge.

Calnan, M. (1987). *Health and illness: The lay perspective.* London: Tavistock.

Calnan, M. (1988). Lay evaluation of medicine and medical practice: Report of a pilot study. *International Journal of Health Services, 18,* 311-322.

Chernin, K. (1981). *The obsession: Reflections on the tyranny of slenderness.* New York: Harper & Row.

Clarke, J. Nancarrow. (1985). *It's cancer.* Toronto: IPI Publishing.

Cohen, M. (1991, June). Gender issues in family medicine research. *Canadian Family Physician, 37,* 1399-1405.

Conrad, P., & Schneider, J.W. (1980). Looking at levels of medicalization: A comment on Strong's critique of the Thesis of Medical Imperialism. *Social Science and Medicine, 14A,* 75-79.

Cornwell, J. (1984). *Hard-earned lives.* London: Tavistock.

Dale, C. (1988). *Sheep's clothing.* Harmondsworth: Penguin.

Devault, M.L. (1990). Talking and listening from women's standpoint: Feminist strategies for interviewing and analysis. *Social Problems, 37,* 96-116.

Ehrenreich, B., & English, D. (1979). *For her own good: 150 years of experts' advice to women.* London: Pluto Press.

Eyles, J., & Donovan, J. (1990). *The social effects of health policy: Experiences of health and health care in contemporary Britain.* Aldershot: Avebury.

Fisher, S. (1988). *In the patient's best interest: Women and the politics of medical decisions.* New Brunswick: Rutgers University Press.

Fraser, N. (1989). *Unruly practices: Power, discourse and gender in contemporary social theory.* Minneapolis: University of Minnesota Press.

Freidson, E. (1970). *Profession of medicine: A study in the sociology of applies knowledge.* New York: Harper & Row.

Gabe, J., & Calnan, M. (1989). The limits of medicine: Women's perception of medical technology. *Social Science and Medicine, 28,* 223-231.

Gordon, J. (1988). Childbirth: The mother's perspective. In P. Tancred-Sheriff (Ed.), *Feminist research: Prospect and retrospect* (pp. 36-48). Montreal: McGill-Queen's Press.

Graham, H., & Oakley, A. (1986). Competing ideologies of reproduction: Medical and maternal perspectives on pregnancy. In C. Currer & M. Stacey (Eds.), *Concepts of health, illness and disease* (pp. 99-115). Leamington Spa: Berg.

Health and Welfare Canada. (1988). *Issues and priorities for women's health in Canada: A key informant survey.* Ottawa: Author.

Hunt, L., Jordan, B., Irwin, S., & Browner, C.H. (1989). Compliance and the patient's perspective: Controlling symptoms in everyday life. *Culture, Medicine and Psychiatry,* 13, 315-334.

Hunt, L., Jordan, B., & Irwin, S. (1989). Views of what's wrong: Diagnosis and patients' concepts of illness. *Social Science and Medicine,* 28, 945-955.

Jagger, A.M. (1983). *Feminist politics and human nature.* Totowa: Rowman & Allanheld.

Kandrack, M.A., Grant, K., & Segall, A. (1991). Gender differences in health related behaviour: Some unanswered questions. *Social Science and Medicine,* 32, 579-590.

Kaufert, P. (1988, Winter). Through women's eyes: The case for feminist epidemiology. *Healthsharing,* 10-13.

Kaufert, P.A., & Gilbert, P. (1987). Medicalization and the menopause. In D. Coburn, C. D'Arcy, G. Torrance, & P. New (Eds.), *Health and Canadian society* (2nd ed.), (pp. 172-184). Markham: Fitzhenry & Whiteside.

Lawrence, M. (1987). *Fed up and hungry: Women, oppression and food.* London: The Women's Press.

Martin, E. (1989). *The woman in the body: A cultural analysis of reproduction.* Boston: Beacon Press.

Miles, A. (1988). *Women and mental illness: The social context of female neurosis.* Brighton: Wheatsheaf.

Murray, T.H. (1986). Regulating asbestos: Ethics, politics, and the values of science. In R. Bayer (Ed.), *The health and safety of workers* (pp. 271-292). Oxford: Oxford University Press.

Pill, R., & Stott, N. (1986). Concepts of illness causation and responsibility: Some preliminary data from a sample of working-class mothers. In C. Currer & M. Stacey (Eds.), *Concepts of health, illness and disease* (pp. 259-277). Leamington Spa: Berg.

Pirie, M. (1988). Women and the illness role: Rethinking feminist theory. *Canadian Review of Sociology and Anthropology,* 25, 628-648.

Redman, S., Hennrikus, D.J., Bowman, J. A., & Sanson-Fisher, R. (1988, February). Assessing women's health needs. *The Medical Journal of Australia,* 148, 123-127.

Reid, J., Ewan, C., & Lowry, E. (1991). Pilgrimage of pain: The illness experiences of women with repetition strain injury and the search for credibility. *Social Science and Medicine,* 32, 601-612.

Riessman, C.K. (1983). Women and medicalization: A new perspective. *Social Policy,* 14, 3-18.

Roberts, H. (1985). *The patient patients: Women and their doctors.* London: Pandora.

Schrecker, T. (1986). *The pitfalls of standards.* Hamilton: Canadian Centre for Occupational Health and Safety.

Statistics Canada. (1990). *Women in Canada: A statistical report* (2nd ed.). Ottawa: Author.

Walters, V. (1991). Beyond medical and academic agendas: Lay perspectives and priorities. *Atlantis,* 17, (1), 28-35

Walters, V. (1992). Women's views of their main health problems. *Canadian Journal of Public Health,* 83, (5), 371-374.

Chapter 15

Corporate Violence and Women's Health at Home and in the Workplace

Ronald Hinch and Walter DeKeseredy
University of Guelph, Carleton University

Introduction

Consistent with American and British studies on violence against women, Canadian research provides strong support for Stanko's argument that "women's lives rest upon a continuum of unsafety" (1990, p. 85). Many women are victimized by a broad range of behaviours that occur in a variety of social contexts, such as within intimate relationships, on the streets, and in the workplace. While most woman-abuse researchers, especially feminists, contend that female victimization is "multidimensional in nature" (DeKeseredy & Hinch, 1991), most focus their attention on the incidence, causes, and consequences of male physical and sexual violence against women in domestic relationships. Compared to the amount of empirical, theoretical, and policy work done on this important issue, an equally if not more serious problem for women — corporate violence at home and in industrial settings — is given short shrift. Much more scholarly attention needs to be paid to this problem because pollution, unsafe products, and the maintenance of hazardous working conditions result in far more deaths and injuries than do acts of conventional criminal violence (Ellis, 1987; Reasons et al., 1981). The main purpose of this article is to review the limited Canadian sociological research on the types of corporate violence women experience in both industrial workplaces and at home.

Violence in the Workplace

Female workers have always experienced workplace dangers. The hazardous effects of lead exposure on pregnant women, for example, was established during the nineteenth century (Klein, 1987). Since then, numerous other workplace health hazards encountered by women have been identified. These risks are presented in Table 1 which shows that virtually all types of work pose some threat to women's physical and psychological well-being.

Exposure to Toxic Substances

One of the most salient problems women experience in the corporate workplace is exposure to toxic substances. Whether it is lead, other metals (for example, mercury), or various chemicals, the toxic hazards encountered by women in the workplace are significant. Most disturbing, however, is the fact that most of the chemical substances currently in use have not been tested to determine human health risks. While more that 500 000 chemical substances are in use, and 3000 new chemicals are introduced each year, only 3 percent have been tested for potential carcinogenic effects on humans (Jones & Nunn, 1986). Thus, many workers, male and female, are presently being exposed to unknown risks.

Industrial workers' exposure to toxic substances is not surprising. However, clerical workers' exposure to toxic substances is surprising. The use of office machinery (e.g., photocopiers) requires the use of toxic substances, such as printing powders or fluids. Similarly, exposure to asbestos, used to insulate heating pipes, etc., is not confined to industrial workers. Wherever asbestos is found, there are always potential threats to people's physical health. This is why asbestos products are used less frequently today than they were in the past. It is also the reason why strict guidelines are in place for asbestos removal in instances where the protective coverings surrounding it have deteriorated to the point where fibres are released into the air.

The full extent of the risk, however, is not known. Experts are divided on the amount of exposure deemed acceptable. As in other instances where exposure levels are regulated by law, such as exposure to radiation, government guidelines are criticized for allowing too much exposure. In general terms, the introduction of toxic substances into the office means more and more office workers risk cancer, respiratory illness, and/or risks to their reproductive health (see Chenier, 1982).

Manufacturers of toxic substances claim their products are safe if used according to instructions, and if proper training is provided. Even so, employers do not always

Table 1   Workplace Hazards

Workplace Hazards	Workers at Risk	Health Problem Caused
asbestos, brake linings, insulation, some textiles, drywall patching, hair dryers, oven mitts, ironing boards, some baby powders)	auto workers, textile workers, insulation workers, anyone working near exposed asbestos fibres	cancer (asbestosis), lung irritations
benzene (in solvents and cleaners)	workers producing or using solvents, plastics, rubbers, glues, dyes, detergents, paints, and petroleum	prolonged menstrual bleeding, postpartum hemorrhaging, birth defects, children have higher rates of leukemia and illnesses from contaminated milk
beryllium	ceramic workers, electronics workers, jewellery makers, lab workers, nuclear technologists	potential lethal, sub-lethal damage
lead	auto workers, ceramic and pottery workers, electronics workers, farmers, pesticide workers, paint makers, paint users, typographers	infertility, miscarriages, stillbirths, menstrual disorders, neonatal death, mental retardation among children of women exposed to lead or lead products
radiation (from VDTs — video display terminals — and various other sources, including x-rays, and radioactive substances)	dental and chiropractor office workers, hospital employees, nuclear industry workers, x-ray technicians	sterility (male and female), premature aging of sex cells, damage to fetus, prenatal death, mental retardation, retardation, leukemia, and cancer
mercury	dentists, dental workers, battery makers, farm workers, jewellery makers, lithographers, pesticide makers, photographic chemical makers and users, and paint manufacturing workers	miscarriages, stillbirths, as well as fetal brain damage and mental retardation
pesticides, insecticides, fungicides	farmers, farm wives, farm workers, anyone using these products	allergies, bacterial and viral infections, lung disease, skin cancer, miscarriages, chromosome changes, birth deformities
hormones (including DES and other estrogen or progesterone drugs)	pharmaceutical workers, lab workers, farmers, and veterinarians	irregular menstruation, infertility, ovarium cysts, breast lumps, cancer of reproductive system, fetuses may develop signs of sexual maturity, such as enlarged breasts, DES may cause cancer in female children and genital abnormalities in male children
vinyl chloride (pipes, siding, furnishings, food packaging, plastic bottles)	workers producing vinyl chloride and polyvinyl chloride and products using these	genetic damage to ovum, miscarriages, stillbirths/fetal death, birth defects, fetuses may develop cancer, bronchitis, skin disease, deafness, vision failure, liver dysfunction

Table I (cont.)   Workplace Hazards

Workplace Hazards	Workers at Risk	Health Problem Caused
anesthetic gases	hospital employees (nurses, doctors, lab technicians, cleaning and laundry workers, cooks, dieticians, and physiotherapists)	spontaneous abortion, congenital abnormalities in children
lint, dust	textile workers, agricultural workers, dry cleaners	cancer, various allergic reactions
ozone and other gases (from photocopiers, carpets, paints, plastics)	photocopier operators, all office workers	eye, nose and throat irritations, cancers
solvents, and other chemicals (in cleaners, glues, or mimeograph machines, benzene-based products, photocopiers	cleaners, mimeograph operators, and photocopier operators, or anyone using these products	skin, eye, nose, and throat irritations: benzene linked to leukemia and genetic effects, chromosome changes, and prolonged menstrual bleeding, as well as postpartum hemorrhage
hair sprays, hair tonics, soaps, detergents, perfumes, nail polish, dyes	hairdressers	bacterial infections, skin irritations, cancer, liver and bladder ailments, respiratory diseases
fatigue (caused by changes in hours of work, stress, noise, loss of sleep)	shift workers, transportation industry workers (flight attendants)	changes in menstrual cycle, body temperature, blood pressure, liver and kidney function
sexual harassment (from male co-workers, bosses, etc.)	all female workers	stress, stress-related illnesses such as ulcers
noise (from office machinery including typewriters, copiers, printers, and industrial machinery	typists, photocopier operators, factory workers, workers working with or near loud machinery	stress, hypertension
heat or heat and humidity	garment and textile workers	heat exhaustion, heat stress, fatigue, irritability, and susceptibility to accidents
poor ventilation (areas at greatest distance from windows and air conditioners	all workers	stress (physical and mental) heart disease, ulcers, hypertension, pneumonitis (a disease caused by build up of bacteria in the cooling fluids of air conditioners which are then distributed throughout a building)
repetitive wrist, arm, and back movements	assembly-line workers, food processing workers, food service workers, keyboard operators	muscle strain, tenosynovitis, other repetitive strain injuries

Table I (cont.)   Workplace Hazards

Workplace Hazards	Workers at Risk	Health Problem Caused
fluorescent lighting	anyone exposed to this light source	has been associated with hypertension in children, and cataracts in adults
prolonged sitting	typists, receptionists, and other workers who sit most of the working day	backstrain, may impede circulation, hemorrhoids
stress (from on the job pressure to perform)	all workers	coronary heart disease, ulcers, hypertension
contact with children	teachers, child-care workers, domestic workers	stress, ulcers, hypertension, contagious diseases
hot stoves, burners, hot water, and knives	all food service workers (cooks, food servers, etc.) and food processing workers	burns, scalding, cuts
gas stoves (carbon monoxide and nitrogen dioxide)	domestic workers, food service workers (cooks)	anxiety, fatigue, rheumatism, arthritis, muscle pain, headaches
microwave ovens (microwaves and radiation)	domestic workers, food service, and food processing workers	cataracts, damage to nerve tissue and white blood cells
frost-free refrigerators (bacteria)	domestic workers, food service workers	respiratory problems

provide their workers with adequate training. Consequently, accidents happen, spills occur, and the workers' health is put at risk.

The gases emitted from petrochemical-based products, including carpeting, office furniture, paint, and cleaning products are also dangerous. This is especially true in sealed buildings dependent on air-conditioning systems for ventilation. Ventilation systems do not always function properly, and are often poorly designed. Thus, sufficient fresh air is not circulated throughout the building. Consequently, harmful gases build up that cause short-term problems, such as headaches and fainting. It is difficult to conclusively determine the long-term health problems related to the build-up of gases and vapours. Generally, the term "sick building" is applied to sealed buildings with inadequate fresh air and a build-up of hazardous gases.

Repetitive Strain Injuries

One of the most common workplace injuries sustained by women are repetitive strain injuries (RSI). RSI are suffered by a wide range of women workers, including grocery-store cashiers, assembly-line workers, and keyboard operators. Most of these injuries are caused by employers who force workers to adapt their body movements to the functions of the machines needed to do the job. This machinery is usually designed to satisfy management needs for increased efficiency and control over the work process. The pressure to get the job done quickly and without error is found in all types of work situations, and frequently results in RSI.

For example, 40 percent of cashiers in grocery stores, most of whom are women, suffer at least one RSI in their lifetime (Shartal, 1988). They are often required to lift from 1 500 to 7 700 kg of food and other items during an eight-hour shift. The lifting, and the twisting and turning of the back required to do it, results in back strain, which in turn leads to lost time on the job, or even permanent disability.

Assembly-line workers also make a number of repetitive movements. For example, according to a woman interviewed by Armstrong and Armstrong (1983, p. 128):

> Basically, I stand there all day and slash the necks of the chickens. You make one slash up on the skin of the neck and then you cut around the base of the neck so the person beside you can crop it. . . . The chickens go in front of you on the line and you do every other chicken or whatever. And you stand there for eight hours on one spot and do it.

The pace at which the chickens are delivered to each worker on the line is determined by assessments of the time it takes to perform each movement. A computer then regulates the conveyer belt. At one poultry-processing plant, employing mostly women on the line, chickens are moved along the line at a rate of 58 per minute, or 3 480 birds an hour (Shartal, 1988, p. 8). This requires individual meat cutters to make 87 separate body movements, including arm and back movements, each minute, or 5 220 movements an hour. The speed of the line and the required number of movements contribute to both mental and physical stress. The mental stress increases the potential for physical problems, such as ulcers, while the physical stress increases the potential for RSI to the back and upper limbs.

When secretaries, bank tellers, ticket agents, and telephone operators are introduced to computer technology enabling more efficient processing of information, there is a sharp decline in job satisfaction and a major increase in stress and RSI. New computer technology allows telephone companies to increase the number of calls operators can take and to continuously monitor each call, the duration of the call, the total number of calls in any given time period (Bernard, 1982; Czerny & Swift, 1988, pp. 92-93). The new technology also allows telephone companies to monitor the time taken for coffee breaks, washroom visits, etc.

Without the new equipment, operators can prolong the time between calls by not responding to their control switches. Hence, they can humanize their work by taking short breaks or having brief conversations with other operators. With computer monitoring, these opportunities for brief contact with other workers declined, and so did job satisfaction. Further, the number of RSI resulting from the various repetitive movements needed to do the job, and from the hours of sitting in one position, increased.

Lack of Training

Many workplace injuries are caused by inadequate training (Reasons, et al., 1981; Simon & Eitzen, 1986). Workers are placed in dangerous situations without preparation, or without being advised of the risks involved. Reasons, et al. (1981), and Simon and Eitzen (1986) point out that some industries have gone to great lengths to cover up the dangers of the substances to which they expose their employees. For example, plutonium workers, like Karen Silkwood, were provided with little or no training in the handling of plutonium, and were not told of its potential, even with low-level exposure, to cause cancer. Similarly, the asbestos industry hid the ill-effects of asbestos for more than 30 years. Even though insurance companies began as early as 1919 to refuse to insure asbestos workers, and the asbestos industry was in possession of clear evidence of the harmful effects of asbestos, the industry denied and covered up that information. The industry even paid for research showing that asbestos was not harmful.

As Armstrong and Armstrong (1983) observed in reference to unskilled labour, especially the unskilled jobs performed by women, employers often assume no training is needed. They believe that packing boxes on an assembly line, or cooking food in a restaurant requires little, if any, instruction. Generally, they receive only a few minutes of instruction from fellow workers. They are shown how to do the job quickly and efficiently. Little or no time is spent on safety training because it is assumed that they know how to work safely. Sometimes, they also work in cramped, poorly designed work stations with little or no first-aid training or with ill-equipped first-aid kits.

Lack of training causes high injury rates, including stress-related injuries. For example, despite the inherent dangers associated with their jobs, food-processing and food-service workers are frequently not trained to use sharp knives, saws, or other equipment (e.g., stoves or burners). However, they are expected to perform a number of tasks in quick succession while using knives and other dangerous equipment. Doing the job quickly means increased risk of injury, in the form of burns (from hot ovens or burners), scalds (from hot water), and cuts (from knives or saws). It also means increased stress from the pressure to perform the job quickly despite its dangers.

Sexual Harassment

In sharp contrast to women, male workers are typically not exposed to sexual harassment. Following Fonow (1983), sexual harassment is defined here as unsolicited, unreciprocated male behaviour that values a woman's sex role over her function as a worker. Key examples of sexual harassment are persistent propositions for dates; suggestions that decisions to hire or promote are dependent on provision of sexual favours; acts of sexual touching; rape; the threat to transfer or the actual transfer of a worker to a more difficult job if sexual favours are not provided; threatened or actual acts of exposure; dirty jokes; verbal threats to perform unwanted sexual acts; and repeated references to either the woman's sexuality or the sexual urges of male co-workers.

Most of the above actions can be processed as criminal events, especially threatened or actual acts of non-consented sexual touching, and demands for sexual favours in exchange for job security or promotion. Nevertheless, these acts are typically processed, if at all, through union grievance procedures, or through other civil-or human-rights procedures.

The painful effects of sexual harassment are worse in situations where supervisors and/or employers know of its existence, but refuse to take action to stop it. This "selective inattention" (Dexter, 1958) is often based on the assumption that sexual harassment is harmless, or humorous, or even flattering. In reality, many victims experience both physical-and mental-health problems. Moreover, some women are unable to do their jobs effectively. Consequently, they are either fired, or they quit their jobs rather than risk further abuse. Sexual harassment can even threaten someone's life. For example, a female factory worker attempted suicide after being sexually harassed almost daily for more than two years (Papp, 1990). When she complained to her union and to management, her co-workers threatened to deny their actions, and management told her to accept an apology and forget about her mistreatment.

The failure of co-workers, supervisors, and employers to try to stop harassment is common. In fact, victims are often blamed for provoking abuse. For example, a woman working in the computer room of a large retailer told her supervisors that her male co-workers were sexually harassing her (Gorrie, 1990). After telling her supervisors that male employees repeatedly used obscene language, bragged about their sexual adventures in her presence, and even stripped down to their underwear when left alone with her, she was told that she was partially responsible. She was blamed for having an outgoing personality, and for getting along well with her co-workers. The fact that she changed clothes in the women's washroom to go jogging during her lunch break was also said to be an indication that her own behaviour was provocative. This amounts to the same type of victim blaming experienced by victims of sexual assault.

Working While Sick or Injured

The refusal to take employee health claims seriously is not limited to cases of sexual harassment. It is a common feature of many women's work settings. Even when they are obviously ill, some employers do not allow women to take time off work:

> Even when I was proofreading, I had a strep throat. I told . . . my supervisor. She called me back because . . . the boss told her to ask me if I could move my hands, could I see good, could I walk to get to work? Then come in because all he needed was for me to move the pencil to read. I didn't go in. But imagine! And this has been done to several people on that job. No compassion shown at all there. None at all. (cited in Armstrong & Armstrong, 1983, p. 193)

In this case, the woman did not give in to the pressure to go to work ill. In other cases, however, women submit to the pressure and continue working. The pressure takes different forms, including threats of job loss and loss of income. Even though employees, male or female, are sometimes permitted a number of sick days each year without fear of job loss, many, especially hourly paid workers, are not paid for those sick days. To avoid income loss, they work.

When injuries are sufficiently serious to force the worker to take time off work, income loss cannot be avoided. Even when the worker is eligible for workers' compensation, she may be without an income for a prolonged period between the injury and the receipt of compensation. When the compensation arrives, it never equals the worker's full pay. Additionally, workers waiting for their compensation cheques often go on welfare.

Workers and their families need to receive their income at regular intervals. Groceries must be purchased and landlords, mortgage companies, and other creditors want their money when it is due. Delays in receiving compensation payments mean angry landlords and creditors. It also means increased stress for the worker.

The Risk of Assault

Many clerical and service-sector workers go to work with the constant threat of danger. Bank tellers, similar workers in other financial institutions, clerks in all-night convenience stores and gas stations, as well as waitresses in restaurants, bars, and nightclubs face potential threats from robbery and assault. For example:

> I've had one night where a bullet went between my legs. In another nightclub, it happened once that a guy grabbed me by the throat — he was actually choking me. Nobody saw me. . . . A customer came by and I kicked him. He saw what was happening and he threw the guy out. I was quite lucky. (cited in Armstrong & Armstrong, 1983, p. 188)

Bank tellers may be given instructions on what to do during a robbery attempt, and may even be compensated for injuries suffered during a robbery, but many other workers do not receive any type of support (Armstrong & Armstrong, 1983). Their fears of assault, including sexual assault, and murder are grounded in stark reality. For example, in the United States, recent reports indicate that 12 percent of all occupational deaths were murders, and that "more working women die of murder on the job than any other occupational accident" (Reuters, 1991, p. B3).

The Domestic Workplace

Some domestic workplace hazards are caused by indirect exposure to toxic substances. That is, women are not directly exposed to the substance, but their husbands or other family members bring the substance into the home on their clothing or on their skin. Men exposed to toxic substances in industrial settings, such as asbestos, chemicals, and radiation, can transfer that exposure to women in the domestic workplace. It is transmitted either during cleaning or during sexual intercourse. Some cases of cervical cancer result from sexual relations with men who were exposed to chemical substances in the industrial workplace (Doyle, 1990).

Other hazards, however, are experienced directly. Many of the toxic substances to which industrial workers are exposed are also found in the home. They are in household cleaners, appliances, building materials (paints, pipes, etc.), and insecticides. It has also been argued that many household accidents may be attributed to corporate efforts to convince women to use certain products (such as household cleaners) that pose safety hazards in home use (Rosenberg, 1990). These latter dangers are the main focus of this section of the paper.

Obviously, men and children are also exposed to these hazards at home. It is reasonable to assume, however, that because women are likely to be at home more than their husbands, and because women are more likely to do household chores that involve using these products, women's exposure to household hazards is a greater threat than men's.

Drugs

Drugs that threaten women's health include those aimed at helping women manage their reproductive life, and pharmaceuticals designed to alleviate stress. In both cases, the pharmaceutical industry has come under extensive criticism for its failure to adequately test products intended for human use, and for marketing drugs which it knows, or has reason to believe, endanger women's health (McDonnell, 1986; Coleman, 1989, p. 43-44). In some cases, drugs are still being marketed to women in the Third World, even though their use is banned in economically advanced nations (Direcks & Hoen, 1986; Duggan, 1986; LaCheen, 1986; Marcelis & Sheva, 1986).

Other marketing practices used by the pharmaceutical industry are also questioned. Ford (1986) notes that drug manufacturers frequently fund not only drug research, but also the journals in which the research is published. The journals also publish advertisements pushing the drugs. Ford found evidence that doctors were advised, by research published in a journal financed by pharmaceutical industry sources, to withhold vital information about the potential hazards of estrogen drugs in the treatment of vaginal atrophy (thinning of the vaginal walls causing dryness). Thus, reliance by doctors on industry-funded research and industry-funded journals is a potential danger to women. Doctors may prescribe drug treatments without knowing all of the side effects of the drug.

Drugs and Reproductive Health: The pharmaceutical industry markets drugs to prevent and diagnose pregnancy, to increase fertility, to control morning sickness, and to induce abortions. Unfortunately, many of these drugs adversely affect women's health. For example, thalidomide, prescribed during the late 1950s and early 1960s to pregnant women as a remedy for morning sickness, was widely marketed before it was fully tested. It was also sold after it caused birth defects. Consequently, thousands of children around the world were born with severe physical handicaps, such as deformed hands, arms, and legs.

Other hormone drugs receive considerable attention from critics of the pharmaceutical industry (Direcks & Hoen, 1986; Ford, 1986; LaCheen, 1986; Marcelis & Shiva, 1986). Drugs containing various combinations of estrogen and progesterone, sometimes separately, sometimes together, pose hazards not only to the workers who make them in the factories, but to the women who use them. DES (diethylstilbestrol), given to prevent miscarriages, and Depo-provera, used as a contraceptive, are known carcinogens. Other estrogen/progesterone (EP) drugs are known to contribute to osteoporosis, and to produce birth defects, including defects in the heart, the circulatory system, the central nervous system, and the limbs.

In some cases, the hazards posed by these drugs were not known prior to being marketed by the pharmaceutical industry. In other cases, the industry brought the drugs to market while in possession of evidence showing their harmful effects. This is certainly the case with all the hormone drugs, such as DES and Depo-provera, currently banned in most economically advanced countries, but still sold to women in the Third World. This is a clear case of the pharmaceutical industry putting profits ahead of the health of female consumers.

Finally, it is no secret that many easily accessible drugs, such as alcohol, tobacco, caffeine, and antihistamines cause health hazards. Alcohol use not only leads to alcoholism, but also contributes to increased rates of heart disease and cirrhosis of the liver. Used in conjunction with sedative-hypnotic drugs (see next section), it can kill, and can cause birth defects. Similarly, lung and heart disease are risks shared by all tobacco users. Use of tobacco products during pregnancy also creates hazards for pregnant women and their babies. Children born of smoking mothers are lighter at birth and have slower rates of physical and mental maturity compared to children born of non-smoking mothers (Simon & Eitzen, 1986, p. 107). Women who smoke during pregnancy also have higher risks of miscarriages, premature births, and still births. Tobacco advertising, while restricted, is also increasingly attempting to capture the market among young females. Finally, antihistamines, found in cold and hay-fever remedies, and caffeine, found in tea, coffee, Coca-Cola drinks, and some cold preparations, are also suspected of causing birth defects.

Drugs and Mental Health: Mood-modifying drugs are overprescribed to women (Harding, 1986). More women than men are prescribed stress-relieving drugs, and despite the fact that women's body size is generally smaller than men's, the average dose given to women is larger than the average dose prescribed to men. Certain women, notably the elderly, are more likely than others to have them prescribed.

That these drugs have been and continue to be overused is shown in the decline in the prescription rates for Darvon (propoxyphene). Harding (1986) reports that in 1977, almost 30 000 people a year were prescribed Darvon in Saskatchewan. By 1982, fewer than 9 000 prescriptions were being written, and the number of physicians prescribing it fell from 717 in 1978 to 383 in 1982. Harding attributes the decline to public concern that this drug was being used irresponsibly. Many women who used it did not need to. However, while the use of this drug declined, the rate of use for sedative-hypnotic drugs increased correspondingly.

The effect of prescribing drugs unnecessarily is deceptively simple. On a societal basis, it is easier to keep those suffering from stress functioning than it is to do something to relieve the sources of stress. In this context, Harding notes that more women than men live in poverty, and that a large segment of the poor are elderly women. Poverty, of course, is associated world-wide with health problems, including stress. Therefore, prescribing mood-modifying drugs provides a remedy for a symptom of poverty, without eliminating the problem.

Harding also attributes the proliferation of mood-modifying drugs to an additional factor. He questions the motives of pharmacy owners who recommended that the Saskatchewan provincial drug-care plan provide prescription drugs at no cost to the elderly. It is well know that the elderly frequently do not buy prescription drugs if they are unable to afford them. Providing free prescription drugs to the elderly, the heaviest users, allows the pharmacist to get his or her dispensing fee. It also increases sales for the pharmaceutical companies.

Toxic Substances

Many of the hazardous gases and toxic substances referred to in Table 1 are also found in products intended for home use. Even though these products are not as dangerous as similar products used in industrial settings, they are still potent enough to cause health problems. Furthermore, while corporations advertise and sell their products by using the happy homemaker image, they rarely specify, even on the packaging, the hazards associated with using the products (Rosenberg, 1990).

Cleaning Products: The most obvious group of toxic substances to which women are exposed in the home are household cleaning products: drain cleaners (lye), toilet-bowl cleaners (ammonia), scouring powder, oven cleaner (lye), chlorine bleach, glass cleaners, disinfectants, all-purpose cleaners, dishwashing detergents, laundry detergents, and furniture polish (Rosenberg, 1990). Many of these products can produce fatal injuries. Lye used in drain and oven cleaners can eat through the skin, damage eyes, and produce extremely dangerous fumes. Similarly, ammonia-based cleaners, when mixed with chlorine-based bleaches, also generate fatal fumes. Other cleaning products irritate skin or eyes, and may be fatal if swallowed by children (many of these products are sold in containers easily opened by children). In many cases, the potential hazards are not clearly specified on product labels. It should also be noted that many of them can be replaced by simple soap and water, or water and vinegar.

Construction Materials: Construction materials are also household hazards. For example, some paints containing lead and/or mercury are still to be found in the marketplace, and are still present in older homes painted with lead-based paint. Furthermore, harmful gases, such as formaldehyde, are emitted from some synthetic fabrics used for carpeting, or furniture made from plywood, or particle board, household solvents, and some foam insulations installed until the late 1970s. The health hazards posed by these products include respiratory ailments, allergies, and cancer (Rosenberg, 1990).

Food Additives: Simon and Eitzen (1986) indicate that there is a problem with food additives and other products mixed with both drinking water and toothpaste. Food additives, such as nitrates, BHT, BHA, sodium benzoate, and benzoic acid, are suspected of causing cancer. Aluminum, used in the form of alum to prevent table salt from caking, is suspected of contributing to Alzheimer's disease. Fluoride added to toothpaste and municipal water supplies, with assurances from manufacturers that the product is safe, is also suspected of causing cancer. Similarly, chlorine added to municipal drinking water is known to cause cancer.

Packaging: Food packaging can be harmful. For example, some manufacturers of cans for food packaging still used lead-based solder. The lead may leach into the food. Similarly, mercury and dioxin, a powerful carcinogen, are found in paper milk cartons. Both leach into the milk after packaging.

Hygiene Products: Some manufacturers market deodorant and/or scented pads and tampons. Although these products contain no noticeable advantages over their non-deodorant and unscented counterpart, and soap and water washing, they are marketed as if they do. Marketing strategies attempt to convince women that they are not really clean unless they use deodorized pads or tampons. Unfortunately, the chemicals used in these products can cause skin allergies.

Further, while tampons are frequently preferred as an alternative to napkins or pads, they can cause *toxic shock*. This deadly illness is caused by staphylococcus bacteria from the vagina or cervix entering the uterus, then the bloodstream. Tampons provide an environment for the proliferation of the bacteria and their resultant toxins. Symptoms of toxic shock include a skin rash, and peeling of thin layers of skin from the body. It may also affect the kidneys, liver, intestines, and stomach. In many cases, toxic shock is first detected as flu-like symptoms followed by a rash. Women who have had vaginal, cervical, or uterine surgery, or have given birth should not use tampons until completely healed.

Pesticides: While there is growing public awareness about the dangers associated with pesticides, many people still purchase them. Consistent with many other harmful consumer products, some pesticides are produced for home use, even though they are banned in other settings. For example, Kepone was so dangerous that its industrial production was banned in the United States. It caused damage to the liver and brain, as well as to male testes. Even so, the U.S. Environmental Protection Agency authorized it for home use. Furthermore, women in households where hang–up antipest strips are used may be exposed to more than 100 hours of DDVP, which is both carcinogenic and suspected of causing genetic defects (Rosenberg, 1990). Other pesticides commonly used in households are diazinon and arsenic.

Other Unsafe Consumer Products

In addition to the products already specified, there is a wide range of consumer products that pose significant health hazards to women. These products range from appliances to IUDs. Again, the producers of these products are frequently knowledgeable of the health hazards, but are not required to notify consumers of the dangers. Sometimes they deliberately misinform consumers of the potential hazards.

Appliances: Rosenberg (1990) provides vital information about the hazards of appliances such as stoves and refrigerators. She notes that gas stoves emit carbon monoxide and nitrogen dioxide. Exposure to these substances may produce anxiety, fatigue, rheumatism, arthritis, headaches, and muscle pain. Microwave ovens, a great convenience in many contemporary homes, produce radiation that may leak through seals and may produce cataracts. The thermal effects of microwaves can also effect nerve tissues and white blood cells. It is usually recommended that users remain at least three feet away from a microwave oven when it is in use.

Self-defrosting refrigerators are convenient, but they pose some health risks. The most significant health hazard is the heat generated to remove ice deposits in the freezer. Heating coils melt the ice and the water vapour collects in the drip pan. The heat from the coils and the water in the drip pans provide an ideal breeding ground for bacteria. The bacteria, which can cause respiratory problems, are then circulated into the kitchen as the refrigerator attempts to dispose of the heat. Given the amount of time spent by some women in the kitchen, this is an obvious health risk for them.

Finally, fluorescent lighting, found in many kitchens, may cause a number of health problems. Prolonged exposure can lead to cataracts and to skin cancer (Rosenberg, 1990).

IUDs: One of the most infamous cases of marketing an unsafe product centred on intrauterine devices (IUDs), such as the Dalkon Shield. Pappert (1986) explains that the Dalkon Shield was simply one of a long list of IUDs. The first such devices were marketed in Germany around 1909. Their use declined rapidly when they were found to produce infections. While other IUDs were tested and marketed over the next 30 years, their use had been thoroughly discredited by the 1940s. It was the concern over rapid population growth in the 1960s that led to the reintroduction of a search for an effective IUD. At that time an organization known as The Population Council began a campaign to reconvince the medical profession that IUDs were safe. They pointed to physicians in Japan and Israel who claimed that their patients had been using the devices without the negative results of earlier IUDs. Pharmaceutical companies quickly entered the market with new IUDs they claimed eliminated earlier concerns about infection.

Unfortunately, the new IUDs did not eliminate infection. They also caused pelvic inflammatory disease (PID) and infertility. IUD users are nine times more likely to develop PID, and are twice as likely to become infertile. More than 200 000 women in the United States are said to have become infertile after using IUDs. By the time these problems were detected, the manufacturers of the Dalkon Shield were faced with more than 300 000 lawsuits from women claiming to have been harmed by the device. Despite its problems, some manufacturers and population-control crusaders still promote their use.

Explaining Corporate Violence Against Women

Corporate violence against women is a product of male domination interacting with capitalist exploitation. In other words, women at home and in industry are exploited because they are both women and workers. In addition, corporate violence against women is an extension of the pattern of male domination that characterizes all of Canadian society (see DeKeseredy & Hinch, 1991). Sexual harassment on the job is clearly an extension of the pattern of sexual assault women experience in other areas of their lives. Drugs that give women the illusion of control over their reproductive systems, but which in fact have a devastating impact on their health and the health of their children, are marketed more for the purpose of profit making than they are for the purpose of giving women control over reproduction. As Duggan (1986, p. 165) explains:

> . . . the technology which allows control of reproduction confers power upon its users only when they have enough information to make truly informed choices.

The information needed to allow women to make informed decisions is frequently suppressed or inaccurately described.

The same may be said of the situation encountered by women who work under hazardous conditions. To the extent that women workers, in either industrial settings or at home, are given false or misleading information about the technology or the products they are using, and to the extent that they have little or no control over working conditions, female workers are disempowered. This leaves them at greater risk of injury and illness.

Of course, with the possible exception of sexual harassment, men face many of these same hazards. They encounter threats to their reproductive systems because of exposure to various toxic substances. They also risk developing cancer and other illnesses as a result of working with or near toxic substances or from using unsafe consumer products. Men, too, are the victims of the corporate need to make profit. No one is immune to these problems.

Conclusion

In this essay, we articulated the various types of corporate violence perpetrated against women. It is evident that women are frequently the victims of deliberate corporate decisions to reduce cost and make profit by sacrificing worker and consumer safety. Our explanation for corporate violence against women maintains that it must be seen as a product of both patriarchy and capitalism. It is this combination of patriarchal and capitalist domination that differentiates the exploitation of women workers from the exploitation of male workers. Both male and female workers experience corporate violence. Women, however, also experience violence against them because they are women. Their concerns about health and safety on the job, whether in the domestic or the industrial workplace, are not taken as seriously as men's concerns in this area. Far too often, it is assumed that because there are fewer women in heavy industry, women's work is not dangerous. What we have tried to do is direct attention to the very real health and safety risks women encounter.

Study Questions

1. In work situations where both men and women face the same danger to their reproductive health, why is it that women, and rarely men, are denied jobs?
2. If it is in the interest of employers to have healthy, productive workers, why do some employers mislead their employees about health and safety hazards?
3. Why do you suppose that only 3 percent of the more than 500 000 chemicals in use have been tested for carcinogenic and reproductive health hazards?
4. Should all consumer products bear similar health warnings to those used on tobacco products?
5. Is there any legitimacy to employer claims that reducing exposure levels to toxic substances would result in either fewer jobs or plant closures?
6. Why are women's occupational health and safety risks taken less seriously than are men's?

References

Armstrong, P., & Armstrong, H. (1983). *A working majority: What women must do for pay.* Ottawa: Canadian Advisory Council on the Status of Women.

Bernard, E. (1982). *The long distance feeling: A history of the telecommunications workers union.* Vancouver: New Star Books.

Chenier, N.M. (1982). *Reproductive hazards at work: Men, women and the fertility gamble.* Ottawa: Canadian Advisory Council on the Status of Women.

Coleman, J.W. (1989). *The criminal elite: The sociology of white collar crime* (2nd ed.). New York: St. Martins Press.

Czerny, M., & Swift, J. (1988). *Getting started on social analysis in Canada.* Toronto: Between the Lines.

DeKeseredy, W., & Hinch, R. (1991). *Woman abuse: Sociological perspectives.* Toronto: Thompson Educational Publishing.

DeKeseredy, W., & Hinch, R. Wife abuse in Canada: The current state of sociological knowledge. *International Criminal Justice Review, Vol. 1,* 35-52.

Dexter, L.A. (1958). A note on the selective inattention in social science. *Social Problems,* 6, 176-182.

Directs, A., & Hoen, E. (1986). DES: The crime continues. In K. McDonnell (Ed.), *Adverse effects: Women and the pharmaceutical industry* (pp. 41-49). Toronto: The Women's Press.

Doyle, L. (1990). Health at home and in waged labour: Part one — hazards of hearth and home. *Women's Studies International Forum, 13,* 501-517.

Duggan, L. (1986). From birth control to population control: Depo-provera in southeast Asia. In K. McDonnell (Ed.), *Adverse effects: Women and the pharmaceutical industry* (pp. 159-165). Toronto: The Women's Press.

Ellis, D. (1987). *The wrong stuff: An introduction to the sociological study of deviance.* Toronto: Collier Macmillan.

Fonow, M.M. (1983). Occupation/steelworker: Sex/female. In L. Richardson & V. Taylor (Eds.), *Feminist frontiers: Rethinking sex, gender and society* (pp. 209-214). Reading: Addison Wesley.

Ford, A.R. (1986). Hormones: Getting out of hand. In K. McDonnell (Ed.), *Adverse effects: Women and the pharmaceutical industry* (pp. 27-40). Toronto: The Women's Press.

Frank, N. (1985). *Crimes against health and safety.* New York: Harrow & Heston.

Goff, C., & Reasons, C. (1978). *Corporate crime in Canada.* Scarborough: Prentice-Hall.

Gorrie, P. (1990, January 23). Victim of harassment told she shares blame. *Toronto Star,* p. D1.

Harding, J. (1986). Mood-modifiers and elderly women in Canada: The medicalization of poverty. In K. McDonnell (Ed.), *Adverse effects: Women and the pharmaceutical industry* (pp. 51-86). Toronto: The Women's Press.

Jones, L., & Nunn, M. (1986). Reproductive hazards in the workplace. *Women and Environments,* 8, 14-16.

Klein, P.V. (1987). For the good of the race: Reproductive hazards from lead and the persistence of exclusionary policies towards women. In B.D. Wright, M.M. Ferree, G.O. Mellow, L.H. Lewis, M.D. Smaper, R. Asher, & K. Claspell (Eds.), *Women, work and technology: Transformations* (pp. 101-117). Ann Arbor: The University of Michigan Press.

LaCheen, C. (1986). Population control and the pharmaceutical industry. In K. McDonnell (Ed.), *Adverse effects: Women and the pharmaceutical industry* (pp. 89-136). Toronto: The Women's Press.

Marcelis, C., & Shiva, M. (1986). EP drugs: Unsafe by any name. In K. McDonnell (Ed.), *Adverse effects: Women and the pharmaceutical industry* (pp. 11-26). Toronto: The Women's Press.

McDonnell, K. (Ed.). (1986). *Adverse effects: Women and the pharmaceutical industry.* Toronto: The Women's Press.

Papp, L. (1990, November 6). Sexually harassed worker wins landmark decision. *Toronto Star,* pp. A1-2.

Pappert, A. (1986). The rise and fall of the IUD. In K. McDonnell (Ed.), *Adverse effects: Women and the pharmaceutical industry* (pp. 167-172). Toronto: The Women's Press.

Parliament, J.B. (1990). Women employed outside the home. In C. McKie & K. Thompson (Eds.), *Canadian social trends* (pp. 99-103). Toronto: Thompson Educational Publishing.

Reasons, C.E., Ross, L., & Paterson, C. (1981). *Assault on the worker*. Toronto: Butterworths.

Reasons, C.E., Ross, L., & Paterson, C. (1986). Your money or your life. In S. Brickey & E. Comack (Eds.), *The social basis of law* (pp. 117–126). Toronto: Garamond Press.

Reuters News Agency (1991, May 3). Work's murder: On-the-job homicide on the rise in the U.S. *The Globe and Mail*, p. B3.

Rinehart, J.W. (1987). *The tyranny of work: Alienation and the labour process* (2nd ed.). Toronto: Harcourt Brace Jovanovich.

Rosenberg, H. (1990). The home is the workplace: Hazards, stress and pollutants in the household. In M. Luxton & H. Rosenberg (Eds.), *Through the kitchen window: The politics of home and family* (2nd ed.), (pp. 37-62). Toronto: Garamond Press.

Shartal, S. (1988). The cutting edge: UFCW members on three fronts of the food industry. *At the Source*, 9, (1), 6-9.

Simon, D.R., & Eitzen, S. (1986). *Elite deviance* (2nd ed.). Boston: Allyn & Bacon.

Stanko, E. (1990). *Everyday violence*. London: Pandora.

Tudiver, S. (1986). The strength of links: International women's health networks in the eighties. In K. McDonnell (Ed.), *Adverse effects: Women and the pharmaceutical industry* (pp. 187-214). Toronto: The Women's Press.

Chapter 16

A Trust Betrayed:
The Sexual Abuse of Patients
by Physicians and Therapists

Linda S. Williams, Health Policy Division, Health Canada, and Carleton University

Introduction

The sexual abuse of patients by physicians and therapists is not a new phenomenon. Hippocrates (circa 460–377 B.C.) was concerned with preventing such abuse when he instituted his oath for new physicians. It has remained a part of each new doctor's promise to serve ever since.

> In every house where I come I will enter only for the good of my patients, keeping myself far from all intentional ill-doing and all seduction, and especially free from the pleasure of love with women or with men . . . (Dorland's Medical Dictionary, 1974, p. 715)

Sigmund Freud, the father of modern psychiatry, also recognized the possibility of sexual intimacy between patient and psychotherapist and warned against its dangers:

> The love-relationship actually destroys the influence of the analytic treatment on the patient; a combination of the two would be an inconceivable thing. (Freud, 1915; 1963, p. 174)

Despite the long-standing nature of this problem, the modern medical establishment has been reluctant to recognize and correct it. In the 1970s, psychologists attempted to remove a male member of the American Psychological Association who raised the question of studying therapist–patient sex, and an early study that revealed the extent of the problem was suppressed (Pope, 1990a). As recently as 1977, Davidson referred to patient-therapist sex as "psychiatry's problem with no name" (p. 43).

Professional research into these issues finally became respectable in the 1970s with the pioneering work of sex therapists William Masters and Virginia Johnson (1966, 1975). They noted that a high percentage of their clients had been sexually involved with their psychotherapists, usually with extremely detrimental results. They called for the prohibition of such behaviour, which they described as rape (Masters & Johnson, 1975). Other early research included Belote, 1974; Chesler, 1972; Dahlberg, 1970; and Kardener et al., 1973.

It is essential to note that the sexual abuse of patients is primarily a gendered phenomenon — most perpetrators are men and most victims are women. This reality, coupled with an increase in the number of women in the mental-health field and the emergence of the modern women's movement, may also have contributed to the public recognition of patient sexual abuse (Bouhoutsos, 1985a).

Professional and public concern prompted the mental-health professions in the United States to revise their codes of ethics in the late 1970s to explicitly prohibit sexual intimacy between practitioner and patient (Pope & Bouhoutsos, 1986). Consequently, most research has taken place only during the last 25 years (Pope, 1990), and mostly in the United States. Most studies have focussed on mental-health practitioners — psychiatrists and psychologists — to whom I shall refer in this chapter as "therapists," but sexual abuse by medical doctors has also been reported. Both groups will be examined in this chapter.

Although Canadian research has been scanty to date, two recent initiatives have focussed attention on this problem in our own country. The first is the formation of a group called CHASTEN (Canadian Health Alliance to Stop Therapist Exploitation Now). This organization consists of mental-health practitioners from nursing, psychology, social work, and psychiatry who assist victims of physician-therapist sexual abuse. CHASTEN also seeks to prevent such abuse through research, lobbying, and educational workshops (CHASTEN, 1991).

The second initiative is at the professional level. On January 28, 1991 the College of Physicians and Surgeons of Ontario established an independent task force to examine physician and therapist sexual abuse in Ontario, and to recommend ways of dealing with the problem. The task force used public hearings, written briefs, and a 24-hour toll-free telephone line to gather information from victims of abuse, their advocates, and a variety of professional organizations. Their recommendations will be presented at the end of this chapter.

The Abuse, the Abusers, and the Victims

The prohibition against sexual contact between patients and healers is based on several factors.

First, the relationship between all health-care practitioners and their patients is understood to be a fiduciary one, that is, it is based on trust and confidence that the needs of the patient are the healer's primary concern. As Feldman-Summers states:

> There is no doubt that physicians, psychiatrists [and] mental health counselors . . . are "fiduciaries." People in these professions as a matter of course hold themselves out as worthy of the trust and confidence of their patients or clients, and routinely profess that they are bound to act in the best interest of those who seek their services. (Feldman-Summers, 1989, p. 193)

A sexual relationship between practitioner and patient creates a clear conflict of interest — whose needs are being met, those of the patient or those of the practitioner? An objective professional relationship with healthy, defined boundaries cannot be maintained when a sexual relationship develops between the parties, and the patient's care will almost certainly be jeopardized.

Second, the power differential between patient and professional is profound. Simply stated, the patient needs the physician or therapist more than the physician or therapist needs the patient. It is highly doubtful that the patient's true informed consent to any sexual activity can be obtained under these circumstances. This power differential is exacerbated if the patient lives in a small town and does not have access to alternative sources of care.

Patients who seek psychiatric help are generally even more vulnerable than those seeking help for physical ailments. They may be emotionally fragile, needy, and suffer from low self-esteem. Any one of these or other emotional states could make them especially vulnerable to the advances of an unethical therapist. Victims of previous sexual abuse and incest are even more vulnerable to (and may be even more damaged by) sexual contact with a therapist (Armsworth, 1989).

Psychiatrists also believe that the psychotherapeutic process involves a phenomenon known as transference in which a patient redirects unconscious feelings, needs, and desires from childhood towards the therapist, who may come to be seen as an object of love or emotional support. Thus the very nature of psychotherapy itself may increase a patient's vulnerability to sexual abuse.

> He was just like the father I had never had. Warm, big and cuddly. He told me to sit next to him, he put his arm around me. I snuggled up, feeling so safe, protected and cared for. Then I felt him take my hand and place it on his thigh. (Penfold, 1987, p. 30)

The sexual abuse of patients takes many forms, including unwanted kissing, fondling of breasts and genitals, sexual intercourse, and rape. Other forms of abuse include legitimate medical procedures performed in a sexualized manner, unnecessary examinations of the breasts, vagina, or rectum, sexually suggestive comments, an erotic embrace, questions about the patient's sexual experience or preferences, or the creation of a sexualized atmosphere.

The following stories are a sampling of the calls received by the 24-hour answering machine made available to the public by the CPSO Task Force.[1]

A woman called to report that she had been sexually abused by her physician [a trusted family doctor] several times between the ages of 16 and 18. . . . During her pelvic examination, he would make comments like, "You are really built to take a man," and he would make attempts to kiss her. He would rub her against his erection and at times, attempt to hug her. . . . Today she says, "I will never forget how awful it felt to be there." (p. 65)

A woman called to testify. She said she went to see a psychiatrist for the treatment of phobias — phobias about being touched. She said the doctor recommended that he desensitize her by touching her. At each treatment, the doctor would fondle and touch her. She felt that this treatment was inappropriate, but she felt powerless and so allowed it to happen. The therapy lasted for 7 years. She said she never got any better. The doctor often saw incest survivors. (p. 63)

A woman called to talk about sexual abuse by her physician when she was between the ages of 6 and 7. She said that she lived in a small village where there was only one physician. This physician repeatedly abused her in her home, and she believed he did the same to her brothers. This stopped when her father hid in the closet one day, and witnessed the abuse. She said that she cannot trust any doctor, be it male or female and wants a hearing. (p. 66)

A male called to report sexual abuse by his male psychiatrist whom he consulted for help with his homosexuality. He reported a lot of hugging. He reported the case to the police and the Attorney General's office and feels that the [complaint] process is much too slow. (p. 64)

A woman called, asking to testify. She said that she had an inappropriate breast examination. She knew that the doctor was attempting to stimulate her by the way he stroked her and the things he said to her. She believed that, in a case of this sort, the College [of Physicians and Surgeons] would see it as minor, and trivialize the problem. (p. 68)

Despite clear prohibitions against sexual intimacy between patients and their physicians or therapists, such behaviour is far from rare. Gartrell et al., (1986) surveyed 1 057 American psychiatrists and reported that 4.1 percent of the male and 3.1 percent of the female respondents admitted to sexual contact with their patients. Pope et al., (1986) found that 9.4 percent of the men and 2.5 percent of the women in their sample of 575

American psychotherapists had engaged in such behaviour. Vinson (1987) reported that on the basis of self-reports it appears that 10-13 percent of male therapists and 2-3 percent of female clinicians are sexually intimate in some way with patients. Malpractice suits for alleged sexual abuse by psychotherapists are now so common in the United States that insurance companies are reducing or eliminating coverage in this area (Pope, 1986). As recently as 1990, the Committee on Women in Psychology of the American Psychological Association felt the need to publish a brochure to inform the public about the harmful effects of patient-therapist sexual intimacy.

The incidence of physician-patient sexual abuse is less well documented. Kardener et al., (1973) surveyed a random sample of 460 male physicians, including psychiatrists, obstetrician/gynecologists, surgeons, internists, and general practitioners, and found that 5-13 percent had engaged in some form of erotic behaviour with patients, including 5-7 percent who admitted to engaging in intercourse. Perry (1976) surveyed 164 female physicians and found no reported incidents of intercourse with patients and a much lower level of other forms of erotic contact. Overall, there appears to be no difference between the rates of therapist-and physician-patient sexual abuse (Borys & Pope, 1989).

No nationwide studies of the incidence of sexual abuse of patients by physicians or therapists have been conducted to date in Canada; however, the results of a survey conducted by Canada Health Monitor and Price Waterhouse Management Consultants, the first of its kind in Canada, show that 8 percent of Ontario women have been sexually harassed or abused by physicians (Task Force, 1991).

The characteristics of abusers are well documented. They are overwhelmingly male (Borys & Pope, 1989). Gartrell et al., (1986) observed that 88 percent of therapist-patient sexual intimacies involved male therapists and female patients; 7.6 percent involved male therapists and male patients; 3.5 percent involved female therapists and male patients; and 1.4 percent involved female therapists with female patients. This pattern is identical to that of sexual abuse in society in general — most sexual abuse is perpetrated by men on women.

Therapists who engage in sexual activities with patients also tend to be significantly older. Gartrell et al., (1989) noted an average therapist age of 43 years, compared to an average patient age of 33 years. These findings were replicated by Bouhoutsos et al., (1983), who reported average ages of 42 and 30 respectively. Offending therapists are also likely to be *more* highly qualified professionally than their non-offending peers (Gartrell et al., 1986, 1989; Pope & Bajt, 1988). They are also "more likely to have undergone personal psychotherapy or psychoanalysis" (Gartrell et al., 1989, p. 7). As Pope (1990a) states, "Sexually abusive psychotherapists cannot be dismissed as the most marginal members of the profession. They are well represented among the most prominent and respected mental health professionals" (p. 233).[2] There is no reported correlation between a therapist's theoretical orientation and patient sexual abuse (Pope, 1990). Most abusers are serial offenders (Gartrell et al., 1987). Holroyd and Brodsky (1977) report that 80 percent of the psychologists in their survey who admitted to having sexual intercourse with a patient had intercourse with more than one.

Aside from being female and younger than their abusers, no other factors have been found to date that predispose patients to the risk of abuse. In their review of the literature, Bates and Brodsky (1989) conclude that "The best single predictor of exploitation in therapy is a therapist who has exploited another patient in the past " (p. 14). Penfold (1987) points out that most women are socialized to be supportive, caring, flirtatious, and sexually available and attractive in their relationships with men, and that these culturally determined self-images and patterns of behaviour make women more vulnerable to therapist sexual abuse than men.

> He told me all his problems. About his wife, kids, job, finances.
>
> He told me that I was the first person who really understood his feelings.
>
> He always flirted with me. He seemed to think that this was the way to make me feel good, to get me out of my depression.
>
> (all quotes from Penfold, 1987, p. 30)

It is important to note that the sexual abuse of patients is not confined to adults. Bajt and Pope (1989) examined 81 instances of therapist sexual abuse of minor patients: 56 percent involved female patients and 46 percent involved males. Female patients were from 3 to 17 years of age; the age range of the males was from 7 to 16. The sexual abuse of children by male physicians has also been reported in Canada, and several cases have reached the courts (see *The Ottawa Citizen*, November 26, 1991; Taylor, 1991).

The Effects of Physician/Therapist Sexual Abuse on the Victims

Besides being highly unethical, it is now widely recognized that sexual contact between patients and health-care providers is harmful to the patient, whether they are seeking psychiatric or medical care.[3] It is important to note that the erotic contact need not culminate in intercourse to result in emotional damage (Vinson, 1987). Bouhoutsos et al., (1983) report that 90 percent of the 559 psychiatric patients examined in their study were negatively affected, either personally or in terms of their therapy. Twelve percent committed suicide, attempted suicide, or required psychiatric hospitalization; 2 percent reported increased drug or alcohol abuse; and 26 percent reported disrupted personal relationships. Other negative effects that have been reported are mistrust of and anger towards men (Feldman-Summers & Jones, 1984); and shame and guilt (Luepker & Retsch-Bogart, 1985). Sexual confusion can result if the abuser was the same sex as a patient who had previously identified as a heterosexual; low self-esteem and an inability to trust one's judgement of an interpersonal situation can also result from this type of sexual abuse (Sonne et al., 1985). A recent Canadian study found that the sexual abuse of patients by psychotherapists undermines the gains in mental health that patients who are not sexually abused generally experience (Valiquette et al., 1991).

Individuals who contacted the CPSO Task Force also reported the following psychological symptoms: intense anxiety, fear, panic, depression, flashbacks, nightmares, and sleep disorders. Physical symptoms such as headaches, ear, nose, and throat problems, digestive difficulties, and sexual dysfunction were also reported. Pope has characterized this constellation of symptoms as the therapist-patient sex syndrome, and states that it is similar to borderline and histrionic personality disorder, posttraumatic stress disorder, rape response syndrome, reaction to incest, and reaction to child or spouse battering (Pope, 1985). The negative psychological effect of therapist abuse on the patient does not appear to differ from the negative effect of physician abuse (Feldman-Summers & Jones, 1984).

The experience of physician or therapist abuse may be so devastating that the victim "may avoid further medical care or travel hundreds of miles to get medical care that feels comfortable to them" (Task Force, 1991, p. 14). In some cases the patient's overall quality of life may be adversely affected.

> Every important area of my life has been significantly harmed. I failed my year at university while seeing this first psychiatrist. I continue to suffer extreme anxiety and depression; I've been underemployed all my professional life; intense hostility toward men — no children, no marriage; after nine years in Ottawa, I have no lasting friend; I cannot feel my body. (Task Force, 1991, p. 72)

The Problems and Outcomes of Reporting Physician/Therapist Sexual Abuse

Just as the effects of physician/therapist sexual abuse on the patient are similar to those experienced by victims of rape or incest, the problems patients have in reporting such abuse are also similar. Very few women who are sexually abused by their physician or therapist ever report their abuse to a regulatory body or to the police. A survey of 559 California patients revealed that only 4 percent made an official complaint, and only half of those were carried through to completion (Bouhoutsos et al., 1983).

Traditionally, women have been taught that keeping any relationship within correct sexual boundaries is their responsibility, and that if sexual activity does occur, it is automatically their "fault." Some victims therefore feel guilty or ashamed of their sexual involvement with a practitioner, and are reluctant to press charges. If the abuser is a psychotherapist, the patient may also retain transference feelings toward the offender and not wish to cause him or her emotional or professional harm by reporting sexual misconduct (Bouhoutsos, 1985; Stone, 1983). Consequently, very few victims report their abuse or press charges (Bouhoutsos et al., 1983).

It was my fault, I seduced him.

I felt so bad about it; like I had toppled him off his pedestal.

(both quotes from Penfold, 1987, p. 30)

Even if a patient does have the courage to report her abuse, she may not be believed. As we have seen, women are the most likely victims of physician/therapist sexual abuse, and it is only since the 1970s that women's charges of sexual abuse, rape, or incest have been taken seriously in any setting. Both law and psychiatry have traditionally viewed these charges with utmost suspicion and often contempt, and "Charges of sex abuse were thus generally attributed to an assumed innate female tendency to make false allegations of a sexual nature against innocent men" (Pope, 1990a, p. 228). Penfold (1987) notes that "Although women who complain of sexual abuse by their therapist are no longer automatically disbelieved, an undercurrent of blame remains. Women victims . . . are seen to be somehow responsible" (p. 30).

The board of inquiry was worse than the abuse; no one believed me.

I told my GP, he didn't believe me. Then I told another psychiatrist, he didn't believe me either.

(Penfold, 1987, p. 30)

Traditional psychiatry has also espoused the notion that "fantasies of being raped are exceedingly common in women, indeed one may almost say that they are probably universal (Wigmore, 1934; 1970, p. 746, cited in Pope, 1990a, p. 228). A woman's report of therapist abuse may therefore be dismissed as a neurotic fantasy, or the acting out of a repressed desire for an incestuous relationship with her father, whom the therapist has come to represent (Freud, 1924; 1952, p. 379; cited in Pope, 1990a, p. 228). The negative, unbelieving, and generally unsympathetic response of individuals or groups who have regulatory authority only tends to exacerbate the negative effects of the initial abuse (Sonne et al., 1985).

He chose to do me harm at a critical turning point in my life. I fled from that psychiatrist, and didn't go near anyone for 10 years until I finally saw a woman psychiatrist, who asked me "Is there any chance you could be imagining this?" [tears] (Task Force, 1991, p. 13)

Some women may also fear the negative consequences of reporting their abuse. As Bouhoutsos (1985) points out, this fear is often all too realistic. The complaint process can lead to disclosure of the patient's sexual history, and the loss of therapist-patient confidentiality. Negative publicity, divorce, and the loss of child custody have also followed disclosure of this type of sexual abuse (Strasburger et al., 1990). Some patients may not report simply because they do not trust disciplinary bodies made up of the abuser's professional colleagues to adequately resolve their complaint (Bouhoutsos, 1985). The investigative process may take several years, and the financial costs of reporting may also be prohibitive.

The doctor told me that I could never afford to go after him, that he had insurance, and that it covered a lawyer, and that I would lose everything, including my farm — a man whose wife was abused. (Task Force, 1991, p. 13)

Reporting of abusers can also be done by colleagues who subsequently treat their victims, but colleagues are usually reluctant to "blow the whistle" on a fellow practitioner who may be a friend or a source of referrals, or they may be concerned with violating the patient's confidentiality (Stone, 1983). Some writers suggest that mandatory reporting of abusive colleagues should be required, with the patient's consent (Strasburger et al., 1990) or without it (Gartrell et al., 1987).

All of these factors combine to produce a situation in which patient sexual abuse is grossly underreported.

Preventing the Sexual Abuse of Patients

What can be done to prevent the sexual abuse of patients by physicians and therapists? Three courses of action have been suggested: education, professional sanctions, and criminal sanctions.

1. Education Numerous writers have called for ethics courses or materials to be included in all graduate psychology or psychiatry training programs to increase practitioners' awareness of the dynamics of sexual attraction to their patients and to prevent patient sexual abuse (Borys & Pope, 1989; Bouhoutsos, 1985; Pope et al., 1986). The

Canadian Psychiatric Association and the Canadian Psychological Association have both called for improvement in the ethics training of Canadian psychologists and psychiatrists (Eberlein, 1988; Pettifor & Pitcher, 1982). In-service training for practitioners has also been suggested (Bouhoutsos, 1985).

Interestingly, calls to improve the ethics training of psychotherapists have appeared concurrently with studies showing that sexual contact between professors and psychology or psychiatry students is also occurring (Carr et al., 1991; Gartrell et al., 1988; Glaser & Thorpe, 1986; Robinson & Reid, 1985). Most of these relationships involve male educators and female students. Since educators are in a position of power vis-à-vis their students, these relationships are generally considered to be unethical (Gartrell et al., 1988; Pope, 1989). As Bouhoutsos (1985) points out, "Modeling of this type cannot help but affect future professional behaviour" (p. 181).

Patient education has also been proposed as a means of preventing sexual abuse. Brochures have been written for patients (Committee on Women in Psychology, 1989), and the Canadian Psychiatric Association suggests that a simplified version of the association's Code of Ethics should be displayed in each psychiatrist's waiting room (Sreenivasan, 1989).

2. Professional Sanctions   Traditionally, doctors and therapists who are convicted of sexual abuse by their professional associations or licensing boards have been dealt with very leniently. Rarely is the practitioner's licence to practise totally revoked. Usually his licence is revoked for a short period, six months to a year, and he may be required to seek psychotherapy and demonstrate that he is rehabilitated before being allowed to return to practise. Supervision by a fellow practitioner for a given period of time may also be a condition of reinstatement for therapists, or a doctor may be required to examine female patients with a nurse present. In some cases, financial damages to the victim may also be awarded.

Why have professional associations been so reluctant to seriously punish their offending members? Pope speculates that:

> The male professional's sense of identification with the male perpetrator (intensified because both roles — health care professional and sex abuse perpetrator — involve being the more powerful member of a private dyad) may . . . elicit the professional's collusion in exonerating the perpetrator's accountability for his acts. . . . Thus the professional is placing an aspect of (perceived) self-interest (based on identification with the perpetrator) above the interests or needs of the victim. (Pope, 1990a, p. 229)

The rehabilitation of offenders is itself a controversial issue. Schoener and Gonsiorek (1988) believe that a comprehensive rehabilitation plan for an offending therapist should include: (1) personal psychotherapy, (2) practice limitations, (3) supervision, (4) change in therapy style, (5) vocational counselling, and (6) organizational changes. Similarly complex plans have also been suggested for offending physicians. However, as Pope states, "At present, the diverse attempts to rehabilitate therapists who perpetrate sexual abuse have not demonstrated success in replicated research studies" (Pope, 1990a, p. 233). As I have stated above, demonstrated rehabilitation is usually a pre-condition for the restoration of an abuser's licence to practise. This contradiction has profound implications for the sanctioning of recognized offenders, and I will briefly discuss this issue further in the final section of this chapter.

3. Criminal Sanctions   At least seven American states have made sexual relations between patient and therapist a criminal offence; in six of these states such actions are felonies, with penalties ranging from large fines to several years in prison (Task Force, 1991), but this development is highly controversial since reporting of offences by colleagues is usually mandatory under this legislation. Some patients may not be ready or willing to testify against their abusers and may be psychologically harmed by being forced to do so (Pope & Bouhoutsos, 1986).

Recommendations of the CPSO Task Force on Sexual Abuse of Patients

On November 25, 1991 the College of Physicians and Surgeons of Ontario published the *Final Report of the Task Force on Sexual Abuse of Patients*. This report was the culmination of ten months of public and private hearings, and round tables on legal issues and education. Three hundred and three detailed reports of sexual abuse were reported to the CPSO Task Force through the public and private hearings, letters, and phone calls to a confidential phone line (Task Force, 1991). A *Preliminary Report* was also published on May 27, 1991.

The cornerstone of the task force's report is the philosophy of Zero Tolerance of the sexual abuse of patients by physicians. This philosophy states that "Zero Tolerance establishes that sexual abuse of patients by physicians is never acceptable and must not be tolerated in our society. It recognizes the seriousness and extent of injury abuse causes, the *risk of harm* posed by abusers, and the need for realistic and effective standards of rehabilitation" (Task Force, 1991, p. 15).

To implement the philosophy of Zero Tolerance, 54 recommendations were made by the task force. The major recommendations include:

I. Penalties for Abusing Physicians   Two levels of penalties have been recommended:

a) Sexual Impropriety   Penalties for this type of abusive behaviour can include reprimand, apology, fine, temporary suspension of licence with conditions or any combination thereof. Sexual impropriety will comprise:

any behaviour, gestures, or expressions that are seductive or sexually demeaning to a patient; inappropriate procedures, including, but not limited to, disrobing or draping practices that reflect a lack of respect for the patient's privacy, (or) deliberately watching a patient dress or undress, instead of providing privacy for disrobing; subjecting a patient to an examination in the presence of medical students or other parties without the explicit consent of the patient or when consent has been withdrawn; examination or touching of genitals without the use of gloves; inappropriate comments about or to the patient, including, but not limited to, making sexual comments about a patient's body or underclothing, making sexualized or sexually demeaning comments to a patient, criticism of the patient's sexual orientation (homosexual or heterosexual or bisexual), making comments about potential sexual performance during an examination or consultation, except when the examination or consultation is pertinent to the issue of sexual function or dysfunction, requesting details of sexual history or sexual likes or dislikes when not clinically indicated for the type of consultation; making a request to date; initiation by the physician of conversation regarding the sexual problems, preferences, or fantasies of the physicians; kissing of a sexual nature. (Task Force, 1991, pp. 23-24)

b) Sexual Violation   The penalty for sexual violation would be a mandatory revocation of the physician's licence for a minimum of five years and a fine up to $20 000. A physician convicted of sexual violation (or sexual impropriety with revocation of licence) could return to practise only if he or she had completed a number of steps which had convinced the college of the applicant's complete rehabilitation.[4]

Sexual violation will comprise:

physician-patient sex, whether initiated by the patient or not, and engaging in any conduct with a patient that is sexual, or may be reasonably interpreted as sexual, including, but not limited to: sexual intercourse, genital to genital contact, oral to genital contact, oral to anal contact, oral to oral contact except CPR, touching breasts, genitals, or any sexualized body part for any purpose other than appropriate examination or treatment or where the patient has refused or has withdrawn consent; encouraging the patient to masturbate in the presence of the physician or masturbation by the physician while the patient is present. (Task Force, 1991, p. 24)

The task force also noted that "Termination of the physician–patient relationship has often been used by a physician intent on sexually abusing to gain sexual access to patients or to rationalize the exploitation." (Task Force, 1991, p. 135)

The task force therefore also recommended that the following guidelines be published by the college:

a physician should not have sexual contact with a former patient for a period of *two years* following the date of the last professional contact with the patient, even if the physician has formally terminated the professional relationship. (Task Force, 1991, p. 133)

In the case of psychotherapists:

> sexual contact with the patient is prohibited during the professional relationship and at *any time thereafter*, due to the lasting nature of transference and the power imbalance, and hence the potential for abuse created. (Task Force, 1991, p. 133)

2. Reporting of Sexual Abuse by Physicians　The task force recommends the mandatory reporting of physician sexual abuse by physicians who are aware of the abuse and the acceptance of reports from third parties who are not physicians, such as friends or partners of the abused person. In both cases, the alleged offender's name would be recorded, along with the reporter's name and a means of contacting the reporter, if they agree, and the patient's name, if they agree. Third-party reports would not lead to an investigation by the college *unless the patient* initiated a formal complaint. If the college receives more than one complaint about an alleged abuser, the evidence would be reviewed and the college would determine if an investigation is warranted. The patient or patients involved would be contacted through the reporting party or parties to see if they might wish to take part in the investigation or make a formal complaint, but they would not be obliged to do so.

3. Education to Prevent Physician Sexual Abuse

a) Education for Physicians　The task force report recommends that medical training at all levels include curriculum on sexual abuse, and that this material be included in examinations and accreditation to practise. The curriculum should include an understanding of the social context and power dynamics of sexual abuse, and information on recognizing and treating previous physician sexual abuse. and guidance on appropriate physician-patient boundaries.

b) Education for the Public　The task force recommends that the task force and other medical groups in Ontario collaborate with patient advocacy groups and abuse survivor groups to produce a patient information brochure on physician sexual abuse. This would be made available in a number of languages, in Braille, and on tape wherever physicians practise in Ontario. This brochure should also contain "The Physicians Commitment to Patients" statement outlining the rights of patients, and this statement should be displayed in poster form wherever physicians practise and in other public places such as community centres, schools, etc. The task force also recommends that the College of Physicians and Surgeons take steps to inform the public in as many ways as possible of the procedure for reporting patient sexual abuse.

Conclusion

The sexual abuse of patients by physicians is a problem as old as medicine itself. Until recently, however, victims suffered in silence, perhaps blaming themselves for their abuse, or were disbelieved and further victimized by those they turned to for help. Thanks to the efforts of activists, both within and outside of these professions, this form of abuse is now beginning to be recognized and dealt with by the appropriate regulatory bodies.

In Canada, the work of the Task Force on Sexual Abuse of Patients, commissioned by the College of Physicians and Surgeons of Ontario, has already had a profound impact on the public's awareness of this form of abuse and on the way in which it is handled. For women, however, learning about patient sexual abuse now means that there is yet another area of their lives where they must be careful, where they must be on guard. In the final analysis, however, this knowledge can be empowering if it prevents such abuse from occurring in the future. A second positive outcome of the public revelation of the nature and frequency of patient sexual abuse is the demystification of the medical profession, a process that had already begun. It is precisely the exalted standing of medical doctors that has protected abusers in the past, and the diminution of this artificially created public esteem can only benefit patients, and ultimately, the profession itself, as it begins to be seen and see itself more realistically.

Although the task force report focusses primarily on medical doctors and psychiatrists, it will no doubt have an impact on other health-care professions, where sexual abuse of patients is also a reality. Similar investigations are now under way in other Canadian provinces.

I would like to close this chapter with a quote from a survivor of physician sexual abuse, who participated in a public hearing of the task force.

> I would like to thank you for providing a safe place for people to speak. . . . I cannot adequately express what that has meant to me, or how grateful I remain to all of you. Thank you so very much. Whatever happens with the recommendations in the final report you have already succeeded. You have brought this issue to the surface and judging by the response of victims, it will not be submerged again. (Task Force, 1991, introduction)

Notes

1. Over 300 calls were received from individuals, health professionals, organizations, and institutions from Ontario and across Canada. Calls ranged from two to 90 minutes, and all were recorded. Most callers described abuse by doctors, but complaints against therapists, teachers, lawyers, judges, clergy, dentists, social workers, and nurses were also received. If the caller wished to receive a response, they were contacted by the task force or a trained counsellor (Task Force, 1991).

2. This point is starkly demonstrated by the 1991 conviction of the former head of the

University of British Columbia Department of Psychiatry, Dr. James Tyhurst, on five counts of sexual and indecent assault involving four female patients over a period of twenty years (LeBourdais, 1991). For a book-length account see Hyde (1991).

3. A few psychologists and psychiatrists have dissented from this majority view in the past and argued that sexual contact between therapist and patient, if carefully undertaken, may not be harmful and may even be beneficial. For a description of this position see McCartney, 1966; Romeo, 1978; and Shepard, 1971.

4. In its *Preliminary Report* published on May 27, 1991, the task force recommended that the penalty for sexual violation should be the permanent revocation of the abuser's licence and a fine. Physicians and some members of the public objected to the stringency of this proposal (see Hall, 1991). By reversing itself on this important recommendation, the task force has left the door open for the *possibility* of rehabilitation; however, the conditions set down in the task force's *Final Report* for proof of rehabilitation are extremely strict. In my opinion, it is doubtful that many offending doctors would be able to meet these requirements for reinstatement (see Laidlaw, 1991).

Study Questions

1. How did the sexual abuse of patients by physicians and therapists come to be recognized as an important social problem?
2. Why is sexual contact between patients and physicians/therapists prohibited by these professions?
3. Describe the physical and emotional effects of physician/therapist sexual abuse on patients.
4. Why do patients, especially women patients, have difficulty reporting sexual abuse by physicians or therapists to the appropriate authorities?
5. What can be done to prevent the sexual abuse of patients? What are the major recommendations of the CPSO Task Force regarding prevention?

Recommended Reading

Burgess, A.W., & Hartman, C.R. (Eds.). (1986). *Sexual exploitation of patients by health professionals*. New York: Praeger Press.

Carr, M., & Robinson, G.E. (1990). Fatal attraction: The ethical and clinical dilemma of patient-therapist sex. *Canadian Journal of Psychiatry*, 35, 122-127.

Gabbard, G.O. (Ed.). (1989). *Sexual exploitation in professional relationships*. Washington: American Psychiatric Press.

Hyde, C. (1991). *Abuse of trust: The career of Dr. James Tyhurst*. Vancouver: Douglas and McIntyre.

Pope, K.S. (1990). Therapist-patient sexual involvement: A review of the research. *Clinical Psychology Review*, 10, 477-490.

Pope, K.S. (1990a). Therapist-patient sex as sex abuse: Six scientific, professional, and practical dilemmas in addressing victimization and rehabilitation. *Professional Psychology: Research and Practice*, 21, 227-239.

Pope, K.S., & Bouhoutsos, J. (1986). *Sexual intimacy between therapists and patients*. New York: Praeger Press.

Task Force on Sexual Abuse of Patients, (1991, November 25). *The final report of the task force on sexual abuse of patients*. Toronto: The College of Physicians and Surgeons of Ontario.

References

Armsworth, M.W. (1989). Therapy of incest survivors: Abuse or support? *Child Abuse and Neglect*, 13, 549-562.

Bajt, T.R., & Pope, K.S. (1989). Therapist-patient sexual intimacy involving children and adolescents. *American Psychologist*, 44, 455.

Bates, C.R., & Brodsky, A.M. (1989). *Sex in the therapy hour: A case of professional incest*. New York: Guilford.

Belote, B. (1974). *Sexual intimacy between female clients and male psychotherapists: Masochistic sabotage*. Unpublished Ph.D. Dissertation, California School of Professional Psychology.

Borys, D.S., & Pope, K.S. (1989). Dual relationships between therapist and client: A national study of psychologists, psychiatrists, and social workers. *Professional Psychology: Research and Practice, 20*, 283-293.

Bouhoutsos, J.C. (1985). Therapist–client sexual involvement: A challenge for mental health professionals and educators. *American Journal of Orthopsychiatry, 55*, 177-182.

Bouhoutsos, J.C. (1985a). Sexual intimacy between psychotherapists and clients: Policy implications for the future. In L. Walker (Ed.), *Women and mental health policy* (pp. 207-227). Beverly Hills: Sage.

Bouhoutsos, J., Holroyd, J., Lerman, H., Forer, B., & Greenberg, M. (1983). Sexual intimacy between psychotherapists and patients. *Professional Psychology, 14*, 185-196.

Carr, M., Robinson, G.E., Stewart, D.E., & Kussin, D. (1991). A survey of Canadian psychiatric residents regarding resident-educator sexual contact. *American Journal of Psychiatry, 148*, 216-220.

CHASTEN (Canadian Health Alliance to Stop Therapist Exploitation Now). (1991, February 19). Brief presented to the College of Physicians and Surgeons task force on sexual abuse of patients. Toronto.

Chesler, P. (1972). *Women and madness.* New York: Doubleday.

Committee on Women in Psychology. (1989). If sex enters into the psychotherapy relationship. *Professional Psychology: Research and Practice, 20*, 112-115.

Dahlberg, C. (1970). Sexual contact between patient and therapist. *Contemporary Psychoanalysis, 6*, 107-124.

Davidson, V. (1977). Psychiatry's problem with no name: Therapist-patient sex. *The American Journal of Psychoanalysis, 37*, 43-50.

Dorlands Medical Dictionary. (1974). (25th ed.). Philadelphia: Saunders.

Eberlein, L. (1988). The new CPA code of ethics for Canadian psychologists: An educational and training perspective. *Canadian Psychologist, 29*, 206-212.

Feldman-Summers, S. (1989). Sexual contact in fiduciary relationships. In G.O. Gabbard (Ed.), *Sexual exploitation in professional relationships* (pp. 193-210). Washington: American Psychiatric Press.

Feldman-Summers, S., & Jones, G. (1984). Psychological impacts of sexual contact between therapists and other health care practitioners and their clients. *Journal of Consulting and Clinical Psychology, 52*, 1054-1061.

Freud, S. (1963). Further recommendations in the technique of psychoanalysis: Observations on transference-love. In P. Rieff (Ed.), *Freud: Therapy and technique* (pp. 167-180). New York: Collier Books. (Original work published 1915).

Gartrell, N., Herman, J., Olarte, S., Feldstein, M., & Localio, R. (1986). Psychiatrist-patient sexual contact: Results of a national survey, I: Prevalence. *American Journal of Psychiatry, 143*, 1126-1131.

Gartrell, N., et al. (1987). Reporting practices of psychiatrists who knew of sexual misconduct by colleagues. *American Journal of Orthopsychiatry, 57*, 287-295.

Gartrell, N., et al. (1988). Psychiatric residents' sexual contact with educators and patients: Results of a national survey. *American Journal of Psychiatry, 145*, 690-694.

Gartrell, N., et al. (1989). Prevalence of psychiatrist-patient sexual contact. In G.O. Gabbard (Ed.), *Sexual exploitation in professional relationships* (pp. 3-13). Washington: American Psychiatric Press.

Glaser, R.D., & Thorpe, J.S. (1986). Unethical intimacy: A survey of sexual contact and advances between psychology educators and female graduate students. *American Psychologist, 41*, 43-51.

Hall, J. (1991, July 30). Report on sexual abuse was unjust. *Toronto Star*, p. A2.

Holroyd, J.C., & Brodsky, A.M. (1977). Psychologists' attitudes and practices regarding erotic and nonerotic physical contact with patients. *American Psychologist, 32*, 843-849.

Hyde, C. (1991). *Abuse of trust: The career of Dr. James Tyhurst.* Vancouver: Douglas & McIntyre.

Kardener, S.H., Fuller, M., & Mensh, I. (1973). A survey of physicians' attitudes and practices regarding erotic and nonerotic contact with patients. *American Journal of Psychiatry, 130*, 1077-1081.

Laidlaw, S. (1991, November 26). Task force backs away from lifetime ban. *The Ottawa Citizen*, p. A4.

LeBourdais, E. (1991). Case involving prominent B.C. psychiatrist puts medical profession on trial. *Canadian Medical Association*, 145, (5), 501-505.

Luepker, E.T., & Retsch-Bogart, C. (1986). Time-limited treatment groups for patients sexually exploited by psychotherapists. In A.W. Burgess (Ed.), *Sexual exploitation by health professionals*. New York: Praeger Medical Series.

Masters, W., & Johnson, V. (1966). *Human sexual response*. New York: Bantam.

Masters, W., & Johnson, V. (1975). *Principles of the new sex therapy*. Paper presented at the annual meeting of the American Psychiatric Association, Anaheim.

McCartney, J. (1966). Overt transference. *Journal of Sex Research*, 2, 227-237.

North Bay doctor found guilty of professional misconduct. (1991, September 7). *The Ottawa Citizen*, p. A13.

Penfold, S. (1987). Sexual abuse between therapist and woman patient. *Canadian Woman Studies*, 8, 29-31.

Perry, J.A. (1976). Physicians' erotic and non-erotic physical involvement with patients. *American Journal of Psychiatry*, 133, 838-840.

Pettifor, J., & Pitcher, S. (1982). Ethical training in Canadian graduate schools of psychology. *Canadian Psychologist*, 23, 235-242.

Pope, K.S. (1985). *Diagnosis and treatment of therapist-patient sex syndrome*. Paper presented at the meeting of the American Psychological Association, Los Angeles.

Pope, K.S. (1986). Research and laws regarding therapist-patient sexual involvement: Implications for therapists. *American Journal of Psychotherapy*, XL, 564-571.

Pope, K.S. (1989). Teacher-student sexual intimacy. In G.O. Gabbard (Ed.), *Sexual exploitation in professional relationships* (pp. 163-176). Washington: American Psychiatric Press.

Pope, K.S. (1990). Therapist-patient sexual involvement: A review of the research. *Clinical Psychology Review*, 10, 477-490.

Pope, K.S. (1990a). Therapist-patient sex as sex abuse: Six scientific, professional, and practical dilemmas in addressing victimization and rehabilitation. *Professional Psychology: Research and Practice*, 21, 227-239.

Pope, K.S., & Bajt, T.R. (1988). When laws and values conflict: A dilemma for psychologists. *American Psychologist*, 43, 828-829.

Pope, K.S., & Bouhoutsos, J. (1986). *Sexual intimacy between therapists and patients*. New York: Praeger Press.

Pope, K.S., Keith-Spiegel, P., & Tabachnick, B. (1986). Sexual attraction to clients. *American Psychologist*, 41, 147-158.

Robinson, W.L., & Reid, P.T. (1985). Sexual intimacies in psychology revisited. *Professional Psychology: Research and Practice*, 16, 512-520.

Romeo, S. (1978, June). Dr. Martin Shepard answers his accusers. *Knave*, pp. 14-38.

Schoener, G.R., & Gonsiorek, J. (1988). Assessment and development of rehabilitation plans for counselors who have sexually exploited their clients. *Journal of Counseling and Development*, 67, 227-232.

Shepard, M. (1971). *The love treatment: Sexual intimacy between patients and psychotherapists*. New York: Wyden.

Sonne, J., Meyer, C.B., Borys, D., & Marshall, V. (1985). Clients' reactions to sexual intimacy in therapy. *American Journal of Orthopsychiatry*, 55, 183-189.

Sreenivasan, U. (1989). Sexual exploitation of patients: The position of the Canadian Psychiatric Association. *Canadian Journal of Psychiatry*, 34, 234-235.

Stone, A.A. (1983). Sexual misconduct by psychiatrists: The ethical and clinical dilemma of confidentiality. *American Journal of Psychiatry*, 140, 195-197.

Strasburger, L.H., Jorgenson, L., & Randles, R. (1990). Mandatory reporting of sexually exploitive psychotherapists. *Bulletin of the American Academy of Psychiatry and Law*, 18, 379-384.

Taylor, P. (1991, March 5). Group seeks removal of MD's privileges. *The Globe and Mail*, p. A5.

Valiquette, M., Sabourin, S., & Lecomte, C. (1991). *The psychological sequelae of sexual intimacy in patient-therapist relationships*. Unpublished paper.

Vinson, J.S. (1987). Use of complaint procedures in cases of therapist-patient sexual contact. *Professional Psychology: Research and Practice*, 18, 159-164.

Chapter 17

The New Reproductive Technologies: Boon or Bane?

Karen R. Grant, University of Manitoba

Introduction

1978. Something unimaginable occurred — the birth of Louise Brown. The world's first "test-tube" baby was a watershed in the field of reproductive medicine, and in the years that have followed, the public remains in awe of the technological wizardry that allows an infertile couple to bear a child of their own. The images of bouncing "miracle" babies are difficult to dislodge from one's consciousness, particularly when we hear of the travails of those couples who have tried — and failed — to conceive a child by conventional means. The burgeoning field of genetic and reproductive engineering, and the associated developments in reproductive technologies, have given the infertile hope that they, too, can realize their dream of having a child.

1984. Another significant date — less for what happened that year, than for what was predicted to happen. George Orwell's prophecy of a world of increased technological surveillance and repression was nightmarish to imagine, much less to see realized in some form. Yet, by all counts, what we have started to see is the kind of reproductive, genetic (and, some would add, social) engineering that Orwell (1949), Huxley (1946), and other dystopian writers (Atwood, 1985) warned us of. In such a "brave new world," we are regularly reminded that "one is never fighting against an external enemy but always against one's own body" (Orwell, 1949, p. 86). Rather than liberating us, developments such as new reproductive technologies (NRT) enslave us to the health system and potentially to iatrogenic (physician-induced) health problems. What is more, these technologies both foster and reinforce an oppressive set of cultural beliefs that demand that we become parents, and not just that, but parents to children with whom we have a genetic link. To this list, feminist critics would add that NRT, reflecting as they do male values, also reinforce gender inequality, rendering women simply "mother machines" (Corea, 1985) and "living laboratories" (Rowland, 1992) in which doctors (most of whom are male) realize their ability to "make" babies.

Miracle or source of tyranny? Boon or bane? It is questions such as these that we attempt to address in this chapter. Following a brief discussion of infertility — the problem NRT were intended to address — and the various technologies, we look at some of the implications of NRT. At the heart of this discussion is an attempt to understand the contradictory nature of NRT. How can one reconcile two competing sets of interests — those of individual women who are themselves infertile or whose partners are infertile and see NRT as offering a "last chance" at genetic parenthood, and those of women as a social group, who risk further domination and control by the technology (and its practitioners) in this "brave new world"? This chapter also explores other social implications of NRT.

The Problem: Infertility

The rise of NRT has, to a large degree, been a response to the problem of infertility. Although some would have us believe that infertility is a new and growing problem, there is little empirical support for such a contention. Infertility has occurred throughout history. In the Old Testament, Sarah's infertility was dealt with by finding a surrogate (Hagar) to bear a child with a genetic link to Abraham. Today, we have numerous examples of infertile couples seeking out surrogates (the "Baby M" case is perhaps the most notorious of these) or enrolling in in vitro fertilization (IVF) programs to deal with their infertility. The problem is not a new one, though some of the "solutions" are very new and different.

Infertility is usually defined as "the inability to conceive a viable pregnancy within one year of [unprotected] intercourse" (Bryant, 1990, p. 2). In other words, while a woman may conceive in this time period, if she does not carry the fetus to term, then she is considered infertile. The one-year criterion is somewhat arbitrary, but is nonetheless an accepted standard. Based on this definition, infertility is said to affect approximately 10 percent of Canadian couples (Bryant, 1990).

In recent years, there has been a barrage of reports that infertility is on the increase. When age is taken into account, the rates of infertility today are actually comparable to those found three decades ago. What is different is the age at which infertility is identified. With women/couples postponing childbearing into their thirties, a point past "peak fertility," there is at least the appearance of an increase in cases of infertility. As well, women have been told that infertility is the price they have paid in their quest for equality in the workplace and in society more generally. Women used to being task-oriented, successful, and in control have suddenly found themselves to be "failures" and unable to control this aspect of their life: fertility. Supposedly, infertility, like the man shortage and superwoman burnout, are all consequences of the feminist movement (Faludi, 1991).

The apparent increase in infertility reflects two other factors. First, the availability of potential adoptees has steadily declined (although many special-needs children continue to await placement) as a result of the availability of abortion on demand, as well as single women opting to keep their babies (Banks, 1991). Second, whereas in the past infertile couples commonly accepted their involuntary childlessness with a degree of shame and fatalism (Rehner, 1989), today medical advances in the fields of reproductive medicine and genetic engineering offer a scientific alternative, including the promise of treatment.

Infertility has been extensively studied by specialists in reproductive medicine. To date, the causes of some forms of infertility are still not understood. Physicians usually differentiate between female-factor and male-factor infertility, and idiopathic infertility (in which the cause is unknown). According to one recent report, infertility is due to female factors in 35 percent of couples, male factors in 35 percent of couples, and a combination of male and female factors in 20 percent of couples. In the remaining 10 percent of couples, the infertility is said to be idiopathic (Banks, 1991).

In both women and men, infertility can result from previous infections or untreated sexually transmitted diseases that have resulted in scar tissue. Such scar tissue may cause blockages in the pathways through which the woman's egg and the man's sperm must travel in order for conception and fertilization to take place. Environmental and occupational exposures may also affect women's and men's fertility.

Female-factor infertility can also be attributed to ovulatory problems as a result of pelvic inflammatory disease (PID). Women using an intrauterine device (IUD) as a form of contraception have a higher risk of PID, particularly those who have used the Dalkon Shield (Clapp & Swenson, 1984). Another common cause of infertility in women is endometriosis. This extremely painful disease occurs when the interior surface of the uterus, the endometrium, begins to grow outside of the uterus, usually in the pelvic area, resulting in scarring or tubal blockages that inhibit fertility. Endocrine problems, which result in irregular menstruation or amenorrhea (absence of menstruation), may lead to difficulties in a woman's ability to conceive. These endocrine problems are usually caused by glandular or hormonal factors, or may be the consequence of protracted use of the Pill (sometimes called the post-Pill syndrome) (Clapp & Swenson, 1984). Women who have had ectopic (tubal) pregnancies and women who have other structural problems in their reproductive systems may also have difficulty conceiving and carrying a fetus to term. For some women, structural problems may be caused by previous in utero exposure to the anti-abortifacient, diethylstilbestrol (DES).[1] For others, structural difficulties may be due to congenital factors. All of these factors, along with problems in a woman's cervical mucus (i.e., abnormalities in pH levels, or incompatibilities in the sperm and cervical mucus) can all result in a woman being defined as infertile.

On the male side of the equation, infertility is usually identified as being the result of low sperm count, or poor quality or motility of sperm. These types of male-factor infertility may be due to a wide range of problems, such as exposure to drugs or environmental toxins, or because of post-pubertal infections such as the mumps. Structural problems that impede the movement of sperm also adversely affect men's fertility. Sexual dysfunction, including premature ejaculation and impotence, can also result in male infertility.

In both women and men, there may be psychological as well as physiological factors that adversely affect fertility. Couples experiencing difficulty in conceiving are often told to "just relax." Though advice such as this is well intentioned, it does little good and often only exacerbates the frustration and anguish that many infertile couples already feel. Described in the literature as suffering a major life crisis (Rehner, 1989; Bryant, 1990; Strickler, 1992; Clapp & Swenson, 1984), the infertile commonly "put their lives on hold," as they relentlessly pursue having a child.

As many couples experiencing infertility discover, the problem is often multifaceted and the diagnosis of the problem is quite involved. Once a diagnosis has been made, there may be treatments employed (e.g., drugs can be used to correct hormone imbalances in women, surgery can be performed to correct structural barriers to conception), but current therapeutics fall short of 100 percent success. Is infertility a "disease"? If so, then the cure must be the ability to have a baby. And just how do we go about "making" babies?

The "Solution": New Reproductive Technologies

For infertile women and men today, the "preferred" medical solution will usually consist of one or more NRT. As Eichler (1991) has noted, however, this term is not entirely accurate. Some NRT are not new at all (e.g., artificial insemination), and some are not technologies (e.g., surrogacy arrangements). While the newest innovations in reproductive medicine were ostensibly developed to assist those who are infertile to bear children, increasingly today many people who are not infertile (according to the definition cited earlier) are using these technologies. This illustrates how easily such technological innovations have become routinized and generalized beyond those for whom treatment was initially intended.

Although hailed in some circles as a sign of medicine's attempts to overcome infertility, NRT have generated an increasing amount of concern. Questions have been raised about the efficacy of some NRT, and the potential short-and long-term health and social consequences of these procedures and technologies. Before considering some of these issues, let's look at the technologies that constitute NRT. To describe the range of reproductive technologies currently in use, I refer to the categories articulated by the National Action Committee on the Status of Women (NAC) in its brief submitted to the Royal Commission on New Reproductive Technologies (1991).[2] The NAC distinguishes between the following: (1) technologies of insemination; (2) techniques of artificial fertilization; (3) prenatal diagnosis; and (4) genetic interventions.

Technologies of Insemination

Technologies of insemination have existed for hundreds of years, although it is only relatively recently that they have been medicalized (Wikler & Wikler, 1991). The two types of insemination are artificial insemination by husband (AIH) and donor insemination (DI). AIH is used in circumstances where a man is unable to ejaculate into his partner's vagina. DI is used in circumstances in which a man produces abnormal sperm, no sperm at all, or if he has had an irreversible vasectomy. DI can also be used to prevent the transmission of hereditary disease[3] (Carver, 1989).

Though conventionally the technologies of insemination are discussed in the context of stable relations between a woman and a man, artificial insemination has been used by single women and lesbian women in order to conceive without sexual intercourse (NAC, 1991). Wikler and Wikler (1991) describe in some detail how simple, low-tech procedures (an ordinary turkey baster will do!), coupled with access to co-operative sperm banks, have allowed women to be self-inseminated. This procedure serves as a challenge to medical control over artificial insemination, as well as our understandings of how and when insemination is used. Obviously, this technology is of use to individuals other than the infertile.

Insemination methods are not without their risks. There is the possibility of the woman being infected during the insemination process, and samples of sperm may be infected with the AIDS virus or other sexually transmitted diseases. Most sperm banks today, however, screen donors and test semen samples for these diseases.

In addition, ethical questions about insemination have been raised. A recent court case involving an American doctor who inseminated dozens of his patients (unbeknownst to them) with his own semen, highlights some of the ethical quandaries raised by insemination. (Dr. Jacobson was sentenced to a 30-year jail term.) Many sperm banks guarantee the anonymity of donors. This raises the difficult question of paternity (biological fatherhood), which may be of significance in terms of the psychological and physical well-being of the offspring resulting from sperm donations.

Techniques of Artificial Fertilization

Several techniques fall into this category, the most common being IVF. In IVF, the union of sperm and egg takes place in a laboratory (the literal translation of in vitro is "in glass"). IVF was first developed in the late 1800s, but the first successful implantation of an embryo in a human did not occur until the mid-1940s. The first live birth of a human was Louise Brown in England in 1978. Canada's first "test-tube" babies (a set of twins) were born in Oakville, Ontario in 1982.

Depending on the circumstances for using IVF, a range of other techniques may be used in conjunction with it (e.g., techniques of insemination, surrogacy). Historically, IVF was developed to assist women whose Fallopian tubes were blocked or malfunctioning, preventing their eggs from getting to the uterus. In such a situation, the proceduralist would "harvest"[4] ripe eggs from the woman's ovary, using a surgical technique called laparoscopy. While under either local or general anesthesia, a doctor inserts a laparoscope into the woman's ovary, punctures the follicle(s), and extracts the egg(s) which are placed into a Petri dish. The woman's partner, meanwhile, will masturbate in order to provide a semen sample. The man's semen, either from the woman's partner or from donor sperm, is then placed in a centrifuge, and the most active sperm are transferred into the Petri dish containing the woman's egg(s). The egg(s) and sperm are incubated for the purposes of fertilization. If fertilization occurs, then the resulting embryo(s) is/are inserted into the woman's uterus, once again using the laparoscope. (If more than one egg is harvested during a laparoscopy procedure, spares will be cryopreserved. This topic is addressed in more detail on the pages that follow.)

Quite commonly, during this process, women will be administered a "hormone cocktail" of superovulatory drugs such as clomiphene citrate (trade name: Clomid), human menopausal gonadotrophin (HMG, marketed as Perganol), human chorionic gonadotrophin (HCG, marketed as Pregnyl), and occasionally, follicle stimulating hormone (FSH) and luteinizing hormone (LH). These cocktails stimulate the woman's ovaries to produce more than one egg during a menstrual cycle, which proceduralists believe will increase the chances of fertilization. Though these cocktails may work in this way, there is also a considerable body of evidence suggesting that women are exposed to serious side effects when on such a chemical regimen (Rowland, 1992; Klein & Rowland, 1988). Hyperstimulation syndrome is not uncommon among women in IVF programs. Among other things, they may experience weight gain, bloatedness, diarrhea, and nausea. Several recent reports have linked hormone cocktails to a rapidly spreading and sometimes deadly form of breast cancer (cited in Rowland, 1992), although physicians working in IVF are quick to dispute this connection as spurious.[5] What is distressing about this is that clinical trials to determine the short- and long-term safety of clomiphene citrate (and the other drugs used in hormone cocktails) have been conspicuously absent in the medical literature. In the face of callous disregard for the health of women in IVF programs, it is no wonder that feminist critics consider that, in IVF, women's bodies are being used as test sites (Klein & Rowland, 1988; Gupta, 1991)!

One other point deserves mention here and that is the incidence of multiple births to women in IVF programs. If more than one egg is harvested and fertilized, it only stands to reason that there is a greater chance of multiple birth. Not uncommonly, such pregnancies are classified as "high risk," and the women involved typically undergo a more interventionist labour and delivery (including Caesarean section). The physical and psychological (not to mention economic) consequences of bearing twins, triplets, or quadruplets are not to be underestimated. However, such considerations often pale when the goal of couples in IVF and their doctors alike is to increase the chance of fertilization.

This is the simplest IVF case. Quite commonly, variations on this theme characterize the procedure. For instance, gamete intra–Fallopian transfer (GIFT) is used where there is either donor sperm or donor eggs, and zygote intra–Fallopian transfer (ZIFT) is used with donor pre-embryos. In some Catholic hospitals, methods of transfer have been developed that circumvent the controversies surrounding the creation of embryos outside of a woman's body (Rowland, 1992). These embryo implantation techniques include pronuclear stage transfer (PROST), transutero-tubal implantation (TUTI), and tubal ovum transfer (TOT). This list is far from complete, but gives some indication of the many and varied ways in which doctors have fashioned a form of "human-made intercourse" (Rowland, 1992, p. 31; NAC, 1991).

If donor gametes (eggs or sperm) or embryos are used in the IVF procedure, they will likely have been cryopreserved (frozen) and then later thawed for implantation in the woman's uterus. As noted previously, spare eggs or embryos are often frozen if more than one egg has been harvested in a laparoscopy procedure. Cryopreservation may cause damage to gametes or embryos, and evidence suggests that the chances of successful implantation of frozen eggs, sperm, and embryos is not very high (Rowland, 1992). Interestingly, IVF researchers contend that cryopreservation techniques obviate the need for women to undergo multiple procedures to extract eggs. With this technology, we are told, a woman in her peak reproductive years can now have several of her eggs preserved for later use, so that she might fulfil career or other personal aspirations. Women with cancer or who have had their ovaries removed can use cryopreservation to, in effect, extend their reproductive life, since it is the age of ova more than the age of a woman's uterus that affects fertility.

However, where there is a brighter side, there is often a darker, or at least unanticipated, side as well. A widely reported case in South Africa in 1987 involved a grandmother surrogate whose daughter's eggs were implanted. The daughter had had a hysterectomy following the birth of her first child. Embryos retrieved from the daughter's intact ovaries were implanted in her mother's womb, and triplets were subsequently born to the grandmother. The triplets were adopted by the daughter and son-in-law (the triplets were a product of their embryo), because by law the grandmother who had gestated them was really the mother! Another curious case involved a British woman who gave birth to "twins" born eighteen months apart (the eggs were harvested at the same time, consequently the children were categorized as twins). Finally, there is the (in)famous Rios case in Australia, which opened up a Pandora's box about IVF and cryopreservation in that country, and which continues to this day. The Rioses were an American couple who had been admitted into an IVF program in Melbourne, Australia. Elsa Rios had had three eggs harvested in a laparoscopy procedure. One egg was implanted, but the pregnancy was later miscarried. The two remaining embryos were being stored in a Melbourne hospital, when the Rioses were killed in an airplane crash. The question that preoccupied Australians for months to follow was what should be done with the spare "orphan" embryos[6] (Albury, 1986). As these cases illustrate, cryopreservation raises complex questions about ownership of embryos, and the parental status of those contributing material toward the embryos or involved in gestation. Rowland cautions us about the uses and consequences of cryopreservation. She describes how some doctors have reportedly used freezing for purely experimental reasons. She further reminds us that "egg freezing . . . opens up an enormous new market which has nothing to do with infertility at all" (1992, p. 35).

IVF techniques have been widely criticized on a number of fronts, the most contentious issues being the costs and the success (or to be more accurate, failure) rates of the procedures. It has been estimated that more than 5000 Canadian couples/women have undergone IVF. Looking at the situation in Ontario, as of 1987, 207 children had been born to 130 couples enrolled in IVF programs throughout the province (Banks, 1991). Conservative estimates of the success rates are rather low (ranging between 0-10 percent, though some centres report rates as high as 15 percent in their promotional materials). And even then, there is much debate as to what constitutes success — the proportion of successful implantations (pregnancies) or the proportion of live births? Though enrollees typically respond that "10 percent is better than 0 percent," the reality of such a high failure rate should give us pause. As a society, we ought to be asking if finite health-care resources should be spent on such an unsuccessful procedure.

And at what cost? Some might say IVF illustrates that some people are prepared to go after a child at any cost. Since many provincial governments consider IVF to be too experimental, they have withheld funding, in whole or in part. (The Manitoba government closed the only IVF program in the province a few years ago.) Waiting lists are notoriously long in IVF programs around the country. Some couples have been prepared to seek IVF out of province (or in other countries). Even where government subsidies of IVF programs exist, couples can expect to pay a substantial portion of the costs out of their own pockets. (It follows that IVF is available largely on the basis of one's ability to pay.) According to Banks (1991), in Ontario, it has been estimated that each IVF baby costs the province $35 000!

In this discussion of IVF, we have only scratched the surface of the issues and controversies that define this technology. The critics have been quite vociferous on matters such as informed consent, safety, and the coercion women feel when enrolled in IVF programs (Rowland, 1992; Klein, 1991; Corea, 1985). The promise of IVF technology, some would say, has not been delivered. Yet, the promise is often compelling enough to keep women coming back for more. An Israeli clinic reminds women that "You're not a failure till you stop trying" (quoted in Solomon, 1988, p. 43). Perhaps the question of who or what is failing needs reconsideration!

Prenatal Diagnosis

Prenatal diagnosis (PND) has introduced revolutionary changes to antenatal care (Bradish, 1987). PND includes a broad range of tests "to analyze the embryo and fetus for the purposes of selective embryo reduction and abortion on the basis of genetically determined characteristics" (NAC, 1991, p. 283). These tests have changed the very essence of birthing by introducing a new level of decision making during pregnancy. Previously, one discovered the sex and the health status of the fetus at birth, and only family history could help to predict the risk of conceiving a child with some genetic disease. Today, "with the analysis of amniotic fluid and cultured fetal cells, ultrasonography, analysis of maternal serum for alpha-fetoprotein and radiography . . . it is now possible to make a more accurate estimation of genetic risks (Paez-Victor, 1988, p. 3). Consequently, new moral, social, psychological, and medical questions arise, such as whether to continue a pregnancy, or whether medical or surgical treatment should be carried out on a woman for the sake of her fetus.

The most commonly used prenatal diagnostic tests are ultrasound, maternal serum alpha-fetoprotein (MS–AFP), amniocentesis, and chorionic villus sampling (CVS). Ultrasound was developed initially to monitor the development of the fetus in utero, and now finds many other applications, including the identification of treatable kidney disease and fetal sex. Most women (85 percent or more, according to one estimate) have at least one ultrasound (if not more) performed during a pregnancy (NAC, 1991). (Some centres will even provide women/couples with a photo or video of the ultrasound! Not surprisingly, the first picture in the family photo albums is often that of the ultrasound.) Despite widespread use of this technology, there have been no systematic studies assessing the long-term impact of ultrasound on women or the fetuses they carry.

The MS-AFP test, a simple blood test, was developed to detect neural tube defects such as spina bifida (where the spinal cord fails to close properly) and anencephalus (a congenital condition in which all or part of the brain is absent). This test can also be used to identify an increased risk of Down's syndrome in the fetus. MS-AFP screening is done on many women as part of routine antenatal care (Greenberg, 1988). In some jurisdictions, women must sign a form to refuse, not consent to, MS-AFP testing.

Both amniocentesis and CVS involve removal of a sample of cells which can be analyzed to determine chromosomal abnormalities such as Down's syndrome. In the case of amniocentesis, a sample of amniotic fluid is removed during the second trimester of the pregnancy (usually around fifteen weeks); in CVS, a sample of the chorionic villus (what will become the placenta) is removed during the first trimester of the pregnancy (usually around ten weeks). Both procedures are done under local anesthesia. CVS is an ultrasound-guided technique (i.e., ultrasound is performed throughout the procedure), while with amniocentesis, ultrasounds are performed before and after the amniotic fluid is removed, to check on the location and viability of the fetus.

While both amniocentesis and CVS are considered safe and effective, they are not without their difficulties and risks. As with many diagnostic tests, there is a risk of false positives (i.e., an incorrect diagnosis that something is wrong). Both of these tests carry a risk of miscarriage — the risk is slightly higher in CVS. Comparative studies of the two methods of testing have, however, reported that the differences are not statistically significant (Canadian Collaborative CVS-Amniocentesis Clinical Trial Group, 1989, 1992). The risk of miscarriage is approximately 1 percent (Daker & Bobrow, 1989), although some studies report higher rates of miscarriage than this. Two recently reported studies have suggested a link between CVS and limb deformities (*Newsweek*, 1992). Critics of this research suggest that the finding of a higher incidence of limb deformities is an anomaly not substantiated in other controlled clinical trials.

One of the major difficulties with amniocentesis has to do with when the procedure is performed (Katz Rothman, 1988). Once a sample has been removed, it must be cultured and the cells analyzed. This process can take up to four weeks, and the waiting period has been found to be fraught with worry for most couples. Should an abnormality be discovered, then a woman (or couple) will need to make a decision as to whether to continue the pregnancy. If she/they decide to terminate the pregnancy, the woman will have to endure a second-trimester abortion, in which she will have labour induced, and she will usually deliver a dead fetus (Rapp, 1984, 1987, 1989; Katz Rothman, 1988). The timing problems of amniocentesis led to the development of CVS. CVS has its own timing problems (Daker & Bobrow, 1989). There is a high rate of spontaneous abortion in the first trimester, test or no test. Furthermore, when ambiguous findings occur with a CVS test, a woman may be referred for an amniocentesis at sixteen weeks. Consequently, yet another invasive procedure will be performed during her pregnancy.

Several commentators have focussed on who is referred for, and has access to, PND (Lippman, 1986, 1991). Normally, one's family history will indicate whether there is a risk of genetic abnormality (e.g., Huntington's disease, cystic fibrosis, some forms of muscular dystrophy). Race and ethnic background may also figure in an assessment of one's risk status — for example, people of African descent have a heightened susceptibility to sickle cell anemia, and Jews of Eastern European (Ashkenazi) descent are prone to Tay Sachs disease (Duster, 1990). In the United States, there have been reports of African Americans experiencing discrimination in connection with PND testing for sickle cell anemia (Duster, 1990). PND for these risks groups is not mandatory, though strongly advised, given the potential health consequences of the aforementioned diseases (sickle cell anemia can be very disabling and Tay Sachs is lethal).

In the last few decades, maternal age has been defined as another risk factor (Elias & Annas, 1987). Genetic research found that with increasing maternal age, there was a greater risk of Down's syndrome. Originally, women aged 40 and over were classified as being high risk (i.e., of advanced maternal age). Today, women aged 35 years and older are routinely referred for PND. The criterion is an arbitrary one, and recently it has been recommended that women 30 years of age will soon be classified as "old." One wonders whether, before long, amniocentesis or CVS will be recommended for all pregnant women!

On the issue of access, it should be noted that a disproportionate number of women using PND (particularly among women of advanced maternal age) are drawn from the higher socio-economic classes (Golbus et al., 1979). Lippman (1991) suggests that the way in which PND is currently offered and used could very well lead to an exacerbation of social inequalities, as the affluent are tested (for many reasons, not necessarily related to the direct costs of screening), while the less affluent and members of some minorities are less likely to be screened. This could lead to the multiplication of stigmatized characteristics (e.g., poor, visible minority, disabled).

According to recent estimates, the number of Canadian women referred for prenatal testing exceeded 22 000 in 1990 (Hamerton & Evans, 1992). Compared to a decade ago, this represents a significant increase in the use of PND. Generally speaking, approximately 50 percent of all pregnant women who are referred for PND actually undergo testing (Elias & Annas, 1987; Daker & Bobrow, 1989). Despite the extensive use of PND, relatively few social and psychological studies have been conducted on the users and refusers of this technology in Canada.

No one disputes the usefulness of PND in identifying potentially debilitating or lethal diseases. However, some would argue that PND has also created the means whereby people can pursue the quest for a "perfect baby" (Chadwick, 1987). Disability rights activists worry that PND is being used for eugenic purposes, and to that end, such testing may lead to even greater intolerance and stigmatization of people with disabilities (Asch, 1988; Asch & Fine, 1988; Saxton, 1987, 1989; Oliver, 1990). Besides, they and others point out, most of the current methods of testing can only tell us a limited amount of information — for example, amniocentesis and CVS can tell the risk of having a child with Down's syndrome, but there is no way of knowing how severe the disability will be, nor whether the child will suffer mostly an intellectual impairment or a physical disability or both.

One final issue regarding PND that merits comment concerns the use of these tests for sex selection. The technology has been developed to separate the X and Y sperm to prevent the transmission of various hereditary diseases. Such therapeutic use of this NRT seldom generates concern. However, the same is not true of the non-therapeutic (and potentially dangerous) use to which such technologies are put, for example, to select the sex of the fetus. In some cultures, the desirability of having sons is well documented (Corea, 1985; Chadwick, 1987). In society at large, there have been reports of couples wishing to control the birth order of male and female children (i.e., an older son, followed by a younger daughter). Critics of this technology claim that PND with selective abortion on the basis of fetal sex could amount to "gynicide," that is, "the use of deliberate systematic measures (as killing, bodily or mental injury, unlivable conditions, prevention of births) calculated to bring about the extermination of women" (Corea, 1985, p. 194). The use of PND in this way helps to ensure a system of patriarchal domination and control. Sherwin says that "catering to gender preferences that have been created in a world which is oppressive to women is likely to reify gender differences found in sexist society and lead to more unquestioning acceptance and exaggeration of these tendencies" (1989, p. 268).

PND clearly has found a place in obstetrical practice, and will likely expand in the years to come. This is because of a new initiative, the Human Genome Project (Beckwith, 1991), which has been funded by several Western governments, including Canada. This research aims to map the genetic structure of humans, thereby identifying the location of various traits. The Human Genome Project will open up a new area of "predictive medicine," in which testing could identify genetic susceptibilities to various diseases and morbid conditions. But Rowland (1992), among others, has raised questions as to whether the Human Genome Project will simply lead to each of us being given "genetic credentials." That such information might result in various forms of discrimination (in the workplace, when we seek health or life insurance, etc.) and breaches of civil liberties is not beyond the realm of possibility (Council for Responsible Genetics, 1990). In other words, "a eugenic dynamic could develop" with these technologies (NAC, 1991, p. 284).

Genetic Interventions

The final category of NRT includes all of the methods of genetic engineering. Included here are the methods of gene mapping already discussed briefly, along with other forms of genetic manipulation and gene transfer (Harris, 1992). Some of the research being done in this area is entirely therapeutic, such as surgery to replace defective genes for healthy ones. Research into Parkinson's disease has shown that the use of brain tissue from aborted fetuses might alleviate the symptoms of this debilitating condition. Such interventions are not without controversy, however. For example, many countries prohibit the use of fetal tissue in this type of research, and those opposed to abortion are fierce objectors to such interventions.

Genetic manipulations involving transgenic transfer (between human and animal species) have also generated some concern. Though researchers involved in such experiments claim that their work is intended strictly for therapeutic uses, or to make a better world (manipulation of genetic material in plants and animals might lead to improvements in the quality or the overall yield of these commodities), some critics worry that a slippery slope leading to scientific and social nightmares might soon be descended. To be sure, we have enough lessons from history of the evil uses to which science has already been put (Hubbard, 1986; Chadwick, 1987; Coney, 1988; Jones, 1981). The question is: will we be wise enough to learn from past tragedies?

The Implications of NRT: A Reason to Celebrate or a Reason to Worry?

As the foregoing discussion has shown, the term NRT includes a wide range of different technologies. It follows then that there are many different questions that arise regarding the various NRT. Instead of looking further at each type of technology, it is instructive to consider the implications of NRT in general. Debate about these technologies comes from a number of corners, but clearly the most vociferous criticism has originated in feminist literature. Broadly speaking, the two issues most often cited by feminist critics concern the physical and other health consequences of NRT, and the social implications of NRT.

Scepticism about the health consequences of some NRT is, by all counts, well founded. The title of a recently published book on NRT, *Living Laboratories* (Rowland, 1992), aptly describes women's bodies as the test sites for experiments in IVF. Many feminist health activists remind us of the less than stellar history of medical interventions into women's bodies, and the consequences of the medicalization of women's lives (Ehrenreich & English, 1978; Kohler Riessman, 1983). One need only look at women's experiences with other medical interventions — thalidomide, DES, Depo Provera, hormone replacement therapy, and even the contraceptive pill — to understand why some researchers and health activists are so apprehensive about NRT. Many technologies that are widely used in medicine today have not been adequately evaluated, as McKinlay (1982) and Cohen and Rothschild (1979) have pointed out. Somehow (and it is no accident), technological innovations have quickly become incorporated into medical practice, without sufficient testing to ensure efficacy and long-term safety (Bunker, 1985). This is true, despite regulatory agencies such as the Laboratory Centre for Disease Control in Ottawa, and the Food and Drug Administration in the United States. Once something has become integrated into medical practice, it is not likely to be abandoned — even when the flimsiest of evidence has provided the technology with a basis for adoption. Consider the recent case involving the silicon breast implant (Regush, 1991).

As noted previously, there is good reason to worry about the physical health consequences of the drug regimens used in IVF programs. Little research has been done on the long-term effects of the hormone cocktails. What research does exist clearly indicates that the combination of drugs is often an assault on women's bodies (Klein & Rowland, 1988). The comparison between clomiphene citrate and DES has already been reported (Rowland, 1992). In the 1950s, DES was billed as "a wonder drug." A generation later, DES was described as "the wonder drug we should wonder about." Is this what we will be saying in the years to come about the drugs women receive in IVF programs? Ann Rochon Ford (1986, pp. 39-40) says:

> it is incumbent upon us to examine at what cost . . . medical advances have been made. In our lifetime, we have seen birth deformities from thalidomide, vaginal cancer from DES and infertility from the Dalkon Shield IUD. How many more discoveries like these will it take before the parties involved — the pharmaceutical industry, doctors, and patients — realize that they are part of a continuum? . . . [W]e must challenge the claim that [medical advances] are always for our own good.

In addition to the potentially iatrogenic diseases of this "treatment," there are also the risks of infection (and where relevant, postoperative complications) from the various invasive procedures that women typically undergo in IVF programs.[7] Should a pregnancy result, evidence shows that most women are classified as "high risk," which becomes a catchword for additional interventions during labour and delivery (Kohler Riessman, 1983). For instance, in Australia, the National Perinatal Statistics Unit reported that the incidence of Caesarean section was significantly higher in IVF deliveries, as compared to natural conceptions (cited in Rowland, 1992, p. 46).

The list of adverse health effects of NRT is not restricted to the physical. One could make just as compelling an argument that the psychological and emotional consequences of NRT exact a significant toll as well. I am reminded of a young woman interviewed on *The Journal* (on CBC), who remarked that she worried about what kind of person she might become if she didn't have a child of her own. Rather than turning the question against herself (as many involuntarily childless individuals do), perhaps it would be useful to look outward. We might also ask for answers about the causes and sources of infertility. Can we prevent infertility? How do assaults on our environment adversely affect fertility?

We might also ask what kind of society would foster such an oppressive system of values that makes individuals believe that they are not whole persons without biological parenthood. Research on women in IVF programs indicates that there are strong pressures to remain in the programs, to keep on trying (Klein, 1989). In a society as pronatalist as ours, there are constant reminders to the infertile of how their bodies have failed them. According to Rowland (1992), it is only a short step for infertile women to embrace a negative self-image. The language to describe the infertile — "barren" — speaks volumes!

The health consequences of NRT do not only affect women, and do not only concern IVF. As there have been more births resulting from NRT, questions have been raised about the consequences for the children born as a result of insemination, surrogacy arrangements, and IVF. What effect will knowledge that one is the product of an anonymous sperm (or egg) donor have on future generations? What will be the impact of court battles when surrogacy contracts go sour, as happened in the Mary Beth Whitehead and William and Elizabeth Stern ("Baby M") case in New Jersey (Harrison, 1987; Katz Rothman, 1987) and the more recent case in California involving Crispina and Mark Calvert and Anna Johnson (Annas, 1991)?

Such questions touch on some of the social implications of NRT. Of particular interest are two interrelated issues: the definition of biological personhood and the definition of parenthood. A child born as a result of NRT might very well have difficulty answering the question "who am I?" By the same token, who will be the child's parents? Betty Lifton, writing about how children will experience the effects of NRT (1988, p. 151), poses the following questions:

Who is my real mother? Who is my real father? Who is the authentic mother? Who is the authentic father? Must a real mother be genetically related? Does a man have the right to detach himself without responsibility from his sperm? And . . . is genetic relatedness necessary for an authentic sense of self?

She goes further in presenting her scenario of the "brave new baby" by asking:

what if he learns that his mother's egg and his father's sperm met in a saucer and he shacked up in a stranger's womb? Would the woman in whose womb he was implanted, on whose body fluid he fattened, on whose umbilical cord he clung, but to whom he was not genetically related, be a stranger, or would she be his mother? What if the brave new baby learns that his father took money as an anonymous donor to a sperm bank or paid money to have his sperm impregnate an anonymous woman? Can a child endure having an anonymous father or an anonymous mother? Would that child feel anonymous or unborn, as many adoptees do? What if he learns that he had a surrogate mother who carried him for a price in her womb and gave him up like a piece of merchandise after he was born? (1988, p. 151; non-inclusive language in original)

With NRT, there are several types of mothers and fathers possible: social and biological (as in the traditional nuclear family); social, but not biological (as in the case of step- or adoptive parents); and biological, but not social (such as when, because of a divorce, a parent is not involved in the raising of the child). To these we add, for women, the question of one's role in gestation. The various combinations and permutations allow for a total of seven types of mothers: traditional mother (uterine, genetic, and social); adoptive or stepmother (social, but not uterine or genetic); birth mother who gives up her child voluntarily or involuntarily or by virtue of a surrogacy contract (uterine and genetic, but not social); egg donor (genetic, but not uterine or social); recipient of a fertilized egg (uterine and social, but not genetic); embryo carrier (uterine, but not genetic or social); and user of an embryo carrier (genetic and social, but not uterine) (Henifen, 1988; Boult, 1990).

Some writers have suggested that these perplexing questions on personhood and parenthood show that public policy has failed to keep up with technology (Yoxen, 1990; Haimes, 1990). (This applies to other medical technologies, for example, the artificial heart.) Our experience with NRT reveals that when public policy lags in the face of revolutionary technological change, it is expedient to hold on to the past. Britain's Warnock Committee recommended that "as a general rule it is better for children to be born into a two-parent family, with both father and mother, although we recognize it is impossible to predict with any certainty how lasting such a relationship might be" (1985, pp. 11-12). Such thinking, which is not unique to Britain, has led to restrictions on access to NRT to those who can best conform to a purely normative and ideological view of the family. But the trouble is that such a view is based on a romantic notion of "the family" that applies less and less to Canadian families.

Furthermore, observations such as these illustrate how problematic NRT are for women as a social group. At the beginning of this chapter, I mentioned the paradoxical nature of NRT, in terms of the competing interests of individual women, as compared to women as a collective. For women whose biological destiny at another time in history might have been to remain childless (or to become an adoptive parent), the miracles of medicine today are such that they can be offered a chance to "beat" their infertility. When the Royal Commission on New Reproductive Technologies travelled across Canada in the fall of 1991, it was not uncommon to hear women enrolled in IVF programs say that they were prepared to subject their bodies and their selves to the drug regimens because "some chance of having a baby was better than no chance." For these women, using IVF (or other NRT) is a matter of personal choice. However, we should be mindful of the choices available to us, as well as the implications those choices will have for all of us.

While not necessarily contending that women who use NRT (and in particular IVF) have been duped, many feminist critics argue that women stand to lose more than they stand to gain by using NRT (Rowland, 1992; Corea, 1985; Klein, 1991; Spallone, 1989; Pauly Morgan, 1989). Steinberg (1990), among others, has described the gendered values of NRT. These technologies have been developed and are used predominantly by male doctors. Even where women are involved as researchers or practitioners, it is undeniable that the community within which they work reflects the patriarchal culture of medicine. Furthermore, despite the advances Canadian women have enjoyed as a result of social and legal change in the past few decades, their status is not at parity with men's, and there are numerous examples one could cite showing a backlash against women's quest for equality (Faludi, 1991). Canadian women continue to experience domination and control — in the workplace, in their homes, in the health-care system. Do NRT simply objectify women's bodies, and commodify motherhood? Do NRT reinforce the alienating view that women are simply vessels (incubators)?

Yoxen (1990) has commented that an "over-individualized notion of the embryo" has emerged with the development of NRT. This idea holds that individual-like properties have been conferred on the embryo. Accordingly, we have begun to see cases in which women's rights have come into conflict with those of the fetus — where women have been compelled to undergo forced Caesarean sections (Annas, 1982, 1986, 1991; Maier, 1989), or where women stand accused of (or have been charged with) fetal abuse for not accessing PND with selective abortion, when they could have, to prevent the birth of a person with a disability. In some instances, there have even been "wrongful life" lawsuits filed against parents (Henifen et al., 1988).

It is abundantly clear that NRT contribute to the further subordination and devaluation of women. The technology has already begun to remove women (either metaphysically, or even ultimately, physically) from reproduction, while (mostly male) scientists go about "making babies." Klein notes that "people, and specifically women, are thus reduced to body parts that can be fragmented, dissected, and recombined at will" (1991, p. 394).

Though NRT are presented to us as a boon — the salvation of the infertile — we would do well to think carefully, critically, and historically about whether these technologies will disempower women (in particular), and foster a "disabling dependence" on medicine (Illich, 1976). Cynthia Carver (1989, p. 56) asks:

> are we as a society promoting these procedures, fostering a fanatical need for pregnancy, exalting the desirability of a "child of one's own" no matter how tenuous the connection of that child to the "parents" and thus creating a research and technological monster with large expenditures and little potential gain to society as a whole?

Before accepting the claim that NRT are a boon, we must insist on rigorous evaluation of these technologies, and a critical social dialogue on the merits and implications of NRT for all of us.

Notes

1. DES was given to women in the 1950s and 1960s to prevent miscarriage. In the decades that followed, it was discovered that many of the children of DES mothers had developed rare forms of cancer and had other reproductive difficulties, including infertility. The irony of DES daughters using IVF does not escape the critics of NRT.
2. In 1989, the Canadian government struck a Royal Commission on New Reproductive Technologies. The mandate of this commission was extensive: to conduct an inquiry into, and make recommendations regarding, the social, ethical, legal, health, and economic implications of NRT for women, men, and society as a whole. The royal commission conducted public hearings across the country in 1990 and 1991, and sponsored a substantial program of research. Its report to government is due to be released in July 1993.
3. Methods have been developed to separate the X and Y sperm, thus ensuring that sex-linked diseases such as bleeding diseases and some forms of muscular dystrophy are not transmitted from one generation to the next. The development of this technique for separating chromosomes has found application for non–disease-related sex selection, about which there is considerable controversy.
4. Take note of the language used in this field. Many NRT were developed in the field of agriculture. The prototypes come from animal husbandry. Corea cautions us that "women may find that the connection men have made for centuries between women and animals still lives on in patriarchal minds, just as it lives on in men's laws and practices. Women and animals remain parts of nature to be controlled and subjugated" (1985, p. 313).
5. At a conference in Melbourne, Australia in May 1992, a woman who had been on superovulatory drugs in an IVF program, and had shortly thereafter developed a virulent form of breast cancer, reported being told by a clinician that "some women get cancer after being on these drugs, and some women just get cancer." The suggestion was,

in other words, that there is no necessary connection between exposure to the superovulatory drugs and cancer.

6. As of this writing, the Rios embryos remain frozen (though their viability after this time is the subject of much conjecture). The ultimate fate of these embryos is hardly inconsequential, since the Rioses left a $7 million (U.S.) estate.

7. Although one often reads about "couples" in IVF programs, we should not forget that it is women's bodies that are the focus of medical intervention even when the source of infertility resides with the male partner. Men may find masturbating into a bottle embarrassing (Beck-Gernsheim, 1989), but who knows what future toll women's bodies will take as a consequence of their exposure to the drugs and procedures used in IVF. What is more, to speak about couples rather than women only serves to render women invisible in this process (Steinberg, 1990).

Study Questions

1. Why is the label NRT inappropriate when describing these technological innovations?

2. What are the health and social implications of NRT such as artificial insemination, in vitro fertilization, and surrogacy? Are there circumstances in which these technologies should or should not be available for use? Who should decide such questions?

3. You have been hired as a consultant to the ministry of health. How would you direct the minister on NRT? Would you recommend a moratorium on NRT developments and research and clinical practice using NRT? Why or why not? What would you recommend the government health department do to deal with infertility?

4. What impact do NRT have on women individually and collectively? How do we reconcile these two potentially competing sets of interests?

5. The best thing about NRT is _____. The worst thing about NRT is _____. Discuss your statements.

Recommended Reading

McNeil, M., Varcoe, I., & Yearley, S. (Eds.). (1990). *The new reproductive technologies*. London: Macmillan.

Overall, C. (1987). *Ethics and human reproduction*. Winchester: Allen and Unwin.

Overall, C. (Ed.). (1989). *The future of human reproduction*. Toronto: Women's Press.

Rowland, R. (1992). *Living laboratories: women and reproductive technologies*. Sydney: Pan Macmillan.

Stanworth, M. (Ed.). (1987). *Reproductive technologies: Gender, motherhood and medicine*. Oxford: Polity Press.

References

Albury, R.M. (1986). Babies kept on ice: Aspects of the Australian press coverage of IVF. *Australian Feminist Studies*, 4, 43-71.

Annas, G.J. (1982). Forced cesareans: The most unkindest cut of all. *Hastings Center Report*, 12, 16-17, 45.

Annas, G.J. (1986). Pregnant women as fetal containers. *Hastings Center Report*, 16, 13-14.

Annas, G.J. (1991). Crazy making: Embryos and gestational mothers. *Hastings Center Report*, 21, 35-38.

Asch, A. (1988). Reproductive technology and disability. In N. Taub & S. Cohen (Eds.), *Reproductive laws for the 1990s* (pp. 59-101). Newark: Women's Rights Litigation Clinic, School of Law, Rutgers University.

Asch, A., & Fine, M. (1988). Shared dreams: A left perspective on disability rights and reproductive rights. In M. Fine & A. Asch (Eds.), *Women with disabilities: Essays in psychology, culture, and politics* (pp. 297-305). Philadelphia: Temple University Press.

Atwood, M. (1985). *The handmaid's tale*. Toronto: McClelland and Stewart.

Banks, K. (1991). Baby chase. *Equinox*, 57, 76-92.

Beck-Gernsheim, E. (1989). From the pill to test-tube babies: New options, new pressures in reproductive behavior. In K. Strother Ratcliff (Ed.), *Healing technology:*

Feminist perspectives (pp. 23-40). Ann Arbor: University of Michigan Press.

Beckwith, J. (1991). Foreward: The human genome initiative: genetics' lightning rod. *American Journal of Law and Medicine*, 17, 1-13.

Boult, B.E. (1990). The need to define the terms "parent" and "parenthood." *Medicine and Law*, 9, 1028-1035.

Bradish P. (1987). From genetic counseling and genetic analysis, to genetic ideal and genetic fate? In P. Spallone & D.L. Steinberg (Eds.), *Made to order: The myth of reproductive and genetic progress* (pp. 94-101). Oxford: Pergamon Press.

Bryant, H. (1990). *The infertility dilemma*. Ottawa: The Canadian Advisory Council on the Status of Women.

Bunker J. (1985, April 25). When doctors disagree. *New York Review of Books*, 32, 7-12.

Canadian Collaborative CVS-Amniocentesis Clinical Trial Group (1992). Canadian multicentre randomized clinical trial of chorionic villus sampling and amniocentesis. Final report. *Prenatal diagnosis*, 12, 385-476.

Canadian Collaborative CVS-Amniocentesis Clinical Trial Group (1989). Multicentre randomized clinical trial of chorionic villi sampling and amniocentesis. *The Lancet*, 1, 1-6.

Carver, C. (1989). The new — and debatable — reproductive technologies. In C. Overall (Ed.), *The future of human reproduction* (pp. 46-57). Toronto: Women's Press.

Chadwick, R. (Ed.). (1987). *Ethics, reproduction and genetic control*. New York: Routledge, Chapman and Hall.

Clapp, D., & Swenson, N. (1984). Infertility and pregnancy loss. In The Boston Women's Health Book Collective (Eds.) *The new our bodies ourselves* (pp. 419-431). New York: Simon and Schuster.

Cohen, L., & Rothschild H. (1979, Summer). The bandwagons of medicine. *Perspectives in biology and medicine*, 531-538.

Coney, S. (1988). *The unfortunate experiment*. Auckland: Penguin.

Corea, G. (1985). *The mother machine: Reproductive technologies from artificial insemination to artificial wombs*. New York: Harper and Row.

Council for Responsible Genetics. (1990). Position paper. *Issues in Reproductive and Genetic Engineering*, 3, 287-295.

Daker, M., & Bobrow, M. (1989). Screening for genetic disease and fetal anomaly during pregnancy. In I. Chalmers, M. Enkin, & M.J.N.C. Keirse (Eds.), *Effective care in pregnancy and childbirth (Vol. 1: Pregnancy, Parts I-V*, pp. 366-381). Oxford: Oxford University Press.

Duster T. (1990). *Backdoor to eugenics*. New York: Routledge.

Ehrenreich, B., & English, D. (1978). *For her own good: 150 years of the experts' advice to women*. New York: Doubleday.

Eichler, M. (1991). *Human rights and the new reproductive technologies: Individual or collective choices?* Toronto: Unpublished manuscript.

Elias, S., & Annas, G.J. (1987). *Reproductive genetics and the law*. Chicago: Year Book Medical Publishers.

Faludi, S. (1991). *Backlash: The undeclared war against American women*. New York: Crown.

Golbus, M.S., Loughman, W.D., Epstein, C.J., Halbasch, G., Stephens, J.D., & Hall, B.D. (1979). Prenatal genetic diagnosis in 3000 amniocenteses. *The New England Journal of Medicine*, 300, 157-163.

Greenberg F. (1988). The impact of MSAPF screening on genetic services, 1984-1986. *American Journal of Medical Genetics*, 31, 223-230.

Gupta, J.A. (1991). Women's bodies: The site for the ongoing conquest by reproductive technologies. *Issues in Reproductive and Genetic Engineering*, 4, 93-107.

Haimes, E. (1990). Recreating the family? Policy considerations relating to the "new" reproductive technologies. In M. McNeil, I. Varcoe, & S. Yearley (Eds.), *The new reproductive technologies* (pp. 154-172). London: Macmillan.

Hamerton, J., & Evans, J. (1992, Summer). Personal communication, Winnipeg.

Harris, J. (1992). *Wonderwoman and superman: The ethics of human biotechnology*. Oxford: Oxford University Press.

Harrison, M. (1987). Social construction of Mary Beth Whitehead. *Gender and Society*, 1, 300-311.

Henifen, M.S. (1988). Introduction. In E. Hoffman Baruch, A.F.D'Adamo, Jr., & J. Seager (Eds.), *Women's health and the new reproductive technologies* (pp. 1-7). New York: Haworth Press.

Henifen, M.S., Hubbard, R., & Norsigian J. (1988). Prenatal screening. In N. Taub, S. Cohen (Eds.), *Reproductive laws for the 1990s* (pp. 129-154). Newark: Women's Rights Litigation Clinic, School of Law, Rutgers University.

Hubbard, R. (1986). Eugenics and prenatal testing. *International Journal of Health Services*, 16, 227-242.

Huxley, A. (1946). *Brave new world*. New York: Harper and Brothers.

Illich, I. (1976). *Medical nemesis*. New York: Bantam Books.

Is my baby all right? (1992, June 22). *Newsweek*, pp. 54-55.

Jones, J.H. (1981). *Bad blood: The Tuskegee syphilis experiment*. New York: Free Press.

Katz Rothman, B. (1987). Comment on harrison: The commodification of motherhood. *Gender and Society*, 1, 312-316.

Katz Rothman, B. (1988). *The tentative pregnancy: Prenatal diagnosis and the future of motherhood*. London: Pandora Press/Unwin Paperbacks.

Klein, R. (1991). Women as body parts in the era of reproductive and genetic engineering. *Health Care for Women International*, 12, 393-405.

Klein, R. (Ed.). (1989). *Infertility: Women speak out about their experiences of reproductive medicine*. London: Pandora Press.

Klein, R., & Rowland, R. (1988). Women as test-sites for fertility drugs: Clomiphene citrate and hormonal cocktails. *Issues in Reproductive and Genetic Engineering*, 1, 251-273.

Kohler Riessman, C. (1983). Women and medicalization: A new perspective. *Social Policy*, 14, 3-18.

Lifton, B.J. (1988). Brave new baby in the brave new world. In E. Hoffman Baruch, A.F. D'Adamo Jr. & J. Seager (Eds.), *Embryos, ethics, and women's rights: Exploring the new reproductive technologies*. New York: Haworth Press, 1988.

Lippman, A. (1986). Access to prenatal screening services: Who decides? *Canadian Journal of Women and the Law*, 1, 434-445.

Lippman, A. (1991). Prenatal genetic testing and screening: Constructing needs and reinforcing inequities. *American Journal of Law and Medicine*, 17, 15-50.

Maier, K.E. (1989). Pregnant women: Fetal containers or people with rights? *Affilia*, 4, 8-20.

McKinlay, J.B. (1982). From 'promising report' to 'standard procedure': Seven stages in the career of a medical innovation. In J.B. McKinlay (Ed.), *Technology and the future of health care* (pp. 233-270). Cambridge: MIT Press.

National Action Committee on the Status of Women (NAC). (1991). The new reproductive technologies: A technological handmaid's tale. *Issues in Reproductive and Genetic Engineering*, 4, 279-296.

Oliver, M. (1990). *The politics of disablement*. London: Macmillan.

Orwell, G. (1949). *1984*. New York: Signet.

Paez-Victor, M.E. (1988). *Risks and values: A study of the social context of prenatal diagnosis and counselling*. Unpublished Ph.D. Dissertation. York University: Downsview, Ontario.

Pauly Morgan, K. (1989). Of woman born? How old-fashioned! — New reproductive technologies and women's oppression. In C. Overall (Ed.), *The future of human reproduction* (pp. 60-79). Toronto: Women's Press.

Rapp, R. (1984, April). The ethics of choice: After my amniocentesis, Mike and I faced the toughest decision of our lives. *Ms.*, pp. 97-100.

Rapp, R. (1987). Moral pioneers: Women, men and fetuses on a frontier of reproductive technology. *Women and Health*, 13, 101-116.

Rapp, R. (1989). XYLO: A true story. In R. Arditti, R. Duelli Klein, & S. Minden (Eds.), *Test-tube women: What future for motherhood* (pp. 313-328). London: Pandora Press.

Regush, N. (1991, April). Health and welfare's national disgrace. *Saturday Night*, pp. 9-18, 62-63.

Rehner, J. (1989). *Infertility: Old myths, new meanings*. Toronto: Second Story Press.

Rochon Ford, A. (1986). Hormones: Getting out of hand. In K. McDonnell (Ed.), *Adverse effects: Women and the pharmaceutical industry* (pp. 27-40). Toronto: Women's Press.

Rowland, R. (1992). *Living laboratories: Women and reproductive technologies*. Sydney: Pan Macmillan.

Saxton, M. (1987). Prenatal screening and discriminatory attitudes about disability. *Women and Health*, 13, 217-224.

Saxton, M. (1989). Born and unborn: The implications of reproductive technologies for people with disabilities. In R. Arditti, R. Duelli Klein, & S. Minden (Eds.), *Test-tube women: What future for motherhood* (pp. 298-312). London: Pandora Press.

Sherwin, S. (1989). Feminist ethics and new reproductive technologies. In C. Overall (Ed.), *The future of human reproduction* (pp. 259-272). Toronto: Women's Press.

Solomon, A. (1988). Integrating infertility crisis counselling into feminist practice. *Issues in Reproductive and Genetic Engineering*, 1, 41-49.

Spallone, P. (1989). *Beyond conception: The new politics of reproduction*. Granby: Bergin & Garvey.

Steinberg, D.L. (1990). The depersonalisation of women through the administration of 'in vitro fertilisation'. In M. McNeil, I. Varcoe, & S. Yearley (Eds.), *The new reproductive technologies* (pp. 74-122). London: Macmillan.

Strickler, J. (1992). The new reproductive technology: Problem or solution? *Sociology of Health and Illness*, 14, 111-132.

Warnock, M. (1985). *A question of life: The Warnock report on human fertilisation and embryology*. Oxford: Basil Blackwell.

Wikler, D., & Wikler, N.J. (1991). Turkey-baster babies: The demedicalization of artificial insemination. *The Milbank Quarterly*, 69, 5-40.

Yoxen, E. (1990). Conflicting concerns: The political context of recent embryo research policy in Britain. In M. McNeil, I. Varcoe & S. Yearley (Eds.), *The new reproductive technologies* (pp. 173-199). London: Macmillan.

Part Five

Health Care
and
the Elderly

Part Five

Introduction

The demographic profile of Canadian society is changing rapidly. It is projected that by the turn of the century the elderly will constitute a significant proportion of the population. Also, the proportion of those commonly referred to as the "old old" or "frail old" is increasing among the elderly group. The increase of the elderly population has important implications for the planning and delivery of health-care services.

It should be noted, however, that the elderly population is by no means homogeneous. Socio-economic status, age, and gender influence the need for health care and other services. In addition to socio-economic diversity and gender, ethnic and cultural differences associated with the process of aging must be taken into account when considering health-related issues. Ujimoto, in Chapter 18, examines the relationship between aging, ethnicity, and health.

Ujimoto argues that an understanding of what is meant by ethnicity is important to an understanding of differential adjustment to aging by ethnic minorities, and for an understanding of their attitudes and behaviour towards aging from a health-care perspective. While the concept of ethnicity can be viewed in several ways, Ujimoto emphasizes that the systematic or integrative approach that draws upon the different conceptions of ethnicity is necessary to comprehend the dynamics of the aging process as it relates to the health status and general well-being of the elderly.

Regardless of ethnic, racial, and cultural differences, all elderly people face some common health problems. There is a normal decline in physical, mental, and functional ability with advancing age. However, as Ujimoto points out, ethnic and cultural differences are important in relation to perceptions of personal health and illness, perceptions of the "seriousness" of the problem, responses to illness, health status, utilization of services, and coping responses and medications used to "manage" physical and psychological stress or illness.

Ujimoto argues that it is important for health-care professionals and other "providers" of health care to recognize ethnic or cultural peculiarities in order to avoid any "cultural misunderstandings." This requires a greater sensitivity to the cultural dimensions of how illnesses are viewed in different ethnic groups. In this regard, an excellent start has been made by the Multicultural Health Coalition in Ontario and Doctors' Hospital in Toronto.

While Ujimoto provides a broader discussion of aging, ethnicity, and health, the focus in Chapter 19 by Tarman is on the elderly, specifically in terms of health-care policy and institutional care.

A variety of institutions provide social and health services for the elderly. Despite the importance of such care, in particular for the "old old" group, there is no uniform and coherent Canadian policy or set of regulations to govern the accommodation standards, funding arrangements, and quality of care. Other than certain conditions that have to be met to retain eligibility for federal cost-sharing arrangements, provinces more or less set their own requirements for the operation and funding arrangements of special-care facilities for the elderly.

Evidence shows that a large number of special-care facilities in Canada are privately owned. There is considerable variation by province in type of ownership.

The discussion on the development of health policy regarding nursing homes in Ontario indicates that the provincial policy has not been oriented toward a complete transformation of the nursing home industry. The provincial government for the most part has been content to "regulate" the industry by requiring certain accommodation and health standards. Though these requirements have had beneficial results, they have also led to an increase in the number and size of facilities with private and corporate ownership. This situation has proved to be advantageous for larger units, enabling them to make large profits. The critics charge that the profit motive is incompatible with quality of care; they advocate the complete transformation of all health-care institutions for the aged to public non-profit facilities.

Chapter 18

Aging, Ethnicity, and Health

K. Victor Ujimoto, University of Guelph

Introduction

It is a well-recognized fact that the demographic profile of Canadian society is changing rapidly. Stone and Fletcher (1980, p. 8) and McDaniel (1986, p. 36) have shown that the proportion of our elderly population has been increasing consistently since 1901. Health and Welfare Canada (1983, p. 12) reports that only 5 percent of the total Canadian population was over 65 years of age in 1901, but by 1981, this proportion had increased to 9.7 percent. Stone and Fletcher (1980, p. 10) predict that the population over 65 will continue to grow until 2016, at which time it is expected to decline. Indeed, recent Statistics Canada (1990) data tend to support this observation. They report that as of 1991, the proportion of the population aged 65 and over is anticipated to be around 11 percent, a 3.7 percent increase since 1971. Statistics Canada (1990) further notes that between 2001 and 2011, the greatest increase will occur in the age 55 to 64 category, an increase from 9.7 percent to 13.1 percent. Subsequently, between 2011 and 2021, this increase will be shifted to the 65 to 74 age category, an increase from 8.3 percent to 11.3 percent. This means that in terms of numbers at least, the elderly are becoming a more significant group today than ever before, and they will continue to have an important impact on Canadian society with reference to issues relating to pension benefits, health, and health systems.

There is another important aspect of demographic change that is occurring — the multicultural nature of Canadian society. This is illustrated in Figures 1a and 1b. The

Figure 1a   Ethnic Origins, Canada, 1986

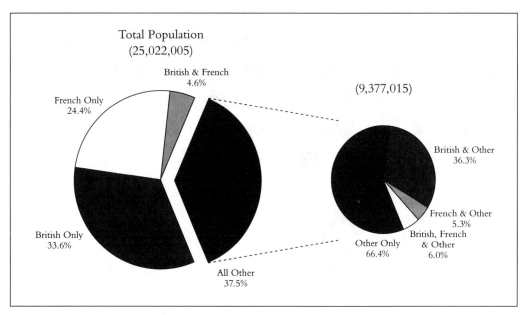

Source: Ledoux, M., & Pendakur, R. (1990). *Multicultural Canada: A Graphic Overview*. Ottawa: Policy and Research Directorate, Multiculturalism Sector, Multiculturalism and Citizenship Canada, p. 7.

aging population is no longer homogeneous, and the ethnic cultural differences associated with the processes of aging must be taken into account when considering health-related issues. The heterogeneity of our aging population is illustrated in Figures 2 and 3. In Figure 2, the 1986 census data reflect a relatively low visible minority age group in the 65 years and over category. Eventually, those who are currently in the 25 to 44 and 46 to 64 age categories will shift into the seniors category. Similarly, in Figure 3, the aboriginal population in relation to the total Canadian population is shown for the various age categories. If the social, economic, and health conditions for the aboriginal populations improve as expected, there should be a reflection of this in the 45 to 64 and 65 years and over age categories in the future.

The heterogeneity of Canadian society is further illustrated by the 1986 census data, which are shown in Figure 4. In Figure 4, the most frequently reported ethnic origins other than the British or French in Canada are provided. It should be noted, however, that the most frequently reported ethnic origins vary across regions and thus future social and health-care policies should recognize this regional variation. These variations in reported ethnic origins are shown in Figures 5a and 5b. In the Atlantic region, the German, Dutch, and aboriginal groups are the highest. In Quebec, the Italian, Jewish, and aboriginals are the largest and in Ontario, the German, Italian, and Dutch. The

Figure 1b   Visible Minority Groups, Canada, 1986

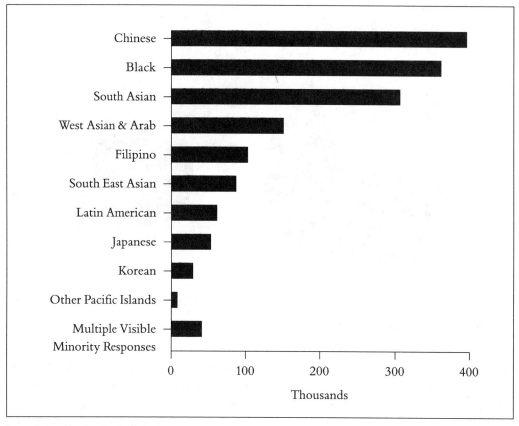

Source: Ledoux, M., & Pendakur, R. (1990). *Multicultural Canada: A Graphic Overview*. Ottawa: Policy and Research Directorate, Multiculturalism Sector, Multiculturalism and Citizenship Canada, p. 45.

Prairie provinces are characterized by a high proportion of the German, Ukrainian, and Scandinavian groups.

In addition to regional variations in the reported ethnic origins of Canadians, there are two other related issues to be recognized when developing health-care policies and services.

First, as illustrated in Figure 6, there may be considerable differences in the ethnic composition of a given metropolitan area in contrast to the regional composition. In British Columbia, for example, the Scandinavians are the second largest ethnic group at the provincial level (see Figure 5b), but the Chinese are the second largest group at the metropolitan Vancouver level. In other words, for the most effective health-care policies and services, they should be geared to reflect the metropolitan ethnic composition rather

Figure 2   Age Distribution, Total & Visible Minority Populations, Canada, 1986

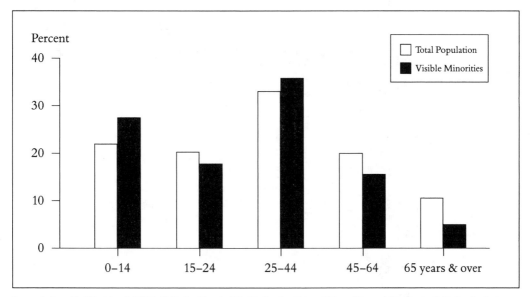

Source: Ledoux, M., & Pendakur, R. (1990). *Multicultural Canada: A Graphic Overview*. Ottawa: Policy and Research Directorate, Multiculturalism Sector, Multiculturalism and Citizenship Canada, p. 47.

Figure 3   Age Distribution, Total & Aboriginal Populations, Canada, 1986

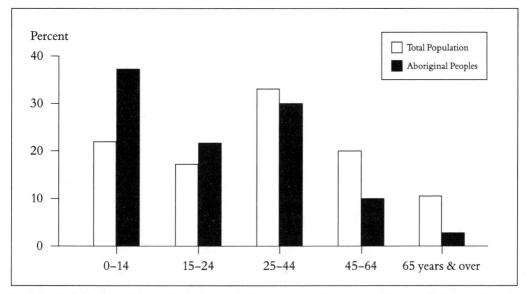

Source: Ledoux, M., & Pendakur, R. (1990). *Multicultural Canada: A Graphic Overview*. Ottawa: Policy and Research Directorate, Multiculturalism Sector, Multiculturalism and Citizenship Canada, p. 55.

Figure 4   Most Frequently Reported Ethnic Origins Other than British or French, Canada, 1986

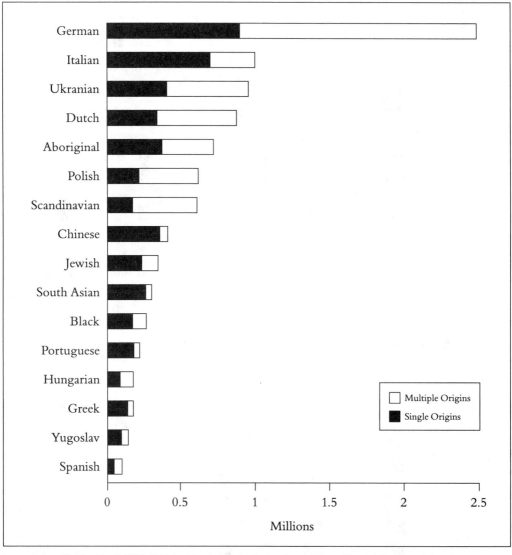

Source: Ledoux, M., & Pendakur, R. (1990). *Multicultural Canada: A Graphic Overview*. Ottawa: Policy and Research Directorate, Multiculturalism Sector,
        Multiculturalism and Citizenship Canada, p. 15.

than the region as a whole. Second, as shown in Figure 7, there are differences in non-official languages reported as mother tongues and non-official languages most frequently reported as home languages. The differences in reported ethnic origins and home languages spoken can be accounted for by ethnic generational differences and new

Figure 5a   Most Frequently Reported Ethnic Origins Other than British or French, Regions, 1986

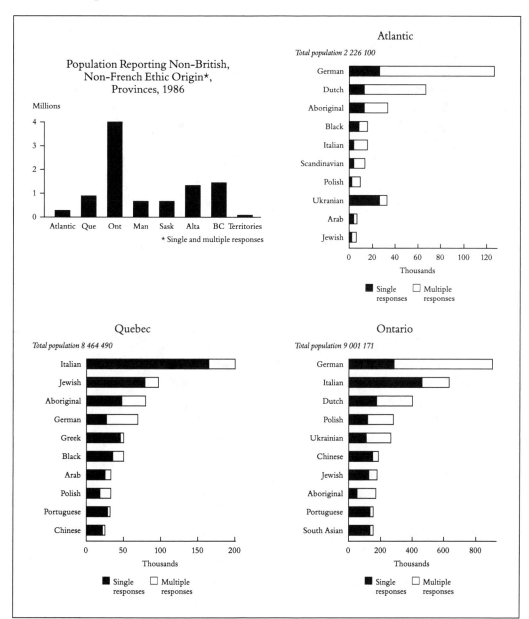

Source: Ledoux, M., & Pendakur, R. (1990). *Multicultural Canada: A Graphic Overview*. Ottawa: Policy and Research Directorate, Multiculturalism Sector, Multiculturalism and Citizenship Canada, p. 17.

Figure 5b Most Frequently Reported Ethnic Origins Other than British or French, Regions, 1986

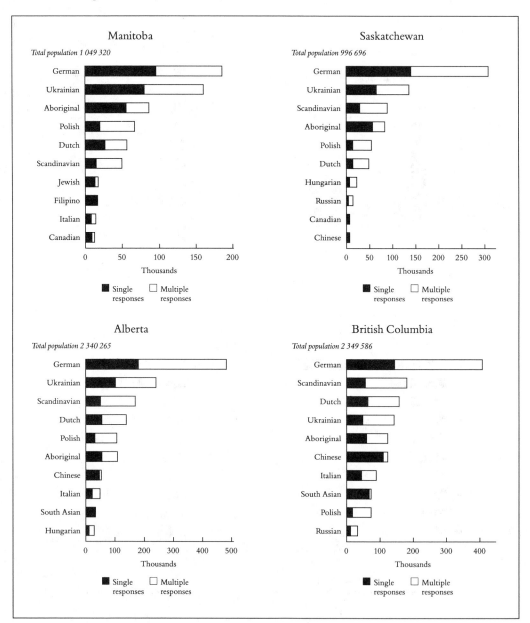

Source: Ledoux, M., & Pendakur, R. (1990). *Multicultural Canada: A Graphic Overview*. Ottawa: Policy and Research Directorate, Multiculturalism Sector, Multiculturalism and Citizenship Canada, p. 19.

Figure 6   Most Frequently Reported Ethnic Origins Other than British or French,
Selected CMAs, 1986

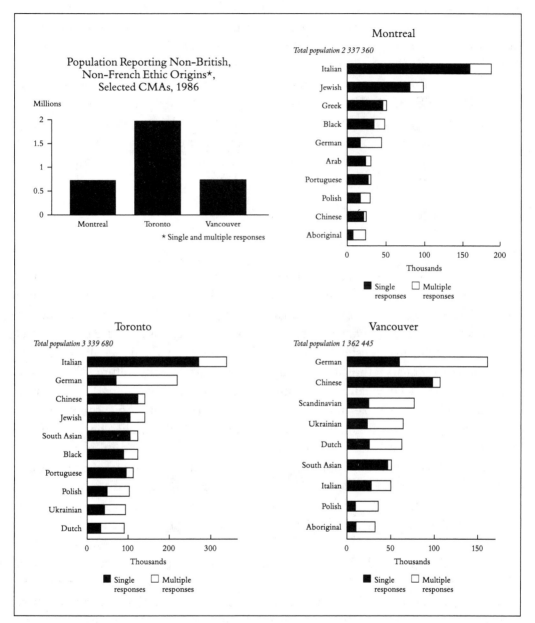

Source: Ledoux, M., & Pendakur, R. (1990). *Multicultural Canada: A Graphic Overview*. Ottawa: Policy and Research Directorate, Multiculturalism Sector, Multiculturalism and Citizenship Canada, p. 21.

immigrants arriving in Canada annually. Given the present demographic trends, we can expect changes that will eventually reflect the current increases in the percentage age distribution of the foreign born. Moreover, as shown in Figure 8, recent emigration to Canada has shifted away from the traditionally European countries to predominantly Asian, African, Caribbean, and South American countries. For an aging and culturally diverse society, it is extremely important to begin to understand the cultural variations that exist today, especially with reference to health-care provision and the well-being of the ethnic minority. Several general questions will be addressed in this paper as follows: What do we need to know about ethnic culture to understand the adjustment to aging by ethnic minorities? What do we need to know about attitudes and behaviour towards aging for effective health care and social support? What can be done to bridge the cultural gap in health care provision?

Ethnicity and Aging

Until very recently, the study of ethnic variations in the aging experience has received very little attention in Canadian gerontological literature. Earlier studies that attempted to examine the relationship between ethnicity and aging failed to differentiate between the various meanings usually associated with the term. One of the first attempts to give a conceptual clarification of what was usually meant by ethnicity is provided by Rosenthal (1986, p. 19). From an extensive review of the literature, she derived the following three conceptions of ethnicity: ethnicity as culture, especially immigrant culture; ethnicity as a determinant of social inequality; and ethnicity as synonymous with "traditional" ways of thinking and behaving. As indicated by Rosenthal, each of the above conceptions of ethnicity will lead to a different model of aging of ethnic families because of the differential emphasis placed on the concept. Therefore, she argues for an integrative approach in which connections or linkages between various conceptions of ethnicity can be drawn together in the study of ethnic families. This approach makes considerable sense especially in the study of some ethnic families in which generational cohorts can be clearly identified and thus different conceptions of ethnicity may be applied to each generation.

The first conception of ethnicity as culture, particularly immigrant culture, takes on added significance if we reconsider the demographic changes noted earlier that are taking place in Canadian society. It will be a fairly safe assumption to make that there will always be an immigrant or first generation of various ethnic groups in Canada. Therefore, the conception of ethnicity as immigrant culture requires a clear understanding of the various elements or components that constitute a given ethnic culture. Most definitions of culture include shared meanings (Gordon, 1964; Fry, 1980; Marshall,

Figure 7

Non-Official Languages Most   Non-Official Languages Most
Frequently Reported as Mother Tongues,   Frequently Reported as Home
Canada, 1986   Languages⋆, Canada, 1986

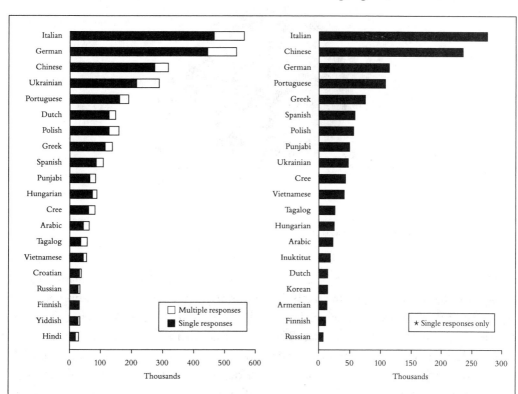

Source: Ledoux, M., & Pendakur, R. (1990). *Multicultural Canada: A Graphic Overview*. Ottawa: Policy and Research Directorate, Multiculturalism Sector, Multiculturalism and Citizenship Canada, p. 27.

1980; Hagedorn, 1986). As described by Hagedorn (1986, p. 36), meanings are usually shared through the various components of culture such as beliefs, norms, mores, values, and symbols.

An interesting point to be made in the definition of culture has been noted by Rosenthal (1986, p. 20) and that is that while some definitions of culture include both shared meanings and patterns of behaviour, others do not. For our purposes, however, it will be argued that the various components of culture such as beliefs held, norms, mores, values, and symbols that constitute the shared meanings are only important in influencing behavioural outcomes. The extent to which each component of culture will influence behaviour will depend on the degree of institutional completeness, a term

Figure 8 World Areas

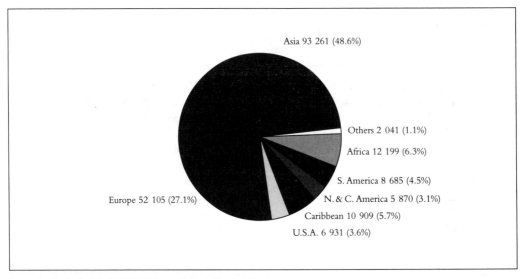

Source: *Immigration Statistics 1989* (1991). Ottawa: Minister of Supply and Services.

developed by Breton (1964, p. 193) to describe the extent to which various social organizations were developed in an ethnic community. For example, depending on one's age at the time of emigration, beliefs held by the immigrant were most likely influenced by the earlier socialization processes. The traditional norms or the rules of behaviour ingrained in the immigrant's mind may or may not be reinforced further depending on the size, density, ethnic composition, and the degree of institutional completeness of one's own ethnic community. Similarly, the enforcement of traditional mores and social interaction patterns based on a system of mutual obligations are also most likely to be influenced by the degree of institutional completeness.

Another important argument that is advanced by Rosenthal (1986, p. 20) is that further distinction must be made between ethnic culture and immigrant culture. She argues that "if the conception of culture is limited to immigrant culture, then ethnic variability in family life should decrease over successive, new immigrant generations." While we have implied previously that immigrant culture is a "transplanted phenomenon," to use Rosenthal's term, and that its influence on behaviour will depend on the degree of institutional completeness, it must be underscored that ethnic cultural characteristics continue to exist, although in slightly modified forms. Some of these characteristics that impinge on the general health status and well-being of the elderly will be discussed later in further detail.

The second conceptualization of ethnicity as a determinant of inequality by Rosenthal (1986, p. 20) draws attention to the ways in which previous research has tended to equate ethnic group with minority group. While the main focus of current debate has been on the lack of distinction between social class and ethnicity (Holzberg, 1982) as key independent variables to account for variations in aging, there are nevertheless several key factors that are relevant to our present discussion on ethnicity and inequality. Since there are several different forms of inequality in Canadian society, we must be extremely careful in selecting the particular form of inequality that we wish to address, not so much in terms of ethnicity, but with reference to our dependent variable, for example, health status and well-being of our elderly.

The most common form of inequality is economic inequality or the variations in one's income and other material resources. A key to understanding economic inequality with reference to ethnic groups is to understand the long history of exploitation, especially of the immigrant or first generation ethnic group, and in many instances, that of institutional racism (Bolaria & Li, 1988). The adverse effects of institutional racism prevented equal access to many institutions and further increased economic inequality.

Another aspect of continued economic inequality that was deeply rooted in institutional racism was the eventual relegation of some ethnic groups to ethnic minority status. The concomitant effects of economic inequality, deprivation, lack of political power, minority status, and hence social inequality, all contributed to the lack of the individual's sense of identity. The sense of who we are and how we relate to others depends on the position we occupy in the Canadian social structure. Another way of looking at this situation is to see which group or groups occupy a dominant position or a subordinate position in terms of influence and decision making. The numerical size of the group, where it is located, its role in the economy, its level of education, and its occupational position all tend to influence not only the identity of the ethnic group members, but also the attitudes of the dominant groups towards the minority group. Attitudes in turn govern social relationships and the degree to which meaningful social interaction can take place. The development of one's ethnic identity and the strengths of this identity in relation to the extent of external or societal constraints is a complex issue that requires further investigation.

The third conception of ethnicity advanced by Rosenthal (1986, p. 20) as being synonymous with "traditional" as opposed to the "modern" ways of thinking and behaving is based on several assumptions and misconceptions. As in the first conceptualization of ethnicity as culture, particularly immigrant culture, there is the implicit assumption that the traditional forms of family life and social discourse are retained and that ethnic culture does not change. Thus, there is a very strong tendency for researchers to over-idealize the ethnic family. Cultural change and generational differences in cultural retention have been subordinated or neglected all together. This tendency to both generalize and idealize the ethnic family in traditional family typology stems partly from the inclination to equate ethnic group with minority group and this latter labelling implying that the ethnic group is a relative newcomer to Canadian society. This implication is often based on a lack of appreciation of the history of the ethnic group concerned, which in many instances goes back several generations. By conveniently disregarding the history and social experiences of the ethnic groups in Canadian society, and also by failing to differentiate between various ethnic groups, it is possible to dichotomize ethnicity in terms of the traditional and modern orientations.

While the limitations of conceptualizing ethnicity in terms of the traditional and modern typology may be fairly obvious, it should be observed that the influence of traditional roles and values are still extremely important to our understanding of the variations in aging, health care, and mental health. Furthermore, it will be equally clear that a simple definition of ethnicity will no longer suffice and that we must draw upon several different conceptions of ethnicity in order to capture the dynamics of the aging process as it relates to the health status and general well-being of the elderly. However, before we proceed to examine the relationship between the various components of ethnicity and the social aspects of aging as they relate to health, a brief overview of what is meant by health, health care, and mental health will be provided.

Aging and Health

The well-being of the individual becomes a primary concern, especially when one approaches retirement age. A crucial variable in assessing the individual's well-being, regardless of one's age, is health. What is meant by health? Shanas and Maddox (1985, p. 701) note that health in the aged is usually defined in terms of the presence or absence of disease, or in terms of how well the aged are able to function. The determination of one's health in terms of the presence or absence of disease is usually considered to be an objective assessment because it is based on medical examinations and laboratory tests to confirm the medical diagnosis. However, Shanas and Maddox (1985, p. 701) note that a truly objective measure of health is difficult to achieve, and that the administration of the laboratory test to measure health varies from time to time. They provide, as an example, physiological measures such as blood pressure readings and glucose levels.

Although Canadian data on the objective measures of health for various ethnic groups are not readily available, it may be instructive to use available data to illustrate the differences in the major causes of deaths in 1988 by age group and sex. These data are provided in Table 1. From Table 1, differences in the major causes of death by age group and sex in Canada can be observed. In the 55 to 64 age category, the 33 percent of male deaths due to heart disease contrasts quite vividly with the 19.3 percent of female deaths

Table 1   Major Causes of Death, By Age Group and Sex, Canada, 1988

	All ages	Age 55 to 64	Age 65 to 74	Age 75 to 84	Age 85 and over
	%	%	%	%	%
Males	100.0	100.0	100.0	100.0	100.0
Heart disease	30.7	33.0	34.3	33.9	34.4
Cerebrovascular disease	5.6	3.6	5.1	7.9	9.1
Atherosclerosis	1.0	0.3	0.5	1.1	3.0
Cancer – breast	—	—	—	—	—
Cancer – lung	8.9	15.5	12.5	7.5	3.1
Cancer – other	18.1	22.3	21.6	17.9	13.6
Diabetes mellitus	1.7	1.5	1.9	2.1	1.7
Pneumonia and influenza	3.2	1.2	2.1	4.3	8.4
All other repiratory diseases	5.9	3.7	6.6	8.3	7.4
Chronic liver disease and cirrhosis	1.3	2.8	1.5	0.5	0.1
All accidents and adverse effects	9.1	5.9	2.7	2.4	2.8
All other causes	14.5	10.0	11.3	14.1	16.5
Total number of deaths	104 106	15 921	27 089	28 541	14 579
Females	100.0	100.0	100.0	100.0	100.0
Heart disease	30.1	19.3	29.3	35.6	37.5
Cerebrovascular disease	9.6	4.9	6.7	11.3	13.6
Atherosclerosis	1.8	0.3	0.5	1.4	4.2
Cancer – breast	5.2	12.3	6.7	3.5	1.6
Cancer – lung	4.5	10.6	8.1	3.1	0.8
Cancer – other	16.7	27.8	23.0	15.4	8.6
Diabetes mellitus	2.4	2.1	2.8	3.2	2.0
Pneumonia and influenza	3.9	1.3	2.0	3.7	7.3
All other repiratory diseases	3.7	3.8	4.6	4.3	3.0
Chronic liver disease and cirrhosis	0.8	2.0	1.2	0.5	0.1
All accidents and adverse effects	4.8	4.1	2.3	2.3	3.0
All other causes	16.6	11.6	12.7	15.7	18.4
Total number of deaths	85 905	8 824	17 109	25 667	24 860

Source: *A Portrait of Seniors in Canada* (1990). Ottawa: Statistics Canada, Housing, Family and Social Statistics Division, Table 6, p. 40.

due to heart disease. According to Statistics Canada (1990), the two leading causes of death in 1985 were heart disease and cancer for both senior men and women.

An alternative way to define health among the elderly suggested by Shanas and Maddox (1985, p. 701) is based on how well the elderly are able to function in terms of day-to-day activities. They argue that the various things that the elderly can do, or think that they can do, are useful indicators of not only their health, but of the kinds of health services that they may require. This functional approach to the assessment of one's health is of particular importance, especially with respect to ethnic minorities, because it assumes that "both the individual and the physicians may have relevant and possibly conflicting information about health status" (Shanas & Maddox, 1985, p. 701). Such conflicting information may easily occur as a result of different perspectives or different cultural perceptions of a given health condition. For example, symptoms such as a headache may be attributed to a particular disease by an elderly ethnic person, while this same symptom may be completely disregarded by the doctor as a sign of old age. Such a problem in the interpretation of the symptom may be doubly troublesome because various ethnic groups have different levels of pain threshold (Hayashida, 1984).

While both the medical and functional models of health evaluation may provide an overall assessment of the elderly person, caution must be exercised if such health assessments are used to decide whether or not the elderly patient should be placed in a given institution. The time and location of the initial health evaluation may be extremely critical in terms of the assessment outcome. Shanas and Maddox (1985, p. 702) report that "different service settings, for example, institutions or mental health clinics attract elderly patients with differing assessment profiles." In this regard, it is of interest to examine a few studies that have compared the functional health evaluation of the elderly in different settings.

One such study that compared the self-assessment of health with objective measures of health is the study by Fillenbaum (1979, p. 45). In this study, Fillenbaum compared these two measures of health assessment by utilizing a sample of older persons who resided in the community and in institutions. The objective measures of health were based on an OARS (Older American Resources and Services) questionnaire, which provided an assessment of the various levels of functioning. Some of the selected items employed by Fillenbaum (1979, p. 46) were as follows:

1. The number of health-related problems reported present in the previous month,
2. The number of different types of medication taken during the previous month, and,
3. The number of different illnesses and disabilities presently affecting the respondent.

Objective measures were compared against the responses to the following subjective questions:

1. How would you rate your health at the present time — excellent (4), good (3), fair (2), or poor (1)?
2. How concerned do you feel about your health troubles — not concerned (4), mildly concerned (3), moderately concerned (2), or very concerned (1)?
3. How much do your health troubles stand in the way of your doing the things you want to do — not at all (3), a little (some) (2), or a great deal (1)?

For the elderly residents of the community, it was found that the self-assessment or subjective evaluations of health reflected the actual state of health as assessed by the objective measures. This probably derives from the fact that those elderly persons who are able to function independently in the community are also in better health, have a higher degree of self-esteem and life satisfaction than those elderly persons who are institutionalized. Indeed, this is indicated in the Fillenbaum study which indicated that for the elderly in institutional settings, the self-evaluations of health were not consistent with the objective measures of health. Fillenbaum (1979, p. 50) concludes that "it is possible that the objective measures used — number of health problems, medicines, illnesses — may not be appropriate where the institutionalized are concerned, or may have a different meaning in institutions."

While these results of the Fillenbaum study may be both time and location specific, the results from an earlier longitudinal study by Maddox and Douglass (1973, p. 87), which compared the medical and self-assessments of the elderly over a fifteen-year period, indicated persistent positive congruency for the two types of health assessment. Of interest is their finding that whenever there was a difference in the physician's and self-assessment of health, the tendency was for the individual to overestimate, rather than underestimate, his or her own health. Maddox and Douglass (1973, p. 92) noted the substantial stability over time in both the self-assessments and physicians' health ratings, however, the self-assessed health rating showed slightly more stability. Their unexpected finding was "the tendency for self health rating to be a better predictor of future physicians' ratings than the reverse." Maddox and Douglass (1973, p. 92) conclude that although their data did not provide a conclusive pattern to confirm or refute the commonly reported findings regarding the two types of health assessment, their data demonstrated that "self-assessment of health is not random but is persistently and positively related to objective evaluations of health status."

An excellent overview of the literature on recent trends in viewing the health status of the elderly from several different perspectives, as well as from several different levels of function, is provided by Shanas and Maddox (1985, p. 703). They draw our attention to the growing acceptance and merging of the medical and functional models of health assessment, especially by those in geriatrics. To underscore this latter observation, they quote the following from the World Health Organization:

> It is now accepted by the medical profession that morbidity should be measured not only in terms of the extent of the pathological process but also in terms of the impairment of the function in the person affected by a pathological condition. . . . Functional diagnosis is one of the most important elements that has been introduced in geriatrics. In this approach a distinction is made between an impairment and a disability caused by a pathological condition.

The utility in employing both models of health assessment becomes evident when we consider the distinction that is made between an impairment and a disability. From the World Health Organization report, Shanas and Maddox (1985, p. 703) note that impairment is "a physiological or psychological abnormality that does not interfere with the normal life activities of the individual." They further note that disability is "a condition that results in partial or total limitation of the normal activities of the individual." It is important to keep these distinctions in mind when considering the health status of aged ethnic minorities. Some types of impairment may eventually result in disability.

The prevalence of selected health problems in Canada in 1985 by age and sex is shown in Figure 9. Statistics Canada (1990) reports that "persons aged 65 and over in 1985, were at least twice as likely to report respiratory troubles, arthritis or rheumatism and hypertension, and at least three times as likely to report heart trouble" compared to the total Canadian population. As illustrated in Figure 9, a slightly higher proportion of male seniors than senior females reported respiratory troubles. In contrast, a higher proportion of senior females reported problems with hypertension and arthritis or rheumatism.

The data for surgical procedures for the population aged 65 years and over are shown in Figure 10. Other than the relatively high proportion of diagnostic and therapeutic procedures shown in Figure 10, the most common surgical procedure for both elderly men and women were operations on the digestive system and abdominal region. For women, the next most frequent operations were those of the musculoskeletal system. For men, the next most frequent operations were those on the genital organs.

While the physiological or physical aspects of aging are important considerations in terms of the functional capabilities of the elderly, it is also important to examine the effects of aging on one's mental health. In order to study the psychological aspects of aging, it is necessary to have an understanding of exactly what is meant by mental health. D'Arcy (1987, p. 425) defines mental health as:

Figure 9   Prevalence of Selected Health Problems, by Age Group and Sex,
Canada, 1985

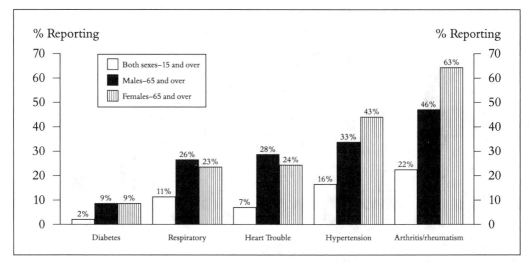

Source: Statistics Canada, Housing, Family and Social Statistics Division. (1990). *A Portrait of Seniors in Canada*. Ottawa: Minister of Supply and Services,
Chart 27, p. 44.

a state in which a person demonstrates his competence to think, feel and (interact in ways that demonstrate
his ability to deal effectively with the challenges of life. The mentally healthy person is accepting of self himself,
able to give as well as receive in relationships and, having realistically evaluated his assets and liabilities, has an
appropriate level of self confidence, making decisions based on sound judgement and accepting responsibility
for his actions.

There are several key components in this definition that merit our attention, particularly with reference to ethnicity and aging. One such component concerns the individual's
ability to think. As noted earlier in our discussion on ethnicity and its synonymy with
traditional ways of thinking, it is quite conceivable that misunderstandings can occur if the
traditional cultural backgrounds of the ethnic groups are not understood. Social behaviour
as outward manifestations of the thinking process may often be interpreted as "bizarre"
when it may be considered "normal" in one's own cultural group. Another important
component that is noted in D'Arcy's definition of mental health is the ability to deal
effectively with various day-to-day situations in life. As noted elsewhere by Ujimoto
(1987a, p. 131), there is accumulating evidence that coping plays a central role in reducing
stress-related illnesses and in promoting good health. The coping strategies utilized by the
elderly who have different socio-demographic characteristics are particularly relevant to
the study of aging and health because constant psycho-social adjustments must be made

Figure 10   Surgical Procedures for the Population Aged 65 Years and Over, by Type of
Procedure and Sex, Canada, 1985–86

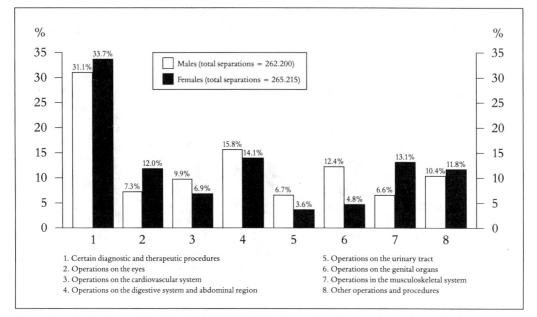

Source: Statistics Canada, Housing, Family and Social Statistics Division. (1990). *A Portrait of Seniors in Canada.* Ottawa: Minister of Supply and Services,
Chart 23, p. 39.

throughout one's lifespan. Therefore, an understanding of the cultural context in which
these adjustments occur is very important.

The final component of D'Arcy's definition of mental health that will be briefly
discussed here concerns the types of social relationships that can realistically occur,
given the limited assets and resources of the elderly. The study of social relationships in
terms of the cultural context in which they occur requires an understanding of the
social exchange mechanisms of the particular group. For example, in the case of the
elderly *issei* (immigrant or first-generation Japanese Canadian) and *nisei* (second generation or Canadian born), it has been observed by Kobata (1979, p. 100), Nishio and
Sugiman (1983, p. 19), and Ujimoto (1987a, p. 116) that traditional Japanese values
influence generational relationships. Intergenerational relationships based on a system
of mutual and moral obligations, as well as on social customs, may be applicable only
to certain groups, and at the same time, there may be less importance placed on them
by subsequent generations. Social relationships based on concepts such as filial piety
and familial dependency in old age are other factors that may intervene in social relationships, depending on the ethnic group.

From our brief discussion of the three components crucial to the definition of mental health provided by D'Arcy, it can be hypothesized that the negative effects of daily-life situations will have a more severe impact on the mental health of recent immigrants to Canadian society than on subsequent generations. The recent arrivals to Canada are the ones who will experience the greatest changes in mental health because of value conflicts and other adjustment difficulties to their new environment. Support for this observation is provided by Kuo (1986, p. 133) who has documented that "an excessive amount of social stress among immigrants — resulting from social isolation, cultural conflicts, poor social integration and assimilation, role changes and identity crises, low socioeconomic status, and racial discrimination — has led to a high prevalence of ill health and psychological impairment among them." The plethora of factors that impinge on one's mental health are extremely difficult to disentangle. As Chappell, Strain, and Blandford (1986, p. 37) have noted, "changes in mental health as we age are less straightforward. Mental health encompasses numerous aspects, including cognitive, psychological and emotional functioning. It is known to be related to both physiological conditions and social environments." At present, the social environment of aged ethnic minority groups is a relatively unexplored area of study.

Although the data on the health status of ethnic groups are not readily available as yet, substantial progress has been made in recent years in obtaining health-related information at the national level. During 1978 and 1979, Health and Welfare Canada and Statistics Canada (1981, p. 14) conducted a survey to obtain data on the health problems and disability of the Canadian population. The data on the health status of Canadians were based on a 12 000 household sample size which provided information on selected health behaviour such as drug use, disability days, accidents, and activity limitations. Table 2 illustrates the distribution of various health conditions.

The data shown in Table 2 refer to the respondents' subjective evaluations of their own health conditions rather than on objective evaluations by physicians. In some instances, the validity and reliability of the responses may be questioned since symptoms of the health disorder were not clearly differentiated from the health disorder itself. It is noted in the Health and Welfare Canada and Statistics Canada (1981, p. 109) report that "some degree of double counting is especially suspected with regard to categories 19 (arthritis and rheumatism) and 20 (back, limb and joint disorders), which were contained in the chronic condition list."

A further caution to be observed concerns the comparability of self-reports of health. Gibson (1991) argues that self-evaluations of health are not "straight forward reflections of clinical status or objective health. Instead, they represent complex constructions that are very likely to be influenced by social and psychological factors." She continues that "despite this knowledge, self-evaluations are still frequently used

Table 2   Distribution of Various Health Conditions

Health Condition	Percent
1. Mental disorders	3.9
2. Diabetes	1.5
3. Thyroid disorders	1.2
4. Anaemia	1.6
5. Headache	4.3
6. Sight disorders	4.7
7. Hearing disorders	4.0
8. Hypertension	6.1
9. Heart disease	3.3
10. Acute respiratory ailments	3.1
11. Influenza	2.7
12. Bronchitis and emphysema	2.2
13. Asthma	2.1
14. Hayfever and other allergies	8.5
15. Dental trouble	6.6
16. Gastric and duodenal ulcers	1.9
17. Functional digestive disorders	2.7
18. Skin allergies and other skin disorders	8.1
19. Arthritis and rheumatism	9.6
20. Back, limb, and joint disorders	9.1
21. Trauma (accidents and injury)	2.4
22. Other	10.4
Total (all conditions) n = 12 000 households	100.0

Source: *The Health of Canadians. Report of the Canada Health Survey* (1981). Ottawa: Health and Welfare and Statistics Canada. Table VI, p. 110.

uncritically in comparisons of the health status of different racial and ethnic groups." Thus, Gibson (1991) argues that any new model of race differences in self-reported health requires a consideration of additional factors that are unique to each social group. Gibson advances the following four issues to be addressed: (1) whether the race differences in the number of chronic conditions indicator is in systematic error, random error, or both; (2) the plausibility of a fourth latent construct (health-service use) that is explained by changes in internal health state; (3) the possibility that a general functional limitation indicator is a measure of both disability and subjective interpretations of health state; and (4) whether disability interpretations of health state are really less valid for blacks than whites.

The impact of life-long patterns of inequality of both health status and economic status and subsequent utilization of health-care services in later life has been examined by Mutchler and Burr (1991). Their analysis of health-care services utilization indicated that black persons made more visits to health-care professionals, but were hospitalized less frequently. This probably reflected the socio-economic status and affordability factors associated with hospital stay. The authors observed that their results were consistent with other studies that indicated health status and health-care utilization to be strongly associated with socio-economic status.

Although socio-economic status may be an important intervening variable between race and health, Mutchler and Burr (1991) note that other characteristics such as "lifestyle, health practices, diet, stress associated with racism and various forms of discrimination, are correlated with but distinct from socioeconomic status, and may be reflected in the health differences observed here." They conclude that future analyses should decompose the direct and indirect effects of race on health status and the utilization of health-care services.

Aging, Ethnicity, and Health

While there are several recent Canadian publications on aging and health, for example, Simmons-Tropea and Osborn (1987, p. 399), D'Arcy (1987, p. 424), Connidis (1987, p. 451), Marshall (1987, p. 473), Chappell (1987, p. 489), Schwenger (1987, p. 505), and Shapiro and Roos (1987, p. 520), the cultural variations in Canadian society and their implications for the future health-care provisions of aging ethnic minorities are not considered. Since this is an important area of study, it is beginning to receive more attention. As noted by Chappell, Strain, and Blandford (1986, p. 30), "the relevance of subculture (ethnic, minority and racial) for the elderly population and, in particular, for the provision of health care is an under-researched area in gerontology. Even though conceptually and theoretically it has been argued that subcultural cohesiveness is likely to result in more social support for its elderly members, this has not been established empirically."

One recent study that examined the relationship between aging and health as interpreted through culture is the study by Rempel and Havens (1986). In this study, they identified the differential perceptions of health of older persons based on twelve different ethnic groups in Manitoba. The Rempel and Havens data analysis (1986, p. 18) indicates that ethnicity and education affect health perception. They note that the Asians and Northern Europeans have the highest positive rating of their own health and the Middle Eastern and Eastern Europeans the poorest health. Because of the small sample size for each of the ethnic groups represented in the sample, caution must be exercised in interpreting the data. The study is nevertheless useful as it suggests several new avenues for future research.

An area of study in health behaviour that is rapidly gaining attention concerns stress and coping behaviour. One study that examines the relevance of ethnicity in relation to stress and coping, particularly with reference to the minority elderly, is the study by Wong and Reker (1985, p. 29). In their comparative study of elderly Chinese and Anglos, Wong and Reker were interested in determining how the Chinese and Anglos differed in their coping behaviour. The three categories of coping strategies that they examined were as follows:

1. Internal strategies are one's own instrumental efforts.
2. External strategies include various forms of dependence on others to reduce stress.
3. Palliative strategies are ways of coping that make one feel better without solving the problem.

Analysis of the Wong and Reker (1985, p. 33) data revealed the presence of several stress–producing health problems noted earlier in Figure 9. In addition to arthritis or rheumatism, eye problems, and other health disorders, other stressful factors that influenced the well-being of the elderly included in-law problems, loss of a spouse, worries about the family, and economic problems. On the basis of their data analysis, Wong and Reker conclude that the "Chinese did not report having more problems, but they perceived their problems, especially the general problem of aging, as more serious than Anglos." The authors note that in addition to the normal biological constraints of aging, there are other compounding factors associated with the minority status of the Chinese aged such as "a language barrier, lack of information, and fear of racial discrimination."

In terms of coping strategies, Wong and Reker (1985, p. 33) found that the Chinese relied more on external and palliative strategies than did the Anglos. Although the Chinese relied more on external help, it is noted that the source of the outside help came primarily from family members and relatives. The Chinese also tended to reminisce and seek refuge in the past rather than attempting to solve a given stress situation, except in coping with health-related problems. Wong and Reker suggest that "Chinese elderly not only experience more stress, but possess less adequate coping resources." Since the aged Chinese sample were all first-generation or immigrant Chinese, while the Anglos were either born in Canada or were long-time residents, the results are perhaps not too surprising. However, they do point out the concerns and health-care needs of the first-generation ethnic minority, and therefore, future health-care policies should not be based on the common assumption that the aged are homogeneous.

A recently completed research project on the well-being of aged Asian-Canadians included the coping inventory developed by Wong and Reker (1983, 1984) noted above.

Table 3   Health Satisfaction of Aged Asian–Canadians by Ethnic Group (n = 774)

Health Satisfaction	Chinese	Japanese	Korean
Dissatisfied	15.7%	10.2%	21.9%
Mixed	8.1	20.1	10.1
Satisfied	76.2	69.7	68.0
	100.0% (223)	100.0% (373)	100.0% (178)

This project by Ujimoto, Nishio, Wong, and Lam (forthcoming), entitled "Comparative aspects of aging Asian-Canadians: Social networks and time budgets" examined the cultural aspects of ethnicity in relation to the allocation of time to various daily activities. By utilizing time-budget data, those activities most predictive of well-being were determined. A description of this research is provided elsewhere by Ujimoto (1987a, p. 130; 1990a, p. 381). Both time-budget and social-network data enable us to differentiate between those individuals who rely upon external resources in order to cope with a stress situation rather than on internal strategies.

The Ujimoto, Nishio, Wong, and Lam (in press) national survey also obtained self-reported data on health satisfaction by Chinese-, Japanese-, and Korean-Canadian elderly. These data are shown in Table 3. Generally, a high proportion of respondents were satisfied with their health. The Chinese respondents appeared to be the most satisfied, followed by the Japanese, but the Japanese elderly tended to have the highest mixed feelings about their health compared to the Chinese and Korean elderly. Of those respondents who were dissatisfied with their present status, the Koreans were the most dissatisfied.

The relatively high percentage of Korean elderly who were dissatisfied with their own self-assessment of health appears to be in contrast to earlier studies which indicated that Koreans were well adjusted. In a study by Kim and Berry (1986) that assessed the mental health of Korean immigrants who resided in Toronto, it was found that the Koreans scored low on the Cawte Stress Scale and also on the Mann Marginality Scale when compared to other groups undergoing acculturation in Canada. Kim (1987) argues that these findings are consistent with several other studies. He notes that several factors may account for the successful adaptation of Korean immigrants. First, Kim states that since Koreans were voluntary migrants, their mental-health status would be better than for others, such as refugees. Second, Kim notes that the Koreans have developed better coping skills to deal with stressful life events. A third factor is that the

Table 4   Health Satisfaction by Generation (n = 774)

Health Satisfaction	First Generation	Second Generation	Kika-Nisei
Dissatisfied	16.3%	8.0%	3.6%
Mixed	13.8	16.8	14.3
Satisfied	69.9	75.2	82.1
	100.0% (621)	100.0% (125)	100.0% (28)

Canadian government selection criteria are such that only the highly educated and those with occupational skills are chosen to immigrate. Finally, the relatively high degree of established Korean community institutions and the policy of multiculturalism both encourage Korean immigrants to retain their cultural identity. How, then, can we account for the relatively high degree of dissatisfaction reported by the Korean elderly?

In terms of the possible contradiction between our data and the previously reported findings, caution must be exercised in interpreting and comparing data. By utilizing the standard stress and marginality instruments, it is conceivable that fairly consistent results can be obtained. However, if we attempt to seek health information from the Korean health professionals themselves, a much different picture emerges. Kim's (1987) intensive interviews with medical and social support staff revealed that the Koreans tended to internalize their problems, thus making it difficult for health-care personnel to assess the real problems.

Kim (1987) reports that the Koreans do not want to admit that they are sick, or to show any signs of weakness and that they tend to somatize their illnesses because of the stigma attached to psychological illnesses. Korean doctors have reported to Kim that many of the Korean illnesses are psychological and stem from loneliness, depression, and anxiety. These, in turn, further aggravate the existing somatic problems. These illness characteristics and behaviour are not limited to the Korean elderly, but are very often manifested by other Asian-Canadian elderly, particularly the first generation. Indeed, Liu (1986) notes that "somatization is culturally sanctioned in Chinese society, it is an adaptive coping response that allows the person to escape stigmatization." Our data in Table 4 below indicate that the highest degree of self-reported health dissatisfaction is by the first generation and the most satisfied are the second generation and *kika-nisei*.

Further insight regarding the relatively high percentage of Korean elderly reporting dissatisfaction with their health can be obtained from our time-budget data. Koreans as a group are extremely devoted to long hours of hard work. More time devoted to work

Table 5 Health Satisfaction by Ethnic Group and Gender (n = 774)

Health Satisfaction	Chinese		Japanese		Korean	
	M	F	M	F	M	F
Dissatisfied	9.2%	20.8%	11.4%	8.6%	12.8%	29.0%
Mixed	6.1	9.6	19.9	20.4	9.0	11.0
Satisfied	84.7	69.6	68.7	71.0	78.2	60.0
	100.9% (98)	100.0% (125)	100.0% (211)	100.0% (162)	100.0% (78)	100.0% (100)

means less time for family and leisure activities, and eventually, this will have an impact on one's health. Kim (1987) reports that about half of the Korean households in Toronto operate a small business; many of them are open from fourteen to sixteen hours per day. A few are open 24 hours per day.

Gender differences in self-reported health satisfaction are shown in Table 5. It will be noted that both Chinese and Korean elderly women report a higher degree of dissatisfaction with their health than do the Japanese elderly women. While both Japanese men and women expressed similar degrees of mixed feelings, both Chinese and Korean elderly men reported higher degrees of health satisfaction. The dissatisfaction expressed by the elderly Korean and Chinese women may stem from the fact that both Chinese and Korean women immigrated to Canada as "captive immigrants," a term used by Kim to describe Korean parents or grandparents who came to Canada because of their sense of responsibility towards their family. In a Korean household that operates a small business or has dual income earners, the baby-sitting role is most often provided by the parents or grandparents. This appears to be the only role given to the elderly Koreans, thus compounding their sense of anxiety and depression. Such a limited role does not provide the elderly with the opportunity to become fully integrated into Canadian society. Kim (1987) notes that the Korean elderly are totally dependent on their children or grandchildren and that "they do not have the cognitive and social skills to participate in the larger society and their adjustment is limited to the ethnic pockets."

Cultural Factors and Aging

One of the key cultural variables that requires examination is the degree of obligations as perceived by the children towards their parents. The concept of filial piety has its roots in Confucianism and involves several types of obligations. According to Osako and Liu (1986, p. 130), the child must obey his or her parents, support them in old age, and must

Table 6 Cultural Factors Considered Important for Successful Aging by Ethnic Group (n = 632)

Cultural Factors	Chinese	Japanese	Korean
Discipline	0.6%	18.4%	1.9%
Patience, tolerance	3.3	20.1	2.5
Filial piety	12.2	7.1	25.5
Group loyalty	1.7	2.7	1.9
Sense of duty	3.3	3.7	3.8
Thriftiness	1.7	1.0	—
Moral obligations	0.6	3.4	8.3
Emphasis on education	17.7	3.1	5.3
Pride in culture, tradition	24.6	8.2	10.8
Honesty, courtesy, manners	—	10.6	0.6
Religious teachings	2.8	2.7	3.8
Traditional family emphasis	1.7	3.7	—
Fatalism	2.2	0.3	—
Deferred gratification	—	1.4	0.6
Martial and traditional arts	—	2.0	—
Modesty	0.6	2.4	—
Self-reliance	6.6	2.4	0.6
Optimism	7.7	—	—
Nothing in particular	12.7	6.8	34.4
	100.0%	100.0%	100.0%
	(181)	(294)	(157)

succeed in one's career to bring honour to parents and ancestors. What happens then, when children do not fulfil the filial roles as expected by their parents? As a partial response to this question, it is suggested that intergenerational conflict is one possible outcome, and in those situations where conflict appears to be minimized, it is the parents who internalize their feelings and suffer the consequences in silence. This tends to be the case for elderly immigrants who arrived more recently than for those immigrants who have become acculturated to Canadian societal norms.

Table 6 illustrates the variations in response to the question "What aspects of your cultural heritage do you feel has enabled you to grow old successfully?" It can be seen from Table 6 that 25.5 percent of the Korean elderly indicated filial piety as the key cultural variable for successful aging. This contrasts with the Chinese and Japanese elderly respondents, of whom 12.2 percent and 7.1 percent respectively indicated filial piety. The Korean elderly also indicated that pride in their cultural heritage was important. It should be observed, however, that the Koreans are the most recent immigrants to Canada among the Asian elderly studied here. This means that most of the socialization had taken place in Korea and thus it can be argued that there is a relatively strong attachment to traditional Korean values. The Chinese tend to fall between the Korean and Japanese responses.

From Table 6, it can be seen that an extremely high percentage of Japanese elderly indicated that discipline and perseverance were important cultural factors that contributed to their successful aging. The Japanese term *gaman* was most frequently cited. According to Kobata (1979), *gaman* is literally translated as "self-control." The outward manifestation of this is the tendency to suppress emotions, whether positive or negative. In traditional Japanese society, *gaman* was seen as virtuous and Kobata argues that "the tendency to suffer in silence with a great deal of forbearance provides some insights into the nature of the family as the source for dealing with problems rather than the outside service providers." It is not suprising, therefore, to note in Table 3 that the Japanese elderly have the highest percentage of mixed feelings regarding their own evaluation of health. Both dissatisfaction and satisfaction appear to be suppressed in comparison to the Korean and Chinese elderly.

Associated with the concept of *gaman* or self-control is *enryo*. According to Kobata, "the norm of *enryo* includes, but is not limited to, reserve, reticence, self-effacement, deference, humility, hesitation, and denigration of one's self and possessions." Because of the plethora of terms that can be associated with *enryo*, it is extremely difficult to assess the well-being of the Japanese elderly. As Kobata notes, "the concept had its origins in the cultural norm of knowing one's position in relation to another when interacting with the others perceived as 'inferior' or 'superior' to oneself." Thus, in interactions with authority figures, for example, doctors, the Japanese elderly very often do not volunteer their true feelings. How can researchers differentiate empirically whether it is *gaman* or *enryo* or both that are operating in order to account for the lack of interaction? This is an extremely crucial aspect to understand if health-care providers are to provide effective care. Our data revealed that 15.7 percent of the Japanese elderly respondents and 6.1 percent of the Korean respondents indicated that *enryo* or reserve was a negative aspect of their culture that impacted on their well-being. This is particularly true in health-care settings in which those who are able to complain the loudest very often receive the most care.

More and more research on various aspects of aging and health are being reported in the literature. However, future studies will have to examine the influence of ethnicity on aging and health in greater detail. As reported by Ujimoto (1987a, p. 117), difficulties with language and the inability to express one's innermost feelings by aged immigrants erect formidable barriers that prevent easy access to the available social, economic, and health support services. Whether it is the lack of health services available in one's own language, or the cultural and psychological barriers that prevent ethnic minorities from utilizing various services, the net result is underutilization of existing health services and facilities by ethnic minorities. Chan (1983, p. 43) found that although the Chinese elderly women in his study were generally aware of medical and dental services in the Chinese community, they were unaware of other services and resources for the elderly available at other institutions and agencies outside of their own community.

While the underutilization of health-care services by various ethnic groups has been noted by Wong and Reker (1985, p. 33), Rempel and Havens (1986, p. 9), and Ujimoto (1987a, p. 117), this is an aspect of aging, ethnicity, and health research that requires a controlled study to determine the reasons. Perhaps there are alternative modes of health care and coping strategies available. We have been alerted to this possibility by a recent study by Hess (1986, p. 314), in which she investigated the differences in over-the-counter (OTC) drug use by two racially and ethnically different groups — the Chinese and Hispanic elders. Hess was interested in determining the variety and amount of OTC preparations that were purchased and used by the two groups for "the relief of common symptoms such as pain, constipation, heartburn/indigestion, nervous tension, 'down in the dumps,' and insomnia/difficulty sleeping." A partial list of OTC preparations used by the Chinese and Hispanic elders are provided in Table 7.

Hess (1986, p. 316) reports that "pain preparations used by Chinese were predomi-nantly topical ointments and balms, while the Hispanics tended to take internal medica-tions for pain." As shown in Table 7, for heartburn or indigestion, the Chinese relied more on various kinds of teas than on OTC drugs. This is one important aspect of health care very often overlooked when a Chinese patient is admitted to a hospital, and instead of Chinese tea, a more potent form of drug is administered. For the remedy of constipa-tion, it may also be noted from Table 7 that the Hispanics tend to use more OTC drugs than do the Chinese. The Chinese tend to rely on natural fruits, vegetables, and folk remedies. Hess concludes that "health care professionals cannot assume that all elderly people are alike in how they approach illness." She argues that "the determination of what preparation to take will depend on a person's perception of the symptoms and their cause." This is usually influenced by the various aspects of ethnicity discussed earlier in this chapter.

An important aspect of health practice to which Hess (1986, p. 317) draws our attention is the Chinese folk practices that "revolve around single dose liquid prepara-tions." In contrast, Western medical practice prescribes multiple dosage of OTC drugs. Hess suggests that this is a confusing concept to the Chinese and that this may explain the Chinese preference for teas and topical preparations for the relief of their health problems.

Table 7 Partial List of OTC Preparations Used By Chinese and Hispanic Elders

| Symptom | Preparations Used by | |
	Chinese Elder	Hispanic Elder

Pain	Absorbine Jr. (topical)
	Anacin (internal)
	Ben-Gay (topical)
	Dr. J.H. Volcanic Oil (topical)
	Essential Balm (topical)
	Infra-Rub (topical)
	Tamenton Heating Oil (topical)
	Tiger Balm (topical)
		Alcohol and camphor (topical)
		Alfalfa tea (internal)
		Anacin (internal)
		Aspirin (plain) (internal)
		  Bayer (internal)
		  Bufferin (internal)
		A.P.C. (internal)
		Balsamo (topical)
		Corn husk/barley/Jamaica (topical)
		Jasmine tea (internal)
		Lemon juice and brandy (internal)
		Mejoral (internal)
		Mentholatum (topical)
		Ruda/Avocado/Seidajal (topical)
		Tylenol (internal)
		Vicks Vaporub (topical)

Constipation	Bok choi (internal) Cascara (internal) Chinese Four-Flavour Teas (internal) Glycerin suppositories (internal) Honey (internal) Maalox (internal) Milk of Magnesia (internal) Po Chai pills (internal) Senna leaves (internal) Wheat and prunes (internal)	Agoral (internal) Ex-Lax (internal) Feen-A-Mint (internal) Gaviscon (internal) Glycerin suppositories (internal) Maalox (internal) Metamucil (internal) Perdiem (internal) Prune juice (internal)
Indigestion (Antacids)	Baking soda (internal) Chrysanthemum crystal tea (internal) Ginseng tea (internal) Maalox (internal) Milk of Magnesia (internal) Mylanta (internal) Po Chai pills (internal) Po Ney tea (internal) Sup Ling Don tea (internal)	Alka-Seltzer (internal) Assorted herbs (internal) Brioschi (internal) Festal (internal) Gaviscon (internal) Maalox (internal) Milk of Magnesia (internal) Mylanta (internal) Pepto-Bismol (internal) Rolaids (internal)
Cold and Cough	Chinese cough syrup (internal)	Vicks Formula 44 (internal)
Skin Problems	Calamine lotion (topical) Desitin (topical) Aveeno Bath (topical) Tashari skin cream (topical)	Tinactin (topical) Hydrogen peroxide (topical)
Eye Strain		Visine
Insomnia/Sleep Difficulties		Warm Milk (internal) Sominex (internal)

Source: Patricia Hess, "Chinese and Hispanic Elders and OTC drugs." In *Geriatric Nursing, American Journal of Care for the Aged*, Vol. 7, no. 6, November/ December, 1986, pp. 314–18.

A theoretical perspective that views the environment and living nature in terms of interacting wholes has created an interest in the holistic approach to medicine and health care. Lock (1978, p. 151) observes that "Western man, having devoted himself for so long to models based on mechanistic and reductionist explanations of the Newtonian tradition can find few examples in his recent history upon which to draw." Therefore, she points to the need "to reach out to other cultures or sub-cultures where illness is not dealt with as though it were reducible to a totally scientific problem." Based upon her extensive research on East Asian medical practices, Lock demonstrates quite forcefully that the concept of holism is culturally determined.

As noted by Ujimoto (1987a, p. 117), some ethnic groups such as the Japanese, Chinese, Koreans, and Filipinos strongly value the emotional and symbolic support provided the elderly members by their families. Lock (1978, p. 151) observes that in East Asian medical practices "the social and cultural dimensions of the *experience* and *meaning* (emphasis added) of illness are assigned at least equal importance to the naming and removal of a specific disease." In Canadian hospitals, this opportunity to discuss and share the "experience and meaning of illness" with family members is often denied the ethnic minority patient and his or her family members. Visits by family members to assist with eating, clothing, bathing, etc., are often viewed as interference with the tasks of the hospital staff. Ujimoto (1987, p. 118) further notes that the situation becomes even more stressful if the aged patient does not understand the medical instructions provided by the hospital staff.

Summary and Conclusion

In this chapter, we examined the relationship between aging, ethnicity, and health. It was shown that changes in recent immigration to Canada and the rapidly aging population strongly indicate a heterogeneous demographic profile. The implications of demographic change on health care were also discussed.

In order to understand the adjustment to aging by ethnic minorities and their attitudes and behaviour towards aging from a health-care perspective, it was argued that an understanding of what we mean by ethnicity is important. While the conception of ethnicity can be viewed in several different ways as noted by Rosenthal (1986, p. 19), such as ethnicity being synonymous with "traditional" ways of thinking and behaving, it was emphasized that the systemic or integrative approach, which draws upon the different conceptions of ethnicity, is necessary to understand the dynamics of the aging process as it relates to the health status and general well-being of the elderly.

Objective and subjective measures of health were discussed. Although it was not intended to provide a comprehensive review of the literature on aging and health, selected examples were noted to give some direction for future research considerations. Access to Canadian data on the health of ethnic minorities continues to be a problem.

The sharing of emotional and symbolic support by the patient with his or her family is an important consideration to be noted, particularly with reference to the East Asian ethnic groups such as the Chinese-, Korean-, and Japanese-Canadians. One way in which cultural misunderstandings may be reduced is to enable health-care professionals to recognize the non-verbal aspects of communication in health care. This requires a greater sensitivity to the cultural dimensions of how illnesses are viewed in different ethnic groups. In this regard, an excellent start has been made in Ontario by the Multicultural Health Coalition, which was established in 1983 to "promote culturally relevant and appropriate programs, services and materials." Through a series of seminars, workshops, and publications, health professionals and educators are gradually being made aware of the health beliefs of over one hundred different ethnocultural groups currently residing in the greater metropolitan Toronto area. Another example of the active role provided in the promotion of multicultural health care is that of Doctors Hospital in Toronto. This hospital serves a community that has some 35 different minority-language groups, and the diverse concerns of the community are discussed regularly by the hospital's director of Community Health Planning.

Significant developments in addressing the concerns of various ethnocultural communities have also taken place in Ontario. In 1988, the Ministry of Health of Ontario (1990, p. 2) established an Advisory Committe on Multicultural Health to the minister of health. The terms of reference for the advisory committee were as follows:

1. To advise the minister of health on means of facilitating access to health care by all ethnocultural communities across Canada,
2. To encourage communications with ethnocultural groups across the province to receive and share information on how to achieve more culturally sensitive health-service delivery,
3. To work in co-operation with the Ontario Advisory Council on Multiculturalism and Citizenship on issues of mutual concern as they relate to health and health care in Ontario.
4. To recommend specific actions or initiatives to the Ministry of Health that might be incorporated into existing and new health programs and services so that they may be more responsive to the needs of ethnocultural groups.

Since its establishment, the Advisory Committe on Multicultural Health has developed a number of important initiatives. It has developed the multicultural health implementation strategy, which provides a set of guidelines to develop culturally sensitive health programs. The advisory committee was instrumental in making available six hundred additional nursing home beds to meet the needs of the ethnocultural communities. Other areas in which the advisory committee is currently active are in cultural interpretation programs, ethnocultural health information services of Ontario, and in the development of a framework to support the access of ethnocultural groups to various health and social services.

In this chapter, we have noted only some of the major issues related to cultural misunderstanding that may affect the well-being and health of the elderly and the provision of health care. Differences in mental health, stress, and coping strategies were discussed with reference to only a few ethnic groups. Further research in this area, particularly with reference to health and aging of ethnic minorities, is urgently required.

Study Questions

1. What are some of the factors that account for the changing demographic profile of Canadian society?
2. What are some of the ways in which ethnicity can be defined?
3. Why is it important to consider the history of ethnic groups in Canada in order to understand the aging process from a life-span development perspective?
4. In what ways do traditional roles and values influence health-care behaviour?
5. What are some of the differences between the medical and functional models of health evaluation?
6. What are the three key components in the definition of mental health?

Recommended Reading

Chappell, N., Strain, L.A., & Blandford, A.A. (1986). *Aging and health care.* Toronto: Holt, Rinehart & Winston.

Driedger, L., & Chappell, N. (1987). *Aging and ethnicity: Toward an interface.* Toronto: Butterworths.

Marshall, V.W. (Ed.). (1987). *Aging in Canada.* Markham: Fitzhenry & Whiteside.

References

American Association of Retired Persons. (1989). *Empowerment of minority elderly.* Conference and Roundtable Discussions. Washington: Author.

American Association of Retired Persons. (1990). *Aging and old age in diverse populations.* Research papers presented at Minority Affairs Initiative Empowerment Conferences. Washington: Author.

Bolaria, B.S., & Li, P. (Eds.) (1988). *Racial oppression in Canada.* Toronto: Garamond Press.

Breton, R. (1964). Institutional completeness of ethnic communities and the personal relations of immigrants. *American Journal of Sociology, 70,* 193-205.

Canadian Public Health Association. (1988). *Ethnicity and aging.* Ottawa: Author.

Chan, Q.B. (1983). Coping with aging and managing self-identity: The social world of the elderly Chinese women. *Canadian Ethnic Studies, 15,* (3), 36-50.

Chappell, N. (1987). Canadian income and health-care policy: Implications for the elderly. In V.W. Marshall (Ed.), *Aging in Canada* (pp. 489-504). Markham: Fitzhenry & Whiteside.

Chappell, N., Strain, L.A., & Blandford, A.A. (1986). *Aging and health care.* Toronto: Holt, Rinehart & Winston.

City of Toronto, Department of Public Health. (1991). *Health inequalities in the city of Toronto: Summary report*. Toronto: City of Toronto, Department of Public Health, Community Health Information Section.

Connidis, I. (1987). Life in older age: The view from the top. In V.W. Marshall, (Ed.), *Aging in Canada* (pp. 451-472). Markham: Fitzhenry & Whiteside.

D'Arcy, C. (1987). Aging and mental health. In V.W. Marshall (Ed.), *Aging in Canada* (pp. 424-450). Markham: Fitzhenry & Whiteside.

Driedger, L., & Chappell, N. (1987). *Aging and ethnicity: Toward an interface*. Toronto: Butterworths.

Economic Council of Canada. (1987). *Aging with limited health resources*. Proceedings of a Colloquium on Health Care. Ottawa: Supply and Services Canada.

Employment and Immigration Canada. (1986). *Immigration statistics*. Ottawa: Minister of Supply and Services.

Fillenbaum, G.G. (1979). Social context and self-assessments of health among the elderly. *Journal of Health and Social Behavior*, 20, (1), 45-51.

Fry, C.L. (1980). *Aging in culture and society*. Brooklyn: J.F. Bergin.

Gibson, Roce C. (1991). Race and the self-reported health of elderly persons. *Journal of Gerontology*, 46, (5), S235-242.

Gordon, M.M. (1964). *Assimilation in American life*. New York: Oxford University Press.

Hagedorn, R. (1986). *Sociology*. Toronto: Holt, Rinehart & Winston.

Hayashida, C. (1984). *Extending the medical center to a multi-ethnic aging population with long-term care needs*. Paper presented at the 37th Annual Scientific Meeting, The Gerontological Society of America, San Antonio.

Health and Welfare Canada. (1983). *Fact book on aging in Canada*. Ottawa: Author.

Health and Welfare Canada. (1988). *After the door has been opened*. Report on the Canadian Task force on Mental Health Issues Affecting Immigrants and Refugees. Ottawa: Author.

Health and Welfare Canada and Statistics Canada. (1981). *The health of Canadians. Report of the Canada health survey*. Ottawa: Minister of Supply and Services Canada.

Hess, P. (1986, November/December). Chinese and Hispanic elders and OTC drugs. *Geriatric Nursing American Journal of Care for the Aging*, 7, 314-318.

Holzberg, C.S. (1982). Ethnicity and aging: Anthropological perspectives on more than just the minority elderly. *The Gerontologist*, 22, 249-257.

Kendall, P.R.W. (1989a). *The Native Canadian community*. (No. 1 in a Series of Ethnocultural and Health Profile of Communities in Toronto). Toronto: City of Toronto, Department of Public Health, Health Promotion and Advocacy Section.

Kendall, P.R.W. (1989b). *The Chinese community in Toronto*. (No. 2 in a Series of Ethnocultural and Health Profile of Communities in Toronto). Toronto: City of Toronto, Department of Public Health, Health Promotion and Advocacy Section.

Kendall, P.R.W. (1989c). *The Italian Canadian community*. (No. 1 in a Series of Ethnocultural and Health Profile of Communities in Toronto). Toronto: City of Toronto, Department of Public Health, Health Promotion and Advocacy Section.

Kendall, P.R.W. (1989d). *The Greek Canadian community*. (No. 1 in a Series of Ethnocultural and Health Profile of Communities in Toronto). Toronto: City of Toronto, Department of Public Health, Health Promotion and Advocacy Section.

Kendall, P.R.W. (1989e). *The Caribbean community in Toronto*. (No. 1 in a Series of Ethnocultural and Health Profile of Communities in Toronto). Toronto: City of Toronto, Department of Public Health, Health Promotion and Advocacy Section.

Kendall, P.R.W. (1989f). *The Sri Lankan Tamil community in Toronto*. (No. 1 in a Series of Ethnocultural and Health Profile of Communities in Toronto). Toronto: City of Toronto, Department of Public Health, Health Promotion and Advocacy Section.

Kim, U. (1987). Illness behavior patterns of Korean immigrants in Toronto: What are the hidden costs? In K.V. Ujimoto & J. Naidoo (Eds.), *Asian Canadians: Contemporary issues* (pp. 194-219). Guelph: University of Guelph.

Kim, U., & Berry, J. (1986). Predictors of acculturative stress: Korean immigrants in Toronto, Canada. In L.H. Ekstrand (Ed.), *Ethnic minorities and immigrants in cross cultural perspectives* (pp. 159-170). Lisse: Swets & Zeitlinger.

Kobata, F. (1979). The influence of culture on family relations: The Asian American experience. In P. Ragan (Ed.), *Aging parents* (pp. 94-106). Los Angeles: University of Southern California.

Kuo, W.H., & Tsai, Y. (1986, June). Social networking, hardiness and immigrant's mental health. *Journal of Health and Social Behaviour*, 27, 133-149.

Kurzeja, P.L., Koh, T.H., & Liu, W.T. (1986). Ethnic attitudes of Asian American elderly. *Research on Aging*, 8, (1) 110-127.

Lam, L. (1982). The Chinese-Canadian families of Toronto in the 1970s. *International Journal of Sociology of the Family*, 12, 11-32.

Ledoux, M., & Pendakur, R. (1990). *Multicultural Canada: A graphic overview*. Ottawa: Policy and Research Directorate, Multiculturalism Sector, Multiculturalism and Citizenship Canada.

Liu, W.T. (1986). Culture and social support. *Research on Aging*, 8, (1), 57-83.

Liu, W.T. (1986). Health services for Asian elderly. *Research on Aging*, 8, (1), 156-175.

Lock, M. (1979). Scars of experience: The art of moxibustion in Japanese medicine and society. *Culture, Medicine and Psychiatry*, 2, 151-175.

Maddox, G.L., & Douglass, E.B. (1973). Self-assessment of health. A longitudinal study of elderly subjects. *Journal of Health and Social Behavior*, 14, 87-93.

Markides, K.S. (1989). *Aging and health: Perspectives on gender, race, ethnicity, and class*. Newbury Park: Sage Publications Inc.

Marshall, V.W. (1980). *Last chapters: A sociology of aging and dying*. Monterey: Brooks/Cole.

Marshall, V.W. (1987). The health of very old people as a concern of their children. In V.W. Marshall (Ed.), *Aging in Canada* (pp. 473-485). Markham: Fitzhenry & Whiteside.

McDaniel, S.A. (1986). *Canada's aging population*. Toronto: Butterworths.

Ministry of Community and Social Services. (1991). *Redirection of long-term care and support services in Ontario. A public consultation paper*. Toronto: Author.

Ministry of Health Ontario. (1990). *Report of minister of health's advisory committee on multicultural health*. Toronto: Author.

Ministry of Health Ontario. (1991). *Guidelines to promote cultural/racial sensitivity and awareness in health care programs and services*. Toronto: Author.

Moon, S.G. (1982). Adjustment patterns among Koreans in Canada. In C. Yunshik, T.H. Kwon, & P.J. Donaldson (Eds.), *Society in transition with special reference to Korea*. Seoul: Seoul National University Press.

Mutchler, J.E., & Burr, J.A. (1991, December). Racial differences in health and health care service utilization in later life: The effect of socioeconomic status. *Journal of Health and Social Behaviour*, 32, 342-356.

Nishio, H., & Sugiman, P. (1983). Socialization and cultural duality among aging Japanese Canadians. *Canadian Ethnic Studies*, 15, (3), 17-35.

Osako, M.M., & Liu, W.T. (1986). Intergenerational relations and the aged among Japanese Americans. *Research on Aging*, 8, (1), 128-155.

Ontario Advisory Council on Senior Citizens. (1988-1989). *Aging together: An exploration of attitudes towards aging in a multicultural Ontario*. Toronto: Author.

Rempel, J.D., & Havens, B. (1986). *Aged health experiences as interpreted through culture*. Paper presented at the Canadian Sociology and Anthropology Association Annual Meeting, Winnipeg.

Rosenthal, C. (1986). Family support in later life. Does ethnicity make a difference? *The Gerontologist*, 26, (1), 19-24.

Schwenger, C.W. (1987). Formal health care for the elderly in Canada. In V.W. Marshall (Ed.), *Aging in Canada* (pp. 505-519). Markham: Fitzhenry & Whiteside.

Shanas, E., & Maddox, G.L. (1985). Health, health resources, and the utilization of care. In R. Binstock & E. Shanas (Eds.), *Handbook of aging and the social sciences* (pp. 696-726). New York: Van Nostrand Reinhold.

Shapiro, E., & Roos, N.P. (1987). Predictors, patterns and consequences of nursing-home use in one Canadian province. In V.W. Marshall (Ed.), *Aging in Canada* (pp. 520-537). Markham: Fitzhenry & Whiteside.

Simmons-Tropea, D., & Osborn, R. (1987). Disease, survival and death: The health status of Canada's elderly. In V.W. Marshall (Ed.), *Aging in Canada* (pp. 329-423). Markham: Fitzhenry & Whiteside.

Statistics Canada. (1984). *The elderly in Canada.* Ottawa: Minister of Supply and Services Canada.

Statistics Canada and Department of the Secretary of State of Canada. (1986). *Report of the Canadian health and disability survey 1983-1984.* Ottawa: Minister of Supply and Services Canada.

Statistics Canada, Housing, Family and Social Statistics Division. (1990). *A portrait of seniors in Canada.* Ottawa: Minister of Supply and Services.

Stone, L., & Fletcher, S. (1980). *Canada's older population.* Montreal: The Institute for Research on Public Policy.

Ujimoto, K.V. (1987a). The ethnic dimension of aging in Canada. In V.W. Marshall (Ed.) *Aging in Canada* (pp. 111-137). Markham: Fitzhenry & Whiteside.

Ujimoto, K.V. (1987b). Organizational activities, cultural factors, and well-being of aged Japanese Canadians. In D.E. Gelfand & C. Barresi (Eds.), *Ethnicity and aging: New perspectives* (pp. 145-160). New York: Springer.

Ujimoto, K.V. (1987c). Sociodemographic factors and variations in the allocation of time in later life: Aged Japanese Canadians. In K. Altergott (Ed.), *Daily life in later life: A comparative perspective* (pp. 186-204). Beverly Hills: Sage Publication.

Ujimoto, K.V. (1990a). Time-budget methodology for research on aging. *Social Indicators, 23,* 381-393.

Ujimoto, K.V. (1990b, March 8). Health care issues for an aging multicultural society: A role for information technology. Paper presented to the House of Commons Standing Committee on Health and Welfare, Social Affairs, Seniors and the Status of Women. In *Minutes of proceedings and evidence of the standing committee on health and welfare, social affairs, seniors and the status of women,* Issue No. 18. Ottawa: House of Commons.

Ujimoto, K.V., Nishio, H., Wong, P.T.P., & Lam, L. (in press). Cultural factors affecting self-assessment of health satisfaction of Asian-Canadian elderly. In R. Masi, K.A. McLeod, & L. Mensah (Eds.), *Multicultural health and culture: Exploring the relationships.* Toronto: Multicultural Health Coalition.

Ujimoto, K.V., Nishio, H., Wong, P.T.P., & Lam, L. (forthcoming). Comparative aspects of aging Asian-Canadians: Social networks and time budgets.

U.S. Department of Health and Human Services. (1985). *Report of the secretary's task force on black and minority health.* Washington: U.S. Department of Health and Human Services.

Verma, R., Chan, K.B., & Lam, L. (1980). The Chinese-Canadian family: A socio-economic profile. In K. Ishwaran (Ed.), *Canadian families: Ethnic variations* (pp. 138-156). Scarborough: McGraw Hill.

Wong, P.T.P., & Reker, G.T. (1983). *Face validity of the coping inventory.* Paper presented at the 12th Annual Meeting of the Canadian Association on Gerontology, Moncton.

Wong, P.T.P., & Reker, G.T. (1984). *Coping behaviours of successful agers.* Paper presented at the 30th Western Gerontological Society Annual Meeting, Anaheim.

Wong, P.T.P., & Reker, G.T. (1985). Stress, coping, and well-being in Anglo and Chinese elderly. *Canadian Journal on Aging, 4,* 29-37.

Yu, E.S.H. (1986). Health of the Chinese elderly in America. *Research on Aging, 8,* (1), 84-109. Annual Meeting, Anaheim.

Chapter 19

Institutional Care and Health Policy for the Elderly

Vera Ingrid Tarman, University of Toronto

Introduction

An increasing proportion of the Canadian population is composed of the elderly. In 1986, the elderly constituted a little over 10 percent of the population (Stone & Frenken, 1988, p. 9). The projection is that by the turn of the century, this proportion will increase to 12 percent, and by the year 2031, the elderly will constitute almost 24 percent of the population (Messinger & Powell, 1987, p. 570; Statistics Canada, 1990, p. 11). Of particular significance in the present context is the increase in the number of people aged 80 and over, commonly referred to as the "old old" or "frail old," within the elderly group. For instance, while in 1986 this group made up 21 percent of the population aged 65 and over, it is estimated that by the year 2001, this will increase to 24 percent (Fact Book, 1983, p. 18; Stone & Frenken, 1983, p. 35). The rapid increase of this population has important implications for the planning and delivery of health-care services for the elderly.

There is a decline in the physical, mental, and functional abilities with increased age. However, it must be emphasized that only a very small minority of the elderly have severe and incapacitating physical and mental conditions. The general notion that old age is synonymous with total dependence on others and that a majority of the elderly are confined to long-term institutional care is not borne out by the data (Chappell et al., 1986).

The elderly population is by no means homogeneous. Socio-economic status, age, and gender variously determine the need for services. For instance, because of higher life expectancy for women, and most likely, for a majority of them, inferior financial status, more women than men are in need of social and health services in old age (Fact Book, 1983). Women stand a greater likelihood than men of living alone. For example, in the 65 to 74 year age group, 30 percent of women and 11 percent of men live alone. However, for those 75 years of age and over, 36 percent of women live alone, in contrast to 16 percent of men. More women than men also end up in institutions and collective dwellings. For those 75 years of age and over, 20 percent of the women, as compared to 13 percent of men, live in collective dwellings. After the age of 80, there is a sharp increase in the proportion of women living in collective dwellings (Fact Book, 1983, p. 68; Shapiro & Roos, 1987, p. 529). Women, therefore, tend to have a higher rate of institutionalization than men.

As noted before, health continues to decline among elderly persons as they continue to age. There is an increased likelihood of dementia. Overall, approximately 5 to 6 percent of the elderly have dementia; however, these figures increase with advanced age — 20 percent of those 80 years of age and over have dementia. Dementia is progressively debilitating and patients require assistance in their day-to-day existence (Chappell et al., 1986). Functional disability, of course, increases with age, and older people also come to suffer from physical diseases, typically chronic conditions such as heart disease, arthritis, and rheumatism (Chappell et al., 1986).

Most elderly Canadians live in private households in a variety of living arrangements — alone, with a spouse, or with relatives. Family and friends continue to be an important source of social support and care for the elderly. A small proportion of the elderly are under institutional care. The figures for 1986 indicate that 12 percent of the elderly (percentage 65 years and over) were under institutional care. The "old old" population is more likely to be under institutional care. The data for 1986 indicate that 34 percent of the "old old" (percentage 85 +) were under institutional care, which includes nursing homes and institutions for the elderly and the chronically ill (Stone & Frenken, 1988, p. 46). Overall, it is estimated that 20 to 25 percent of the elderly can expect to spend some time in an institution (long-term care facility) before they die (Chappell et al., 1986). If the current demographic trends hold, the important age and gender differences are likely to be even more significant in terms of need and demand for social and health services for the elderly, not only in the community but also in institutions. With an increase of the "old old" population, the demand for and reliance on institutional care is likely to increase further, unless, of course, some alternatives to institutional care (such as community-based homemaker services) are developed.

In spite of the importance of institutional care for the elderly, in particular for the "old old" group requiring extended-care facilities, there is currently no uniform and coherent policy in Canada to regulate the standard of accommodation, funding arrangements, and quality and standards of care. Institutional care, like most other health services, is a provincial responsibility, and thus is subject to variation across the country.

This chapter provides an overview of the special-care facilities in Canada. A detailed discussion is presented on the development of health policy regarding nursing homes in Ontario, with particular emphasis on the funding and regulatory arrangements affecting these institutions and the consequences of provincial policy for the nursing-home industry.

Special-Care Facilities in Canada

There is a variety of institutions providing social and health services for the elderly population. These vary considerably by province. Other than specifying certain conditions that have to be met in order to remain eligible for federal cost-sharing arrangements, provinces make their own decisions regarding the organization and funding of programs.

Data on special-care facilities for the aged are presented in Table 1. It is evident that a large number of special-care facilities are privately owned. This includes proprietary, for-profit institutions that are owned by "private individual, partnership or corporation, regardless of financial aid received by owner or residents, and operated for a profit." (Statistics Canada, 1987). Public ownership refers to those institutions that have municipal, provincial, or federal ownership.

There is considerable variation through the province in type of ownership. For instance, a large proportion of the number of facilities and the number of beds in Quebec, Saskatchewan, and Alberta are under public ownership. On the other hand, in Newfoundland, Prince Edward Island, Nova Scotia, Manitoba, and British Columbia, a very large number of special-care facilities are privately owned.

Institutions also vary in terms of the type and level of care provided. According to federal guidelines issued in 1973, there are five levels of institutional care. These are (1) residential, which includes custodial-care institutions such as rest homes, hostels, and homes for the aged; (2) extended care, which includes nursing homes and their equivalents; (3) chronic hospitals; (4) rehabilitation; and (5) acute hospital care (Kane & Kane, 1985, p. 58; for a detailed description of Ontario's scheme, see Gross & Schwenger, 1981, pp. 28-44).

In spite of these guidelines, there continues to be provincial diversity in funding, health-care provision for the elderly, and even the use of nomenclature for various institutions (Kane & Kane, 1985, p. 59). For instance, the chronic, rehabilitation, and acute hospitals (levels 3 to 5) are automatically funded by all provincial health-insurance programs. Services provided by levels 1 and 2, however, are fully funded only in the provinces of Manitoba and British Columbia. Nursing-home care, specifically, is funded as a universal benefit in Ontario, Manitoba, British Columbia, Quebec,

Table 1 Number of Special-Care Facilities* and Beds for the Aged† — Canada and Provinces, 1986

Province	Public		Private	
	No.	Beds	No.	Beds
Newfoundland	3	576	77	2 741
Prince Edward Island	7	572	23	574
Nova Scotia	21	1 889	91	4 336
New Brunswick	3	290	233	5 789
Quebec	506	27 386	188	7 819
Ontario	96	18 863	537	43 810
Manitoba	30	1 174	99	7 293
Saskatchewan	102	5 057	43	3 444
Alberta	177	10 496	59	5 898
British Columbia	3	160	309	18 462
Northwest Territories & Yukon	4	80	1	4
Canada	952	67 143	1 647	92 170

* Special-care facilities—facilities that provide a measure of care. Data cover residential units only. These facilities are in general maintained for residents who are chronically ill or disabled, in contrast to, for example, a hospital where patients are accommodated on the basis of medical need and are provided with continuing medical care and supporting diagnostic and therapeutic services.

† Aged—those who receive a level of care and whose reason for residing is due principally to the aging process.

Source: Statistics Canada. *List of Canadian Hospitals and Special Care Facilities, 1986.*

Saskatchewan, and Alberta, but not in the four Atlantic provinces. Home-care insurance, as well, is developed (or is in the process of developing) in the same provinces that presently fund nursing homes (Kane & Kane, 1985, p. 15).

It is apparent from the above that in spite of some commonality, there continues to be considerable diversity in the organization of institutional and other health facilities for the elderly. Consequently, it is difficult to present a meaningful analysis, given the time and space, of health-care policy for the aged in the Canadian context. Therefore, the remainder of this chapter deals with the special-care facilities in Ontario and examines the development of health policy towards nursing homes in that province.

Special-Care Facilities in Ontario

Ontario is the most populated province in Canada. A little over 35 percent of the Canadian population lives in Ontario. It also has the largest population of elderly people.

Table 2   Ontario Special-Care Facilities* and Beds for the Aged† — Selected Years

Year	Public		Private Profit		Private Non-Profit	
Year	No.	Beds	No.	Beds	No.	Beds
1980	88	17 883	96	9 189	376	24 185
1982	88	18 079	94	9 513	341	24 550
1984	95	18 746	102	9 864	433	33 226
1986	96	18 863	108	10 184	424	33 626

* Special-care facilities—facilities that provide a measure of care. Data cover residential units only. These facilities are in general maintained for residents who are chronically ill or disabled, in contrast to, for example, a hospital where patients are accommodated on the basis of medical need and are provided with continuing medical care and supporting diagnostic and therapeutic services.

† Aged—those who receive a level of care and whose reason for residing is due principally to the aging process.

Source: Statistics Canada, *List of Canadian Hospitals and Special-Care Facilities, 1980-1986.*

Almost 37 percent of Canada's elderly live in Ontario (Stone & Frenken, 1988, p. 2). Ontario's "old old" population is also quite high. In 1981, almost 40 percent of the elderly were over 75 years of age.

The data on special-care facilities for the elderly in Ontario are presented in Table 2. It is evident that Ontario continues to rely very heavily upon private facilities to provide special-care services for the elderly. In fact, there was a substantial increase in the number of private, for-profit facilities and beds from 1981 to 1986. This is particularly important in view of the discussion that follows regarding incompatibility between the profit motive and quality of care (Baum, 1977; NDP Task Force, 1984; Social Planning Council of Metropolitan Toronto, 1984).

Various provincial regulations govern the funding and operation of institutions for the elderly in Ontario. Although some services for the elderly are covered by other ministries, long-term care in Ontario is primarily within the jurisdiction of the two provincial ministries, the Ministry of Health and the Ministry of Community and Social Services (ComSoc). Both subsidize residential and extended-care services in the community.

Long-term institutional services in Ontario can be placed under the residential, extended care, chronic, and rehabilitation levels of the federal paradigm mentioned earlier. There is some overlapping of services among long-term care institutions. Nursing homes, which fall under the label of extended care (defined as 1.5 hours of nursing and personal care a day in Ontario), are allowed to offer some residential care. Homes for the aged, which are municipal or charitable non-profit institutions funded and regulated by the Ministry of Community and Social Services, are expected to offer custodial rather than health care (Gross & Schwenger, 1981, p. 36). Individual homes offer on average of 60 percent of their beds as extended care (Blake, 1972). Total provincial expenditure for homes for the aged in 1989 was approximately $358 million (Strategies for Change, 1990, Appendix I).

The definition of Ontario nursing homes comes from the 1972 Nursing Homes Act, which states that a nursing home is "any premise maintained and operated for persons requiring nursing care, or in which such care is provided to two or more unrelated persons." In order to maintain a licence and receive funding, nursing homes must offer at least 75 percent of their beds to patients who require "extended care," that is, 1.5 hours or more of nursing and personal care. In actual fact, nursing homes provide over 94 percent of their beds at this level of health care (Hansard, 1984, p. 4853). In 1989, nursing homes received a total of $395.1 million from the Ministry of Health (Strategies for Change, 1990, Appendix I).

While the notion of a nursing home as a business is not incorporated into the legislated definition, it must be noted that nursing homes, as opposed to homes for the aged, are and have been, by and large, private, for-profit entities. Currently, 86 percent of homes are private, for-profit entities (Ministry of Health, 1991).

The Development of Health Policy Regarding Nursing Homes in Ontario

The development of health policy concerning nursing homes in Ontario may best be discussed in two parts. The first will examine the time period beginning with the General Welfare Assistance Act of 1949, which represents the provincial government's first involvement with the nursing-home industry. The primary concerns raised during this time, which extends until the 1972 Nursing Homes Act, relate to the necessity for provincial licensing, uniformity of standards, and universal funding for nursing homes.

The second part deals with what may be characterized as "quality of care issues." The focus is on the debate between various interest groups — government, the opposition party, nursing-home operators, and other interested groups. Provincial policy has been primarily oriented toward reforms. Critics of the proprietary (for-profit) institutions argue that there is a basic contradiction between the profit motive and quality of care that cannot be resolved by reform and more regulation.

I. The Call for Provincial Licensing and Insurance

The debate surrounding nursing homes until 1972 was dominated by two issues: the need for provincial licence and regulation, and the necessity for nursing-home insurance.

Before the amendment to the General Welfare Assistance Act of 1957, which represented the provincial government's first action towards the funding and regulation of homes, nursing homes were for the most part unlicensed, small, private households. The Ontario Health Survey estimated that there were approximately 487 nursing and boarding homes in Ontario, which gave in-bed care suitable for the elderly (Davis, 1950, p. 166).

Upon the implementation of the General Welfare Assistance Act, homes that received payments for their indigents were expected to conform to regulations suggested by a draft provincial bylaw. This act thus represented the first action of government towards recognizing homes as being more than small businesses. Nursing homes were beginning to be seen as providing care for the old and infirm. This required, therefore, some acknowledged standards of care; however, the proposed standards were not generally accepted as adequate.

The basic problem with the act was that it did not address the lack of uniformity of regulations across the province. Homes that did not receive payments did not have to be licensed, or even declare their existence, and of those homes that did receive subsidies, it was up to the individual municipalities to interpret and enforce the suggested provincial regulations.

This variation of standards in nursing homes became an issue shortly after the introduction of the Hospital Insurance and Diagnostic Services Act of 1957 (see LeClair, 1975). Nursing homes were excluded from this federal-provincial cost-shared health-insurance program because they were too disparate and unregulated. Also, they were not seen as providing health care (Blake, Dreezer, & Corder, 1986).

Thus, by the late 1950s, two issues emerged that would shape the history of nursing homes until 1972: inadequate standards and the desire for more extensive government subsidy. These two issues dominated the debate concerning nursing homes. All the parties — nursing-home owners, consumers of nursing-home services, government representatives — were in agreement (though for different motives) in their demand for adequate and uniform standards for health-care services for the elderly.

Nursing-home proprietors, through a newly formed association, lobbied for the extension of universal hospital insurance to cover nursing homes. They were thus motivated to push for provincial licence and uniform regulation of homes in order to receive this funding from the Department of Health, or failing that, to increase their subsidy under the Department of Welfare (Associated Nursing Homes Incorporated, 1964).

The need for provincial licensing and regulations was also becoming obvious to consumers of nursing-home care. In the early 1960s, families of patients had begun to write to their members of parliament and to the media about the poor conditions that they had found in homes. The Ontario Welfare Council released an interim report in 1965, citing 165 homes out of 425 as giving inadequate care (Hansard, 1965, p. 4444).

There was pressure within the provincial government itself, by officials who worked with nursing homes, to seek uniform regulation. This was because a certain percentage of nursing homes at this time were being used as "auxiliary hospitals" wherever there was a shortage of hospital beds. By 1964, there was also a percentage of homes that were licensed as Homes for Special Care, that is, that housed ex-psychiatric patients. Officials found that when they looked for suitable homes to which they could transfer patients, many were not adequate for their purposes (Blake, Dreezer, & Corder, 1986; Blake, 1972).

Despite the apparent congruity of interests of various parties, the government was somewhat reluctant to take steps to transform private institutions for the elderly. Nursing homes continued to be treated as custodial-care institutions rather than as health-care institutions. The government, however, did pass additional regulations and increased funding to the municipalities.

The response in 1965, for example, to the growing concerns over the quality of nursing-home care, was simply to tighten up the General Welfare Assistance regulations, and to increase its municipal payments.

The provincial Nursing Home Act of 1966 stipulated that all nursing homes in Ontario be licensed under the Department of Health. But it was still left to the municipalities to interpret, add to, and enforce the provincial regulations (see An Act to Provide for the Licensing and Regulation of Nursing Homes). This act, therefore, did not establish uniform standards for nursing homes across the province.

Under the Nursing Home Act of 1966, nursing homes were still not considered eligible for provincial hospital insurance, despite their having been taken over by the Department of Health. They were still being funded, on a means-test basis, by the Department of Welfare, now named the Department of Family and Social Services. They were still primarily seen as offering custodial rather than health care.

The extension of hospital insurance was seen, however, as necessary for the Nursing Home Act to be effectual. The act had been modelled after the Homes for Special Care Act, in that nursing homes were now officially expected to act as inexpensive substitutes for hospital beds, of which there was an increasing shortage (Hansard, 1966, p. 1087). However, unlike Homes for Special Care, nursing-home beds were not subsidized and consequently could not fulfil the function of a hospital bed, since people were reluctant to transfer patients from the hospital to a facility that they had to pay for.

Despite its failure to provide uniform funding and regulations, this act did have a significant effect on the nursing-home industry in other respects. Many previously unlicensed or smaller homes were forced to close down because they could not afford to adapt to the new regulations. According to one source, as many as 70 homes closed down in the period of a year and a half (Hansard, 1968, p. 2342). "In the Canadian nursing home industry," the Financial Post forecast, "the days of the 'ma and pa' homes may be numbered" (Bruchovsky, 1970, p. 21).

Bruchovsky further states: "Emerging are corporate chains, building large and modern facilities and very intent on expansion." Indeed, by 1970, in the space of less than five years, there were six public investor-owned chains in Canada, with at least two operating in Ontario. There was a growing optimism about the financial feasibility of nursing homes, and of the profit that could be generated from a nursing-home business (Bruchovsky, 1970, p. 21).

At this juncture, the provincial government passed additional regulations. The Nursing Home Act of 1972 signalled at last the greater willingness of the provincial government to become involved with nursing-home care. These regulations were to be enforced by the Ministry of Health, rather than the municipalities. This act also provided the extended-care hospital insurance for nursing home residents, (and some homes for the aged residents), under the newly amalgamated Ontario Health Insurance Plan (Nursing Home Act, 1972).

The act thus signalled a turning point for the government in its recognition of the changing function of nursing homes. The role of nursing homes was shifting from profit and "custodial-care" to "health-care" institutions for the old and infirm.

An equally important feature of the act was the control government took over the numbers and allocation of beds to be licensed. There was systematic effort to distribute beds across the province so that rural as well as urban communities would have access to nursing-home care. The allocation of beds would be based on demonstrated need. The utilization of the district-health councils one year later was an effort to formalize this system of demonstrated need to 3.5 beds per 1 000 population (Potter, Hansard, 1973, p. 2170).

There was also a decided effort to control the costs and thus the numbers of beds that government had to subsidize (Hansard, 1972, p. 799; Chatfield, cited by Engel, 1973, p. 17). This was a valid concern as federal aid towards nursing homes would not be forthcoming until the Extended Care Block grant in 1977 (Blake, Dreezer, & Corder, 1986).

Government, by controlling beds in this way, was thus able to provide the popular extended-care insurance within its own regional and budgetary constraints. This rationing strategy, however, in some areas inadvertently created a shortage of nursing-home beds.

The situation proved to be advantageous for the larger nursing-home chains. The smaller "independent" nursing homes could not compete with larger "corporate" institutions, and were forced to close down. It has been estimated that 148 homes closed down after 1971, as a result of the inability of homes, particularly smaller homes, to comply with regulations (Duggan, 1985). According to the Nursing Home Association, the low per-diem rates of the extended-care subsidy made it difficult for homes to afford the higher standards required by the act. Nursing homes, in order to be licensed, were required to provide extended-care insurance for 75 percent of their beds. Nursing homes could not offset this cost by charging extra fees to their clients, as the 1973 amendment to the Nursing Home Act disallowed any charge that exceeded the fee schedule (Potter, Hansard, 1973, p. 326).

The smaller nursing homes already in existence could not compete with the larger homes. Also, new small enterprises were not viable because of the large capital outlay required to open new premises (Hansard, 1972, p. 1277). These conditions contributed to the increase of larger homes that could afford the capital costs and still make a profit with the extended-care subsidy.

It is not surprising to find, therefore, that since 1971 the average size of homes has increased from 44 beds to 89 beds (Scully, 1986, p. 13). By 1983, 41 percent of the nursing-home beds in Ontario were owned by the ten largest nursing-home companies active in Ontario (Privatization Project, Feb. 1984). By 1991, there were 259 corporate-owned homes (three or more homes owned by one company) out of 337 homes (spokes-person for the Ministry of Health, 1991). The act thus created a situation that favoured the emergence of larger homes and which enabled them to make, according to the Financial Post (Engel, 1973), record profits.

Linda McQuaig of the *The Globe and Mail* (1984) analyzed this favourable situation for the large nursing homes as analogous to the taxicab business.

> Like the taxicab business, nursing homes benefit from a licensing system that limits competition. . . . But the nursing home business has another advantage not enjoyed by the cab industry: a huge and growing demand for its services. In the taxi business, it would be comparable to an ever present and growing line-up of customers ready to jump in as soon as the cab is empty. . . . And payment is guaranteed . . . to continue the taxi analogy, it would be as if all those customers lined up to get into the cab had government charge accounts . . . under the current system . . . private nursing home operators, in many ways, are enjoying the best that both the private and public sectors have to offer. The firms are assured of government subsidies and provincially set prices but also enjoy benefits of private enterprise profits.

It was also during this time that various interest groups entered into the controversial debate concerning the type of ownership of homes (for-profit versus non-profit) and quality of care. For instance, the private contenders, such as the Nursing Home Association, called for a higher per diem, or for less governmental control of the competitive forces of the private nursing-home marketplace (Duggan, 1985; ONHA). The public or non-profit advocates, such as the New Democratic Party (1984) or the Social Planning Council (1984; see also Concerned Friends, 1984) felt that the profit motive was incompatible with quality of care, even in the best of conditions, and called for the creation of non-profit nursing homes (for a review of arguments, see Tarman, 1990).

In summary, the provincial policy, particularly the Nursing Homes Act of 1972, has had some beneficial results. The act provided uniform operating standards for nursing homes and called for equitable distribution of facilities across the province, so that rural as well as urban residents would have access to them. Many small nursing homes, because of the costs, could not comply with the standards and had to close down. New small enterprises were not viable because of the large capital outlay required to open new facilities. This situation favoured the emergence of larger homes under corporate ownerships. This created a basic contradiction between the profit motive and provision of quality care for the elderly.

2. The Calls for Quality Care

The second part of this history looks at the issues that emerged as a result of the 1972 Nursing Homes Act. Government remained hesitant to intervene in nursing-home matters until the early 1980s, when policy towards homes shifted and became strongly reformist in nature.

Because of the repercussions of the nursing-home legislation, the government has, through the years, been somewhat reluctant to enforce regulations and address the suggestions for nursing-home reform put forth by many groups. Government has been hesitant to intervene and further jeopardize the profit interests of the nursing-home business. This led to a series of confrontations in the late 1970s among the Ministry of Health, nursing homes, and the public.

The ministry, for example, was reluctant to prosecute nursing-home owners for any violations of standards, particularly if it would result in the closing of homes. The ministry was not anxious to exacerbate the bed shortage, particularly in rural areas (Hansard, 1978, p. S-1113). It preferred instead to advise and seek co-operation from nursing-home operators. As one spokesperson for the regulatory authority in the Ministry of Health explained: "Let me stress that we are not anxious to close any nursing home because the need for such institutions is great. We would prefer to develop an atmosphere of co-operation which would be of mutual benefit" (cited in Baum, 1977, p. 70).

The ministry, furthermore, was reluctant to make inspection reports pertaining to nursing homes' compliance with regulations and standards available to the public. The ministerial response was based on considerations of confidentiality; that is, the records were confidential for medical reasons; instead, only summaries of the reports would be given (Hansard, 1978, p. 4621; 1981, p. 584).

The same arguments were made to protect the confidentiality of profits and losses of nursing homes. The provincial government argued that to demand such information was an invasion into private property rights (Hansard, 1983, p. 1189). There was a concern raised by some (Concerned Friends, 1984) that profits generated from nursing-home care were not being reinvested into the homes (in terms of upkeep), but were instead going into other business ventures such as life insurance and computer technology.

As a result, beginning as early as 1977, there were calls for an inquiry into nursing homes. The ministry, however, felt that a highly publicized inquiry was too expensive and quite unnecessary (Timbrell, Hansard, 1977, p. 2454). Instead, it granted slight improvements to the inspections procedure and amended a regulation in the Nursing Homes Act in 1980 (Hansard, 1978, p. S-1094; 1980, p. 5029).

Calls to make nursing homes non-profit were also continuously opposed. The fundamental and growing concern held by many (NDP, 1984; Concerned Friends, 1984; Social Planning Council, 1984), was that nursing homes, as proprietary institutions, were more interested in making a profit than in providing good-quality care. To reduce costs, nursing-home operators, for example, followed the practice of contracting out health and maintenance services, to avoid hiring the better-paid unionized workers (Hansard, 1977, p. 629; 1983, p. 3039; NDP, 1984, p. 22). To increase their incomes, some institutions were levying additional charges for necessary services, such as laundry or transportation, that were not covered under the extended-care or resident co-payment fees (Social Planning Council, 1984, p. 101). Some nursing homes also practised what is referred to as "cream-skimming," that is, accepting only the least problematic and thus least costly patients into their homes (Social Planning Council, 1984, p. 19).

There was an implicit concern in the government, however, that without the profit motive many nursing-home operators would lose incentive, close down homes, and thus exacerbate the bed shortage. The general response to the call to make nursing homes non-profit was that problems in quality of care in nursing homes resulted more from a faulty inspections procedure than from the type of ownership (Hansard, 1978, p. 2409).

The issues that emerged in the late 1970s indicate that government was reluctant to intervene into the "business matters" of the nursing home industry. The 1972 Nursing Homes Act, which was intended to improve the conditions of nursing homes, was inadvertently the cause for potentially greater problems within them. Yet government was hesitant to intervene still further, as it seemed that increased state intervention would jeopardize private involvement in nursing-home care. It seemed inevitable that even more small homes would close down if forced to conform to regulations; as well, the larger homes would lose incentive to provide care if their profit-making mechanisms were challenged and/or curtailed.

Since the early 1980s, however, there has been a detectable shift in government's priorities regarding nursing-home policy. Highly publicized events and the growing strength of public interest groups have elicited a decisive increase in governmental intervention. These interventions have promoted nursing homes as reliable health-service entities.

Some examples of intervention bear mention, as they are in sharp contrast to government's previous reluctance to interfere in the private market. In 1983, the Minister of Health made inspection reports available to the public (Norton, 1983, p. 8). Not incidental to this reform was the nursing-home industry's own initiative to accredit nursing homes by the Canadian Council on Hospital Accreditation. The Ministry of Health publicly supported this action (Norton, 1983, p. 15; Hansard, 1984, p. S-53).

The focus on resident and family input into homes increased in the 1980s. In 1983, the Minister of Health set policy to ensure that residents be informed of their right to form a resident's council (Norton, 1983). In 1987, the Ministry of Health passed the Nursing Homes Ammendment Act, which included an extensive Residents' Bill of Rights. The 1987 legislation also called for a broader role for the non-profit sector in institutional care, as well as for increased consumer input into the development of higher standards of care.

Finally, in 1990 an interdisciplinary effort of the Ministries of Health and Community and Social Services, and the Office of Senior Citizens' Affairs presented *Strategies for Change*. This is a blueprint for the reform of all long-term care services in Ontario. It proposes a more efficient, better co-ordinated service delivery system, which promises better access to nursing-home services and even greater consumer input. This document does not, however, address the profit/non-profit mix of nursing homes.

Recently it appears that the government has been more willing to intervene to ensure uniform standards through various regulations, as well as to be more receptive to public input and public surveillance of nursing homes through the 1987 nursing-home legislation and the 1990 proposed reform of long-term care.

Summary and Conclusions

A variety of institutions provide social and health services for the elderly population. In spite of the importance of institutional care for the elderly, in particular the "old old" group, there is a lack of a uniform and coherent Canadian policy and regulation that govern the standards of accommodation, funding arrangements, and quality and standards of care. As in other matters of health care, institutional care is a provincial responsibility. Other than certain conditions that have to be met to maintain their eligibility for federal cost-sharing arrangements, provinces more or less set their own requirements for operation and funding arrangements of special-care facilities for the elderly.

Data show that a large number of special-care facilities in Canada are privately owned, which includes proprietary, for-profit facilities. There is considerable variation in provinces of type of ownership. For instance, Quebec is one of the provinces with a high proportion of facilities and beds under public ownership. In Ontario, on the other hand, a very large number of the facilities are under private ownership. In fact, there was a substantial increase from 1981 to 1983 in the number of both privately owned facilities and beds in Ontario.

The discussion on the development of health policy regarding nursing homes in Ontario indicates that the provincial policy has not been oriented toward a complete transformation of the nursing-home industry. The provincial government for the most part has been content to "regulate" the industry by requiring accommodation and health standards. Though these requirements have had beneficial results, they have also led to an increase in the number and size of facilities under private and corporate ownership. This situation has proved to be advantageous for larger units, enabling them to make large profits. The critics charge that the profit motive is incompatible with quality of care. The data presented above suggest that nursing homes use various strategies to cut costs or levy additional charges to residents for necessary services, or practise what is referred to as "cream-skimming."

This continued reliance on proprietary facilities is particularly significant in view of the current concern about health costs and quality of care. Institutional care is quite expensive, whether provided by public or private facilities. The proprietary institutions, however, are more likely to be oriented to profit and less concerned about quality of care. The debate about health costs in addition to health-promotion strategies perhaps should also include the current organization and financial arrangements of health-care institutions (in this case, special health-care facilities for the elderly) and health-care delivery systems. The critics of the proprietary, for-profit institutions advocate their complete transformation to public non-profit facilities. Government "reforms" such as various regulations, legislation, and the new policy blueprint do not alter the basic contradiction between profit and quality of care, nor do they significantly improve the quality of care or reduce the cost of health-care services for the elderly.

Study Questions

1. Briefly discuss the development of policy regarding nursing homes in Ontario and its impact on the provision of health services for the elderly.
2. It is argued that reforms do not resolve the basic contradiction between profits and quality of care. Discuss this in view of the material presented in this chapter.
3. Why, in your opinion, has the provincial government been content to "regulate" the nursing-home industry rather than transforming it completely to a non-profit, public ownership industry?
4. Discuss briefly the mechanisms used by the owners to reduce costs and how these interfere with the provision of care.
5. How would you explain the continued existence of privately owned, special-care facilities in the context of universal public funding of health-care services?

Recommended Reading

Chappell, N., Strain, L., & Blandford, A. (1986). *Aging and health care: A social perspective*. Toronto: Harcourt Brace Jovanovich.

Gross, M., & Schwenger, C. (1981). *Health-care costs for the elderly in Ontario: 1976-2026*. Toronto: Ontario Economic Council, Occasional Papers 11.

Kane, R.L., & Kane, R.A. (1985). *A will and a way: What Americans can learn about long-term care from Canada*. Santa Monica: Rand Corporation.

Social Planning Council of Metropolitan Toronto. (1984, October). *Caring for profit: The commercialization of human services in Ontario*. Christa Freiler, Project Director. Toronto: Author.

Tarman, V. (1990). *Privatization and health care: The case of Ontario nursing homes*. Toronto: Garamond Press.

References

Alberta Nursing Home Review Panel. (1982). *Report and recommendations*. Ministry of Hospitals and Medical Care.

An act to provide for the licensing and regulation of nursing homes. (1966). *Revised Statutes of Ontario* (Chap. 99). Toronto.

Associated Nursing Homes Incorporated. (1964, July). A report concerning nursing homes and nursing home residents in the province of Ontario to the senate of Canada special committee on aging. In *History of associated nursing homes incorporated (Ontario): 1959-1964*. Toronto: Ontario Nursing Homes Association.

Baum, D.J. (1977). *Warehouses for death: The nursing home industry*. Don Mills: Burns and MacEachern.

Blake, B. (1972, October 15). Speech to OHA Small Hospital Forum. Toronto.

Blake, B., Dreezer, S., & Corder, D. (1986, October). Interview with spokespersons at Ministry of Health. Toronto.

Bruchovsky, A. (1970, March 21). Nursing homes plan to grow with 'good quality care.' *Financial Post*, p. 21.

Chappell, N., Strain, L., & Blandford, L. (1986). *Aging and health care: A social perspective*. Toronto: Harcourt Brace Jovanovich.

Concerned Friends of Ontario Citizens in Care Facilities. (1984, September). Consumer concerns and recommendations related to nursing home care in Ontario. A brief to the Honourable Larry Grossman, Minister of Health. Toronto: Author.

Davis, G. (Chairman). (1950). Report of the Ontario Health Survey Committee. Vol. 1. Toronto: Ontario Health Survey Committee.

Duggan, R. (1985, September). Interview with spokesperson at Ontario Nursing Home Association. Toronto.

Engel, R. (1973, May 12). Nursing home concept catching on. *Financial Post*, pp. 17-18.

Estes, C.I., Gerard, L.E., Zones, J.S., & Swan, J.H. (1984). *The political economy, health and aging*. Boston: Little, Brown & Company.

Fact book on aging in Canada. (1983, October 24-27). Second Canadian Conference on Aging. Ottawa: Government of Canada.

Gross, M., & Schwenger, C. (1981). *Health care costs for the elderly in Ontario: 1976-2026*. Toronto: Ontario Economic Council, Occasional Papers 11.

Hansard official report of debates, 1960-1986. Toronto: Legislative Assembly of Ontario.

Kane, R.L., & Kane, R.A. (1985). *A will and a way: What Americans can learn about long-term care from Canada*. Santa Monica: Rand Corporation.

LeClair, M. (1975). The Canadian health care system. In S. Andreopoulos (Ed.), *National health insurance: Can we learn from Canada?* (pp. 11-89). Malabar: Robert E. Krieger.

Messinger, H., & Powell, B. (1987). The implications of Canada's aging society on social expenditures. In V.W. Marshall (Ed.), *Aging in Canada* (pp. 569-585). Markham: Fitzhenry & Whiteside.

McQuaig, L. (1984, May 17). Nursing homes flourish under taxpayer's umbrella. *The Globe and Mail*, p. M2.

Ministry of Health. (1991, July). Telephone interview with the spokesperson for the Ministry of Health. Toronto.

NDP Caucus Task Force Report. (1984, June). *Aging with dignity*. Toronto: Author.

Norton, K. (1983, September 22). Remarks by the Honourable Keith Norton, Minister of Health, to the Ontario Nursing Home Association. Toronto.

Nursing Homes Act, 1972. (1972). *Revised statutes of Ontario, 1972* (Chap. 11, p. 87). Toronto.

Ontario Nursing Home Association's Role Study Task Force. (1983). *Position paper and recommendations regarding the role of nursing homes as developed by the ONHA*. Toronto: Author.

Panitch, L. (1977) The role and nature of the Canadian state. In L. Panitch (Ed.), *The Canadian state: Political economy and political power* (pp. 3-27). Toronto: University of Toronto Press.

Privatization Project. (1984, February). Toronto: Social Planning Committee of Metro Toronto.

Scully, D. (1986, February). History of nursing homes in Ontario. *Ontario Nursing Home Journal*, 2, (1), 12-15.

Shapiro, E., & Roos, N. (1987). Predictors, patterns and consequences of nursing-home use in one Canadian province. In V.W. Marshall (Ed.), *Aging in Canada*. (pp. 520-537). Markham: Fitzhenry & Whiteside.

Social Planning Council of Metropolitan Toronto. (1984, October). *Caring for profit: The commercialization of human services in Ontario*. Christa Freiler, Project Director. Toronto.

Statistics Canada. (1981-1987). *List of Canadian hospitals and special care facilities, 1980-86*. Ottawa: Statistics Canada, Health Division.

Statistics Canada. (1990). *A portrait of seniors in Canada: Target group project*. Ottawa: Minister of Supply and Services.

Stone, L., & Frenken, H. (1988). *Canada's seniors: 1986 census of Canada*. Ottawa: Minister of Supply and Services.

Strategies for change: Comprehensive reform of Ontario's long-term care services. (1990). Toronto: Queen's Printer.

Swartz, D. (1977). The politics of reform: conflict and accommodation in Canadian health policy. In L. Panitch (Ed.), *The Canadian state: Political economy and political power* (pp. 311-42). Toronto: University of Toronto Press.

Tarman, V. (1990). *Privatization and health care: The case of Ontario nursing homes*. Toronto: Garamond Press.

Part Six

Mental Illness,
Psychiatry,
and Sociology

Introduction

A number of previous readings in the text indicate that while there has been a general improvement in the health status of the Canadian population, substantial disparities in life expectancies and mortality rates continue to persist across income and occupational groups and for the unemployed and Native Canadians. Evidence presented in Chapter 20 by Stolzman shows that disparities in the rates and types of mental disorders also prevail across social classes, with the rates of mental disorders being highest in the lower classes.

Stolzman discusses different theoretical interpretations of the relationship between class and mental disorder. After a brief outline of the genetic and social selection hypotheses, explanations that emphasize causation are discussed in more detail. The societal reaction model maintains that the purported higher prevalence of mental disorder in the lower classes is primarily an artifact of class bias as to who gets labelled as mentally ill in society. The social stress hypothesis attributes the proclivity of lower-class persons to become mentally disordered to the pressures and deprivations associated with their life circumstances. A modified version of this interpretation argues that lower-class people are more prone to psychological disturbances because they have fewer and less adequate resources for coping with stress than do people in higher social class positions. The examination of all these factors to promote a comprehensive understanding of the connections between social class and mental disorder is stressed.

Stolzman also examines differences in psychiatric treatment by social class. It is contended that a two-tiered mental health-care system, in which higher-class patients receive quality psychotherapy while lower-class patients are relegated to custodial care or less effective organic treatments, persists in North American society.

In conclusion, Stolzman proposes some reforms aimed at reducing the unequal allocation of psychotherapy. One of the reforms suggests that medical students in psychiatry do substantial course work in the humanities and social sciences. This would expose students to various psychosocial factors that impinge upon mental health and psychiatric care, and help to alleviate an apparent obliviousness to these factors that is fostered by existing medical education and training.

In Chapter 21, Dickinson also notes that although the Canadian health-care system has many strengths, mental health is becoming a major problem. He argues that because it is primarily an illness-care system, it is not equipped to deal with the chronic and degenerative health problems that predominate. It has been estimated that at least one in eight Canadians will experience a mental health problem serious enough to require hospitalization. In the United States, the estimated figure is as high as one in five. While the numbers of mental hospitals and patients in them have decreased over the past few decades, the number of persons receiving in-patient psychiatric services in general hospitals has increased. Since many people are never admitted to hospital for treatment of their mental health problems, an unknown number are seen as out-patients or receive no help and add to the growing ranks of the homeless. The cost of mental health problems was estimated to be more than $136 billion in 1992 in the United States; in Canada, the cost of hospital days alone exceeded one billion dollars in 1978.

Dickinson describes how various solutions to the problem of mental disorders follow from the ways in which the problem is defined. In Western societies, confinement in asylums was the main solution to the problem of mental illness up until the 1960s. By the end of the 1980s, there were a number of distinct groups, each with different ideas about the nature of the problem and the most appropriate solution to it, all trying to have their interests entrenched in policy: medical professionals and others who maintained that the problem was really mental illness and should be treated like every other illness; non-medical professionals such as social workers, psychologists, and other psychother-apists who argued that the problem was various types of psycho-social problems in living, requiring their therapeutic assistance; and members of the psychiatric consumer/survivor movement who maintained that whatever the true nature of the problem, those suffering from it should be responsible for its definition and solution.

A number of common themes in current policy initiatives are examined: an increased emphasis on mental health promotion and the prevention of mental dis-orders; the protection of human rights and freedoms; a greater emphasis on commu-nity care; and co-ordination of service planning and development. Dickinson discusses some of the contradictions embedded within and between these themes. He suggests that rather than being the solution to existing problems, current initiatives may indeed be creating new ones.

Chapter 20

The Distribution and Treatment of Mental Disorders by Social Class: A Review of the Research and Theoretical Interpretations

James D. Stolzman, Dalhousie University

Introduction

Sociology's distinctiveness as a perspective on human behaviour is founded on the observation that the way in which groups and societies are organized or structured has a profound effect on how its members think, act, and feel. A key aspect of any society's structure is its system of stratification. This term refers to the social arrangements whereby people receive unequal amounts of, and have unequal access to, whatever is considered valuable in that society. Most writers on stratification agree that foremost among the valued resources distributed in society are wealth, social prestige, and power.

Canada, along with most other Western industrial capitalist nations, has what sociologists call a class type of stratification system. In a class system the various occupational positions form a hierarchy based primarily upon inequalities of wealth, property, and income. Compared to other types of stratification systems, class societies are relatively open. This is to say that they permit individuals to move up or down the hierarchy on the basis of their personal qualities and achievements. Consequently, class societies are typically highly competitive. While existing inequalities of power and privilege may interfere with its realization, the ideal of equal opportunity is central to the beliefs that serve to legitimize this type of stratification system.

In class-stratified societies, the inequalities of wealth and power tend to be manifested in a variety of ways. Social research has repeatedly demonstrated that people's standing in the class system partly determines the kinds of lives they lead, the kinds of attitudes they hold, and the kinds of opportunities that are available to them. Indeed, social class has proved to be sociology's most powerful explanatory variable; it correlates with a multitude of behaviour patterns, beliefs, lifestyles, and "life chances." By the latter term I mean the probability of securing resources that will promote and enhance the quality of one's life. These might include the opportunity to get a good education, to hold a rewarding job, to live a long life, to travel extensively, and to be healthy, both physically and mentally.

The last point brings us to the subject matter of this chapter. Other chapters in this volume have underlined the fact that physical health and illness are unequally distributed across the stratification system. More specifically, "social class gradients of mortality and life expectancy have been observed for centuries, and a vast body of evidence has shown consistently that those in the lower classes have higher mortality, morbidity, and disability rates" (Syme & Berkman, 1981, p. 35). Why this is so is a matter of some controversy that will be considered here only insofar as it bears on the one facet of the issue — namely, the relationship between social class and mental disorders.[1] Discussion of this issue will begin by surveying some of the major studies that have helped to establish that such a connection is real. I will then identify and comment upon various interpretations that have been offered to explain the nature of the relationship between social class and mental disorder. The chapter will conclude with an examination of how social class affects the type and quality of treatment received by the mentally ill.

Empirical Research on Class and Mental Disorder

One of the first systematic studies in the social epidemiology of mental disorder was conducted by Faris and Dunham (1939) in Chicago during the 1930s. They combed the admission records of both public and private mental hospitals to identify approximately 35 000 persons who had received psychiatric care over a twelve-year period. They then plotted the addresses of these individuals on large census maps of the city. What this procedure revealed, among other things, was that the highest rates of schizophrenia were found in inner-city districts where persons of low status were concentrated. The more affluent areas of the city, on the other hand, tended to be the districts where the least number of mental patients and ex-patients resided. While Faris and Dunham's conclusion that poverty led to a higher incidence of mental disorder was challenged on a number of methodological and theoretical points, their study did lend credibility to the notion that people's position in the class structure had implications for their mental health.

The most famous study to pursue this implication was carried out by Hollingshead and Redlich (1958) in New Haven, Connecticut in the early 1950s. These authors were concerned that previous research such as Faris and Dunham's, may have underestimated the extent of mental disorders in the middle and upper classes, because it was based solely on hospital admissions. Hollingshead and Redlich sought to remedy this deficiency by undertaking an ambitious case-finding procedure. A thorough examination of the records of hospitals, clinics, and psychiatrists in private practice enabled them to identify a total "psychiatric population" of almost 2 000 New Haven residents. For purposes of comparison, the authors also gathered information on a large random sample of the general population of New Haven. To determine a person's social standing, Hollingshead and Redlich devised a composite index that encompassed occupation, education, and location of residence. Utilizing this index, they divided the community into five social classes. Next they compared the social class distribution of the general (non-patient) population with that of psychiatric patients. The logic of this research design was that if there were no relationship between social class and the incidence of mental disorders, then each of the five classes should be present in the psychiatric population in roughly the same percentage as it was in the general population. Hollingshead and Redlich's data clearly indicated that this was not the case. Instead, the social-class breakdown of the two populations showed that the highest class in New Haven was significantly underrepresented, the three middle or in-between classes were moderately underrepresented, and the lowest class was substantially overrepresented. For example, although the lowest social class, according to Hollingshead and Redlich's index, included just under 18 percent of New Haven's citizens, it contributed nearly 37 percent of the psychiatric patients. What is more, this strong association between social class and being a mental patient still existed after the authors controlled for the effects of sex, age, race, and marital status. Their findings also revealed an interesting pattern with respect to class and the type of mental disorder. What they discovered was that members of the lower classes were more likely to be diagnosed as suffering from relatively severe disorders (psychoses), whereas members of the higher classes were more frequently diagnosed as having milder disorders (neuroses).

As its authors were well aware, a major limitation of Hollingshead and Redlich's study was that their data pertained only to the relationship between social class and the prevalence of *treated* mental disorders. They realized, however, that there are very good grounds for assuming that those who receive psychiatric or other treatment for their problems by no means constitute all the mentally disordered persons in society. For this reason, it is not possible to speak of the "true" or "total" prevalence of mental disorders unless one has taken measures to locate such untreated cases. In the absence of such measures, studies such as Hollingshead and Redlich's do not necessarily indicate that persons of the lower class are more apt to be psychologically disturbed. It might only mean that they are more likely than their higher-class counterparts to visit a psychiatrist or to end up in a mental institution. What is needed to determine the relation between class and the actual prevalence of mental disorders in society is a procedure for assessing mental health in the general population, quite independent of whether those judged to be disordered are receiving treatment of any kind. Despite this shortcoming of their study, Hollingshead and Redlich can be credited with marshalling impressive evidence to suggest that there is an inverse relation between social class and rates of treated mental disorders. They also laid the groundwork for subsequent studies that were designed to approximate the distribution of untreated disorders in the population.

A study conducted by Leo Srole (1962) and a number of his associates in the 1950s attempted to ascertain the true prevalence of mental disorder among a large cross section of persons who lived in the Midtown Manhattan area of New York City. Over 1 600 adults in a sample of randomly selected households were interviewed. Information was collected on their personal background, past history of psychological distress and psychotherapy, and responses to an index of psychiatric symptoms that was constructed for the study. The interviewers also rated the respondents' tension level both at the beginning and at the conclusion of the interview. All of these data were then turned over to a team of psychiatrists, which was asked to evaluate the respondents' mental health in terms of four categories, ranging from "well" to "impaired." Perhaps the most remarkable finding of this study was that less than 20 percent of those interviewed were assessed as well or relatively free from noticeable psychiatric symptoms. This rather amazing fact aside, the research once again showed that class (or what the authors called "socio-economic status") exhibited a substantial and consistent relation to rated psychiatric condition. To illustrate, Srole and his colleagues found that their lowest socio-economic group had almost twice the percentage of respondents considered "psychiatrically impaired" as did the higher socio-economic group. Moreover, the latter had approximately three times the proportion of people diagnosed as "well" compared to the low-status group.[2]

Another major epidemiological survey of mental disorder was the so-called Stirling County survey carried out by Leighton et al., (1963) in a rural area of Nova Scotia during the late 1950s.[3] One aspect of the study involved examining the records of local hospitals and physicians. Information obtained in this manner permitted the investigators to determine the prevalence of treated cases and to select a sample of previously hospitalized mental patients for interviewing. But, like the researchers of the Midtown Manhattan study, Leighton et al., were interested in the prevalence of untreated disorders. Thus they developed a questionnaire and inventory of psychiatric symptoms that were administered to a random sample of over 1 300 Stirling County residents. The data collected from these interviews were then evaluated by at least two psychiatrists to assess the likelihood of respondents being considered mentally ill if they had been diagnosed by a psychiatrist applying the prevailing standards of the profession. The results of this study again suggested that the incidence of untreated cases in the population at large is extremely high. While it was not the focus of their research, Leighton et al., did include a measure of socio-economic status and, once again, they found that mental disorder was most common among members of the lowest socio-economic category.

These studies are commonly acknowledged to be the classical research ventures in this area of inquiry. Subsequent research has generally confirmed the patterns reported above. Myers and Bean (1968), for example, did a follow-up study of New Haven ten years after Hollingshead and Redlich's that corroborated the main findings of the original study. In 1974, Dohrenwend and Dohrenwend exhaustively analyzed the findings of all published studies on the true prevalence of psychopathology by social class. While acknowledging the difficulty of comparing results of studies based on what are often very discrepant methodologies, they nevertheless assert that the most consistent finding has been that lower socio-economic status is related to differential rates of mental disorder. The Dohrenwends reported that of 33 communities studied by various researchers, 28 yielded the highest rates of psychological disturbance in the lowest class. This general pattern also squares with the results of a variety of social surveys carried out in recent decades that indicate persons in the lower classes are, on average, more unhappy, more worried, and less hopeful about the future than are persons in the middle and upper classes.[4]

To summarize, the proposition that a relationship exists between social class and mental disorder can be regarded as fairly well established. However, the coarse generalization that social class and mental illness are inversely related cannot be accepted without a couple of important reservations or provisos. First of all, it seems clear that this pattern does not apply to all types of disorders. In their aforementioned review of studies in this area, the Dohrenwends found that the relationship held most strongly for personality disorders and schizophrenia. But no relationship was discovered between socioeconomic status and the prevalence of affective psychoses (i.e., severe mania and/or depression). They also noted that the situation with respect to the class distribution of less severe disorders, the neuroses, is inconclusive. Slightly more than half of the studies examined showed an inverse relationship between class and the prevalence of neuroses, but a sizeable minority revealed either a positive relationship or no relationship. In other words, some mental disorders and even certain types of disorders appear to be exceptions to the generalization. Secondly, although it is true that most studies have reported the prevalence of serious psychological impairment to be greatest in the lowest socioeconomic category, there is at best only a very moderate inverse association among the remaining strata designated in these studies. Again, major differences in both the conceptual frameworks and methodologies employed by the various researchers make the drawing of such conclusions questionable, but it appears that there is insufficient evidence to warrant inferences of the sort that rates of mental disorder are "higher in the middle class than the upper class" or are "lower in the 'upper middle' than the 'lower middle' class." To the extent that the purported inverse relationship between social class and mental disorders implies such notions, the generalization is misleading on a second count.

These cautions and qualifications notwithstanding, I would not quarrel with Grusky and Pollner's (1981, p. 92) observation that "the relation between social class and mental disorder is virtually incontestable." To this point, however, I have only attempted to summarize the body of empirical research that allows one to make this claim. But these research findings still need to be interpreted; the facts do not "speak for themselves" in this regard. So the next task is to look at how these researchers and other social scientists have sought to *explain* the relationship between class and mental disorder.

Theoretical Interpretations

Several interpretations have been formulated to explain the relationship between social class and mental disorder. As a sociologist, I am inclined to favour interpretations that emphasize the impact of the social environment on people's mental health. Theories along these lines are known as "social causation" explanations. Most of the discussion that follows will be devoted to outlining the rationales of the leading sociological perspectives that fall under this general heading. However, before turning to these social causation explanations, I will briefly mention two other interpretations that seek to explain the class-mental disorder relationship without reference to social or environmental effects.

Genetics

There is, first of all, the genetic explanation that argues that mental disorders are transmitted through heredity. Studies of monozygotic twins and adopted children have established that genetic transmission plays some part in people's susceptibility to schizophrenia and other psychiatric disorders. It is also apparent from these studies that genetic factors alone cannot provide a sufficient explanation of schizophrenia or account for why it is so prevalent in the lower class.

Social scientists have been critical of both the biological determinism and the ideological conservatism implicit in this viewpoint. However, it should be noted that this explanation does not necessarily imply that persons of the lower class are genetically inferior. Rather, one can postulate that if vulnerability to mental disorder is inherited, then there must have been high rates of such disorders among the parents and grand-parents of those afflicted. And because disorders such as schizophrenia are usually debilitating, downward social mobility in earlier generations would almost certainly have occurred and thus, eventually resulted in a concentration of genetically susceptible people in the lower class. The rationale of this extrapolation for the genetic hypothesis is in fact very similar to the next interpretation I will consider, the "social selection" hypothesis.

Social Selection

This explanation accepts that there is a definite relationship between social class and mental disorders, but maintains that this is because low class standing is a *consequence* rather than a cause of poor mental health. One variant of this explanation, dubbed the "downward drift" hypothesis, posits that psychologically disturbed persons typically experience a reduction of their ability to function successfully in their occupations, and therefore gradually drift down the social ladder and into the lower class.

The other version of this school of thought posits that poor mental health works not so much to cause downward mobility as to limit or retard upward mobility. According to this way of thinking, the prevalence of mental disorders in the lower class is largely due to the fact that its mentally healthy members are more likely to achieve upward mobility, thus leaving behind a cohort of persons whose aggregate level of mental health has been diminished by the departure of such individuals.

There are empirical studies that have been made which lend some support to both versions of the social selection hypothesis.[5] That is, it seems true that psychological impairment both restricts some persons from moving up the class hierarchy, and is a contributing factor in the case of some who "skid" downward. Having conceded this point, however, I would hasten to add that social selection, either by itself or in conjunction with the genetic explanation, is not adequate to fully explain the higher incidence of mental disorder in the lower social classes. Furthermore, I concur with Cockerham (1981, p. 187) who states:

> When the question is whether social class position helps to promote mental disorder (social causation) or whether mental disorder causes social class position (social selection), most likely the former . . . is correct. That is, social class position contributes to the onset of mental disorder to a more significant degree than does the mental disorder causing social class position.

It now remains to explore the social causation explanation. This interpretation appears in a number of guises. All of them are in agreement that the preponderance of mental disorder in the lower class is mainly attributable to social factors, but they differ in their assessment of which features of the environment are most salient. In this connection, one can single out the following perspectives: societal reaction, social stress, and differential coping resources. Each of these will be discussed in turn.

Societal Reaction

The first perspective to be considered takes a radically different point of departure when analyzing what is ordinarily called "mental illness." Proponents of the societal reaction model (also known as "labelling theory") fundamentally challenge the medical conception of mental disorder that informs modern psychiatry as well as public attitudes on the subject. The view that most people in our society have come to accept is the one put forth by the medical profession, which essentially contends that mental disorders are illnesses much like cancer, tuberculosis, or influenza. According to the medical model, mental "illness" is either likened or attributed to a disease entity lodged in the individual's mind and/or body, that manifests itself in observable symptoms. Labelling theorists tend to be extremely skeptical about this whole formulation. Echoing the maverick psychiatrist Thomas Szasz (1961) — who went so far as to claim that mental illness is a myth — they view the latter as a label applied to certain people who either violate society's rules or express unacceptable ideas in an unusual idiom. In short, mental disorders are understood as deviant behaviour.

A distinctive aspect of this perspective is that it does not centre its attention on trying to explain what makes the deviant "tick." Its focus is rather on the social context within which such transgressions occur. This alternative vantage point is largely premised on the observation that deviance is a status conferred upon a person by other members of society. Labelling theorists think it telling that many acts of rule-breaking do not result in the rule-breaker being branded as deviant. Such conduct frequently goes unrecognized, or is rationalized away, by members of the community. (For example, middle-class male vandalism may be dismissed as nothing more than "boys will be boys.") On the other hand, if and when labelling takes place, the "deviant" is expected to conform to the prescriptions of the role in which she or he has been cast. Once a person has been labelled as "crazy," for instance, others will expect that person to behave abnormally and may give him or her little chance to act like a "sane" person. As Scheff (1984) has argued, where bizarre behaviour is defined and reacted to as signs of mental illness, a self-fulfilling process is initiated that can culminate with the labelled individual capitulating to social pressures and rewards, and accepting the proffered role of a mentally ill person.

The nature of society's reaction is thus seen as the crucial factor influencing what comes of misbehaviour. If the community response is to ignore or downplay such conduct, labelling theorists would predict that it will be of transitory significance because it is not likely to make a lasting impact on the rule-breaker's self-identity or social status. If, however, displays of such behaviour are acknowledged and responded to by significant others in the community, the individual may be launched on a "career" of ever more extensive and identity-altering deviant acts.

The critical stance causes labelling theorists to take quite a different view on the question of why rates of mental disorder are usually higher in the lower class. To begin with, they allege that such data are not what they pretend to be — that is, objective measures of mental disturbance. In their judgement, these data merely reflect the number of persons who have been classified as mentally ill by the arbitrary standards of the psychiatric profession. On this score, societal reaction theorists are fond of citing research which demonstrates that psychiatric diagnosis is notoriously unreliable. They note that psychiatrists routinely infer the presence of "illness" in their patients from unconventional behaviour and/or beliefs. Their ostensibly objective inference that particular actions or ideas are "symptoms" of an underlying pathology is said to actually entail a subjective judgement that is bound to be coloured by the psychiatrist's own political and moral standards. To be sure, these ideas may be shared by other members of his or her profession, and beyond; however, labelling theorists will correctly reply that bias can be collective as well as individual.

Defenders of the societal reaction model emphasize that psychiatrists occupy position of power and privilege in contemporary society. Like other dominant groups, psychiatrists are said to be favourably situated to create and impose their own particular interest, values, and views of the world on other, less privileged members of society. That such efforts are not always successful is said to be attested to by the fact that psychiatry's criteria for evaluating what is "healthy" or "normal" in human beings have come under attack in recent decades as harbouring biases of various types. Blacks and women, for example, have charged that psychiatry's prototype of health belies that fact that its practitioners are overwhelmingly white and male.[6] Following this same logic, it has been argued that the apparent concentration of mental illness in the lower class is at least partly an artifact of a middle-class bias that pervades psychiatric thought and diagnosis. This argument rests upon the truth that a number of attitudes, values, and skills relevant to psychological assessment vary considerably by social class. For example, introspection, emotional control, and intellectual autonomy all tend to be more valued in the middle and upper classes than in the lower class. Given the highly subjective nature of psychiatric diagnosis, these class differences in cognitive abilities and value orientations may have the effect of predisposing psychiatrists to evaluate the mental health of lower-class patients unfavourably. The intrusion of such class prejudice could mean that part of what are seen as psychiatric symptoms in lower-class people are simply their distinctive social-class characteristics.

The societal reaction approach by no means regards the sort of class bias just described as confined to the formal procedure or psychiatric diagnosis. Inasmuch as middle-class norms and values tend to prevail in most spheres of everyday life (e.g., schools, the mass media), lower-class people who act in an odd or obnoxious manner run a greater risk of being labelled "crazy" than do their higher-class counterparts. In other words, if the labelling theorists are right, the middle-class bias of psychiatry only reinforces the prejudices in the society at large, which brings greater numbers of lower-class people to its attention in the first place.

Another relevant feature of this explanation concerns the differential ability of persons by class to resist the labelling process, in the psychiatric setting as well as in society generally. Labelling theorists maintain that even though the severity of their psychological distress may be equivalent, higher-class persons ordinarily enjoy numerous advantages (e.g., access to expert legal counsel) over lower-class persons of having their "symptomatic" behaviour disregarded or minimized by the community, thereby reducing the possibility of their becoming officially designated as psychiatric cases. All of these considerations have led critics of the medical model to assert that the mentally disordered suffer not so much from internal predispositions to "illness" as from external "contingencies" that render them vulnerable to being defined by society as mentally ill.

Social Stress

A second type of social causation explanation is the social stress hypothesis. In contradistinction to the societal reaction hypothesis, this interpretation does not dispute the claim that mental disorder is most prevalent in the lower class. It accepts this as fact and seeks to account for it by suggesting that members of the lower class are subjected to greater stress by virtue of living in deprived social conditions.

The supposition that something about the lower-class environment is stressful appears to be well founded. However, there is not consensus when it comes to specifying exactly what features of the lower-class life situation produce stress. Overcrowded housing, broken homes, and social isolation are but some of the items mentioned in this connection. The most commonly cited factor, however, is the economic insecurity of lower-class life. Unemployment and/or the threat of job layoffs are most acutely felt by persons in lower social-class positions. Apart from the ample social scientific research attesting to the negative consequences of being without work, it is surely no secret that unemployment tends to erode family relationships and create feelings of despair and worthlessness. Little wonder, then, that fluctuations in the level of unemployment have been shown to be the single most important source of changing admission rates to mental hospitals.[7]

For those in the lower class who manage to find employment, the jobs available frequently have several features believed to be associated with stress. In addition to being low-paid, a majority of lower-class workers hold jobs that are thought to require little skill, are repetitive and monotonous, involve being controlled by others, and are easy to get locked into for life. Moreover, many of these jobs take place in work settings where there are serious problems of comfort, health, and safety.[8] Such working conditions, it is hypothesized, are likely to be hazardous to people's emotional well-being, to say nothing of their physical health.

Other commentators have pointed out that the hazards of belonging to the lower class are not restricted to the material hardships dictated by economic status. A proper assessment of the stresses facing lower-class persons also needs to take into account the whole climate of degradation that envelops low status in a class-stratified society. This is to say that, over and above the disadvantages deriving from lack of money or power, lower-class people must endure repeated affronts to their dignity and selfhood. Where class inequality prevails, people's worth tends to be measured by their financial and occupational success. Honour and esteem are accorded to those who achieve such success; disrepute befalls those who do not. That these judgements are often shared by lower-class persons themselves has been documented by Sennett and Cobb in a study aptly entitled "The Hidden Injuries of Class" (1972). Through intensive interviews with a number of blue-collar workers in the Boston area, the authors uncovered a tragic sense of failure and self-devaluation in these people. The depth of these feelings was perhaps most poignantly conveyed by their proclaimed efforts to ensure that their children should not follow in the parents' footsteps. Working-class people, Sennett and Cobb (1972) observe, ask their children to take their parents' lives as a warning rather than a model.

The stress of such emotional wounds is probably compounded by the tendency, common among lower-class persons, to blame themselves for their subordinate position in society. That is, when asked about the reasons for their low status, they frequently mention their perceived laziness, stupidity, or some other nameless personal deficiency as key determinants.[9] This definition of their predicament means that the anger or sense of injustice that lower-class people commonly feel about their lowly position in society is more likely to be turned inward rather than directed against the social sources of their misery. Sennett and Cobb detected something of this nature in the Boston workers they interviewed. As they put it, "they are both angry and ambivalent about their right to be angry" (Sennett & Cobb, 1972, p. 79). It almost goes without saying that such ambivalence and suppressed rage is frequently the stuff of emotional disturbance.

Coping Resources

It is arguable whether the proclivity of lower-class persons to blame themselves for their disadvantaged situation directly adds to the stresses they already encounter. What seems more certain is that self-blame detracts from their ability to cope effectively with the myriad pressures surrounding life at the bottom of the class hierarchy. This may be, in fact, generally why stress manages to adversely affect the mental health of the lower classes. Langner and Michael (1963), two of Srole's colleagues in the previously discussed midtown Manhattan study, had found that membership in the lower class did involve being subjected to more measurable life stress than did membership in the higher classes. However, they further disclosed that at any given level of stress, persons in the lowest socio-economic category were more likely to become mentally disturbed than persons of middle- or upper-class standing. Indeed, Langner and Michael found that the more sources of stress, the greater was the class difference in the proportion of people who manifested psychiatric symptoms. What these findings seemed to be suggesting was that stress affects the mental stability of the underprivileged more severely than it does that of the relatively privileged. This finding has more recently been confirmed by Kessler (1979) and other investigators. Realization of this point has, in turn, prompted a shift in thinking among some advocates of the social stress hypothesis. Proponents of this interpretation are now less inclined to subscribe to the notion that the relationship of class to mental disorder is primarily attributable to the sheer amount of stress people endure by virtue of their socio-economic position. The strong suspicion is that there are important class differences in how effectively people deal with stress.

This modified interpretation suggests that irrespective of whether lower-class members are confronted with greater stress as a result of living in deprived social circumstances, they are at a disadvantage in their ability to cope with it. The disadvantage is said to derive from the fewer and poorer coping resources at their disposal. Lower-class people are in a weak position in this respect because the stress-producing circumstances they face are usually less alterable by individual action than are those confronting middle-class persons. It will be recalled that much of the stress in the lower-class environment probably stems from remote, impersonal economic forces over which most members of society, but especially those in the lower class, have precious little control. Similarly, lower-class persons, almost by definition, have little money or power to either escape or mitigate stressful experiences. Research by Liem and Liem (1978) has also shown that lower-class people are more prone to find environmental stress psychologically distressing, because their interpersonal relationships and weak ties to the community typically afford less social support to buffer the stress than is enjoyed by those in the higher classes. All in all, then, the lower class appears to suffer from a poverty of external coping resources, which exacerbates an already stressful situation.

Sociologist Melvin Kohn (1977) has pursued a rather novel tack in analyzing this issue. Kohn persuasively argues that certain features of lower-class life and socialization patterns impair its members' internal resources for dealing effectively with stress. Without discounting the liabilities engendered by their lack of external resources, Kohn postulates that the constricted conditions of life experienced by people in the lower class foster conceptions of social reality that diminish their ability to deal effectively with stress. Kohn's own research demonstrated that there are important social class differences in how children are taught to perceive, assess, and deal with reality. Unlike middle-class parents who encourage their children to act according to their own judgement and moral standards, lower-class parents are less concerned with self-direction and place a much greater emphasis on obedience to external authority. Kohn submits that this fundamental class difference in value orientations — the premium on self-direction at higher-class levels and on conformity at the lower-class levels — is not accidental but reflects significant divergences in life circumstances. He is worth quoting at length on this point.

> The essence of higher class position is the expectation that one's decisions and actions can be consequential; the essence of lower class position is the belief that one is at the mercy of forces and people beyond one's control, often, beyond one's understanding. Self-direction — acting on the basis of one's own judgement, attending to internal dynamics as well as to external consequences, being open-minded, being trustful of others, holding personally responsible moral standards — this is possible only if the actual conditions of life allow some freedom of action, some reason to feel in control of fate.
>
> Conformity — following the dictates of authority, focusing on external consequences to the exclusion of internal processes, being intolerant of non-conformity and dissent, being distrustful of others, having moral standards that strongly emphasize obedience to the letter of the law — this is the inevitable result of conditions of life that allow little freedom of action, little reason to feel in control of fate. (1977, p. 189)

Kohn does not deny that the conformist value system may in some ways be adaptive for coping with the standard exigencies of lower-class existence. However, rigid adherence to norms or authority can also prove to be disastrous to people when they are confronted with new situations and new problems that require an innovative response. In sum, the conformist value system may be too simplistic to provide people with a sufficient sense of life's complexities, and too inflexible to provide them with the cognitive tools they need to meet the dilemmas and crisis situations that invariably arise in a rapidly changing world. For Kohn, then, insofar as lower-class people subscribe to such an orientation, they may be ill-prepared to adequately cope with the stresses they encounter.

A Note on Theoretical Divergence in Sociology

This completes my survey of the theoretical interpretations that have been advanced to explain why rates of mental disorder are related to social class. Representatives of the contending schools of thought often engage one another in scholarly debate over how adequately the various interpretations are able to account for the presumed facts pertaining to this issue. Such controversy is commonplace in modern social science. Because the competing theoretical perspectives are often tied, wittingly or unwittingly, to different ideological positions and/or social policy implications, the tenor of these debates may give outsiders the impression that the validity of the rival interpretations is mutually exclusive. I think it is accurate to say that the literature on the relationship of class to mental disorder could easily lead one to assume that it is not possible to accept certain interpretations unless one rejects others. I hope that my review of these different theories has discouraged readers from adopting such an assumption. In my opinion, all of the hypotheses discussed contain elements of truth that can contribute to a comprehensive understanding of why mental disorder is more common at the lower end of the social scale. The fact that lower-class persons are more apt to suffer from psychological distress than middle-or upper-class persons may very well be the result of a combination of interacting factors that includes genetic susceptibility, social selection, differential labelling, environmental stress, and inadequate coping resources — and perhaps still others that have thus far eluded our attention. This posture is not meant to deny that some of the foregoing factors will prove to have greater explanatory power than others. By the same token, some of the interpretations I have reviewed will probably prove more influential than others in shaping society's mental health policies. But, given the present state of our knowledge about this complex problem, future theorizing, research, and policy debates will likely stand to benefit from an appreciation of all the perspectives outlined in this chapter. One such policy issue concerns the type of psychiatric treatment people receive when they become mentally disordered. The way in which social class standing affects such treatment will now be explored.

Differences in Psychiatric Treatment by Social Class

It has long been observed that class differences in the prevalence of mental disorders are compounded by what is tantamount to a two-tiered system of mental health care. That is, the poor are said to be disadvantaged relative to the rich not only because they are more likely to experience some form of debilitating psychological distress, but also because they tend to receive less adequate treatment for their disorders.

This double standard in the distribution of mental health services was most conspicuous in the early decades of this century. Kupers has noted that two quite distinct psychiatries co-existed at that time.

> One was practiced in asylums, the other in consulting rooms. In the asylum inmates were chained to the wall, forced into icy baths, and severely reprimanded for every bizarre act. In the consulting room the analysand was listened to with compassion and taught how to understand anxieties and dreams and how to use that understanding to create a richer life. (1981, p. 13)

The clientele of these two psychiatries was clearly differentiated along social-class lines. Psychoanalytic therapy "was practised in the consulting room among the affluent, and services for the poor consisted only of asylum practice" (Kupers, 1981, p. 20).

By mid-century, the old-style asylums had given way to the public mental hospitals and veterans' hospitals. In the transition, the line distinguishing the two types of psychiatric treatment became less distinct. However, the persistence of a double standard was attested to by Hollingshead and Redlich's previously discussed study of New Haven. Their research documented that higher-class patients tended to receive individually oriented therapy involving verbal interaction between the patient and the psychiatrist, whereas lower-class patients were far more likely to receive organic therapies (e.g., drugs, electroshock, psychosurgery) or "custodial" care. As Gallagher rightly remarks, the latter category is really a euphemism or "polite term for no treatment at all" (1980, p. 268). An especially telling statistic emerging out of Hollingshead and Redlich's research was that more than 600 persons in their psychiatric population of 1900 plus were judged to have received custodial care only; over 90 percent of these patients were from the two lowest social strata in the study's five-class scheme. Thus, Hollingshead and Redlich concluded with good reason that social class position strongly affects the type of treatment rendered to persons in need of psychiatric help.

This particular finding of the New Haven study provoked considerable controversy. Some critics seized upon it as ammunition to indict the whole mental health care system for providing quality therapy to higher-class patients while relegating lower-class patients to custodial care or less effective therapeutic programs. Defenders of the system argued that the prevailing therapy of choice, psychoanalysis, did not lend itself to treating the sort of severe disorders of psychoses most often found in the lower classes. Others went a step further and claimed that lower-class persons were generally not suitable candidates for social psychological or "talking" therapies aimed at equipping patients with insight into their emotional problems. According to this argument, lower-class people lacked the motivation, verbal skills, and/or self-awareness to benefit from the sort of therapeutic techniques that had proved successful with their more affluent, better educated clients. The critics regarded this defence as itself a sign of the middle-class bias permeating psychiatric thought and practice.

In retrospect, it appears that this issue temporarily subsided because it had arisen at a time when psychiatric treatment and mental health policies were beginning to undergo some rather substantial changes. In the middle 1950s, chlorpromazine and other psycho-tropic medications were developed. The administration of these drugs enabled many mental patients, including some of the more severely disturbed, to function better without impairing their consciousness. The popularity of these drugs spread rapidly. One of the most significant consequences of their wholesale adoption by psychiatry was that large numbers of patients were helped enough to be discharged from mental hospitals. The diffusion of drug treatments and the declining mental hospital population also gave hope to many psychiatrists and other mental health professionals who saw in these developments new opportunities to both treat and prevent mental illness. Their belief was that the potential for reducing the severity and duration of mental disorders, if not their cure, was contingent upon returning patients to the community, where family and friends could help create conditions that would permit ex-patients to work and to live more or less normal lives. Institutional mental health care was also increasingly coming under attack as being hopelessly custodial. Such misgivings with the large, overcrowded state/provincial mental hospitals were related — probably not coinciden-tally — to the recognition that these institutions required enormous and ever-increasing outlays of tax revenue for their maintenance alone.[10] By the early 1960s, the confluence of all these factors had set the stage for a major shift in social policy: the establishment of community mental health centres. In the decade between 1965 and 1974, a multitude of public clinics and outpatient mental-health facilities were set up in communities across North America.[11]

The community mental-health movement was partly inspired by a wish that such centres would engender a more democratic dispensation of therapy. The vision was that as the archaic mental hospitals were phased out, sufficient resources would then be available to provide low-income clients with quality mental-health care. With the advantage of hindsight, it is today fairly safe to say that the egalitarian ideals of this movement have, by and large, not been translated into reality. To be sure, "deinstitu-tionalization" has meant the return of many mental patients to the community. Never-theless, the double standard of mental health care is by no means a thing of the past. By all accounts, the chronically disordered patients who remain warehoused in mental hospitals are still drawn disproportionately from the lowest social strata. Moreover, it is questionable whether life for many of the former mental patients who now reside in the community has been positively affected by this policy. Kupers assesses the situation as follows:

> The treatment they receive at public clinics rarely includes much in-depth psychotherapy, and usually involves the administration of large doses of psychotropic medications plus training in skills of daily living and appropriate behaviour. In other words, the goals of treatment are more like the old asylum psychiatry, with its stress on external constraint and moral training, than they are like the self-discovery and self-expansion of consulting room therapy. The locked doors and straitjackets of the asylum have merely been replaced by the medications prescribed in public clinics. Thus the mental patients have been ghettoized in the community, and many people are wondering whether their plight there is any better than it was in the asylums. (1981, pp. 22-23)

The trends described by Kupers have been accelerated in recent years by often severe budgetary cutbacks that have been imposed on public clinics and outpatient facilities. Despite such diminished resources, therapists working in such settings are obliged to treat anyone in their geographic or catchment area who cannot afford private therapy. Many of these persons have little or no desire to undergo therapy, but have been pressed into seeking help by parents, schools, the courts, or other authorities. Under these circumstances, staff are only able to see most clients briefly and they manage to cope with the situation by resorting to the prescription of drugs, which many concede serve more as social control mechanisms than as effective psychotherapy.

Psychiatrists and non-medical therapists working in the private sector operate under conditions that are vastly more conducive to the practice of quality psychotherapy. For one thing, therapists in private practice are normally in a position to select their clients from a pool of persons who have voluntarily sought out their services. And, as Szasz (1970) has argued so vociferously, a precondition for avoiding the social control functions of traditional psychiatry is that both parties, client and therapist, freely enter into the therapeutic relationship. In-depth psychotherapy, in which the therapist does not simply dispense advice to clients about how to live their lives, but attempts to help each of them find his or her own path virtually always requires a great deal of time. As long as the client can afford to pay, there is a greater likelihood in private therapy that the time needed to sort out emotional conflicts and to arrive at such self-discovery can be arranged.

On the other hand, this is not to suggest that quality therapy is easily procured. One result of the over success of the pharmacological revolution referred to earlier has been the rise of a new generation of psychiatrists who have largely given up the psychotherapeutic orientation of their professional predecessors. The once-dominant psychoanalytic view of mental disorders as intrapsychic conflicts rooted in childhood experiences is probably now subscribed to by only a relatively small fraction of North American psychiatrists. In its place, the new psychiatry favours a physiological model of madness and tends to embrace drug treatment as the most promising therapeutic strategy. Of course one can still find psychiatrists who remain committed to psychosocial conceptions of mental disorders and to non-organic therapies. There are also a large number of psychiatrists in private practice who advocate the use of tranquillizers and antidepressant medications as an adjunct to other therapies aimed at self-exploration and self-clarification. This combined approach — which, incidentally, appears to be highly effective — is quite different from the situation in public clinics and hospitals, where the use of drugs is essentially an *alternative* to in-depth therapy.

In sum, to the extent that higher-and lower-class patients are generally treated by psychiatrists working in the private and public sectors respectively, the description of the mental health-care system as "two-tiered" would seem to be justified. Indeed, this charge of a double standard in treatment is even more warranted when one considers the various and sundry non-medical psychotherapies (e.g., Gestalt therapy, psychodrama, primal therapy) that have gained a following in recent decades. For both economic and cultural reasons these alternative therapies cater almost exclusively to the middle-class clientele.

At this point, it is perhaps worth speculating about what accounts for these class differences in psychiatric treatment. Radicals tend to explain the inequitable distribution of mental health care as a predictable by-product of the dominant socio-economic structure of society. In this view a class-stratified society ensures that important life chances, including the opportunity to receive quality psychotherapy, are bound to be unequally allocated. The double standard is thus understood as an instance of class discrimination against society's underprivileged members. For these critics, the villains in the story are the psychiatrists and other mental health professionals in positions of authority, whose class bias allegedly disposes them to pursue mental health policies that perpetuate inequalities in treatment.

I confess to having some sympathy with elements of the radical critique. More specifically, as long as the economic conditions of life are class-divided, I would contend that it is naïvely unsociological to believe that these divisions will not somehow be reflected in most areas of social life. But having conceded this, I cannot accept the implication of some radicals that the differential psychiatric treatment by social class is a matter of design or deliberate policy. Building on some of the research I have reviewed in this chapter, I would instead offer a more benign interpretation. In this connection I see the double standard as partly attributable to, and reinforced by, a curious affinity that exists between certain aspects of the different world views held by middle-class mental health professionals and their lower-class patients.

On the psychiatrists' side, their characteristic values and view of the world incline them to truly believe that lower-class people are generally unable or unwilling to take advantage of quality, insight-oriented therapy. And while I would agree that such a presumption is based upon class prejudice, it must be appreciated that if this is how they define the situation, then their practice of treating low-income clients with drugs or some other somatic methods actually makes sense. Strangely enough, the values or world view of their lower-class patients frequently mesh with this definition of the situation. For example, there is plenty of research indicating that lower-class persons tend to view their mental or emotional problems in physical terms. (Attributing psychological distress to one's "nerves" is perhaps the most common expression of this conception.) Richard Lichtman has nicely summarized some significant social class differences in how such matters are typically perceived. In his words,

> the poor are not simply less wealthy than the rich. Their world is qualitatively different. They do not even regard their bodies as the more prosperous do; their bodies are alien, incomprehensible, dangerous, unworthy of care, naturally given to misuse and decay, and a comforting explanation for their social inadequacy. They are far more likely to accept the impairment of their bodily and mental functioning as a "normal" fact of the world, to be borne like other natural hazards of existence, and manipulated for whatever comfort it may offer. (1968, p. 47)

This way of thinking may well be generated by ignorance, indoctrination, and/or alienating life circumstances. But again, insofar as such notions are defined as valid, lower-class patients adhering to them are likely to welcome organic treatments as appropriate, and to regard insight-oriented therapies as irrelevant to what they believe ails them.[12]

Conclusion

I will conclude by briefly considering the social policy implications of the interpretation just presented. To reiterate, I acknowledge the radicals' polemical point that the double standard in mental health care cannot ultimately be eliminated in the absence of society-wide transformation and "destratification." However, this certainly does not mean that anything short of a full-fledged social revolution will be of no avail in addressing this or related problems. If the argument put forth above is correct, a number of possible reforms might be pursued to ameliorate the situation. To begin with, medical schools could be enjoined to insist that students electing to specialize in psychiatry do substantial coursework in the humanities and social sciences. It is at least arguable that the commonly narrow, exclusively scientific education and training presently received by most psychiatrists fosters obliviousness to the psychosocial factors impinging on mental health and psychiatric care. Secondly, if mental hospitals and public clinics caring for the poor are to do more than medicate and otherwise control their large numbers of clients, massive budgetary increases will obviously be needed. Kupers reports that many mental health professionals employed in the public sector are initially motivated to provide meaningful psychotherapy to their lower-class patients, but along with the aforementioned inadequacies in their medical training, the obstacles presented daily by swelling caseloads and diminishing financial resources eventually produce staff "burnout" or demoralization. Finally, I would recommend that governments could reduce the double standard by making information and subsidies available to low-income persons who might benefit from any reputable non-medical therapies that are locally available.[13]

Such reforms are by no means a panacea for remedying the deficiencies inherent in the two-tiered system. But, if there are any lessons to be learned from the tragic experience of the community mental health movement, one of them may be the realization that there are no quick, inexpensive, or strictly medical solutions for overcoming the inequitable distribution of mental health-care services.

Notes

1. I will generally employ the term mental "disorders" rather than mental "illness" throughout this chapter because the former concept is non-committal on the controversial issue of whether a medical conception of psychological disturbance is appropriate or not.

2. Srole et al., (1962) also found that persons who had been downwardly mobile were much more likely to be rated as psychiatrically impaired than were those who had moved up the stratification system.

3. "Stirling County" was a pseudonym adopted by the authors of this study to conceal the identity of the area in Nova Scotia they investigated.

4. For example, see Bradburn and Caplovitz (1965).

5. See, in particular, the study by Harkey, Miles, and Rushing (1976).

6. See Grier and Cobbs (1968) and Greenspan (1983) for critiques of traditional psychiatry from a black and feminist viewpoint, respectively.

7. The classic study documenting this relationship is Brenner (1973).

8. See Rinehart (1975) for a useful discussion of the blue-collar work environment and its psychological consequences.

9. The social sources and political consequences of this pattern are discussed in Della Fave (1980).

10. Scull (1977) has in fact attempted to demonstrate that the impetus for deinstitutionalization was neither the advent of psychotropic drugs nor the belief that it represented a better form of psychiatric treatment. He argues that the real force behind this policy shift was economic; governments perceived it as a way to save large sums of money.

11. American accounts of the rise of the community mental health movement commonly treat it as originating in the United States. For the record, it should be pointed out that the province of Saskatchewan was among the earliest pioneers of this movement.

12. Kupers (1981) reports cases in his experience as a psychiatrist in public clinics where low-income clients would begrudgingly attend psychotherapy sessions only out of fear that non-attendance might result in termination of their drug prescriptions.

13. For a very different analysis of the failure of mental health policy than the one advanced here, see Isaac and Armat (1990).

Study Questions

1. How does the relationship between social class and mental disorder correspond with what you have learned in other chapters about the unequal social distribution of physical disease? To what extent do the factors that give rise to high rates of physical illness in the lower class strike you as also responsible for the high rates of mental disorder in this class?

2. Contrast the medical and societal reaction models of mental disorder. What do you see as the main strengths and weaknesses of labelling theory's critique of the medical conception of mental illness?

3. To what extent do you think social class and other types of bias enter into psychiatric diagnosis? Do you think it is possible to devise standards of mental health that are free of such bias?

4. Summarize what Kohn sees as the major differences between middle-class and lower-class value orientations. With a friend or acquaintance whose social class origin is quite different from your own, discuss how each of you was socialized in terms of the distinction between self-direction and conformity. Do the results of this exercise support Kohn's thesis?

5. What social policy implications follow from each of the theoretical interpretations of the relationship between class and mental disorder discussed in this chapter?

6. Unlike the United States, Canada has a universal, government-sponsored health-care system that provides for both hospitalization and private psychiatric treatment. Do you think our health-insurance programs have substantially weakened the double standard of mental health care? Why or why not?

Recommended Reading

Archibald, W.P. (1978). *Social psychology as political economy* (pp. 123-185). Toronto: McGraw-Hill Ryerson.

Dohrenwend, B.P., & Dohrenwend, B.S. (1969). *Social status and psychological disorder.* New York: John Wiley and Sons.

Hollingshead, A.B., & Redlich, F.C. (1958). *Social class and mental illness.* New York: John Wiley and Sons.

Kohn, M.L. (1981). Social class and schizophrenia: a critical review and a reformulation. In O. Grusky & M. Pollner (Eds.), *The Sociology of Mental Illness: Basic Studies* (pp. 127-142). New York: Holt, Rinehart & Winston.

Kupers, T.A. (1981). *Public therapy: The practice of psychotherapy in the public mental health clinic.* New York: Free Press.

Scheff, T.J. (1984). *Being mentally ill: A sociological theory* (2nd ed.). New York: Aldine.

Sennett, R., & Cobb, J. (1972). *The hidden injuries of class.* New York: Alfred A. Knopf.

References

Bradburn, N., & Caplovitz, D. (1965). *Reports on happiness.* Chicago: Aldine.

Brenner, M.H. (1973). *Mental illness and the economy.* Cambridge: Harvard University Press.

Cockerham, W. (1981). *Sociology of mental disorder.* Englewood Cliffs: Prentice-Hall.

Della Fave, R. (1980). The meek shall not inherit the earth: self-evaluation and the legitimacy of stratification. *American Sociological Review, 45,* 955-971.

Dohrenwend, B.P., & Dohrenwend, B.S. (1974). Social and cultural influences on psychopathology. *Annual Review of Psychology, 25,* 417-452.

Faris, R., & Dunham, W. (1939). *Mental disorders in urban areas.* Chicago: University of Chicago Press.

Gallagher III, B. (1980). *The sociology of mental illness.* Englewood Cliffs: Prentice-Hall.

Greenspan, M. (1983). *A new approach to women and therapy.* New York: McGraw-Hill.

Grier, W., & Cobbs, P. (1968). *Black rage.* New York: Basic Books.

Grusky, O., & Pollner, M. (Eds.). (1981). *The sociology of mental illness: Basic studies.* New York: Holt, Rinehart and Winston.

Harkey, J., Miles, D., & Rushing, W. (1976). The relation between social class and functional status: A new look at the drift hypothesis. *Journal of Health and Social Behaviour, 17,* 194-204.

Hollingshead, A., & Redlich, F. (1958). *Social class and mental illness*. New York: John Wiley and Sons.

Isaac, R.J., & Armat, V. (1990). *Madness in the streets: How psychiatry and the law abandoned the mentally ill*. New York: Free Press.

Kessler, R. (1979). Stress, social status and psychological distress. *Journal of Health and Social Behaviour*, 20, 259-272.

Kohn, M. (1977). *Class and conformity: A study in values* (2nd ed.). Chicago: University of Chicago Press.

Kupers, T. (1981). *Public therapy: The practice of psychotherapy in the public mental health clinic*. New York: Free Press.

Langner, T., & Michael, S. (1963). *Life stress and mental health: The Midtown Manhattan study*. London: Free Press of Glencoe.

Leighton, D.C., Harding, J., Macklin, D., Macmillan, A., & Leighton, A. (1963). *The character of danger: Psychiatric symptoms in selected communities*. New York: Basic Books.

Lichtman, R. (1968). *Toward community: A criticism of contemporary capitalism*. Santa Barbara: Center for the Study of Democratic Institutions.

Liem, R., & Liem, J. (1978). Social class and mental illness reconsidered: The role of economic stress and social support. *Journal of Health and Social Behaviour*, 19, 139-156.

Myers, J., & Bean, L. (1968). *A decade later: A follow-up of social class and mental illness*. New York: John Wiley and Sons.

Rinehart, J. (1975). *The tyranny of work*. Don Mills: Longman Canada.

Scheff, T. (1984). *Being mentally ill: A sociological theory* (2nd ed.). New York: Aldine.

Scull, A. (1977). *Decarceration: Community treatment and the deviant*. Englewood Cliffs: Prentice-Hall.

Sennett, R., & Cobb, J. (1972). *The hidden injuries of class*. New York: Alfred A. Knopf.

Srole, L., Langner, T., Michael, S., Opler, M., & Rennie, T. (1962). *Mental health in the metropolis*. New York: McGraw-Hill.

Syme, S.L., & Berkman, L. (1981). Social class, susceptibility, and sickness. In P. Conrad & R. Kern (Eds.), *The Sociology of Health and Illness: Critical Perspectives* (pp. 35-44). New York: St. Martin's Press.

Szasz, T. (1961). *The myth of mental illness*. New York: Harper & Row.

Szasz, T. (1970). *Ideology and insanity: Essays on the psychiatric dehumanization of man*. Garden City: Doubleday-Anchor.

Chapter 21

Mental Health Policy in Canada: What's the Problem?

Harley D. Dickinson, University of Saskatchewan

Introduction

There is a growing recognition that despite its many strengths our health care system has a number of weaknesses. One of the most significant weaknesses is that it is not primarily a health care system, rather it is an illness care system. As such, it is a more or less effective means for dealing with acute injuries and illnesses, but it is less adequate as a solution to the chronic and degenerative health problems which currently predominate in Canada. Among the "new" public health problems, mental health ranks high (Epp, 1986). As a consequence, considerable attention has been recently devoted to developing mental health policy in Canada (Epp, 1988).

The scope of the problem is substantial. It has been estimated, for example, that at least one in eight Canadians will experience a mental health problem serious enough to require hospital treatment (Statistics Canada, 1981). In the United States, it is estimated that the figure is as high as one in five Americans (Health Beat, 1992, p. 20). In addition, both the number of persons and the proportion of the population receiving treatment has been increasing over time.

Although there has been a decrease in the number of mental hospitals and the number of patients in those hospitals over the past several decades, there has been an increase in the number of persons receiving in-patient psychiatric services in general hospitals. Blishen (1991, pp. 36-38) shows that between 1969 and 1982 mental disorder rose from the fifth to the first leading cause of hospitalization measured as a rate of patient days per 1 000 population in general and allied special hospitals. Many more people are never admitted to hospital for treatment of their mental health problems. Thus, an unknown number are (1) seen by physicians on an out-patient basis; or (2) seen by various non-medical mental health professionals; or (3) receive informal support and help from family, friends, or other volunteers; or (4) receive no help or services and contribute to the growing homeless populations that currently characterize modern urban societies.

It is difficult to know the total cost of mental health problems. American estimates place them at more than $136 billion in 1992 (Health Beat, 1992, p. 20). In Canada it has been estimated that in 1978, the cost of hospital days alone exceeded one billion dollars. Bland (1988, p. 1) states that hospital costs have since increased. Costs associated with non-institutional treatment are additional to these figures. It is also estimated that direct hospital costs are at least matched by various indirect costs, including those associated with lost productivity, unemployment, and the personal suffering and reduced quality of life experienced by the mentally disordered and their families (Bland, 1988, p. 1). The existing mental health-care system seems to be overwhelmed and incapable of effectively dealing with these problems. The reasons for this are the subject of debate.

In this chapter, I will provide an overview of some of the main dimensions of disagreement. It consists of two main sections. In the first, I will describe how various solutions to the problem of mental disorders follow from the ways in which the problem is defined. The second section will briefly outline a number of common themes and trends present in current mental-health policy debates. The central argument is that current policy initiatives undertaken within a health promotion policy framework reflect an attempt to establish an accommodation between differing and potentially incompatible definitions of the problem while at the same time containing costs.

The Sociology of Mental Illness and Mental Health

One problem that all societies must solve is what to do with individuals who engage in socially disruptive forms of deviant behaviours. The first, and arguably the most important, step in solving this problem is its definition, since the way in which a problem is defined determines the type of solution that is implemented. If troublesome behaviours are defined as criminal, for example, legal solutions will be devised; if the problems are seen as biological in nature, medical solutions will be developed; if the problem is seen to be spiritual in origin, a religious or magical solution will be developed. If there is uncertainty concerning the nature of the problem, there will also be uncertainty concerning the nature of the solution to be applied.

In Western societies it is generally agreed that the solution to the problem of what to do with deviant individuals has evolved through a series of steps from religious, to legal, to medical forms of management and control (Manning, 1989; Kittrie, 1972; Conrad & Schneider, 1980; Scull, 1982, 1983; Freidson, 1970). The origin of the modern medicalization of social control is generally placed sometime between the end of the eighteenth and nineteenth centuries. Although there is disagreement over why confinement in asylums became the dominant means for managing madness and controlling the insane at that time, there is widespread agreement that it signalled a major step towards the medicalization of Western social control practices (Scull, 1982, 1983, 1991; Foucault, 1973; Conrad & Schneider, 1980). I have argued elsewhere (Dickinson, 1989) that even though the origin of the modern struggle to medicalize psychiatry can be traced to the end of the eighteenth century, it was not successfully completed until the 1960s.

The strategy of confining the mentally ill in asylums remained the dominant solution to the problem until the 1960s. Since then there has been a marked demise of the asylum as the principal means and location for managing mental illness and a rise of various community-based alternatives. Although there is general agreement that this transformation heralded a major, perhaps even revolutionary change in the nature and organization of psychiatry, there is little agreement concerning either the causes or consequences of those changes.

A number of different accounts of this transformation have been proposed (Busfield, 1986; Cohen, 1985; Dickinson, 1989; Ralph, 1983; Scull, 1983). Although it is not possible here to review them all comprehensively, I will provide a brief sketch of the main aspects of the differing descriptions and explanations of the transition from asylum to community psychiatry.

The first, and probably most popular, account of the transformation is the "march of medical science" story (Cohen, 1985). This well known and widely accepted account postulates that advances in modern medical science resulted in the discovery of new and true knowledge about the nature and causes of mental illness and that knowledge replaced the ignorance, superstition, and myths of previous generations. Specifically, new scientific knowledge led to the development of new forms of medical treatment that replaced the old asylum system, which was discredited as ineffective at best and brutally inhumane at worst.

Central to this account is the claim that modern medical science demonstrated that "madness" and "insanity" were really "mental illnesses." Given this claim, it followed that mental illness should be treated in the same way and in the same locations as other illnesses. In this regard, the asylum was seen as an obstacle to the humane and effective medical treatment of the mentally ill (Goffman, 1961). The asylum was more like a prison than a hospital, and its radical reform or replacement was seen as imperative.

From this point of view, the transition from asylum to community psychiatry was essentially a triumph of science and humanitarian concern, the realization of which was made possible by the discovery of powerful psychotropic drugs in the 1950s.

To the extent proponents of this rather celebrationist history acknowledge that there are problems with community psychiatry, they are generally seen to be the result of lack of resources, therefore, the solution is simply more of the same. Another more critical explanation argues that the demise of the asylum and the rise of community psychiatry is best understood as the substitution of one form of social control with another that was neither more humane nor scientifically justified than that which it preceded (Scull, 1983; Ralph 1983). From this perspective, the transition from asylum to community psychiatry is best understood in political and economic terms. Scull (1983), for example, claims that in the post-War period a growing fiscal crisis of the state resulted in efforts to reduce costs. In response to the imperative of cost cutting, the state began to divest itself of responsibility for the institutional care or control of various deviant populations, especially the mentally ill. Thus, the emptying and abandonment of the asylums, a process to be termed decarceration, was driven by economic and political imperatives, not the progressive and humanitarian advances of medical science.

Despite the differences between the "march of medicine" and the critical "fiscal crisis" perspectives for understanding the development of community psychiatry, they both share the view that the object of treatment, or mistreatment, is the same — mental illness and the mentally ill.

The claim, or assumption, that the domain of psychiatry is mental illness, however, has not gone unchallenged. Indeed, Szasz (1972, p. 12) has proclaimed that mental illness is a myth, and that psychiatric "treatment," especially involuntary treatment, is best understood not as the application of medical science to the identification and treatment of mental illness, but rather as a form of torture. This view, variously expressed, is termed anti-psychiatry.

Anti-psychiatry shares with the critical perspective outlined above the belief that the primary function of psychiatric diagnosis and treatment is the social identification, classification, and control of deviance. It is not so much that anti-psychiatrists don't agree that persons diagnosed and treated as mentally ill have problems, but rather they disagree about the true nature of those problems. Szasz (1972), for example, argues that the problems currently being diagnosed and treated as medical problems by psychiatry are really best understood as psycho-social problems in living. Conceived of in this fashion, it follows that individuals suffering from such problems should not be labelled as mentally ill nor treated by medically trained psychiatrists. Rather, they should be helped to solve their problems in living by those more suited to doing so, namely psychologists or other types of non-medical psychotherapists.

Another branch of the anti-psychiatry movement argues that even this position is wrong. Laing and Esterson (1964), for example, argued that persons labelled as mentally ill were neither ill nor were their problems in living the primary problem. Rather, it was suggested that such individuals were responding to an insane and maddening social reality in a sane and rational fashion. From this perspective, the problem was not the individuals who refused to voluntarily deform themselves in order to conform to social demands and expectations, but rather the social institutions of bourgeois society, particularly the family and the economy. The so-called mentally ill were really reacting against the soul destroying demands of family and society by embarking on a journey of individual growth and personal development that threatened the status quo. Thus, madness was a proto-revolutionary act that was suppressed by the counter-revolutionary oppression of psychiatry. The role of the radical, anti-psychiatric therapist in this rebellion against conformity and oppression was to aid and abet the rebels in their emancipatory journey through madness.

Despite the obvious and substantial differences between these two versions of anti-psychiatry, they share a significant common component, namely, they both reserve a privileged position for the professional, medical and/or non-medical therapist in defining the real nature of the experience and the nature of the appropriate response or solution to it. An alternative perspective on the appropriate role of professionals in the definition of mental health problems and their solutions is provided by the mental patients'/consumers' rights movement.

These movements emerged in contemporary forms concomitant with the rise of community psychiatry. The culmination of efforts to medicalize psychiatry in the 1960s facilitated many of the mentally ill being given the same rights as other medical patients. These rights included the right to informed treatment, the right to receive adequate treatment in the least restrictive environment, the right to refuse treatment, and various other protections against the possibility of unjust and involuntary detention and treatment.

The extension and realization of these rights fundamentally altered the nature of the doctor-patient relationship. In most cases, the psychiatric patient was empowered relative to the physician/psychiatrist and came to have a greater say in the definition of their problems and the determination of solutions.

This empowerment of patients was further advanced in the context of the Szaszian critique of psychiatry. Indeed, if mental illness did not exist as illness, then it followed that it was not a medical problem and therefore medical solutions were unwarranted. If those diagnosed as mentally ill in reality were experiencing various psycho-social problems in living, they should be helped to identify and deal with those problems by those trained to do so — psychiatric social workers, psychologists, or other types of non-medical psychotherapists — or by themselves.

This rejection of medical dominance was encouraged by various non-medical mental health professions as part of their own struggles to achieve professional autonomy in the context of a newly emerging community psychiatry (Dickinson, 1989). One consequence of the competing claims concerning the nature of the problem and the most appropriate solution to it was that patients/clients came to have a choice of treatments available to them and consequently came to act more as consumers.

An outcome of these developments has been the emergence of a consumer advocacy ethic grounded in the more or less explicitly stated assumption of consumer sovereignty. In the context of a "service provider-consumer" relationship the balance of power, at least in principle, shifts significantly toward the consumer who plays a leading role in determining the nature of the demand for services and how they are to be provided.

In practice, the sovereignty of the consumer is frequently moderated by a number of factors, including the fact that the consumerist ethic is often mediated through advocacy/ support groups that may not be controlled by those with mental health problems. Specifically, many so-called consumer advocacy groups are dominated by the families of those with mental health problems or by various professional interests. This creates the potential for a conflict of interests between those who propose to speak for the service consumers and to define their needs and the service users themselves.

Recognition of this conflict of interests has contributed to the emergence of another branch of the anti-psychiatry movement generally referred to as the mental patients' liberation movement or psychiatric survivors' movement (Chamberlin, 1990; Burstow & Weitz, 1988; Olsen, 1993). This movement, which is the most radical in its definition of the situation, has essentially rejected the validity of claims that professionally dominated service delivery, whether medical in nature or not, is anything but an oppressive form of social control. Having said that, it must be pointed out that the consumers'/ survivors' movement, at least as it has evolved in Canada since the 1970s, is not homogenous in terms of membership nor in terms of ideologies (Olsen, 1993). Chamberlin (1990, p. 323) notes that despite the lack of organizational and ideological unity, the movement is held together by its commitment to a two-fold common mission, namely, the development of self-help alternatives to medically based psychiatric treatment, and the securing of full citizenship rights for individuals labelled "mentally ill." In practical terms, proponents of the anti-psychiatric perspective endorse the empowerment of service consumers in defining and resolving their problems.

By the end of the 1980s, the mental health field, then, had a number of distinct groups, each with different conceptions of the nature of the problem and the most appropriate solution, attempting to secure the attention of policy makers in order to have their interests and perspectives entrenched in policy. To summarize, these groups were medical professionals and others who maintained that the problem was really mental illness and should be treated like every other illness; non-medical professionals, such as social workers, psychologists, and other types of psychotherapists who maintained the problem was really various types of psycho-social problems in living that required their therapeutic assistance for its correct identification and solution; and finally members of the psychiatric consumers'/survivors' movement who maintained that whatever the true nature of the problem was, those suffering from it should be primarily responsible for its definition and solution. In the following section, I will attempt to show that current policy initiatives can be understood as efforts to accommodate these different and potentially incompatible perspectives and interests while at the same time responding to demands for cost containment.

Current Policy Proposals and Developments

In Canada, mental health, like health in general, is a provincial responsibility. Each province/territory, therefore, is developing its response to the problems of mental health relative to its own unique circumstances. Despite this, mental health policy in all jurisdictions is developing within the health promotion framework and consequently is characterized by a number of common themes and trends (Macnaughton, 1992; Epp, 1988, 1986; Health and Welfare Canada, 1990).

Four of these identified by Health and Welfare Canada are an increased emphasis on mental health promotion and the prevention of mental disorders; the protection of human rights and freedoms; a greater emphasis on community care; and concern for the co-ordination of service planning and development (Health and Welfare Canada 1990, p. 169). The balance of this chapter will be devoted to an examination of these themes and to some of the contradictions embedded within and between them as a means for accommodating the three conceptions of the nature of the problem outlined above.

Mental Health Promotion and Prevention of Mental Disorders

The promotion of mental health as a policy objective presupposes a definition of mental health. There is, however, no widely accepted definition. For that reason, Health and Welfare Canada proposed the following interactive definition:

> Mental health is the capacity of the individual, the group and the environment to interact in ways that promote subjective well-being, the optimal development and use of mental abilities (cognitive, affective and relational), the achievement of individual and collective goals consistent with justice and the attainment and preservation of conditions of fundamental equality (Epp, 1988, p. 7).

An important aspect of this interactive definition is that mental health is not defined in terms of the absence of mental disorders/illnesses. Thus, mental health and mental illness are not seen as lying at opposite poles on a single continuum. Rather, it is suggested that they lie on separate continuums. Mental disorders, then, are conceptualized as existing on a continuum with maximal mental disorder at one pole characterized by the greatest severity, frequency, and range of psychiatric symptoms, and absence of mental disorder at the other pole characterized by freedom from psychiatric symptoms (Epp, 1988, p. 9).

Mental health, on the other hand, is seen as lying on a continuum with optimal mental health at one pole where individual, group, and environmental factors work together effectively to ensure subjective well-being, optimal development and use of mental abilities, the achievement of goals consistent with justice, and conditions of fundamental equality, while at the other pole is minimal mental health characterized by subjective distress, impairment or underdevelopment of mental abilities, failure to achieve goals, destructive behaviours, and entrenchment of inequalities caused by con-tradictory interactions between individual, group, and environmental factors (Epp, 1988, p. 8, Figure 2). Given this conceptualization, the absence of psychiatric symptoms in itself does not imply optimal mental health. Similarly, the presence of mental disorders, or psychiatric symptoms, does not preclude the possibility of enhancing mental health. Rather, "mental disorder may be regarded as one of several possible obstacles" to the achievement of mental health (Epp, 1988, p. 8).

The promotion of mental health, therefore, is the same for all individuals regardless of whether they suffer from mental disorders. It involves eliminating or minimizing the barriers to the achievement of empowering interactions between individuals, groups, and the environment (Epp, 1988, p. 9). These interventions can be aimed at individuals or they can be directed towards altering social and organizational structures and policies so as to facilitate the achievement, maintenance, or restoration of mental health.

Conceptually and practically, the prevention and treatment of mental disorders is distinct from the promotion of mental health, although in a number of aspects they intersect. Little is known about the underlying causes of many of the major mental illnesses/disorders, although there is an emerging consensus that they result from bio-logical, developmental, and/or psycho-social factors and "can — in principle, at least — be managed using approaches comparable to those applied to physical disease (that is prevention, diagnosis, treatment and rehabilitation)" (Epp, 1988, p. 8).

Despite this consensus concerning the mutifactoral causes of mental disorders/illnesses, little can be done in the way of primary prevention, that is, prevention of the onset of mental disorders. Secondary prevention, or the prevention of relapse through the management of symptoms, has been facilitated by "pharmacological and other modalities" (Epp, 1988, p. 8), although there is still considerable controversy concerning both the effectiveness and appropriateness of chemotherapy and other forms of treatment directed towards symptom management. Currently, attention is being devoted to what is termed tertiary prevention, that is, prevention or minimization of the degree of disability associated with mental disorders. In more concrete terms, tertiary prevention is directed towards minimizing the need for expensive in-patient and residential treatments. Tertiary prevention efforts, whatever their focus, attempt to identify and mobilize resources in the form of self-help or mutual-aid and to minimize reliance on expensive professional services whenever and to whatever extent possible. I will return to this topic below.

Like current efforts to prevent mental disorders, mental health promotion practices are premised on the ideal of consumer involvement and empowerment. As we have seen, a contradiction can exist between the ways in which different stakeholders understand the nature of the problem and approach its solution. Policy makers recognize at least some of the potential problems in this regard created by the distinction between mental health and mental disorders presented above:

> Only by recognizing the importance and interaction of these two areas of endeavour can we avoid the two
> "blind alleys" of the mental health policy debate: exclusive reliance on medical treatment technologies on the
> one hand, and anti-professionalism and exclusive reliance on individual initiative or volunteer action on the
> other" (Epp, 1988, p. 10).

Problem recognition is a first step towards its resolution. In this quote, it is clear that policy makers recognize the existence of two approaches to the problem of mental health/illness, namely the medical and the anti-professional, anti-psychiatric approach. The distinctions and potential conflicts between the medical and the anti-medical professional models, however, is not recognized. Without concrete proposals for how proponents of the contending positions are to co-operate, calls for various stakeholders to work together may be dismissed as hopelessly naive, or even worse, as an effort to obscure continued forms of psychiatric oppression or professional dominance behind an ideological facade of co-operative partnership. The current emphasis on human rights and freedoms in the mental health arena and policy deliberations may be intended to forestall the latter interpretation.

Protecting Human Rights and Freedoms

The protection of human rights and freedoms has been a perennial concern relative to the social management and control of madness/mental illness. Over the last two centuries, the power to define and treat the mad/mentally ill has alternated between the state delegation of power to the medical profession in order to enable the timely diagnosis and treatment of the problem for the protection of both the individual and society, and a system that was legally dominated in order to ensure due process to those thought to be mentally ill/mad so as to protect them from unjust and unfair commitment and involuntary treatment.

In the face of recent attempts to demonstrate the truth of the claim that mental illness was really an illness that should be treated like every other illness, there emerged a growing recognition of the rights of mental patients to be informed of treatment, to refuse treatment, and to be treated in the least restrictive setting and manner possible. This impetus to mental patients' rights paradoxically received added impetus as a result of the post-1960s anti-psychiatry movement, which maintains, as we have seen, that mental illness is a myth and that the system of medically dominated diagnosis and treatment predicated upon the medical model was a violation of human rights.

These general factors contributed to a growing consensus that patients/consumers should have a significant, if not a predominant say, in defining the nature of their problem and the nature of the most appropriate solution(s). Consumer participation in these processes is currently seen as an effective means to protect their rights and freedoms (Health and Welfare Canada, 1990, pp. 173-174).

The forces described above that contributed to an emphasis on consumer participation as a means of ensuring the protection of individual rights and freedoms was given added impetus with the adoption of the Canadian Charter of Rights and Freedoms in 1982. In 1987, a draft of a Uniform Mental Health Act was prepared by a committee of the Uniform Law Conference of Canada (Uniform Law Conference 1987). The draft of the Uniform Mental Health Act, although it has no legal status, was intended to serve as a guide for the legislative incorporation of the requirements of the Charter of Rights and Freedoms into provincial and territorial legislation.

Despite the fact that there is an increasingly explicit commitment to consumer empowerment and participation in problem definition and solution formulation in the mental health field, a contradiction that is evident in the model mental health act remains. The contradiction resides in the fact that mental health policy and practice has a dual function: it is intended to provide care and treatment to those in need and it is intended to protect others from mentally disordered individuals who may be dangerous. Indeed, in the 1987 model mental health act, the protection of society from danger and the terms and conditions for providing involuntary "treatment" to those considered dangerous is the dominant concern (Health and Welfare Canada, 1990, pp. 173-74).

It is obvious that the provision of involuntary examination, custody, care, treatment, and restraint is inevitably going to conflict with the principle of consumer control and voluntary participation. In practical legal terms, this contradiction can be expressed as a conflict between society's right to provide involuntary treatment in order to protect its members and the individual's right to refuse treatment.

Recent efforts to resolve this contradiction have resulted in the introduction of mandatory community treatment orders. These orders enable the courts to require individuals to take their medications and to appoint someone, often a physician, to ensure that they do. It is generally thought that many individuals caught in the revolving door of hospitalization–release–hospitalization could have that cycle broken if they would stay on their medications while in the community. Community treatment orders are an attempt to prevent re-hospitalization and to that extent are part of the tertiary prevention efforts mentioned above.

In reference to this, a potential contradiction can be seen to exist between the principles of protecting individuals' rights to refuse treatment, particularly if they are no immediate danger to themselves or others, and the commitment to community care and least-cost solutions of tertiary prevention (i.e., the prevention of the need for expensive in-patient treatment).

Community Care

The emphasis on community care is often interpreted to mean the establishment of a more "balanced" configuration of institutional (i.e., in-patient and other residential treatment services), and community-based (i.e., out-patient and non-residential) services and supports of various types. More specifically, it refers to a further reduction in the use of long-term residential care facilities and expensive in-patient services in general hospitals.

The fact that the majority of mental health care costs are associated with the provision of general hospital–based treatment and care is generally taken as indicative of the failure of the 1960s and 1970s deinstitutionalization movement (Simmons, 1990; Lurie, 1984; Trainor et al., 1992). It is important to note, however, that during the first phase of the development of community psychiatry, the substitution of general hospital based in-patient treatment services for mental asylum/hospital services was seen as a major advance (Dickinson, 1989; Tyhurst et al., 1963).

The current commitment to reduced in-patient services is accompanied by the recognition that a range of housing alternatives are required "in order to provide for people at various levels of individual functioning, while allowing the appropriate degrees of professional supervision and personal autonomy" (Health and Welfare Canada, 1990, p. 170).

It is explicitly stated that the service users are to have a central role in the development and co-ordination of community psychiatric services: ". . . the involvement of service consumers is an essential part of planning and developing services which will meet their needs" (Health and Welfare Canada, 1990, p. 170). It is also made explicit that the satisfaction of those needs will involve the co-ordinated identification, use, and development of various "informal and natural support networks with respect to care and rehabilitation efforts" (Health and Welfare Canada, 1990, p. 170). The identification and mobilization of these informal community-based resources for the provision of care and rehabilitation services signals a commitment to least-cost solutions and constitutes a mainstay in mental health promotion efforts. Given that this priority will likely be pursued via the re-allocation of resources from the medically dominated hospital sector, which is devoted to the problem of mental disorders, to the non-medical community mental-health care system primarily concerned with the problem of promoting mental health, it seems likely that putting commitment to the principle of community care into practice will not be easy or conflict free. Recognition of this potential underpins a commitment to coordination in service planning and delivery.

Coordination of Service Planning and Delivery

Accurate identification of needs is the foundation of service planning and delivery. It is generally believed that once the prevalence and types of needs are accurately identified, rational decisions can be made concerning the (re)allocation of mental health resources, both financial and human. Related to this is the proposition that accurate assessment of needs, especially at the individual level, allows for the development of individualized service delivery plans. This is deemed essential, both to minimize the possibility of necessarily institutionalizing individuals and inadvertently creating dependance, and in order to reduce the risks that individuals with some kind of service needs fall between the cracks in an uncoordinated system.

The priority currently given to coordination in policy planning and service delivery is at least partly a response to these general concerns. More specifically it is a response to widespread criticism of the initial phase of the deinstitutionalization movement of the 1960s and 1970s. A problem with that first phase of community psychiatry was that it over emphasized efforts at deinstitutionalization, which in practice often amounted to little more than depopulation of the old asylums. The depopulation of asylums, which was made possible as a result of the successful medicalization of psychiatry (Dickinson, 1989; Dickinson & Andre, 1988), was roundly criticized because it failed to adequately establish community-based services and resources. This failure had a number of consequences, all of which are considered to be negative, and are referred to in various ways, but they generally include what is termed ghettoization and trans-institutionalization.

Ghettoization of the mentally ill is seen to be a result of the abandonment of discharged patients into a community setting that is not equipped or willing to provide the services and supports for them (Scull, 1983; Dear & Wolch, 1987). A consequence of this lack of adequate community psychiatric or mental health services is that discharged mental patients, who usually have few resources or money, tend to drift towards low rent inner city neighbourhoods. Increasingly, those with mental disorders contribute to the growing population of homeless that are a ubiquitous and distressing feature of contemporary Western societies.

The problems associated with ghettoization, magnified by cutbacks to welfare and social services and increasing levels of apparently permanent un- and underemployment, creates a crucible for crime. The mentally ill are both victims and offenders. A consequence of this is that many discharged mental patients are caught up in the criminal justice system. This is often referred to a the criminalization of mental illness and it is an aspect of transinstitutionalization. Transinstitutionalization is the process of shifting individuals with mental disorders from one institutional setting to another without really solving the problem that motivated the discharge from mental hospitals in the first place. Indeed, most analysts agree that transinstitutionalization exacerbates the problem because individuals end up in institutional settings even less equipped to provide appropriate services and support than were the old mental hospitals. This is often seen to be a particular problem for the aged mentally disordered who, it is frequently maintained, are often simply drugged and warehoused in long-term care facilities.

In an effort to avoid and correct these problems, decentralization and regionalization have been enthusiastically embraced as a means for coordinating mental health program planning and development. The anticipated advantages of decentralization and regionalization are twofold; it is hoped it will enable the identification of location-specific service delivery needs and that it will facilitate the creation of local commitment to the mobilization and reallocation of resources within the communities most directly affected. This last point is particularly important in light of the commitment to self-care and mutual-aid as essential elements in the new health promotion framework (Epp, 1986, 1988).

The commitment to decentralization and regionalization is expressed in varying degrees in different provinces, but generally it entails a transfer of at least some executive and fiscal responsibility to new administrative structures. This transfer of power or responsibility is seen to have both positive and negative effects. On the positive side it is argued to be an extension of democratic decision-making into new areas of community life. On the negative side it is argued that it simply results in the transfer of difficult and divisive resource allocation decisions to local communities. Both of these have the consequence of politicizing decisions at the community level, and thereby intensifying the struggle for control of available resources.

The nature of the membership of the new and proposed regional planning and administrative bodies emerging in various forms and with various degrees of autonomy across the country is important if the hopes for increased democratization are to be achieved. There are a number of "stakeholders" or vested interests in the mental health field who do not share a common definition of the nature of the problems to be solved, nor as a result, do they share a common vision of the most appropriate solutions to be applied (Boudreau, 1991a, 1991b, 1987; White & Mercier, 1991; Dickinson, 1989; Dickinson & Andre, 1988). Furthermore, it is not apparent that any consensus can be reached on these issues.

Attempts to skirt these issues by selective participation in planning and administration of mental health services will undermine the legitimacy of these new initiatives and, consequently, their likelihood of success. Sensitivity to this potential problem is crucial given the importance to the health promotion framework of securing both individual, family, and community participation in the planning and provision of services and support for those with mental health problems and mental disorders.

Conclusion

This chapter has focussed on selected aspects of the problem definition components of current policy initiatives in the mental health field and their relationship to key elements of the proposed reforms of mental health-service delivery systems. I have argued that lack of consensus about the causes of mental disorder and the nature of mental health problems contribute to the institutionalization of contradictions at the level of the service delivery structure.

More specifically, I argued that current policy initiatives appear to be directed toward establishing a compromise between three conceptions of the problem to be solved and the best way to solve it. Despite the laudable intentions behind these policy proposals, it is not clear that they can be effectively put into practice in the form of a comprehensive and integrated mental-health care services system. The problem is that the stakeholders, which include both medical and non-medical professional interests and the non-professional interests of service users and their advocates, don't necessarily agree on the nature of the problem nor on the nature of the best solution. Policy initiatives, then, may have the unintended consequence of locking proponents of conflicting and possibly irreconcilable positions into a system of perpetual conflict. Thus, rather than being the solution to existing problems, current initiatives may simply be creating new ones.

Study Questions

1. Identify and discuss the relationships between the three main approaches to defining the problem of mental disorders/health presented in this chapter.
2. What are the four main issues common to mental health policy debates and reforms currently taking place in Canada?
3. Outline and discuss the relationship between the anti-psychiatry movement and the psychiatric consumers'/survivors' movement.
4. The distinction between mental disorders and mental health problems is intended to avoid the two "blind alleys" of mental health policy debate. Outline and discuss.

Recommended Reading

Dickinson, H.D. (1989). *The two psychiatries: The transformation of psychiatric work in Saskatchewan, 1905-1984.* Regina: CPRC.

Epp, J. (1988). *Mental health for Canadians: Striking a balance.* Ottawa: Health and Welfare Canada.

Health and Welfare Canada. (1990). *Mental health services in Canada, 1990.* Ottawa: Author.

Scull, A. (1983). *Decarceration: Community treatment and the deviant — A radical view* (2nd ed.). Cambridge: Polity Press.

Szasz, T.S. (1972). *The myth of mental illness: Foundations of a theory of personal conduct.* Frogmore, St. Albans, Herts.: Paladin.

References

Bland, R.C. (1988). Prevalence of mental illness. *Annals of the Royal College of Physicians and Surgeons of Canada, 21,* 89-93.

Blishen, B.R. (1991). *Doctors in Canada: The changing world of medical practice.* Toronto: University of Toronto Press in association with Statistics Canada.

Boudreau, F. (1987). The vicissitudes of psychiatric intervention in Quebec. In E.M. Bennett (Ed.), *Social intervention, theory and practice* (pp. 295-323). Lewiston and Queenston: The Edwin Mellen Press.

Boudreau, F. (1991a). Stakeholders as partners? The challenges of partnership in Quebec mental health policy. *Canadian Journal of Community Mental Health, 10,* 7-28.

Boudreau, F. (1991b). Partnership as a new strategy in mental health policy: The case of Quebec. *Journal of Health Politics, Policy and Law, 16,* 307-330.

Burstow, B., & Weitz, D. (Eds.). (1988). *Shrink resistant: The struggle against psychiatry in Canada.* Vancouver: New Star Books.

Busfield, J. (1986). *Managing madness: Changing ideas and practices.* London: Unwin Hyman.

Chamberlin, J. (1990). The ex-patient's movement: Where we've been and where we're going. In D. Cohen (Ed.), Challenging the therapeutic state: Critical perspectives on psychiatry and the mental health system. *The Journal of Mind and Behavior, 11,* (3, 4), 323-336.

Cohen S. (1985). *Visions of social control: Crime, punishment and classification.* Cambridge: Polity Press.

Conrad, P., & Schneider, J. (1980). *Deviance and medicalization: From badness to madness.* St. Louis: C.V. Mosby.

Dear, M., & Wolch, J. (1987). *Landscapes of despair: From deinstitutionalization to homelessness.* Princeton: Princeton University Press.

Dickinson, H.D. (1989). *The two psychiatries: The transformation of psychiatric work in Saskatchewan, 1905-1984.* Regina: Canadian Plains Research Centre.

Dickinson, H.D., & Andre, G. (1988). Community psychiatry: The institutional transformation of psychiatric practice. In B.S. Bolaria & H.D. Dickinson (Eds.), *The sociology of health care in Canada* (pp. 295-308). Toronto: Harcourt Brace Jovanovich.

Epp, J. (1986). *Achieving health for all: A framework for health promotion.* Ottawa: Health and Welfare Canada.

Epp. J. (1988). *Mental health for Canadians: Striking a balance.* Ottawa: Health and Welfare Canada.

Foucault, M. (1973). *Madness and civilization: A history of insanity in the age of reason.* New York: Vintage Books.

Freidson, E. (1970). *Profession of medicine: A study in the sociology of applied knowledge.* New York: Harper & Row.

Goffman, E. (1961). *Asylums: Essays on the social situation of mental patients and other inmates.* New York: Anchor Books.

Health and Welfare Canada. (1990). *Mental health services in Canada, 1990.* Ottawa: Author.

Health Beat. (1992, May/June). Research for mental disorders gets shortchanged. *Natural Health: The Guide to Well-Being,* 20.

Kittrie, N. (1972). *The right to be different.* Baltimore: Penguin.

Laing, R.D., & Esterson, A. (1964). *Sanity, madness and the family (Volume 1): Families of schizophrenics.* London: Tavistock Publications.

Lurie, S. (1984). More for the mind, have we got less?" In M.D. Nair, R.C. Hain, & J.A. Draper (Eds.), *Issues in Canadian social services.* Toronto: Canadian Council on Social Development, 166-185.

Macnaughton, E. (1992). Canadian mental health policy: The emergent picture. *Canada's Mental Health,* 4, 3-10.

Manning, N. (1989). *The therapeutic community movement: Charisma and routinization.* London: Routledge.

Olsen, D. (1993, February). *The movement.* Unpublished paper.

Ralph, D. (1983). *Work and madness: The rise of community psychiatry.* Montreal: Black Rose Books.

Scull, A. (1991). Psychiatry and social control in the nineteenth and twentieth centuries. *History of Psychiatry,* 2, 149-169.

Scull, A. (1983). *Decarceration: Community treatment and the deviant — A radical view* (2nd ed.). Cambridge: Polity Press.

Scull, A. (1982). *Museums of madness: The social organization of insanity in nineteenth-century England.* Harmondsworth: Penguin.

Simmons, H. (1990). *Unbalanced: Mental health policy in Ontario, 1930-1989.* Toronto: Wall & Thompson.

Statistics Canada. (1981). *One of eight: Mental illness in Canada.* Ottawa: Statistics Canada in collaboration with the Canadian Mental Health Association.

Szasz, T.S. (1972). *The myth of mental illness: Foundations of a theory of personal conduct.* Frogmore, St. Albans, Herts.: Paladin.

Trainor, J., Church, K., Pape, B., Pomeroy, E., Reville, D., Teft, B., Lakaski, C., & Renaud, L. (1992). Building a framework for support: Developing a sector-based model for people with serious mental illness. *Canada's Mental Health,* 40, 25-29.

Tyhurst, J.S. et. al. (1963). *More for the mind: A study in psychiatric services in Canada.* Toronto: Canadian Mental Health Association.

Uniform Law Conference of Canada. (1987). Proceedings of the Sixty-ninth Annual Meeting, Appendix F — Uniform Mental Health Act. Victoria: Uniform Law Conference.

White, D., & Mercier, C. (1991). Reorienting mental health systems: The dynamics of policy and planning. *International Journal of Mental Health,* 19, 3-24.

Health-Care Professions and the Division of Labour

Part Seven

Introduction

The established professions resist and oppose any perceived or actual threat to their monopolistic position, either by the state or by other professions. The first two chapters in this section discuss the medical profession's opposition to alternative medicine and to midwives; the third chapter deals with the dental profession's opposition to a provincial dental plan; while the fourth chapter discusses the need for change in the division of labour in health care.

A significant amount of health care in Canada is provided by various practitioners in the alternative health-care system. In Chapter 22, Northcott examines the various terminologies used to distinguish the dominant and alternative health-care systems. Wardwell's (1979) typology of health-care practitioners (parallel, limited, ancillary, marginal, quasi) is discussed.

The various therapies that overlap both the scientific and alternative health-care systems are examined. These include midwifery, holistic health care, self-care, feminist health care, and quackery. Skrabanek and McCormick's (1990) typology for alternative health care is described. Categories include: medication, manipulation, devices, mind cures, and occultism. The following alternative therapies are then discussed by category: homeopathy, naturopathy, herbal remedies, osteopathy, chiropractic, acupuncture, massage, radionics, selected mind cures, folk medicine, and diagnostic techniques such as iridology.

A review of the research literature is provided, and it is argued that a substantial minority of the population uses alternative health care in a given year. Users tend to represent a socio-demographic cross-section of the general population, and tend also to use scientific medicine concurrently. It is further suggested that despite the hostile rhetoric, there appears to be a trend towards the convergence of both systems.

The status of midwifery vis-à-vis conventional medicine is also ambiguous. It has re-emerged in Canada in two general forms: community midwives who manage home deliveries; and nurse-midwives operating more autonomously within institutions such as hospitals or birth centres. Burtch, in Chapter 23, provides a brief outline of the historical antagonisms between traditional midwives and physicians, and of current applications of legal sanctions to birth attendants. The central theme is that provincial quasi-criminal law — such as the B.C. Medical Practitioners Act — and the federal Criminal Code have been used to consolidate the powers of the medical profession in managing births. A related point is that the state does not act merely in an instrumental way.

A structuralist interpretation of the role of the state, and especially of its legal apparatus, is applied to current attempts to legalize midwifery practice and place it on a more autonomous footing. Burtch argues that although resistance to the midwifery movement rests upon material and ideological concerns, the public interest is also served by the consequent establishment of controlling general regulation standards of training and professional practice.

Croucher, in Chapter 24, describes the response of a professional association to the introduction of a government-organized children's dental-care plan in Saskatchewan. This plan relied on "expanded duty" dental nurses to provide services through clinics based in the school system, working with a minimum of supervision by dentists.

In opposing this plan, the College of Dental Surgeons of Saskatchewan used an ideology containing both "parochial" and "ecumenical" elements. More stress was laid upon the parochial issue of the autonomy of the dentist. In this case this referred to the need for greater supervision of the dental nurse, along with a preference for a service modelled on the existing private fee-for-service model.

By presenting these arguments, the profession overlooked the existing poor health of the children of Saskatchewan and the maldistribution in the supply of services.

Objective evaluations of the performance of the dental plan have demonstrated the value-laden basis of the dental profession's ideology. Changes in the epidemiology of dental disease, coupled with a greater supply of dentists, have resulted in the recent "arm's-length" involvement of the profession in the plan.

Chapter 25 is also concerned with changes to interpersonal relationships in health care. Arguing that the division of labour in health care in Canada is unethical, Storch begins by describing how it developed, strongly influenced by policies in the United States and Britain. She notes that although major advances have been made in the way that physicians, nurses, physiotherapists, nutritionists, occupational therapists, psychologists, and social workers interrelate in the care of patients, these advances are inconsistent across regions, hospitals, and even across hospital and health-care units. Research findings support the conclusion that collaboration, allowing input from two or more different health professionals, can lead to better outcomes for the patient because decisions are based on more complete information and shared decision making. The author suggests that changing the division of labour in health care will require political will since traditional values and power structures will have to change. She posits that with greater refinement in measuring outcomes, assessing processes, and clarifying inputs there will be greater precision in matching patient needs with health professional knowledge and skills so that the abilities of all on the health-care team are maximized.

Chapter 22

Alternative Health Care in Canada

Herbert C. Northcott, University of Alberta

Introduction

Discussions of health care in Canada tend to focus on a long list of practitioners and agencies including, for example, the medical doctor, nurse, pharmacist, rehabilitation medicine therapist, hospital, nursing home, and government-sponsored health-care insurance program. Nevertheless, a significant amount of health care in Canada is provided by practitioners not included among the usual components of the health-care delivery system as listed above. The purpose of this chapter is to describe the alternative health-care delivery system in Canada and its relationship to the dominant health-care system. To accomplish this purpose, it is necessary first to review and select an appropriate terminology, and second, it is helpful to briefly examine the relationships of the various practitioners within the conventional health-care system so that comparisons and contrasts can be made with the various practitioners in the alternative health-care system.

One might think that selecting a terminology would be an easy task. After all, it might be reasonably concluded that all that is needed is one term to describe the dominant health-care system and a second term to describe the alternative. Indeed, the previous sentence suggests that the terms "dominant" and "alternative" might be adequate to this task. The problem is that the literature is replete with synonyms and related terminologies, each with differing connotations and implications. For example, the terms "dominant" and "alternative" imply that alternative health care is inferior to the dominant system. While the dominant system does enjoy a more widespread acceptance, a higher social standing, and greater power and political clout, not everyone, certainly not alternative health-care practitioners and their clients, will agree that the alternative system is inferior. Consequently, other terminologies are examined in the following paragraphs.

Because the dominant system of health care has come to be based heavily on the scientific method while alternative health care tends to be less scientific in orientation, the dichotomy "scientific-unscientific" is often utilized. Because scientific medicine has developed in the West (primarily in Europe and North America) and in recent centuries (particularly in the twentieth century), the descriptions "modern" and "Western" are often added to the term "scientific." Further, because science is based on a "rational" system of thought, the dominant health-care system tends to be described as modern, Western, rational, and scientific. In contrast, alternative health care tends to be described as non-modern, non-Western, irrational, and unscientific, terms that seem pejorative, especially when used in combination with one another.

Because the current dominant system of health care has been prominent for some time, it is therefore occasionally referred to as the "traditional" system. By implication, alternative health care is "non-traditional." This terminology is problematic, however, in that the term traditional is widely used to describe long-standing systems of "folk" medicine. Further, many of the modern alternative health-care therapies have more in common with ancient folk medicine than with modern scientific medicine. In other words, it can be argued that the term "traditional" is better applied to the alternative health-care system than to the dominant science-oriented health-care system.

Even the term "medicine" is ambiguous. This term is often used to refer to the dominant system characterized above as modern, scientific, rational, and Western. However, consider Ayurvedic medicine, an "alternative" system of health care indigenous to India, and consider also the "medicine man" (or woman) who is typically viewed as an alternative practitioner (the medicine man's contributions to modern medicine notwithstanding, e.g., morphine, quinine, cocaine, digitalis).

Turning to a religious metaphor (recall that both modern and alternative medicine have their roots in ancient systems that combine proven knowledge with magic and religion), modern medicine is frequently described as "orthodox" and alternative health care as "unorthodox" or "heterodox." Continuing the metaphor, alternative therapies are sometimes referred to as medical "cults." Unorthodoxy, of course, implies heresy, a connotation that some find unhelpful and unwelcome. Alternatively, a legal metaphor provides the labels "legitimate" and "illegitimate." Again, such terminology is value laden, judgemental, and subjective in that legitimacy depends on your point of view. As terminology is typically selected according to the point of view of the dominant system, the term illegitimate is then applied pejoratively to alternative health care.

The "official-unofficial" typology is a bureaucratic metaphor, while organizational metaphors provide the following: "organized-unorganized," "included-excluded," "center-fringe," and "mainstream-periphery." Social metaphors describe alternative health care as "marginal," "deviant," or "irregular." Building on the deviance theme, alternative health care is occasionally and more aggressively labelled as "quackery" and alternative health-care practitioners as "quacks" or "charlatans." These terms imply practice based on fraudulent and/or erroneous methods. Quackery tends to be seen, therefore, as inefficacious (except by the placebo effect), illegitimate, and while occasionally sincerely misguided, too often cynically motivated in an attempt to exploit the vulnerable and the gullible. The term quack, then, serves to defend the practitioner of scientific medicine by discrediting practitioners of alternative health care. Because of the value judgement, bias, and politics inherent in the term, it is too inflammatory a concept to be applied to alternative health care generally.

There is another set of descriptors used to distinguish the dominant and alternative health-care systems. While the terms discussed above tend to reflect favourably on the dominant system and unfavourably on the alternative system, there are terms that tend to do just the opposite. For example, critics of the dominant system see it as impersonal, disease-oriented, and overly specialized and fragmented. By contrast, the strengths of the alternative system are often said to be a personal, holistic, and health (wellness) orientation (Edginton, 1989, pp. 172-173). Nevertheless, these descriptors fail to provide a simple, non-evaluative terminology that adequately captures the essential differences between the dominant and alternative health-care systems.

Finally, the dominant and alternative health-care systems have been described above in language that implies that each system is integrated, unified, and monolithic. While this characterization does apply to a considerable degree to the dominant health-care system, it does not accurately describe the alternative system. The "alternative" system includes a diverse range of practices and practitioners. This diversity includes everything from chiropractors to faith healers. Furthermore, these various practitioners do not constitute an integrated, unified system of health care. Nevertheless, the simplification is perhaps useful. That is, given the predominance of scientific medicine in our society, it is helpful to classify any given health care practitioner as either a member of the dominant health-care system or as an alternative practitioner.

Just the same, rather than thinking of the dominant and alternative systems as dichotomous monoliths, it is helpful to think of a continuum on which various practitioners from both schools can be located. However, before examining this continuum, it is necessary to finally settle on a terminology. For the purposes of the following discussion, the dominant health-care system will be identified as "scientific" medicine while the term "alternative" will be used to group and characterize the diverse components of the non-dominant health-care system. It is hoped that this terminology is reasonably descriptive while at the same time minimally evaluative. While our culture does tend to have a favourable disposition toward science (the mad scientist notwithstanding), alternatives can be either better, comparable, or worse. In other words, this terminology does not necessarily elevate one system and denigrate the other. Further, Skrabanek and McCormick (1990, p. 103) argue that "Two things distinguish alternative medicine. The first is that it does not derive from any coherent or established body of evidence. The second, that it is not subjected to rigorous assessment to establish its value." In other words, alternative medicine is not scientific, science being both a systematic body of knowledge and theory as well as a particular method for assessing validity and efficacy. In short, the non-dominant system of medicine truly represents an "alternative" to "scientific" medicine.

Before examining the various components of the alternative health-care system, it is helpful to examine the relationships among the various practitioners of scientific medicine in order to develop a continuum that can be extended to alternative health-care practitioners. The prototypical practitioner of scientific medicine is the medical doctor. All other practitioners of scientific medicine tend to be classified in relation to the medical doctor. Wardwell (1988, p. 187) identifies "parallel" practitioners such as osteopathy which have become similar to the medical doctor in theory, training and practice but nevertheless maintain a distinct identity. Furthermore, Wardwell (1979) identifies "limited" and "ancillary" medical practitioners. Limited medical practitioners such as dentists and optometrists practise limited specialties within scientific medicine independent of the control of medical doctors. On the other hand, ancillary medical practitioners such as nurses, pharmacists, and rehabilitation therapists are controlled to varying degrees by the medical doctor. Wardwell (1979) also identifies two categories of alternative practitioners: "marginal" practitioners such as chiropractors and naturopaths and "quasi-practitioners" such as faith healers. Marginal practitioners are located near the boundary separating scientific and alternative medicine while quasi-practitioners are far removed from scientific medicine having a fundamentally different view of health and illness (e.g., a view based on psychological, metaphysical, or religious assumptions rather than physiological premises).

It is interesting to note that health-care therapies are not necessarily static. For example, scientific medicine is evolving as medical theories are proven or disproven, as treatments are found to be effective or ineffective, and as gaps in knowledge are filled. Further, alternative health-care therapies may also develop an increasing knowledge base and may even converge with scientific medicine. Indeed, Biggs (1988, p. 331), commenting on Wardwell's work on chiropractic, observes that chiropractic may be evolving from a marginalized position in the alternative health-care system into either a parallel profession or a limited specialty within scientific medicine. The next section of this chapter will discuss chiropractic and various other alternative health-care therapies.

Alternative Health-Care Therapies

Alternative health care includes many diverse practitioners and systems of healing and health promotion. In this section, a typology of alternative health-care therapies will be developed and selected therapies will be examined. First of all, however, midwifery, holistic health care, self-care, feminist health care, and quackery, each of which overlap with both the scientific and alternative health-care systems, will be discussed.

In Canada today, a midwife trained as a nurse and practising in the hospital under the direction of the physician is an ancillary practitioner within the scientific health-care system. Alternatively, a midwife trained in modern birthing techniques (but not necessarily trained as a nurse) who is practicing in the community (e.g., attending home births) independent of the control of the physician is a marginal practitioner in the alternative health-care system with a claim to being, and a likelihood of becoming, a limited practitioner in the scientific health-care system. Midwifery is currently legal in Newfoundland (Burtch, 1993, p. 513) and there are movements to legalize midwifery in other provinces. For example, Alberta and Ontario have both announced intentions to legalize midwifery (*Edmonton Journal*, April 8, 1991, p. A10; 1991, June 12, p. A1). In contrast, a lay midwife trained in a traditional system of folk medicine is and will likely remain a member of the alternative health-care system. (For discussions of midwifery in Canada, see Burtch, 1993; Clarke, 1990, p. 272-78.)

Like midwifery, holism has a long history. Holism reflects the orientation of many ancient therapeutic systems. Modern scientific medicine has been widely criticized for its physiological, specialized, and fragmented approach to the whole person. Accordingly, it is claimed by many that a more holistic approach is superior. Holism emphasizes the interdependence of body, mind, and environment (physical, social, etc.). The emotions and spirit are often added to this list of interdependent parts. Holism opposes the separation of mind and body and rejects the reductionism and fragmentation of modern scientific medicine, arguing instead that the whole is greater than the sum of the parts and that therefore the "whole person" must be treated instead of some limited and diseased aspect of the person. Holism emphasizes harmony, wellness, prevention, and self-help. Holism is a philosophy and therapeutic orientation claimed by some practitioners of scientific medicine (including some doctors, nurses, and rehabilitation therapists) and by many diverse practitioners of alternative health care (including chiro-practors, naturopaths, and folk healers). (For discussion and analysis of the modern holistic health "movement" see Alster, 1989; see also Stalker & Glymour, 1985; Hast-ings, Fadiman, & Gordon, 1980; English-Lueck, 1990; Lowenberg, 1989.)

Self-care (also referred to as self-help) also overlaps with both scientific medicine and alternative health care. That is, self-care, with or without the advice of lay others in one's social network (e.g., spouse, parents, other relatives, friends, and so on), may draw from either scientific medicine or alternative health care. For example, self-prescribing an over-the-counter analgesic or cough medication is consistent with scientific medi-cine. In contrast, self-prescribing an old family or home remedy such as an herbal tea or dietary prescription (consider the legendary chicken soup) would more likely constitute alternative health care. In other words, self-care is not necessarily alternative health care nor is it necessarily scientific medicine. Indeed, it may be either depending on whether or not the remedy self-prescribed is recognized by the scientific medicine community or claimed by alternative health-care practitioners.

Feminist health care tends to overlap with midwifery, holistic health, and self-care. The women's health movement objects to male-dominated medicine and seeks to deme-dicalize many aspects of female life (e.g., pregnancy, menopause) thereby wresting control of women's bodies away from male doctors and returning that control to women themselves. It is important to note that feminist health is not opposed to scientific medicine per se, but rather is opposed to the male domination of health and the exploita-tion of women's health by means of definitions, diagnoses, and treatments that disadvan-tage women. While the emphases on nature, holism, and self-responsibility are consistent with the orientation of alternative health, nevertheless, feminist health care draws from both scientific medicine and alternative health care.

Quackery, like midwifery, holistic health care, self-care, and feminist health care cannot be designated as a component of either scientific medicine or alternative health care. Quackery, that is, fraudulent practices, flourish today as in the past (Coe, 1978, pp. 238-44). In one sense, quackery, because it is fraudulent, is neither a part of scientific medicine nor of alternative health care. Quackery, however, may pretend to be either. For example, psychic surgery — ostensibly an alternative health-care therapy — has been fraudulently practised (American Cancer Society, 1990). On the other hand, many modern products are marketed under the guise of scientific medicine. Coe (1978, p. 240) states that there are three major areas for such quackery: foods and nutrition, mechanical and electrical devices, and drugs and cosmetics. Coe (1978, p. 240) notes that these various products are "cloaked in scientific terminology" and attended by "false or misleading claims." Furthermore, Coe (1978, p. 238) notes that if the definition of quackery is extended to include "error" as well as fraud, then erroneous practices have been and will yet be found among the practitioners of both scientific medicine and alternative health care. (For discussions of quackery, see Porter, 1989; Bynum & Porter, 1987; Jameson, 1961; Holbrook, 1959; and Young, 1967, 1961.)

In summary, issues such as quackery, holistic health care, self-care, feminist health care, and midwifery cut across both scientific medicine and alternative health care. The following will provide a typology and discussion of alternative health-care therapies.

A typology for alternative health care is provided by Skrabanek and McCormick (1990, p. 104) who divide alternative therapies into several categories (note that actual practitioners may combine several different categories in a holistic approach). The categories are: (1) medication, for example, homeopathy, herbalism, and other forms of medicines not recognized by modern, science-based pharmacology; (2) manipulation, for example, chiropractic, reflexology, acupuncture; (3) devices, for example, ozone generators, negative ionizers, radionics; (4) mind cure, for example, faith healing, mental imaging; and (5) occultism (magic), for example, pyramidology, psychic surgery. Complex systems of folk medicine, incorporating some or all of these various categories, and alternative diagnostic techniques can be added to this list. Medication, manipulation, and devices can all ultimately be placed on a scientific basis and might therefore be classified in Wardwell's (1979) term as marginal alternative therapies. Mind cure might appear at first glance to be more exotic but nevertheless has a potential for convergence with modern psychology that has achieved limited specialty status within scientific medicine. Occultism continues to have virtually nothing in common with scientific medicine, being based on entirely different philosophical premises (i.e., the supernatural versus the natural). Nevertheless, despite the potential for placing many alternative therapies on a scientific basis, these various therapies as practiced today remain alternatives to scientific medicine. Selected alternative therapies are discussed in the following pages.

Category 1. Medication

Homeopathy

Homeopathy was established in the early 1800s by Samuel Hahnemann, a German physician. Homeopathy is based on the law of similia (like cures like) and the law of infinitesimals (the smaller the dosage, the more potent the effect) (Twaddle & Hessler, 1987, p. 187; Coulter, 1984). In other words, homeopathy treats symptoms of disease by medicating with diluted substances which undiluted would produce the symptom being treated, hence "homeo" meaning the same (Skrabanek & McCormick, 1990, p. 105). (In contrast, modern scientific medicine is often referred to as allopathic medicine because it is based on the assumption that opposites cure (Clarke, 1990, p. 263). In other words, allopathic medicine uses treatments, for example, that surgically remove diseased tissue or oppose disease pathogens — consider antibiotics and their effects.) Homeopathy is fairly widely practised today by medical doctors in countries such as France, West Germany, and Britain (Skrabanek & McCormick, 1990, p. 106).

Naturopathy

Naturopathy originated in the late 1800s, building on the philosophy and practice of homeopathy. Naturopathic medicine emphasizes natural, drugless healing and the preservation of health by use of such "natural" treatments as nutrition, herbal remedies, and mind-body therapies such as yoga. In Canada, the Ontario College of Naturopathic Medicine was founded in 1978. (See Twaddle & Hessler, 1987, pp. 188-190; Clarke, 1990, pp. 268-272).

Herbal Remedies

Herbal remedies have long been a part of traditional systems of folk medicine. In the twentieth century in America, Thomsonianism promoted self-administered natural herbal remedies, and Graham (the Graham cracker) promoted natural foods. In the early twentieth century, Bach touted his flower remedies. While some herbal remedies, or at least their active ingredients, have been incorporated into the modern pharmacopoeia and while a healthy diet continues to be a standard prescription, nevertheless, both herbal remedies and natural foods (consider "health foods," organically grown foods, "no-additives," fibre, vitamin C, and so on) have a current popular appeal. (See Kaslof, 1980; Rothstein, 1988; Fulder, 1984; Hufford, 1988, pp. 234-237; Whorton, 1988.)

Category 2. Manipulation

Osteopathy

Osteopathy was founded by Andrew Still in the United States in the nineteenth century following the American Civil War. Osteopathy originally viewed disease as primarily a result of problems with the skeletal and muscular systems resulting in obstruction of the circulatory system. Accordingly, it was thought that disease was curable through physical manipulation. Osteopathy has converged with modern scientific medicine and in the United States today is a parallel medical profession more or less equal to the medical doctor. In the United Kingdom, osteopathy is now a specialty taken following the medical degree. (See Twaddle & Hessler, 1987, pp. 188-192). In Canada, osteopaths have a very different status than their American or British counterparts. In Canada, there are no osteopathic schools of medicine and osteopaths cannot be licensed except as "drugless practitioners." Further, their services are usually excluded from health-care insurance coverage (Sutherland & Fulton, 1988, pp. 93, 206).

Chiropractic

Shortly after the establishment of osteopathy, Daniel D. Palmer and his son B.J. founded and promoted a second school of manipulation therapy in the United States known as chiropractic. This school focused more exclusively on the spine and taught that most disease originates from spinal misalignments placing pressure on the nerves (Twaddle & Hessler, 1987, p. 188). Diseases were therefore thought to be curable through the physical manipulation of the spine. Chiropractic has divided into two schools: the "straights" who adhere to the original teachings of the Palmers and the "mixers" who have adopted such methods of treatment as nutrition and physical therapy in addition to spinal manipulation (Clarke, 1990, p. 266). Mixers now predominate and in Canada, the Canadian Chiropractic Association represents mixers solely (Clarke, 1990, p. 267). The Canadian Memorial Chiropractic College (established in 1945) offers a four-year Doctor of Chiropractic degree, often following a Bachelor of Science undergraduate degree. Chiropractic increasingly functions as a limited specialty like dentistry or optometry (Sutherland & Fulton, 1988, p. 215). Chiropractors are licensed in all Canadian provinces except Newfoundland. Chiropractic, where licensed, is covered by medical care insurance (up to a limited number of visits per year, except in Saskatchewan where there is full coverage). (See Clarke, 1990, pp. 267-268. For additional discussions of chiropractic in Canada, see Biggs, 1988; Coburn & Biggs, 1987; and Coulter, 1987. For a discussion of chiropractic in the United States, see Wardwell, 1988.)

Acupuncture and Acupressure

Acupuncture is a component of traditional Chinese medicine. Acupuncture involves the insertion of needles into the body just below the skin along certain lines known as meridians. Manipulation of the needles is thought to control pain and both cure and prevent disease. (For discussions of acupuncture, one for and one against, see Skrabanek, 1985 and Bresler, 1980.) In acupressure, and in Japanese Shiatsu, a practitioner's fingers are utilized instead of needles. Acupuncture and acupressure are techniques used by both scientific medical practitioners and alternative practitioners. In Canada, Sutherland and Fulton (1988, p. 93) note that coverage of acupuncturists' services under the provincial health insurance plans is "variable."

Massage

In addition to manipulation therapies such as acupressure and chiropractic, there are other forms of therapy involving massage (Frager, 1980). These include the gentle Esalen massage, the more aggressive Swedish massage, Rolfing, and reflexology which involves the manipulation of "reflex points" primarily on the feet and hands.

Category 3. Devices

Radionics

In radionics, an electronic device is used to diagnose disease by assessing electromagnetic vibrations and energy levels. A variety of treatments, electronic or otherwise, might then be employed including use of a treatment device that emits healing vibrations. (See Skrabanek and McCormick, 1990, pp. 118-119; Fulder, 1984, pp. 239-247.)

The *Edmonton Journal* (May 26, 1991, p. E6) reports that at the 1991 14th annual alternative medicine show, one could purchase a MRT-Bioenergizer that was said to pump "ionized plasma energies from a coil to treat everything from ulcers to cardiovascular disease to cerebral palsy." The price was $248.

Category 4. Mind Cures

"Mind cures" or mind–body therapies assume that the mind and body are interrelated and that mental states can both cause and cure disease. For example, it is widely argued today that psychological or psychosocial stress can affect physical health (e.g., Selye, 1976). Similarly, it is often argued that certain mental states are health promoting — consider for example, Antonovsky's (1987) discussion of the healthful effects of a "sense of coherence." There are a wide variety of mind-body therapies practised including meditation, relaxation therapy, Yoga, visualization, biofeedback, the Lamaze childbirth method, bioenergetics (Reichian psychotherapy), autogenic therapy, and faith healing (Fulder, 1984, pp. 208-218). A common element in all of these mind cures is the key role that the individual plays in implementing these therapies. In biofeedback, for example, a person learns to influence and regulate physiological responses such as the heart rate. Biofeedback is used in both scientific medicine and alternative health care (Young, 1985). Similarly, the Lamaze method for childbirth, which utilizes patient–controlled breathing rhythms, is widely used today in the birthing rooms of scientific medicine. Visualization (also known as mental imaging) is a mental strategy used by patients to "fight" cancer and other diseases and is used in conjunction with conventional therapies (Friedlander, 1985). Faith healing, while still relying on the individual patient, bridges the mental and the spiritual. Faith healing may use faith, prayer, the "laying on of hands," and/or practitioners such as Christian Science healers.

Category 5. Supernatural Cures

Supernatural cures assume that there are metaphysical, supernatural, and/or transcendent forces that can both cause and cure disease. For example, it might be argued that disease is caused by malevolent spirits, black magic, disobeying the gods, or being out of harmony with cosmic vital forces. Accordingly, it might be argued that disease is cured or prevented and health promoted by appealing to protective spirits, white magic, obedience to the gods, and/or seeking to harmonize with or draw upon cosmic vital forces.

Folk Medicine

Extensive systems of health care exist that defy neat classification into the categories used above but nevertheless provide alternatives to scientific medicine. Native American healers, for example, incorporate the supernatural with mental, medicinal, and manipulative therapies, and with devices (an amulet, for example) in a comprehensive health-care system. Similarly, Ayurvedic medicine (from India), traditional Chinese medicine, and Mexican folk medicine all comprise alternative systems of health care.

Diagnostic Techniques

Finally, there are certain diagnostic techniques, such as iridology, which are part of the alternative health-care system.

Iridology

Iridology is a diagnostic technique rather than a therapy. Iridology involves the examination of the iris of the eye for the purpose of assessing the state of the various components of the body, each of which is thought to be reflected in a specific area of the iris (Worrall, 1985).

The next section of this chapter will examine the uses of alternative health care, focussing on their social characteristics and on their motivations.

Who Uses Alternative Health Care and Why?

In Canada, chiropractic is probably the most commonly used alternative health-care therapy. Sutherland and Fulton (1988, p. 97) report that from 5 to 15 percent of the population, depending on the province, visit a chiropractor at least once a year. By comparison, 80 to 85 percent visit a medical doctor at least once a year. Biggs (1988, p. 335) reports that the Canadian Chiropractic Association estimates annual utilization at six to ten percent of the population. Biggs (1988, p. 336) further reports that data from the Saskatchewan Medical Care Commission show 10 percent of that province's population utilized chiropractic services at least once in 1985-86. Similarly, a survey of a representative sample of 307 adult Edmontonians in 1988 found that 11 percent had visited a chiropractor at least once in the previous twelve months (Northcott & Bachynsky, 1990). Turning to the characteristics of the users of chiropractic, Coulter (1987) surveyed a random sample of 658 Canadian chiropractic patients and found that they represented a cross-section of the Canadian population. (See also Coburn & Biggs, 1987, p. 380).

The *Edmonton Journal* (May 26, 1991, p. E6) (see also the *Canadian Medical Association Journal*, 1991, p. 469) reports that "a poll of 2000 Canadians by the Canada Health Monitor found that one in five Canadians used some form of alternative therapy in the first six months of 1990." Of these, half visited a chiropractor. Similarly, Northcott and Bachynsky (1990) found that 21 percent of a representative sample of Edmontonians (N = 307) surveyed in 1988 used some form of alternative therapy (including 11 percent who used chiropractic) in the previous twelve months. Users did not appear to differ from non-users on selected socio-demographic characteristics such as age, sex, and socio-economic status.

There are a number of different reasons why people might use alternative health care (see, for example, Coe, 1978, pp. 242-244; Wolinsky, 1980, pp. 296-297; Biggs, 1988, p. 330). It has been suggested that users of alternative health care are:

1.   socially marginal, i.e., poor, uneducated, ignorant, superstitious, gullible;
2.   hypochondriacs with psychosomatic problems;
3.   incurable, having diseases or conditions for which scientific medicine has not found a cure;
4.   members of subcultures, including ethnic groups that endorse alternative systems of health care (e.g., folk medicine);
5.   motivated by fear, hope, "grasping at straws";
6.   alienated from scientific medicine because of its fragmentation, specialization, depersonalization, and/or dissatisfaction with previous results of care;
7.   drawn to the more holistic, personalized, health promotion orientation of alternative health care and to its emphasis on self-care and personal responsibility for health; and
8.   convinced by personal experience and/or by testimonials that alternative health care "works."

This list implies that users of alternative health care tend to be distinct from users of scientific medicine. Nevertheless, studies tend to show that users of alternative health care represent a socio-demographic cross-section of the general population, and furthermore, that users of alternative health care tend to be concurrently users of scientific medicine (Coulter, 1987, p. 391; *Canadian Medical Association Journal*, 1991, p. 469;

Shapiro, 1983; Cassileth, et al., 1984; Kronenfeld & Wasner, 1982; Donnelly, et al., 1985; Fulder & Munro, 1985; Furnham & Smith, 1988; Kestin, et al., 1985; Smart, et al., 1986; King, et al., 1988; and Verhoef, et al., 1990). These studies suggest that people in the developed world generally rely on scientific medicine but turn readily to alternative health care when scientific medicine is perceived to fail them or reveals its limits. Furthermore, many use both systems concurrently or in turn, trying one and then the other, until they find the therapy that seems to give the best results for their particular ailment. In short, users of health care generally tend to be eclectic and pragmatic, searching for and using whatever works, whether scientific medicine or alternative health care. Thus, there is no obvious polarization of health-care users into separate camps: one relying on scientific medicine while avoiding alternative health care; the other relying on alternative health care while avoiding scientific medicine. Rather, users of health care tend to be relatively ecumenical, willing to find solace for their health-care problems in either health-care system.

The Relationship Between Scientific Medicine and Alternative Health Care

The official rhetorics emanating from both scientific medicine and alternative health care suggest that the relationship between these two systems has long been one of overt hostility and acrimony. At the material level, this hostility derives from a power struggle — a struggle for control of clients' bodies, minds, and ailments as well as a struggle for control of the dollars spent by clients and governments on health care. Furthermore, there is also a struggle for the mantle of legitimacy which is conferred by both public acceptance and official governmental recognition (e.g., favourable legislation, fee payment via governmental health-care insurance). However, the hostility between scientific medicine and alternative health care represents more than a political struggle; it also represents a moral struggle, a "holy war" in which truth and mortal salvation are the stakes. Scientific medicine accuses alternative health care of error, fraud, and exploitation of the ignorant and gullible, often, it is alleged, with disastrous consequences for the health of the client. In turn, alternative health care accuses scientific medicine of failure to treat the whole person and of failure to recognize a variety of natural and supernatural sources of health, often, it is alleged, with disastrous consequences for the health of the client. It would appear, if the official rhetorics are to be believed, that the line is intractably drawn between these two opposing camps, the separate dogmas defined, and the impass defended by hot and vitriolic rhetoric. Nevertheless, this characterization greatly overstates the apparent polarization of scientific medicine and alternative health care. Indeed, a closer examination suggests that the rhetorics obscure the realities.

First of all, historically, scientific medicine and alternative health care share common heritages. Second, many alternative therapies have been developed by medical doctors (e.g., homeopathy, visualization, biofeedback) or are used by medical doctors (e.g., acupuncture). Third, health-care therapies often evolve and may converge (e.g., osteopathy and scientific medicine; chiropractic, physical therapy and orthopedics). Fourth, scientific medicine and alternative health care often have more in common than they admit. For example, alternative health care tends to be results oriented (the beginning of scientific validation?) while scientific medicine does recognize that mind and body are interdependent (e.g., consider psychosomatic medicine and the recognition that cure is often facilitated when a client has faith in the practitioner, in the therapy prescribed, and in the possibility of a positive outcome). Further to this point, consider the World Health Organization's definition of health (complete physical, mental, and social well-being) which is echoed by Health and Welfare Canada (Epp, 1986). Note that this holistic definition of health, an emphasis usually attributed to alternative health care, is advanced by bastions of scientific medicine. In short, alternative health care and scientific medicine may not be as distinct practically or ideologically as official rhetorics imply. Fifth, practitioners of scientific medicine and of alternative health care increasingly refer clients to each other (consider chiropractic, for example). Sixth, while nonmedical practitioners of alternative health care are usually prevented by law from "practising medicine," many practitioners of scientific medicine practice various alternative health-care therapies. In short, scientific medicine and alternative health care are not as distinct as the common rhetorics imply.

The fairly widespread practice of alternative health care by medical doctors has been documented in the Netherlands (Visser & Peters, 1990; Knipschild, et al., 1990), Britain (Wharton & Lewith, 1986; Jones, 1987; Nelson, et al., 1990; Goldstein, et al., 1988), New Zealand (Hadley, 1988; Marshall, et al., 1990), and the United States (Cassileth, et al., 1984). Indeed, some researchers use the term "complementary medicine" (e.g., Wharton & Lewith, 1986; Hadley, 1988) in preference to "alternative medicine." Furthermore, some analysts have noted the possibility of, and/or commented on the degree of integration of alternative health care within scientific medicine (e.g., Visser & Peters, 1990; Goldstein, et al., 1988). Similarly, the possibility of "convergence" implies that either system, or both, might move in the direction of the other. Finally, it is commonly noted that modern societies are "medically plural." Medical pluralism implies a diversity of health-care options all incorporated (even if somewhat loosely) into one health-care delivery system. In other words, this terminology undermines the rhetoric that speaks of the polarization of health-care systems into a hegemony ruled by scientific medicine and an outcast group of alternative health-care practitioners. Instead, medical pluralism implies an accommodation and an integration of diverse parts. While the vitriolic and dogmatic rhetoric is still present and while idealogues continue to wage battle, nevertheless, many practitioners and their clients draw upon both systems, suggesting trends towards convergence or at least towards accommodation and integration.

Acknowledgements: Research assistance was provided by Erica Van Roosmalen, Robert Lewis, and particularly Lynn Skillen.

Study Questions

1. Discuss the various labels applied to scientific medicine and alternative health care. Select an appropriate terminology and justify your choice.
2. Discuss midwifery, holistic care, self-help, feminist health care, and quackery in terms of their relationships to alternative health care and scientific medicine.
3. Provide a typology of alternative health-care therapies and select and discuss an appropriate alternative therapy to illustrate each category in your typology.
4. Who uses alternative health care and for what reasons?
5. Discuss the relationship between scientific medicine and alternative health care. Discuss present trends and future possibilities.

Recommended Reading

Alster, K.B. (1989). *The holistic health movement.* Tuscaloosa: University of Alabama Press.
Fuller, R.C. (1989). *Alternative medicine and American religious life.* New York: Oxford University Press. (For a different but provocative approach.)
Gevitz, N. (Ed.). (1988). *Other healers: Unorthodox medicine in America.* Baltimore: Johns Hopkins University Press.
Stalker, D., & Glymour, C. (Eds.). (1985). *Examining holistic medicine.* Buffalo: Prometheus.
Young, J.H. (1961). *The toadstool millionaires: A social history of patent medicines in America before federal regulation.* Princeton: Princeton University Press.
Young, J.H. (1967). *The medical messiahs: A social history of health quackery in twentieth-century*

America. Princeton: Princeton University Press.
Wardwell, W.I. (1988). Chiropractors, evolution to acceptance. In N. Gevitz (Ed.), *Other healers: Unorthodox medicine in America* (pp. 157-191). Baltimore: Johns Hopkins University Press.

References

Alster, K.B. (1989). *The holistic health movement.* Tuscaloosa: University of Alabama Press.
American Cancer Society. (1990). Psychic surgery. *CA*, 40, 184-188.
Antonovsky, A. (1987). *Unraveling the mystery of health: How people manage stress and stay well.* San Francisco: Jossey-Bass
Biggs, L. (1988). The professionalization of chiropractic in Canada: Its current status and future prospects. In B.S. Bolaria & H.D. Dickinson (Eds.), *Sociology of health care in Canada* (pp. 328-345). Toronto: Harcourt Brace Jovanovich.
Bresler, D.E. (1980). Chinese medicine and holistic health. In A.C. Hastings, et al. (Eds.), *Health for the whole person* (pp. 407-426). Boulder: Westview.
Burtch, B.E. (1993). Promoting midwifery, prosecuting midwives: The state and the midwifery movement in Canada. In B.S. Bolaria & H.D. Dickinson (Eds.), *Sociology of health care in Canada* (this volume). Toronto: Harcourt Brace and Company.
Bynum, W.F., & Porter, R. (Eds.). (1987). *Medical fringe and medical orthodoxy 1750-1850.* London: Croom Helm.
Canadian Medical Association Journal. (1991). One in five Canadians is using alternative therapies, survey finds. *Canadian Medical Association Journal, Vol. 144,* 469.

Cassileth, B.R., Lusk, E.J., Strouse, T.B., & Bodenheimer, B.J. (1984). Contemporary unorthodox treatments in cancer medicine: A study of patients, treatments, and practitioners. *Annals of Internal Medicine*, 101, 105-112.

Clarke, J.N. (1990). *Health, illness, and medicine in Canada*. Toronto: McClelland and Stewart.

Coburn, D., & Biggs, C.L. (1987). Legitimation or medicalization? The case of chiropractic in Canada. In D. Coburn et al. (Eds.), *Health and Canadian society* (2nd ed.), (pp. 366-384). Markham: Fitzhenry & Whiteside.

Coe, R.M. (1978). *Sociology of medicine* (2nd ed.). New York: McGraw-Hill.

Coulter, H.L. (1984). Homeopathy. In J.W. Salmon (Ed.), *Alternative medicines: Popular and policy perspectives* (pp. 57-79). New York: Tavistock.

Coulter, I.D. (1987). The chiropractic role: Marginal, supplemental or alternative health care? An empirical reconsideration. In D. Coburn, et al. (Eds.), *Health and Canadian society* (2nd ed.), (pp. 385-398). Markham: Fitzhenry & Whiteside.

Donnelly, W.J., Spykerboer, J.E., & Thong, Y.H. (1985). Are patients who use alternative medicine dissatisfied with orthodox medicine? *Medical Journal of Australia*, 142, 539-541.

Edginton, B. (1989). *Health, disease and medicine in Canada*. Toronto: Butterworths.

English-Lueck, J.A. (1990). *Health in the new age: A study in California holistic practices*. Albuquerque: University of New Mexico Press.

Epp, J. (1986). *Achieving health for all: A framework for health promotion*. Ottawa: Health and Welfare Canada, Minister of Supply and Services Canada.

Frager, R. (1980). Touch: Working with the body. In A.C. Hastings et. al. (Eds.), *Health for the whole person* (pp. 209-225). Boulder: Westview.

Friedlander, E.R. (1985). Dream your cancer away: The Simontons. In D. Stalker & C. Glymour (Eds.), *Examining holistic medicine* (pp. 273-285). Buffalo: Prometheus.

Fulder, S. (1984). *The handbook of complementary medicine*. Great Britain: Coronet Books.

Fulder, S.J., & Munro, R.E. (1985). Complementary medicine in the United Kingdom: Patients, practitioners, and consultations. *Lancet*, 2, 8454, 542-545.

Furnham, A., & Smith, C. (1988). Choosing alternative medicine: A comparison of the beliefs of patients visiting a general practitioner and a homoeopath. *Social Science and Medicine*, 26, 685-689.

Goldstein, M.S., Sutherland, C., Jaffe, D.T., & Wilson J. (1988). Holistic physicians and family practitioners: Similarities, differences and implications for health policy. *Social Science and Medicine*, 26, 853-861.

Hadley, C.M. (1988). Complementary medicine and the general practitioner: A survey of general practitioners in the Wellington area. *New Zealand Medical Journal*, 101, 766-768.

Hastings, A.C., Fadiman, J., & Gordon, J.S. (Eds.). (1980). *Health for the whole person: The complete guide to holistic medicine*. Boulder: Westview.

Holbrook, S.H. (1959). *The golden age of quackery*. New York: MacMillan.

Holistic medicine: Cure or quackery? (1991, May 26). *Edmonton Journal*, p. E6.

Homebirth advocates plan rally at nurse's trial. (1991, April, 8). *Edmonton Journal*, p. A10.

Hufford, D.J. (1988). Contemporary folk medicine. In N. Gevitz (Ed.), *Other healers: Unorthodox Medicine in America* (pp. 228-264). Baltimore: Johns Hopkins University Press.

Jameson, E. (1961). *The natural history of quackery*. London: Michael Joseph.

Jones, L. (1987). Alternative therapies: A report on an inquiry by the British Medical Association. *The Skeptical Inquirer*, 12, 63-69.

Kaslof, L.J. (1980). The therapeutic use of plants. In A.C. Hastings et al. (Eds.), *Health for the whole person* (pp. 263-276). Boulder: Westview.

Kestin, M., Miller, L., Littlejohn G., & Wahlqvist M. (1985). The use of unproven remedies for rheumatoid arthritis in Australia. *Medical Journal of Australia*, 143, 516-518.

King, D.E., Sobal, J., & DeForge B.R. (1988). Family practice patients' experiences and beliefs in faith healing. *Journal of Family Practice*, 27, 505-508.

Knipschild, P., Kleinjnen, J., & ter Riet, G. (1990). Belief in the efficacy of alternative medicine among general practitioners in the Netherlands. *Social Science and Medicine*, 31, 625-626.

Kronenfeld, J.J., & Wasner, C. (1982). The use of unorthodox therapies and marginal practitioners. *Social Science and Medicine*, 16, 1119-1125.

Lowenberg, J.S. (1989). *Caring and responsibility: The crossroads between holistic practice and traditional medicine*. Philadelphia: University of Pennsylvania Press.

Marshall, R.J., et al. (1990). The use of alternative therapies by Auckland general practitioners. *New Zealand Medical Journal*, 103, 213-215.

Nelson, M.V., Bailie, G.R., & Areny, H. (1990). Pharmacists' perceptions of alternative health approaches — A comparison between U.S. and British pharmacists. *Journal of Clinical Pharmacy and Therapeutics*, 15, 141-146.

Northcott, H.C., & Bachynsky, J.A. (1990). *The utilization of prescription medicines, nonprescription medicines and alternative health care therapies*. Edmonton Area Series Report No. 70. Edmonton: Population Research Laboratory, Department of Sociology, University of Alberta.

Porter, R. (1989). *Health for sale: Quackery in England 1660-1850*. Manchester: Manchester University Press.

Report endorses midwives: New legislation pledged. (1991, June 12). *Edmonton Journal*, p. A3.

Rothstein, W.G. (1988). The botanical movements and orthodox medicine. In N. Gevitz (Ed.), *Other healers: Unorthodox medicine in America* (pp. 29-51). Baltimore: Johns Hopkins University Press.

Selye, H. (1976). *The stress of life* (revised ed.). New York: McGraw-Hill.

Shapiro, E. (1983). The physician visit patterns of chiropractic users: Health-seeking behavior of the elderly in Manitoba, Canada. *American Journal of Public Health*, 73, 553-557.

Skrabanek, P. (1985). Acupuncture: Past, present, and future. In D. Stalker & C. Glymour (Eds.), *Examining holistic medicine* (pp. 181-196). Buffalo: Prometheus.

Skrabanek, P., & McCormick, J. (1990). *Follies and fallacies in medicine*. Buffalo: Prometheus.

Smart, H.L., Mayberry, J.F., & Atkinson, M. (1986). Alternative medicine consultations and remedies in patients with the irritable bowel syndrome. *Gut*, 27, 826-828.

Stalker, D., & Glymour, C. (Eds.). (1985). *Examining holistic medicine*. Buffalo: Prometheus.

Sutherland, R.W., & Fulton, M.J. (1988). *Health care in Canada: A description and analysis of Canadian health services*. Ottawa: Canadian Public Health Association.

Twaddle, A.C., & Hessler, R.M. (1987). *A sociology of health* (2nd ed.). New York: Macmillan.

Verhoef, M.J., Sutherland, L.R., & Brkich, L. (1990). Use of alternative medicine by patients attending a gastroenterology clinic. *Canadian Medical Association Journal*, 142, 121-125.

Visser, G.J., & Peters, L. (1990). Alternative medicine and general practitioners in the Netherlands: Towards acceptance and integration. *Family Practice*, 7, 227-232.

Wardwell, W.I. (1979). Limited and marginal practitioners. In H. Freeman, S. Levine & L. Reeder (Eds.), *Handbook of medical sociology* (3rd ed.), (pp. 230-250). Englewood Cliffs: Prentice Hall.

Wardwell, W.I. (1988). Chiropractors, evolution to acceptance. In N. Gevitz (Ed.), *Other healers: Unorthodox medicine in America* (pp. 157-191). Baltimore: Johns Hopkins University Press.

Wharton, R., & Lewith, G. (1986). Contemporary medicine and the general practitioner. *British Medical Journal*, 292, 1498-1500.

Whorton, J.C. (1988). Patient, heal thyself: Popular health reform movements as unorthodox medicine. In N. Gevitz (Ed.), *Other healers: Unorthodox medicine in america* (pp. 52-81). Baltimore: Johns Hopkins University Press.

Wolinsky, F.D. (1980). *The sociology of health*. Boston: Little, Brown and Company.

Worrall, R.S. (1985). Iridology: Diagnosis or delusion? In D. Stalker & C. Glymour (Eds.), *Examining holistic medicine* (pp. 167-179). Buffalo: Prometheus.

Young, J.H. (1961). *The toadstool millionaires: A social history of patent medicines in America before federal regulation*. Princeton: Princeton University Press.

Young, J.H. (1967). *The medical messiahs: A social history of health quackery in twentieth-century America*. Princeton: Princeton University Press.

Young, L.D. (1985). Holistic medicine's use of biofeedback. In D. Stalker & C. Glymour (Eds.), *Examining holistic medicine* (pp. 341-359). Buffalo: Prometheus.

Chapter 23

Promoting Midwifery, Prosecuting Midwives: The State and the Midwifery Movement in Canada

Brian E. Burtch, Simon Fraser University

Introduction: The State and Health Care

We are sophisticated enough to see that the law often selects the immoralities with which it chooses to deal on a political basis. The more powerful a group is, the less its immoralities will be legally prohibited (Wexler, 1976, p. 358).

The status of Canadian midwives has been debated for many decades. In the past fifteen years this debate has become more prominent as nurse-midwives have sought greater independence in their work, and community midwives have attended thousands of home births in various Canadian provinces. Barrington (1985, p. 38) estimated that in 1984 just over 100 community midwives were assisting home births in Canada.

This chapter provides an overview of key developments in the contemporary midwifery movement, emphasizing the pivotal role of the state, and especially the provincial governments, since the administration of health care is within their bailiwick, as set out in the British North America Act. The Canadian state has a contradictory position here (Gavigan, 1986). On the one hand, it claims to protect the freedoms of individuals, to ensure equal justice, and to encourage certain forms of competition; on the other hand, the state has limited the freedom of women in reproductive choices, including childbirth (Currie, 1986), and has utilized the criminal sanction for abortion (Gavigan, 1984; Osborne, 1987). Another contradiction emerges with respect to the application of the medical model for pregnancy, a state that is not inherently a disease state.

The orthodox perspective on medicine is largely empirical, disease-oriented, and professional; this leads to minimal emphasis on social theory, non-organic sources of diseases, and non-professional action in promoting health (Doyal, 1979). Medical research and practice are to a large extent centred on individual pathology and curative medical treatment. Heroic medicine and high-technology approaches to illness coexist, reinforcing the medical sphere: "The availability of high-technology medicine and the publicising of individual medical breakthroughs (whatever their real value) are important window-dressing in maintaining support for the existing system" (Doyal, 1979, p. 43).

Doyal's analysis also emphasizes the imperatives of production of commodities, the entrenchment of authority relations, and the division of tasks in the health sector along lines of race, class, and gender. A similar analysis of the health-care sector is articulated by the Women's Work Project (1976, p. 19); that is, between 75 and 85 percent of lab technicians, licensed practical nurses, and manual services aides were women, with 80 to 90 percent of the latter occupations comprised of non-white workers (1970 data from New York City hospitals). In their more general analysis of sexual stratification in the Canadian work force, Phillips and Phillips (1983) state that two features of the work force at the turn of the century are still evident: gender differentials in income (women earn approximately 60 percent of men's wages, averaged for full-time work), and the concentration of women's paid employment in specific groupings.[1]

The key to Doyal's analysis, then, is the dialectical relationship between domination and exploitation on the one hand, and changing patterns of health and health services on the other. Her analysis features a distinctly Marxist twist in its interpretations of advances in medicine and improved medical care as either (1) concessions to the working class, thereby mitigating developed class struggle, or (2) a service ultimately on behalf of a dominant class whereby the availability of a healthier, more reliable work force is ensured through health-care programs and the like.

Spitzer (1983) reviews the emerging theories of law that move beyond simple instrumentalism and economism. Structuralism (exemplified by Althusser) and culturalism (exemplified by E.P. Thompson) are the major competing theories. Both attempt to redefine the nature of relationships among human actors, external structures, and law. A structuralist premise is that although the law is in some sense relatively autonomous, along with other superstructural features of society, the vectors of legal regulation are ultimately traced back to the economic system. The reformulation of this structuralist approach by Poulantzas (1973, 1978) involved a recognition of the role of the law as an apparatus that preserves "real rights" of dominated classes. He added the caveat that these rights are embedded within a dominant ideology.[2]

The relationship between law and that state has thus undergone a contemporary re-evaluation among Marxists and neo-Marxists. As Spitzer (1983, pp. 114-117) indicates, the shortcomings of legal economism and of structuralism have generated a more vital paradigm of law in which law arises from an "ideological pool" comprising beliefs and assumptions from all social classes. In turn, the relatively autonomous role of the state — which is not governed by the will of a dominant class but rather exercises power against some of its powers — reflects the contradictory nature of legal ideology and the law as practice.

Eisenstein (1981, p. 222) portrays the state as an agency that constrains radical alternatives, including radical feminism. The structure of the state is such that it cannot allow women's equality with men. The "sexual ghetto" of lower-paid occupations is perpetrated by the state as an employer and as an arbiter of social conflicts. Through the agency of law, the state mystifies what women are and what they do; law serves to constrain people's actual options, and yet it can establish "positive rights." Eisenstein recognizes the political power of the state over women, while endorsing progressive struggles to secure the recognition of the state. The implications of such struggles are developed in the next section, with specific reference to Canadian midwives.

The Midwifery Movement and the State

The practice of midwifery is a complex phenomenon in Canada and other industrialized societies. While midwifery has been defined generically as the act of attending a person in childbirth, it is better understood as an occupation. In contrast to the traditional (lay) midwife in developing countries, North American midwives include certified nurse-midwives (who trained to practise in hospitals, having completed nursing training followed by a a midwifery apprenticeship), and community midwives who attend home births and are generally not members of a professional nurses' association. The techniques of practice and rigours of training vary considerably within these forms of midwifery. Nevertheless, legal regulation of birth attendance influences all forms of midwifery. This regulation is most significant for community midwives whose practice may be a violation of provincial medical acts and other quasi-criminal statues, and community midwives are also more likely to be prosecuted for criminal negligence in the event of the death or injury of an infant during labour or delivery.

There are important links between contemporary health-care regulations of midwives in advanced capitalist societies and the historical transformation of birth from a local, private event to a public, medical matter. The perception of midwives has historically been negatively stereotypical — as witches, harridans, or meddlesome ignorant women (Donnison, 1977, pp. 28-29; Evenson, 1983, p. 313). A closer look at contemporary midwives in a British Columbia study indicates that they are not easily categorized:

midwives vary in experience, professional training, and philosophies of birthing and politics, to name only a few aspects.[3]

Common ground for midwives, however, can be determined. First, there seems to be a general agreement that pregnancy is not synonymous with disease. Morbid situations will develop, but generally birth can be managed skilfully and safely with a lower rate of obstetrical intervention, including induction and augmentation of labour, instrumental delivery via forceps or Caesarean section. Obstetrical intervention is often recast as obstetrical interference.

Second, midwives tend to agree that they could operate more autonomously than is currently provided for under provincial law (which requires the direction of a physician, or a delegation of responsibly from a physician to a non-physician, were applicable). The dependent status of midwives is thus generally seen as contrived, and not associated with legitimate differences in skills between physicians and trained midwives in the management of uncomplicated pregnancies. This dependent relationship is often linked with the economic interest of physicians in attending births and the sense of control that physicians, especially male physicians, can exert over parturient patients and the nursing staff that assist doctors in childbirth care (see Buckley, 1979; Oakley, 1984)

Third, women's right to be informed and to make decisions about maternity care is vital to the midwifery debate. Women should have some say in the location and the manner of birth.

Fourth, the question of iatrogenic (physician-induced) practice is often brought forward. Reliance on such procedures as the lithotomy (prone) delivery position, use of drugs to induce labour and to relieve pain, lack of continuity of care (through the prenatal period, labour, delivery, and after birth), and the overarching ideology that birth is essentially a medical event are all seen as factors contributing to substandard maternity care.

Differences within the movement occur at various points. First, there is an ongoing debate over the importance of nursing training as a prerequisite to midwifery training. Some favour direct entry into a midwifery program that incorporates some aspects of orthodox nursing curricula, while others maintain that formal criteria are not a necessary condition for midwifery practice. Second, there has been a movement toward establishing guidelines (or standards) for practice. Some midwives' associations discourage their members from managing breech deliveries at home, or insist that women should be transported to hospital if twins are suspected, if amniotic fluid is stained with meconium, or in other atypical circumstances. Others believe that automatic contraindications to midwifery management in domiciliary births are unnecessary and should be left to the midwives' judgement.

A third issue is where midwives prefer to practise — at home, in clinics or in hospitals. Benoit (1988) found that midwives who had practised in Labrador and New-foundland often preferred to practise in a clinic-like setting. This arrangement allowed them considerable autonomy in their practice, provided access to various medical resources, and ensured that they were not isolated from other midwives. Benoit (1988) nevertheless cautions that midwives disagreed among themselves over various issues, and that some clients proved especially demanding for isolated, outport midwives dependent on their clients' patronage.

Another point of disagreement involves the necessity of midwives working with physicians and the delegation of ultimate responsibility for maternal and infant welfare to physicians (e.g., College of Nurses of Ontario, 1983). The counter-position is that midwives should be allowed to work independently of physicians, at least in cases of uncomplicated deliveries (Van Wagner, 1984).

The author's fieldwork on midwifery in British Columbia allows a few impressions on the implementation of midwife attendance. First, community midwives are able to use a variety of resources in conducting their work. There are legal resources available to them through legal advice, sometimes involving litigations, sometimes not. Likewise, there are legal defences available to midwife-defendants. As demonstrated by recent criminal prosecutions of the Halifax midwives and a birth attendant in Victoria (see p. 516), these defences have been successfully employed against criminal charges. The various court-situated contests over midwifery and birth-related issues have been accompanied by some political support from opposition parties. In Ontario and British Columbia, for example, the New Democratic Parties — through caucus or private mem-bers' bills — have supported the legalization of midwifery in their provinces (Cooke, 1984; Stephens, 1984). The National Action Status on the Committee of Women also passed a resolution in 1984 in support of midwifery legalization in Canada (Sweet, 1985). Second, many practising midwives are aided by the material and emotional support of "significant others" — spouses, other midwives, neighbours, family mem-bers — that allows them to practise midwifery alongside other responsibilities of income, child care, and the like. Third, opportunities for counter-hegemonic powers are evident. In one instance, recounted to the author by a Lower Mainland midwife, the threat of prosecution for the unlawful practice of midwifery under the Medical Practi-tioners Act was not followed through, ostensibly because as a politicized midwife she was prepared to muster considerable support in defence of community midwifery (Burtch, 1987).

Fourth, midwives do work in conjunction with sympathetic physicians and other personnel with respect to backup and transfers of women into hospital. Fifth, midwives utilize various forms of medical technology (oxygen for resuscitation, sutures) and a variety of communications devices (telephone, message recorders, "beepers") to contact fellow midwives, clients, and other concerned parties.

Two other resources that community midwives have developed are media exposure (through letter-writing campaigns to newspapers and contributions to such periodicals as *The Maternal Health News*) and fee increases for birth attendance. The latter resource is especially important in light of the relatively low incomes generated by community midwifery and the economic strain on family earnings. Apparently, the "service" orientation of the mid-1970s has been succeeded by higher fees (approximately $600 for prenatal, labour and delivery, and postnatal care).

These resources must be placed in a larger context of midwifery containment. Community midwives remain liable to quasi-criminal prosecution for the unlawful practice of midwifery. They are occasionally faced with the real possibility of criminal prosecution, their personal incomes are far below those of physicians and below those of obstetrical nurses working full-time. Nurse-midwives face constraints under the existing law and the policy position of their college and the College of Physicians and Surgeons. Recent initiatives to establish midwifery on a more autonomous footing required the unpaid involvement of nursing professionals in the Low-Risk Clinic in Vancouver. There has also been a reluctance to recognize midwives as midwives, since midwifery is seen as a physicians' monopoly under current legislation.

Legal Constraints on Midwifery

The practice of midwifery is, for the most part, both constrained and facilitated by its legal status. A key element in the involvement of the state — through its legal powers — in what was previously a localized, neighbourhood event in North America, has been the assumption that midwifery practice is more hazardous than physicians' attendance. A related assumption is that midwives require supervision by physicians, although legislation such as the Midwives' Act in England has established a basis for self-regulation by midwives to a considerable degree. A further assumption of liberal democratic theory is that legal constraints on midwives stem from a public consensus on the appropriateness of restricted birth practices. This includes broad powers of medical practice and self-regulation with respect to medical events. In contrast, there has been a counter-interpretation of medical power as the securing of powerful interests, rather than protection of the general interest in health-related events.

The following sections cover some cases in which midwives faced prosecution under quasi-criminal law (literally, an offence to which a penalty is attached) or under criminal law, such as allegations of criminal negligence causing death. These prosecutions — and the potential for such prosecutions — have hindered the implementation of midwifery services in Canada, including recruitment of new midwives. Nevertheless, the legacy of recent case law is that Canadian midwives have not been successfully prosecuted through criminal or quasi-criminal law.

Unlawful Practice of Medicine: Quasi-Criminal Sanctions

The civil status of lay midwives and nurse-midwives in Canada has, with few exceptions, served to limit their practice. In nineteenth-century Ontario, for instance, the right to practise midwifery independently of legislation governing the practice of physic or surgery gradually gave way to the monopolization of childbirth attendance by medical personnel. It is noteworthy that the initial, statutory monopoly status gave way to an explicit recognition of the right of women in Upper Canada to practise midwifery without a licence. Moreover, even as this legislation reintroduced the ban on lay midwifery, enforcement was problematic due to the limited number of doctors and the lack of doctors in what was then a predominantly rural region (Biggs, 1983). Specifically, Section 49 of the Ontario Medical Act held that:

> it shall not be lawful for any person not registered to practise medicine, surgery of midwifery for hire, gain, or hope of reward, and if any person not registered pursuant to this Act, for hire, gain or hope of reward practises or professes to practise medicine, surgery, or midwifery, he shall upon summary conviction thereof before any Justice of the Peace, for every such offence, pay a penalty not exceeding $100 nor less than $25.

An important qualification at this point in legal regulation was that the alleged illegal practices must in fact trench on medical practice, and that isolated episodes would not sustain a conviction. As J.A. Garrow (1906) indicated in *Re Ontario Medical Act*,

> The thing practised must, to be illegal, be an invasion of similar things taught and practised by the regular practitioner, otherwise it does not affect the monopoly, and is outside the statute. And it must be practised as the regular practitioner would do it — that is, for gain, and after diagnosis and advice. And it must be more than a mere isolated instance, which is sufficient to prove a "practice." (p. 513)

The obligation to prove more than a single act had been upheld in a number of precedents. In *Regina v. Whelan* (1900) the conviction of a Toronto midwife under Section 49 of the Ontario Medical Act was reversed on appeal. The Appeal Court found that the Crown had not established that the midwife had practised medicine on more than one occasion, and further that she had not always received financial gain through her actions. The necessity to prove that financial gain was received and that the illegal practice of medicine occurred repeatedly was crucial in the acquittal of the accused in *Regina V. Armstrong* (1911). The judge held:

> Before an accused person can be convicted of falsely pretending to heal the sick, it is necessary that it be shown that the accused was in the habit of so pretending, or at least that there had been continuous treatment, the principle being the same as practising medicine for gain or hope of reward. An isolated case is not sufficient to secure a conviction.

Subsequently, in *Regina v. Cruikshanks* (1914), Justice Simmons confirmed that a single act does not constitute the practice of medicine or a trade.

Nonetheless, as the state has deliberated over birth-related law, the criterion for an offence has been broadened. In Ontario, the common-law rule that "practice" implied repetition of the offending act was altered such that proof of performance of a *single* act in the practice of medicine on one occasion was deemed sufficient to establish the practice of medicine. Another criminal conviction of a midwife in the Northwest Territories was also quashed. In *Rondeau* (1903) the court held that Section 60 of the Medical Profession Ordinance did not include "midwifery" as a form of practice to be covered along with "medicine" and "surgery." Accordingly, since Section 60 had been composed with reference to the earlier Ontario Medical Act — which prohibited midwifery, medical, and surgical practice by unregistered persons, the court overturned the conviction. Ironically, the decision in *Rondeau* was brought forward in the 1990 trial and acquittal of Noreen Walker, an Edmonton midwife charged with practising medicine without a licence (see below).

Legal prohibitions on the practice of medicine thus serve to protect unregistered practitioners to a degree. In another case, an orderly accused of practising midwifery and with practising medicine, both for "hope of reward," was acquitted on both counts. The court held that the accused orderly had assisted a woman following delivery when no doctor was available to her; that is, he acted under emergency circumstances and did not attempt to charge for his attendance. On the second count, although the accused had on two occasions filled in blank prescription forms, taken patients' temperatures, and given instructions as to treatment, there was no proof of payment or of request for payment by the orderly (*Regina v. Ornavowski*, 1941).

Reference to case law also reveals the opposite effect: persons practising medicine on more than one occasion, and seeking payment for their advice, could be convicted as in *Provincial Medical Board v. Bond* (1890) in Nova Scotia. About two decades later, in a case heard in Saskatchewan, Justice Trant declared that the rights of unregistered practitioners are limited and sharply defined. They must not offer diagnosis, give advice, or prescribe medicines (*Regina v. Raffenberg*, 1909).

The recent trial of Noreen Walker in Alberta is more in keeping with the courts' reluctance to find for the prosecution, following charges against midwives. In 1990, Ms. Walker, a community midwife who had been practising for over a decade in the Edmonton area, was charged with practising medicine without a licence (Jimenez, 1990). This was an unusual case, since neither the mother nor the infant suffered any injury at the home birth near Castor, Alberta. The author was one of the three expert witnesses asked to speak in Ms. Walker's defence. Her lawyer requested a directed verdict of not guilty, meaning that the trial judge could acquit the defendant without hearing from the defence witnesses. On June 6, 1991 the judge accepted the defence motion for a directed verdict, and found the defendant not guilty. It was significant that the judge remarked on the differences between practising medicine and practising midwifery, thus reaffirming the midwives' general contention that midwifery cannot simply be subsumed as part of medical practice. The defence was also aided by a provision in Alberta's legislation that allowed for midwifery practice under certain conditions.

One twist in the Walker case was the high level of public support manifested in Alberta (see Burch, in press), most tangibly through the $20 000 raised for her defence fund. The fundraising was obtained from former clients, sympathetic practitioners (most notably, generous funding from two chiropractic clinics), and a cross section of people convinced that midwives ought not be artificially constricted in their right to practise. Another twist in the Walker case was a letter published in The *Edmonton Journal*, written by a descendant of Mrs. Rondeau, the midwife charged at the turn of the century in northern Alberta. The letter read in part:

> In the early part of this century, midwives played a major role in country life in Alberta. They were the only caregivers in many areas. Walker is not the first midwife in Alberta to face charges. My great-grandmother, Sarah Rondeau, was a practicing midwife in the Morinville area. She faced charges on more than one occasion and was acquitted. Even the local doctor testified on her behalf. I doubt that she would have believed that midwives would still lack legal recognition almost 100 years after she practiced. Isn't it time we gave midwives and midwifery the recognition they deserve? Midwives are professional and expert in normal pregnancy and childbirth. Midwifery legislation is most certainly long overdue! (Cust, 1991)

The status of Canadian midwives is either unsettled or illegal, with the exception of trained midwives who act as obstetrical nurses, under the supervision of a physician, or nurses who work in remote regions of Canada. Barrington (1985, pp. 140-141) reported that the legal status of Canadian midwives practising in the mid-1980s was uncertain in many jurisdictions. She noted that there were no separate midwifery acts as such, with most provinces and territories providing medical and nursing acts. Even where mid-

Table I   Legal Status of Midwifery in Canada

Jurisdiction	Current Legislation	Criminal Prosecution	Other Charges[1]	Legal Status
Newfoundland & Labrador	Midwifery Act	None	None	Legal, but few mid-wives practise.
Nova Scotia	Medical Act	Carpenter et al. (1983) case dismissed	None	No distinct status.
New Brunswick	Medical Act	None	None	Not illegal, but few registered.
Prince Edward Island	Medical Act	None	None	No provision for licensing midwives.
Quebec	Medical Act	None	None	Considering midwifery legislation; some pilot projects.
Ontario	Health Disciplines Act	None	None	1991, announced intention to legalize under Midwive's Act. Legislation not yet proclaimed.
Manitoba	Medical Act	No	No	No distinct status.
Saskatchewan	Medical Professions' Act	None	None	No distinct status.
Alberta	Medical Professions' Act	None	Walker (1991) directed acquittal	1992, legalized under Health Professions Act.[2]
British Columbia	Medical Practitioners' Act	Le May/Sullivan (1985/1991) (1991 acquittal by Supreme Court of Canada)	None	1993. B.C. Health Minister announced intention to legalize under Health Professions Act.[3]
Yukon & North West Territories	Medical Profession Ordinance	None	None	No distinct status.

1. Reference is made only to criminal prosecutions and quasi-criminal charges since 1980. For earlier refernces, see accompanying text in this chapter.

2. Supreme Court of Canada.

3. The Midwives' Association of B.C. has been invited to apply for standing under Bill 31, the Health Professions Act.

Source: Adapted from Barrington, E. (1985). *Midwifery is catching*. (pp. 140-141). Toronto: NC Press.

wives might be registered as bona fide practitioners, the colleges governing such registrations had not made provision for practising midwives, as a rule.

Significantly, a number of provinces have since expressed interest in providing a legal status for midwives. In Ontario, for instance, a 1987 report on the implementation of midwifery services was followed by legal provision for midwifery training, accreditation, and practice distinct from nursing or medicine. The statutes governing birth are not as far-sighted in other jurisdictions in Canada, with midwives still seeking legal status which safeguards their professional autonomy (see *Burtch, Midwifery and the Law*, 1991).

The practice of midwifery in British Columbia is legally protected as the bailiwick of medical practitioners. Section 72 of the provincial Medical Practitioners' Act stipulates that:

> (1) A person who practises or offers to practise medicine while not registered or while suspended from practice under this Act commits an offence. (2) For the purposes of and without restricting the generality of subsection (1), a person practises medicine who . . . (d) prescribes or administers a treatment or performs surgery, *midwifery* or an operation or manipulation, or supplies or applies an apparatus or appliance for the cure, treatment or prevention of a human disease, ailment, deformity, defect or injury . . . (British Columbia, 1979, emphasis added).

One episode in which an alternative practitioner (not a midwife) was acquitted has been documented in Alberta. In *Regina v. Wong* (1979) the court held that the art of acupuncture was not recognized by the Alberta College of Physicians and Surgeons as a branch of medicine; moreover, acupuncture was not taught in North American medical education. A later conviction of an acupuncturist in British Columbia occurred, however, despite the reasoning in *Wong*.

Under Section 83 of the Medical Practitioners' Act the minimum penalty for a first offence for practising medicine or midwifery when unregistered is set at $100 or imprisonment (Section 87); this rises to $300 or imprisonment for a second conviction, and imprisonment only for a third or subsequent conviction.[4] Under Section 73 there are several exceptions to the broad ambit of medical practice set out under Section 72. Specifically, the following practitioners do not practise unlawfully while registered under their respective acts: chiropractors, dentists, naturopaths, optometrists, pharmacists, podiatrists, psychologists, nurses, and dental technicians. Orthoptic technicians, physiotherapists, and dieticians may also be exempt from Section 72. Emergency procedures are permitted under the Health Emergency Act; domestic administration of family remedies is permitted; and religious practitioners "who practise the religious tenets of their church without pretending a knowledge of medicine or surgery" are exempted under Section 74 of the act.

Liabilities associated with childbirth become even more complex when one considers the liabilities of parents. In the United States the parents' duty of care has traditionally begun with the birth of a child: there has been no obligation on the part of the mother, for instance, to seek medical assistance prior to the birth of a child. Nevertheless, there appears to be a shift in legal opinion whereby parental failure to obtain medical care in circumstances where such care is clearly warranted ought to be culpable (see Annas, 1978, pp. 19-20). Parental liability is also an issue with respect to responsibility surrounding midwifery attendance in jurisdictions where it is illegal. On one level, Klein (1980, p. 6) indicates that the choice of birth setting — and, by extension, the choice of birth attendants — is the responsibility of the expectant mother. The Freemont Birth Collective linked their philosophy of parental responsibility and decision making with a non-hierarchical approach to birth management:

> Working as a team throughout pregnancy and labor, prospective parents and workers all share in the responsibility for the situation. The woman who is pregnant or in labor, and her support people, are the ones who ultimately make the decisions about what to do, how to proceed. Especially because we're not certified in any way, we're concerned that people analyze their level of comfort working with us. We encourage people to educate themselves as much as possible, consult the statistics we have kept, ask us lots of questions, talk to others who have experienced obstetrical care in other settings, and to make conscious decisions to really think about what they want and make intelligent judgments. (1977, p. 20)

Control over birthing decisions, including who may attend births, can be tied in with a general ideological framework of resistance to patriarchy's control over women, and especially its fear of women's power.[5] On another level, legal actions are conventionally brought against the birth attendant, not the expectant mother. This locus of responsibility avoids a direct confrontation with parental rights, at the same time locating the legal conflict as essentially a property dispute pertaining to occupational licensure.

The wide ambit of medicine today corresponds to structuralist imagery of social control: herein the mechanics of touch, palpation, measuring, listening to the pregnant woman or the baby may be construed as the province of licensed physicians or licensed midwives exclusive of parental preferences or the right of women to attend births. A crucial point here is that the consolidation of the "medical gaze" (Foucault, 1973) as a superior method of health care is realized, in part, through legal prohibition and prosecution.

Criminal Prosecution of Birth Attendants

The criminal prosecution of midwives, while less prevalent than quasi-criminal actions launched against midwives, is nonetheless crucial to an understanding of legal encumbrances on midwives: criminal prosecution carries the possibility of severe dispositions, including life imprisonment in Canada in cases involving criminal negligence causing death (Bourque, 1980); moreover, criminal actions appear to be increasing as home birth has become more prominent in recent decades.

A case in point in British Columbia is the prosecution and acquittal of a spiritual healer (and former doctor) on a charge of criminal negligence causing death. In *Regina v. Marsh*, an infant death was attributed to cerebral hemorrhage due to a tear in the tentorium of the skull. This tear was associated with birth trauma, according to the autopsy report (Proceedings at Trial, Oct. 11, 1979, p. 64).

The legal actions that followed this infant death were twofold. First, a charge of criminal negligence causing death was eventually laid against the birth attendant, a former physician who had been dropped from the rolls of the College of Physicians and Surgeons of British Columbia. Second, a quasi-criminal action alleging that her actions contravened the British Columbia Medical Practitioners Act was successfully brought against the defendant (McIntyre, 1983).

Margaret Marsh was acquitted of a charge of criminal negligence causing death. In his "Reasons for Judgement," Judge Millward (1980) stated:

> Mrs. Marsh first became aware of the unusual and dangerous position of the child when the first foot appeared. By then, the evidence clearly shows it was too late to save the child from the injury that it suffered, or at least on the evidence, it is most unlikely, given the situation, that is, a lack of skilled personnel present, the distance in time and space from the hospital, and the lack of any previous arrangements having been made. . . . On that finding, and with reference to the acts of omissions of Mrs. Marsh from the point in time when the foot first emerged, there cannot be a finding of criminal negligence causing death arising out of those acts or omissions, and accordingly, if any criminal liability is to attached, it must be found in her acts or omissions prior to that point in time. . . . a most important point, in my view, is that there is no evidence whatever of any doubt, in the mind of Mrs. Marsh as to the position of the child at that point.
>
> Accordingly, while Mrs. Marsh may have been incompetent, yet I am faced with the evidence of eminent authorities called both by the Crown and by the Defence, to the effect that even the most expert and experienced practitioners do make mistakes from time to time in detecting the position of fetuses in circumstances similar to those which were obtained here.
>
> I am faced with that clear evidence and a total lack of any positive evidence of a wanton or willful disregard. I am unable to conclude that any act or omission of Mrs. Marsh, prior to the emergence of the foot was indeed negligent, and certainly I am unable to conclude that it was criminally negligent.

Since the 1980 decision in *Marsh*, three midwives have faced criminal prosecution in Halifax. The three defendants were charged with criminal negligence causing bodily harm on January 27, 1983, following the transfer of an infant to hospital. This charge was later raised in the summer of 1983, a few weeks after the infant's life support system was disconnected, to criminal negligence causing death.

At a preliminary inquiry to determine whether the defendants would be brought to trial, Judge Gunn decided that the women would not be brought to trial due to lack of evidence. Witnesses at the preliminary inquiry made three key observations: first, that the infant suffered a hemorrhage to the portion of the brain that governed breathing; second, that this injury was not attributable to the midwives' care; and third, that similar injuries have been noted among babies delivered in hospital settings under medical care (Alternative Birth Crisis Coalition, 1984).

The 1986 trial of midwives Gloria LeMay and Mary Sullivan resulted in conviction. This trial represented a break from the tradition of acquittal of midwife-defendants in criminal law in Canada. In finding the defendants guilty of criminal negligence causing death, following attempts to assist at a home birth on May 8, 1985, the trial judge concluded that they failed to use reasonable knowledge, skill, and care in managing the birth (Edge, 1986; Mate, 1987). The midwives were each given a suspended sentence, placed on probation for two years, and obliged to perform 200 hours of community service.

This conviction was appealed to the Supreme Court of British Columbia. The charge of criminal negligence causing death was removed, but a charge of criminal negligence causing bodily harm (to the mother) was substituted. This second decision was then appealed to the Supreme Court of Canada. The LeMay–Sullivan case was finally decided by the Supreme Court in 1991, six years after the original charge. The Supreme Court acquitted the defendants. The LeMay–Sullivan case was a landmark case, especially with regard to the legal status of the fetus prior to expulsion from the mother (the court held that the fetus was not a person, prior to delivery). It was also another indication of the failure of court proceedings against the unregulated and alegal/illegal status of midwifery.

Canadian case law reveals few instances in which charges of criminal negligence causing death have been brought against doctors attending births. In *Simard* (1964) the initial conviction of a physician for criminal negligence was quashed on appeal to the Quebec Court of Queen's Bench. The newborn child died of a cerebral hemorrhage a few days following delivery by forceps; however, the appeal judges clearly felt that the facts of the case did not warrant the jury finding of guilt. These facts included the wish of the mother to not be delivered in a hospital but rather at a clinic, her failure to follow Dr. Simard's suggestion of an X-ray for suspected cephalo-pelvic disproportion, and the mother's early departure from the clinic against the doctor's advice. The court also accepted expert testimony vindicating the use of chloroform and forceps, and rejected contrary opinion on this point.

Civil Suits against Birth Attendants

Malpractice suits against physicians are proportionately fewer on a per capita basis in Canada than in the United States. Coburn (1980, p. 14) reported that while 20 000 malpractice suits were launched in the United States in one year, only 200 to 300 were initiated in Canada. MacIsaac (1976, p. 204), using data from the Canadian Medical Protective Association, reported that between 1966 and 1970 the number of monetary settlements against its members averaged 18 per year; in 1971, only 22 monetary settlements resulted from 131 writs against its members. Coburn goes on to suggest that judges in Canada are generally sympathetic to physicians because of a common status. This notion of class affinity is developed further in Miliband (1973), with respect to the British judiciary, and Olsen (1980) makes a similar point. At the same time, there is little evidence of civil suits launched against community midwives by their clients. It is noteworthy, however, that as American nurse-midwives have become established as professionals in institutional (hospital and clinic) settings, they are increasingly subject to malpractice actions (Sinquefield, 1983).

Conclusions

There is ample evidence to support the viewpoint that dominant groups invoke their powers to exclude competing groups and that exclusory tactics are intimately connected with powers legitimated by the state (see Giddens, 1982). Approximately 99 percent of births in British Columbia now occur in hospital settings (Tonkin, 1981, p. 11). Hospital-based birth attendance is either directed by physicians or, less commonly, responsibility may be delegated to nursing personnel. Physicians' incomes (on average) remain well above average incomes for North Americans, while as a rule midwives' incomes are markedly lower, especially with respect to community midwifery.

Nevertheless, the available material on midwifery practice in Canada and preliminary data collected by the author reflect initiatives to counter the dominant status of hospital-based obstetrics. Indeed, as has been noted above, attempts to use the courts to prosecute midwives under the Criminal Code have not always been successful. Even quasi-judicial hearings, such as coroners' inquests, do not automatically reinforce the authority of medical control over birth. Two coroners' inquiries in Ontario have recommended legal recognition of midwives and establishment of a provincial school of midwifery (Ontario Association of Midwives and the Nurse-Midwives' Association of Ontario, 1983, p. 4).

Legal struggles and the continuing dominance of physician authority in Canadian maternity care touch directly on Balbus's (1978, p. 77) criticism of Western legal ideology for its adherence to formal, abstract equality of citizens despite substantive inequalities before the law. If midwifery is taken as one instance of a "rights struggle," Sumner's (1981) call for further struggles seems apropos, as does Beirne and Sharlet's (1980) observation that struggles for such rights as the right to abortion, prisoners' rights, redress of racial and sexual discrimination, and so forth are to be encouraged.

Theoretically, some have favoured "democratic relativism" (Feyerabend, 1980) as a means of protecting unorthodox forms of medicine and healing and thereby permitting comparisons of the various forms of health care. The point remains that implementation of such a thoroughly pluralistic ideal has not been secured in Western public policy (McRae, 1979). The presence of these specific struggles in maternity care should not overshadow the continuing protection of professional attendance and medical dominance in the Canadian context and elsewhere.

A key point is the yawning gap between the demonstrated ability of midwives to manage uncomplicated deliveries — often with birth outcomes superior to those associated with conventional medical attendance in North America — and the persistence of legal controls that buttress the professional dominance of obstetricians and general practitioners. By vesting policing powers with the medical colleges, and through the occasional prosecution of alternative practitioners, the implementation of safe, pluralistic maternity care services remains greatly constrained. As indicated above, however, the rekindling of more autonomous midwifery in community settings and in hospitals is tied in with a measure of human agency; so also is the continuing practice of midwifery through limitations on the state and the medical profession.

To the extent that legal statutes often retard the implementation of midwifery services for expectant mothers and their families, Canadian public policy seems grossly out of step with virtual world-wide recognition of midwives in health systems. Indeed, the literature on birth outcomes continues to support the argument that midwives can not only practice as safely, or more safely than other professionals, but that they appear especially adept in reducing unnecessary interventions and measures applied to labouring women (Tew & Damstra-Wijmenga, 1991). This aspect of midwifery care, in light of patterns of increasing interventions (such as Caesarean section) in some jurisdictions (Francome, 1986), makes a strong argument for promoting, not prosecuting midwives. Moving toward the turn of the century, in spite of an ideology of medical control and supervision over birth (as a medical event), midwives and some legislators are holding fast to the importance of providing midwives with legal standing, and sufficient powers and resources to enable them to practise in their own right.

Notes

1. See also Eisenstein (1981, p. 209) regarding the low proportion of U.S. women in professional occupations such as law and medicine. The partial segregation of women into occupational groupings — in the health sector and other sectors — is thus linked with market forces. These forces in turn reinforce patriarchal elements in the economy, yet these relations of production in capitalist countries also carry benefits for women, including increased income and consumption levels, greater mobility, and personal independence (Lim, 1983, p. 83).
2. Many contemporary scholars have grappled with the theoretical and practical implications of retaining parliamentary democracy and the rule of law. For a review of some problems associated with idealist and materialist approaches, see Sumner (1981).
3. An elaboration of midwifery practice in British Columbia is available in Barrington (1985) and Burtch (1987).
4. It must be kept in mind that the court has the power to dismiss charges against defendants when the information is insufficient. In one instance, where a defendant was charged under the British Columbia Medical Act, the information alleging the unlawful practice of medicine was quashed. The evidence failed to set forth the act or acts constituting the alleged offences and failed to name the persons with whom the defendant was alleged to have unlawfully practised medicine (Regina v. Kripps, 1977).
5. Gordon and Hunter (1977/78, p. 12) define patriarchy as "a specific organization of the family and society, in which heads of families controlled not only the reproductive labor, but also the production of all family members."

Study Questions

1. Discuss the reasons why Canada is the only industrialized nation that has not legally recognized midwifery as an occupation.
2. How have historical restrictions on the licensing of health practitioners affected Canadian midwives? Consider the *number* of midwives now operating autonomously in Canada and the degree to which their work can be criminalized or otherwise regulated.
3. Reconsider stereotypical images of midwifery, especially surrounding competency of midwives and infant safety. Whose interests are served by the charge of "meddlesome midwifery"?
4. Outline possible contradictions between patients' interests and professional interests in maternity care.
5. What does the instance of midwifery lobbying suggest with respect to the place of human agency in political struggles? To what extent is innovation possible? To what extent are alternative measures in health care structured by the state and the professions?

Recommended Reading

Arney, W.R. (1982). *Power and the profession of obstetrics*. Chicago: University of Chicago Press.

Buckley, S. (1979). Ladies or midwives? Efforts to reduce infant and maternal mortality. In L. Kealey (Ed.), *A not unreasonable claim: Women and reform in Canada, 1880s-1920s* (pp. 231-252). Toronto: Women's Press.

DeVries, R. (1985). *Regulating birth: Midwives, medicine, and the law*. Philadelphia: Temple University Press.

Donnison, J. (1977). *Midwives and medical men: A history of inter-professional rivalries and women's rights*. London: Schocken.

Doyal, L., & Pennell, I. (1979). *The political economy of health*. London: Pluto Press.

Mehl, L., Peterson, G., Whitt, M., & Howes, W. (1977). Outcomes of elective home births: A series of 1146 Cases. *Journal of Reproductive Medicine*, 19, (5), 281-290.

Oakley, A. (1986). *The captured womb: A history of the medical care of pregnant women*. London: Basil Blackwell.

Spitzer, S. (1983). Marxist perspectives in the sociology of law. *Annual Review of Sociology*, 9, 103-124.

References

Alternative Birth Crisis Coalition. (1984). News analysis: Canada midwives on trial. *ABCC News*, 111, (3), 304.

Anderson v. Chasney and Sisters of St. Joseph. (1949). 2 W.W.R. 337, 57 Man. R. 343 (1949) 4 D.L. R. 71, reversing in part (1948) 4 D.L.R. 458. Affirmed 1950 4 D.L.R. 223 (Can.).

Annas, G. (1978). Homebirth: Autonomy vs. safety. *Hastings Center Report*, 8, 19-20.

Arney, W.R. (1982). *Power and the profession of obstetrics*. Chicago: University of Chicago Press.

Badinter, E. (1981). *The myth of motherhood: An historical view of the maternal instinct*. London: Souvenir Press.

Balbus, I. (1978). Community form and legal form: An essay on the 'relative autonomy' of law. *Law and Society Review*, 2, 77.

Barrington, E. (1985). *Midwifery is catching*. Toronto: NC Press.

Beirne, P., & Sharlet, R. (1980). *Pashukonis: Selected writing on Marxism and law*. London: Academic Press.

Benoit, C. (1988). Traditional midwifery practice: The limits of occupational autonomy. *Canadian Review of Sociology and Anthropology*, 26, (4), 633-649.

Biggs, C.L. (1983). The case of the missing midwives: A history of midwifery in Ontario from 1795-1900. *Ontario History*, 75, 21-35.

Blackburn, R. (Ed.). (1972). *Ideology in social science*. London: Fontana/Collins.

Bourque, P. (1980). Proof of the cause of death in a prosecution for criminal negligence causing death. *Criminal Law Quarterly*, 22, (3), 334-343.

Buckley, S. (1979). Ladies or midwives? Efforts to reduce infant and maternal mortality. In L. Kealey (Ed.), *A not unreasonable claim: Women and reform in Canada, 1880s-1920s* (pp. 231-252). Toronto: Women's Press.

Burtch, B.E. (1987). Community midwifery and state measures. *Contemporary Crises*, 10, 399-420.

Burtch, B.E. (in press). Law, medicine, and the midwifery movement in Canada. In R.S. Ratner (Ed.), *State hegemony in Canada: Order, resistance, and change*. Vancouver: University of British Columbia Press.

Burtch, B. (Executive Producer), Neville, K., & Doherty, M. (Directors). (1991). *Midwifery and the law*. [Videotape]. Vancouver: Simon Fraser University and the Knowledge Network.

Coburn, D. (1980). Patients' rights: A new deal in health care. *Canadian Forum*, 60, (699), 14-18.

College of Nurses of Ontario. (1983). *Guidelines for registered nurses providing care to individuals and families seeking alternatives to childbirth in a hospital setting*. Toronto: CNO (Photocopy).

Cooke, D. (1984, December 4). Government should recognize midwifery. *NDP News*, p. 30.

Currie, D. (1986). Reproductive rights: Implications for feminist jurisprudence and the state. In D. Currie & B.D. MacLean (Eds.), *The administration of Justice* (pp. 35-47). Regina: Social Research Unit, Department of Sociology, University of Saskatchewan.

Cust, K. (1991, June). Midwifery has always been a part of humanity. [letter to the editor]. *Edmonton Journal*.

Donnison, J. (1977). *Midwives and medical men: A history of inter-professional rivalries and women's rights*. London: Schocken.

Doyal, L., & Pennell, I. (1979). *The political economy of health*. London: Pluto Press.

Edge, M. (1986, October 10). Midwives may face jail in December. *Vancouver Sun*.

Eisenstein, Z. (1981). *The radical future of liberal feminism*. New York: Longman.

Evenson, D. (1983). Midwives: Survival of an ancient profession. *Women's Rights Law Reporter*, 7, (4), 313-330.

Feyerabend, P. (1980). Democracy, elitism, and scientific method. *Inquiry*, 23, (1), 3-18.

Fottler, M.D., Gibson, G., & Pinchoff, D.M. (1980). Physician resistance to manpower innovation. *Social Science Quarterly*, 61, (1), 149-157.

Foucault, M. (1973). *The birth of the clinic: An archaeology of medical perceptions*. New York: Vintage Press.

Francome, C. (1986, January 17). The fashion for caesareans. *New Society*, pp. 100-110.

Freemont Birth Collective. (1977). Lay midwifery — Still an 'illegal' profession. *Women and Health*, 2, (3), 19-27.

Gavigan, S. (1984). The criminal sanction as it relates to human reproduction. *Journal of Legal History*, 5, (1), 20-43.

Gavigan, S. (1986). Women, law and patriarchal relations: Perspectives within the sociology of law. In N. Boyd (Ed.), *The social dimensions of law* (pp. 101-124). Scarborough: Prentice-Hall.

Giddens, A. (1982). *Profiles and critiques in social theory.* Berkeley: University of California Press.

Gordon, L., & Hunter, A. (1977/1978). Sex, family and the new right: Anti-feminism as a political force. *Radical America,* 12, (1), 8-25.

Hamowy, R. (1984). *Canadian medicine: A study in restricted entry.* Vancouver: Fraser Institute.

Hart, N. (1982). Is capitalism bad for your health? *British Journal of Sociology,* 33, (3), 435-443.

Jimenez, M. (1990, November 10). Midwife must stand trial, judge decides. *The Globe and Mail.*

Klein, S. (1980). *A childbirth manual.* Victoria: B.C. Photocopy.

Labonté, R. (1983). Good health: Individual or social? *Canadian Forum,* 63, (727), 10-13, 70-91.

Lim, L.Y.C. (1983). Capitalism, imperialism and patriarchy: The dilemma of third-world women workers in multinational factories. In J.C. Nash & M.P. Fernandez-Kelly (Eds.), *Women, men, and the international division of labor* (pp. 70-91). Albany: State University of New York Press.

MacIsaac, R.F. (1976). Negligence actions against medical doctors. *Chitty's Law Journal,* 24, (6), 201-206.

Mate, G. (1987, January 8). It's time to legalize midwifery. *The Globe and Mail.*

Medical Practitioners' Act. (1979). R.S.B.C.

McIntyre, G. (1983, February 18). Midwives ask for sanction of law. *The Province.*

McRae, K. (1979). The plural society and the western political tradition. *Canadian Journal of Political Science,* 12, (4), 675-689.

Mehl, L., et al. (1977). Outcomes of elective home births: A series of 1,146 cases. *Journal of Reproductive Medicine,* 19, (5), 281-290.

Miliband, R. (1973). *The state in capitalist society.* London: Quartet Books.

Millward, P. (1980). Reasons for judgement. *Regina versus Marsh.* Victoria: County Court of British Columbia.

Oakley, A. (1984). The captured womb: A history of the medical care of pregnant women. London: Basil Blackwell.

Olsen, D. (1980). *The state elite.* Toronto: McClelland and Stewart.

Ontario Association of Midwives and the Nurse-Midwives' Association of Ontario. (1983, December). *Brief on midwifery care in Ontario.* Brief submitted to the Health Disciplines Review Committee, Toronto, Ontario.

Ontario Medical Act. (1906).

Osborne, J. (1987). The crime of infanticide: Throwing out the baby with the bathwater. *Canadian Journal of Family Law,* 6, (1), 47-59.

Phillips, P., & Phillips, E. (1983). *Women and work: Inequality in the labour market.* Toronto: James Lorimer.

Poulantzas, N. (1973). *Political power and social classes.* London: New Left Books.

Poulantzas, N. (1978). *State, power, socialism.* London: New Left Books.

Provincial Medical Board v. Bond. (1890). *22 Nova Scotia Reports,* 153.

Regina v. Armstrong. (1911). *Canadian Criminal Cases,* 18 (72) (Sask.).

Regina v. Cruikshanks. (1914). 6 W.W.R. 524, 7 Alta. L.R. 92, 23 C.C.C. 23, 16 D.L.R. 536 (C.A.)

Regina v. Kripps. (1977). 4 B.C.L.R. 364 (Provincial Court).

Regina v. Marsh. (1980). (Victoria: Unreported).

Regina v. Ornavowski. (1941). W.W.R. 103 (Sask.).

Regina v. Raffenberg. (1909). *Western Law Reports,* 12, 419.

Regina v. Rondeau. (1903). *Territories Law Reports,* 5, 478-483.

Regina v. Whelan. (1900). 4 *Canadian Criminal Cases,* 277 (Ontario).

Regina v. Wong. (1979). 6 W.W.R. 163 (Prov. Ct.).

Simard v. the Queen. (1964). *Criminal Reports (Canada),* 43, 70-82.

Sinquefield, G. (1983). A malpractice dilemma: Defining standards of care for certified nurse-midwives. *Journal of Nurse-Midwifery,* 28, (4), 1-2.

Spitzer, S. (1983). Marxist perspectives in the sociology of law. *Annual Review of Sociology,* 9, 103-124.

Stephens, R. (1984, March 16). Ontario midwives merit legal status, NDPer says. *The Globe and Mail.*

Sumner, C. (1981). The rule of law and civil rights in contemporary marxist theory. *Kapitalistate,* 9, 63-91.

Sweet, L. (1985, April 8). Midwives are battling for their freedom. *The Toronto Star*, p. C1.

Tew, M., & Damstra-Wijmenga, S. (1991). Safest birth attendants: Recent Dutch evidence. *Midwifery*, 7, 55–63.

Tonkin, R. (1981). *Child health profile: Birth events and infant outcome, British Columbia*. Vancouver: Hemlock Printers.

Van Wagner, V. (1984). *The current politics of midwifery in Ontario*. Paper presented at the 20th Annual Meeting of the Canadian Sociology and Anthropology Association, University of Guelph.

Wexler, S. (1976). The intersection of law and morals. *Canadian Bar Review*, 54, 351–359.

Women's Work Project of the Union for Radical Political Economists. (1976). USA — Women health workers. *Women and Health*, 1, (3), 14–23.

Chapter 24

Professions, Ideology, and Change

Ray Croucher, London University

Introduction

Changes in health-care delivery systems are often assumed to confer benefits on both the consumer and the profession concerned. These may accrue, for example, from the provision of a more universally available service, or one financed through government revenues, and, therefore, with no direct financial penalties to the patient. The health profession's interests are assumed to complement those of the consumer, and vice versa.

It has become clear, however, that the narrow occupational interests of the health profession do not necessarily coincide with the wider, public interest. Apparently contradictory consequences may arise, for example, dentists' opposition to the establishment of a dental program intended to provide comprehensive dental services to schoolchildren, without financial penalty, through the use of an expanded-duty dental auxiliary. Why would dentists oppose such a plan? What arguments could they use to justify opposition?

This chapter provides answers to these questions through an examination of the development of a dental plan in the province of Saskatchewan. Although the details of developments discussed are unique to that province, the issues are universal and relevant to any areas where the professionally dominated model of service delivery operates.

The concepts of professionalism and professional ideology, which are useful in explaining the response of dentists to the Saskatchewan Dental Plan, are introduced in the following section. Next is a detailed discussion of the extent and distribution of dental disease, and of the supply of dental services in Saskatchewan before the plan was introduced. The dental profession's response to the proposed dental plan is then examined in light of the previous discussion of professionalism and professional ideology. After a brief evaluation of the plan's effectiveness, the chapter concludes with a general overview of the changing patterns of dental health in Canada and elsewhere, the increase in the supply of dentists, and the ways in which these factors are influencing dentists' patterns of practice.

Professions and Ideology

One way in which professions have set about differentiating themselves from other groups in society is to claim a set of distinguishing attributes. The most commonly accepted attributes are a prolonged specialized training in a body of abstract knowledge, a commitment to acting in a disinterested and responsible way towards their clients, and the possession of autonomy. Freidson (1970, p. 82) believes that autonomy is the key feature and defines it as "a position of legitimate control over work." The profession may exercise autonomy by determining standards of education, by the licensing of professional practice, and by shaping legislation that concerns the profession.

The right of the profession to self-regulation comes through discussion between the professional association and government officials. Hall (1969, p. 75) describes this as being given "community sanction." Through the efforts of the professional association, a monopoly is granted to all members of the profession. The community as a whole believes it will benefit greatly by granting this monopoly.

In addition to self-regulation and professional autonomy, the profession will also seek to define how other should behave in matters concerned with its work. This definition of behaviour may have internal significance to the profession, involving the conditions of work of other people in its division of labour. Freidson (1970, pp. 48-49) enumerates several conditions of work associated with the medical profession:

1. Much of the technical knowledge that paramedical workers acquire during their training and use in their work tends to have been discovered or enlarged upon or, at the very least, approved of by physicians
2. The tasks performed by paramedical workers tend to assist rather than to replace the focal tasks of diagnosis and treatment
3. Paramedical workers tend to be subordinate, in that their work tends to be performed at the request or "order of" physicians, and is often supervised by them
4. The prestige accorded paramedical occupations by the general public tends to be less than that accorded to physicians

This definition of behaviour may also be of external significance, that is, of the profession, presuming "to tell society what is good and right for the individual and for society" (Hughes, 1958, p. 79). Davis (1980, p. 44) notes that "it has generally been the clinician's concept of dental practice that has dominated the deployment of resources and that has also tended to govern our ways of thinking about the problems of oral health in society."

These professional privileges may be legitimated through the use of an ideology — "a set of ideas which explains why professional autonomy is not desired out of self-interest, but is a requirement for offering the best possible service in the public interest" (Daniels, 1973, p. 39). Presumably, professional ideology will bear out claims to knowledge. Thus, while the division of labour is initially established by associations and legislation, continuous political activity is required to maintain and improve the profession's position in the marketplace and the division of labour surrounding it. The ideology is used to defend the status quo. To limit its basis to purely professional issues would be erroneous. Bottomore (1971, p. 33) emphasizes that "there are many potential sources of ideology: ethnic and linguistic groups, occupational groups, generations, groups resulting from cultural or regional affinities and traditions as well as social classes." Stamm (1978, p. 407) notes that the Canadian climate of entrepreneurial activity has fostered strong independent professions that have chosen to operate in the private sector using a direct-payment fee-for-service arrangement.

Professional socialization is also important, providing not only a body of knowledge but also a set of norms and values. Goode (1957, p. 194) notes that "though the profession does not produce the next generation biologically, it does so socially through its control over the selection of professional trainees."

The impact of an ideology upon the wider society may be understood in terms of its "parochial" and "ecumenic" content. "Parochial" ideas have particular meaning for the profession, while "ecumenic" ideas are relevant to the concerns of lay persons entirely apart from their dealings with the occupation in question (Dibble, 1963, p. 230). Dibble suggest that the ideology of higher-ranking occupational groups will often be more widely diffused throughout society. It follows that the parochial concerns of a professional association may have a greater impact if they are linked to the values held by society at large.

There is a close relationship between these ideas and those of the professional association with which this chapter is concerned, namely, the College of Dental Surgeons of Saskatchewan. Created under the terms of the Saskatchewan Dental Act, it was granted the powers of licensing and disciplining its members. It concerns itself, in addition, with the promotion and protection of the dental health of the public. No conflict of interest is perceived in the simultaneous serving of both public and professional interests.

The above discussion provides a framework for explaining the response of the dental profession to the Saskatchewan Dental Plan. However, it would be useful to first discuss briefly the status of dental health and dental services in Saskatchewan before introduction of the plan.

Dental Health and Dental Services in Saskatchewan Before 1972

This section reviews the rationale behind the decision to introduce proposals for a dental plan in Saskatchewan in 1972. Firstly, the children of Saskatchewan suffered from poor dental health. A survey of nearly 7 000 schoolchildren in 1951 found an average of 3.2 decayed, missing, and filled teeth in one provincial health region, and an average of 2.9 decayed, missing, and filled teeth in another. McPhail et al., (1972, p. 288) reported a survey carried out in 1954 of 3 470 schoolchildren aged seven to seventeen, who resided in rural and urban communities in the southern geographical third of the province. It found that only 13 percent of the children examined needed no treatment at all, while 29 percent needed at least four fillings, and 8 percent needed at least four teeth extracted. Prior to treatment at the beginning of the first year of operation of the Saskatchewan Dental Plan, 10 924 six-year-olds were examined. The annual report concluded that "the dental health of children enrolled in the Dental Plan is very poor. Enrollees had, on average, 5.01 decayed teeth and only 1.10 filled teeth" (Saskatchewan Dental Plan, 1976, p. 20). Twelve percent of the children examined needed no treatment at all.

For comparison, a survey of children's dental health in England and Wales carried out in 1973 found that six-year-olds had, on average, 3.7 decayed and filled teeth, of which 2.8 teeth were decayed (Todd, 1975, p. 243). Thirty-three percent needed no treatment. These clinical data hid great variations when socio-economic variables were considered. McFarlane (1964, p. 90) had concluded a review of the impact of socio-economic variables upon the utilization of dental-health services by noting that "levels of income and education, and, in general, position in the social class structure, determine to a great extent the degree of demand for and the utilization pattern of dental services irrespective, relatively speaking, of need." He also found areas of residence to be relevant. This was illustrated by McCormick's study of 11 993 Grade 1-8 schoolchildren, which found that "more than half (57%) of rural Manitoba schoolchildren seek to obtain some dental treatment, but that these children do not necessarily receive all the treatment they require" (1966, p. 280).

Additional data relating to the utilization of dental services was collected as the result of a World Health Organization International Collaborative Study carried out during 1968 and 1969. Data were collected by interview from both urban and rural areas of the province. A total of 3 584 interviews with families were conducted (Josie, 1973, p. 29).

The data from this study show a differential utilization of the dental services by area of residence. Respondents from the rural area had a markedly lower level of utilization. Only 39 percent had seen a dentist in the previous twelve months, compared to 52 percent of the urban respondents. Sixty-one percent of the rural residents reported not having seen a dentist for one or more years, compared to 48 percent of the urban residents. This category includes those who had never seen a dentist. Further analysis showed that 75 percent of the rural respondents who had visited a dentist in the previous month had done so to relieve a symptom rather than for a preventive "checkup," compared to 51 percent of the urban respondents.

Analysis of the factors of age, income of family head, and education of family head emphasizes the influence of area of residence upon dental visits.

In the urban area, the youngest age group was two or three times more likely to have seen a dentist in the previous month than its counterpart in the rural area. It might be anticipated that this age group as a whole would make more visits than other age groups, because dental decay is more prevalent among younger people. This indeed was true for the urban area, but not in the rural area where there was little variation between age groups.

This urban/rural disparity can also be observed when the income and education of the head of the family are considered. In urban areas there was a positive relationship between income, education, and dental visits: those with high incomes (above average) were twice as likely to have visited a dentist in a one-month period than persons from a low-income (below average) group. Those from households where the head had a university education were about three times as likely to have visited a dentist, compared to those where the head of the household had only elementary education. This positive relationship between income, education, and dental visits was less pronounced in rural areas.

In summary, the data from the study conducted by the World Health Organization and other studies showed a differential access to services by area of residence, income, and education. It is apparent that the need for dental treatment was not being met. In addition, substantial socio-economic barriers existed to prevent an equitable and accessible utilization of dental services prior to the introduction of the Saskatchewan Health Dental Plan in 1974.

Saskatchewan residents also suffered from an inadequate supply of dental services. The province had never been adequately served by dentists, as measured by the dentist/

patient ratio. In Canada as a whole, there had been a slight improvement in the ratio from 1957 (one dentist for every 3 031 population) to 1973 (one dentist for every 2 581 population). Saskatchewan had the second-worst dentist/patient ratio of all the Canadian provinces: in 1973 it was one dentist for every 4 049 population (Chebib, 1973; Saskatchewan Department of Health: Health Personnel Inventory, 1972-74; College of Dental Surgeons of Saskatchewan, Annual Register, 1975).

There was also a wide variation in the supply of dental services. The two major urban centres, with less than one-third of the population, were served by over one-half of the dentists. In 1972, there were twenty rural communities with populations of 1 000 or more that did not have a resident dentist (Saskatchewan Debates and Proceedings, 1972-74; Saskatchewan Department of Health: Health Personnel Inventory, 1972-74).

There was apparently little prospect of improving this situation. Prior to the opening of the College of Dentistry in 1968, prospective dentists had to attend dental schools outside of the province, usually in Alberta or Ontario. It was felt that graduated dentists were then reluctant to return to Saskatchewan, having made personal and professional contacts elsewhere. In the years 1972-79, 29 dentists graduated from the newly opened College of Dentistry in Saskatchewan. Twenty-four of them set up practice in the main population centres (McPhail, 1976, p. 1). It was also apparent that the province suffered from a net out-migration of dentists. While a surplus of 38 new dentists over those retiring was created between 1957-70, there was also a loss of 32 moving out of the province in the same period. They formed part of the Canadian pattern of westward interprovincial location.

Those dentists working in the province reported a high degree of "busyness." In 1968 the Canadian Dental Association reported that 39 percent of Saskatchewan dentists were too busy to treat all those requesting appointments, and that Saskatchewan dentists were seeing a higher-than-average number of patients — 2 991 in that year, compared to the Canadian average of 1 926. Seven percent of the province's dentists felt that they could have taken on an additional 400 patients each, resulting in perhaps 5 600 more patients being served (Canadian Dental Association, 1968).

The nature of dental problems resulted in a minimal division of labour. The dental hygienist was the dental profession's preferred "expanded-duty" auxiliary, being allowed to "work in the mouth" removing hard deposits from the teeth and providing instruction in oral hygiene. The hygienist's predominantly preventive role contributed to improved efficiency and productivity in dental practices. Hygienists worked under the supervision of the dentist, without impinging on the dentist's right to diagnose and plan treatment. However, in 1972, there were only 30 dental hygienists licensed to practise in the province.

The Saskatchewan Dental Plan: The Government Proposal

Recognition of Saskatchewan's dental-health problems led the government to consider the introduction of a system established in New Zealand in 1921. In that country, dental nurses provided basic dental services to schoolchildren. By 1979, nineteen other countries were using a similar auxiliary. A scheme using dental nurses had been in operation in the Yukon since 1962. Following a successful experiment in one Saskatchewan community, proposals for a universal and comprehensive dental service for children aged three to twelve were prepared. This service would be universal in attempting to remove the existing financial and geographic barriers to dental care, and comprehensive in providing as complete a set of services as possible. Use of the school system to provide clinics was proposed to allow easy access to, and treatment of, the child population. It was also anticipated that dental health education could be organized through the school system. The program would be financed from general provincial revenues with no premiums or individual levies. Recognizing the problems in the supply of dental services, the government proposal advocated the use of an expanded-duty dental auxiliary, the dental nurse, modelled on the New Zealand auxiliary. It was anticipated that 107 such dental nurses would eventually be employed, along with twelve dentists to be designated as regional dental consultants. Rather than providing services, their task would be to monitor the work of the dental nurses. The dental nurse, envisioned as the key person in a clinic, was described by the proposal (1972, p. 14) as: "the principal officer of a dental clinic and (performing) dental inspections, restorations and extractions within her competence."

The Response of the Dental Profession: I

An advisory committee was set up by the provincial government, and input was invited from the public. Thirty-eight groups or individuals replied, including seven from dental associations. A major feature of the professional response to the government's proposals was to emphasize what have been characterized as "parochial" issues, issues of concern primarily to the profession and the existing organization of dental care. A primary stress was on the necessity for direct "supervison" of the dental nurse. An example of the type of argument used was contained in the submission of the College of Dental Surgeons of Saskatchewan (1973, p. 8), which stated: "a registered dentist must examine the patient and prescribe, preferably in writing, the treatment plan, and delegate appropriate procedures to the nurses. *The flow of communication in this regard must always be from the dentist to the nurse*" (emphasis in original). Supervision had to be direct, as had occurred traditionally. The new Saskatchewan dental nurse posed a threat to the traditional dental division of labour, as the dental nurse would be expected to recognize when a child needed treatment beyond her competence and refer that child to a dentist.

The professional association acknowledged the need for an auxiliary to assist in the more efficient delivery of dental care, and proposed using the dental hygienist. Hygienists in the province were prepared to accept direct dental supervision, as shown by this quotation from the brief presented by the provincial Dental Hygienists' Association (1973, p. 1): "Dentist not doing examination, diagnosis, and treatment planning . . . is totally inadequate, as we know from our training that you cannot be educated in two years to do real examinations."

Associated with the need for direct supervision was an argument for quality. A connection was implied between quality and the already existing organization of dental service i.e., fee-for-service private practice, where the dentist had complete autonomy. The articulation of the issue of "quality" provides an example of the sometimes contradictory nature of the ideas contained in an ideology. While the profession recognized the need for quality dental services, it also deemed itself the only group able to properly assess this, suggesting that the public might be a poor judge: "Any plan that offers services previously not available, is likely to be acceptable to them and viewed with considerable enthusiasm" (Canadian Dental Association, 1973, p. 8). The definition of quality was partial, relating as it did only to the presence of the dentist in supervison but not considering issues such as the equitable distribution and supply of dental personnel throughout the province. A quality program would be more expensive, as it would need to employ more supervisory dentists. It would also delay the introduction of the program until sufficient labour was available.

"Ecumenic" ideas — those reflecting the values of the wider society — were also articulated, although with much less frequency. One example was the issue of "freedom." The College of Dental Surgeons of Saskatchewan, claiming to protect the public interest, argued that a choice of services be made available, either through schools or using existing dental practices, stating: "The college feels that it should be the right of parents to be able to have a freedom of choice as to who provides services for their children under the plan" (1973, p. 73). The distribution and availability of existing dental services was such that many children had no choice at all. It is interesting to note that the College of Dental Surgeons also proposed the compulsory attendance of parents during treatment.

A second "ecumenic issue" was "personal responsibility" as a key to good dental health: "It is up to the child and his parents to achieve the goal of dental health — it cannot be given" (College of Dental Surgeons of Saskatchewan, 1973, p. 29). Two points should be noted. First, many children needed "catch-up" restorative treatment. Second, to place the responsibility solely on the individual is to fail to recognize the impact of many wider social factors, for instance, the use of sugar in food manufacturing, on dental disease. This factor can be tackled most successfully through fiscal measures and innovative nutrition policies (Ringen, 1979).

A third issue used was "universal availability." It was anticipated that the plan would include all children regardless of economic status, geographic location, race, colour, or creed. However, this "ecumenic" concern conflicted with the more strongly held "parochial" value of "quality": *We feel it is much more important to introduce a programme of the highest possible quality, rather than to institute a universal programme of dubious value*" (College of Dental Surgeons of Saskatchewan, 1973, p. 6; emphasis in original).

It should be noted that in presenting these priorities, the dental association was reflecting the feelings of its members. One conclusion of a survey of Saskatchewan dentists conducted in 1972 was that:

> a preponderance of Saskatchewan dentists contend that examination, diagnosis and treatment planning should be done by a dentist. Certain other duties must be delegated to a dental nurse and performed either under "in-office" or "intermittent" supervison of a dentist. (Thomson et al., 1973, p. 53)

Disentangling Quality Care from Professionalism

Despite the misgivings expressed by organized dentistry in the province, the Saskatchewan Dental Plan started operation in 1974. By the year 1983-84, 161 784 children and adolescents were enrolled in and receiving services from the plan. After ten years of operation, it was possible to evaluate the validity of the dental profession's ideological claims about the organization of the dental plan. In particular, the "parochial" claims could be evaluated; that is that only a high quality of service would be acceptable to the population of the province and that a quality service could only be provided through a much higher degree of involvement of the dentist.

An initial evaluation of the quality of service provided by dental nurses was undertaken in 1976. Three academic dentists from outside Saskatchewan assessed the treatment provided for children. An important feature of their study design was the decision to base their sampling on classrooms and to examine every child in each classroom. This enabled comparisons between the dental work provided by dental nurses and that provided by dentists in private practice. A second important feature was that the examiners worked "blind"; that is, they were unaware of whether the treatment provided for a child had been done by a dental nurse or a dentist. A major finding of this evaluation was that, for whatever type of filling being considered, those placed by dental nurses were significantly superior to those placed by the dentists working in private practice. Of the fillings placed by dentists, 21 percent were rated as "unacceptable" and 1 percent as "superior," while only 4 percent of the dental nurses' fillings were rated as "unacceptable" and 48 percent as "superior." "Unacceptable" meant that in the opinion of the examiners, the filling should be redone. The evaluators commented in their report upon the issue of supervision. Noting that it had been controversial and that direct supervison of the dental nurse was not provided by a dentist, they concluded: "On the basis of the data presented here, it would be difficult to insist that more direct supervision of dental nurses take place without making the same suggestion in the case of dentists" (Ambrose et al., 1976, p. 15).

A second evaluation of the plan was undertaken in 1980. The evaluation was based on data routinely collected during its operation. For some of the issues involved in the evaluation, it was possible to make comparisons with other provinces.

It was found that enrollment by parents of children in the plan had averaged 83 percent and that at least three-quarters of this group would receive complete care every year. When those children who received only partial care from the plan were included, along with those who might be receiving treatment from a private dentist, it was suggested that the level of dental-care utilization by Saskatchewan's children might approach 90 percent, higher than anywhere else in North America.

Comparisons with children's dental plans provided in other provinces showed that actual utilization was about 20 percent higher than in Newfoundland, Nova Scotia, and Quebec, and similar to that in Prince Edward Island. It should be noted that the fee-for-service private-practice delivery model is used in the first three provinces, while Prince Edward Island organizes its services for children in a way similar to Saskatchewan.

The costs of providing treatment for each enrolled child were also compared with the other provincial schemes. The evaluator concluded that "costs, despite the provision of more services and wider coverage (utilization) under the Saskatchewan Health Dental Plan, are actually lower than or equal to the costs of the other provincial insurance children's plans" (Lewis, 1981, p. 73).

The most important finding was that a child enrolled in the plan would be likely to develop less decay and receive less treatment as he or she got older. This has been corroborated by data collected routinely by the dental plan, which shows that in 1984-85, the five-year-old child entering the plan had an average of 2.16 decayed teeth, while an eleven-year-old child had on average only .55 decayed teeth. In addition, the percentage of five-year-old children with no decay and no restorations had increased from 19 percent in 1975-76 to 43 percent in 1984-85 (Young, 1986, p. 828).

The ultimate test of any health program is its long-term influence on the health status of a population. In this case, the improved long-term oral health status of Saskatchewan's population is being considered. Lewis (1981, p. vi) concluded that "the performance to date gives early indications of the likely achievement of this long-term goal."

The Response of the Dental Profession: 2

At the same time as the dental plan developed its therapist–based services, the supply of dentists was increasing. From 1971 to 1981 the number of dentists in Canada grew by 52 percent. This growth came about as a result of more dentists' graduation from the expanded educational system. The population of Canada grew by only 12 percent in the same time period. From 1981 to 2001 the expected increase in dental graduates will be 40 percent, while the population is projected to increase by 19 percent. Although Saskatchewan was underserviced in dental terms in the past, in the future it is expected that the supply of dentists will grow at a rate above the Canadian average. The dentist/population ratio has dropped from 1: 4 191 in 1971 to 1: 2 941 in 1981 to a projected 1: 2 234 in 2001 (House et al., 1983, p. 89). The number of dentists in the province grew from 189 in 1961 to 333 in 1981 (McDermott & Oles, 1982, p. 721). Rather than being too busy to take on new patients, dentists are presently facing the challenge of a possible shortage of patients needing the services they have traditionally supplied (*Journal of the Canadian Dental Association*, 1981, p. 630). The fear is that in the major population centres the supply of dental labour will exceed the demand for dental treatment (McDermott & Oles, 1982, p. 723).

This issue, coupled with a changed provincial administration perhaps more willing to recognize the "parochial" ideological concerns of the profession (*Journal of the Canadian Dental Association*, 1982, p. 500), may have been responsible for the decision by dentists to become involved in the dental plan. From 1981 adolescents aged fourteen years and up, who were enrolled in the plan, were to receive their dental care in private dental offices. This was presented as a bridging exercise to encourage the transition from the plan to seeking (and eventually paying for) care from a dentist in private practice upon leaving school. Covered services were provided at no charge to parents.

Two issues emerged from this plan. First the provincial department of health designated schools either dental-plan or general-practice schools. The dental-plan schools had care provided by teams of dental nurses (now called "dental therapists") in school clinics, and were situated predominantly in the two major centres of population. General-practice schools were located in rural areas to encourage and support the continuing equitable availability of dental services for the whole population of these areas.

The second issue was the payment mechanism negotiated. This is described as "a modified capitation payment system," which maintains a facade of "at arm's length" involvement by the government. For every adolescent attending a participating dentist, a capitation payment is made to the College of Dental Surgeons of Saskatchewan by the provincial government. In turn, the college has negotiated payment with participating dentists on a fee-for-service basis. By this mechanism, dentists' anxieties about government interference with their professional authority can be smoothed, and their autonomy of practice maintained. The College of Dental Surgeons acts, in effect, as a clearing house, transferring fee accounts from individual dentists to the provincial Department of Health, where they are processed and a payment list generated for return to the college. A cheque is then drawn on the funds previously made available through the capitation payment received from the government. Ninety-five percent of registered general dental practitioners in Saskatchewan take part in the adolescent program.

Changing Patterns of Oral Health: International Comparisons

An earlier section, reviewing the rationale behind the proposals for a dental plan, described data relating to dental health and indicated that there were substantial socio-economic barriers to the equitable and accessible utilization of dental services. Patterns of access to services related to area of residence, income, and education. This section will review patterns of dental health, the variation in these patterns within populations, and explanations for these variations.

Before pursuing these objectives, two comments are appropriate. Firstly, if trends are to be examined and comparisons made, there is a need for repeated cross-sectional surveys of the same population using the same methods and procedures. Over the past 30 years, oral-health surveys have been conducted on children and adults in the United Kingdom at ten-year intervals. Secondly, there is the need for a reference point against which countries and populations can be compared. This has been provided by the World Health Organization, which has developed a series of global indicators of oral health that are achievable by the year 2000. These are:

1. At age 5-6 years 50 percent of children should have no dental decay.
2. At age 12 years children should have an average of three decayed, missing and filled teeth.
3. At age 18 years 85 percent of this group should retain all their permanent teeth.
4. At age 35-44 years 75 percent of this group should have at least 20 natural teeth.
5. At age 65 years 50 percent of this group should have at least 20 natural teeth (Barmes, 1983, p. 60).

Throughout this section the second goal — that children aged twelve years should have an average of three decayed, missing, and filled teeth (DMFT) — will be used for comparison.

In global terms there has been a basic difference in trends in oral health between the technically developed countries and the developing countries. In the technically developed countries there has been a dramatic reduction in dental decay among children, while in developing countries there has been, with a few exceptions, an increase in dental decay among children (Beagrie, 1986, p. 53). Using the goal that children aged twelve should have an average of three DMFT, data available in 1986 showed that:

1. In 58 developing countries and 7 technically developed countries the goal had been achieved.
2. In 32 developing countries and 21 technically developed countries the goals had yet to be achieved.
3. Eleven of these technically developed countries would achieve the goal, given the current trend in decreases in dental decay.
4. Sixteen of the developing countries from the first group had deteriorating trends in dental decay, which would mean that what had been achieved would be lost i.e., the average would move from below to above DMFT.

These changing patterns of dental decay in developing countries have been related to changes in sugar consumption. Akpabio (1987, p. 23) notes that sugar consumption in developing countries is rising and points out that in Nigeria, for example, between 1969 and 1975 total sugar consumption rose by 70 percent from 96 million kilograms to 137 million kilograms. He further argues that sugar is one of the first foods to respond to a rise in income in low-income countries, and that this will be mainly consumed in processed foods such as soft drinks, biscuits, and cakes.

The reduction in decay in technically developed countries has been ascribed to the use of fluoride in toothpaste, improved awareness about health in general and oral hygiene in particular, changes in the nutritional value of food, and the increased prescribing of antibiotics. The role of the increased availability of dental services has been questioned (Ryan & Grainger, 1983, p. 7; Graves & Stamm, 1985, p. 698).

Stamm (1978, p. 408) has noted that there exists a paucity of data about the prevalence, incidence, and distribution of dental disease in Canada. However, using the WHO goal it is possible to make the following comments:

1. Within Saskatchewan the average number of DMFT in 12-year-olds had declined from 5.23 in 1978 to 3.67 in 1984 (Young, 1986, p. 828).
2. Within Alberta the average number of DMFT in 13-year-olds had declined from 4.74 in 1978 to 3.09 in 1985 (Lizaire et al., 1987, p. 847).
3. Within Quebec the average number of DMFT in 13-to 14-year-old children had declined from 8.9 in 1977 to 6.01 in 1984 (Payette et al., 1988, p. 186).

Payette et al., (1988, p. 188) also report DMFT data within Canadian provinces, which range from 6.5 to 3.1. Most provinces have averages towards the top end of the range, while Ontario reported the lowest average. These surveys were carried out at the beginning of the 1980s. It may be concluded from this data that Canada constitutes one of the 32 technically developed countries that has yet to achieve the WHO goal for oral health in its twelve-year-old population, and that the provinces of Alberta and Ontario will probably have achieved the goal by the year 2000.

In comparison, the 1983 average DMFT in the United Kingdom for twelve-year-olds was 3.1, ranging from 2.9 in England to 4.8 in Northern Ireland (Todd & Dodd, 1985, p. 38). Further, twelve-year-old children from families of non-manual occupational backgrounds were less likely to have experienced decay and were less likely to have had teeth extracted.

This variation between oral health and socio-economic status has been reported consistently. Carmichael et al., (1980, p. 163) reviewed 40 studies from technically developed countries investigating socio-economic status and decay experience. Thirty-three reported a higher decay experience in the lower social classes. Akpabio (1987, p. 23) reviews literature that suggests that in developing countries children from a higher socio-economic status will have greater decay experience because of their families' greater access to sugar.

This socio-economic patterning has also been reported in Canada:

1. A survey carried out in Atlantic Canada to assess the dental treatment needs of children aged 6-7 and 13-14 years showed that 21 percent of the younger age group needed no treatment. Additional data also showed that children from rural areas, with parents possessing below-average levels of education and occupational background, were likely to need more treatment than their counterparts from urban areas with parents of above-average levels of education and occupational background (Banting et al., 1985, p. 20).
2. Stamm et al., (1980, p. 130) showed that in Quebec, decay experience had a clear relationship with a child's socio-economic status, average DMFT ranging from 6.4 for children in Blishen Group 1 to 9.7 for children in Blishen Group 7.

Thus, while there is less overall decay experience and need for treatment, the socially disadvantaged continue to be penalized. Various competing explanations for this inequality have been presented (Townsend & Davidson, 1982). One explanation attempts to explain it in terms of knowledge, attitudes, and behaviour. People from lower socio-economic groups are less healthy because they indulge in more health-damaging behaviours, are less knowledgeable, and do not plan their lives. This assumes in the case of dental decay that individuals can choose to change their diet (reduce their sugar consumption) once they are made aware of the consequences. This kind of explanation tends to be favoured by health professionals. Shaw et al., (1987, p. 201) ascribe the poor oral health of a community of Cree Indians in Northern Quebec to poor parental co-operation following the introduction of a preventative program.

A more challenging explanation argues that inequalities in health have their origins in material deprivation. Factors such as poor-quality housing, hazardous domestic environments, occupational hazards, and poverty interact to produce differences. A Swedish study (Embom et al., 1986) compared the oral health of miners to a matched group of white-collar workers. The miners were more likely to report jaw problems, which were ascribed to atmospheric pollution and work-induced stress.

The degree to which these inequalities will be reduced by making services more available is questionable. There has been a large increase in the availability of dental services in Saskatchewan since 1972. There has also been an improvement in the decay experience of children. While the availability of dental services has a role to play in providing treatment, it must be emphasized that improvements in dental health have been ascribed to other factors indicated earlier. In addition, the services offered in Saskatchewan have been curative rather than preventative in their approach (Young, 1986, p. 828), focussing on the increased targeting of services for the smaller number of children with dental decay. This approach has only a minor impact on the distribution of disease in a population. Indeed, Beagrie (1986, p. 53) argues that the expansion of dental schools in Canada during the 1960s came *after* the decay rate for Canadian children had peaked in 1950 at 12 DMFT. Dental health was improving before the supply of dentists increased.

Conclusion

This paper has described the background of the development of public dental health services in Saskatchewan and the basis of the arguments used to oppose their introduction by the dental profession. It illustrated the use of an ideology based on claims to knowledge in order to protect the basic attributes of professional status: the autonomy to diagnose disease, prescribe treatment, and delegate duties to other members of the dental team. In seeking to justify this status quo, the dental profession oversimplified and distorted the reality of dental health for the population of Saskatchewan. Objective evaluations have demonstrated the ability of the Saskatchewan Health Dental Plan to provide a better quality of treatment than that given by dentists. Furthermore, this care has been provided at a lower cost for more members of the child population than in other provinces.

A number of factors have resulted in changes to the operation of the plan. These have included changing disease patterns, and increasing number of dentists, and growing provincial deficits. Initially these factors resulted in dentists becoming involved in the plan in a way designed to preserve the appearance of professional power. In 1987 however, the provincial government of the day effectively eliminated the Dental Plan as part of a cost–cutting strategy. That government, itself committed to privatization and deficit reduction, was more receptive to the ideological claims of the dental profession. One consequence of this was that those dental services previously provided free for schoolchildren under the plan were no longer provided or provided by privately practising dentists on a fee-for-service basis.

An initial argument of this chapter was that the narrow occupational interests of the health profession may not necessarily coincide with the wider, public interest. This has been demonstrated in one particular case, where control of the dental division of labour was sought. Other examples exist to further support this argument: the original introduction of the dental nurse in New Zealand (Gruebbel, 1950, p. 425) and the experiment with a dental auxiliary in the United Kingdom (Hallett, 1950, p. 39) provoked similar opposition from the dental profession in those countries.

The introduction of medical-care insurance has shown the medical profession to be concerned about defending its mandate to define the terms of medical practice. During 1962, medical doctors in Saskatchewan went on strike to resist the introduction of medical-care insurance by the provincial government. The intention of the legislation was to provide universal coverage for all of the population and to furnish a comprehensive range of medical-service benefits, financed through government revenues. The chief arguments used by doctors related to interference with professional standards and independence. Badgley and Wolfe point out that doctors "wanted a monopoly only if they controlled it, and did not have to negotiate the price of the product they were selling to consumers" (1967, p. 46).

A comparison between the ideology expressed by the Canadian Medical Association in opposing publicly administered and financed medical-care insurance and the ideology of the dental profession in Saskatchewan reveals a similar emphasis on the importance of professional control of change (Croucher, 1976, p. 97; Blishen, 1969, p. 151).

The introduction of the National Health Service in the United Kingdom in 1948 provides a third example of "parochial" professional attitudes. General practitioners went on strike to protest its introduction and, again, its aim was to make good health care available to the whole population without financial barrier (Murray, 1971, p. 1).

These examples suggest that broad comparisons may be made between the ideologies used by different health professions when the changes in health-care policy introduced are perceived as challenges to their autonomy. On these occasions the needs of the public are displaced by more parochial occupational concerns.

Above all it is very clear that a successful approach to oral health problems, such as those found in Saskatchewan, does not require the current focus on the lengthy training of dentists. The primary emphasis should be on preventing oral disease by developing an integrated range of different categories of oral-health workers, rather than producing dentists with clinical expertise.

Study Questions

1. Autonomy has been described as a key attribute of professional status. Find examples of its use by other professionals, analyzing why it is being used in each situation.
2. In Saskatchewan, the subordinate members of the dental division of labour, that is, dental hygienists, readily accepted the claims made by dentists. Need this always be the case? Find examples where this ready acceptance has not happened, and try to determine why.
3. It has been suggested that a major source of an ideology is in the process of professional socialization. What other sources of ideology are there, and what role might they play?
4. What data are available on dental health in your province? Have any changes in the organization of dental services evolved as an outcome of these data? Analyze the role played by the dental profession in these changes.
5. What other factors besides the availability of dental services are important for the promotion of good oral health?

Recommended Reading

Davis, P. (1980). *The social context of dentistry*. London: Croom Helm.

Freidson, E. (1973). Professions and occupational principle. In E. Freidson (Ed.), *Professions and their prospects*. New York: Sage Publications.

Locker, D. (1989). *An introduction to behavioural sciences and dentistry*. London: Routledge.

Taylor, M.G. (1960). The role of the medical profession in formulation and execution of public policy. *Canadian Journal of Economics and Political Science*, 26, 108-127.

Thomson, H.E., Mann, J.R., & McPhail, C.W.B. (1973). Dentists' attitudes to prepaid children's dental care programs and expanded duty dental auxiliaries in Saskatchewan. *Journal of the Canadian Dental Association*, 39, 47-54.

Wardwell, W.I. (1972). Limited, marginal and quasi-practitioners. In H.E. Freeman, S. Levine, & L.G. Reeder (Eds.), *Handbook of medical sociology*. Englewood Cliffs: Prentice-Hall.

References

Akpabio, S.P. (1987). *Achieving oral health by the year 2000*. London: University College.

Ambrose, E.P., Hord, A.B., & Simpson, W.J. (1976). *A quality evaluation of specific dental services provided by the Saskatchewan dental plan final report*. Regina: Saskatchewan Health Dental Plan.

Badgley, R.F., & Wolfe, S. (1967). *Doctors' strike: Medical care and conflict in Saskatchewan*. Toronto: Macmillan.

Banting, D.W., Hunt, A.M., & Baskerville, J.C. (1985). *Summary report: Atlantic Canada children's oral health survey*. London: Faculty of Dentistry, University of Western Ontario.

Barmes, D.E. (1983). Indicators for oral health and their implications for developing countries. *International Dental Journal*, 33, 60-66.

Beagrie, G.S. (1986). Dental manpower. *Journal of the Canadian Dental Association*, 52, 52-55.

Blishen, B.R. (1969). *Doctors and doctrines: The ideology of medical care in Canada*. Toronto: University of Toronto Press.

Bottomore, T. (1971). Class structure and class consciousness. In I. Meszaros (Ed.), *Aspects of history and class consciousness*. London: Routledge and Kegan Paul.

Canadian Dental Association. (1968). *Survey of dental practice, 1968*. Toronto: Canadian Dental Association, Bureau of Statistics.

Canadian Dental Association. (1973). *Brief submitted to the minister's advisory committee on dental care for children, province of Saskatchewan*. Ottawa: Canadian Dental Association.

Canadian Dental Association. (1981). Saskatchewan facing manpower crisis. *Journal of the Canadian Dental Association*, 47, 630-631.

Canadian Dental Association. (1982). New Saskatchewan health minister pledges consultation with dental colleges. *Journal of the Canadian Dental Association*, 48, 500.

Carmichael, C., Rugg-Gunn, A., French, A., & Cranage, J. (1980). The effect of fluoridation upon the relationship between caries experience and social class in 5-year-old children in Newcastle and Northumberland. *British Dental Journal*, 149, 163-167.

Chebib, F.S. (1973). *Dentists in Canada*. Winnipeg: University of Winnipeg, Publications Office.

College of Dental Surgeons of Saskatchewan (1973). *Brief submitted to the minister's advisory committee on dental care for children, province of Saskatchewan*. Saskatoon: College of Dental Surgeons of Saskatchewan.

College of Dental Surgeons of Saskatchewan. (1975). *Annual register*. Saskatoon: College of Dental Surgeons of Saskatchewan.

Croucher, R. (1976). *Professionalism and dental care legislation in Saskatchewan*. Unpublished Master's Thesis. Saskatoon: University of Saskatchewan.

Daniels, A.K. (1973). How free should professions be? In E. Freidson (Ed.), *Professions and their prospects*. New York: Sage Publications.

Davis, P. (1980). *The social context of dentistry*. London: Croom Helm.

Dibble, V.K. (1963). Occupations and ideologies. *American Journal of Sociology, 68*, 229-241.

Embom, L., Magnusson, T., & Wall, G. (1986). Occlusal wear in miners. *Swedish Dental Journal, 10*, 166-170.

Freidson, E. (1970). *Profession of medicine*. New York: Dodd, Mead and Co.

Goode, W.J. (1957). Community within a community: The professions. *American Sociological Review, 22*, 194-200.

Graves, R.C., & Stamm, J.W. (1985). Decline of dental cares: What occurred and will it continue? *Journal of the Canadian Dental Association, 51*, 693-699.

Gruebbel, A.O. (1950). Dental public health services in New Zealand. *Journal of the American Dental Association, 41*, 275-283; 422-436.

Hall, R.M. (1969). *Occupations and the social structure*. Englewood Cliffs: Prentice-Hall.

Hallett, G.E.M. (1950). Public dental service in Great Britain with reference to the New Zealand scheme. *British Dental Journal, 90*, 38-41.

House, R.K., Johnson, G.C., & Edwards, F.A. (1983). Manpower supply study scenarios for the future: Dental manpower to 2001. *Journal of the Canadian Dental Association, 49*, 85-98.

Hughes, E.C. (1958). *Men and their work*. Glencoe: Free Press.

Josie, G.H. (Ed.). (1973). *Report on basic Canadian data. World Health Organization international collaborative study of medical care utilization*. Saskatoon: University of Saskatchewan,

Department of Social and Preventative Medicine.

Lewis, D.W. (1981). *Performance of the Saskatchewan health dental plan, 1974-80*. Regina: Saskatchewan Health Dental Plan.

Lizaire, A.L., Hargreaves, J.A., Finnigan, P.D., & Thompson, G.W. (1987). Oral health status of 13-year-old school children in Alberta, Canada. *Journal of the Canadian Dental Association, 53*, 845-848.

McCormick, C.H. (1966). Availability and utilization of dental services by rural Manitoba children. *Journal of the Canadian Dental Association, 32*, 275-280.

McDermott, R.E., & Oles, R.D. (1982). Dentist-to-population ratios in Saskatchewan: A realistic appraisal. *Journal of the Canadian Dental Association, 48*, 721-723.

McFarlane, B.A. (1964). *Dental manpower in Canada*. Royal Commission on Health Services. Ottawa: Queen's Printer.

McPhail, C.W.B. (1976). Personal communication with author.

McPhail, C.W.B., Curry, T.M., Hazelton, R.E., Paynter, K.J., & Williamson, R.G. (1972). The geographic pathology of dental disease in Canadian Central Arctic populations. *Journal of the Canadian Dental Association, 38*, 288-296.

Murray, D.S. (1971). *Why a national health service?* London: Pemberton Books.

Payette, M., Plante, R., & L'Heureux, J-B. (1988). Comparison of dental caries and oral hygiene indices for 13-14-year-old Quebec children between 1977 and 1984. *Journal of the Canadian Dental Association, 54*, 183-190.

Ringen, K. (1979). The new ferment in national health policies: The case of Norway's nutrition and food policy. *Social Science and Medicine, 13C*, 33-41.

Ryan, K., & Grainger, R.M. (1983). Reduction in dental caries prevalence and treatment needs for elementary school children from 1972-1982. *Journal of Ontario Dental Association, 60,* (5), 7.

Saskatchewan (1972-74). *Debates and proceedings of the legislature*. Regina: Queen's Printer.

Saskatchewan Dental Hygienists' Association. (1973). *Brief submitted to the minister's advisory committee on dental care for children, province of Saskatchewan*. Regina: Queen's Printer.

Saskatchewan Department of Health. (1972). *A proposal for a dental program for the children of Saskatchewan*. Regina: Queen's Printer.

Saskatchewan Department of Health. (1974). *Health personnel inventory*. Regina: Queen's Printer.

Saskatchewan Department of Health. (1976). *Saskatchewan health dental plan. Report of first year of operation*. Regina: Queen's Printer.

Shaw, L., Clark, D.C., & Edger, N.P. (1987). The oral health status of Cree children living in Chisasibi, Quebec. *Journal of the Canadian Dental Association*, 53, 201-205.

Stamm, J.W. (1978). An overview of dental care delivery systems in Canada. *International Dental Journal*, 28, 406-420.

Stamm, J.W., Dixter, C.T., & Langlais, R.P. (1980). Principal dental health indices for 13-14-year-old children in Quebec. *Journal of the Canadian Dental Association*, 46, 125-137.

Thomson, H.E., Mann, J.R., & McPhail, C.W.B. (1973). Dentists' attitudes to prepaid children's dental care programs and expanded duty dental auxiliaries in Saskatchewan. *Journal of the Canadian Dental Association*, 39, 47-54.

Todd, J.E. (1975). *Children's dental health in England and Wales, 1973*. London: Her Majesty's Stationery Office.

Todd, J., & Dodd, P. (1985). *Children's dental health in the United Kingdom, 1983*. London: Her Majesty's Stationery Office.

Townsend, P., & Davidson, N. (1982). *Inequalities in health: The black report*. Harmondsworth: Penguin Books.

Young, W. (1986). Targeting preventive services in the Saskatchewan dental plan. *Journal of the Canadian Dental Association*, 52, 827-830.

Chapter 25

Division of Labour in Health Care: Pragmatics and Ethics

Janet Storch, University of Calgary

Introduction

In 1967, an article appeared in the *Archives of General Psychiatry* called "The Doctor-Nurse Game." In this article, Stein, a psychiatrist, described the interactional framework of the doctor-nurse relationship as fitting a game model, noting that the underlying attitudes which demand that this game be played are unfortunate because they create "serious obstacles in the path of meaningful communications between physicians and nonmedical professional groups."

Stein described the "game" as one in which the physician (by tradition) has total responsibility for making decisions regarding management of his patients' treatment. Among the many forms of data the physician uses to guide his decisions are recommendations he receives from the nurse. However, in order to be acceptable, these recommendations have to be provided in such a manner that the nurse does not appear to be insolent. Stein suggested that the object of the game was that the nurse must appear to be passive while taking initiatives and making significant recommendations; the physician, in requesting a recommendation from the nurse, must do so without any appearance of asking for advice; that open disagreement must be avoided at all costs; and that there are rewards and penalties for not playing the game well.

Stein also provided an analysis of the genesis of the game in medical student training wherein the student was led to believe in medical omnipotence and infallibility, which disallowed accepting advice from nonphysicians. Thus, when medical interns became physicians and entered the patient-care units, they were obliged to learn to play this game to succeed. Conversely, nurses were taught the game early in their training, with an indoctrination about the superiority of medical knowledge requiring utmost respect from the subservient nurse. Such a posture disallowed the nurse from making an independent recommendation to the doctor that might be interpreted as questioning the physician's knowledge and insulting or belittling the physician. Stein suggested that the game persisted because of "stereotyped roles of male dominance and female passivity," and because it effectively supported and protected "a rigid organizational structure with the physician in clear authority" (p. 703).

Since Stein's article was written over a quarter century ago, there have been numerous changes in the doctor-nurse relationship. Nurses no longer are required to stand to attention when physicians enter the nursing station or unit; student nurses no longer repeat the Nightingale Pledge, which includes the phrase, "with loyalty will I endeavour to aid the physician in his work . . ."; and there has been a remarkable de-militarization of the hospital as an institution. However, the removal of all these trappings does not necessarily mean that a spirit of true collegiality, collaboration, and mutual respect presently exists among all members of the health-care team, nor that there is open and honest dialogue in a spirit of equality. Further, the concept of patient "ownership" by the physician persists. And while Stein suggested that the "inhibitory effect on open dialogue" among health professionals was "stifling and anti-intellectual," of far greater significance is the fact that such open dialogue and interdisciplinary respect (as well as the perpetuation of physician ownership of the patient) is contrary to good patient care and good outcomes of care.

Although one cannot deny that major advances have been made in the way physician, nurses, physiotherapists, nutritionists, occupational therapists, psychologists, social workers, and chaplains interrelate in the care of patients, these advances are not consistent across regions, across hospitals, or even across hospital and health-care units. Further, current professional legislation and current structures in hospitals and other health agencies continue to support a division of labour in health care that is *not ethical*.

In this chapter, a defence of the hypothesis that *the division of labour in health care is unethical* will be provided by noting how it developed and is perpetuated in Canada; how it violates ethical principles; why there is an imperative for change; what evidence exists for signs of change; and what future directions will be necessary to accomplish the change.

The Division of Labour in Health Care

The "division of labour" is a concept with roots in economics and in sociology. Adam Smith, the eighteenth-century economist, used the term to refer to the "extreme specialization in the process of production that results from subdividing work into limited operations performed by separate workers to raise the productivity of labour." Later, Charles Babbage (1832) noted an added advantage which was to separate work into components, some of which were simpler than others, enabling an employer to purchase cheaper and less-skilled labour to do the simpler jobs rather than expensive skilled workers doing the whole process. While sociologists such as Comte and Durkheim recognized the division of labour as holding the potential to increase social solidarity by creating mutual relationships of dependence between individuals, the potential for divisiveness was also recognized. Marxist sociologists held that it produced social conflict and was the primary cause of social inequality. Many of these sociologists observed the extreme division of labour found in many firms was not technically required for efficiency, but that managers (and others) used it to increase their power in the workplace by weakening the control over production of some skilled workers.

The division of labour in health care in Canada has been profoundly influenced by developments in the United States and the United Kingdom and has been characterized by differentials in power not always congruent with differentials in level of skill. The fact of the dominance of the physician in health care has been well recognized in Canada since the early 1900s. In both the United States and Canada the position of the medical profession has rested on three spheres; the *cultural authority* of medicine, particularly as more scientific approaches to medicine developed in the late 1800s, thereby convincing people of their own inadequacy in dealing with their health problems; the *market authority* of medicine through licensing bodies, limits on medical education, and resistance to salaried positions; and the *political authority* of medicine in its influence on the policies of governments (Starr, 1978).

In the United States in the 1760s, the profession of medicine began to take shape through the work of a small medical elite in urban centres who pushed for medical licensure and medical institutions. Even though this time period predated significant developments in medical science, these medical practitioners were intent on confining licensure to one type of practitioner to exclude midwives, homeopaths, eclectics, and other irregulars. Until the 1870s, this group struggled against considerable odds in its attempts to control the practice of medicine, but with the achievements of medical science between 1890 and 1920, the rise of medicine to its modern status and authority was possible. These same problems of weeding out irregular practitioners and establishing a unified and homogeneous occupation characterized Canadian medicine in the late 1800s. Prior to Confederation, legislation was passed in Upper Canada in 1865 creating a college of Physicians and Surgeons in Canada, and prior to that in 1847, a similar act was passed in Lower Canada. Although these acts still included homeopaths and eclectics, their power and potential to practise increasingly diminished. The legislation was challenged from without and from within, particularly since Canadian medical schools became affiliated with universities (Coburn, Torrance, & Kaufert, 1983).

In addition to suppressing quacks and improving medical training, the medical profession also "gained dominance and restricted activities of other health occupations such as pharmacy" (p. 412). Pharmacists had been able to counter-prescribe, thereby acting as primary-care healers and sharing a function of doctors, unity the early 1900s when (under considerable pressure) they "struck a tacit bargain with medicine," giving up the right to counter-prescribe in exchange for an agreement from doctors not to dispense drugs. Prior to this event, midwifery had been gradually outlawed, first in towns then in cities. Most of the other relatively new health occupations came within the official medical division of labour, for example, physiotherapy, occupational therapy, medical laboratory, x-ray technology — these were born under medical control and thus became labelled as "para-medical" occupations. The terminology here is of interest in itself as the power of vocabulary is consequential. Technically, one would have assumed that these emerging professions, rather than being labelled para-medical, might have been labelled "para-patient" occupations to indicate the primacy of their obligation to the patient.

Nursing was an older, recognized occupation but, like pharmacy, began to restrict its functions to take a recognized but subordinate place in the official division of labour, thus by the early 1900s becoming subordinate to the medical profession. It is of interest to note that in 1901 there were 280 nurses in Canada compared to 5 422 physicians and surgeons, but by 1921 (twenty years later) there were over 20 000 nurses (Coburn, 1987). The nurse to physician ratio remains roughly 4:1. Before 1900, nurses worked largely in private duty, but as hospitals developed, private duty practice decreased and nursing became increasingly subject to physician and hospital control, including a strong medical influence on nursing education and delineation of nursing practice and an expected loyalty to physician and to hospital (Coburn, 1988).

But, over the years, there has been a progressive drive toward greater independence and autonomy, precipitated in part by a felt dissonance between absolute loyalty to the physician and hospital and an obligation to the patient. The former hospital directives and mottoes of hospital schools of nursing which commanded silence regarding the internal affairs of the hospital, including physician errors (Coburn, 1987) were simply no longer viable, and an impetus to change and to effect more "professional" alliances became a pressing matter. The code of ethics adopted by the CNA in 1985 and revised in 1991 is testimony to a profound shift in allegiances (*Code of Ethics for Nursing, 1991*). For example, one set of obligations in the code is that nurses must not "participate in efforts to deceive or mislead clients about the cause of an alleged harm or injury resulting from unethical or incompetent practice." This is a far cry from the silence traditionally demanded of nurses.

Thus "the major trend in relationships between nursing and medicine has been the ever-increasing separation of nursing from medicine" and nursing's increasing occupational autonomy (Coburn, 1987). In contrast to the old deference, there is often open antagonism, conflict, and lack of collaboration. Nurses find their circumscribed role increasingly difficult, given the tremendous advances that have been made in their own nursing knowledge and skill development. They, and other health professionals, are restricted in the application of their knowledge and skill by structural (i.e., legal, traditional, bureaucratic) barriers.

In 1990, another article was published, this one in the *New England Journal of Medicine* entitled "The Doctor-Nurse Game Revisited." Stein and two medical colleagues noted that one of the players (the nurse) in the Doctor-Nurse Game had decided unilaterally to stop playing it. Nurses were attempting to change nursing to move from dependency to mutual interdependency and autonomy. According to Stein and his colleagues, these changes were being accomplished through education in colleges and universities. The effect of this change on nurses was that they felt freer to challenge and question physicians, while physicians responded to the change with feelings of puzzlement, confusion, betrayal, and sometimes anger. Physicians who had not perceived nurses to be subservient in the first place were confused about the nurses' efforts to gain greater equality. Some physicians, who perceived the nurse's role as primarily carrying out doctors' orders, concluded that nurses had stopped "doing nursing" and preferred to work with licensed practical nurses or nursing assistants who did as they were told. And while most nurses and physicians are gaining some comfort with the changed relationship, some still prefer the former hierarchical model which provided greater security in "knowing one's place" (Ornstein, 1990).

Why Is this Division of Labour Unethical?

The division of labour in health care in unethical because it contravenes a set of ethical principles: justice, beneficence, respect, and autonomy.

In time of shrinking resources in health care, the inability to maximize the use of valuable human resources in patient care is unjust. Legal and traditional practice restrictions, which disallow nurses from serving as primary-care providers to the elderly, the worried well, and numerous other populations where the fit of knowledge and skill to need is excellent, must be viewed as unethical.

Fragmentation of care, buck passing, and lack of holistic care are logical outcomes of systems that highly regulate which professionals may perform set practices, independent of the patient's pressing problems and independent of matching knowledge and skills to patient need. More harm than good is often the logical result, and the ability to benefit the patient is restricted.

Lack of mutual respect for the contributions each professional can make to the health-care team is yet another ethical problem of the current division of labour in health care. Competent, capable, and autonomous judgements of other health professionals are frequently disallowed, to a point where many capable and competent health profession-als are convinced (indoctrinated to believe) that they are incompetent to make those judgements — only a physician can do so. In effect, they are disempowered members of the health-care team. How could this sort of structure, this division of labour, possibly be ethical?

For numerous reasons, including issues of justice, respect, and beneficence, a change in interprofessional relationships in health care would seem urgently needed. The degree of interprofessional conflict, competition, and mutual devalution is not acceptable if the goal is quality patient care. Better collaboration and communication are not just ideals to pursue for the sake of peace in the health-care family. Rather, collaboration and good communication have a positive impact on patient care since many areas of expertise are essential for humane and competent care.

One research study documented the effects of nurse–physician collaboration on the outcomes for patients in intensive care units (Knaus, Draper, Wagner, & Zimmerman, 1986). When the outcomes of 5 030 patients from the intensive care units of thirteen hospitals were studied, some significant differences between predicted and observed death rates were found. After controlling for numerous variables, differences appeared to relate to the interaction and communication between physicians and nurses. "As a general rule, in the five best hospitals, physicians respected the nurse's capabilities and readily listened to and trusted what the nurse had to say regarding a patient's condition and course of treatment. As a result, the nurses would not hesitate to convey information to the physician" (Draper, 1987). Other research findings have also supported these conclusions (Baggs et al., 1992). Since collaboration allows input from two or more different types of health professionals, it can lead to better outcomes because decisions are based on more complete information and shared decision making.

Signs of Change and the Means of Change

A number of recent reports, position papers, and commissions across professional associations and across the provinces have highlighted the need for better collaboration between physicians and other members of the health-care team. Throughout the profes-sional journals there is a call for increased collaboration for more harmonious relations for better patient care. If one believes that there is a twelve-step program of rehabilitation of these relationships similar to the twelve-step program for alcoholics, then at least the first step — that is, acknowledging that there is a problem and being able to talk about it — has been reached.

Fundamental to improved relationships is a mutual respect and trust. This necessitates a clear understanding of the unique knowledge and skill of each type of health professional and a clarification of expectations. It also means valuing the expertise each discipline has to offer. For example, historically, medicine has focussed on diagnosis and treatment of disease as defined in biophysical terms, a very worthwhile and valuable expertise; nursing has focussed on responses to illness — on "the subjective experiences and practical problems experienced by patients," also a very worthwhile and valuable set of knowledge and skills (Campbell-Heider & Pollock, 1987).

To accomplish change that leads to respect and trust in one another's knowledge and skills, the education of health professionals would have to be modified to increase opportunities for dialogue and mutual decision making. Multidisciplinary courses in communications, bioethics, and other endeavours are well-suited to increase the sensitivity of students to one another's values and beliefs. Such sensitivity enables students-turned-professionals to see other's positions as not wrong or better, but different. Doctors and nurses, for example, do think differently about patient care, and they do approach patients from a different ethical perspective (Grundstein-Amado, 1992; Pike, 1991). These differences become problematic only when health professionals refuse to take time to understand each other.

Institutional structures and processes tend to foster and perpetuate the current division of labour and diminish the team spirit in health care. For example, the standard practice in many hospitals is that each patient has a designated physician as specified by a sign on the patient's door, a doctor's name on the chart, and an arm bracelet linking doctor and patient. The implication here is one of ownership — ownership by a physician. Other health professions act by permission of that physician or his designate and all activities are then driven by the physician's signature. This sort of linkage system cannot function to ensure the best use of human resources, the best sort of collaboration, or the best outcomes for patient care.

A structure presently in the process of adoption in many Canadian hospitals is an organizational structure called the "Johns Hopkins model." In this model, each specialty area in the hospital is designated as a functional unit headed by a physician chief who reports to the chief executive officer of the hosptial. Reporting to the physicians are a nursing director and an administrator; these three form a triumvirate accountable for the costs of the unit. The model has been adopted by many hospital administrators, who see it as a means to cost control by holding the physician chiefly accountable for costs of the unit. However, notably absent from consideration in its implementation is the fact that it is a return to clear subordination of nurses and all other health professionals. As one author asks: "Why does it appear to be so difficult to involve physicians in cost control unless they are granted final authority? Surely in this day and age, all professionals must accept cost control as a facet of their daily individual practice" (Besel, 1988). Another author adds that "A coordination technique which subordinates significant elements of decision-making regarding nursing resources to medicine . . . will inevitably compromise the commitment and professionalism of nursing" (Meilicke, 1990).

If better collaboration is to become a reality, institutional structures must support collaborative work. There must be "equality or parity among partners" of the health-care team and enough control over "part of an enterprise to make sharing a meaningful concept." To accomplish this goal, there would have to be equal power to influence decisions relating to caregiving through acceptance of shared priorities and regulatory stands (Fagin, 1988). A recent pilot study on clinical ethics committees in hospitals in Canada (Storch & Griener, 1992) provides initial evidence that much remains to be done to improve interdisciplinary dialogue and decision making in matters of ethics. The perceptions of physicians, nurses, social workers, chaplains, and others were markedly disparate about the utility of ethics committees for enhanced ethical decision making and about the value of interdisciplinary discussion.

Inevitably, achieving better collaboration will also have to involve changes in legislation to permit all health professionals to utilize their knowledge and skills to meet patients' needs, rather than legislation which serves professional needs. The restrictive power of the Medical Profession Act, among others, must give way to "enabling" legislation for all health professionals. Codes of ethics may also have to be modified to better recognize and account for other health providers.

There are promising signs of change that will need to be cultivated to ensure their positive outcomes. Many of these changes are being precipitated by recognition of scarce resources requiring creativity and fresh thinking about how to maintain and improve the quality of care provided as resources decrease. Discussions around the Barer and Stoddart Report (1991) regarding utilization of medical resources have raised awareness about different modes of delivery involving other health-care professionals. Many provincial goverments have also begun to look at more efficient and effective ways to deploy human resources in health care. And concepts such as case management have been adopted in many hospitals, in many instances leading to improved collaboration on the health-care team.

According to Webster's dictionary, collaboration can have two meanings: (1) the act of working together, as in writing a book; (2) cooperation with the enemy. Pike (1991) describes collaboration between physicians and nurses on one unit of Beth Israel

Hospital in which the meaning of collaboration came to life. She states: "Collaboration has come to imply trust and respect not only of one another, but also of the work and perspectives each contributes." It suggests "a bond, a union, a depth of caring about each other and the relationship. It incorporates notions of a synergistic alliance that maximizes the contributions of each participant" (p. 352). There is a sharing of responsibility and accountability for patient care.

Too often nurses assert that they are the ones who care while physicians are preoccupied with cure. But when nurses and physicians work together in true partnership rather than inequality, nurses soon discover that "they are not alone in their caring . . . that physicians also care deeply about their patients, and also agonize over moral dilemmas. Unfortunately, like their nurse colleagues, most have previously done so in isolation" (p. 354). When nurses understand that this is so, they are able to express their concerns about patients and communicate "with dignity, not contempt."

Conclusions

Changing the division of labour in health care will require political will, since traditional values and power structures will need to change. Change will be required in institutional structures from self-serving to patient-serving modes. Change will be required in thinking about health-care teams, with the potential of rotating captains or (using a new analogy) quarterbacks. Above all, change will be needed to truly *value* the contribution of each discipline comprising the team.

The climate for enhanced interprofessional relationships is ripe and the potential for a more ethical division of labour is possible. With greater refinement in measuring outcomes, assessing processes, and clarifying inputs will come greater precision in determining the level and type of knowledge and skill required by each group of clients/ patients. This precision will allow matching patient needs with health professional knowledge and skills so that the talents and abilities of all involved in health care are maximized. Such alignments will ensure a more ethical division of labour.

★ *This text was first printed in* Humane Medicine, *published by the Canadian Medical Association.*

Study Questions

1. How did a division of labour in health care evolve in Canada, particularly with reference to nursing tasks and medical tasks?
2. Is the Doctor-Nurse Game a suitable analogy to physician-nurse interaction? If so, why? If not, why not?
3. How is the division of labour in health care perpetuated?
4. Would you agree that the division of labour is a matter of ethics?

Recommended Reading

Coburn, D. (1988). The development of Canadian nursing: Professionalization and proletarianization. *International Journal of Health Services*, 18, (3), 437-456.

Coburn, D., Torrance, G., & Kaufert, J. (1983). Medical dominance in Canada in historical perspective: The rise and fall of medicine? *International Journal of Health Services*, 13, (3), 407-432.

Stein, L. (1967). The doctor-nurse game. *Archives of General Psychiatry*, 16, 699-703. Also published in *American Journal of Nursing (1968)*, 68, (1), 101-105.

Storch, J., & Griener, G. (1992). Ethics committees in Canadian hospitals: Report of the 1990 pilot study. Healthcare Management Forum, 5, (1), 19-26.

References

Baggs, J.G., Ryan, S.A., Phelps, C., Richeson, C.E., & Johnson, J.E. (1992). The association between interdisciplinary collaboration and patient outcomes in a medical intensive care unit. *Heart and Lung*, 21, (1), 18-24.

Barer, M., & Stoddart, G. (1991). *Toward integrated medical resource policies for Canada*. Report prepared for the Federal/Provincial/Territorial Conference of Deputy Ministers of Health. Ottawa: Health and Welfare.

Besel, L. (1988). Beyond the Johns Hopkins model. In L. Besel & R. Stock (Eds.), *Benchmarks*, 2, (pp. 1-12). Toronto: Carswell.

Campbell-Heider, N., & Pollock, D. (1987). Barriers to physician-nurse collegiality: An anthropological perspective. *Social Sciences and Medicine*, 25, (5), 421-425.

Coburn, D. (1987). I see and I am silent: A short history of nursing in Ontario. In D. Coburn et al., (Eds.), *Health and Canadian society* (2nd ed.), (pp. 441-462). Markham: Fitzhenry & Whiteside.

Coburn, D. (1988). The development of Canadian nursing: professionalization and proletarianization. *International Journal of Health Services*, 18, (3), 437-456.

Coburn, D., Torrance, G., & Kaufert, J. (1983). Medical dominance in Canada in historical perspective: The rise and fall of medicine? *International Journal of Health Services*, 13, (3), 407-432.

Code of ethics for nursing. (1991). Ottawa: Canadian Nurses' Association.

Draper, E.A. (1987). Effects of nurse-physician collaboration and nursing standards on ICU patients' outcomes. *Current Concepts in Nursing*, 1, (4), 2-9.

Fagin, C. (1988). Why the quick fix won't fix today's nursing shortage. *Inquiry*, 25, 309-314.

Grundstein-Amado, R. (1992). Differences in ethical decision-making processes among nurses and doctors. *Journal of Advanced Nursing*, 17, 129-137.

Knaus, W.A., Draper, E.A., Wagner, D.P., & Zimmerman, J.E. (1986). An evaluation of outcome from intensive care in major medical centers. *Annals of Internal Medicine*, 104, 410-418.

Meilicke, C. (1990). Nurses and physicians in the modern hospital: Watering the garden. *Canadian Journal of Nursing Administration*, 3, (4), 19-22.

Ornstein, H. (1990). Collaborative practice between Ontario nurses and physicians: Is it possible? *Canadian Journal of Nursing Administration*, 3, (4), 10-14.

Pike, A. (1991). Moral outrage and moral discourse in nurse-physician collaboration. *Journal of Professsional Nursing*, 7, (6), 351-363.

Starr, P. (1982). *The social transformation of American medicine*. New York: Basic Books.

Stein, L. (1967). The doctor-nurse game. *Archives of General Psychiatry*, 16, 699-703. Also published in *American Journal of Nursing*, (1968) 68, (1), 101-105.

Stein, L., Watts, D., & Howell, T. (1990). The doctor-nurse game revisited. *The New England Journal of Medicine*, 322, (8), 546-549.

Storch, J., & Griener, G. (1992). Ethics committees in Canadian hospitals: Report of the 1990 pilot study. *Healthcare Management Forum*, 5, (1), 19-26.

Part Eight

Nurses' Education and Work

Part Eight

Introduction

There has been considerable change in the form and content of nursing education and work. The ramifications of these changes are discussed in this section.

Rejecting theories of modernization and industrialization and stressing the value of a historical materialist and feminist approach, Warburton and Carroll, in Chapter 26, analyze class and gender implications of hospital nursing by placing it firmly within industrial and domestic social relations that are capitalist and patriarchal. Particular emphasis is placed on nurses' subordination to male physicians and hospital administrators. The class and gender composition of Canadian nursing is illustrated with Canadian census data, and materials from recent research on Canadian nursing are used to examine the impact of managerial strategies on the nursing labour process, especially those taken in response to the prevailing fiscal crisis of the capitalist state. Nurses' commitment to professionalism and the more recent shift to unionism are studied in light of their exposure to a process of proletarianization that puts them into situations resembling those of industrial workers. For many of them, this leads to increased class consciousness. Gender issues, however, are becoming more prominent in this field and it may well be that, as in other struggles involving workers in institutions of social reproduction, the pursuit of justice and equality for women will become a major field for political action in the coming decades.

The demand for improvements in the education of nurses has been a continuing focal point in nurses' quest for professional status. Wotherspoon, in Chapter 27, examines the relationship between the development of nursing education in Canada and the nature of control over the nursing profession.

It is argued that concepts of nurses' professionalism are limited by their uncritical acceptance of social structures and occupational practices. Alternatively, it is proposed that nursing be conceptualized according to the social relations that develop around the employment of nurses in health-care work. Viewed in this way, nursing education can be understood as an arena within which competing conceptions of nursing are given shape.

Data reveal that while nurses in this century have made substantial improvements in income levels and working conditions, their subordinate status has been maintained by corporate, state, and medical intervention in health-care policy and nursing education. Despite nurses' efforts to improve their educational qualifications and overall quality of their training programs, serious inadequacies remain on both accounts. In conclusion, Wotherspoon states that if present trends continue, nurses may become channelled into two separate streams — a highly educated, male-dominated elite, and a feminized pool of less educated nurse practitioners.

Campbell, in Chapter 28, discusses the structure of stress in nurses' work. This chapter is based on research that focusses on the document-based control methods whereby nurses' labour processes can be subordinated to fiscal restraint policies. Hospital nursing in Canada has been reorganized during the last decade by, and in response to, the introduction of documentary systems of managing nurses' work. Management priorities emphasize increased efficiency and productivity — but do so at a cost to both nurses' and patients' well-being. The stress nurses feel arises not only from an increased pace of work, but through losing control over the quality of care they are able to deliver. Nursing management technology, such as patient classification, flexible staffing methodologies, and documentary assessment of nursing "quality," even as they improve hospital administration and bring nursing into the era of modern document-based administrative practices, externalize control and bypass nurses' professional judgement.

The impact of the oft-held view that nursing is women's work, that it taps into "female" characteristics and is thus a woman's job, is explored by Stelling in Chapter 29. Using data gathered from two studies, Stelling proposes that many of the problems facing nurses today stem from this association. It is argued that nurses' complaints about being too busy and not having enough time to do nursing are less about time than about their lack of autonomy and ability to control the definition of their work — time, then, is a metaphor for work and control.

To date, much of the existing data on risk and work hazards has focussed on workers employed in mining and manufacturing, traditionally male-dominated fields. In Chapter 30, Walters examines the risks nurses associate with their work and the ways they react to these risks. The data, drawn from interviews with 123 nurses, yields some interesting conclusions. Very few nurses, although aware of hazards in their work, pursued issues that worried them. Moreover, collective expression of their concerns through processes established by occupational health and safety legislation was rare. Despite their recognition of hazards, nurses presented little challenge to conventional definitions of acceptable risk. Using their accounts, factors that shape their constructions of risk are discussed, as is the nature of workers' participation in occupational health and safety. In particular, the constraints arising from social conditions in the workplace, the content of professional ideology, and the influence of gender are emphasized. It is these factors that help to stifle nurses' concerns.

Chapter 26

Class and Gender
in Nursing

Rennie Warburton & William K. Carroll, University of Victoria

Introduction

In the analysis of health-care systems, nursing is of obvious importance since nurses provide most of the direct care that hospital patients receive. But the work that nurses do has implications reaching well beyond the issue of health-care delivery. This chapter analyzes the place of nursing within the social relations of capitalist society, drawing out some implications for the consciousness and action of nurses as primarily female workers.

Until recently, sociological approaches to nursing were simply applications of concepts embedded in the theory of "industrial society." According to this approach, in the past two centuries human societies have been undergoing a process of "modernization," characterized by such trends as industrialization, institutional differentiation, increasing affluence and social mobility, and professionalization. This perspective placed great emphasis on the socialization process through which individuals learn the values and skills appropriate to their roles in a complex social system; it paid little attention to issues of women's oppression and class conflict (Corwin, 1961; Smith, 1981; MacLean, 1974). Nursing was viewed within the distinct social institution of medicine as a highly specialized occupation, whose mainly female practitioners had to be carefully prepared for dedicated, demanding, and responsible tasks requiring high levels of knowledge and expertise and a clear sense of their role in an increasingly complex division of labour. Due to the advancement of medical science and the progress brought about by industrialization, nursing was seen as a quasi-profession aspiring to the status already achieved by physicians, mainly by insisting on higher educational requirements (Etzioni, 1969). The two professions of nursing and medicine were seen to be mutually interdependent (Diamond, 1984, p. 13). The sexual division of labour, in which female nurses typically worked for male doctors, was attributed to culturally given, normative expectations concerning sex roles, for example, nurses were mainly women because women were expected to perform mother-surrogate roles by providing tender, loving care (Thorner, 1955; Schulman, 1972; Cockerham, 1982, p. 178). This sort of uncritical, ahistorical, and optimistic analysis was typical of North American sociology during the period of economic expansion following World War II, when unemployment was minimal, average living standards the highest in the world, and sociologists concerned that their work should remain "value-free," that is, strictly confined to explaining social behaviour rather than evaluating the quality of contemporary society. In fact a lot of their sociology, far from being value-free, was actually a justification of the existing structure of society.

In the past two decades, several developments have occurred to undermine that approach. The realization on the part of thousands of women that scholarship generally, and sociology in particular, had totally neglected women's oppression has had special significance for research and theory on nurses (Diamond, 1984; Game & Pringle, 1983). The persistence of other kinds of social inequality in North America, especially the large incomes of the medical profession and the huge profits of health-sector corporations compared to the deprivations of the poor and of ethnic minorities, has lead to serious criticism of both the quality of life and the economic structure of capitalism. Studies of the rise of medical dominance and of the "American health empire" were part of this development (Freidson, 1970; Ehrenreich & Ehrenreich, 1970; Coburn et al., 1983). One of its main features has been a growing interest in applying Marxist theory, suppressed for decades in North American intellectual discourse with the attack on socialist trade unionism after the First World War and the cold-war McCarthyism which followed the Second World War (Navarro, 1983). This resurgence of Marxism should not be seen as a fad or the product of extremist radicalism. It is based on the capacity of Marxist-influenced analyses to further the explanation of social situations and processes in capitalist societies. Compared to liberal or value-neutral sociology, its strength lies in its concern with historical and dialectical analysis of the origins of contemporary social structures, the persistence of class-related struggles, and the tendency for capitalism to undergo recurrent crises. These strengths persist in spite of the demise of state-socialist societies in recent years. Thus the social relations that presently surround nursing as a position within advanced capitalism are viewed not as the effect of "modernization," but

Table 1   Class Composition of Canadian Nurses, 1931–1981

	Graduate Nurses				Nurses in Training			
Year	Wage Earner	Self-Employed	Unpaid	Total	Wage Earner	Self-Employed	Unpaid	Total
1931	47.81	43.06	9.13	100	71.01	0.00	28.99	100
1941	79.52	10.78	9.70	100	45.60	0.00	54.40	100
1951	99.97	0.03	0.00	100	100.00	0.00	00.00	100
1961	96.27	3.71	0.02	100	99.79	0.15	00.06	100
1971	99.12	0.72	0.17	100	99.95	0.00	00.00	100
1981	99.41	0.54	0.04	100	00.00	0.00	00.00	0

Source: For 1931–1971, Census of Canada various years. For 1981, Statistics Canada special tabulation.

as the provisional outcome of struggles based on opposing interests and unequal power among classes and gender groups.

Nursing and Modern Capitalism

To analyze a social practice we must situate it within the economic, political, and ideological relations of the society in which it appears. In the case of contemporary nursing this means recognizing that we are dealing with capitalist societies where the capitalist mode of production dominates the economy, deeply influences the political system, and appropriates the relations and practices of civil society (Urry, 1981).

The hallmark of capitalism is the selling of one's capacity to labour to an employer who uses it to make a profit on the sale of commodities produced by employees, the owners of that labour power. No other economic system throughout human history has operated in that way. In order to establish itself, capitalism had to replace, or maintain for its own purposes, previous modes of production, including aboriginal production systems, feudal agriculture, slavery, and independent commodity production. The latter involves the owner of the means of productions using his or her own labour power to produce commodities. Self-employed, "private duty" nurses who sell their services for a fee are a good example of independent commodity producers. The rise of modern hospitals has reduced their numbers within the nursing labour force from a majority of nurses as recently as 1932 (Weir, 1932) to a minute proportion, as Table 1 illustrates.

Capitalism's main effect on nursing, therefore, has been to make it a form of wage-labour used in hospitals, that is, to *proletarianize* nurses. Contrary to the beliefs of many nurses and public perceptions of nursing as a profession, it is crucial to view nurses as skilled members of the working class. Becoming proletarianized, however, does not preclude being concerned with"credentialism," for example, the pursuit of university degrees as minimum qualifications which enhance the status of nursing (Coburn, 1988, p. 441).

At first glance, the establishments in which nurses are employed as hourly wage-earners do not appear to be capitalist because they do not produce commodities to realize a direct profit, particularly not in Canada, where hospitals are state-funded institutions. But Bellaby and Oribabor (1977, pp. 802-805) have demonstrated that hospital treatment is itself a commodity. It has obvious use-value to the patient, but also exchange-value inasmuch as it competes with alternatives such as osteopathy, chiropractic, and faith healing, which usually have to be paid for. It also helps to realize capitalist profit by consuming commodities from other branches of the health-care industry: the machines and apparatuses of medical technology, pharmaceutical products, etc. Finally, by emphasizing the individual source and nature of medical problems, the impersonal treatment of patients as "cases," and their helpless, subordinate status vis-à-vis physicians and other medical personnel, hospital treatment helps perpetuate the social and psychological conditions on which capitalist corporations depend for their continuing domination of the labour process.

A similar point can be made if we examine hospital treatment from the perspective of nurses. Their work situation in hospitals is structured in terms of capitalist relations of production, which involve the direct subordination of workers to managerial dominance. There is a basic division between rank-and-file and supervising nurses. The latter manage nursing divisions, assisted by head nurses, the equivalent of forepersons in industry. Below them are general duty registered nurses, followed by licensed practical nurses, nursing aides or assistants, and student nurses. These objective relations produce support for existing hierarchies of class power and divide nurses from each other as workers. Campbell's study of hospital nurses in Ontario shows how a two-tiered occupation is being created as those who manage nursing are split off from those who give nursing care (Campbell, 1984, p. 12). The same point was made by Carpenter (1977) in an analysis of nurses' experience in Britain. Head nurses in particular are being drawn more and more into management (Campbell, 1984, p. 173). However, a certain ambiguity exists because nurses also supervise and give orders to other hospital workers, for example, cleaners, orderlies, kitchen staff. We suggest that this ambiguity in their position tends to reinforce their commitment to professionalism and has inhibited the development of working-class consciousness.

There is still another sense in which hospital nursing must be viewed within the context of an advanced capitalist system. Because they are accountable to governments, modern state-funded hospitals are subject to evaluations of efficiency and cost accounting like those used in the private corporate sector. In part, this is due to the responsibility governments feel to ensure that funds are well spent, but it also places hospitals, and nurses as their primary employees, in competition with other recipients of state expenditures, including corporations which seek subsidies, grants, research and development funds, highways, cheaper electric power, and other infrastructural services.

In recent years, these competitive pressures have intensified. Economic stagnation and fiscal crisis have prompted governments in the capitalist democracies to shift funding priorities away from the social programs and demand management of the Keynesian welfare state, to the "supply-side" private investment incentives of neo-conservatism (Wolfe, 1983).

In coping with these changing state priorities, hospital management has adopted measures of nurses' work performance, job evaluations, methods of speeding up the delivery of nursing services, definitions of optimum staffing requirements, etc. Campbell (1989) discusses them under patient classification systems and quality assurance assessment. These "efficiency measures" make excellent sense from the standpoint of hospital administrators, whose objective is to obtain maximum production and consumption for every dollar invested. But Campbell's study of measures to produce efficiency among hospital nurses indicates that, though the record-keeping practices yield documented, measurable information, they are wrongly viewed as the neutral application of modern technology in the pursuit of efficiency. While they may keep costs down, they are means of reinforcing the power of employer over employee, devices of so-called "objective" management that displace nurses' control over their practice, thereby contributing to their proletarianization (Campbell, 1984; Coburn, 1988, p. 438). Campbell argues that even though these "accounting" processes may organize higher-status "occupational content" into nurses' work, their most significant effect is an increase in managerial control over nursing knowledge. They also intensify nurses' workloads, increase job frustration, devalue nurses' knowledge, and displace their professional judgement (McSwain, 1991).

In this sense, the incorporation of "efficiency measures" into nurses' labour process may be viewed as an extension of the proletarianization process outlined by Wagner (1980, p. 279), which included creation of "a stable and loyal staff and the development of a hospital hierarchy based on Tayloristic principles of dividing the work process into the smallest possible components and giving cheaper work to unskilled and semi-skilled workers." The proletarianization of nurses, however, has also entailed a process of *ideological subordination*, similar to that experienced by professionals in profit-making organizations. Employed professionals are increasingly required to faithfully serve "organizational interests, even where basic professional ideals — in this case of service to clients — are thereby sacrificed" (Derber, 1983, p. 324).

Campbell (1984, p. 182) claims that erosion of the quality of nursing care is one consequence of these subordinating and cost-cutting measures. High-quality care can be maintained as long as the staff is adequate to provide good care according to nurses' traditional standards. This includes the chance to take responsibility and enjoy self-respect by applying one's skills and energy to meet a patient's needs. However, Campbell's informants commented that their work had been intensified beyond the level at which they could guarantee good care.

In 1985, we obtained evidence that, to some extent, supports this analysis in a survey of 179 registered nurses at a large acute-care hospital in Victoria, British Columbia, which was affected by the provincial government's neo-conservative austerity program of 1982-1984. In response to a question on how often they found it stressful to have insufficient time to complete all of their nursing tasks, only 9 percent of respondents said "never," 44 percent "occasionally," 31 percent "frequently," and 13 percent "very frequently." Ninety-two percent agreed that the restraint program had directly affected nurses' working conditions at the hospital. When asked how restraint had affected their working conditions, 77 percent of these respondents spontaneously mentioned insufficient staffing, 38 percent mentioned bed shortages, and 22 percent mentioned a heavier workload. Similarly, 76 percent of respondents agreed that the government's restraint program had directly affected patients' safety at the hospital. In describing the effects of restraint on patients' safety, 69 percent cited understaffing, 28 percent cited inadequate monitoring of patients, 26 percent cited patient overcrowding, and 22 percent cited inadequate patient care.

The close connection between nurses' working conditions and quality of care they are able to give patients has important implications for their role in class struggles. Insofar as restraint-motivated "efficiency measures" bring an erosion of both working conditions and the quality of care, it is likely that nurses' collective struggles will increasingly centre on these related issues. For instance, in 1986, the chairperson of the B.C. Nurses' Union Bargaining Committee gave the following description of two of the union's contract proposals:

> One of our proposals is for formal recognition of the right of nurses to use the grievance procedure to correct patient care problems. This is something that has been denied us. Another proposal deals with the effects of poor scheduling on us and our patients. Right now, nurses can be required to work eight days, or nights, in a row. We want six to be the maximum, so nurses can give the best possible care without the extra burden of unnecessary fatigue. (Timmivaara, 1986)

Proposals such as these, explicitly linking hospital nurses' interests as workers to the interests of their predominantly working-class clientele, exemplify a broader tendency in the labour movement to establish worker-consumer alliances. As Bernard (1986, p. 382) points out,

> Labour is trying to increase its strength by breaking down the separation between producers and consumers. Unions are making issues such as deregulation, centralization, and care of the handicapped into issues of public policy. Workers as the producers and deliverers of services are beginning to recognize that they have expertise and the right to propose their own alternatives.

In their work as deliverers of health care, nurses are in a position to contribute to this widening of the labour movement's agenda.

Male Dominance, Medical Dominance, Managerial Dominance, and Nurses' Struggles

As important as it is to situate nurses in the context of their developing class relations, it is equally crucial to recognize the fact that nurses perform a particular form of "gendered labour." Throughout history, healing, caring, and looking after others have been typical of women's activity. As one sociologist put it, "the experience of caring is the medium through which . . . women gain admittance into both the private world of the home and the public world of the labour market" (Graham, 1983, p. 30). Together with child care, cleaning, teaching, secretarial and social work, waitressing, and other typical female service jobs, nursing has been a major avenue for many women to move out of confined, dependent, domestic roles. The growth of nursing as a feminized occupation in Canada is illustrated in Table 2. Entering nursing, however, has not freed women from patriarchal relationships in the workplace or in the home.

The earliest hospital nurses were either nuns, who worked in charitable hospitals, or poor women like Charles Dickens's character Sairey Gamp, who staffed the workhouses where the destitute spent the end of their lives. The nineteenth-century reforms attributed to the influence of Florence Nightingale were efforts on the part of women of the respectable classes to open up working opportunities, mainly for women of bourgeois or petty-bourgeois origins who needed alternatives to either marriage or burdensome and inactive spinsterhood (Gamarnikow, 1978, pp. 111-112). For this reason, good manners, cleanliness, respectability, and other middle-class virtues and behaviour patterns have been stressed in nursing training.

The granting of opportunities for wage-earning and service occurred within patriarchal settings. Nursing was one of those "natural" spheres of activity for women that

Table 2 Gender Composition of Canadian Nurses,* 1901–1981

Year	Percent Female	Nurses† as % of Female Labour Force	Nurses as % of Total Labour Force
1901	100.00	0.12	0.02
1911	97.78	1.54	0.21
1921	98.96	4.36	0.67
1931	100.00	4.79	0.81
1941	99.41	4.63	0.92
1951	98.21	4.36	0.96
1961	96.84	4.79	1.31
1971	95.84	3.53	1.21
1981	95.39	3.79	1.54

* Includes graduate nurses and nurses-in-training   † Includes female nurses only

Source: Census of Canada, various years.

was rooted in the institution of the family. According to one protofeminist speaker in 1885:

> to enlarge the working sphere of woman to the measure of her faculties, to give her a more practical and authorized share in social arrangements which have for their object the amelioration of suffering, is to elevate her in the social scale. (Gamarnikow, 1978)

However, the Nightingale reformers did not upset the power and control that the medical profession had secured over the health system since the early nineteenth century (Larson, 1977; Coburn et al., 1983). Medical dominance in health care did not simply emerge as a matter of course or as a simple manifestation of superior knowledge. It involved weeding out the unqualified, obtaining the support of universities and the state, and restricting the activities of competitors like pharmacists — and nurses! (Torrance, 1981, p. 16). Judi Coburn (1981, p. 184) writes of the "housewife-cum-nurse-doctor-apothecary" who, in the 1870s, administered care in remote communities. She points out how women, once independent practitioners, were denied training and thus relegated to a subservient position within the medical profession. Complete subservience to the doctor and silent obedience to his authority were stressed in nursing training. Thus the development of nursing as a specific location within the division of health-care labour must be viewed as an integral aspect of the rise of medical dominance. As sex-segregated occupations, both medicine and nursing have been historically constructed and ideologically legitimated on the basis of predominant gender relations in capitalist society.

Melosh's phrase "the physician's hand" captures the essence of nurses' work as subordinate to physicians in the medical hierarchy (Melosh, 1982, pp. 6-10). Gamarnikow (1978) claims that nursing is united by a common recognition of the existence and nature of boundaries between itself and medicine, boundaries that reflect unequal professional power and that have been justified by a naturalistic ideology that asserts a biological basis for the sexual division of labour. She sees medical dominance contained in the limits on access to patients by practitioners of other health occupations, through the monopoly of initial intervention which designates the patient qua patient: "Once the health care process is under way, nursing consists of a variety of tasks, some of which are ordered by the doctor, and others which reflect current ideas about providing a healthy environment" (Gamarnikow, 1978, p. 106). Physicians are not the only patriarchal group with which nurses have had to contend. Hospital administrators and members of governing bodies also have been overwhelmingly male.

The major implications of nurses' status as female employed workers have been that they have been incorporated into hospital settings in subordinate, passive roles under the control of male superiors. This situation was facilitated by nurses' adoption of occupational values of dedicated service and commitment to patient care, values rooted in the Catholic religious tradition of "sisters of charity" and the devoted activities associated with Florence Nightingale. For several decades in the early part of this century, this ideology was instilled into student nurses by an often cruel regime run by autocratic matrons, the appointed representatives of the male-dominated hospital hierarchy. Wagner (1980, pp. 200–281) notes how the professional associations fostered loyalty and sympathy for the hospitals and developed an aura of prestige around nursing.

The use of student nurses in hospitals up to the 1930s, paid only in the form of room and board plus training, was one of the most blatant forms of the exploitation of women in recent times. For example, students comprised the entire ward of the largest training hospital in Canada, working as unpaid, sweated labour. A common type of exploitation involved sending student nurses out to do private nursing, the fees being paid to the hospital (Coburn, 1981, p. 189). The Weir Report of 1932 documented frank admissions by nursing school superintendents in Ontario that a cheap labour supply was the prime reason for the existence of training schools.

The low-grade working conditions of hospital nurses in this period were demonstrated by Weir (1932) and by Eaton (1938). According to Weir, inadequate education, low wages, and working hours which were so long that nurses had insufficient time for study and recreation, were widely prevalent. Eaton reported twelve-and sixteen-hour working days as normal. Both of these reports advocated an eight-hour workday for nurses.

Like most other workers, nurses eventually organized to improve their situation. The earliest nurses' groups were formed by the most highly trained who, in imitation of the medical profession, sought to control the quality of nursing by improving the level of nurses' education and restricting entry to the properly qualified. Judi Coburn compares the struggle for registration to the closed shop movement among unions. In arguing for protection against lower-paid practical nurses, graduates were not so much seeking professional recognition similar to that enjoyed by lawyers and doctors, but the privileges of the labour aristocracy. In excluding experienced but unqualified practical nurses, the nursing elite helped to perpetuate the exploitation of cheap nursing labour (Coburn, 1981, p. 195). Goldstone (1981, p. xx) observed in her study of nurses in British Columbia that the graduates who pressed for legalization of nursing registration showed no interest in pressing for improved remuneration or working conditions. They were more concerned with abolishing the oppressive schools of nursing, and in the decades following the passing of nurses' registration acts, a large proportion of schools in Canada were closed. Nurses' educational aspirations shifted to the pursuit of recognition by universities of nursing as a degree-worthy discipline; the breakthrough came with the establishment of a degree program at the University of British Columbia in 1919 (Canadian Nurses' Association, 1968).

Concern over working hours led to the struggle for an eight-hour day, pitting nurses against physicians and hospital administrators who were determined to discourage such unionist behaviour (Coburn, 1981, p. 197). The importance of class struggle in understanding modern nursing can be seen further in the organizing that occurred during the Second World War. Faced with competitive rivalry from trade union organizing attempts, nurses across the continent responded to their working conditions with collective bargaining measures (Wagner, 1980, p. 288). In Canada, this began with the formation of negotiating committees within nurses' associations. Several labour unions attracted lower-echelon, practical nurses into membership, but registered nurses remained opposed to unionization per se. They had, nevertheless, accepted the principle of collective bargaining as a means of resisting managerial dominance.

As bargaining occurred and nurses' remuneration increased, a rift developed within the professional associations between those who felt they should confine themselves to clinical issues, improvements in the quality of nursing, professional ethics, etc., and those who identified with the struggle for better working conditions. Many, of course, saw no incompatibility between the two types of activity, but the outcome has been the emergence of unions of registered nurses in most provinces during the past fifteen years. Other levels of nursing, including licensed practical nurses, have joined various hospital workers' unions. An instructive example of nurses' turn toward unionism and collective action arose in British Columbia in 1983, when the nurses' union joined the Solidarity Coalition, an alliance of labour, women's and community groups, in its protests against the Social Credit government's attacks on social services and trade-union rights. The strike by the British Columbia Nurses' Union in 1989 had among its primary objectives the attainment of wage parity with predominantly male occupations (British Columbia Nurses' Union, 1989, p. 9). In 1991, nurses in Manitoba participated in the longest nursing strike in Canadian history, which involved more workers than any strike in that province since 1919 (McSwain, 1991, p. 17). These trends all point to nurses becoming increasingly conscious of their situation as employed workers, albeit with a commitment to professional notions of high-quality service, devotion to duty, and to keeping abreast of improvements in knowledge and nursing skills. These aspects of nurses' professionalization can, as Coburn (1988, p. 453) contends, be seen as part of efforts to gain control over the labour process.

This is not to say, however, that registered nurses have acquired a high degree of class consciousness, explicitly aligning them with other sections of the working class. As Judi Coburn (1981, p. 200) says, many nurses have remained "workers who have not seen themselves as workers." She goes on to describe how they perpetuate divisions between themselves and other hospital workers by identifying with the status of the medical profession. To Coburn, it is not surprising, therefore, that nurses are still faced with the competition of less-skilled women whose cheap labour is a boon to hospital administrators.

We have already noted nurses' subordination to the male dominance and class-based authority of doctors and hospital administrators. Insights into the gendered context in which they work have led to proposals for the application of feminist principles in nursing education and practice. Kagan-Krieger (1991) claims that higher value is placed on treatment-oriented care and on technological innovations such as diagnostic imaging, computerized X rays, and life-support equipment than on caring and nurturing. She advocates a feminist approach based on co-operation, solidarity, and empowerment to help nurses overcome such contradictions and the oppressive work demands they face. There is, therefore, strong evidence that class and gender concerns are coming together as powerful forces for heightening nurses' political consciousness in the face of government austerity, managerial controls, anti-labour sentiments, and blatant sexism (Campbell, 1989, pp. 26-27).

But their work setting is only one field in which nurses are subject to the effects of class and patriarchy. The other major arena where these relations are found is the home. Like other women, nurses face varying circumstances on the domestic scene. Some are secondary income earners in fairly wealthy households. Others are single parents or other prime income earners with families. Some live in relatively egalitarian households, others in traditional, patriarchal ones. Whatever the structure of their household, most nurses are heavily involved in domestic labour, which one would expect to have an effect on their consciousness of class and gender. However, in our research on nurses in

Victoria, the only aspect of gender consciousness that distinguished nurses living in traditional patriarchal nuclear families from others was their reluctance to support universal day care (Carroll & Warburton, 1989, p. 141).

Conclusion

In this chapter we have indicated how class and gender relations provide the broad framework in which contemporary struggles of nurses can be understood. By this we do not mean that nurses' efforts to research their delivery of care and to improve the services they offer are not important. Indeed, they are highly significant. But those services are being threatened as the current crisis of the international economy and of capitalist states within it leads to public expenditure cutbacks becoming part of nurses' reality. What, then, of the future?

There is no sign of massive revival of the prosperity that prevailed in the 1950s and 1960s. Consequently, the quality of nursing and health care generally will be jeopardized as governments continue to cut back on medical insurance and hospital funding. To the extent that nurses collectively resist the proletarianized working conditions, pay restraints, and job insecurity that result from such cutbacks, it is conceivable that increasing numbers of nurses will discover what they have in common, not only with other health-care workers, but with the rest of the working class. Indeed, as deliverers of human services, nurses are in a position to help broaden the agenda of the labour movement by linking their struggles for improved working conditions to the struggle for improved health care for the population at large. Such linkages have significance precisely because struggles in the sphere of reproduction — whether over health care, education, or the family — have become central to the politics of advanced capitalism (Urry, 1981).

A similar point can be made concerning nurses' role in the struggle for gender justice. As Melosh (1982, p. 219) has noted, nurses' experience of paid work does not merely reinforce women's subordination, it also heightens the contradictions of gender inequality. Unlike full-time homemakers, nurses occupy a position of economic independence from which they make indispensable contributions in the social provision of health care. As organized female workers subordinate to primarily male physicians and administrators, nurses have considerable scope to challenge and disrupt existing notions of "women's place." This could mean attacking the sexual division of labour on both the industrial and domestic fronts, an enterprise that Maroney (1983, p. 65) deems essential to the long-term solidarity of "a working class that has two sexes."

Sociological projections are always hazardous and usually a source of future embarrassment, as the practical actions of women and men ruthlessly defy our neat causal frameworks. Nevertheless, this analysis does suggest a working hypothesis of modest scope. As skilled female workers engaged in the reproduction of labour power, nurses may play a strategically significant role in the working–class and feminist struggles of the late twentieth century.

Study Questions

1. What ambiguities are found in the class location of nurses?
2. In what ways do nurses face gender subordination?
3. How does class struggle manifest itself among nurses?
4. What are the implications of hospital management "efficiency measures" for the quality of patient care?
5. Examine the shortcomings of mainstream sociology and modernization theory for the study of nursing.
6. Are nurses professionals or skilled workers?

Recommended Reading

Ashley, J. (1979). *Hospitals, paternalism and the role of the nurse*. New York: Teacher's College Press.

Ehrenreich, B., & English, D. (1973). *Witches, midwives and nurses: A history of women healers*. Westbury: Feminist Press.

Game, A., & Pringle, R. (1983). *Gender at work*. Sydney: Allen and Unwin.

Gibbon, J.M., & Mathewson, M.S. (1947). *Three centuries of Canadian nursing*. Toronto: Macmillan.

Kramer, M. (1974). *Reality shock: Why nurses leave nursing*. St. Louis: C.V. Mosby.

References

Bellaby, P., & Oribabor, P. (1977). The growth of trade union consciousness among general hospital nurses. *Sociological Review*, 25, (4), 801-822.

Bernard, E. (1986). Labour tactics today. In W. Magnusson et al. (Eds.), *After Bennett* (pp. 368-382). Vancouver: New Star Books.

British Columbia Nurses Union. (1989, July-October). A chronology of the dispute. *BCNU Reports*, pp. 3-11.

Campbell, M. (1984). *Information systems and management of hospital nursing: A study in the social organization of knowledge*. Ph. D. Thesis. University of Toronto.

Campbell, M. (1988, Autumn). Management as ruling: A class phenomenon in nursing. *Studies in Political Economy*, 27, 53-86.

Campbell, M. (1989, October). Nurses battle for quality health care. *Canadian Dimension*, 25-26, 47.

Canadian Nurses' Association (1968). *The leaf and the lamp*. Ottawa: Canadian Nurses' Association.

Carpenter, M. (1977). The new managerialism and professionalism in nursing. In M. Stacey et al. (Eds.), *Health and the division of labour*. London: Croom Helm.

Carroll, W.K., & Warburton, R. (1989, Fall). Feminism, class consciousness and household-work linkages among registered nurses in Victoria. *Labour/Le Travail*, 24, 131-146.

Coburn, D. (1988). The development of Canadian nursing: Professionalization and proletarianization. *International Journal of Health Services*, 18, (3), 437-456.

Coburn, D. et al. (1983). Medical dominance in Canada in historical perspective: The rise and fall of medicine? *International Journal of Health Services*, 13, (3), 407-431.

Coburn, J. (1981). I see and am silent: A short history of nursing in Ontario. In D. Coburn et al. (Eds.), *Health and Canadian society*. Markham: Fitzhenry & Whiteside.

Cockerham, W.C. (1982). *Medical sociology (2nd ed.)*. Englewood Cliffs: Prentice-Hall.

Corwin, R.G. (1961). The professional employee: A study of conflict in nursing roles. *American Journal of Sociology*, 66, 604-615.

Derber, C. (1983). Ideological proletarianization and post-industrial labour. *Theory and Society*, 12, (3), 309-341.

Diamond, T. (1984). Elements of a sociology for nursing: Considerations on care-giving and capitalism. *Mid-American Review of Sociology*, 9, (1), 3-21.

Eaton, R. (1938). *Report of the advisory committee on labour conditions in hospitals*. Victoria: Provincial Secretary and Ministry of Labour.

Ehrenreich, B., & Ehrenreich, J. (1970). *The American health empire: Power, profits and politics*. New York: Random House.

Etzioni, A. (1969). *The semi-professions and their organization: Teachers, nurses and social workers*. New York: Free Press.

Freidson, E. (1970). *Professional dominance*. Chicago: Aldine.

Gamarnikow, E. (1978). Sexual division of labour: The case of nursing. In A. Kuhn & A.M. Wolpe (Eds.), *Feminism and materialism: Women and modes of production*. (Chapter 5). London: Routledge and Kegan Paul.

Game, A., & Pringle, R. (1983). Sex and power in hospitals: The division of labour in the health industry. In A. Game & R. Pringle (Eds.), *Gender at work*. (Chapter 5). Sydney: George Allen and Unwin.

Goldstone, I.L. (1981). *The origins and development of collective bargaining by nurses in British Columbia, 1912-1976*. M.Sc. Thesis, University of British Columbia.

Graham, H. (1983). Caring: A labour of love. In J. Finch & D. Groves (Eds.), *A labour of love*. London: Routledge and Kegan Paul.

Kagan-Krieger, S. (1991, September). Nursinged and feminism. *The Canadian Nurse*, 30-32.

Larson, M.S. (1977). *The rise of professionalism: A sociological analysis*. Berkeley: University of California Press.

MacLean, U. (1974). *Nursing in contemporary society*. London: Routledge and Kegan Paul.

Maroney, H. J. (1983, September/October). Feminism at work. *New Left Review*, (141).

McSwain, K. (1991, December). If we are professionals, why are we on strike? *The Canadian Nurse*, 17-19.

Melosh, B. (1982). *The physician's hand: Work, culture and conflict in American nursing*. Philadelphia: Temple University Press.

Navarro, V. (1983). Radicalism, marxism and medicine. *International Journal of Social Services*, 13, (2), 179-202.

Schulman, S. (1972). Mother surrogate — After a decade. In E. Jaco (Ed.), *Patients, physicians and illness* (pp. 233-234). New York: Free Press.

Smith, J.P. (1981). *Sociology and nursing*. Edinburgh: Churchill Livingstone.

Thorner, I. (1955). Nursing: The functional significance of an institutional pattern. *American Sociological Review*, 20, 531-538.

Timmivaara, S. (1986, May 18). Nurses want fair deal. *Victoria Times-Colonist*, p. A4.

Torrance, G.M. (1981). Introduction. In D. Coburn et al. (Eds.), *Health and Canadian society* (pp. 1-28). Markham: Fitzhenry & Whiteside.

Urry, J. (1981). *The anatomy of capitalist societies*. London: Macmillan.

Wagner, D. (1980). The proletarianization of nursing in the United States, 1932-1946. *International Journal of Health Services*, 10, (2), 271-290.

Weir, G.R. (1932). *Survey of nursing education in Canada*. Toronto: University of Toronto Press.

Wolfe, D. (1983). The crisis in advanced capitalism: An introduction. *Studies in Political Economy*, 11, 7-26. Journal of Health Services, 10, (2), 271-290.

Weir, G.R. (1932). *Survey of nursing education in Canada*. Toronto: University of Toronto Press.

Wolfe, D. (1983). The crisis in advanced capitalism: An introduction. *Studies in Political Economy*, 11, 7-26.

Chapter 27

Nursing Education:
Professionalism and Control

Terry Wotherspoon, University of Saskatchewan

Introduction

The first Canadian training school for nurses opened in St. Catharines, Ontario, in 1874. According to "The First Annual Report of The St. Catharines Training School and Nurses' Home, July 1, 1875,"

> the skilled nurse, by minutely watching the temperature, conditions of skin, pulse, respiration, and the various functions of all the organs, and reporting faithfully to the attending physician, must increase the chances of recovery two-fold. (cited in Gibbon & Mathewson, 1947, p. 145)

Clearly, "nursing skill" meant "service" in a dual way, with both the patient and the physician being served. The emergence of the hospital system within the context of burgeoning industrial capitalism set the tone for a nursing force characterized by a unique blend of Christian dedication, Victorian femininity, medical faith, and labour discipline. In this context, nurse training was oriented to produce a cheap, subservient, readily available work force armed with a basic knowledge of hospital and sanitary procedures.

In the 1990s, primary responsibility for nursing education no longer lies with hospitals but, instead, is part of the general university and community college systems. A discourse emphasizing faithful service has been supplanted by symposia on credentialling, specialization, nursing research, and medical technology. Nursing, laying claims to professionalism, has proceeded to organize a basis of skill and privilege around a unique body of nursing knowledge.

This chapter is concerned with the development of nursing education in Canada. The transformation that has just been described is interpreted in conjunction with the observation which Celia Davies (1980) makes that nursing education in Britain and the United States emerged as a compromise arising from inadequate resources. In particular, I emphasize the ways in which contradictions in the provision and utility of the education of nurses in Canada have served to limit nurses' position in the Canadian health-care system. Since the nineteenth century, with the emergence of the well-known "Nightingale system," prescient nurses and nursing supervisors have recognized the potential value of training for the establishment of a distinct sphere of nursing activity within the overall health-care system. However, the nature of that training and role has been subject to varying, often conflicting, conceptions by groups within nursing and interests outside of nursing. Ultimately, then, the development of nursing and nurse training must be understood as part of a wider network of social, political, and economic relations.

Nurses and Professionalism

Professionalism is the key concept in most recent analyses of nursing. Nurses are regarded either as constituting a profession, with their traditional low status a relic of the past, or as falling short in their drive to professionalism, in which case the reasons for their failure become the focus of analysis.

A typical expression of the first view is the statement that nursing has been involved in a "progressive development toward professionalism" (Elliott, 1977, p. 69). Three interrelated factors are commonly cited to highlight this apparent evolutionary progress: the specialization and bureaucratization of health care, increasingly sophisticated medical technology, and the growth of nurses' own professional awareness (Innis, 1970; Kelly, 1985). As health care has become a more comprehensive, sophisticated enterprise, new medical knowledge and health-care functions have become unequally distributed among participants in the health-care system. This has afforded nurses the opportunity to organize and push for increased status and responsibility; nurses have willingly emulated the medical profession with the assumption that full professionalism is an inevitable outcome. In this evolutionary mode, the role of education is clear — education is the vehicle for professional status. More education for more nurses, built around a distinct scientific core of nursing knowledge, would allow nurses simultaneously to adapt to a changing world and to occupy a position of enhanced importance in the division of labour in health care (Canadian Nurses' Association, 1986; Rogers, 1978).

As desirable as this image is from a nursing perspective, it fails to analyze adequately the wider context within which nursing operates, and it ignores many of the major constraints that continue to act upon nursing. Arising from the blend of optimism and frustration that has marked nurses' ongoing struggles for status, this viewpoint has interpreted the substantive gains that nurses have made against a backdrop of influential individuals and interest groups which seem to have no enduring connection to other aspects of social structure. The real historical barriers to nursing status seemingly can be dissipated merely through hard work and upgrading of skills on the part of nurses.

The second viewpoint paints a less flattering image of nurses. It takes as its starting point the obstacles that nurses face in their quest for status, and concludes that nurses are at best a semi-or para-profession, most likely doomed to an eternal inferiority to the medical profession (Cockerham, 1986; Wolinsky, 1980). Probably the clearest manifestation of this perspective is the fact that nursing is virtually ignored or given only passing consideration in much of the literature on the sociology of medicine. Against the visible unity and autonomy of the (predominately male) medical profession, the service orientation of the internally divided (predominately female) nursing ranks seems highly appropriate. This patronizing and accusatory view is expressed clearly by Oswald Hall (1970, p. 12), to whom:

> it seems clear that, to date, nurses have not tried seriously to focus their work efforts in a scientific mould. While medical care has been specializing along new types of diagnosis and treatment at a bizarre speed, nursing has shown no such trend.

We are left with the impression that no matter how strongly nurses have struggled in the past to establish their occupational status, they have not worked hard enough. Ironically, however, this view fits nicely with the first position on nurses' professionalism, differing primarily in the assessment of the likelihood of nurses' success in achieving professionalism.

Unfortunately, the debate over whether or not nursing is a profession tends to divert attention from questions of greater significance. Professionalism is assumed to be a desirable attribute, without any critical appraisal of the conditions within which professionalization occurs or of the strategic importance of professionalism as an ideological position. (See Johnson, 1972 for an extended critique of this approach.) Instead, the circumstances under which the health–care system and the role of nursing within it have developed are attributed to grand, amorphous tendencies such as "progress," "technological change," and "interest-group politics" without any sustained analysis of social relations in which these processes are grounded. Therefore, occupational roles and training are treated as neutral phenomena, given shape by the whims and visions of individuals acting as part of a seemingly natural evolution of social forces.

An alternate explanation of the development of nursing and nurse education focusses on the particular social relations that give shape to and are influenced by nursing. Nurses are recognized as dependent wage earners who pose problems of cost and control to their employers (Cannings & Lazonick, 1975; Warburton & Carroll, this volume; White, 1990). Nursing emerges from and acts upon distinct social structures and practices that are characterized by regular, often contradictory, patterns. Consequently, issues concerning the training and welfare of nurses, although important in their own right, are viewed as meaningful only when interpreted in the context of wider trends associated with health-care organization, policy, and finance.

Nurses as Salaried Employees

One clear indication of the status of nurses is expressed by the relative incomes of nurses and other health-care workers. As the data in Table 1 indicate, the incomes of nurses have increased steadily both in absolute terms and in comparison with the average income of the Canadian work force as a whole. Of the three tabulated health occupational categories, nurses have made the greatest relative gains. However, nurses' salaries still remain, on average, just below the national average for all occupations and less than one-third of the average for physicians and surgeons.

The most common justification for the latter trend is that medical training is more arduous and is of much longer duration than nurse training. Therefore, in accordance with a functionalist analysis of stratification, the higher salaries of doctors are seen to represent a "payoff" for the years of training and sacrifice undertaken by the individual in order to fill the important medical positions (Davis & Moore, 1945). This correlation between years of training and occupational income is borne out, in broad terms, by general surveys of the labour force that reveal that workers with higher levels of education are likely to be found in higher income categories. (See, for example, the monthly reports issued by Labour Canada under the title of *The Labour Force*.) As such, it serves as a rallying point for nursing advocates who argue that more and better-quality education is necessary for higher status. There are, though, some problems in this analysis. The income-education linkage is more likely to be a product of initial privilege or class power than an indicator of true market value (Bowles & Gintis, 1976). Moreover, the whole question of what constitutes recognized training must be considered. Historically, as will be discussed below, nurses have been trained on the job, providing cheap hospital labour in a prolonged apprenticeship period that is not regarded in the same way as is, for example, medical-ward experience and internship. At the same time, the fiscal returns and inducements for nurse training are not nearly as significant as a "reward for education" argument would have us believe. In 1975, for example, the mean salary for a public-health nurse, with both a university certificate in public-health nursing and a university degree, was $224 less than the mean salary for a public-health nurse with the same certificate but without the degree (based on data from Statistics Canada, 1976, p. 77). In 1987, staff nurses in Saskatchewan with a baccalaureate degree in nursing received a monthly salary allowance that was only $5.65 greater than that received by staff nurses with a one-or two-year nursing diploma (based on data from the Saskatchewan Union of Nurses, 1986). These examples illustrate that the financial "inducements" in themselves are hardly incentives or rewards for nurses to take the additional two or more years of formal education that a university degree requires.

A second argument for the relatively low wages that nurses receive is that nurses are much more poorly organized and less assertive than is the medical profession. Certainly doctors have benefited tremendously from the strength and ability of organizations like the Canadian and American Medical Associations to promote their own interests. In contrast, nursing leaders have chronically lamented the seeming inability of nurses to mobilize into a cohesive, powerful force. Unfortunately, advocates of these arguments tend to regard nurses and doctors as two independent rather than interdependent groups, and to confuse cause and consequence. While the medical and nursing professions each have their unique histories, the picture is incomplete without an analysis of how the medical profession has been able to advance in large part at the expense of nursing, through the subordination and guided development of nursing by doctors, health-care policy-makers and managers, and the structure of health-care systems.

This suggests the need for a relational analysis that can account for contradictions and constraints in nursing development. We can illustrate this type of analysis by returning to Table 1 and taking note of the third category of health occupations, after doctors and nurses. The wage levels of nursing aides, assistants, and orderlies have remained relatively constant, at between 56 and 69 percent of average occupational earnings. This implies that nursing, as an intermediate health occupation, can both exert pressure on and be subject to pressure from at least two levels — doctors and managers from above and auxiliary health-care workers from below. Therefore, by way of example, health-care administrators make decisions influenced by the fact that individual nurses are less costly than physicians, but more costly than auxiliary health-care workers. At the same time, nurses have reason to fear that they are potentially more dispensable to the health-care system than are doctors under present circumstances. Nurses, for example, are excluded from legislation that enables physicians and surgeons to prescribe medication or perform surgery. These relations are intensified with the introduction of new medical technology and health-care treatment models that serve to redefine the place and role of various health-care workers. If the diagnosis of a cancer, for example, can be made by a laboratory technician with the aid of a sophisticated instrument, and

Table 1 Employment Income for Selected Health Occupations: Average and Ratio to Average Canadian Occupational Income, 1931–1986

Census Year	Physicians and surgeons		Nurses		Nursing aides, assistants, & orderlies		All Canadian Occupations	
	Average employment income ($)	Ratio to Canadian average	Average employment income ($)	Ratio to Canadian average	Average employment income ($)	Ratio to Canadian average	Average employment income ($)	Ratio to Canadian average
1931	3 095*	3.65*	580	0.68	524	0.62	848	1.00
1941	2 693*	3.10*	596	0.69	486	0.56	868	1.00
1951	2 936*	1.59*	1 107	0.60	1 074	0.58	1 851	1.00
1961	13 836	4.34	2 421	0.76	1 847	0.58	3 191	1.00
1971	25 308	4.69*	4 344	0.81	3 572	0.66	5 391	1.00
1981	52 839	3.87	13 036	0.96	9 301	0.68	13 635	1.00
1986	85 023	3.17	26 123	0.98	18 430	0.69	26 781	1.00

* Figures for 1931 to 1951 do not include income for self-employed physicians and surgeons, and hence are likely to under-represent actual physician and surgeon incomes for those years. 1986 figures are for full-year, full-time workers.

Source: Calculated from census data.

can be treated with drugs prescribed by a physician, where does the nurse fit in? At another level, a greater integration of the health-care system with other social and educational services could provide opportunities for nurses to enhance their role in health care, or it could have the effect of making nursing a redundant occupation, as social workers, auxiliaries, or other new occupations begin to provide nursing services.

Viewed in this context, nursing education is a significant variable in the development of the health-care system. Education acts as a conduit for nursing knowledge, status, and credentials, but it also serves to stamp into place particular conceptions of nursing. More precisely, while the provision of educational opportunities is generally associated with the advancement of nursing, it is also a factor in the historical subordination of nurses.

Work and Education in the Canadian Context

Nursing education, like other forms of vocational training, began outside the formal system of public education in Canada. Mass public schooling emerged through the attempts by nineteenth-century school reformers to ensure the transformation of individuals into morally disciplined political subjects within a sphere of state rule (Curtis, 1983; Corrigan, Curtis, & Lanning, 1987). Vocational training was more strictly concerned with imbuing persons in specific jobs with the competencies and discipline that would make them productive workers. Once established in the throes of industrial development, however, the state public school system was subject to conscription by private capitalist interests concerned with obtaining at public expense a cheap, compliant, and differentiated labour force; schooling thus became penetrated by the logic of vocationalism (Bowles & Gintis, 1976; Schecter, 1977). However, a contradictory dynamic was generated by subordinate social groups that saw in public schooling a vehicle for upward social mobility and participation in hitherto closed political channels (Carnoy & Levin, 1985). A major consequence of the struggles that ensued over the nature and content of state schooling was the emergence in the twentieth century of the education system as the primary channel of individual access to the job market.

The developing linkage between school and work provided a focal point for the energies of competing social interests. The educational credential provided a screening mechanism for employers, a "meal ticket" for individuals, and an instrument to guarantee status for certain prestigious occupational groups such as medical doctors. Little overt challenge was presented to the tacit consensus that formal schooling was a legitimate educational and selective enterprise. Instead, conflict centred around the amounts and content of formal education appropriate to particular occupations or positions in the labour force. As debate concerning how much and what kinds of education a person needed to enter, certain jobs began to dominate educational discourse; wider questions about the structures of education and work were no longer issues. The ground rules for work and schooling solidified, with only the details open to contention (Wotherspoon, 1987).

Nurse training, which began in Canada within the hospital system, was absorbed into the state education system only through a protracted series of developments. The interconnection of such factors as the rising cost to hospitals of providing nurse training, corporate and state intervention in the health-care system, and the organized efforts of nurses accompanied a transformation in nursing work away from a strictly supervised feminine servitude to a bureaucratically organized wage-labour force. In the following sections, I outline the development of nurse training in Canada and discuss the nature of the Canadian nursing labour force.

The Development of Nursing Education in Canada

The formal training of nurses in Canada began in the 1870s for the purpose of producing hospital personnel who could adequately carry out doctors' orders (Mussallem, 1965, pp. 5-6). In the mid-nineteenth century, nursing was nearly unique as an occupation legitimately open to women. Nursing was established from the outset of the development of medial science as an auxiliary occupation, concerned primarily with "caring" rather than "curing," or hygiene rather than medical treatment (Gamarnikow, 1978; Corea, 1985). The medical division of labour, reproducing the patriarchal structure of the bourgeois home and workplace, was clear — men were doctors and women were nurses.

Nursing, nonetheless, did present opportunities, however limited, for the career advancement of a select group of women. Early nursing promoters, such as Florence Nightingale in Britain and Isabel A. Hampton in North America, saw that an inexpensive, regimented nursing force could provide the necessary foothold to establish nursing in the health-care process. The advantage of this strategy to solidify nursing status through the promotion of its ethos of service was that nursing could develop as a relatively autonomous enterprise, hierarchically organized around hygienic ideals under the supervision of women (Carpenter, 1977, pp. 166-67). However, the development of this autonomy was highly constrained.

Hospital administrators quickly came to appreciate the value of nurses for developing a clientele and providing inexpensive labour. With a nursing force at hand, public hospitals could shift their image and emphasis from providing a repository for the terminally ill to serving as a centre for treatment and recovery. The possibility that patients could be ministered back to health was crucial for an emerging industrial nation that required a continuous supply of able-bodied workers. Hospitals, in becoming important centres of health care, simultaneously began to train and contain nurses. Thus, generally following the pattern of industrialization in Canada, the number of hospital schools of nursing increased from one in 1874 (in St. Catharines) to 20 in 1900, 170 in 1909, and approximately 220 in 1930 (Canadian Nurses' Association, 1968, p. 33; Duncanson, 1970, p. 112).

In this context, nurse training accomplished several contradictory functions. Extending over a two-to three-year period, training programs ensured that a supply of nurses was continually available for hospital service. The exploitation of the nurse trainee prevailed over educational aims so that lecture and study time was a "privilege" granted only in the interstices of up to 15 hours of daily ward duty (Duncanson, 1970, pp. 112-113; Mussallem, 1965, p. 6). Nurse training programs dampened the hostilities of doctors, who scorned nurses as unskilled and uneducated. At the same time, doctors who were suspicious that they might some day be displaced by trained nurses found that they could advance their own interests by involvement in the nurse-training program as lecturers and moral guardians. Discipline over nurse trainees was further maintained by a highly regimented supervisory structure, constant surveillance facilitated by the establishment of dormitories, and inculcation of virtues of obedience and commitment, and the absence for most trainees of any occupational alternatives.

The advantages in terms of costs and services that nurses offered to the hospital system were also used by nursing leaders in the early part of the twentieth century as levers for gaining certain concessions, including reductions in the workday, specified educational time allocations, formalized instruction, and more standardized curricula (Duncanson, 1970, p. 113; Mussallem, 1965, p. 7). Trained nurses, working to enhance their own status in contrast with untrained nursing personnel, organized local, national, and international associations to provide a body for political lobbying. Nursing, as promoted by nursing administrators, was to be of service because it brought to the health-care sector a cultivated worker who conformed to high standards of female gentility and passivity (Coburn 1987, p. 448). In 1893, the American Society of Superintendents of Training Schools for Nurses of the United States and Canada was formed by 40 nursing-school superintendents in order to push for better-quality and more uniform nursing educational standards. This society laid the groundwork for a dominion-wide nursing organization, the Canadian National Association of Trained Nurses, established in 1908, which in 1924, with 52 affiliated member organizations, became the Canadian Nurses' Association, or the CNA (CNA, 1968, pp. 36-38). These organizations focussed the profession's energies on a drive for the establishment of registries of trained nurses, which received some degree of legislative recognition in all nine provinces between 1910 and 1922 (CNA, 1968, p. 38). They also began, especially with the aid of a 1914 Special Committee report on education, a lengthy campaign to have nursing education incorporated into the state educational system (King, 1970, p. 69).

In the midst of these developments, the fundamental contradiction between state and private demands for low-cost but widespread health-care services on the one hand, and nurses' demands for adequate training and remuneration on the other, intensified. In the early decades of the twentieth century, health-care services were becoming instituted as a regular social provision, in conjunction with the rise of a stable national work force. Exacerbating this trend was the success of the medical profession in acquiring greater influence with the health-care system. In this, the medical associations were aided by the large corporate foundations, especially the Carnegie Foundation, which sponsored the influential Flexner Report of 1910. In the wake of the report, major recommendations to reduce the number of North American medical schools and the supply of medical graduates, and to tighten control over medical education standards were quickly adopted (MacFarlane, 1965, pp. 19-21).

The data in Table 2 reveal the impact of these events on the medical and nursing labour forces. The supply of physicians was greatly moderated, especially in the period from 1911 to 1921, when the population per physician ratio actually increased, meaning that there were fewer physicians per capita in 1921 than in 1911. However, medical care was at that time highly labour-intensive so that, with fewer doctors, either patients received less medical attention, doctors worked harder, or other health-care personnel filled the void. The rapid increase in the nursing labour force (which grew by nearly four times between 1911 and 1921, and which has maintained an average annual rate of increase of 56.5 percent between 1911 and 1989, compared to an average annual rate of 8.9 percent for doctors over the same period), suggests the importance of the latter possibility. Lower-cost nurses, trained for dedicated service and disciplined by social and labour market conditions, served, in effect, to subsidize the greater occupational rewards that doctors were in a position to enjoy.

With an expanded and diversified health-care role, though, nurses were also able to assert more strongly their monetary and educational demands. However, as with doctors, nurses' progress in this regard was highly dependent upon the intervention of external agencies. A university degree program in nursing, the first in Canada, was established at the University of British Columbia in 1919 and, with the efforts and financial assistance of the Canadian Red Cross Society, public health nursing programs were developed in six universities by 1920-21 (King, 1970, p. 70). However, as King (1970, pp. 71-72) indicates, there were serious inadequacies in the early university nursing programs in terms of both upgrading nursing skill and raising nursing status relative to other university-educated occupational groups: "In the teaching of nursing great emphasis was placed on technical skill, following orders, and adhering to established practice; the intellectual component was subservient to the daily round."

There is evidence, too, of a strong occupational split in nursing between nursing

Table 2   Number of Physicians and Nurses, and Population per Physician and Nurse in Canada, 1901–1989

Year	Physicians		Nurses	
	Number	Population per physician*	Number†	Population per nurse*
1901	5 442	978	280	19 014
1911	7 411	970	5 600	1 284
1921	8 706	1 008	21 385	410
1931	10 020	1 034	20 462	506
1941	11 873	968	25 826	441
1951	14 325	976	41 088	325
1961	21 290	857	70 647	258
1971	32 942	659	148 767	146
1981	45 542	538	206 184	119
1982	47 384	521	214 989	115
1983	48 860	510	218 344	114
1984	49 916	503	222 960	113
1985	51 948	487	229 650	110
1986	53 207	479	237 181	107
1987	55 275	467	241 955	107
1988	57 405	455	249 827	104
1989	58 942	449	252 189	105

* Based on census data.

† Registered nurses for 1941 to 1975; census figures for 1931 (graduate nurses) and earlier years (nurses). Excludes Newfoundland prior to 1961; excludes Yukon and Northwest Territories prior to 1941. The 1921 figure includes nurses-in-training. Figures from 1981 to 1989 include only nurses registered during the first four months (3 in Quebec) of the registration period and registered in the same province in which they work or reside.

Source: For 1901 to 1971, Statistics Canada. (1983). *Historical Statistics of Canada* (2nd ed.). Ottawa: Minister of Supply and Services, Series B82-92.

      For 1981 to 1989, Health and Welfare Canada. (1991). *Health Personnel in Canada*. Ottawa: Author.

supervisors and instructors, who had been trained in and had advanced through the hospital service system, and nurses who saw the need to develop the profession through university education and research (King, 1970, pp. 73–75). The latter group was given support by George Weir in the 1932 report *Survey of Nursing Education in Canada*, co-sponsored by the CNA and the Canadian Medical Association. The report's primary recommendation was that nursing schools be removed from hospital control and placed under the auspices of the provincial education systems.

With the onset of the international economic crisis in the 1930s, the fate of this recommendation was suspended between conflicting interests. In the early part of the decade, expenditures on health services declined (Statistics Canada, 1983), placing increased pressures on the existing health-care system and on its labour force to operate more efficiently. At the same time, these conditions provoked intensified efforts from several quarters for an overall upgrading of the health-care system. Potentially militant trade unions and the unemployed, subject to severe social and economic dislocation, posed a worrisome threat to state and corporate interests. A series of social reform measures, including health-insurance schemes, was introduced by provincial and federal legislatures as part of an attempt to pacify the working class and stabilize economic conditions (Swartz, 1977).

Corporate interests also played a more direct role, primarily through their charitable foundations which provided financial assistance and funded research for selected health, education, and welfare projects, in order to secure social harmony, develop a stable work force, and promote a favourable investment climate. In the field of health care, the W.K. Kellogg Foundation has a history of prominence, having contributed over $263.5 million to various health-care programs, mostly in the United States, Canada, and Latin America, between 1930 and 1980 (Kellogg, 1979, p. 112). Of that total, $822 000 were spent between 1944 and 1952 to provide staff, consultative services, and curricular and instructional resources for twelve university nursing schools (ten in the United States and two in Canada), and a grant of over $165 000 served to establish an experimental undergraduate nursing program, grounded in basic science training, at the University of Saskatchewan, beginning in 1952 (Kellogg, 1955, pp. 143-48).

At the same time, other pressures were mounting to push training of nurses out of the hospitals. Nurses, who in the 1930s often accepted board and lodging from their hospital employers in lieu of full salary payment, began in the 1940s to return to the community and, simultaneously, to demand higher wages (CNA, 1968, p. 34). A similar situation developed for nurses in training who exchanged fees and labour in return for training and services. The Department of National Health and Welfare estimates that by 1960, the average direct annual cost to the hospital per student was $1 000 (Mussallem, 1965, p. 40). Because hospitals compensated for this cost by extracting unpaid or underpaid labour from nursing students and by underpaying nursing instructors, a generally unsatisfactory situation prevailed. Moreover, low wages and low levels of government educational assistance made it economically unviable for most nurses and nursing teachers to extend their education beyond the minimal time period required for graduation from basic training, especially when the training program was prolonged excessively by the priority of work over training in the hospital system. Consequently, it is not surprising that Mussallem (1965), in a study prepared in the early 1960s for the Royal Commission on Health Services in Canada, indicts the nursing education system of the time as haphazard, outdated, educationally unsound, and inadequate for the needs of nurses and the health-care system.

The Royal Commission's report itself recommended a reduction in the time span of the diploma program from three to two years and a separation of nurse training from hospital demands for nursing service, and stressed that the increasing need for qualified nurses required the co-ordinated development of nursing education programs integrated into the general system of higher education in Canada and the provinces (Duncanson, 1970, pp. 122-123). While the Royal Commission inquiry was being conducted, nurses' organizations, educational institutions, and the Ontario government cooperated in an initiative that led to the establishment in 1964 of a nursing diploma program at the Ryerson Polytechnical Institute. By 1968, in the wake of this precedent, 26 nursing diploma programs were offered in institutions other than hospital schools of nursing across Canada; by 1977, full-time enrollment in community college nursing diploma programs was 17 789, as compared to 5 136 in hospital programs (CNA, 1981, p. 2; Statistics Canada, 1977). A similar expansion was underway in university degree nursing programs, with more programs, greater numbers of students, and the establishment of graduate degree programs.

Recent Trends in Nursing Education and the Nursing Labour Force

The move away from hospital-based nurse training has been associated with a general improvement in the overall status of nurses, but it has not solved several fundamental problems associated with training and maintaining a nursing labour force. There are presently two main educational streams for entry into nursing practice: university degree programs of three to five years in length, and nursing diploma programs, offered mainly through the community college system, of one to three years in length. In 1989, there were 110 initial diploma programs and 22 baccalaureate programs in nursing in Canada (Statistics Canada 1991e, pp. 1-2), compared with 170 hospital schools and 16 university baccalaureate programs in 1963 (Mussallem, 1965, p. 11). However, despite a recent trend to emphasize the importance of the degree qualification in nursing, by the end of the 1980s about 75 percent of nursing graduates continued to receive their initial training in diploma programs (see Table 3).

The provision of nursing education through the public education system has ensured that certain levels of funding, facilities, and standards will be maintained for nurse training, sheltered from the vagaries of hospital administration. At the same time, though, new sets of constraints emerge as nursing education is forced to compete for resources with other educational and state priorities. Insofar as the educational credentials of teachers, a major cost factor in postsecondary educational institutions, are linked to promotion and salary scales, nursing education is relatively inexpensive. In 1989-90, for example, only 22.7 percent of full-time university nursing teachers had completed

Table 3 Numbers of Nursing Graduates from Initial Diploma and Basic Baccalaureate Programs in Canada, and Number of Immigrant Graduate Nurses Entering Canada, 1962–1989

| Year | Number of nurses graduating from Canadian programs | | | Number of immigrant graduate nurses* |
	Initial diploma programs	Basic baccalaureate programs†	Total	
1962	6 246	148	6 394	1 621
1963	6 764	171	6 935	1 879
1964	7 107	154	7 261	1 967
1965	7 154	206	7 360	2 829
1966	7 167	220	7 387	3 732
1967	7 249	273	7 522	4 262
1968	7 591	300	7 891	3 375
1969	7 978	381	8 359	3 248
1970	8 212	413	8 625	2 274
1971	9 543	515	10 058	989
1972	9 596	487	10 083	892
1973	8 985	609	9 594	1 418
1974	9 205	694	9 899	1 702
1975	8 933	845	9 778	1 839
1976	9 087	954	10 041	1 130
1977	6 203	977	7 180	607
1978	7 403	1 455	8 858	405
1979	6 680	1 330	8 010	467
1980	6 685	1 453	8 138	653
1981	6 478	1 425	7 903	977
1982	6 621	1 590	8 211	999
1983	6 761	1 686	8 447	358
1984	6 871	1 729	8 600	300
1985	7 218	1 957	9 175	283
1986	6 762	2 037	8 799	387
1987	7 054	2 221	9 275	730
1988	6 981	2 265	9 246	1 044
1989	7 117	2 313	9 430	1 185

* Immigrants who indicated that nursing is their intended occupation.

† Figures from 1978 and later include graduates of post-RN baccalaureate programs.

Source: Health and Welfare Canada. *Canada Health Manpower Inventory* (Annual series, 1969, 1976, 1985): Mussallem, H.K. *Nursing Education in Canada*. Ottawa: Queen's Printer; and Health and Welfare Canada. (1991). *Health Personnel in Canada 1989*. Ottawa: Minister of Supply and Services.

doctorates, compared with an overall Canadian university teacher average of 67 percent (Statistics Canada, 1990, p. 42; Statistics Canada, 1991b, p. 211). In addition, such low-cost highly specific programs as computer-assisted instruction and self-directed learning modules are becoming prominent features of university nurse education programs (Crawford, 1978; Hannah, 1978). These programs, besides reducing the costs of education relative to more open-ended discovery and analysis-based courses, prepare the student for work roles that are highly structured and involve few opportunities for the worker to exercise discretion on the job.

But despite the potentially lower cost of nursing education programs, there are indications that governments have made only limited commitments to support nurse-training programs, particularly at the university level. If we return to Table 3, we observe that immigration has provided Canada with a major source of trained nurses, especially in the late 1960s and early 1970s during the transfer of nursing education out of hospitals. By importing trained labourers (although not all workers will necessarily become employed in their intended occupations), Canada is able to transfer the cost of educating a substantial pool of workers to the countries of origin and gain in the process a cheap, often docile work force (Bolaria, 1987). Depending upon where the workers are placed in job situations, this will either ensure that lower-paid positions are constantly filled (as opposed to increasing wage levels), or reduce the overall costs of maintaining a trained work force.

The lack of government support for nursing education, especially at the university level, is also revealed in the problems that nurses face in upgrading their basic training. Nurses often discover that they are left out of decisions to introduce, and shut out from training to operate, new medical technology (Wallis, 1978). A recent survey reveals that absence of credit courses for upgrading training at work, lack of time off to attend classes that are offered, and lack of financial assistance are common problems for nurses working in Canadian hospitals and health-care institutions; nurses in at least one institution have even held bake sales and auctions in order to raise money for a tuition-assistance fund (Allen, 1985, p. 12). Significantly, according to 1988 data, only 29 508 (or 14 percent) of the 210 506 registered nurses employed in nursing in Canada have an academic degree (Statistics Canada 1990, p. 30). Moreover, as some of the trends noted above suggest, even the attainment of a university degree does not guarantee that nurses will be prepared to step into decisive, autonomous health-care positions. There does not appear to be a significant change from the days of hospital service for nurse trainees. Nonetheless, there is evidence that the state has channelled funds into specific vocational streams, such as psychiatric nursing and dental nursing since the 1960s in response to political, economic, and employment relation factors (Dickinson, 1987; Statistics Canada, 1977).

A major consequence of these trends is the possible bifurcation of nursing. In accordance with the degree/diploma distinction, two streams are emerging — one more highly skilled and educated and the other service-oriented and less educated — reminiscent of the separation of trained nurses from untrained nursing personnel in the early part of the twentieth century. This is consistent with the demands of nursing organizations in the 1960s for an increased recognition of the dual educational credential system (CNA, 1968, p. 4), but contains implications for the organization of nursing that may well undermine the very cause nurses are championing.

Hospitals remain the major workplace for Canadian nurses regardless of educational background, employing several times more nurses than do all other categories of nursing employer (see Table 4). However, some variation occurs with respect to educational credentials. Nurses with only basic diploma training are overrepresented in hospitals, nursing homes, and doctors' offices (i.e., while 68 percent of all employed nurses in 1983 had only basic diploma training, the respective proportions within these workplaces of nurses with basic diplomas were 72, 78, and 80 percent). These are workplaces that tend to be characterized by direct personal or bureaucratic supervision and strict delineation of authority. Conversely, nurses with bachelor's degrees or higher are overrepresented in jobs in community health and in educational institutions, which carry the possibility of greater autonomy and decision-making authority. Similar trends are observable with respect to nursing positions. Table 4, incorporating 1990 data, shows that basic diploma nurses, who predominate numerically, are overrepresented in general-duty nursing positions and underrepresented in directorial, senior supervisory, and teaching positions, while the opposite holds for degree nurses.

A second related aspect of bifurcation is observable in the gender structure of the occupation. Nursing remains an overwhelmingly feminized occupation — in 1988, only 3 percent of registered nurses employed in nursing in Canada were male (Statistics Canada 1990, p. 13). Nonetheless, 29 percent of male nurses held directorial, supervisory, head nurse, or instructor positions while only 19 percent of female nurses held such positions (Statistics Canada 1990, p. 17). Moreover, according to 1986 census data, female nurses who worked on a full-time, full-year basis, earned an average of $171 less in yearly income than their male counterparts (Statistics Canada, 1989, p. 110).

These conditions are exacerbated by the actions of legislators and administrators empowered with financing and regulating the health-care system, especially in the context of general demands to reduce overall levels of government spending. Health-care services have consumed steadily greater shares of national resources, increasing from $7.8 billion (or 7.4 percent of GNP) in 1972 to $47.9 billion (or 8.6 percent of GNP) in 1987 (Statistics Canada 1991a). Hospital expenditures, in turn, have consumed in recent years over 40 percent of these total health expenditures, and nursing costs have been a major component of hospital expenditures; in 1987-88, for example, nursing

Table 4   Nurses Registered in Canada and Employed in Nursing — Type of Employer (1983), and Position (1990), by Highest Level of Education in Nursing

	Highest level of education, expressed as percentage of nurses within each type of employment situation or position				
Type of Employer, 1983	Total number	Registered nurse diploma	Post-basic diploma or certificate	Bachelor's degree	Master's degree or higher
Hospital	130 375	72	19	8	1
Community health	16 325	45	27	27	1
Home for aged, nursing home	11 019	78	17	4	1
Educational institution	4 912	27	15	48	10
Physician's office, family practice unit	4 477	80	15	5	1
Other types of employer	5 998	64	22	12	2
Not stated	3 517	72	28	8	2
Total — percent	100	68	20	11	1
— number	176 623	120 940	34 708	18 816	2 013
Position, 1990					
Director, assistant/associate director	4 278	39	25	28	7
Supervisor/coordinator assistant supervisor/coordinator	8 609	53	23	22	1
Clinical specialist	1 362	37	19	28	16
Instructor	4 492	21	13	56	11
Head nurse	8 174	57	26	16	1
Staff nurse	124 925	72	16	11	<1
Other	10 730	57	20	20	2
Not stated	61 395	68	19	11	1
Total — percent	100	67	18	14	1
— number	223 965	150 931	40 139	30 304	2 591

Source: 1983 data calculated from Canadian Nurses' Association, *Nursing in Canada 1983*. Statistics Canada and Canadian Nurses' Association, 26; 1990 data calculated from Statistics Canada. (1991). *Nursing in Canada 1990*. Health Reports Supplement No. 22. Catalogue 82-003S22. Ottawa: Minister of Industry, Science and Technology, 12.

costs constituted 35 percent of the total operating costs of $15.5 billion for Canadian public hospitals (Statistics Canada 1991c, p. 66).

Consequent to the growth of the health-care system have been increasingly sustained legislative and managerial efforts to make the operation of the system more efficient and accountable. Initiatives such as community health centres, prescription drug assistance programs, and concentration of hospital systems, regardless of their possible medical merits, have the clear effect of increasing the output of hospital workers while shifting some health-care services from hospitals to less expensive and less labour-intensive in-home and community alternatives (Salmon, 1984). At the same time, institutional health care is being reorganized primarily through innovations in the supervision patterns of hospital and nursing-home employees in order to increase centralized managerial control and maximize employee productivity (Carpenter, 1977). Nursing, as the largest single category of health-care workers, remains central to the politics and structure of health care in Canada.

The observed tendencies toward bifurcation in nursing suggest that any benefits from a restructured organization of health-care services will be distributed in a highly asymmetrical fashion. Within nursing, males and nurses with degrees, especially post-graduate degrees, are moving into positions likely to serve as bases for further consolidation of authority and resources. While the resources that go into nursing education, as well as nursing initiatives in the direction of credentialling, the development of nursing knowledge, and specialization may serve to upgrade the status of nursing as a whole, they are more likely to be channelled towards the minority of nurses who can use credentials and authority positions to their advantage. If these initiatives do enable nurses on the whole to legitimize their claims to greater proportions of health-care resources, nursing administrators are liable to rely less upon nurses and more upon lower-paid auxiliaries to provide health-care services. The upper stream of credentialled nurses, with the assistance of agencies such as the Kellogg Foundation, which has recently funded major projects in nursing research, accreditation, and doctoral studies (CNA, 1983, pp. 29-30), may be able to insulate itself from the erosion of the profession as a whole by strengthening its own claims to essential health-care skills and knowledge which it alone possesses.

The trend towards greater professional recognition of nursing is represented especially in the recent CNA focus, reinforced through complementary positions advanced by several provincial nursing associations, on "entry into practice," which calls for a minimum requirement of a complete baccalaureate degree as the standard for entry into nursing practice by the year 2000 (CNA, 1982, p. 1; Registered Nurses' Association of British Columbia, 1983). As the CNA itself admits, such a goal seems difficult to attain, given the current slow rate of increase in the proportion of student admissions to degree nursing programs relative to diploma programs, and the continuing lack of funds to expand degree nursing programs (1986, p. 5). Instead, support given to degree programs and nursing research may be channelled into specialized programs supporting the small proportion of nursing practitioners who, on the basis of the degree credential, may stake sole claim to the title of "nurse." In 1989, over 24 000 students nationally were enrolled in diploma programs in nursing, compared to just under 11 000 in the longer degree programs (Statistics Canada, 1991e, pp. 1, 5). At the same time, fiscal and administrative support previously given to nursing diploma programs is likely to be directed to promoting the expanded production of auxiliary health-care workers. Paradoxically, then, by advancing credentialling and research policies in the interest of the profession as a whole, nurses may be contributing to their own division into a highly skilled and educated nursing elite and a mass of undertrained, low-paid support workers.

Nurses are increasingly cognizant of their uncertain status within a changing health-care sector. In many cases they have been able to use the realities of chronic shortages of health-care workers to their advantage, gaining concessions in wages and improved professional working conditions from their employers. At the same time, however, they have had to rely upon collective action to make any substantive gains or even to hold their ground against reductions in health-care services and expenditures. As an indication of mounting tensions within the health-care sector, nurses in Quebec and the four Western provinces have engaged in strike action since early 1988. In the process, nurses have been forced to rethink their status as workers and as professionals. While the service ethic remains an important component of nurse training and work, nurses have shown through their struggles that the nature of that service can no longer be bound within restricted terms of docility.

Conclusions

This chapter has emphasized how the transformation of nursing from a subordinate service occupation into a more specialized and sophisticated profession has been rendered more apparent than real in many key respects through a series of external and internal constraining factors. Education has been a crucial channel for the occupational development of nursing, serving both to advance and to suppress its status. The pattern of nursing and nursing education in Canada has followed the interplay of nurses' organized efforts to establish their occupation with the development of a Canadian labour force in general and a health-care labour force in particular. The frequent success of corporate, state, and medical interests in guiding the development of nursing has had a significant impact on the present status of nursing as a wage labour force divided by education and gender. Nurses, though, have come to recognize within the past decade and a half that their status as the largest single health-care occupation is a potential power base (Ferguson, 1985; Lerner, 1985; Mussallem, 1977). By promoting their ability to serve client needs and health-care priorities rather than economic or systemic requisites, while simultaneously avoiding the trap of accepting a professional ideology as substitute for actual resources, nurses may yet succeed in their quest for status. To this end, nurses are beginning to align themselves with other groups of workers, particularly teachers, who face similar threats and challenges. The consequences of nurses' development of a political strategy are significant, for without a clear analysis of their occupational situation, nurses are likely to suffer, as will the quality of the health services that they are able to provide.

Study Questions

1. Which factors have facilitated the emergence of nursing as a prominent health-care occupation? Which factors have served to constrain the development of nursing in Canada?
2. Discuss the relationship between nursing and the development of the medical profession.
3. What implications have changes in medical technology and in the organization of health-care services had for the development of nursing?
4. Discuss the ways in which the state education system is subject to pressures from various social interests, as illustrated by the example of nursing.
5. How does the development of nursing compare with trends in other related occupations such as teaching and social work? Should nurses have the right to strike?

Recommended Reading

Cannings, K., & Lazonick, W. (1975). The development of the nursing labor force in the United States: A basic analysis. *International Journal of Health Services*, 5, (2), 185-216.

Corea, G. (1985). *The hidden malpractice: How American medicine mistreats women*. New York: Harper & Row.

Davies, C. (Ed.). (1980). *Rewriting nursing history*. London: Croom Helm.

Innis, M.Q. (Ed.). (1970). *Nursing education in a changing society*. Toronto: University of Toronto Press.

Kerr, J., & MacPhail, J. (1988). *Canadian nursing: Issues and perspectives*. Toronto: McGraw-Hill Ryerson.

Stacey, M., Reid, M., Heath, C., & Dingwall, R. (Eds.). (1977). *Health and the division of labour*. London: Croom Helm.

White, J. (1990). *Hospital strike: Women, unions, and public sector conflict*. Toronto: Thompson.

Wotherspoon, T. (Ed.). (1987). *The political economy of Canadian schooling*. Toronto: Methuen.

References

Allen, M. (1985, May). Baccalaureate education remains an enigma for many nurses. *Canadian Nurse*, 81, (5), 12.

Bolaria, B.S. (1987). The brain drain to Canada: The externalization of the cost of education. In T. Wotherspoon (Ed.), *The political economy of Canadian schooling* (pp. 301-322). Toronto: Metheun.

Bowles, S., & Gintis, H. (1976). *Schooling in capitalist America*. New York: Basic Books.

Canadian Hospital Directory. (1984). *Canadian hospital directory statistical compendium*.

Canadian Nurses' Association. (1968). *The leaf and the lamp*. Ottawa: Author.

Canadian Nurses' Association. (1981). *The seventh decade 1969-1980*. Ottawa: Author.

Canadian Nurses' Association. (1982). *Entry to the practice of nursing: A background paper*. Ottawa: Author.

Canadian Nurses' Association. (1983). *Nursing in Canada 1983*. Ottawa: Statistics Canada and Canadian Nurses' Association.

Canadian Nurses' Association. (1986, October). Collaboration between nurse educators in the use of nursing education resources. *Entry to Practice Newsletter*, 2, (5).

Cannings, K., & Lazonick, W. (1975). The development of the nursing labor force in the United States: A basic analysis. *International Journal of Health Services*, 5, (2), 185-216.

Carnoy, M., & Levin, H.M. (1985). *Schooling and work in the democratic state*. California: Stanford University Press.

Carpenter, M. (1977). The new managerialism and professionalism in nursing. In M. Stacey, M. Reid, C. Heath & R. Dingwall (Eds.), *Health and the division of labour* (pp. 165-193). London: Croom Helm.

Coburn, J. (1987). I see and am silent: A short history of nursing in Ontario, 1850-1930. In D. Coburn, C. D'Arcy, G.M. Torrance & P.K. New (Eds.), *Health and Canadian society: Canadian perspectives* (pp. 441-462). Markham: Fitzhenry & Whiteside.

Cockerham, W.C. (1986). *Medical sociology* (3rd ed.). Englewood Cliffs: Prentice-Hall.

Corea, G. (1985). *The hidden malpractice: How American medicine mistreats women*. New York: Harper & Row.

Corrigan, P., Curtis, B., & Lanning, R. (1987). The political space of schooling. In T. Wotherspoon (Ed.), *The political economy of Canadian schooling*, (pp. 21-43). Toronto: Methuen.

Crawford, M.E. (1978, February). The curriculum revision process — experienced at the college of nursing, the University of Saskatchewan. In *Perspectives: Nursing education, practice and research* (pp. 1-16). Proceedings of the 1978 Annual Meeting of the Western Region — Canadian Association of University Schools of Nursing. Calgary: The University of Calgary.

Curtis, B. (1983, Winter). Preconditions of the Canadian state: Educational reform and the construction of a public in Upper Canada, 1837-1846. *Studies in Political Economy*, 10, 99-121.

Davies, C. (1980). A constant casualty: Nurse education in Britain and the USA to 1939. In C. Davis (Ed.), *Rewriting nursing history* (pp. 102-122). London: Croom Helm.

Davis, K., & Moore, W.E. (1945). Some principles of stratification. *American Sociological Review*, 10, 242-249.

Dickinson, H.D. (1987). Vocational education and the control of work: The case of psychiatric nursing in Saskatchewan. In T. Wotherspoon (Ed.), *The political economy of Canadian schooling* (pp. 231-251). Toronto: Methuen.

Duncanson, B. (1970). The development of nursing education at the diploma level. In M.Q. Innis (Ed.), *Nursing education in a changing society* (pp. 109-129) Toronto: University of Toronto Press.

Elliott, M.R. (1977). Nursing and interdisciplinary practice. In B. LaSor & M.R. Elliott (Eds.), *Issues in Canadian nursing* (pp. 43-72). Scarborough: Prentice-Hall.

Ferguson, V. (1985). Overview of the concepts of power, politics, and policy in nursing. In R.R. Wieczorek (Ed.), *Power, politics, and policy of nursing* (pp. 5-15). New York: Springer.

Gamarnikow, E. (1978). Sexual division of labour: The case of nursing. In A. Kuhn & M. Wolpe (Eds.), *Feminism and materialism — Women and modes of production* (pp. 96-123). London: Routledge & Kegan Paul.

Gibbon, J.M., & Mathewson, M.S. (1947). *Three centuries of Canadian nursing*. Toronto: Macmillan of Canada.

Hall, O. (1970). Social change, specialization, and science: Where does nursing stand? In M.Q. Innis (Ed.), *Nursing education in a changing society* (pp. 3-15). Toronto: University of Toronto Press.

Hannah, K.J. (1978, February). Overview of computer-assisted learning in nursing education at the University of Calgary. In *Perspectives: Nursing education, practice and research* (pp. 43-56). Proceedings of the 1978 Annual Meeting of the Western Region — Canadian Association of University Schools of Nursing. Calgary: The University of Calgary.

Health and Welfare Canada. (1985). *Canada health manpower inventory 1985*. Ottawa: Minister of National Health and Welfare.

Innis, M.Q. (Ed.). (1970). *Nursing education in a changing society*. Toronto: University of Toronto Press.

Johnson, T. (1972). *Professions and power*. London: Macmillan.

Kellogg, W.K. Foundation. (1955). *The first twenty-five years: The story of a foundation*. Battle Creek: Author.

Kellogg, W.K. Foundation. (1979). *The first half-century 1930-1980: Private approaches to public needs*. Battle Creek: Author.

Kelly, L.Y. (1985). *Dimensions of professional nursing* (5th ed.). New York: Macmillan.

King, M.K. (1970). The development of university nursing education. In M.Q. Innis (Ed.), *Nursing education in a changing society* (pp. 67-85). Toronto: University of Toronto Press.

Lerner, H.M. (1985). Educating nurses for power. In R.R. Wieczorek (Ed.), *Power, politics, and policy of nursing* (pp. 90-95). New York: Springer.

MacFarlane, J.A. (1965). *Medical education in Canada*. Royal Commission on Health Services Special Study No. 13. Ottawa: Queen's Printer.

Mussallem, H.K. (1965). *Nursing education in Canada*. Royal Commission on Heath Services Special Study No. 16. Ottawa: Queen's Printer.

Mussallem, H.K. (1977). Nurses and political action. In B. LaSor & M.R. Elliott (Eds.), *Issues in Canadian nursing* (pp. 154-181). Scarborough: Prentice-Hall.

Registered Nurses' Association of British Columbia. (1983). *Entry into the practice of nursing in the year 2000: Position statement of the registered nurses' association of British Columbia*. Vancouver: Author.

Rogers, M.E. (1978). Emerging patterns in nursing education. In J.A. Williamson (Ed.), *Current perspectives in nursing education: The changing scene, Vol. 2* (pp. 1-8). St. Louis: C.V. Mosby.

Salmon, J.W. (1984). Organizing medical care for profit. In J.B. McKinlay (Ed.), *Issues in the political economy of health care* (pp. 143-186). New York: Tavistock.

Saskatchewan Union of Nurses. (1986, December). Private correspondence with author.

Schecter, S. (1977). Capitalism, class, and educational reform in Canada. In L. Panitch (Ed.), *The Canadian state: Political economy and political power* (pp. 373-416). Toronto: University of Toronto Press.

Statistics Canada. (1976). *Compendium of selected health manpower statistics 1976*. Ottawa: Statistics Canada.

Statistics Canada. (1977). *Survey of vocational education and training 1976-77*. Ottawa: Minister of Supply and Services Canada.

Statistics Canada. (1983). *Historical statistics of Canada* (2nd ed.). Ottawa: Minister of Supply and Services Canada.

Statistics Canada. (1989). *Canadians and their occupations: A profile*. Census Canada 1986. Catalogue 93-157. Ottawa: Minister of Supply and Services Canada.

Statistics Canada. (1990). *Nursing in Canada 1988*. Catalogue 83-226. Ottawa: Minister of Supply and Services Canada.

Statistics Canada. (1991a). *Canada year book 1991*. Catalogue 11-402E. Ottawa: Minister of Supply and Services Canada.

Statistics Canada. (1991b). *Education in Canada: A statistical review for 1989-90*. Ottawa: Minister of Industry, Science and Technology.

Statistics Canada. (1991c). *Hospital annual statistics, Vol. 5 — Administrative and support services and finances*, 3, 1. Catalogue 82-003S20. Ottawa: Minister of Industry, Science and Technology.

Statistics Canada. (1991d). *Nursing in Canada 1990*. Health Reports Supplement No. 22, 3, 2. Catalogue 82-003S22. Ottawa: Minister of Industry, Science and Technology.

Statistics Canada. (1991e). *Nursing in Canada: Nursing education program 1989*. Health Reports Supplement No. 22, 2, 4. Catalogue 82-003S. Ottawa: Minister of Supply and Services Canada.

Swartz, D. (1977). The politics of reform: Conflict and accommodation in Canadian health policy. In L. Panitch (Ed.), *The Canadian state: Political economy and political power* (pp. 311-343). Toronto: University of Toronto Press.

Wallis, M. (1978, February). The technological society — its implications for nursing. In *Perspectives: Nursing education, practice and research* (pp. 81-91). Calgary: Proceedings of the 1978 Annual Meeting of the Western Region — Canadian Association of University of Schools of Nursing. Calgary: The University of Calgary.

Warburton, R., & Carroll, W.K. (1993). Class and gender in nursing. In B.S. Bolaria & H.D. Dickinson (Eds.), *Sociology of health care in Canada* (2nd ed.), (this volume). Toronto: Harcourt Brace & Company.

Weir, G.M. (1932). *Survey of nursing education in Canada*. Toronto: University of Toronto Press.

White, J. (1990). *Hospital strike: Women, unions, and public sector conflict*. Toronto: Thompson Educational Publications.

Wolinsky, F.D. (1980). *The sociology of health: Principles, professions, and issues*. Toronto: Little, Brown & Co.

Wotherspoon, T. (1987). Conflict and crisis in Canadian education. In T. Wotherspoon (Ed.), *The political economy of Canadian schooling* (pp. 1-15). Toronto: Methuen.

Chapter 28

The Structure of Stress
in Nurses' Work

Marie L. Campbell, University of Victoria

Introduction

Cost control in the Canadian health-care system has been a major preoccupation of policy-makers since the advent of medicare in the late 1960s. Revisions of federal-provincial funding arrangements during the 1970s and 1980s, and an increasingly neo-conservative cast to governmental fiscal policies continue to be reflected in social policy. Among other expectations, health-care institutions have come under considerable pressure to deliver services faster and cheaper. To a large extent, management has come to be accepted as the answer to the problem of doing more with less. During this time, hospitals in Canada have undertaken significant administrative reforms, introducing new management technologies and systems that are aimed in the short run at improving management control, and ultimately at improving operational cost effeciency and cost effectiveness.

This chapter describes one of the earliest, and subsequently most widely used, instances of such reform in hospitals — the nursing workload measurement and staffing system, based on classifying patients' needs for nursing care. According to Bennett and Krasny (1977), nursing services in hospitals were the focus early on of important administrative efficiency measures. In hindsight, it is easier to see the revolutionary significance of nursing management techniques such as "patient classification" being introduced into nursing. Patient classification generates objective information about nurses' work, in this case about the amount of nursing care that is "necessary" for specific patients, information on which objective staffing decisions depend. Previously, nursing staff was attached to hospital wards on the basis of their size, patient census, and historic staffing patterns, with periodic adjustments made on the basis of "local" nursing knowledge. The new information makes possible the calculation and enforcement of "productivity" expectations, that is, how much work a nurse is expected to get through in a day. The long-term effect of "managing" nursing productivity objectively has been to force nurses to readjust their traditional beliefs about patients' needs and bring them more in line with the new realities of funding.

Since the implementation of this management technology in hospital nursing, the systematic construction of information and its transfer from the point of service "production" to management has become the central organizing feature of health-service administration. Major expenditures on computers, software, and information management personnel have followed, as health-service institutions have come to rely on management practices in which systematic information is integral. Krawczyk (1989) reports that Canadian hospital administrators feel that they must continue to increase their investment in information systems in order to properly account for their expenditures. The accepted approach to savings is now through detailed financial controls and local accountability for resources, making paperwork, or its electronic equivalent, a paramount and routine part of health-care work. An organization's strategic plan, within the dominant perspective of information-based management or the "accounting" approach to administration, while focussed obstensibly on managing the service delivery mission economically, becomes a plan for elaborate documenting of service to "capture costs" as information.

While this accounting approach now represents mainstream thought, not only of administrative practice but also within the health professions, new voices are being raised in criticism. Accounting analysts such as Chua (1991) are sceptical that the numbers produced through managerial accounting systems actually relate very closely to the hospital activities and patients they claim to represent. Chua argues that the social manufacture of accounting data does, however, alter power relations, transferring dominance to those who can claim, on the basis of the data, to "know" more (p. 31). This is the crux of the argument being presented here in relation to nurses, the new knowledge of nursing-care needs that patient classification generates, and the altered structure of decision making about nurse staffing. Beyond that, as developed in this analysis, are the personal costs to nurses and patients that such a transformation of effort, power, and control introduces.

This chapter deconstructs the managerial accounting methods by which hospital managements sought to build the kind of knowledge needed to maximize the usefulness of nursing labour, and thereby to improve its efficiency as nursing productivity became a key topic of concern in the early 1980s. The analysis casts doubt on the overall success of these methods, even as they speeded up the pace of nurses' work. The cost to the nurses involved, it is argued, is so high as to directly undermine their capacity to work effectively; a concern that, incidently, is borne out by the crisis in nursing that overtook the health-care system during the eighties.

This analysis sheds some light on the trouble nurses continue to experience as nursing is more explicitly managed. The social organization of "cost efficiency" in their work exacts both a personal and a professional toll when nurses are expected to accept personal responsibility for delivering a safe and sufficient level of care under conditions that become less and less capable of sustaining this work. Experiencing an increased pace of work and heavier workloads, they speed up their work and make personal contributions from their unpaid time. Yet nurses working under these conditions suffer frustration, anxiety, and self-blame about the care they are able to give. These are the experienced features of the now common workplace syndrome which Freudenberger (1975, 1980) and Vash (1980) have called "stress" and "burnout," but which is argued here to have an explicitly organized character. The following analysis shows an accounting approach to "efficiency" to be a double-edged sword, attacking nursing labour costs on one side and nurses' physical and mental well-being on the other.

The Structure of Management Control

To understand the structure of stress on nurses, one needs to investigate how efficiency measures reorganize their work. Figure 1 offers a "route-map" of the structural analysis that links policy and organizational processes to "stress" effects.[1] As Smith (1984) has argued, the capacity to organize and control local activities in line with ideas arising elsewhere is a contemporary and distinctive feature of corporate capitalism. The documentary processes described in this article help solve a particular problem in hospital management as health care is increasingly incorporated into the ruling apparatus of Canadian society. Until recently, the work of *professional employees* was conducted under professional supervision, relatively autonomous of managerial control. The new methods make it possible for managerial decisions and organizational priorities to be embedded, through objective processes, in nurses' practice. In this way, policy decisions made elsewhere in the health-care system pervade nursing care. The "problem" of nurses' autonomy from managerial control is thus addressed as individual hospital managements are brought under central policy control. Nurses' control over their own labour process became problematic to hospital managers only when health-care policy took a direction at odds with nurses' ideas.

Health-care policy deliberations in the 1960s contained rudimentary ideas about the

Figure 1   Organization of Cost-Constraint in Hospital Nursing: A Route-Map of
Documentary Methods & Results

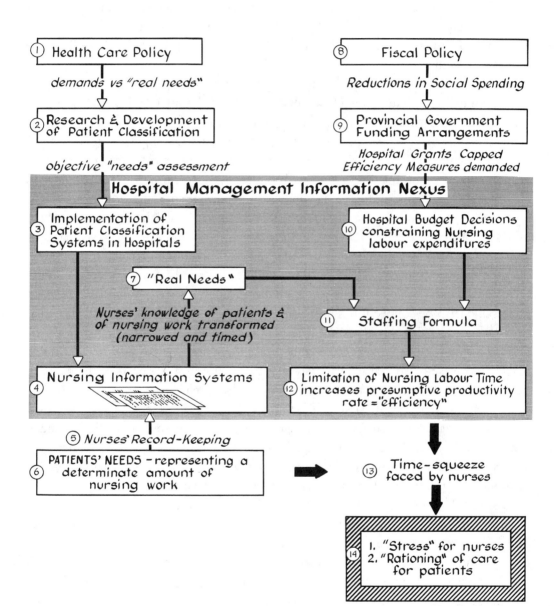

utility of measuring "needs" for health services rather than responding to public demand. The notion that Canadians demand more health services than they really need was formalized in policy documents such as the *Report of the Task Force on the Cost of Health Services*, published in 1970. Those task force recommendations were the launching point for research and development of management systems in which nursing services were to be related to patients' needs (Vol. 1, pp. 43-45.) The assumption behind the R and D programs was that nurses were unreliable at differentiating "real needs" from patients' excessive demands. Patient classification systems, such as those developed from work carried out by the Saskatchewan Hospital Systems Study Group (1967, 1970, 1973, etc.) were to make determinations of need more objective and rational.

When a patient classification system is implemented in a nursing department, assessment of patients' needs for nursing care takes place *in the management system*, as contrasted to individual decision making by nurses about what to do for individual patients. To nurses who are introduced to a patient classification system, the whole process is represented by a document (i. e., a patient classification form, which they are expected to fill out once a day) (Figure 2). Filling out the form puts in motion a process that has a definite effect, at least when it is used as part of a staffing system; nurses are aware that the number of staff made available to do the work on a hospital ward is a reflection of what they have reported in their Patient Classification Forms. Nurses are given to understand that the connection is more direct than it really is. This is what makes their troubles about staffing so distressing to them. During implementation of patient classification systems, nurses are encouraged to revise the wording on the form, and to add new categories, etc., so that it accurately reflects the important aspects of their care of patients. Later, when they have carefully recorded their knowledge of individual patients, and have received classification ratings which result in too few nurses to do a good job, they are confused. The structure of decision making remains unclear to them, and the decision itself, mysterious. But the system has provided officially sanctioned knowledge, built on what they themselves have reported. Nurses are thus implicated in its production in a way that binds them to its staffing outcome.

To begin to understand what has happened to transform what they have said into an organizational decision that may seem "wrong," one must see that the patient classification form is only one piece in a documentary decision-making process. It refers back to research and development work and forward to staffing decision procedures. There is room for a calculated reshaping of nurses' accounts in both those processes. The patient classification data collection form is one of a series of documents in which "what nurses know" is systematically transformed into information with a special character appropriate for semi-automated and objective decision making. The patient classification form collects up, from several documents, specific kinds of information about patients; the form then physically travels out of a ward into a central office, where compilations are made mechanically. (Computer applications can, of course, speed up the processing time, by removing the necessity for paper to be routed around the hospital.)

In patient classification, nurses' knowledge of their patients is being used to classify them into several levels of need for nursing care. This step is carried out as a record keeping, in addition to nurses' daily work. Nurses categorize what they know about their patients, including the daily plan of work in the form specially constructed for this purpose. The categories of the patient classification form provide a kind of conceptual template for nurses to use to mentally scan a particular patient and estimate, according to a standard guide (see Figure 2), the amount of time needed to carry out the major features of that patient's therapeutic regime. A nurse need not be familiar with a particular patient to "classify" the patient; she or he consults and interprets other records, showing both retrospective accounts of care given and current plans for ongoing therapeutic activities (Figure 3).

The patient classification technique gets nurses to express, in concrete terms, tied to actual activities, the amount of time they expect planned-for care of a particular patient to take. Nurses' responses about major features of their patients' needs for nursing intervention *indicate* "automatically," referencing background research, which level of care a patient falls into. Work analysis and time studies (the R & D work) have provided a body of data, on the basis of which standard schedules of tasks and standard times per task are defined. Patient classification information supplied by nurses offers *the indicators* necessary to relate individual patients to standard interventions, or at least, what is crucial for the management decisions to be taken, to the *amount of time* that standard interventions take standard nurses to complete in a research setting. These standard times are then substituted for nurses' individual time estimates in calculating staff allocations. This constitutes the first kind of reshaping of nurses' practical knowledge alluded to above.

There is yet more restructuring of "what nurses know" before a staffing decision is arrived at. My discussion of the intended uses and unintended effects of document-based decision making awaits some consideration of this second kind of reshaping. The actual staffing decision makes use of more information than nurses' transposed choices about patients' nursing care needs from the classification form. That initial step has produced an generalizable account of "nursing care needs" in an information form ready for processing with budget information, to determine staffing levels, objectively. It is this latter capacity that makes patient classification useful as a technique for improving "efficiency" of nursing labour. Nurses' pace of work can be manipulated when staffing decisions incorporate patient classification information. A determination is made of the amount of paid labour time that will "match" a definite amount of work (estimated in

Figure 2   Patient Classification

UNIT: _____   TEAM: _____   TO-DAYS DATE: _____

* For Full Description of Care — Please See Guidelines

Rm. No.	Patient's Name	PERSONAL CARE							NUTRITION			ACTIVITY			TEACHING & EMOTIONAL SUPPORT				TREATMENT OBSERVATION			PAT. CLASS
		1	2	3	E3	1	2	3	1	2	3	1	2	3	1	2	3	E3	1	2	3	

Rater: _____

Direct Nursing Care in 24 Hrs.
 Time Values:
 Factor 1 — 30 min.
 Factor 2 — 30-60 min.
 Factor 3 — 60-120 min.
 Factor E3 — over 120 min.

Column headings (diagonal):
PERSONAL CARE: SELF CARE / ASSISTANCE / COMPLETE CARE / OVER 120 MIN. REQUIRED 24 HRS. / MINIMUM ASSISTANCE / PARTIAL ASSISTANCE
NUTRITION: NEEDS TO BE FED / MINIMUM SUPPORT / REQUIRES ASSISTANCE
ACTIVITY: FULLY DEPENDENT / 0-30 Min./24 Hrs / 30-60 Min./24 Hrs / 60-120 Min./24 Hrs
TEACHING & EMOTIONAL SUPPORT: 0-30 Min. / 30-60 Min. / 60-120 Min. / OVER 120 Min. 24 Hrs
TREATMENT OBSERVATION: 24 Hrs. 1 / 24 Hrs. 2 / 24 Hrs. 3 TOTAL / PAT. CLASS

TOTALS	Team Sub Total	1		2	3	4	5	Team Census
	Combined Totals	A		B	C	D	E	Unit Census

Figure 3 A Nurse's Worksheet

INDIVIDUAL CARE PLAN

STANDARD CARE PLANS
IN USE:

DATE	PROBLEMS/NEEDS (NURSING DIAGNOSIS)	EXPECTED OUTCOMES	DEAD-LINES	CHARTING	NURSING ACTIONS

NURSES WORKSHEET (TO BE COMPLETED IN PENCIL)

DATE   DAILY CLASSIFICATION   DIAGNOSIS: DOCTOR:

VITAL SIGNS   DATE

T.P.R.:   APEX: I.V. THERAPY

B/P

INTAKE: OUTPUT:

OTHER:

PERSONAL CARE: SELF   ASSIST   TOTAL   TREATMENT/THERAPY

ACTIVITY: SELF   ASSIST   TOTAL

NUTRITION: SELF   ASSIST   TOTAL

DIET:

FOOD ALLERGY:

ELIMINATION: SELF   ASSIST   TOTAL   TEACHING NEEDS:

OTHER: DISCHARGE PLANS/LONG TERM GOAL

relation to care levels). Reducing slightly the labour time allowed means that nurses have to speed up to handle the designated work.

Matching staff allocations to care levels gives a hospital management more control over a nursing work force. Previously, staffing was a very imprecise procedure. Basic decisions about how many nurses to assign to a nursing unit depended upon historical experience of the workable ratio between nurses and patients; patient census was the only "hard data" available to modify historical staffing complements. This gave hospital managements very little control over the productivity of their nursing force. Census information (or how many beds were filled each day) did not communicate anything about acuity (how ill a patient was); therefore it could not be used to discriminate effectively about differing staff levels needed in units with the same number of patients. Previously, head nurses would be able to demand additional staff when, in their professional judgement, they needed more. Individual head nurses, like individual staff nurses, would have varying ideas about what amount of care was necessary, how fast nurses could work, etc.; head nurses would also have varying capacities to make their nurses work speedily, and hospital managers had no objective information about which head nurses were more "successful" in this regard. In particular, hospitals had no control over nurses' beliefs and commitments to giving "good care." As the policy cited earlier suggested, the costs of health services were alarming Canadian policy-makers into believing that nurses were being too generous, and that their choices should be curbed. Patient classification is the instrument by which that can be accomplished, although not directly.

To implement changes that make use of patient classification information, new staffing methodologies were developed. "Flexible" staffing, for instance, is an innovation that operates on patient classification information. It is a method in which a minimum number of permanent staff is maintained, and "floating" staff are assigned on a daily basis to those units in which classification figures show more staff to be needed. This not only provides for efficient use of staff by assigning them where and when they are needed, but allows the hospital to make use of cheaper labour (casual workers, not in the permanent work force.) Given the local availability of a pool of young, married nurses who are content with part-time or temporary work, this staffing procedure can be implemented very effectively.

Economical staffing decisions depend both on the way that "real needs" are constructed through patient classification, and on how those data are manipulated with budget information. Regarding the first, "real needs" information is a minimized version of what nurses have said about their patients. The "real needs" coming out of the information system are standardized needs, trimmed of individual differences that nurses see in patients or those that they bring to the workplace as their own special characteristics. Aggregated, they represent a standardized and minimized estimate of the work contained in a nursing unit (hospital ward) of actual patients. Organizing staffing in relation to "real needs" improves efficiency by making nurses responsible for caring for a determinate number of patients in a determinate amount of paid labour time. In principle, staff allocations can be made precisely, matching exactly the standard time of aggregated "real needs." Presumably, every minute of a nurse's paid labour time can be allocated to work that must be done to meet the patients' minimal needs. In principle, patient classification gives hospitals the capacity to keep nurses working without any wasted time.

Of course, nursing management is not quite as straightforward as it appears on paper. For one thing, objective information about needs is still an estimate, produced daily, in relation to a patient population that is extremely changeable. Patients' conditions change all the time and, for efficiency reasons, hospitals move patients in, through their facilities, and out again rapidly. So the apparent precision that the management system offers is reduced by variations in the work which are not reflected in the objective information. Also, time studies of nursing have been most successful in reflecting those aspects of the work nurses do directly with the patient. But nurses' work is by no means limited to the bedside. They organize and co-ordinate an environment that houses patients and has many aspects similar to running a hotel; they work in concert with a variety of auxillary service providers. In addition, nurses provide a supportive environment for the practice of medicine, and articulate their caring work to physician's orders and practical needs. Nurses take responsibility for managing the patient's whole therapeutic regime, organizing his or her movements to other hospital departments for special treatments, etc. They are involved with the public, communicating with families and other visitors, some of whom need special attention, instructions, and interpretation. These and many other background tasks, apparently peripheral but actually necessary to adequacy of care, are part of nurses' work. Quite indeterminate features of the work are estimated in a nursing management system and are given a quantitative expression in the "real needs" figure.

When standard times were developed, researchers also included in their calculations the varying amounts of time nurses spend "unproductively," that is, not engaged in any observably determinate nursing task. It is assumed that nurses can reduce such "wasted" time if they are organized properly. Hospitals set presumptive productivity expectations when information about patients' needs, standard nursing time, and its costs are compiled and correlated with budget information. A staffing formula brings this information together. The productivity expectation influences the amount of money that can be "saved" on nursing labour. To increase the pressure on nurses to work harder, the staffing formula is shifted to reduce the time allowed for what I have called the indeterminate work. This simply cuts back on the total time estimated for a nurse to complete all the needed care. The effect, with a professional work force, is to increase the pace of work. Nurses take as their own responsibility the additional "cost" of completing their assigned patients' care, when less time is allocated in which to do it.

Policing how nurses spend their time is not really necessary, as long as they maintain their high level of professional commitment to their patients. When less time is made available for the total care of their patients, not only do nurses speed up, but they work on unpaid time, according to the nurses I interviewed. In addition, they also curtail the range of services and attention they give to patients. This happens through "prioritizing" their work, an approach to nursing that is a professionally sanctioned method of nursing decision making. In other words, nurses, as part of their trained competencies, "manage" their work by discriminating between more or less crucial nursing actions. Making decisions about cutting out some of the nursing care their patients actually need puts nurses under even more pressure. When something has to go it requires a high level of competence to judge which of the list of tasks nurses regard as necessary should be left out. This new responsibility for making rationing decisions in an ad hoc manner has nurses, at the lowest organizational levels, making choices that may have life-and-death implications. Nurses have to make such consequential decisions "on the run," as a matter of daily routine. While nurses have always been on this important front line of decision making, the pressures on them have increased. Raising nurses' productivity has this contradictory outcome: services are reduced and those reduced services are spread over a greater number of patients.

The efficiency effect has not come about through precise specification and control of the *labour process* of nursing, in the way Braverman (1974) and others have described scientific management of other types of work. Nursing still has the form of professional work, in which the practitioner chooses how to apply his or her knowledge and skills, in relation to each patient. It has, as well, the character of women's work, in which women "pick up the pieces" of whatever needs to be done to advance a project; the hospital unit is particularly reliant on nurses seeing what needs to be done and doing it, even if it is not in their job description. The nursing program is laid out in documents, but *how* that work gets done — the specificity of each general task, the order in which they are done, the care and attention to detail — is not defined. "Morning care," even for the same patient, could be a quick face-wash and tidying of the bedclothes, or a complicated bed-bath, including time spent helping the patient to dress and move about with tubes, drains, etc., in place. Leaving decisions about what care can be hurried over, skimped on, or deleted completely, is, to overstressed nurses, hardly a rational way to manage health care. In fact, this feature of "efficiency" makes something of a mockery of the previous attention given to measuring and matching "needs" and work accurately.

Yet, this is the practical outcome of implementing budget cuts through organizational systems of objective managerial control. The nursing management system described here channels fiscal decisions made elsewhere into nurses' interactions with patients and their families. The system is both an advance in managerial technology and a questionable incursion into professional practice. The increasing use of objective management systems in nursing has been part of the "corporatization" of hospitals and widespread adoption of more business-like management practices in public administration. Provincial governments play an active role in encouraging hospitals to implement nursing management information systems, although the relationship between public hospitals and provincial governments does not allow the government to direct a hospital's actions. Statutory funding arrangements give the governments certain powers, however. Hospital administrators negotiate annual block grants on the basis of budget forecasts, developed from historical data and projected changes. Such negotiations take place within conditions established by political priorities and government fiscal policies. Among other fiscal restraint actions, provincial ministries have required hospitals to demonstrate managerial effectiveness; use of a patient classification system is treated as the best way of managing the nursing labour budget. In Ontario, for instance, hospital nursing departments have introduced objective management techniques, either in response to budget cuts already experienced, to help "rationalize" difficult staffing decisions, or to implement new management systems on the recommendation of (invited) ministry consultation. Taking the ministry's advice about managerial methods may be a precondition for a favourable hearing in funding talks, even if a hospital does not plan to use patient classification information for staffing decisions.[2]

Internal hospital decisions about the amount of budget allocated to nursing labour are constrained by earlier decisons at the ministry level, for example, the 1981 Ontario decision to stop reimbursing hospital cost overruns. At the hospital level, the nursing labour budget is finally decided in relation to other hospital priorities and pressures, as well as by considering the estimates prepared by nurse executives. Nurses' productivity, when it is treated as indefinitely expandable, appears as one solution to funding problems. The staffing decision taken through applying the staffing formula determines what nurses' productivity *must be*. The administrative capability to assess "needs" at the point of service production finally comes down to this "efficiency" use. In the "efficiently" organized hospital, there is more work to do than is provided for in purchased hours of labour. This disjuncture must be accommodated somehow, through nurses' efforts. The management idea is that not only does less work really need to be done, but that nurses can actually work faster if they are pressured. The management system turns that idea into a staffing quota with a definite productivity expectation.

The new and difficult conditions being organized in hospital nursing have had a number of organized responses. For instance, nurses' unions have begun to intervene to help nurses take a collective stand on "safety to practice" issues. Initiated by the Ontario Nurses' Association around a landmark case at Toronto's Mt. Sinai Hospital, several provincial nursing unions have now negotiated "professional responsibility" or "professional accountability" clauses. Such contract provisions provide nurses with routine administrative mechanisms to bring organizational problems affecting their practice to the attention of administrative superiors.[3]

The profession has also acted in response to the deficiencies recognized in nurses' increasingly pressured decision making. New systems to support clinical decision making have been developed and implemented through nursing's official regulatory bodies, officially sanctioned nursing school curricula, and professional associations. Hospitals have come to see the usefulness of objective assessment of the "quality" of nursing care using these information systems. "Quality assurance," as a management technique, requires yet more record-keeping from nurses, adding to the weight of paperwork for which they are responsible. To assess its adequacy, objectively, that is, documentarily, nurses' work must be conceptualized and recorded in special documents. Not only does this mean additional time spent in record-keeping, but it ties nurses even more tightly into the management-controlled, time-constrained version of nursing care. Their "product," at least its documentary reflection, is available to management scrutiny. Nurses become individually responsible for results identifiable in documents.

Meanwhile, the "quality assurance" system obscures the existence of time pressures on nurses. The staffing system has determined what is enough labour-time to get the work done; the quality assurance system sets objective outcomes for the work. The problem for nurses and their patients occurs when a discrepancy exists between the official version of needs and what nurses find to do in the actual workplace. Officially and organizationally, however, the disjuncture between nurses' professional judgement of what needs to be done for adequate care of patients and the "real needs" time allotments can be ignored. Officially, "quality of care" is defined documentarily, within the constraints of any specified and budgeted-for labour time. It has nothing to do with nurses' concerns about what else might be done to provide "good care."

With the new professional reliance placed on management information systems, a hospital loses any administrative-level knowledge that a problem exists for nurses and patients. Objective information, reported through proper channels, replaces procedures for listening to and relying on experienced professionals. Only nurses at the front line are aware of the disjuncture and what it means. And they are silenced and disempowered.

Nurses' control over their practice is lost when they can no longer control staffing decisions. Nurses continue to be held responsible for the outcome of their work in hospitals, while the conditions being organized there are outside their control. Working conditions may deteriorate, but the demands on nurses stay as high as ever. Nurses' own expectations of themselves as professionals also remain constant. Yet, they see that learning to fulfil documentary requirements will get them "full marks" on the new documentary monitoring system of "quality of care." Recognition for exercising their judgement, for extending themselves to meet needs they identify in their patients, is systematically erased. Nurses interviewed in the course of this study (Campbell, 1984) complained that their job satisfaction was declining, both because their work was not valued and because they felt they were no longer able to care for patients properly. They felt that paperwork had become more important than patient care. Nurses who have other options "flee the profession," as noted in a *Globe and Mail* article (1986). Others carry on and feel anxiety and self-blame. Talking about how she managed to get through a day's work when she did not have time to care for all her assigned patients, one nurse explained:

> Some patients take a lot more time (than I have to give). When you see that they need it, you have to take time from someone else who doesn't know how much care they are getting. It's not really fair (to the unconscious or confused patient) but that's the way you have to do it. (Campbell, 1984, p. 114)

Stress Effects

It is in such a context that nurses suffer "stress" effects. They absorb, on a continual basis, the risks involved in working with sick people under conditions of fiscal restraint. The pressures on them are heightened by coming under increasing (management) scrutiny. Failure to measure up to new demands can be reflected in poor performance evaluations, which have cumulative effects, and might even result in job loss. Walker (1986) gives the following definition of stress:

> The most popular version of the concept is Selye's (1956), which posits a physiological response to internal or external events or "stressors" that cause the body to mobilize for fight-or-flight by releasing adrenalin into the system. Since this is an animal response no longer appropriate to modern life, the body must react in other ways and the person experiences anxiety which must be controlled. This process is generally destructive if extreme, prolonged or frequent. (p. 14)

Burnout is a contemporary term that denotes a person's "response to a prolonged unavoidable and excessive stress in a work situation," according to Walker(1986, p. 15).

The literature that describes and analyzes burnout, Walker has argued, is part of the organization of managerial and therapeutic responses to "the problem." The popularization of this literature makes it possible for readers to recognize a constellation of symptoms, in themselves and others, as burn-out. This conceptual framework has administrative usefulness, as well. Through its use, burnout victims can be fitted into socially acceptable therapeutic categories, and organizationally sanctioned methods of handling workers' problems can be introduced. The range of responses to burnout runs the gamut from tranquillizers and rest cures for individuals to worker participation in management. In special burnout programs, workers are taught how to live with the new organizational realities and suffer less pain.

Nurses are among the people who are showing such symptoms. They experience them individually and personally. One of the popular versions of burnout, as the notion is applied to nurses, is that professionals, especially those in the "helping professions," expect too much of themselves. The concept of burn-out as an explanatory system helps to bypass the structural analysis, with its political implications. The preceding analysis of "cost-efficient" organization of the nursing labour process shows a different side to nurses' stress. Such personally experienced reactions have a definite and consciously planned etiology in the workplace. Pushing this analysis a little farther opens up larger social policy questions behind such organizational change.

We might ask who, in a democratic society, has the right to make the kind of health-care decisions that are being made "technologically" now. Is the Canadian public willing to "save money" in health care by putting its health-care workers and their service product at risk? When the stress symptoms that nurses suffer are restored to their proper administrative context, they lead analysis back to such fundamental questions. Retracing the organizational elements of nurses' problems can be the basis for rethinking the almost universally favourable response to attempts to improve hospital workers' "productivity" and "efficiency" and to bring modern management methods into hospitals. We have seen the latter providing the organizational capacity to erode health services, an outcome of which the Canadian public strongly disapproves. But such an administrative attack on health and social services, instituted through routine, even apparently progressive-appearing, organizational and professional practices, is less viable than cutting programs, shutting hospitals, or applying user fees. It may, therefore, be harder to resist.

Acknowledgements: The author gratefully acknowledges financial support from two sources: a National Health Student Fellowship for the original research, first reported in a doctoral dissertation; and a Social Sciences and Humanities Research Council Post-doctoral Fellowship during revision of this chapter.

Notes

1. The account given in this chapter draws on research carried out for my doctoral dissertation (Campbell, 1984). One hospital's nursing information and management systems were studied as an entry point for analyzing how a nursing labour process *could be controlled* through such information-based methods. More than a case study, the research offers a structural analysis of the managerial processes through which funding processes link specific policies to definite outcomes in geographically dispersed organizations. One particular patient classification system, from a possible dozen or so that are in common use across the country, was analyzed and is described here. The claim that I make is that regardless of the particularities of these systems, the *processes* I describe are the same wherever document-based decision making is done.

2. Unpublished notes for a 1981 update of Buchan's 1979 survey of staffing methodologies in use in Canadian hospitals suggests that this is a more or less standard practice in Ontario. Since then, other provincial governments have made funds available for hospitals to hire private consulting firms to introduce patient classification systems. Patient classification continues to be an important part of the nursing management repertoire, but is used less for staffing than in the beginning. Patient classification's newest potential use is in costing out nursing, to support nursing department claims for its share of funding allocated to hospitals on the basis of case-mix groupings according to P. Mehmert et al., in the article, "Computerizing nursing diagnosis" in *Nursing Management, 20*, (7), 24-30, 1989.

3. Clause 10 in the (1984) ONA collective agreement provides the following protection for nurses: "In the event that the Hospital assigns a number of patients or a workload to an individual nurse or group of nurses such that she or they have cause to believe that she or they are asked to perform more work than is consistent with proper patient care, she or they shall . . . (follow a specified procedure which includes a written complaint, attempting to solve the problem through a hospital committee set up for that purpose, or, failing that, forwarding the complaint to an Independent Review committee empowered to carry out and report on its own investigation)" (p. 7).

Study Questions

1. This article suggests that managing a hospital is not exactly like running a business. Identify some of the differences and some of the similarities. To become more "business-like" about hospital management, there must be trade-offs; what are they?

2. Physicians' training gives them skills in diagnosing and treating the symptoms that individual patients complain of. New diagnostic technology and improvements in medicine support an approach that focusses on the individual. How would an environmental approach to understanding stress differ from the current medical approach? Why might it be difficult for the medical profession to incorporate such an approach into their practice?

3. Professionals are expected to work independently to serve their patients or clients, whereas one expects non-professionals to require more supervision and external controls over their work. From what you have read about nurses in this article, do you consider them to be professionals? Why? Does the notion of "professionalism" adequately explain the differences in how physicians' and nurses' work is organized?

4. Nurses in Canada are now largely unionized under provincial labour laws. Very few physicians belong to unions. From the article, and from what you know about the medical profession, can you suggest why nurses need the protection afforded by collective bargaining more than doctors do?

Recommended Reading

Durber, C. (1982). *Professionals as workers: Mental labor in advanced capitalism.* Boston: G. K. Hall.

Torrance, G. (1987). Hospitals as health factories. In D. Coburn et al. (Eds.), *Health and Canadian society* (2nd ed.), (pp. 479-500). Markham: Fitzhenry & Whiteside.

VanLoon, R. (1978). From shared cost to block funding and beyond: The politics of health insurance in Canada. *Journal of Health Politics, Policy and Law*, 454-477.

Vayda, E., Evans, R., & Mindell, W. (1979). Universal health insurance in Canada: History, problems, trends. *Journal of Community Health, IV*, (3), 217-231.

Wahn, M. (1987). The decline of medical dominance. In D. Coburn et al., (Eds.), *Health and Canadian society* (2nd ed), (pp. 422-440). Markham: Fitzhenry & Whiteside.

Walker, G. A. (1986). Burnout: From metaphor to ideology. *Canadian Journal of Sociology*, 11, (1), 35-55.

White, R. (Ed.). (1985/1986). *Political issues in nursing: Past, present and future (Vols I and 2)*. Chichester: John Wiley & Sons.

References

Bennett, J., & Krasny, J. (1977, March 26 — May 7). Health care in Canada. *The Financial Post*. (Reprint of series).

Buchan, I. (1979). *Nurse staffing methodology in Canada*. Ottawa: Canadian Nurses' Association.

Campbell, M.L. (1984). *Information systems and management of hospital nursing: A study in social organization of knowledge*. Unpublished Ph.D dissertation. Toronto: Department of Education, University of Toronto, Department of Sociology in Education, OISE.

Canada Committee on the Cost of Health Services. (1970). *Task force reports on the cost of health services in Canada*. Ottawa: Queen's Printer.

Chua, W. F. (1991, July 8-10). *The social manufacture of hospital product costs*. (Paper presented at the 3rd International Perspectives on Accounting Conference). University of Manchester.

Freudenberger, H. (1975). Staff burn-out syndrome in alternative institutions. *Psychotherapy: Theory, Research and Practice XII*, 17-22.

Freudenberger, H. (1980). *Burn-out: The high cost of high achievement*. New York: Anchor Doubleday.

Giovannetti, P., & McKague, L. (1973). *Patient classification. System and staffing by workload index: A working manual*. Saskatoon: Hospital Systems Study Group.

Holmlund, B. (1967). *Nursing study phase 1, University Hospital*. Saskatoon: Hospital Systems Study Group.

Krawczyk, M. (1988, June). Is MIS investment the key to solid hospital management? *Health Care*, 10-11.

Sjoberg, K., & Bicknell, P. (1968). *Patient classification study*. Saskatoon: Hospital Systems Study Group.

Smith, D.E. (1984). Textually mediated social organization. *International Social Science Journal*, 36, (1), 59-75.

Vash, C. (1980). *The burnt-out administrator*. New York: Springer.

Walker, G. (1986). Burnout: From metaphor to ideology. *Canadian Journal of Sociology*, 11, (1), 35-55.

Chapter 29

Staff Nurses' Perceptions of Nursing: Issues in a Woman's Occupation

Joan Stelling, McGill University

Introduction

The 1980s were witness to increasing concern about the viability of our health-care system and the health of its component parts — a concern that is continuing into the 1990s. One of the worrisome areas has to do with nursing — shortages of nurses and high rates of turnover of hospital nursing staff in particular. This concern is evident in a proliferation of research on factors related to burnout, turnover, and retention of nurses, as well as in popular publications such as *Who Cares: The Crisis in Canadian Nursing* (Growe, 1991) and *Second Opinion: What's Wrong with Canada's Health Care System and How to Fix It* (Rachlis & Kushner, 1989). Working conditions in nursing have also been highlighted in recent documentary films (Sky, 1991; Tree & Huycke, 1991; Carota & Carota, 1991).

At 274 000 (in 1989), registered nurses comprise the largest category of workers in the health-care system, outnumbering physicians by more than four to one (Department of National Health and Welfare, 1990). Almost all registered nurses (90 percent) work in nursing; most (72 percent) are employed by hospitals (Statistics Canada, 1990). Among hospital nurses, 81 percent work as general-duty staff nurses, the bottom, or entry-level, position for newly graduated nurses (Statistics Canada, 1990). Hospitals depend on nurses to look after patients. Among all hospital employees, it is the nursing staff that is on the wards 24 hours a day, seven days a week. When there are not enough nurses, hospitals are forced to close beds. Bed closures affect patients, physicians, and all categories of hospital employees.

There are numerous signs that all is not well in nursing. Nurses have been vocal about their dissatisfaction with working conditions. There were nursing strikes in Alberta and Saskatchewan in 1988, a near miss in Manitoba in the same year, and strikes in British Columbia and Quebec in 1989. The complexity of nurses' work has been increasing. For a variety of reasons, the patients who are in hospital are sicker and require more care than was the case a few years ago. Corley and Mauksch estimate that the number of medications and treatments ordered for hospitalized patients has quadrupled in the past 30 years (1988, p. 141). As patient care has become more complex, the demand for registered nurses has increased, as has the pressure on nurses to continually upgrade their knowledge.[1] At the same time, rising costs have made provincial health ministers and, in turn, hospital administrators reluctant to provide resources sufficient to support the kind of staffing nurses think is necessary. As a result, the workloads are heavy and many nurses work overtime and extra shifts. In a Quebec survey, conducted by the Federation quebecoise des infirmieres et infirmiers, 78 percent of nurses surveyed reported working overtime, "without pay, staying late or reporting in early or by cutting short their rest periods and meal periods" (Ordre des infirmieres et infirmiers du Quebec, 1989, p. 17). Heavy workloads and excessive overtime, in combination with limited autonomy, relatively low pay, and little chance for advancement, can contribute to a disaffection with, and desire to change, one's job. Rachlis and Kushner believe that "unless steps are taken to make nursing more professionally and financially rewarding, we'll continue to lose nurses to other fields" (1989, p. 313).

There seems little reason to expect things to improve in the near future. In 1988 Employment and Immigration Canada reported a current shortage of nurses and predicted that it would persist, and perhaps worsen, during the 1990s (Employment and Immigration Canada, 1988). It is important to note that the financial aspect is only one of several factors contributing to nursing's problems. Making nursing more professionally rewarding, as advocated by Rachlis and Kushner (1989), would include such things as providing more opportunities for advancement, granting nurses' autonomy and control over their work, and increasing the recognition of their contribution to, and role in, health care.

In this chapter, data from general-duty staff nurses in Montreal provide the starting point for an examination of nursing and some of the factors underlying its current malaise. The data were collected from 85 nurses working in three Montreal hospitals. They come from two different research projects:

1. Study A: From 1984 to 1986 the author spent periods of six to nine months observing and interviewing staff nurses on each of three wards in a pediatric hospital. This research was undertaken at the behest of nursing administrators who

wanted to know how the recently implemented "primary nursing" was working.[2] In-depth, open-ended interviews were conducted with 51 nurses on the three wards. The interviews, which lasted approximately an hour, were tape-recorded.

2. Study B: This was a project designed to investigate invisible work in nursing. To elicit data, pictures of staff nurses at work were used as an interview tool to obtain detailed descriptions of nursing work from other staff nurses. There are two types of data from this project. The first comes from the arguments and discussions of the panel of five nurses who spent five days working together to select the pictures to be used for the interviews. The second comprises the interview data; twenty-nine staff nurses from three different hospitals were interviewed in this project.

I begin with a brief consideration of nursing as a woman's occupation, and then go on to look at the way these nurses talked about nursing and their work, what they liked about it, and what they disliked and/or found stressful. The data are subsequently discussed and interpreted in light of the sex-typing of nursing and its autonomy and ability to control its work.

Nursing — A Woman's Occupation

Nursing is the quintessential woman's occupation. Not only are almost all (97 percent) nurses women, but the image of nursing and nursing work is strongly linked to images of women, "womanhood," and mothering, and to beliefs about the "natural" endowments of women (Hughes, 1980; Corley & Mauksch, 1988; Reeder & Mauksch, 1979; Reverby, 1987; Coburn, 1987). The cultural assumption that women are "naturally" or "innately" qualified to be nurses belittles the knowledge and skill that the work requires and belies its complexity. The linkage between images of nursing and of women can also be seen in the mass media's treatment of nursing. Television series between 1950 and 1980 portrayed nurses as compassionate, self-sacrificing, and maternal (Kalisch, Kalisch, & Scobey, 1983). In addition, they were handmaidens, dependent on doctors to tell them what to do, with no patient care functions of their own.

> Their duties are only indirectly related to patient care. Nurses deliver medicine and food, monitor equipment, make notations in charts, push wheelchairs and carts, answer the phones, file things at the nursing station, and take orders from doctors. (p. 180)

Most series showed nurses as dependent on physicians to tell them what to do and to supervise their doing it. Hughes's analysis of the printed media (magazines, novels, newspapers) led her to a similar conclusion: "The public continues to view the nurse as dependent upon physician supervision and unable to function without medical direction" (1980, p. 69). In a recent American study, high-school sophomores held similar images of nursing. When compared to their ideal careers, nursing was found lacking in many things; among these were opportunities to be a leader, make decisions, be powerful, be appreciated, and be respected (Marriner-Tomey, Schwier, Maricke, & Austin, 1990).

By contrast, when nurses themselves talk about nursing, its work is portrayed as independent of and quite different from medicine. It differs in its orientation to, and emphasis on, the patient as an individual, and its focus on relational work with patients. It is not defined by medical orders. This kind of image is conveyed by the nurses appearing in recent documentary films on nursing (Skye, 1991; Tree & Huycke, 1991; Carota & Carota, 1991), as well as by the data from nurses in Montreal. There is still a strong connection with images of women, but the subservient, handmaiden image is notably absent.

Nurses Talk about Nursing

A Caring Profession

"A caring profession" is the phrase one of the Montreal nurses used to characterize nursing, and, indeed, nursing and caring seem to be inextricably linked. Leininger says caring is "the central and unifying domain" of nursing knowledge and practice (1981, p. 3). Caring suggests "being concerned" about someone, as well as "looking after" or "providing for." The nurses' concern is evident in the emphasis they gave to their role in providing support and empathy to patients and helping them manage their problems and deal with hospitalization.

> Just to be there and be able to help this person through it. (How do you help them?) In your support; in your being there . . . both physical and mental. Holding them when they need to be held, and talking, and the caring again. (A, ch. 1, p. 3)
>
> Just to get him through the next few days until he's feeling better and he can go home with his parents, get him through the worst, the sickest part of his hospitalization . . . it's just taking care of them for the time that they're in hospital and trying to do as much — not only as much for them as I can, but trying to help them cope with their hospitalization. (A, ch. 1, p. 115)

The nurses talked about looking after, or "taking care" of those who are sick and doing whatever is necessary to help them get better.

> When somebody gets ill, there's certain basic needs that they can't do themselves anymore . . . and we take on those needs for a little while. We take care of them, basically. (A, ch. 1, p. 6)
>
> Taking care of people that can't . . . look after themselves while they're sick; making sure that they're okay and all their needs are fulfilled . . . (What kinds of things does taking care of them involve?) Everything, from washing them to feeding them to giving them medication to changing dressings — to make sure they get well as fast as possible, make sure they don't have to come back. (A, ch. 1, p. 10)

The "taking care" includes attending to "the need for food, for care, for attention" (A, ch. 1, p. 19). The act of caring is thus very encompassing; it can include whatever is thought to be needed by the patient.

The nurses also emphasized their role in teaching patients and families about things which are specific to the patient's particular condition, as well as broader aspects of prevention and health behaviours. A staff nurse on a pediatric ward said:

> How I see nursing? It's somebody who can help prevent, and to give advice to people, and working a lot in the community about that. I see nursing like a change agent, somebody who . . . can teach people that it's better to prevent the disease, than heal the disease . . . somebody who can help to prevent. (Do you see that in the nursing role in the hospital as well?) Yes, in clinic . . . Even in the ward, when you know that somebody came for a treatment, and if something had been done right at home, the patient wouldn't have (had to) come here. There's a place for prevention; tell the parents how to manage. Sometimes it's only how to feed a baby. . . . It's always time to do prevention. You just have to notice how parents manage with their child and you can help them with many things. (A, ch. 3, p. 12)

These nurses saw themselves as a link between patients and other health professionals involved in patient care. One said, "I'm the link between medical care and emotional care and all types of care" (A, ch. 1, p. 2), and another, "You're not treating; you're just helping someone to be treated" (A, ch. 3, p. 6). They talk about being a "spokesperson" or "advocate," stressing the role of an agent who represents the patient's interests to other health professionals and monitors the treatment and care of the patient. One said she felt like a "watchdog for the patient . . . you just sort of have to make sure that everything goes along . . . as it should" (A, ch. 3, p. 2).

> We're standing for the patient's rights, like there's a bunch of blood tests or something that were done the day before and aren't really necessary to be repeated; ask a doctor if it's really necessary that they are done again, and let him know they were done; try to decrease the invasive procedures to the child as much as possible; avoid doctors waking kids up. (A, ch. 2, p. 9)
>
> I find I'm much more involved in . . . relating to, involving myself with other professionals, and getting involved with the doctors and really becoming involved in the whole care of this patient, not just helping

them. . . . Initially I thought I was just going to follow orders, but now I've found that I don't just do that; I
think a lot more. I more or less involve myself in saying, "Well, why is this happening to him? Why did you
decide to do this, rather than this?" (A, ch. I, p. 12)

Thus they portrayed nursing as the centre of care, describing their role as a pivotal
one so far as patient care is concerned. They talked not only about providing care
themselves, but also about seeing that patients receive appropriate care and treatment
from others. This is quite different from the peripheral role seen in the television series.
The nurses' descriptions do not convey a picture of the nurse as subservient to and
dependent on the physician. Even the one who had expected that kind of role found that
her work was not circumscribed by physicians' orders.

The way they talked about nursing points to the importance the nurses placed on
their interaction and relational work with patients.[3] They talked about how much
patients need emotional support, comfort, and teaching, as well as about the satisfaction
they get from meeting these needs. They talked, for example, about the importance of
empathy, of listening, of working to calm people and allay the anxiety of those faced
with disfiguring surgery or death. Good relationships with patients are critical to these
aspects of nursing work. In addition, getting to know their patients facilitates decisions
about nursing interventions. The process of establishing and using such relationships
requires skill and is often time-consuming and emotionally draining. One nurse said
that to build a "trust relationship," it is important to be open and not hide behind the
professional role:

They have to feel that they can connect to something, or to somebody that is there behind — behind the roles
. . . you have to give them some opening where they can reach out to you. (B, p. 207).

Recent research in nursing defines caring as "a nurturing way of relating to a valued
other toward whom one feels a personal sense of commitment and responsibility"
(Swanson, 1991, p. 165). Both the specific activities described by the nurses and the
emphasis placed on the interactional and relational work can be subsumed by this
definition.

The Dark Side of Caring

When asked what they disliked about nursing, the two most common complaints were:
having to do work that is not nursing and that they think they shouldn't have to do,
and being understaffed and overworked. On the surface, these things have more to do
with working conditions than with nursing per se. Nonetheless, they can be seen,

respectively, as (1) related to the centrality of caring in nursing and nursing's link with motherhood and, (2) a manifestation of the low value placed on caring.

Non-Nursing Work

Citing a study by the Ontario Nurses' Association, the Order of Nurses of Quebec reports that non-nursing work takes up 30 percent of nurses' time (Ordre des infirmieres et infirmiers du Quebec, 1989, p. 24). In an editorial titled "Fatal Availability," Curtin suggests that the shortage of nurses may be an artifact of the amount of time nurses spend on non-nursing.

> We may, indeed, have plenty of nurses; it's just that nurses don't have enough time to provide good nursing care and perform the chores — at one time or another — of almost every direct care-related department in the hospital . . . wouldn't it be worthwhile to see what might happen if "support" services really did support patient care — all the time, every day, even on weekends? (1988, p. 9)

The panel of nurses who selected pictures to be used in the interviews in Study B spent a lot of time talking about the "non-nursing" work that nurses do, arguing that they shouldn't have to do it. Those interviewed shared the panel's views on this. The non-nursing work included work the nurses thought belonged to others such as secretaries, porters, orderlies, housekeeping staff, kitchen staff, and maintenance workers. They disliked non-nursing work because much of it is seen as menial work. One nurse said it made him feel like "a maid with a diploma," while another said "if there is a spill or an accident anywhere, there is a nurse coming in with a mop, you know. Looks very professional!" (B, p. 226).

They also dislike it because it takes time away from nursing, which is particularly annoying when they have a heavy workload.

Even though they dislike it and think it should be done by others, they reported doing a lot of non-nursing work, saying that it is often easier and faster to do it than to get the "right" person to do it. Much of the non-nursing work is done during evening and night shifts and on weekends, when the "right" person is off duty. Departments charged with maintaining and repairing equipment, for example, are likely to be closed after four or five o'clock in the afternoon and on weekends; many hospital wards have clerical staff for only 35 hours a week; during the other 133 hours, it is the nurses who pick up the slack. They often justified doing this work on the grounds that it was in their patients' best interests or that the patient would suffer or be uncomfortable if they didn't. One of the panel nurses said, for example, "you make a snack for somebody because it's — they haven't eaten. I mean you have to provide nutrition — but it's still not our job to make food."

There are two complementary ways of looking at the prevalence of non-nursing work in nursing. It can be seen as a function of the association between nursing and women's work, in particular the frequent analogy between the work of nurses and that of mothers. Several of the nurses drew this analogy, saying that they did these things much as a mother would at home. Non-nursing work can also be viewed in the context of the definition of care. Arguing that nursing has been shaped by the "obligation to care," Reverby describes caring as "an unbounded act, difficult to define, even harder to control" (1987, p. 1). Certainly it is clear that an ideology of patient care that gives nursing the responsibility of looking after the patient's best interests makes it very difficult to impose limits or boundaries on nursing work. Both motherhood and nursing are shaped by the obligation to care; both are charged with (and take on) the responsibility of looking after those in their care. That responsibility and the "best interests" of their charges can provide a justification for almost any activity. Such justifications are used by nurses to rationalize their non-nursing work; they also serve to support others' expectations that nurses will "pick up the slack."

Too Much Work

Staff nurse complaints about being understaffed and overworked are widespread (Corley & Mauksch, 1988). Nurses studied by Prescott and Bowen identified workload, staffing, and time with patients as the most influential factors in their decisions to resign from their jobs (1987). Workload has been found to be a major source of stress among nurses (Walters & Haines, 1989) and to be related to nurse burnout (Robinson et al., 1991). Workload was clearly an issue for the Montreal nurses, as well. Having too much work and too few nurses were identified as conditions that they most disliked and that they found stressful.

One of the things that happens when staffing is short is that the nurses feel simply overloaded with work. They talked about "running all the time," things being hectic or crazy, working overtime (often without pay), and being exhausted by the end of their work day.

> You work hard. You work hard. . . . We don't have to be there until 7:30, and I would come on at 7:00 to get started. And sometimes give up that coffee break — never lunch. And we're supposed to get off at 3:30, and often, often it would be 4:15 — and never apply for overtime because they make it very hard to get it. (B, p. 103)
>
> Sometimes the expectation that people have from you — patients or co-workers or supervisor — that it doesn't matter if you miss lunch or coffee or supper, or you work late. That's expected of you. Nurses are never supposed to go on coffee break on time; you're never supposed to sort of leave for lunch on time. Or you can miss supper, and you won't be paid overtime . . . when you're very busy and you're tired, well that's

expected. And I feel very responsible for my patients . . . but it's sort of — we are overloaded. We are. There's a lot of expectations from us, in terms of the work load. (A, ch. 2, p. 6)

The extra pressure. Like when you're in the middle of a hurricane. Very often I feel like everyone wants you at the same time. You cannot do what you have to do, because you're missing — it could be equipment or somebody else you need who's not there, not available — and you have about three people calling you at the same time, and then another problem arises. (A, ch. 3, p. 6)

One of the younger nurses said the hectic pace did not bother her, although she wasn't sure that would continue to be the case:

If you love what you are doing, you don't see that as a big thing. But . . . (if you) see what you do during one day, and if you think about it, it's crazy. You know, it's — now it's really — you're not stopping. Like I said before, sometimes we don't even have time to go to eat. So that's hard on your body — that's — so — I don't know if, in the long run, I'm going to feel the same way, you know? But I enjoy working as a nurse now. (B, p. 104)

The flip side of too much work is too little time. For these nurses, time is a critical resource. When it is in scarce supply, their work day is not only hectic, but they are unable to do their work the way they think it should be done.

I guess the worst part about nursing is when it's so busy that you don't know what you're doing any more. And you're just running like crazy, and you're not doing a good job, and you know it. And you leave the floor when you finish 1-2 hours late for your shift, and you know that you missed something and somebody could have had better care than they got. That's one of the bad things. (A, ch. 2, p. 9)

When the floor is busy and you don't have time to do your job right . . . you leave and you have a feeling that you could have done more, and you didn't give all the time that you should have given and that the patient needed. I think that's frustrating. (A, ch. 1, p. 1)

Being too busy to "do your job right" is frustrating for these nurses, and it increases their anxiety about safety and potential mistakes. One talked generally about the risk of mistakes. "It's people's lives, really. They could make mistakes that, uhm, could be serious . . . especially when things are too busy, really too busy (B, p. 103)."

Another related an experience she had on the night shift when working with one other nurse and one assistant:

The floor was 36 kids . . . and I was sick all night, but I kept on because [the supervisor] said, "Go lie down an hour, but you have to stay." . . . We were both really scared, because we had meds to give to 36 kids . . . we were responsible for everything . . . so, it's scary. Sometimes I find that the floor is unsafe. (A, ch. 1, p. 7)

Nurses interviewed by Walters and Haines were similar in their concern about safety and their belief that work overload compromised safety (1989).

The Montreal nurses also reported that being too busy made it impossible to do some of the work that they believed important and found satisfying.

> A big frustration, of course, is knowing that all this stuff should be done — setting the lady's hair, getting her ready for her birthday party — but not having the time because there aren't enough nurses. . . . Knowing that that is part of nursing, and enjoying doing that sort of stuff, and knowing that it's important, but not doing it, and that (causes) a lot of frustration. And resentment. (B, p. 103)
>
> I feel we are becoming technicians, in a way, whose main concerns are sort of vital signs, medications, and dressings. And that is what you base your day on, not the interaction between the nurse and the patient. Some days I feel I haven't done anything but sort of vitals and dressings and pills and that, I feel, it's awful. It's — I don't get anything out of that. That — that's a job . . . it's just tasks, and I do them because they have to be done, but that's not what I went into nursing for. (B, p. 218)

It is not that the nurses think that vital signs, medications, and dressings are unimportant or unnecessary or that they are not a nursing responsibility. To paraphrase one of the respondents, they are tasks that have to be done; they are a nursing responsibility, but they do not epitomize nursing.

Campbell reports that nurses learn to deal with time pressures by assigning different levels of priority to the things that need doing; when they are short of time, they give patients fewer services and less attention (1988). She argues that having to make "decisions about cutting out some of the nursing care their patients actually need puts nurses under even more pressure" (1988, p. 400). The problem, from the perspective of nurses, is that nursing gets slighted in favour of other aspects of nurses' work. Masson describes nursing as time-dependent, arguing that as the operating room is essential to surgeons, so time is necessary to nurses — without it, they cannot do nursing:

> When time is lacking, they are able to perform only those functions that revolve around medications, medically prescribed procedures, and machines. (Masson, 1985, p. 72)

In other words, the "caring" work of nursing takes second place to the work ordered by physicians. When it is not possible to do everything, such physician-derived tasks assume a higher priority than the interaction and relational work that nurses place at the heart of nursing and which many see as the most satisfying part of their work. Whether a nurse opts to omit some of this work or tries to "do it all," she is likely to come away with a sense of a "job not well done." In either case there are repercussions for her satisfaction with her work, her sense of effectiveness, and her self-esteem.

Discussion

There is a real incongruity between nurses' portrayal of their occupation as independent and nursing-defined and the amount of autonomy and control they are able to command. That autonomy and control can be seen to reflect the value placed on nursing, which, in turn, is limited by the belief that nursing is a woman's occupation.

Autonomy and Control

The lack of formal power and authority makes it difficult if not impossible for nursing to control its working conditions and protect its "right to nurse." Frisch, Dembach, and Shannon (1989) report that the head nurses in their sample often felt powerless, that is they had "responsibility without comparable authority" (p.11). But if that is true of head nurses, it is at least equally true of staff nurses, who have, at best, a tenuous hold on power. In many instances, their frustrations are exacerbated by their powerlessness. To quote one of the nurses in the documentary *The Right to Care*, "They expect us to know all, be all, and do all, but we don't have the power to change anything."

Nursing has been, and in many ways continues to be, a subordinate occupation. Nurses, as women, lack the power and autonomy enjoyed by physicians who carry an aura of male power and authority. The limitations on nurses' autonomy and ability to control their work are at odds with their description of nursing as a discipline in its own right, different and separate from medicine. The argument made here is that issues of autonomy and control underlie the dark side of nursing. Two different examples are used to illustrate this: nursing's preoccupation with safety and mistakes and the opportunity to nurse.

The Preoccupation with Safety and Mistakes

There are many indicators of nursing's preoccupation with issues of patient safety and potential mistakes. Hospital nursing departments have a proliferation of policy and procedure manuals to explain the "correct" way to do specific procedures and treatments.[4] Nursing administrators stress the importance of being "safe," and not having enough nurses to provide safe care is seen as a valid reason to limit the number of patients admitted to a hospital or a specific ward. In pediatric hospitals staff nurses keep a close eye on new medical students and interns to make sure that they do not leave a baby unattended while the crib-side is down; in nursing homes, using physical restraints to keep a patient in bed or in a wheel chair is rationalized on the grounds of patient safety. A column titled "Medication Errors" is a regular feature in *Nursing 91*, an American magazine for nurses. New nurses are warned that they must always check the medications that have been ordered for their patients, that the Nuremburg laws apply and "following orders" is no excuse. Finally, in many hospitals nurses are required to file written reports of "incidents." Incidents include errors of commission, such as giving the wrong medication; errors of omission, such as not giving a medication or failing to record something in a patient's chart; and "accidents," such as a patient falling out of bed or a visitor slipping on a wet floor. The emphasis on safety, on mistakes, and on having a written, signed record of incidents can contribute to the occupational stress experienced by staff nurses when circumstances, such as time pressures, work against error-free performance.

More important here, however, is the question of why nursing seems so concerned about these issues. Since the mistakes of health professionals can have serious consequences for patients, this preoccupation may seem unremarkable or natural. But physicians' mistakes can be equally fateful, yet there is no comparable preoccupation in medicine. Physicians are more likely to talk about "errors of judgement" and to believe that all that can reasonably be expected is that they "do their best, under the circumstances" (Stelling & Bucher, 1973). Paget (1988) found medical mistakes to be actions that *become* wrong — they are defined retrospectively, in light of "new" information; as one of her respondents said, "The errors are errors now, but weren't errors then." Medical errors are seen as an inevitable by-product of the nature of the work and the state of medical knowledge. Thus they are both expected and attributed to the work, not the worker. For nursing, the high salience of potential mistakes suggests that they are expected. In this case, however, they are attributed to the worker, not to the work. Nurses are held responsible, often blamed, for their errors. Unlike physicians, they do not have a "licence to err."

As a subordinate occupation that operates in an arena where mistakes are both likely and potentially disastrous and that is held culpable for errors, nursing needs to protect itself.[5] The preoccupation with safety and mistakes can be seen as a way of doing this. The emphasis on safety, incident reports, and procedure manuals are safety nets designed to "catch" or prevent mistakes. They have a protective function, too, when they serve as evidence that nursing has done everything possible to prevent mistakes and thus is not to be blamed when they happen.

Safety nets may catch mistakes, but they also ensnare the nurse's autonomy. Nurses are urged to "be professional" and to "exercise judgement," at the same time that they are expected to abide by procedure manuals and accept supervision. It seems that the nurse's freedom to exercise professional judgement is contingent on not making a mistake.[6]

Thus the emphasis on safety and mistakes is seen to derive from nursing's subordinate position;[7] it also serves to reinforce that subordinate status by contributing to the constraints on nurses' autonomy and control.

The Opportunity to Nurse

Complaints about too much work and too little time are not unique to nursing; they can be heard in other occupations as well. It is not possible to say whether time deprivation is worse in nursing, but its meaning may be different. One might ask in what other occupations is it seen to result in the core work of the occupation being routinely pushed aside in favour of peripheral tasks and work that belongs to others.

Let us reconsider Masson's (1985) characterization of nursing as time-dependent, and her argument that depriving nurses of time means they can only do medical tasks, not nursing. Her argument seems to make sense and to help explain many of the things the nurses said about their work. But if depriving them of time means they can do medical, but not nursing, work, then it would seem that the real issue is not the amount of time, but the lack of power to control how the available time will be used. More generally, nurses' complaints about lack of time and their attribution of time pressure to such things as understaffing and others' unrealistic expectations can be seen as statements about the lack of power to impose their definitions of nursing work and to exercise control over their workload and conditions of work. Time thus becomes a metaphor for autonomy and control. If time is a metaphor, decreasing the time deprivation might have little effect on the opportunity to nurse.

Valuing Nursing

Nursing's association with images of women and mothers rebounds on the way it is valued in our society. Nursing centres around the act of caring, something which has been assumed to be the natural domain of women, and which is accomplished through the interactional and relational work for which women are assumed to be naturally talented. The assumption or belief that what women do is a product or expression of their "nature" is not without consequences. Our culture puts a high value on acquired knowledge and skills and little value on those believed to be innate or natural. Work that is attributed to women's natural capabilities carries little value as such.

> Since interactional work is related to what constitutes being a woman, with what a woman is, the idea that it is work is obscured. The work is not seen as what women do, but as part of what they are. (Fishman, 1982, p. 180, emphasis in original.)

The fact that it is work is not always recognized, even by the women who do it. The panel nurses tended to reject pictures that showed a nurse who was "just chatting" or "just talking" on the phone or "just comforting" someone. Reverby (1987) describes nursing as being obliged to care in a society that does not value caring. Nurses, of course, are part of that society and influenced by it; however great the importance they give to caring, they often have trouble defining it as work. Nursing's lack of power to define and control its work and to enforce its priorities is generated and supported by the low value placed on caring.

Nurses' commitment to their patients and their peers, their somewhat doubtful recognition of relational work as real work, and their inability to give it a high priority ranking, contribute to the amount of overtime they work and to their failure to consistently report or claim this work. Several nurses told us that they would claim overtime if it was due to a medical emergency, but not if they were late because they had taken the time to be with a patient. In many hospitals, nurses must justify their overtime claims, and they find this easier to do when it is "medical," not nursing, work that has made them late. The medical work is easily recognized as work, whereas the interactional work of nursing is often suspect — for those who require that overtime be justified, as well as for the nurses themselves.

As nursing work is suspect, so is the professional commitment of nurses. Corley and Mauksch (1987) say that nurses' commitment to their patients is dismissed by being:

> defined as fitting into a female stereotype and, thus, as a natural by-product of a female role. . . . A set of
> characteristics, which otherwise would earn applause and prestige, can be neutralized if not trivialized when
> identified with the presumed natural consequences of low status attributes. (p. 136)

An illustration of the way nurses' commitment is overlooked can be found in the work of Zerubavel (1981). In a sociological analysis of time, he talks about professional commitment in terms of temporal boundaries. He argues that because physicians do not leave the hospital or their office until they have finished their work and, furthermore are "on call" even when not physically present, their commitment is not bound by time and is, accordingly, seen as very strong. By way of contrast, he comments on the "rigidity" of these boundaries for nurses, saying that "unlike physicians, nurses stop working not upon having completed their daily work assignments, but rather when the clock indicates the end of their shift. (p. 162)

He notes that nurses regularly do stay late, but dismisses this observation, saying they only do this to complete work that was scheduled for their shift. Thus it seems that tasks that would be work if done during the nurse's shift fail to qualify if done when she is off duty. Zerubavel also says, parenthetically, that it is usually impossible for nurses to finish their charting on time, and hence:

> (It is not unusual that a nurse would leave the hospital only about an hour, or even an hour and a half, past the
> official end of her shift.) On such occasions, however, they are clearly not expected to fulfill and assume any
> other nursing duties and responsibilities. (p. 165; parentheses in original)

So it also seems that if she is not available to take on other nursing duties, she is not working. One could argue, however, that it is only when she is "off duty" that she is able to control the interruptions and say, "Don't bother me, I'm busy." If she were able to exercise that control during her shift, there might be less need to stay late. But Zerubavel doesn't ask why it is impossible for nurses to finish on time, or whether the frequency of overtime might have some relevance to commitment.

There is an irony here. Women are supposed to give first priority to their families, and are consequently assumed or expected to have a lesser commitment to their careers. Somehow nurses' commitment to their patients, which is manifest in the way they talk about nursing and their work, in the overtime they work, and in their willingness to "pick up the slack," seems to be equated to women's "natural" commitment to their families and thereby deemed irrelevant to their professional commitment. Thus it becomes invisible and doesn't count as commitment.

This lesser commitment is often used to rationalize women's lower salaries and poor representation in the ranks of upper management. Yet hospitals, and other sectors of health care, bank heavily on nurses' occupational commitment to their patients. They bank on that commitment, for example, when they assume that nurses will provide care in spite of increasing workloads, or that they will pick up the slack left by other departments whose staff do not work 24 hours a day. As Corley and Mauksch point out:

> Awareness of the level of commitment among nurses served as a basis and justification for neglect and reduced responsibility on the part of other hospital workers, regardless of occupation . . . the knowledge of the commitment among nurses absolves others, particularly those in positions of power, from a sense of guilt or failure. (1987, p. 141)

On the one hand, nurses' caring and commitment does not translate into either power or high financial reward because they are assumed to come from the natural attributes of nurses as women. On the other hand, it is assumed that nurses have the knowledge and skills necessary to cover for staff in other departments and that they can be counted on to do so. Talking about the range of tasks nurses undertake, especially during off hours, one of the Montreal nurses remarked, "Just ask a nurse. She can do anything!"

The perception that nurses' work is women's work has consequences for the nature of the rewards, as well as for the problems and frustrations of nursing work. So long as that perception remains, and so long as the image of women is such that their work is devalued, accomplishing real change in nursing may depend on significant change in the status of women and the value of their work.

The question of cui bono is also relevant here. Those who benefit from the way nursing work is structured and rewarded are likely to resist changing it. If nursing was granted more power and autonomy, the use of that power to change its work priorities would have repercussions for all the other occupations in the health-care system, as well as for the organizations that administer health care. Given the value Canadians place on their health-care system, however, public perception of the "crisis" in nursing as a serious threat to the health-care system could trigger changes in spite of the opposition of other occupations. To this end, the sympathetic portrait drawn by such authors as Growe (1991) and Rachlis and Kushner (1987) may stand nursing in good stead.

Acknowledgements: One of the research projects reported here (Study B) was supported by two grants from the Social Sciences and Humanities Research Council of Canada. Darcie Olijnek was an important and valued colleague on this project: the contributions of Dawn Fowler and Ian Graham were critical in the development and early stages of the research. I would also like to acknowledge and thank Sara Frisch for her review and criticism of earlier drafts of this paper.

Notes

1. The Canadian Nursing Association wants all new nurses to have a baccalaureate degree by the year 2000. Whether they will accomplish this remains to be seen. Of those graduating in 1989, approximately 25 percent came out of degree, as opposed to diploma, programs. (Health Personnel in Canada, 1989).
2. Primary nursing is a way of organizing nursing care such that each nurse has full responsibility for the care of patients assigned to her. This contrasts with "team nursing," for example, in which a team leader decides what care patients need and then assigns specific duties to the nurses on her team.
3. Relational work is broadly defined as work that is involved in dealing with, managing, changing, or controlling behaviour, feelings, and emotions. It may be done with, or directed at, oneself or others, including co-workers and patients (Stelling & Olijnek, 1991).
4. Nurses who move from one hospital to another may find that what is defined as the right way to do a procedure is hospital specific, rather than standard across all hospitals.
5. The Susan Nelles case strengthened and reinforced nurses' perception of their vulnerability and cupability when something goes wrong.
6. In earlier work we have argued that it is unrealistic to expect nurses to take responsibility for making decisions unless they have the authority and the leeway to make the wrong decision. (Stelling et al., 1988)
7. Sara Frisch has suggested that guarding the safety of those deemed incapable of looking after themselves is also part of the role of mother, and that nursing's concern with safety may thus be another manifestation of the links between nursing and the more generalized roles of women (personal communication).

Study Questions

1. Nursing has been called a subordinate occupation. What do you think this means? How, or in what way, is it subordinate? Why is this so? What contributes to or supports its subordination?
2. Assuming that nurses are to be granted the power and autonomy to define and control their work and working conditions, consider the consequences of this for patients, nurses, other health-care workers, hospitals, and the health-care system.
3. How would nursing look or be different if it were a man's occupation?

4. Are there similarities between nursing and other occupations considered to be particularly appropriate for women, such as elementary-school teachers or secretaries?

Recommended Reading

Campbell, M.L. (1988). The structure of stress in nurses' work. In B. S. Bolaria & H. D. Dickinson (Eds.), *Sociology of health care in Canada* (pp. 393-405). Toronto: Harcourt Brace Jovanovich.

Coburn, J. (1987). I see and am silent: A short history of nursing in Ontario, 1850-1930. In D. Coburn, C. D'Arcy, G.M. Torrance, & P. New (Eds.), *Health and Canadian society: Sociological perspectives* (pp. 441-462). Markham: Fitzhenry & Whiteside.

Corley, M. C., & Mauksch, H. O. (1988). Registered nurses, gender, and commitment. In A. Statham, E.M. Miller, & H.O. Mauksch (Eds.), *The worth of women's work: A qualitative synthesis* (pp. 135-149). Albany: State University of New York.

Growe, S.J. (1991). *Who cares: The crisis in Canadian nursing.* Toronto: McClelland & Stewart.

Reeder, S.J., & Mauksch, H. (1979). Nursing: Continuing change. In H.E. Freeman, S. Levine, & L.G. Reader (Eds.), *Handbook of medical sociology* (pp. 209-229). Englewood Cliffs: Prentice Hall.

Reverby, S. (1987). *Ordered to care: The dilemma of American nursing, 1850-1945.* Cambridge: Cambridge University Press.

Walters, V., & Haines, T. (1989). Workload and occupational stress in nursing. *The Canadian Journal of Nursing Research*, 21, (3), 49-58.

References

Campbell, M.L. (1988). The structure of stress in nurses' work. In B.S. Bolaria & H.D. Dickinson (Eds.), *Sociology of health care in Canada* (pp. 393-405). Toronto: Harcourt Brace Jovanovich.

Carota, L. (Director and Producer), & Carota, L. (Producer). (1991). *A nurse's opinion* [Film]. Produced by East in Motion Pictures, Montreal: National Film Board of Canada.

Coburn, J. (1987). I see and am silent: A short history of nursing in Ontario, 1850-1930. In D. Coburn, C. D'Arcy, G.M. Torrance, & P. New (Eds.), *Health and Canadian society: Sociological perspectives* (pp. 441-462). Markham: Fitzhenry & Whiteside.

Corley, M.C., & Mauksch, H.O. (1988). Registered nurses, gender, and commitment. In A. Statham, E.M. Miller, & H.O. Mauksch (Eds.), *The worth of women's work: A qualitative synthesis* (pp. 135-149). Albany: State University of New York.

Curtin, L.L. (1988, December 12). Fatal availability. *Nursing Management*, 19, 9-10.

Department of National Health and Welfare. (1990). *Health Personnel in Canada, 1989.* Ottawa: Department of National Health and Welfare.

Devault, M. (1984). *Women and food: Housework and the production of family Life.* Ph.D. Dissertation, Northwestern University.

Employment and Immigration Canada. (1988). *The labour market for nurses in Canada: A summary discussion and analysis.* Ottawa: Employment and Immigration Canada.

Fishman, P.M. (1982). Interaction: The work women do. In R. Kahn-Hut, A. Kaplan Daniels, & R. Colvard (Eds.), *Women and work: Problems and perspectives* (pp. 170-180). New York: Oxford University Press.

Frisch, S. R., Dembeck, P., & Shannon, V. (in press). *What stresses head nurses? How do they cope?* Paper presented at 2nd Management of Nursing Practice Research Conference, Halifax, January, 1989. (This paper is "in press" at the Canadian Journal of Nursing Administration.)

Growe, S.J. (1991). *Who cares: The crisis in Canadian nursing.* Toronto: McClelland & Stewart.

Hughes, L. (1980, April). The public image of the nurse. *Advances in Nursing Science*, 3, (3), 55-72.

Kalisch, P.A., & Kalisch, B.J. (1984). Sex role stereotyping of nurses and physicians on prime-time television: A dichotomy of occupational portrayals. *Sex Roles*, 10, (7/8), 533-553.

Kalisch, P.A., Kalisch, B.J., & Scobey, M. (1983). *Images of nurses on television.* New York: Springer Publishing Company.

Leininger, M.M. (1981). The phenomenon of caring: Importance, research questions, and theoretical considerations. In M.M. Leininger (Ed.), *Caring: An essential human need* (pp. 3-15). Thorofare: Charles B. Slack.

Marriner-Tomey, A., Schwier, B., Maricke, N., & Austin, J. (1990). Sophomore high school students' perceptions of ideal and nursing career choices. *Nursing Forum*, 25, (2), 27-30.

Masson, V. (1985). Nurse and doctors as healers: Personal observations on the relationship — and the distinctions between nursing and medicine. *Nursing Outlook*, 33, (2), 70-73.

Ordre des infirmieres et infirmiers du Quebec. (1989). *The facts: Hypertension: An urgent need for action.* Montreal: Ordre des infirmieres et infirmiers du Quebec.

Paget, M.A. (1988). *The unity of mistakes: A phenomenological interpretation of medical work.* Philadelphia: Temple University Press.

Prescott, P., & Bowen, S. (1987). Controlling nursing turnover. *Nursing Management*, 18, (6), 60-66.

Rachlis, M., & Kushner, C. (1989). *Second opinion: What's wrong with Canada's health care system and how to fix it.* Toronto: Collins.

Reeder, S.J., & Mauksch, H. (1979). Nursing: Continuing change. In H.E. Freeman, S. Levine, & L.G. Reader (Eds.), *Handbook of medical sociology* (pp. 209-229). Englewood Cliffs: Prentice Hall.

Reverby, S. (1987). *Ordered to care: The dilemma of American nursing, 1850-1945.* Cambridge: Cambridge University Press.

Robinson, S.E., Roth, S.L., Keim, J., Levenson, M., Flentje, J.R., & Bashor, K. (1991). Nurse burnout: Work related and demographic factors as culprits. *Research in Nursing and Health*, 14, 223-228.

Sky, L. (Director and Producer) (1991). *The right to care* [Film].Toronto: Sky Works.

Statistics Canada (1990). *Nursing in Canada: Registered nurses, 1989. Health Reports*, supplement No. 22, Volume 2 (3). Ottawa: Statistics Canada.

Stelling, J., & Bucher, R. (1973, September). Vocabularies of realism in professional socialization. *Social Science and Medicine*, 7, 431-446.

Stelling, J., & Olijnek, D. (1991). *Paradoxes of nursing work.* Paper presented at the annual meeting of the Canadian Sociology and Anthropology Association, Kingston, Ontario.

Swanson, K. M. (1991). Empirical development of a middle range theory of caring. *Nursing Research*, 40, (3), 161-166.

Tree, T., (Director and Producer, Pax Productions) & Huycke, S. (Producer, National Film Board of Canada) (1991). *Nursing: The heart of the system* [Film]. Toronto: Magic Lantern.

Walters, V., & Haines, T. (1989). Workload and occupational stress in nursing. *The Canadian Journal of Nursing Research*, 21, (3), 49-58.

Chapter 30

The Social Construction of Risk in Nursing: Nurses Responses to Hazards in their Work

Vivienne Walters, McMaster University

Introduction

The identification of hazards in the workplace is not simply a matter of scientific documentation of the health consequences of exposure. Risk is not an inherent property that only has to be identified. It is a social concept, and the social construction of risk involves complex social processes, wherein risks are categorized as acceptable or unacceptable, and associated physical or mental states as normal or pathological. The data produced by scientific experts — medical researchers, epidemiologists, industrial hygienists — are only one element in these processes. Indeed, experts themselves may dispute whether or not a particular substance is to be regarded as a hazard (Murray, 1988; Schrecker, 1988). As Nelkin and Brown (1984) note, risk is embedded in social and political relationships, and perceptions of risk depend as much on the social context as on the nature of the hazards.

A classic case study of the processes involved in the social construction of a disease is Smith's (1981) research on black lung. She looks at the different and changing constructions of black lung among workers and within medicine. Workers who had once accepted the symptoms of black lung as "normal," came to see it as an occupational disease. Smith describes the conditions under which definitions changed, and the struggles that led to a societal recognition of black lung as a disease eligible for compensation. Among the factors influencing societal constructions of risk are the relations between capital, labour, and the state; the resources they can draw upon; and the extent to which they can harness scientific knowledge to their own ends. For example, concepts of risk will reflect the extent to which employers can resist the recognition of hazards and the extent to which workers can press alternative definitions. When working conditions are redefined as hazardous, and illnesses and injuries are recognized, there is the potential for improvements in working conditions.

The role of labour in the social construction of risk is critical. A growing body of research suggests that the greater the strength of workers; movements and the greater workers' participation in the identification of hazards, the better their working conditions, their health and safety, policies to regulate the work environment, and compensation for illness and injury (Dwyer, 1983; Elling, 1986; Gardell, 1982; Grunberg, 1983; Navarro, 1983, Sass, 1986; Smith, 1981; Walters, 1983). Conditions of work and concepts of risk and pathology can thus be shaped by workers collectively asserting their claims and pressing their definitions — through political representation and through their unions. Worker participation has also been recognized in law; occupational health and safety legislation defines participatory rights that provide for the collective representation of workers' concerns. Such legislation can modify the balance of social relations of production, the degree of change being assessed in terms of the participation and control afforded to labour (Elling, 1986; Walters, 1991).

What is uncertain is the role that rank–and–file workers play in these aspects of the social construction of occupational health and safety. Research has tended to focus on the most pronounced conflicts over health and safety and on the role of organized labour. Few studies have explored workers' perceptions and responses, and relatively little is known about their general awareness of hazards, how they deal with them, and whether they seek to collectively challenge definitions of acceptable risk (Nelkin & Brown, 1984). Moreover, research has tended to focus on workers in mining and manufacturing and, consequently, on male workers.

This chapter will focus on nurses. It will look at the results of a study of nurses' perceptions of hazards at work and their reactions to them. This is an example of how workers do not necessarily press for change, even though they may be very aware of hazards in their work. As Nelkin and Brown (1984) have shown, and Weitz (1989) too in relation to AIDS, in the face of uncertain risk, several reactions are possible. Denial, acceptance, adaptation, and protest may all merge together. The recognition of risk does not necessarily mean that workers will seek more information, that they will act to reduce the risk, or that they will attempt to collectively redefine concepts of risk. This chapter explores some of the constraints that influence nurses' responses and shape their role in the social construction of risk.

Occupational Health and Safety Legislation

In the province of Ontario — the location of this research — legislation furnishes workers with a modest degree of participation in occupational health and safety. This is prescribed in the principle of "internal responsibility," which recognizes workers' participatory rights and encourages the resolution of issues at the workplace, with minimal intervention or regulation by the state. A primary element of the internal responsibility system at the workplace is the Joint Health and Safety Committee (JHSC), on which both management and workers are equally represented. Most workplaces employing more than twenty workers are required to establish such a committee, the task of which is generally to advise on health and safety matters. Their decision-making role is limited; JHSCs were not designed to intrude on management's right to manage. Workers select their own health and safety representatives and these, in theory, play an important role in transmitting workers' concerns to the JHSC, as well as channelling information to workers. Workers' representatives also have rights to inspect the workplace and to investigate accidents. Alongside these mechanisms for dealing with issues, workers have the right to refuse work they believe to be unsafe — a right that allows an immediate response to unsafe or unhealthy working conditions. In these ways, the legislation recognizes differences of interest between workers and their employers, while also providing a structure for co-operation. Workers can thus participate in processes that help to define hazards and give a collective voice to individual concerns. The internal responsibility system strengthens collective choice mechanisms in the unionized sector and extends it to the non-unionized labour force (Riddell, 1986, p. 63).

The Sample

The data presented in this chapter are from interviews with 123 nurses.[1] The sample was drawn from two hospitals in southern Ontario and it includes nurses who worked in a general ward and in the operating room, as well as intravenous nurses. One was a non-unionized hospital with 435 beds in which the administration provided us with a list of nurses from which we drew a random sample in the areas we had selected for the study. The other was a unionized hospital in two locations, with 415 and 722 beds respectively. In the absence of co-operation from the administration, we worked through the nurses' union. On our behalf, the union sent out letters to those of its members who were working in the areas of interest to us. The letters explained the research and asked nurses to indicate if they did not want their name released. From those who remained, we selected a random sample. The response rate in the non-union hospital was 73 percent and 64 percent in the unionized, which yielded 62 and 61 interviews respectively.[2]

Respondents were usually interviewed in their homes. The questionnaire was structured, though it contained many open-ended questions. Typically, interviews lasted for about 2 hours, although they ranged from 45 minutes to 4 hours. Interviewing was done by trained interviewers during the last few months of 1984 and early 1985.

Ninety-eight percent of the sample were women. Forty-one percent were in part-time employment, though there were variations between the two hospitals. Only 31 percent of the unionized nurses were working part-time, while 52 percent of the non-unionized nurses were thus employed. Eighty percent of the sample were registered nurses and the data for them and for the registered nursing assistants have been analyzed together, with no attempt to distinguish between them. Twenty-one percent of the sample were 30 years or age or less; 47 percent were aged between 31 and 40; 27 percent were between 41 and 50 years; and 5 percent were over 50. Thirty-seven percent had worked for their current employer for less than 5 years; 18 percent for between 5 and 9 years; 26 percent for 10 to 14 years; and 19 percent for 15 years or more. Compared with data for nurses in the province of Ontario, this sample mirrored the distribution of males and females and full-and part-time nurses, but it had a higher representation in the under-40 age groups and a lower proportion of nurses aged over 50.

The Hazardous Nature of Nursing

The focus of research into workplace hazards has very often been on industrial work, yet the health-care sector, and nursing in particular, are by no means immune to occupational hazards (Zoloth & Stellman, 1987). In fact, recent reviews have indicated that the health and safety risks are high compared to most industries (Clever & Omenn, 1988). Among the hazards identified are heavy lifting, cuts, burns, infections, noise, radiation, anesthetic gases, ethylene oxide, cytotoxic drugs, and stress (Coleman & Dickinson, 1984). Not all hazards are equally severe in each clinical area of nursing, and in this sample, intravenous nurses and those working in operating rooms were especially likely to be exposed to radiation, anesthetic gases, and ethylene oxide.

The nurses in this study recognized the hazardous nature of their work. Ninety-five percent of them felt that their work might damage their health. Among the primary health hazards they identified were infectious diseases — a problem that can be compounded by lack of information and having to work under pressure.

We come into contact with a lot of infectious diseases. It's not that you don't take the proper precautions but that you don't know what you are dealing with. In emergencies we may deal with patients who are hemorrhaging. We are putting IVs into them and we aren't expected to glove or gown. You can get blood all over you. If the person has hepatitis you are at risk, and with AIDS . . .

Anesthetic gases, radiation, and ethylene oxide were recognized as carcinogens and reproductive hazards, as well as having some acute effects.

> It's the anesthetic gases. They have good systems, but there's still leakage. Some days I get a real bad headache and I know that's a side effect of the gases. There's leakage from the mask on the patient when they don't fit, and they never do. The X rays. You wear the lead apron but sometimes you're exposed for hours and there is no protection for your thyroid glands. It can sterilize you.

And new issues were emerging, though nurses had worked without protective equipment for years.

> There are some concerns about chemotherapy drugs. We have been working with them for years, but now they are beginning to consider wearing gloves. What about the years we've been working without protection?

Among the more dramatic descriptions of safety hazards was violence from patients.

> Patients hurting you. More the adult patients. They can become violent and attack. Usually it's a confused patient. The big kids who are retarded often are afraid of us and strike out. I've never been hurt, always been lucky and dodged. I've had the odd bite, from children usually.

Other threats to safety included cuts and pricks from "sharps," slips (especially on newly cleaned floors), and back problems due to lifting patients — most keenly felt by older nurses.

> The lifting has always been the biggest problem. I have to be careful. My back isn't the best and my knees are kind of creaky. It's just wear and tear. As I get older, I notice it more and more.

The possible magnitude of the health effects was rated as little by 36 percent, moderate by 46 percent, and 16 percent said they were likely to be affected a great deal. Of the 277 health effects they mentioned, 44 percent had either been experienced already by the respondent or else observed in a fellow nurse.

We asked respondents whether they felt stress as a result of their work, and 87 percent reported that they did.[3] Heavy workload was by far the main cause, being mentioned by 71 percent of those who experienced stress.

> It's quite a heavy workload, much worse than when I first started here. The number of nurses doesn't go with the rising number of patients. With the chemotherapy there's been at least a 10-percent increase in the number of patients without an increase in the number of nurses.

It's trying to get your work done on time. You are covering two or three floors. If you are taking blood samples and the doctors want it for a certain time, you have to get the sampling done. If I am called to do other jobs, I don't have enough time to do my own.

Other features of the work were also implicated. For example, the stress associated with professional dominance and with conflicting expectations.

I find working with doctors in general to be stressful. They usually think they are gods and we have to walk down around their feet. They tend to take advantage of their position. They think they can say anything to you and you have to grovel. It makes us anxious. Also dealing with the demands of the patients' families causes stress. They can be very demanding. If you have 16 patients to take care of and each family wants special attention, that can make you anxious too. You just can't meet their demands. Sometimes we get angry.

Clearly, the overwhelming majority of the sample considered their work to be hazardous and they recognized a range of threats to their health and safety.

Coping with Hazards

If workers acknowledge a wide range of health and safety problems in their work, how do they deal with them? We used three indices of actions: Had the nurses sought any information on health and safety matters during the past year and, if so, who had they approached? Had they refused to work because they feared for their health or safety? And could they recall a situation during the past five years when they had worried about their health or safety? If they did give such an example, we probed to find out what they had done to deal with it. Thus, we aimed to find out whether they had acted on their concerns and also whether they had made use of the internal responsibility system. The latter was assessed on the basis of their refusal of unsafe work and their use of health and safety representatives, either as a source of information or to report a problem.

Only 25 percent of nurses had asked for information on health and safety issue in the past twelve months. None had refused to work. And of the 79 nurses who described a hazard that had worried them, 75 percent had taken some form of action beyond accepting the problem or working with greater care, though a quarter of them had simply discussed the problem with their colleagues.

Very little use was made of the internal responsibility system. Health and safety representatives were seldom mentioned by the 59 nurses who followed through on an issue that had concerned them. Only 3 percent had gone to their representative. It was much more likely that nurses raised the issue with their supervisor (32 percent). Similarly, among the 31 nurses who had asked for information during the past year, only 16 percent had approached their health and safety representative, whereas 39 percent had gone to their supervisor and 45 percent had approached the department responsible for health and safety at the hospital.

The tendency to favour lines of authority in the hospitals rather than using their own health and safety representatives was also apparent in responses to two hypothetical examples we presented to respondents. The purpose of these examples was not to gauge how individuals would react, but to assess their awareness of resources — the range or possible responses with which they were familiar. In the first case, they were presented with a low level risk to their health and safety; what would they do to deal with the situation? Respondents were more likely to mention supervisors than health and safety representatives: 82 percent said they would approach their supervisor, while 35 percent said they would raise the problem with their health and safety representative. In the second case, they were asked who they would approach if they wanted information on the composition and health effects of a chemical with which they were working. Here, the patterns were similar: 78 percent of nurses said that they would speak with their supervisor and 26 percent mentioned their health and safety representative as a source of information. Again, nurses placed relatively little emphasis on the internal responsibility system and procedures for collective protection and the expression of their own interests. They were more likely to rely on authority structures in the hospital.

Nurses were most likely to define their control over their health and safety in individualistic terms. Seventy-six percent said they had either a great deal or a moderate amount of control over their health and safety, and just 24 percent said they had none or very little. The vast majority of the examples they gave referred to ways in which individuals alone can try to avoid or minimize hazards — by taking care, wearing personal protective equipment, following safe working practices, using proper "body mechanics," and not cutting corners.

> Don't be foolish. Use care. Be careful how you handle the drugs and the equipment. Use common sense.

This theme of individual responsibility is consistent with a dominant ideology that places both responsibility and blame on the individual (Crawford, 1984; Dickinson & Stobbe, 1988; Knowles, 1990). Collective approaches involving a group protest or the use of procedures established under the legislation were seldom mentioned. Only a few nurses described how the Occupational Health and Safety Act (sometimes referred to as Bill 70) gave them added control over their conditions of work and said that they had heard of it being used successfully.

> I only know about it because one of the girls on our staff was union president and gung ho about health and safety things. She told me that the girls in the ICU used Bill 70 to get more staff. In the surgical unit too, I think.

What is it, then, that helps to foster this individualistic emphasis and inhibit reliance on more collective strategies? The interviews provide some clues to the reasons that nurses did not pursue their concerns more frequently and why collective action was rare.

Lack of Knowledge and Perceptions of Hazards

Given the apparent lack of salience of existing legislation for nurses, it may come as no surprise that they were not very familiar with their rights under the legislation nor with the identity of their health and safety representative.[4] Asked about the content of the current occupational health and safety legislation, only 34 percent could name at least one of its provisions. (Several nurses believed that they had no right to refuse work and they they would be disciplined if they did so. "The College of Nurses has an act that says you are not allowed to refuse. The patient comes first." "It's the Health Disciplines Act. I'm not allowed to walk off the job. Some nurses have been disciplined for this." "In my job we don't have the right to say no.") Moreover, only 55 percent of the nurses could identify their health and safety representative. It may be misleading to dwell too long on the importance of knowledge in initiating action. However, this is one factor which may help to explain the lack of use of the internal responsibility system (Walters & Denton, 1990) and account for the pervasive sense of fatalism in these interviews.

Another theme concerned the hazards themselves — their history, their multiplicity, their perceived seriousness, and whether their effects were viewed as immediate and certain. These may be less a comment on the hazards themselves than an example of how nurses rationalize away the degree of risk. Several nurses argued that it seemed a little pointless to start using the protective equipment which had just recently been introduced when they had worked for so many years without it.

> Older nurses like me, we're inclined to say "look, if something is going to happen to me, it will." It's too late to wear gloves because we didn't for years before that.

Another, referring to nuclear medicine procedures, reasoned that she had resigned herself to the hazard, given that it was just one of so many.

> Nobody ever does too much about it. I've put up with it. I hope nothing will come of it. I'm denying the worry. I guess I know that I'm being exposed to so many other things in my environment that I say, what's one more thing?

The fact that only 16 percent felt that their work would affect their health a "great deal" may help to explain their responses; the perceived threats were not yet serious enough to prompt action. Moreover, some nurses acknowledged that problems were not so immediate and certain as to compete with the many other demands on their time.

> We talk among ourselves. We have the same concerns, but I think everyone is so busy trying to do their own job. And as soon as we get out of there we concentrate on our personal lives. Because no one has had a disaster happen to them, we haven't wanted to cause a problem.

One nurse suggested that the hazards themselves could inhibit action — that the stress they experienced could lead to a "lackadaisical and don't care attitude."

These two issues, nurses' lack of knowledge of their legal rights and their perceptions of hazards, help to explain their responses to risk. However, two other themes in the interviews provide a broader framework within which we can, in turn, understand knowledge and perceptions. The nature of social relations in the workplace and the content of professional ideology may both contribute to nurses' lack of awareness of health and safety policy, the way they appear to rationalize away risk, and their emphasis on individual responsibility.

Social Relations in the Workplace, Professional Ideology, and Gender

The extension of class relations into public health care and the subordinate role of nurses (Campbell, 1988a; Carroll & Warburton, 1989; Coburn, 1988; Warburton & Carroll, 1988) are important in understanding their responses to hazards. The nurses echoed themes that are familiar among other workers (Elling, 1986; Nelkin & Brown, 1984; Walters & Haines, 1988b) and that point to their inability to reconcile their desire for health with their dependence on a wage. They needed their jobs and some worried about the future when they would no longer be fit enough to work.

> How much longer can my back take it? I decided to put up with it because I have to. I'm part-time and when I don't work I don't get paid. We need the money and I enjoy nursing, but there is no compensation for low back strains, so I've never bothered anyone. I can't pinpoint the problems as starting in any one situation. To claim compensation you have to give a specific time when you were injured. What's going to happen when I really hurt my back? Where will I go and what will I do?

Others felt that they had to weigh whether or not their job was on the line.

> I might refuse to work, but I wouldn't do this if I felt I couldn't afford to be fired.

> We can't do anything about it. Quit your job. They wouldn't miss you, lots of people to take your place. They would tell you to get a new job if you didn't like it.

You could refuse. But who would do that? We all need our jobs.

Such fears were compounded when nurses were hassled.

If you make waves, you are hassled . . . . One person who was complaining about something . . . had to work at New Years. For two years in a row. I've never seen anything done outside the contract, nothing overt. There are ways they can do things though, like shifts or holidays. They would have a difficult time firing you, instead they just make things difficult for you, so you may resign. Ease you out of your job — move you around so you can't stand it.

I could go to the supervisor, but then you're causing unnecessary trouble. They would watch you and make life difficult for you. So I don't follow through.

Less threatening, but no more encouraging, was the trivialization of nurses' complaints through jokes — a response that refers the problem back to the individual.

The men often say that it's just your time of the month.

We've complained several times about the anesthetic gases, but they've never done anything about it. They joked and said breathe a little oxygen from the masks.

Or else it was the impression of an unsympathetic administration.

If we do voice our concerns, it gets to our personal care co-ordinator and no further. They say, if you don't like your job, you can find another area to work in.

The importance of the broader social and economic context beyond the workplace also emerged in the interviews. For example, several nurses referred to ways in which they absorbed the consequences of budget cutbacks and the fiscal crisis in the health-care sector. As well as heavy workloads, there were other effects of the tightening of purse strings and these can help to alter expectations and reinforce a sense of powerlessness.

I'm worried about reproductive problems. There's nothing you can do about it. It goes with the job. There are new suction machines coming out that work better. But right now it's the budget-cutbacks at [the hospital] and in health care in general.

Management's hands are tied because it's dollars that dictate everything.

I went to my union, talked to them, talked to the head nurse. There's not enough money for more staff. You still worry about it, but the bottom line is no money.

Such observations point to the ways in which nurses' responses to hazards are shaped by social relations in the workplace and the broader socio-economic context. Whether or not nurses make use of their legal rights can be affected by their dependence on a wage, their subordination to medical and administrative authority, and their lack of control over their conditions of work.

In these respects, nurses experience constraints that are similar to those in other types of wage work. Yet there are also elements of their work environment that are more distinctive, and these too are central to an understanding of their responses. Nursing involves caring and service-oriented work in which lives may be at stake, and historically this has been given a strong emphasis within the occupational culture (Fox, 1989). As opposed to the conflict between health and productivity which touches industrial workers, nurses may experience a tension between safeguarding patients' health and protecting their own. For nurses, productivity is not more goods turned out, more ore mined. Instead, it is defined as the care and comfort of patients and their return to better health. In its more dramatic forms, it saves lives. As such, the tension may be more difficult to resolve, because it involves the health and welfare of others.

> It's not like car assembly. When you are dealing with human lives, there are situations that arise that prevent you following exact rules.

Patients' needs may be seen as having priority over family responsibilities.

> I cannot leave a patient who has run into problems and get home to my children at the time I should and this is stressful.

They may also be seen as coming before nurses' own health and safety.

> We have always been told that we went into the medical profession to help the sick — it's our job to take the risk of health and safety hazards.

One nurse described how she considered refusing to work when she was to take part in surgery on an AIDS patient. She decided not to because "I'm a nurse and it's my job." Another said, "We can't judge an AIDS patient. We are professionals. We have to take care of ourselves, but we have to do the job."

Within such comments there are indications of a professional ideology that emphasizes service over contract and that may help to inhibit nurses' actions concerning their own health and safety. Nurses may be caught between a contractual emphasis in their dealings with the hospital administration and their very different conception of their obligations to their patients. In the strikes and protests of nurses in Canada and Great Britain during the past few years, they appear to have resolved such tension by portraying their actions as being in patients' interests — arguing that failure to pay attention to nurses' concerns has led to a deterioration in the quality of care provided. In this sense there is a basis for an alliance between patients/consumers and nurses, an alliance which the leadership of nurses' organizations has emphasized (Warburton & Carroll, 1988). But, such links are seldom emphasized with respect to occupational health and safety, and were not articulated in this rank-and-file sample. There was little evidence of an ideology that would support collective action and transform nurses' health and safety problems into issues of broader significance. Instead, there is still a culture which focusses on the dedication and commitment of nurses in their caring roles. These co-exist uneasily with concerns about working conditions and may help to stifle their collective expression. Only a few respondents seemed to feel a measure of frustration that as nurses, they were not prepared to push their concerns.

> We talk among ourselves. We talk to our supervisor. But you don't accomplish anything. We had thought to go to the union but never did. As nurses, we are not as militant as perhaps we should be. We are easily intimidated.
>
> The radiation is something we all discussed. I don't think we pushed it enough. We could have taken it further but we didn't. We're conditioned that way. We don't buck the system. You get into that whole mentality. Nurses are generally very compliant and they are encouraged to stay that way.

This tension may also be exacerbated by gender — by the greater encouragement of women to defer to the needs of others. In this chapter I have relied on nurses' own accounts of the constraints they perceive and the issue of gender was not raised in any of the interviews. Yet, it is important to recognize that this may be relevant to the experience of nurses and to other forms of women's work. Risk and danger are typically associated with the work of men and their "macho" occupational cultures. Less frequently do we recognize the socially sanctioned risks faced by women in their caring, service-oriented roles and pressures they experience to defer to the needs of others (Graham, 1985; Heller, 1986). This may well be a silent influence on the culture of nursing. As Reverby (1990) has argued, nursing reflects all the ambivalences of womanhood. It embodies many of the characteristics and responsibilities associated with women, at the same time that it reflects the dilemmas and challenges that women face — the tension between caring for others and asserting self, the contradiction between altruism and autonomy. Historically, the naturalistic ideology that defines women as suited for such caring roles has served to subordinate women to both medical and administrative authority (Gamarnikow,

1978). While feminism has provided an alternative ideology (Gray, 1989), its impact is still uncertain (Carroll & Warburton, 1989).

In sum, it is helpful to view nurse's responses to risk in terms of these aspects of their work: their lack of control as wage workers, subject to medical and administrative authority; the content of their professional ideology; and the influence of gender. It is the convergence of these that may help to explain their individualization of risk and their lack of use of collective strategies to challenge definitions of acceptable risk. No doubt some of these patterns may have changed. However, it would be unwise to overestimate the degree of change. A review of selected nursing publications suggests that occupational health and safety has not received a higher profile in the latter part of the 1980s.[5] If anything, it may have received slightly less attention. From 1985 to 1990, the *College Communique* published by the College of nurses did not focus on health and safety. With the exception of AIDS,[6] *The Canadian Nurse* devoted less attention to hazards in 1990 than it did in 1985. Only the newsletter of the Ontario Nurses Association (*ONA News*) has discussed occupational health and safety regularly, but even this coverage became less frequent in 1989 and 1990. There is little to suggest that nurses have been encouraged to change their responses to hazards. And there are other reasons for being cautious in our estimates of change. Carroll and Warburton (1989) have outlined the contradictory features of nurses' location in the hospital hierarchy, the other conflicting pressures they experience, and the ambiguities of consciousness these produce. They conclude that future changes are unlikely to occur in a linear fashion and that nurses will continue to be pulled in different directions.

Conclusions

In this study, there was little evidence of an assertive occupation predisposed to collective action in relation to health and safety. Nurses did not present a challenge to what was viewed as problematic in occupational health and safety, and thereby tended to confirm existing definitions and approaches to risk. The possibility of reshaping concepts of acceptable and unacceptable risks may be greatest where standards are least distinct at present — occupational stress, for example. But there is little to suggest that these rank-and-file nurses were collectively expressing their concerns about stress or any other health and safety problems they had experienced. With respect to health and safety, at least, nurses did not seem to emphasize a difference between their own interests and those of the hospital, for they relied heavily on hospital structures for information and representation. Moreover, their assumption of individual responsibility for health and safety was often matched by its more negative form — that of blaming oneself or others. Nurses described each other as too careless, as needing to concentrate more on their jobs, and it was pointed out that "rules are only as good as the worker." One nurse commented, "If I'm in a hurry and don't lift properly, or roll the bed properly, it's my fault, not theirs." At neither the individual nor the collective level were conceptualizations of hazards challenged.

These findings, along with those for industrial workers (Walters & Haines, 1988b) and similar patterns identified in studies in the U.S. (Nelkin & Brown, 1984; Frenkel & Priest, 1979), suggest that workers play a limited collective role in challenging the social construction of risk in the workplace. Insofar as this does occur at the level of rank-and-file workers, it is in a form more subtle than has been captured in research to date. On the other hand, it may be the case that workers' strong consciousness of hazards is only mobilized under certain conditions or through the initiative of health and safety representatives or other levels of organized labour.

The data discussed here point to ways in which nurses' experiences are similar to those of other workers, yet also distinctive with regard to features of their work and their professional ideology. Such observations hint at the two seemingly contradictory processes of development in nursing which Coburn (1988) has described: professionalization and proletarianization. Carroll and Warburton (1989) use Wrights' concept of the "semi-autonomous worker" to help capture nurses location in "a complex and contradictory network of collegial and authority relations" (1989, p. 136). On the one hand, nurses have followed a process of professionalization, and it is within their professional ideology that we can locate their apparent difficulty in resolving contradictions between patients' and nurses' interests. Yet alongside such developments in the profession, nursing has also been proletarianized — a process accompanied by a growth in unionization and the emergence of an "industrial climate" (Kahn & Westley, 1984) in hospitals. The historical shift to wage labour was followed by rationalization and an intensification of labour (Campbell, 1987, 1988a, 1988b; Coburn, 1988; Warburton & Carroll, 1988). Within these trends we can locate other issues identified here — conflicts between health and the need for a wage, the limits imposed by "cutbacks," and nurses' subordination to their employers and, within the medical hierarchy, to medicine. Viewed thus, nurses' lack of pursuit of their health and safety concerns may be understood in terms of constraints arising from both wage labour and their professional ideology. At the same time, permeating the effects of class and professional ideology is the influence of gender. In this respect too, there is evidence of contradictory pressures on nurses.

In more practical terms, these data point to problems within the internal responsibility system. Nurses' concerns are not expressed through the channels intended to serve this purpose. Health and safety representatives do not have strong ties with nurse and communication between JHSCs and the work force is poor. One strategy might be to educate nurses regarding their legal rights and make them more aware of processes for dealing with health and safety issues. But knowledge is not a panacea. The discussion here has also pointed to the importance of developing a fuller understanding of other factors that prevent nurses from acting on their concerns. At a time when their workloads are increasing and fiscal constraints can lead to a deterioration in working conditions, it is important to look more closely at what limits nurses' participation.

Acknowledgements: The research was funded by the Social Sciences and Humanities Research Council and by supplementary grants from the Labour Studies Programme and the Arts Research Board of McMaster University. Ted Haines was my co-investigator. Thanks are due to Dorothy Pawluch for helpful comments on an earlier draft of the chapter; to Brenda Nussey and Lynda Hayward for their help with the computer analysis; and to Kelly Ronalds-Potts for the content analysis of recent nursing publications.

Notes

1. The nurses were a subset of a larger sample that totalled 492 (Walters & Haines, 1988a). The rest of the respondents were composed primarily of industrial workers drawn from six workplaces, including a carpet manufacturer, two steel companies, and aluminum cans, rubber, and brake manufacturing. There were also 58 other employees of the hospitals — in housekeeping and laboratories. The data on industrial workers are discussed in Walters and Haines (1988b).
2. There were very few significant and consistent differences between unionized and non-unionized nurses, therefore the data are presented for both hospitals combined. The lack of variation on the basis of unionization is interesting, but unfortunately there are insufficient data for each hospital to help us understand why this was so.
3. Nurses' responses to occupational hazards were sometimes quite different from those of industrial workers. This was one such instance. Only 59 percent of industrial workers reported job-related stress.
4. Nurses were much less likely than industrial workers to know anything about the legislation, to know their health and safety representative, and to refer to a representative as a resource they have used or could use in the future. In all these respects, they showed less familiarity with the "internal responsibility system" and less propensity to make use of it.

5. The publications cited here were reviewed by Kelly Ronalds-Potts. She also noted a strong emphasis on individual responsibility. It is consistent with this individualistic emphasis that nurses appear to be leaving the profession because of poor occupational health and safety conditions ("Poor Occupational Health and Safety Conditions: A Factor in Nurses Leaving the Profession," ONA News, March 1990).
6. AIDS is a clear exception and is an interesting example of the social construction of risk; why AIDS and not other hazards at work?

Study Questions

1. Does the impact of work on health vary in relation to gender?
2. What is meant by the social construction of risk? Can you think of an example — a specific hazard or a particular occupation — that illustrates the processes involved as constructions of risk change over time.
3. Would you expect to find differences in the hazards encountered by unionized and non-unionized workers?
4. Health promotion often stresses the importance of educating people about health risks. So too, "right-to-know" legislation regarding occupational hazards assumes that behaviour is influenced by knowledge. What are the limits of such an assumption? What other strategies to improve health are necessary?

5. What are the different implications of conceptualizing nurses as workers or as professionals?

Recommended Reading

Coburn, D. (1988). The development of Canadian nursing: Professionalization and proletarianization. *International Journal of Health Services*, 18, 437-456.

Lowe, G.S. (1989). *Women, paid/unpaid work and stress*. Ottawa: Canadian Advisory Council on the Status of Women.

Nelkin, D., & Brown, M.l (1984). *Workers at risk*. Chicago: University of Chicago Press.

Occupational health and safety concerns of Canadian women. (1991). Ottawa: Labour Canada.

Reverby, S. (1990). A caring dilemma: Womanhood and nursing in historical perspective. In P. Conrad & R. Kern (Eds.), *The sociology of health and illness: Critical perspectives* (3rd ed.), (pp. 184-195). New York: St. Martin's Press.

Smith, B.E. (1981). Black lung: The social production of disease. *International Journal of Health Services*, 11, 343-359.

References

Campbell, M.L. (1987). Productivity in Canadian nursing: Administering cuts. In D. Coburn, C. D'Arcy, G. Torrance, & P. New (Eds.), *Health and Canadian society: Sociological perspectives* (2nd ed.), (pp. 463-475). Markham: Fitzhenry & Whiteside.

Campbell, M.L. (1988). The structure of stress in nurses' work. In B.S. Bolaria & H.D. Dickinson (Eds.), *Sociology of health and health care in Canada* (pp. 393-405). Toronto: Harcourt Brace Jovanovich.

Campbell, M.L. (1988a). Management as "ruling": A class phenomenon in nursing. *Studies in political economy*, 27, 29-51.

Carroll, W. K., & Warburton, R. (1989). Feminism, class consciousness and household-work linkages among registered nurses in Victoria. *Labour/Le travail*, 24, 131-145.

Clever, L. Hawes, & Omenn, G.S. (1988). Hazards for health care workers. *American Review of Public Health*, 9, 273-303.

Coburn, D. (1988). The development of Canadian nursing: Professionalization and proletarianization. *International Journal of Health Services*, 18, 437-456.

Coleman, L., & Dickinson, C. (1984). The risks of healing: The hazards of the nursing profession. In W. Chavkin (Ed.), *Double exposure: Women's health hazards on the job and at home* (pp. 37-56). New York: Monthly Review Press.

Crawford, R. (1984). A cultural account of "health": Control, release and the social body. In J. B. McKinlay (Ed.), *Issues in the political economy of health care* (pp. 60-103). New York: Tavistock.

Dickinson, H.D., & Stobbe, M. (1988). Occupational health and safety in Canada. In B.S. Bolaria & H.D. Dickinson (Eds.), *Sociology of health care in Canada* (pp. 426-438). Toronto: Harcourt Brace Jovanovich.

Dwyer, T. (1983). A new concept in the production of industrial accidents: A sociological approach. *New Zealand Journal of Industrial Relations*, 8, 147-160.

Elling, R.H. (1986). *The struggle for workers' health: A study of six industrialized countries*. Farmingdale: Baywood.

Fox, R.C. (1989). *The sociology of medicine: A participant observer's view*. Englewood Cliffs: Prentice Hall.

Frenkel, R.L., & Priest, W.C. (1979). *Health, safety and the worker: An in-depth consideration of hazards and effects as revealed by survey data*. Report summary. Cambridge: MIT, Center for Policy Alternatives.

Gamarnikow, E. (1978). Sexual division of labour: The case of nursing. In A. Kuhn & A.M. Wolpe (Eds.), *Feminism and materialism: Women and modes of production* (pp. 96-123). London: Routledge & Kegan Paul.

Gardell, B. (1982). Scandinavian research on stress in working life. *International Journal of Health Services*, 12, 31-41.

Graham, H. (1985). Providers, negotiators, and mediators: Women as the hidden carers. In E. Lewin & V. Olesen (Eds.), *Women, health and healing* (pp. 25-52). New York: Tavistock.

Gray, D.E. (1989). Militancy, unionism and gender ideology: A study of hospital nurses. *Work and Occupations*, 16, 137-152.

Grunberg, L. (1983). The effects of the social relations of production on productivity and workers' safety: An ignored set of relationships. *International Journal of Health Services*, 13, 621-634.

Heller, A. Fochs (1986). *Health and home: Women as health guardians*. Ottawa: Canadian Advisory Council on the Status of Women.

Kahn, J.Y., & Westley, W. (1984). *The working environment in Canadian hospitals: Constraints and opportunities*. Ottawa: Labour Canada.

Knowles, J.H. (1990). The responsibility of the individual. In P. Conrad & R. Kern (Eds.), *The sociology of health and illness: Critical perspectives* (3rd ed.), (pp. 376-386). New York: St. Martin's Press.

Murray, T.H. (1988). Regulating asbestos: Ethics, politics, and the values of science. In R. Bayer (Ed.), *The health and safety values of science* (pp. 271-292). Oxford: Oxford Unversity Press.

Navarro, V. (1983). The determinants of social policy: A case study: Regulating health and safety at the workplace in Sweden. *International Journal of Health Services*, 13, 517-561.

Nelkin, D., & Brown, M.S. (1984). *Workers at risk*. Chicago: University of Chicago Press.

Poor occupational health and safety conditions: A factor in nurses leaving the profession. (1990, March). *ONA News*, 17, p. 3-4.

Reverby, S. (1990). A caring dilemma: Womanhood and nursing in historical perspective. In P. Conrad & R. Kern (Eds.), *The sociology of health and illness: Critical perspectives* (3rd ed.), (pp. 184-195). New York: St. Martin's Press.

Riddel, W.C. (1986). *Canadian labour relations*. Toronto: University of Toronto Press.

Sass, R. (1986). Workplace health and safety: Report from Canada. *International Journal of Health Services*, 16, 565-582.

Schrecker, T. (1988). *The pitfalls of standards*. Hamilton: Canadian Centre for Occupational Health and Safety.

Smith, B.E. (1981). Black lung: The social production of disease. *International Journal of Health Services*, 11, 343-359.

Walters, V. (1983). Occupational health and safety legislation in Ontario: An analysis of its origin and content. *Canadian Review of Sociology and Anthropology*, 20, 413-434.

Walters, V. (1991). State mediation of conflicts over work refusals: The role of the Ontario labour relations board. *International Journal of Health Services*, 21, 717-729.

Walters, V., & Denton, M. (1990). Workers' knowledge of their legal rights and resistance to hazardous work. *Relations Industrielles*, 45, 531-547.

Walters, V., & Haines, T. (1988a). Workers' perceptions knowledge and responses regarding occupational health and safety: A report on a Canadian study. *Social Science and Medicine*, 27, 1189-1196.

Walters, V., & Haines, T. (1988b). Workers' use and knowledge of the internal responsibility system: Limits to participation in occupational health and safety. *Canadian Public Policy*, XIV, 411-423.

Warburton, R., & Carroll, W.K. (1988). Class and gender in nursing. In B.S. Bolaria & H.D. Dickinson (Eds.), *Sociology of health care in Canada* (pp. 364-374). Toronto: Harcourt Brace Jovanovich.

Weitz, R. (1989). Uncertainty and the lives of persons with AIDS. *Journal of Health and Social Behaviour*, 30, 270-281.

Zoloth, S., & Stellman, J. (1987). Hazards of healing: Occupational health and safety in hospitals. In A.H. Stromberg, L. Larwood, & B.A. Gutek (Eds.), *Women and work: An annual review, Volume 2*, (pp. 45-68). Beverley Hills: Sage.

Part Nine

Environment, Work, and Illness

Part Nine

Introduction

In the realm of medical practice, disease is attributed to "malfunctioning" of the human body, although, increasingly, social-psychological factors are being recognized as influential in disease processes. The treatment model associated with this conception of disease emphasized that normal, or healthy, functioning can be restored through "technological fixes" and/or individual behaviour modification techniques. This clinical model, although effective with regard to some disease processes, obscures the social nature of disease and undermines the importance of social and work environments to health and sickness. As readings in this section indicate, social and work environments, inequalities of class, production processes, unemployment, lack of job security, social isolation, personal subordination, and exploitation all contribute to ill health.

Chapter 31 by Harding sets out the general global evidence that supports moving towards an environmental health perspective. It is argued that industrial and other activities that undermine the sustainability of the world's ecosystems will increasingly endanger human health. The fact that much of this activity involves transforming natural substances, and not only the adding of synthetic toxins to the environment, is not accepted as any justification for these dangerous industrial practices.

Next, the environmental degeneration of the Great Lakes and the growing contamination of the Canadian food chain and food supply are discussed to show concretely the interdependence of environmental and human health. In both systems, it is argued, production and consumption for profit encourage such environmental degradation.

Finally, the rising rate of cancer deaths in Canada is explored as an environmental health crisis. The highly individualistic lifestyle approach to cancer prevention and the related biomedical model are rejected in favour of a much more encompassing environmental health approach that would involve the social control and social change of industry. Rising rates of death from lung cancer and smoking are discussed as a case in point.

The chapter concludes that dominant political ideologies and social sciences have both largely accepted the trade-off of environmental health for economic growth, but that changing broad-based public opinion now provides the opportunity for alliances committed to fundamental alternatives.

Shields and Dickinson, in Chapter 32, provide data on the number, rate, and costs of work-related injury, illness, and death in Canada. The authors then review the main policy responses to the problem of worker health and safety. They identify and discuss the two main policies that have been developed historically: a laissez-faire, market-oriented policy, and a social-insurance policy based on the principle of compensation. Today, all provinces and territories have some form of workers' compensation in place. Recent issues and problems surrounding current occupational health and safety policy and practice are discussed, and a number of forces pressing for change are identified. The authors conclude with the suggestion that the application of a health-promotion policy to the issues of worker health and safety requires the democratization of the workplace.

Bolaria, in Chapter 33, extends the topic of occupational illness and death to farmers, farmworkers, and their families. The evidence presented in this chapter shows that farmworkers are exposed to numerous health hazards. Many of the accidents and fatalities in agriculture are associated with farm machinery, which claims 150 to 200 lives in Canada every year. Farmworkers suffer from exposure to pesticides; safety regulations are either nonexistent or not enforced. The working and living conditions of farm labourers also contribute to their ill health — inadequate sanitation and hygiene facilities and poor water supply have created a high incidence of infectious diseases. Since young children are an important source of farm labour, they are also subject to injury and health risks. The author discusses explanations of agricultural injury, illness, and death in terms of three categories: individual, technical, and labour process. It is suggested that self-employed farmers, because of constraints imposed by economic and market forces, are pressured to adopt farming practices that expose them and their families to numerous occupational health hazards. Bolaria argues that the health, health care, and safety of farmworkers should be analyzed in the context of class relations at the workplace, where employers control the labour process.

Over the past few years, Canadians have demonstrated their concern about environmental conditions, especially as it relates to health. Chemicals pose a particular hazard to human and animal health. Excluding skin cancer, over one in three Canadians will develop some form of cancer during their life. Child lead poisoning, linked to poor grades and co-ordination, is a major public-health issue. Excessive exposure to radiation is known to cause cancer, leukemia, and genetic changes. While environmental conditions affect the health of the whole population, the socially and economically disadvantaged — women and racial minority workers, those living near hazardous industries, families and children of workers who are employed in those industries — suffer a disproportionate burden of the illnesses associated with hazardous industries and environmental degradation.

Chapter 31

Environmental Degradation and Rising Cancer Rates: Exploring the Links in Canada

Jim Harding, University of Regina

Introduction

Environmental health problems involve industrial, military, and other pollutants that detrimentally affect the earth upon which we live, the atmosphere that shields us from cosmic rays, the air we breathe, the water we drink, and the food we eat. When the health of the environment is threatened, it is not only the human species that is endangered; the world's ecosystems, and the detrimental effects of failing to care for them, are shared by all life on this planet.

The notion of environmental health has developed recently in certain parts of the world in response to the acceleration and convergence of environmental crises. Canadian research, politics, and public opinion have lagged behind with regard to the threats to environmental health for a number of reasons, including the seeming vastness of Canada and the associated myth of its infinite natural resources, the relatively small and highly concentrated population, and the dominance of urban living and ideology. All these relate to Canada's political economy, which from its origins has been organized primarily around export of raw materials and staples to the more urbanized and industrialized areas of the United States and western Europe.

There has been some official recognition, mostly unheeded, of the growing health risks from exposure to environment contaminants. A decade ago, the Science Council of Canada released a report entitled *Politics and Poisons*, which focussed on growing knowledge about the risks from asbestos, lead, mercury, oxides of nitrogen, radiation, and vinyl chloride. It noted that these were studied as "separate cause-and-effect models" and, furthermore, that those substances were "not necessarily the six most dangerous or difficult materials which our society handles." It emphasized that: "The impact of collective exposure to the broad spectrum of toxic substances at or below the permissible levels at which each is viewed safe demands serious consideration" (1977, p. 5).

While there have been such pockets of consciousness, the environmental health perspective has mostly been treated as a radical fringe in a society that still tends to act as a junior partner in American-based industrial growth and military dominance. Even the nationalist and antiwar organizations that have emerged to counter growing global disparities, the cold war, and the arms race have failed to grasp the full implications of military-industrial societies (and their hinterlands) for the declining health of the environment. For many years, environmental scientists have warned that some industrial activities (including the use of fluorocarbons in aerosol propellants, supersonic jets, and atomic tests) may reduce the earth's ozone layer that shields us from ultraviolet rays causing skin cancer. The U.S. Environmental Protection Agency has estimated that every percentage point reduction in atmospheric ozone will result in an additional 200 000 cases of skin cancer worldwide.

In the mid-1980s, atmospheric research confirmed that in a ten-year period there had been a 40-percent decrease in the ozone layer around the South Pole, which had resulted in a "hole" the size of the United States. Industry and government both continued to stall on any action until, in 1988, scientists confirmed "that up to 3 percent of the ozone layer over the more populated Northern Hemisphere had been destroyed" (Roan, 1989, viii).

Chlorofluorocarbons (CFCs) are now considered to be the main cause of ozone depletion. This depletion not only leads to increases in skin cancer (a 5 to 6 percent increase in melanoma for every 1 percent decrease in ozone), but may also lead to crop failures and death of micro-organisms, and contribute to global weather changes. Though the 1988 Montreal Accord restricting the international use of CFCs is a start, much more needs to be done to ban and replace such industrial production practices, which degrade ecological and human health.

Since human evolution occurred with the aid of the protective layer of atmospheric ozone, which built up over eons, it is tantamount to reversing evolution to continue practices that can undermine conditions indispensable to life.

Preparations for nuclear war, of course, are the greatest threat to global environmental health. The use of only a small number of the stockpiled weapons is considered sufficient to create the ecological devastation of a "nuclear winter." It is probably no coincidence that the far-right political groups most committed to the continued dominance of the U. S. military-industrial system are also attacking the evolutionist theories that could provide us with some foresight and ability to prevent such catastrophic events.

Many industrial practices, including those in agriculture, energy and mining, and forestry can, and do, have dramatic negative consequences for ecosystems that evolved over long periods of time. In both the Canadian and U.S. grain belts, for example, a half-century of unecological farming practices has reduced organic matter in the soil, which took thousands of years to develop, by 50 percent (Goldsmith, 1977). Reasons for this include the cultivation of areas not appropriate for agriculture, monoculture, the reliance on annual crops, the export and decline of soil nutrients, dependence upon chemicals, and the growing disregard of conservation practices associated with the increase in farm size and use of farm technology. We have been relatively slow to recognize the environmental damage, as well as the threat to limited food-growing areas in an era of rising world population, from these "modern" agricultural techniques. Famines in Africa are the result of unecological forestry and farming practices, including concentrated land ownership and control (Timberlake, 1985).

There is little awareness of the long-term risks from petroleum-dependent technologies. Manufacturers' additives to petroleum fuel that are based on efficiency, not environmental quality of life (like food additives), are part of this risk. The amount of lead that falls on the Greenland icecap has grown sixteenfold since the turn of the century. Though evidence continued to be amassed that the body burden from lead (especially children) was increasing, the federal government continued to push back the date for mandatory unleaded gasoline through the 1980s.

The massive world trade and transportation of oil also pose largely ignored threats to the world's oceans. A background paper for the 1972 United Nations Conference on the Human Environment noted that

> of the 2.2 billion tons of oil produced annually in the world, about 10 million tons of related material end up in the oceans from accidental or negligent discharge at sea, from rivers and sewers and — probably the largest source — from the fallout of hydrocarbons emitted on land by motor vehicles. (Main, 1972, p. 9)

Some argue that this cumulative pollution could interfere with the ability of the oceans to sustain life. Moving Canada and other industrial societies to more self-sufficiency in energy — using conservation and renewables — is essential to reverse this trend.

An awareness that uranium mining and nuclear power will threaten environmental health for many thousands of years is also developing (Harding, 1978). The most widely recognized dangers are the production of nuclear weapons, which has been interlocked with the commercial nuclear industry from its beginnings, and the long-lived radioactive wastes that come from both weapons and nuclear power plants. Dangers from the buildup of long-lived (e.g., 250 000 years) radioactive tailings at mine sites, unfortu-nately, have received less attention. According to Bertell (1985), mounting radioactivity in the biosphere will not only increase cancers, but will weaken the ability of our immune systems to protect us in a declining environment.

This is of particular importance to Canadians, since Canada is presently the world's largest uranium producer. Ten million tonnes of tailings remain as an ecological debt near the ghost town of Uranium City. There are 100 million tonnes of uranium tailings in northern Ontario; another 25 million tonnes, with much higher levels of radioactiv-ity, are being created at open-pit uranium mines in northern Saskatchewan.

The debate over nuclear power has polarized those who have an almost religious faith in industrial technology and those who are beginning to rethink social structures and technological designs in more ecological terms. In this polarization, those who see environmentally induced cancers growing with the nuclear and chemical industries have even been called "apocalyptics." Efron (1984, p. 58), discounting the scientific legiti-macy of their environmental pronouncements, asserts that the apocalyptics real "objects of denunciation were man, America, science, technology, industrial production, the profit and market system and economic growth and capitalism." Efron is particularly concerned about the alleged commitment of the apocalyptics to "the redistribution of American wealth, and the wealth of the other great industrial nations, to the Third World countries" (1984, p. 44). She argues, at great length, and apparently with the endorsement of several (unidentified) U.S. scientists, that the dangers of cancer from industrial synthetics have all been based on a logical flaw that forgets that industry "had simply dug up or chopped down the earth's own materials" (1984, p. 121). Criticizing Epstein's list of major industrial carcinogens, for example, Efron writes:

> Asbestos is a natural mineral; arsenic and chromium are elements and natural metals; and petroleum is a natural fossil fuel. These carcinogens . . . are processed by industry, but they are actually natural sub-stances. . . . They are chemicals; everything is chemicals; Epstein is chemicals. (1984, p. 132)

Later she notes that tobacco also is a natural substance. According to her peculiar logic, this means that the smoking industry is less blameworthy for the worldwide epidemic of lung cancer.

Efron's criticisms of many proponents of environmental health is based upon a semantic trick, one used continually by industry itself. Because not as much attention has been given to the natural basis of many industrial and other carcinogens, those created by industry, or those to which industry has greatly increased public exposure, are somehow not valid issues. Her position is all the more indefensible because, even though she deliberates extensively about how few chemicals have actually been tested, and how a complete, pure science is not the foundation of concerns about environmental health, she acknowledges that the incidence of cancer and the threat from carcinogens is on the rise (1984, pp. 128, 178). Like so many others trying to hide their allegiance to industry behind "pure" science, Efron has simply failed to grasp that this is not an abstract controversy over definitions of "natural," but an issue of increasing environmental health risks.

In the controversy over nuclear energy, it would be foolish to deny that uranium is a natural element, or that unmined uranium-bearing ore releases background radiation. It is, however, a most pernicious semantic distortion to call the greatly increased exposure of humans to lung-cancer-causing alpha-emitters from the radon gas in uranium tailings something natural. These tailings have entered the air and waterways through mining and milling practices, and it has been shown that existing technology cannot isolate these or prevent them from moving into biological pathways (Torrie, 1980). It is this transformation of a natural system, and not the fact that there is radioactivity in the earth, that is the crucial environmental health and, I might add, ethical issue. One would have to be slightly mad to say that it does not matter that contemporary industrial practices may be increasing the amount of skin cancer due to their impact on the protective ozone layer, just because ultraviolet rays are naturally created.

The Declining Health of the Great Lakes

Let us now turn our attention to the decline of one large ecosystem in particular. The degradation of the Great Lakes is probably one of the greatest assaults on the environmental health of any bioregion in Canada's short history.[1] With one-fifth of the world's fresh surface water, the Great Lakes are not only a Canadian, but also a global, ecological treasure. Since the time of Canadian and U.S. industrialization, this glorious water system has been treated as a liquid dump for industrial waste and human excrement. A source of drinking water for nearly 40 million people, and home to many more millions of wildlife, this liquid dump is now rising to haunt us.

Over 1 000 chemical and metal pollutants already have been detected in the lake system (Keating, 1986), and the advancing technology of detection has just begun to be applied. These pollutants come mainly from the factories along the lakes and rivers, from agriculture and other run-off, and from the ecologically abnormal concentration of urban population clustered along the lakes.

The extent to which some of these toxins have moved through the Great Lakes is astonishing. In the mid-1970s, for example, taconite, containing cancer-causing asbestos, covered 500 square miles of the Lake Superior lake bed on the American side. There were also traces of the same kind of asbestos on the Canadian side near the intake system for Thunder Bay's drinking water (Harding, 1978). Public concern after asbestos was found in drinking water samples was one of the reasons the city finally built a water filtration system.

Not only many resource industries, but the hub of manufacturing in Canada stretches along the Great Lakes from Hamilton to Oshawa. This so-called "golden horseshoe," Canada's symbol of industrial wealth and power, contains nearly 50 sources of industrial pollution and 30 sources of municipal sewage. For many years, untreated industrial and human wastes were dumped directly into the lake system from both sides of the border.

Referring to Toronto and the lack of ecological consciousness, for example, Keating (1986, p. D5) notes that

> the city's three main rivers are major sewers themselves, polluted with 14 chemicals, including PCBs, at up to 1400 times the provincial objective for water quality. Along the same heavily settled stretch of Lake Ontario, there are 38 municipal drinking water intake pipes and 25 for industries, including food processing.

In recent years, illness rates in areas adjacent to the 200 or so chemical dumps along the Niagara River have been higher than expected. This has resulted in an increase in militant local opposition (Freudenberg, 1984, pp. 42-45). The industrial dumps in this area epitomize "the dark side of economic growth" (Capra, 1982). Keating (1986, p. D5) shows the extent of the problem: "The four biggest, Love Canal, Hyde Park, S-Area and 102nd St., contain 245 000 tonnes of chemical wastes, enough to fill 10 000 tanker trucks stretching bumper to bumper from Toronto to Niagara Falls." The Niagara River provides 80 percent of the water flowing into Lake Ontario, which supplies water for 4.5 million Canadians.

The industries and municipalities polluting the Great Lakes typically claim to have cleaned up their acts and/or deny any responsibility for endangering health. Cancer rates in Canada tend to be higher in the heavily urbanized areas around the lower Great Lakes and St. Lawrence River (especially Montreal Island). It is difficult, however, to establish a causal connection between one pollutant from one polluter and an increase in the rates for particular types of cancer.

Animal studies, however, are useful in this regard, because almost all substances that have been found to cause cancer in humans also do so in other mammals (Epstein, 1978). A Greenpeace study of the relationship between industrial pollutants and mortality and morbidity rates of the endangered beluga whale has found that despite past protective efforts, the beluga population is characterized by a high incidence of diseases such as hepatitis, dermatitis, septicemia, perforated ulcers, pulmonary abscesses, bronchial pneumonia, and bladder cancer. These diseases are "readily traceable to severe environmental disturbance." According to Greenpeace,

the probable cause of bladder cancer is the carcinogen benzo(a)-pyrene or B(a)P, one of the most dangerous of the polycyclic aromatic hydrocarbon (PAH) chemicals. Besides causing cancer, B(a)P breaks down the immunological system in mammals, producing an AIDS-type syndrome. (Greenpeace, 1986)

The probable source of the carcinogen benzo(a)-pyrene is the Alcan Aluminum plant on the Saguenay River 100 kilometres upstream from the belugas' main habitat. Belugas are not the only victims of this unregulated chemical: it also has been implicated in over 70 cases of bladder cancer among Alcan workers. This chemical assault on the beluga can be seen as an ecological crime in itself and as an early warning of similar dangers to humans. Either way, it is clearly in the human interest to become more involved in the protection of the health of environments we share with other species.

The consumption of water also threatens the health of the environment. Next to the United States, Canada has the highest per capita consumption of water in the world, over 90 percent of it by industry (including irrigation). This amounts to 4 100 litres per capita per day. The U.S. figure is 6 300 litres. In Canada's "chemical valley" along the St. Clair River south of Sarnia, nearly 2 billion litres of water are used daily for cooling, mixing, and discharging wastes (Keating, 1986, p. D5).

In the mid–1970s, 140 cubic metres of water per second were being taken from, but not returned to, the Great Lakes. The amount of water extracted from the Great Lakes, if unchecked, could increase sixfold within 50 years. Authorities are already predicting a lowering of lake levels, with the potential of further destruction of natural habitats and an increased concentration of pollutants by an inhibition of the ability of the lakes to cleanse themselves.

Pressure from the United States to divert waterways south from Canada continues to grow, especially after the Mulroney government passed the U.S.-Canada Free Trade Agreement. Such diversion projects would have untold ecological implications, as well as affecting aboriginal land claims and Canadian autonomy. Conservation practices and a shift to creating sustainable communities will ultimately be required to avert these dangers.

Increasing Contamination of the Food Chain

While exposure to water and airborne toxins is cause for growing concern, Epstein (1978, p. 441) claims "food is the most important single source of exposure to a wide variety of synthetic chemicals." Davies's (1986) study of Toronto supermarket food, which found PCB, dioxin, and several other persistent chemicals, confirms this. On the basis of this study, Davies estimates that 86 percent of non-occupational exposure to these chemicals comes from the food we eat.

Food and diet are now considered important causes of cancer, even more important than smoking. It has been estimated that 35 percent of all cancers are related to food and diet (United States Congress, 1981, p. 108). Many factors have been implicated, including fat, meat, and low fibre consumption, elements and chemical reactions in food, deficiencies in essential elements and vitamins, imbalances in diet, certain methods of cooking, environmental pollutants, and industrial additives.

Food additives have been linked to health problems. Pim (1981, p. 27), for example, lists 68 additives used in the Canadian food industry for which "there is some evidence of health effects." They include eighteen preservatives, fourteen colourants, ten texture agents, eight flavourers, two acid/base balancers, one flour bleacher, and one sequestering agent. Also included are fourteen common additives, such as monosodium glutamate (MSG), various nitrites, and butylated hydroxy-toluene (BHT). These latter alone represent about 20 percent of the food additives permitted in Canada, and do not include any of the hundreds of flavourings currently used (Pim, 1981, p. 37).

Eight of these additives are known or suspected carcinogens, seven others have been found to produce tumours, three have been linked to birth defects (teratogenic), and one has been linked to genetic changes (mutagenic), as well as a range of conditions from allergies to hyperactivity.

The food and chemical industries deny that these additives place humans at risk. Their self-interested viewpoint is that you cannot extrapolate from effects on other animals to humans, or that the amounts are too small to hurt humans. There are too many people, however, who have directly experienced undesirable effects of these additives or seen their children react to them to believe these disclaimers. At present, pressure is mounting to ban the sulphites (widely used in salad bars, canned foods, jams, wines, and beers) because they have been linked to several fatal allergic reactions across Canada. The history of testing and regulation suggests it is more prudent to be suspicious than trusting of these additives, especially when the testing is done by individuals or institutions whose economic interests stand to be affected by the findings (Pim, 1981, p. 43). Since the food laws were tightened in the mid-1960s, the number of additives presently suspected is about the same as the number of additives that have been removed from use, because since that time a similar number of new additives have found their way into the food supply (Pim, 1981, p. 37). Clearly we are faced with a revolving door of food additives.

Food additives, however, like industrial chemicals, are presumed innocent until proved guilty. Guilt is difficult to establish, often requiring years of exposure and enough victims to be "statistically significant." In some cases, due to legal and regulatory definitions, an additive is not even regulated. Several flavour-enhancers, including MSG (which some consider a psychoactive drug), for example, are not defined as additives, and remain unregulated. One consequence of this is that there is no limit on the quantity of these substances which may be used. Also, since ingredients are simply listed in descending order by weight, a person has no knowledge of the quantity of additives consumed. Some labels are so imprecise, listing only "colours" or "flavours" etc., that it is impossible to know exactly what is being consumed; furthermore, manufacturers and suppliers of bulk foods, baked goods, fast food, and restaurant meals are not required to divulge such information to consumers. This lack of adequate regulation makes a mockery of claims of consumer protection because it is impossible for persons with fatal allergies to some additives to know if those substances are contained in purchased products. Even when ingredients are listed, they may not be reliable or complete; chemicals from packaging materials and residues from agricultural herbicides, insecticides, fertilizers, hormones, and antibiotics, for example, do not have to be listed on labels.

The number of unidentified chemicals consumed is substantial. About 300 chemicals are used in agricultural production. In Saskatchewan alone, farmers spend 250 million dollars annually on a wide range of chemicals. Agricultural chemicals are such big business that Saskatchewan's Progressive Conservative government brought the chemical industry to the grain belt supposedly as a way of diversifying and stabilizing the economy.[2]

Even in a time of growing environmental consciousness, centralized economic powers and regional disparities lead parochial politicians to go on trying to buy votes by selling the health of the future. People along Lake Ontario, concerned about chemically contaminated drinking water, might even support moving the chemical industry to the Prairies.

The fundamental question regarding food additives is, Why do food products need all those colours, flavours, preservatives, and stabilizers? It is not because this is the best way to produce nutritious food; rather, these substances are used by a food industry wherein production is motivated above all by profit, not by the satisfaction of needs or the protection of health.

Causes of Death and Environmental Health

Even with the direct evidence of declining environmental health, some people go on believing that this has no bearing on human health. The major causes of death in contemporary Canada highlight the linkages. Ischaemic heart disease (involving restricted arteries), cancer, and cerebrovascular diseases, are among the leading causes of death for all Canadians. Of the five major causes of death, apparently only the categories "all other causes" and "accidents, poisoning and violence" are not linked to environmental health. If the quality of the social environment is related to the larger issues of environmental health, as it must be through occupational health, however, many of these apparently unrelated causes of death, such as accidents, would also be included as environmentally related.

Statistics Canada recognizes these interconnections in the observation that "the foremost killers are those which are a combination of habits of life, environment, and heredity" (1983, p. 19). There is continuing disagreement, of course, concerning the relative importance of environment versus heredity as causes of death. For mostly economic and ideological reasons, the dominant approach to prevention in recent years has focussed upon the individual's so-called lifestyle. Of the eight risk factors listed by Peron (1985, p. 136), seven — cholesterol, blood pressure, alcohol, smoking, obesity, sedentary living, and not using seatbelts — are lifestyle variables. The fact that "industrial and urban pollution" is treated as only one category suggests a bias towards a pre-environmental view of health.

This is not to downplay the fatal implications of individually consumed toxins from food, cigarettes, or beverages. However, focussing on "the habits of life" tends to reinforce the treatment orientation of technological medicine, and to emphasize control of the individual rather than control of the institutions of society. The main ideological effect of the lifestyle approach, therefore, has been a general acceptance of the present organization of industry, and its pollution, as a given.

The social control of the individual may be beginning to pay off. There is evidence that lifestyle-related causes of death are starting to contribute less to the overall death rate. A slight decrease in the percentage of all deaths attributable to circulatory ailments, for example, was observed between 1970-72 and 1975-77. This applied to both Canadian men and women born during the same periods (Peron, 1985, p. 156).

Though these small changes (1 percent or less) are not compelling, it is noteworthy that the percentage of all deaths was down for all major causes of death except cancers. Though there were various changes in specific kinds of cancers, one must be careful of interpreting "cancer" as an aggregate trend since it includes around 200 specific diagnoses. This exception warrants further examination.

Environmental Degradation and Rising Cancer Rates

Federal government figures indicate a growth in the role of cancer in the deaths of Canadians through the 1970s and 1980s, both in terms of absolute numbers and as a rate

Table I   Deaths from Cancer, 1973-1988

Year	Number	Rate per 100 000
1981	40 362	165.9
1982	41 901	170.4
1983	42 796	172.2
1984	44 784	178.5
1985	46 157	183.2
1986	47 243	186.3
1987	48 460	189.1
1988	50 613	195.2

Source: *Cancer in Canada*. Ottawa: Statistics Canada, 1979-1988.

per 100 000 population (see Table 1). The probability of developing some form of cancer is now so high, and apparently continuing to grow, that it should be a major issue of politics and policy. The fact that it is not has much to do with the preponderance of pre-industrial and pre-environmental views of disease.

Peron (1985, p. 140) includes calculations of the cumulative incidence of cancer in Canada for the years 1969-72 to all sites of the body for people up to 75 years old. These calculations went from a high 31.5 percent for males in British Columbia to a low of 20.5 percent for females in Quebec. The highest rate for women, 28.6 percent, was also in British Columbia and the lowest rate for men, 24 percent, was also in Quebec. Remember, these are averages and, therefore, tend to obscure important differences, including rural-urban and regional variations.

Differences in the cumulative incidence of cancer warrant more in-depth analysis. Peron (1985, p. 140) has noted that "the values obtained vary sufficiently to underline the differential vulnerability of provincial populations to various forms of cancer or cancer in general." Thus, one should examine the role of environmental factors, lifestyle factors, and industrial and urban pollutants in the unequal distribution of cancer across Canada.

Cancer, Gender and Region: The Case of Smoking

Data indicate there are important gender differences in types and rates of cancer in Canada. In 1981, for example, lung cancer accounted for more deaths among males aged 40-84 than any other cancer. Lung cancers were reported that year as causing one-third of all deaths by cancer for men, compared to 12 percent for women. In contrast, in 1981, breast cancer accounted for more deaths among females aged 30–74 than did any other cancer.

This striking comparison shows that men and women have been facing different risks in an era of rising cancer. Not all major cancer trends, however, suggest this. Cancer of the large intestine and rectum accounted for one-third of deaths for men 35 and older as well as for women 45 and older. Such things as common diets probably contribute to an equalization of this form of cancer. It is known that the rate of lung cancer among women is getting closer to that of men as they become integrated into the mainstream workforce and adopt such practices as smoking.

There are also important differences in reported deaths from cancer for men and women over their life cycle. This can be shown by contrasting the major sites of fatal cancers for young, middle-aged, and older Canadians. For example, in 1981, for both males and females up to 24 years, leukemia and lymphatic cancers accounted for almost half the fatal cancers. But gender differences became quite pronounced by mid-life. For men 45–49, lung cancer accounted for the most fatal cancers, while for women of these ages this was the case with breast cancer. Gender differences persisted into old age. Lung and breast cancers accounted for the second most cancer deaths for the oldest men and women, those 85 and over; however, prostate and intestinal–rectum cancers accounted for the most cancer deaths in this group, for men and women respectively.

These differences are not necessarily persistent, nor are they well understood. Such factors as kinds of exposure, latency periods for different cancers, effectiveness of treatment, and survival rates, among others, would all have to be carefully considered. Smoking and exposure to airborne carcinogens in the workplace probably explain the higher lung cancer rate in men. This suggests that an understanding of cancer mortality rates requires an understanding of the organization of production and consumption and its role in environmental contamination. The role of smoking, of course, complicates the situation. It seems nonsensical and counter-productive, however, to view smoking simply as an individual, lifestyle problem.

Even federal health researchers acknowledge this. A report entitled *Cancer Patterns in Canada 1931-1974*, for example, distinguishes "environmental" from "lifestyle" factors by suggesting that "the exposure of an individual is involuntary to the former but not the latter" (1977, p. 4). The fact that nicotine is an extremely dependency-producing drug that is widely and persuasively advertised by the cigarette industry, combined with the fact that smoking patterns are characterized by important gender and socio-economic differences, however, suggest that use of the term "voluntary" is quite misleading in the case of smoking.

It is increasingly being recognized that most cancer is environmentally caused. The authors of *Cancer Patterns*, reporting on international variations in cancer mortality rates, for example, stated that "at least 80 percent of all human cancer is environmentally determined and thus theoretically preventable" (1977, p. 3). In spite of this, the debate about lung cancer and smoking is usually depicted in narrower individualistic terms. Worldwide smoking patterns, however, directly relate to the degree to which human activities have become integrated into industrialization. Mass production (e.g., 5 000 cigarettes per minute), and mass promotion of tobacco as a commodity for sale and profit may not be a sufficient cause, but they are a necessary cause, of damage from mass heavy smoking. The fact that smoking and lung cancer is increasing as Western production and consumption patterns spread to developing countries, and that smoking and lung cancer are on the increase as women become more integrated into mainstream industrial workstyles, show the stupidity of postulating individualistic reasons for different rates of these fatal cancers.

The view of smoking as fundamentally a lifestyle problem has even been used to try to disprove that environmental cancers are on the rise. For example, it is not that uncommon to attribute rising cancer rates in Canada primarily to lung cancer caused by smoking. On the basis of overall and lung cancer death rates reported in *Cancer in Canada* from 1976-80, however, this is not the case. Lung cancer deaths in that period went from 48.8 to 54.4 per 100 000. The overall cancer death rates for these years rose from 151.5 to 165.3 per 100 000. Subtracting lung cancer deaths from the total cancer deaths accounts for only 5.6 of the 13.8 per 100 000, or 40.5 percent of the increase.

This should come as no surprise, since other cancer rates have also been on the rise. Skin cancer (malignant melanoma) for both men and women, for example, doubled between 1951-1970 (*Cancer Patterns, 1931-1974*, 1977, p. 5). With the interpretation that "excessive exposure to sunlight appears to be a factor" (1977, p. 5), there was a tendency to ignore environmental health, especially the role that a reduced ozone layer may be playing in this trend.

This is not intended to downplay the relationship between smoking and lung cancer but, rather, to suggest this rise constitutes only one part of a larger and more detrimental set of problems of environmental health. There is a sense in which smoking is undeniably an environmental health problem. This is shown by looking at the complete tobacco industry rather than just focussing on individual consumption and risk. This is what Taylor (1985, pp. 252-253) does when he reports that:

> it has been estimated that around 150 large trees are needed to cure just over one acre of tobacco. (It has been said — although challenged on the grounds that no such calculation is possible — that 300 cigarettes consume one Third World tree.) A quick calculation shows why the horizons are bare; the average size of a tobacco allotment in Rio Grande Do Sul is about four acres. Therefore, in one year, the area's 100,000 tobacco farmers need the wood of 60 million trees — or nearly 1.5 million acres of forest.

The fact that this aspect of the smoking and lung cancer epidemic has not become part of the mass definition of the problem, not even among most anti-smoking environmentalists, goes to show the way in which individualistic biomedical biases permeate the cancer controversy. In fact, smoking, as an activity of production as well as consumption, threatens our health through contributing to environmental degradation in a very direct way.[3]

As stated earlier, significant regional differences in cancer rates continue to be documented. These trends, at the very least, provide descriptive (though not yet explanatory) evidence that cancer must be seen in large part as an environmental health problem.

A volume was prepared on cancer for the *Mortality Atlas of Canada* using cancer mortality by census division for the years 1966–76. One major conclusion was that there was:

> substantial spatial variation for all cancer sites combined and for several individual cancers including stomach, large intestine (except rectum) and lung. Mortality rates for certain sites such as male lung cancer tended to be high in major urban areas whereas the high rates for other sites such as stomach tended to occur in rural and semi-rural census divisions. (1980, p. 6)

There are major problems interpreting such spatial differences. The authors estimated that between 1966–71, 10 percent of Canadians 45 years and older moved. Furthermore, there can be the averaging-out of high rates for some groups within census regions. An obvious problem is that the number of smokers within census divisions is not considered, although surveys could be used to help control for this. Lack of standardized data across provinces, the notorious problem of long latency periods for many cancers, and the fact that mortality data do not indicate actual cancer or survival rates, or account for treatment efficacy, can all further complicate interpretation.

Nevertheless, the extent of some of the spatial differences is suggestive. For all cancer sites, the rate for men was "significantly higher in census divisions of several large cities (Winnipeg, Toronto, Montreal) and several less densely populated census divisions of Quebec" (1980, p. 15). Furthermore, the fact that there was "less spatial variation (for females) than was observed for males" (1980, p. 15) should make us consider the health implications of the division of labour by gender.

Evidence for this exists in Epstein's analysis of the *Cancer Atlas*, which lists cancer rates in over 3 000 counties in 48 U.S. states. He notes that:

> males show a striking variation in distribution of cancer mortality rates, with the highest rates of certain cancers in counties with heavy concentrations of petrochemical industries. . . . The fact that the corresponding

cancer rates among women in some cases show less striking variations strongly suggests the cancers in the men are substantially occupational in origin. (1978, pp. 50-51)

It is unlikely that the differences in lung cancer rates across Canada can be explained without reference to occupational and industrial exposures. The rates for males were much higher in the densely populated manufacturing areas, such as Greater Vancouver, Metropolitan Toronto, Hamilton-Wentworth, and the Island of Montreal.

Generally, cancer rates for the period 1966-76 were higher in the eastern than western half of Canada. Because of the long latency periods for cancers, the trends probably tell us more about past than present risks to Canadians. Risks from increased use of agricultural chemicals, for example, were likely not yet reflected.

In exploring these gender and regional differences, I am not claiming that the nature of environmentally caused cancer is well understood. I do believe, however, that the evidence and the prerequisites of prevention compel us fundamentally to alter our perspective in order to facilitate such understanding. The importance of this is shown, in particular, when we begin to realize the potential cancers that can come from continued disruptions in global ecological systems, such as the ozone layer around the earth. The supreme irony regarding cancer prevention is that we cannot afford the time for pure epidemiological or toxicological research, which requires exposure of large populations, and large numbers of victims, if we are to redirect our social, economic, and political institutions for a more sustainable future.

That is not to say that we cannot or should not learn from these research methodologies. This is possible as long as we continually place the results in the broader context. This is not, however, the way industrial and regulatory bodies usually use the data and tentative conclusions. A few years ago, a task force report was released on budworm spraying in New Brunswick, one of the most contentious environmental health issues in the Atlantic provinces. Officials supporting expanded spraying across Canada, supposedly as a means to make the exploitation of our diminishing forests more competitive with other lumber-exporting countries, jumped to the conclusion that "a casual link between spraying and any cancer excess has not been established" (New Brunswick Task Force, 1984, p. 138). What was not mentioned was the qualifying statement that "apparent excesses of the incidence [of cancer] for certain anatomical sites were identified in New Brunswick compared to Nova Scotia. Suggestions of association of the spray program with some of the anatomical sites cannot be ruled out" (1984, p. 137). Nor did these pro-spraying officials acknowledge the admission by the authors that the study "does not meet current toxicological standards which require two such studies in different species" (1984, p. 137).

Overcoming Social Antagonisms

If we are to change or adequately control activities that jeopardize environmental health, we will have to have a clearer understanding of the roots of these activities. Some people now argue that the roots of environmental decline are more anthropomorphic than industrial and/or capitalist. One of the arguments for this view is that socialist industrial societies, too, have had major environmental health programs. Certainly, the USSR (as it was formerly known) proved capable of bringing devastation to major ecosystems, as the accident at its electrical and military nuclear power plant at Chernobyl in 1986 attests.

The critical study of environmental health certainly requires a vigilantly independent stance. The anthropomorphic ideology that is associated with the dominance of nature (including humankind), however, is probably part of the industrial epoch. Capitalist and socialist forms of production and consumption both have originated and developed with this epoch. Due to the fundamental commitment of capitalism to exploitation, expansion, centralization, and profit, however, the prospects of an environment-compatible post-industrial socialism seem greater.

That is not to say that the seeds of such politics or economics are within today's ruling socialist or social democratic parties or governments. For the most part they have been as fully committed to the assault on environmental health as have been the ruling capitalist parties. Both have been assisted by the conventional assumption of growth-oriented economics that:

> public expenditure on health is "social" expenditure, involving "wealth-consumption." Thus the need to safeguard health, e.g., by safety or pollution-control measures is seen as a cost. Measures to create a healthier physical and social environment which would enable people to live healthier lives are not recognized as productive investment in society's most important resource and capital asset, namely its people. (Robertson, 1985, p. 10)

The dominant social sciences have been no more sensitive to the realities of environmental health. For the most part, all social sciences accept, as an unstated assumption and value, domination of nature as a necessary condition for economic growth. Furthermore, most social scientists have an urban and northern hemispheric perspective on the world, and tend to be more removed from the devastation brought to environmental health at the front end of extraction, or at the point of production. It has been indigenous people, trade unions at the shop level, and peace groups who have brought to light the military-industrial links behind environmental devastation.

By the mid-1980s, opinion polls suggested that most Canadians were beginning to break from the aspect of the dominant ideology of industrial capitalism that traded off environmental health for economic growth. Over 80 percent in a 1984 poll indicated they "do not believe that environmental laws should be relaxed to achieve economic growth [and feel] that protecting the environment is more important that keeping prices down." Over 90 percent believed "that every major economic project should be proven environmentally sound before it can go ahead" (Environment Canada, 1986, p. 20). This shows a trend towards support for prevention instead of clean-up.

At the same time, there were signs by the late 1980s that industry might try to highjack, and in the process divert, public concern for environmental health by creating a lucrative "green products" market. Instead of primary prevention through reductions in, and replacements for, toxic industrial practices and products, there is pressure to simply recycle wastes as a means to stimulate more economic growth. Rather than making the necessary transitions to renewable energy and fundamental conservation, existing governments are still showing themselves to be susceptible to the promotions of the nuclear industry, which falsely tries to market itself as the environmental energy option.

Ecosystems do not operate in terms of antagonisms between economic classes, genders, town and country, or the northern and southern hemispheres. It was just a matter of time, therefore, before our ecological interdependence was recognized. How much this recognition of interdependence will contribute to the resolution of the antagonisms that underlie the environmental health crisis and cancer epidemic facing humankind will depend upon our ability to organize effective alliances for this purpose.

Notes

1. While the pollution of the Great Lakes has received more attention and affects many more people directly, the degradation of the prairie bioregion due to cultivation and agribusiness has likely had the greatest ecological effect as anywhere in Canada. The loss of wildlife and wildlife habitat, of short and tall grasses and other indigenous plants, has transformed the Prairies from a rich ecosystem into a resource extraction industry for "mining the soil." There is some hope that the organic farming movement may begin to reverse this damage.
2. This is the same logic that informed previous attempts by NDP Premier Blakeney to develop and expand uranium mining and refining. Blakeney's plan, which failed due to an unexpected public opposition, was to diversify the provincial economy by building a uranium refinery in the south of the province.
3. The steady depletion of the world's forests, particularly the rain forests of Central and South America, constitutes one of the greatest ecological crimes of all times. This is not only destroying the regional habitats of indigenous people and many of the world's endangered species, but also, if unchecked, will permanently disrupt the globe's photosynthesis cycles of oxygen creation and carbon absorption. Since these forests are the "winter homes" of many of Canada's summer songbirds, these too are now at risk.

Study Questions

1. In what major ways do the environmental health perspectives differ from the more biomedical views of sickness and health?

2. What evidence exists for linking rising cancer rates or other illnesses to environmental degradation?
3. What are the major consequences of viewing smoking and lung cancer as a problem of environmental health rather than simply of lifestyle?
4. What social and economic ideologies do you think presently inhibit the achievement of global environmental health?
5. What do you think are the major implications of the environmental health perspective for social science in Canada?
6. What do you think are the main problems with Canada's existing system for protecting environmental health?

Recommended Reading

Bertell, R. (1985). *No immediate danger: Prognosis for a radioactive earth*. London: Women's Press.
Capra, F. (1982). *The turning point: Science, society and the rising culture*. New York: Simon & Schuster.
Epstein, S. (1978). *The politics of cancer*. San Francisco: Sierra Club Books.
Freudenberg, N. (1984). *Not in our backyards: Community action for health and the environment*. New York: Monthly Review Press.
Goldsmith, E. (1977, June). The future of an affluent society — the case of Canada. *Ecologist*, 7, (5), 160-194.
Howard, R. (1980). *Poisons in public: Case studies of environmental pollution in Canada*. Toronto: James Lorimer.
Keating, M. (1986). *To the last drop: Canada and the world's water crisis*. Toronto: Macmillan.
Pim, L. (1981). *Additive alert: a guide to food additives for the Canadian consumer*. Toronto: Doubleday.
Roan, S.L. (1989). *Ozone crisis*. Toronto: John Wiley & Sons.
Supply and Services. (1986). *State of the environment report for Canada*. Ottawa: Author.
Taylor, P. (1985). *The smoke ring — Tobacco, money and multi-national politics*. London: Sphere Books.
Troyer, W. (1977). *No safe place*. Toronto: Clarke, Irwin.

References

Bertell, R. (1985). *No immediate danger: Prognosis for a radioactive earth*. London: Women's Press.
Cancer Institute of Canada. (1987-1990). *Canada cancer statistics, deaths from cancer in Canada, 1987, 1988, 1989, and 1990*. Toronto: Canadian Cancer Society.
Capra, F. (1982). *The turning point: Science, society and the rising culture*. New York: Simon & Schuster.
Crawford, R. (1978, January-February). Sickness as sin. *Health PAC Bulletin*, 80, 10-16.
Davies, K. (1986). *Human exposure routes to persistent toxic chemicals in the Great Lakes basin: A case study*. Toronto: Department of Public Health.
Doyal, L., et al. (1983). *Cancer in Britain*. London: Pluto.
Efron, E., (1984). *The apocalyptics: Cancer and the big lie*. New York: Simon & Schuster.
Epstein, S. (1978). *The politics of cancer*. San Francisco: Sierra Club Books.
Franson, R.T., et al. (1977, October). *Canadian law and the control of exposure to hazards*. Ottawa: Science Council of Canada, Background Study No. 39.
Freudenberg, N. (1984). *Not in our backyards: Community action for health and the environment*. New York: Monthly Review Press.
Goldsmith, E. (1977, June). The future of an affluent society — the case of Canada. *Ecologist*, 7, (5), 160-194.
Greenpeace, (1986). *The history of the beluga whales in the St. Lawrence*. Vancouver: Author (pamphlet).
Harding, J. (1978, Winter). The worldwide public health hazards of the nuclear industry. *Alternatives*.
Harding, J. (1978, March-April). Asbestos in the great lakes. *New Ecologist*, 2.
Harding, J. (1983). Mercury poisoning. In Ryerson (Ed.), *Sociology: A critical perspective*. Toronto: Holt, Rinehart and Winston.
Harding, J. (1984, March 17). *The ecology of health*. Paper presented to the Consumer Health Organization of Manitoba, Winnipeg.
Harding, J. (1991). Ecology and social change. In P. Li & B.S. Bolaria (Eds.), *Sociology*. Toronto: Copp Clark Pitman.

Health and Welfare. (1981). *Major causes of cancer deaths in Canada*. Ottawa: Author.

Health and Welfare, Statistics Canada. (1980). *Mortality atlas of Canada, Vol. 1: Cancer*. Ottawa: Authors.

Higginson, J. (1969). Present trends in cancer epidemiology. In *Canadian cancer conference* (pp. 40–75). Toronto: Pergamon Canada.

Howard, R. (1980). *Poisons in public: Case studies of environmental pollution in Canada*. Toronto: James Lorimer.

Keating, M. (1986). *To the last drop: Canada and the world's water crisis*. Toronto: Macmillan.

Keating, M. (1986, October 18). Soiling the sweetwater seas. *The Globe and Mail*, p. D5.

Main, J. (1972). *Pollutants: Poisons around the world*. New York: United Nations.

National Health and Welfare. (1977, March). *Cancer patterns in Canada, 1931-1974*. Ottawa: Bureau of Epidemiology.

New Brunswick Task Force on the Environment and Cancer. (1984, March 16). *Final report*. Ministry of Health, Government of Province of New Brunswick.

Peron, Y., & Strohmenger, C. (1985, November). *Demographic and health indicators: Presentation and interpretation*. Ottawa: Statistics Canada.

Pim. L. (1981). *Additive alert: A guide to food additives for the Canadian consumer*. Toronto: Doubleday.

Roan, S.L. (1989). *Ozone crisis*. Toronto: John Wiley and Sons.

Robertson, J. (1985). *Health, wealth and the new economics: An agenda for a healthier world*. New York: Intermediate Technology Group of North America.

Science Council of Canada. (1977, October). *Policies and poisons: The containment of long-term hazards to human health in the environment and in the workplace, Report No. 28*. Ottawa: Author.

Starrs, C. (1982, January). *Environmental ethics and beyond: The human side of the non-environment relationships*. Ottawa: Public Policy Concern.

Statistics Canada. (1983, May). *In sickness and in health: Health statistics at a glance*. Ottawa: Author.

Statistics Canada. (1989). *Canada year book 1990*. Ottawa: Author.

Statistics Canada. (1990). *Health reports, 1 and 2*. Ottawa: Centre for Health Information.

Statistics Canada. *Cancer in Canada, 1979 to 1988*. Ottawa: Author.

Supply and Services. (1986a). *Canada's environment: An overview*. Ottawa: Author.

Supply and Services. (1986a). *State of the environment report for Canada*. Ottawa: Author.

Taylor, P. (1985). *The smoke ring — tobacco, money and multi-national politics*. London: Sphere Books.

Timberlake, L. (1985). *Africa in crisis: The causes, the cures of environmental bankruptcy*. London: Earthscan.

Torrie, R.D. (1980, August 6). *Uranium mine tailings — what the record shows: A review of evidence presented to the British Columbia Royal Commission on Uranium Mining*. Paper presented to Select Committee on Ontario Hydro Affairs, Toronto, Queen's Park.

Troyer, W. (1977). *No safe place*. Toronto: Clarke, Irwin.

United States Congress. (1981). *Assessment of technologies for determining cancer risks from the environment*. Washington: Office of Technology Assessment.

Chapter 32

Health for Sale: The Political Economy of Occupational Health and Safety

John Shields and Harley D. Dickinson, Ryerson Polytechnical Institute, University of Saskatchewan

Introduction

Although most Canadians work to make their living, for many their wages cost them their health. It has been estimated, for example, that each year since 1976 over 1 000 000 Canadian workers have been injured in work-related accidents (Labour Canada, 1991, p. 12). In 1990, almost 587 000 workers, or approximately 58 percent of those injured, were injured seriously enough to require time off work (Statistics Canada, 1991. p. 7). The average length of time lost by each injured worker is estimated to be about 30 working days.

Many work-related accidents result in death. In the eleven years between 1979 and 1989, 11 913 work-related deaths were reported. Of these, the families of 9 228 were compensated (Statistics Canada, 1992: Table 6.15, p. 162). Although the number of workplace fatalities is down from previous decades, this does not necessarily mean that work is getting safer. Table 1 clearly shows that since 1965 the number of disabling injuries has increased dramatically, although the number of non-disabling injuries has fluctuated, reaching a high of approximately 648 000 in 1980 to a low of about 417 206 in 1989.

Most of the figures discussed above are related to workplace injuries. Many workers, however, suffer and die from work-related illness. It is difficult to get an accurate picture of the extent of work-related illness for a number of reasons. Among other things, there is a lack of knowledge about the substances the worker may have been exposed to, and, if known, whether the substances were safe or toxic. These difficulties are compounded by

Table I   Historical Summaries of Occupation Injuries

	Number of Employees (000's)	Non-disabling		Disabling		Fatal		Total
		Total**	%	Total	%	Total	%	
1965	6 862	490 850	66.1	250 914	33.8	1 118	0.15	742 882
1966	7 152	512 275	65.4	269 609	34.4	1 198	0.15	783 082
1967	7 379	512 762	65.5	269 308	34.4	1 058	0.14	783 128
1968	7 537	500 587	65.6	261 440	34.3	928	0.12	762 955
1969	6 591	504 587	63.4	289 819	36.4	1 001	0.13	795 407
1970	6 692	491 099	61.9	301 653	38.0	918	0.12	793 670
1971	6 850	480 475	60.5	312 302	39.3	924	0.12	793 701
1972	7 109	489 831	55.6	390 612	44.3	1 078	0.12	881 521
1973	7 491	547 256	55.5	438 384	44.4	1 124	0.11	986 764
1974	7 861	573 281	54.7	473 726	45.2	1 456	0.14	1 048 463
1975	8 014	547 147	55.3	441 008	44.6	957	0.10	989 112
1976	8 148	572 062	54.7	472 372	45.2	936	0.09	1 045 370
1977	8 371	586 267	56.2	455 402	43.7	813	0.08	1 042 482
1978*	8 525	592 327	55.0	484 386	45.0	811	0.08	1 077 524
1979	8 843	630 118	54.0	536 387	45.9	944	0.08	1 167 449
1980	9 034	648 272	53.3	566 949	46.6	967	0.08	1 216 188
1981	9 340	622 208	51.5	584 443	48.4	967	0.08	1 207 618
1982	9 039	496 437	48.9	518 751	51.1	861	0.08	1 016 049
1983	8 767	462 704	48.5	490 463	51.4	718	0.08	953 885
1984	8 902	510 652	49.3	524 948	50.7	744	0.07	1 036 344
1985	9 209	504 424	46.9	570 616	53.0	733	0.07	1 075 733
1986	9 845	474 624	44.2	598 424	55.7	762	0.07	1 073 810
1987	10 134	421 564	40.8	612 127	59.2	796	0.08	1 034 487
1988	10 285	446 522	41.0	642 849	59.0	867	0.08	1 090 238
1989P	10 518	417 206	38.8	656 658	61.1	869	0.08	1 074 733
Average	8 340	521 421	53.3	456 542	46.6	942	0.10	978 905

* 1989 figures do not include the Northwest Territories

Compensated fatalities are used to calculate total injuries and all rates. In some instances, the number of compensated cases may exceed the number of reported cases because cases reported in a particular year may not be settled until subsequent years.

** Includes only those claims to which $100 or more in medical assistance was provided.   P = Preliminary

Source: Labour Canada. (1991). Table 1A, p. 23, Cat. no. L151-2238/91B.

a number of other factors, including the long latency period between first exposure and the appearance of symptoms, and the actual processes by which exposure levels are set and safety regulations enforced.

It is estimated, for example, that some cancers don't appear until ten to twenty years after exposure to the cancer-causing agent. This makes it difficult to determine with any accuracy whether or not the worker was exposed to a disease-causing agent, or whether the exposure was of sufficient duration and intensity to have caused the illness. The determination of safe exposure levels to substances is notoriously difficult. One reason for this is that often considerations other than the health and safety of workers influence decisions (Sentes, 1985). In setting the asbestos exposure levels in Quebec in the 1970s, for example, it has been suggested that economic factors were given priority. According to Doern (1977, p. 6) the director of the Quebec Asbestos Mining Association suggested that setting the exposure limit at 2 fibres per cubic centimetre of air, as it was in Ontario, instead of the 5 fibres proposed for Quebec, was unrealistic "because it would cost the companies too much."

Similarly, under the existing worker's compensation systems in Canada, both employers and compensation boards have an interest in reducing the number of accepted claims because of the costs involved. This contributes to a tendency to adopt a "negative assumption" concerning the relationship between disease and occupation (Ison, 1978). Generally, the onus is put on the claimant to prove that she or he has been exposed to a known disease-causing agent in the workplace. This is difficult to do. As a result, many work-caused illnesses are not diagnosed as such nor compensated.

Worker-related injury, illness, and death are the source of much personal suffering, both for those directly affected and for family and friends. There are also direct financial costs to those affected in the form of lost income and earning power, as well as a host of direct costs to society as a whole. Table 2, for example, shows that in 1989 it was estimated that the total payments for work injuries exceeded $3.8 billion (Labour Canada, 1991, Table 2B, p. 26). These costs included $468 553 000 for medical aid; $298 826 000 for hospitalization costs; $1 907 000 for funerals expenses; $1 286 028 000 for pensions; and $1 768 158 000 in the form of compensation for lost earnings (Labour Canada, 1991, Table 2B, p. 26).

Labour Canada estimates that indirect costs may be four times higher, although there is some suggestion that this may be too high (Labour Canada, 1991, p. 13). If the usual 4:1 multiplier is applied to the almost $4 billion direct-cost figure, however, one comes up with an estimate of indirect costs. If the two figures are added, it results in an estimated $19 billion in total costs associated with the existing worker's compensation system. These costs are additional to the estimated $61 billion expended in 1990 by governments on the Canadian health-care system in general.

In terms of time lost, the figures are also staggering. It is estimated, for example, that work-related injuries and illnesses cost the Canadian economy an average of almost 19 million person-days for each of the years between 1987 and 1989 (Labour Canada, 1991,

Table 2   Work Injury Cost, in Thousands of Dollars, Canada, 1965-1989

Year	Total Claims	Total Payments	Total Payroll	Work Injury Cost per $100 Payroll	Payment per Claim
1965	741 764	178 731	28 201 000	0.63	0.24
1966	781 884	208 069	31 878 000	0.65	0.27
1967	782 070	216 446	35 303 000	0.61	0.28
1968	762 027	233 793	38 444 000	0.61	0.31
1969	795 407	274 481	40 663 000	0.68	0.35
1970	793 670	307 711	44 088 000	0.70	0.39
1971	793 535	318 992	48 458 000	0.66	0.40
1972	880 454	367 683	53 923 000	0.68	0.42
1973	985 640	426 162	62 923 000	0.68	0.43
1974	1 047 077	521 396	74 509 000	0.70	0.50
1975	988 155	657 291	86 727 000	0.76	0.67
1976	1 044 505	774 518	100 059 000	0.77	0.74
1977	1 039 650	857 301	110 076 000	0.78	0.82
1978	1 071 484	966 655	119 764 000	0.81	0.90
1979	1 167 220	1 115 914	88 223 000*	1.26	0.96
1980	1 216 188	1 355 410	98 757 000*	1.37	1.11
1981	1 207 618	1 613 228	112 370 000*	1.44	1.34
1982	1 015 049	1 969 913	121 557 000*	1.62	1.94
1983	953 885	2 217 947	127 406 000*	1.74	2.33
1984	1 036 344	2 488 240	140 691 000*	1.77	2.40
1985	1 075 773	2 731 405	148 509 000*	1.84	2.54
1986	1 073 813	3 131 723	162 904 000*	1.92	2.92
1987	999 444	3 406 681	n/a	n/a	3.41
1988	1 089 955	3 659 307	n/a	n/a	3.36
1989P	1 074 455	3 857 522	n/a	n/a	3.59

* Excluding P.E.I. and N.W.T.   P = Preliminary

Source: Labour Canada. (1991). Table 2A, p. 25 and Table 2B, p. 26 for years 1987-89, Cat. no. L151-2238/91B.

p. 14). This compares to an estimated 4.6 million person-days per year lost to various types of work stoppages (Labour Canada, 1991, p. 14).

As staggering as these costs are, they do not reflect either the total extent or costs of work-related injuries, illness and death. There are several reasons for this. First, not all claims for work-related injuries and illnesses are accepted as legitimate. Second, not all workers are covered by worker's compensation boards or commissions. Although it is true that approximately 80 percent of Canadian workers are covered, this still leaves 20 percent of the Canadian work force who are not included in the figures. This means that the figures presented could be underestimated by as much as 20 percent (Labour Canada, 1991, p. 16).

Another reason for underrepresentation is related to the fact that only accepted claims, that is, claims that are accepted as compensatable by the various worker's compensation boards and commissions, are included. This excludes both those whose claims are not accepted and those who never submitted claims for various reasons.

Other factors result in the underrepresentation of the true incidence of work-related injury and illness. The fact that both employers and employees have a financial interest in not reporting injuries or illnesses is important in this regard. The employees' interest is related to the fact that compensation payments are significantly less than regular incomes. Employers' interests in non-reporting are based on the fact that workers' compensation premiums, which are paid by employers, are directly related to the number of claims. Hence, the more claims, the greater the cost to employers. This mutuality of interest often results in employer and employee agreeing to the reassignment of the affected worker to a lighter duty job. The extent of the underreporting of work-related accidents is thus probably quite high. There is a growing concern, however, from a number of quarters, concerning the adequacy of both existing occupational health and safety policies and workers' compensation systems.

In the sections that follow we briefly review the main policy responses to the problem of worker health and safety. We identify two main policies that have been developed historically: a laissez-faire, market-oriented policy, and a social-insurance policy based on the principle of compensation. Following this we discuss a number of issues and problems surrounding current occupational health and safety policy and practice, and identify a number of forces pushing for change. We conclude with the suggestion that the application of a health-promotion policy to the issues of worker health and safety requires the democratization of work relations.

Policy Responses to the Problem of Occupational Health and Safety: From Laissez Faire to Compensation

The dominant solution to the problem of worker health and safety in capitalist societies until the twentieth century has been to do nothing. This classical laissez-faire response was based on the belief that free-market forces would both compensate workers for increased risk and provide incentives for business to improve working conditions. It was generally thought that those involved in dangerous work would be paid higher wages to compensate for the increased risk. Higher wage costs for employers would build in an incentive for them to reduce the incidence of sickness and injury in their operations leading, in the long run, to safer work sites for employees and lower wage cost to employers (Digby & Riddell, 1986, p. 294).

Although the laissez-faire policy may have resulted in lower wage costs for employers, both historical and contemporary evidence indicates that in many cases the most dangerous jobs were also the lowest paying (Kalwa, 1981; Bolaria, 1991, p. 237; Shields, 1988). This clearly suggests that the assumptions underpinning the laissez-faire, market-oriented approach were incorrect; workers neither had complete knowledge of the health and safety risks involved in their jobs, nor were labour markets completely free (Lanoie, 1992).

The failure of the laissez-faire policy response to result in either increased worker compensation in the form of higher wages or in improved working conditions, in turn, resulted in workers seeking compensation for occupational injuries and illnesses through the courts. This was, however, a lengthy, costly, and difficult process for workers to undertake. For a worker to be successful in the courts, she or he had to prove that they had not willingly assumed the risk and thereby waived their rights to sue, and that the injury was caused by defective machinery or "improper procedures or negligent supervision" on the part of the employer (Morton, 1990, p. 86).

Besides the difficulty inherent in proving these points, British common law, which extended to Canada, provided employers with three major legal defences that were difficult for workers to overcome. The employer might argue that the worker had contributed to the injury through his or her own negligence, or that a fellow worker was at fault and, therefore, should be sued, or "that the accident was really no one's fault, but due to an ordinary trade risk" (Millis & Montgomery, 1938, pp. 190-191).

These legal defences, combined with the fact that workers often simply could not afford to take their employers to court, resulted in a small number of cases being brought before the courts and an even smaller number being successful. By the turn of the century, however, the number of workplace injuries and deaths began increasing sharply, largely as a result of increased mechanization and the associated speeding up of work processes. Between 1900 and 1905, for example, the accident rate in Ontario's industries increased by 250 percent (Campbell, 1981).

This resulted in an increase in both the absolute number of claims brought against employers and in the number of successful actions. When workers were successful, employers were often obliged to pay heavy damage awards. These unpredictable costs were sometimes ruinous for a company, forcing them out of business, and this outcome was of little benefit to either the individual worker or to the other workers who lost their jobs. Thus, both workers and employers had an interest in developing a new system of compensation, regardless of who was at fault (McGilly, 1990, pp. 107-108).

It was out of this collective interest that Canada's first efforts to create an alternative to the laissez-faire policy approach developed. The first concrete step in that process was the 1914 Ontario Workmen's Compensation Act. From the point of view of workers, the act provided "compulsory income protection against one of the major risks to the continuity of income in industrial society — work related sickness, disability, or death" (Guest, 1985, p. 39). Also, because it provided workers with a measure of financial protection against workplace risk on a collective rather than individual basis, the worker was not "dependent upon the solvency of a particular firm" (Marsh, 1975, p. 126).

This was, of course, a major benefit to employers, who no longer had to fear bankruptcy as a result of worker compensation awards. Also, because the program bypassed expensive litigation (it was no-fault insurance), and was administered publicly rather than on a private profit basis, considerable savings were realized by capital (Marsh, 1975, pp. 126-128).

Thus, while at first sight it might seem that workers' compensation is primarily an attempt to insure workers against the risk of work-related injury and death, in reality a major effect was to insure employers against the risk of lawsuits from injured workers for damages. Largely for this reason, contributions to the workers' compensation fund are made only by employers. Assessments are made on an industry-to-industry basis, with the most dangerous industries paying the highest premiums (McGilly, 1990, pp. 104-105). Because of this, some employers resisted the introduction of workers' compensation legislation. In exchange for assuming all costs, however, they gained complete freedom from the threat of ruinous lawsuits by employees. The legislation restricted compensation to the coverage of impaired earning capacity, however. A number of elements of common lawsuits were excluded, including "pain and suffering," lost income potential, and punitive damages (King & McCombie, 1981, p. 35). This feature limited the compensation options of workers.

Thus, workers' compensation was developed as a trade-off between capital and labour, and the essence of the act remains little changed today. The philosophy behind this scheme limited employer liability for workplace injury and death, while at the same time providing workers and their families with a limited, but guaranteed, level of compensation for occupational injuries.

Over the years, other provinces followed Ontario with their own workers' compensation legislation: Nova Scotia in 1915; British Columbia and Manitoba in 1917; Alberta and New Brunswick in 1918 and 1919 respectively. Saskatchewan, Quebec, and Prince Edward Island waited until 1929, 1931, and 1949 respectively to enact legislation (Reasons et. al., 1981, pp. 163-164). Today, all provinces and territories have some form of workers' compensation system in place.

Recent Issues Surrounding Workers' Compensation Policy

Although the workers' compensation system as we now know it embodies a number of advantages to both workers and employers, it has continued to be the object of considerable conflict. Employees and their organizations have attempted to extend the range, level, and duration of compensation, while employers have tried to lower compensation payments by restricting the range of compensatable injuries and illnesses, as well as the level and duration of payments. In addition, more recently, an employer initiative has emerged to change the basis for financing the workers' compensation system, from one funded by employer premiums to one financed by taxpayers in general (Brown & Crossman, 1981, p. 12).

One area of continual struggle centres on the issue of what is to be considered a compensatable workplace injury or illness. In many cases this is not a problem, especially with regard to traumatic accidents and the injuries caused by them. In other cases, however, the problem of determining if there is an injury, and if it was work related, is difficult. Perhaps these problems are best illustrated in reference to back injuries (Doran, 1988).

Related to this problem is the issue of duration of compensation. Despite the fact that the pain and disability of an injury are often of long duration, workers' compensation boards are hesitant to extend compensation for "continuing pain and chronic problems" experienced by workers after the period of initial injury (Papp, 1992, p. A17).

The problem of reaching agreement about the "compensatability" of a claim for work-related illnesses is even more pronounced. It is not surprising that physicians employed by workers' compensation boards have been hesitant to acknowledge the fact that many workplace materials and conditions contribute to ill health. As we have seen, this hesitation is exacerbated by the fact that in many cases neither the worker nor the physician knows what substances the worker has been exposed to, nor whether or not they are toxic. This lack of knowledge stems from a number of factors, including the nature of current testing procedures and the fact that many safe substances form toxic by-products when combined with other substances (which may also be safe in themselves). Synergistic effects like these make it even more difficult to know to what one has been exposed.

A further manifestation of the struggle over what is considered to be compensatable is found in attempts to secure compensation for the negative health effects of workplace stress and sexual harassment. Recent workers' compensation board rulings in favour of claimants with regard to sexual harassment in Saskatchewan (Weils, 1992), have contributed to a renewed interest in finding an alternative basis for financing the workers' compensation system.

One proposal currently under consideration is to establish the funding of workers' compensation on the same basis as other health and welfare services. That is, financing it out of general tax revenues rather than from employer contributions. The concept of "universal social insurance," which has also been labelled "universal accident and disability insurance," is traditionally a part of the social democratic political agenda supported by labour. Certain sectors of the capitalist corporate community, however, have also come to see potential advantages to this system. While insurance companies, because of their vested interests, are opposed to a universal insurance scheme, firms in industrial sectors characterized by high worker injury and illness rates clearly see the advantage of shifting responsibility for compensation from themselves to "society at large" (McCombie, 1982, p. 13).

This appears to be becoming increasingly attractive to many elements of the corporate community, especially in light of increasing numbers, types, and costs per claim (see Table 2). One advantage of a fully socialized system is that it would be easier to reform compensation to include important sectors of the labour force, such as domestic workers, farm workers, and housewives, and also to include diseases such as "alcoholism, stress and mental disorders" (McCombie, 1982, p. 13), which are presently outside the bounds of compensation.

Such a recasting of the system, while allowing labour to extend the reach of compensation, might also act as a disincentive for industry to improve workplace health and safety conditions. If the costs of compensation are excluded as a direct factor in the cost of production, some firms may become even less interested in investing money into improving health and safety conditions at work. A socialized system of workers' compensation could turn out to be a Faustian bargain. Since the heaviest tax burden falls upon blue-and white-collar employees, they themselves would be the largest contributors to this socialized scheme. Because workers' compensation was developed, in part, as an insurance plan to protect employers from liability, the question becomes whether it is fair that business be allowed to escape the full burden of the premiums.

A further issue is the contradiction that arises concerning the funds generated for the program. In 1977, for example, all Canadian workers' compensation boards had approximately a $2.4 billion investment portfolio. Rather than using the funds for research into occupational health and safety in order to create some concrete improvements in working conditions, the boards have tended to use these funds to finance industry. In British Columbia in the early 1980s, for instance, the Board used 44 percent of its portfolio in investments in B.C. Hydro and Power Authority and B.C. Railway bonds. B.C. Hydro has been under continuous attack by environmentalists, trade unionists, Native peoples, and other public interest groups who have opposed many of its projects "on the grounds of environmental pollutions and resource giveaways" (Paterson,

1981, p. 7). While the B.C. Workers' Compensation Board is run hypothetically in the interests of workers, it is clear that labour has little or no control over the funds that have been invested in industries that have harmed the living and working environment.

More recently, funding controversies have centred around the issue of unfunded liabilities. "Unfunded liability" refers to the excess of claims over the ability of the fund to pay, either currently or in the future. In Canada's industrial heartland, Ontario and Quebec, this has recently become a major concern for employers. In 1989, for example, the workers' compensation deficit in these two provinces was over $9 billion (McGilly, 1990, p. 114). By 1995, in Ontario alone, the liability is projected to reach $12.5 billion. This means that assessments against employers will have to be raised by up to 23 percent in Ontario, from the industry average of $3.16 per every $100 of coverage to $3.88. Consequently, business is applying increasing pressure to control the cost of compensation (Lester, 1992, p. 8). This can be accomplished in a number of ways, namely by lowering the amount of benefits awarded, making it more difficult to qualify for compensation, and, as some business leaders are calling for, making employees share in the funding of workers' compensation (McGilly, 1990, pp. 114-115; Papp, 1992, p. A17).

Governments have started to respond to some of these employers' concerns. Some provinces have begun to reduce their benefit levels from 90 percent of net income to a figure closer to the American average of 66 percent (Lanoie, 1992, p. 64). In 1989, Ontario changed the basis of its compensation by introducing a dual system of awards. In the case of partial disability, for example, the board makes a discretionary assessment of what the "deemed" earning capacity of the worker will be after the injury or illness, compares this to what the worker was earning before, and pays the difference (McGilly, 1990, p. 103; Coalition against Bill 162, 1989, p. 12). There are already many incidences in which the Ontario board has made "deeming" awards, even though the injured worker has not been able to find a job in which she or he is able to earn the "deemed" portion of their income (McGilly, 1990, p. 103). This is a "reform" that in effect will serve to lower many injured workers' levels of compensation.

A further development worthy of note concerns the substantial transformations taking place within the modern labour force. Workers' compensation, along with other state welfare programs, were based on the premise of a particular pattern of work that became predominant in advanced capitalist economies between the middle of the nineteenth and third-quarter of the twentieth centuries. This form of work organization, which came to be seen as the cultural standard, was characterized by full-time employment, concentrated in the industrial goods manufacturing sector, with male workers earning a wage sufficient to support financially dependent families. The archetype of this standard form of work was the automobile assembly line.

Since the 1960s, however, changes to the structure of the economy and the nature and organization of work have led to the emergence of a labour force that is increasingly female, centred in the service sector of the economy, and embracing non-standard work forms, especially part-time work (Shields, 1991, p. 46). Today, about 43 percent of the Canadian labour force is female (Chawla, 1990, p. 65). About one-third of the total labour force is employed in various non-standard work patterns (part-time, temporary, casual and seasonal work, and self-employment) (Brett, 1992, p. C1) and increasingly people are working in the service sector, which currently accounts for about 70 percent of all employment.

All predictions are that the new work force working in new, non-standard work relations is likely to continue to grow, that is, various types of part-time service sector jobs are becoming the new standard. A major reason for this is that the new work patterns and conditions are beneficial to employers. For example, the productivity of part-time workers may be higher than that of full-time workers because they can be used during peak work times and thus labour more intensively during this short period (Dickinson, 1991). Part-timers also provide greater flexibility to management because they can be let go more easily and cheaply — "often without notice or pay and without damaging the morale of the full-time labour force" (Shields, 1991, p. 46).

The workers' compensation implications of such a labour-force change are profound. For instance, because the compensation system only provides successful claimants payments based upon a percentage of their existing wage, members of the new labour force are disadvantaged since they generally earn low wages. Part-time workers in Ontario would be eligible for only 90 percent of their part-time wage. But many of such workers are involuntarily working part-time. A workplace injury or illness may keep them trapped in a part-time job that does not provide an adequate living wage.

Temporary and contract workers also do not enjoy the right to be offered re-employment in the workplace at which they were injured, unless they have been employed there for over a year, an unusual circumstance. Non-standard workers very often do not enjoy the same workers' compensation rights as standard full-time workers, partly because they are non-unionized and have been unable to successfully negotiate adequate protection or compensation coverage.

The disadvantages faced by women workers are often aggravated. First, they are on average a low-wage segment of the work force, receiving only about 65 cents for every dollar a man makes. Also, workers' compensation boards often display sexist attitudes towards women claimants when making policy decisions. Women typically are not viewed as suitable candidates for job retraining or upgrading because they are not perceived as "legitimate family breadwinners" (Clark & Gray, 1991, p. 42). Moreover, women are often denied financial claims or the right to rehabilitation on the grounds that they are not really sick or injured but just "hysterical" or "anxiety-ridden" (Clark &

Gray, 1991, p. 19). All of this can seriously affect their ability to reenter the labour force at a similar level of pay and skill.

Broadening the Agenda: Beyond Compensation to Occupational Health and Safety Promotion

Historically, the first policy response to occupational health and safety concerns was a laissez-faire, market-based approach. This was followed by the institutionalization of a state-administered injury and illness compensation system. Since the 1970s, legislated reforms in various Canadian jurisdictions have moved increasingly in the direction of occupational health and safety promotion and injury and illness prevention. To the extent that this is the case, policy developments in this area have mirrored health-policy initiatives in general.

In the area of health policy in general, the first attempt to formulate the basis for a health-promotion strategy was the so-called Lalonde report entitled *A New Perspective on the Health of Canadians*. This report proposed that health and illness must be understood as more than simply medical questions. Indeed, it was suggested that a variety of factors, including genetics, lifestyle, environment, and the nature of health-care services themselves, all contributed to health and illness (Lalonde, 1974). This report, although generally well received, was also criticized for focussing too much on individual lifestyles as the cause of illness and injury and for underplaying the health effects of political and economic structures on health and illness (Bolaria, 1979).

The Lalonde report was followed about a decade later by the Epp Report. This report, entitled *Achieving Health for All: A Framework for Health Promotion*, was an attempt to address the shortcomings of the previous policy paper and to outline a comprehensive strategy for the positive promotion of health and prevention of illness and injury (Epp, 1986). One of its main elements was an attempt to escape the problems of victim-blaming that characterized previous efforts to highlight the importance of lifestyle as a determinant of health and illness. This was to be done through efforts to empower people so that they could exert control over their environments in order to maximize the health-promoting aspects and minimize the illness-generating components. This was to be achieved, in part, by having policy makers in various spheres include health promotion and injury-and illness-prevention considerations in the formulation of policy.

Although little headway has been made in relation to inserting health concerns into all policy agendas, there is evidence of movement in that direction. Policy initiatives in the area of workers' compensation, for example, began to move towards a new set of workers' rights, namely: "the right to refuse unsafe work, the right to participate in joint health and safety committees, and the right to know about occupational hazards"

(DeMatteo, 1988, p. 20). This was done, it was argued, to give workers more control over their work environment.

Although the establishment and recognition of these rights in principle is an important advance, a number of economic factors have prevented their full implementation.

One of the major impediments is the fact that the majority of work sites are not unionized. Workers operating in non-union settings find using the right to refuse unsafe work particularly problematic because of the real threat of employer reprisal (Miller, 1988, p. 31). From management's perspective there exists a fear "that to formally recognize a worker's right to challenge a supervisor's orders in one set of circumstances (such as refusing to do an unsafe job), may somehow lead to a weakening of management's basic rights to direct other aspects of their operation" (Aykroyd, 1978, p. 10). While there has always been a common-law right to refuse work under unsafe conditions, the scope of this basic right and the circumstances under which it can be exercised have never been precisely defined (Eady, 1982, p. 11). The same type of haziness exists in current legislation, and because of this, very often little protection is afforded to workers who refuse a job on this premise.

The rules guiding the right to refuse unsafe work have also largely neutralized the impact of this right. Dangers have tended to be interpreted narrowly by both management and government, thereby greatly limiting the potential power of this provision (De Carlo, 1989, p. 9). Consequently, few employees are willing or able to exercise their rights due to fear of management retaliation (Lewis, 1986, p. 28).

Even the existence of unions does not alter this situation very much. The statutory joint health and safety committees, for example, are based upon the false assumption that both parties have equal power to act in relation to health and safety issues. The great majority of such issues, however, necessitate the spending of money, and many employers are unwilling to give over decisions concerning investments in new and safer plant and equipment to workers. Even if employers were inclined to invest money in the promotion of healthy work environments, they are generally loath to give up fundamental management rights, such as the right to make investment decisions, to do so. This point was clearly made by DeMatteo (1988, p. 20):

> Investment decisions central to health protection remain a managerial prerogative. Employers, not workers, make decisions about the installation of local ventilation or the rate at which fresh air will be drawn into the workplace.

Thus, the workers' right to participate in health and safety issues is limited. Labour's involvement remains at the level of consultation rather than at the level of equal participation (Tucker, 1992, p. 115).

The workers' right to know about workplace hazards is equally problematic. Too often knowledge about health and safety is viewed as strictly scientific and technical. The assumption is that if workers have access to this information they can then control workplace health and safety problems because of the further assumption that knowledge equals power. But the critical question of who is controlling the production of this knowledge in the first place is ignored. The readily available "knowledge" is not neutral. For instance, the standards for proving whether a given level of a toxic substance is safe or not are set by government and industry on grounds that are sensitive to corporate priorities for profitability rather than based on purely objective scientific grounds (Sentes, 1985). It is a significant reflection of the unequal power balance in the workplace that chemicals and other dangers on the job "are presumed innocent until they are proven guilty beyond a reasonable doubt" (DeMatteo, 1988, pp. 20-21). Clearly, the workers' well-being is not the highest priority in such a calculation.

Conclusion

Hazards that accompany the work process have always been considered part of the job, if they have been considered at all. This attitude is the result of a system that has evolved around the belief that work is a privilege rather than a right. Moreover, even when health and safety in the workplace has been taken up as a significant issue, it most often has been approached as either a personal problem of the injured worker or as a technical problem that can be fixed through tinkering with lighting level and worker-education campaigns.

These factors are important, of course, but they are inadequate for a complete understanding of the nature of workplace health and safety concerns. Control over the nature and organization of work is a political issue that exists at several levels. At the most abstract level it is a question of social-class relations and struggle. That is to say, occupational health and safety issues involve questions of power conflicts between management and workers — struggles over the right to safety versus the right to corporate profits.

Only when the workplace becomes democratized, that is, when workers gain real control over decision-making powers with regard to investments, job design, new technology, etc., will they be able to effectively participate in decisions that tackle the underlying problems of job hazards. This will also necessitate workers increasing their influence over the health and safety bureaucracy of the state (Tucker, 1992, p. 120). Only under these conditions will workers be able to begin to realize the slogan "our health is not for sale."

Study Questions

1. To whose ultimate advantage was the development of workers' compensation schemes?
2. What are some of the difficulties in the way in which liberal ideology approaches occupational health and safety questions?
3. Identify some of the limitations of the current workers' compensation program for meeting the needs of the new labour force and suggest ways in which it could be modified to meet new conditions.
4. What are the possibilities and what are the limits, under the logic of capitalism, for improving health and safety conditions in the workplace?
5. Explain why occupational health and safety issues are, in essence, matters that involve class struggle?

Recommended Reading

Dickinson, H.D., & Stobbe, M. (1988). Occupational health and safety in Canada. In B.S. Bolaria & H.D. Dickinson (Eds.), *Sociology of health care in Canada* (pp. 426-438). Toronto: Harcourt Brace Jovanovich.

Doran, C. (1988). Canadian workers' compensation: Political, medical, and health issues. In B.S. Bolaria & H.D. Dickinson (Eds.), *Sociology of health care in Canada* (pp. 460-472). Toronto: Harcourt Brace Jovanovich.

Guest, D. (1985). *The emergence of social security in Canada.* (2nd ed., ch. 4). Vancouver: University of British Columbia Press.

Lanoie, P. (1992). Government intervention in occupational safety: Lessons from the American and Canadian experience. *Canadian Public Policy*, 18, (1), 62-75.

Reasons, C.E., Ross, L.L., & Paterson, C. (1981). *Assault on the worker: Occupational health and safety in Canada.* Toronto: Butterworths.

Walters, V. (1983). Occupational health and safety legislation in Ontario: an analysis of its origins and content. *Canadian Review of Sociology and Anthropology*, 20, (4), 413-434.

References

Aykroyd, C. (1978). An examination of the right to refuse unsafe work. *Labour Research Bulletin*, 6, (6), 10-11.

Bolaria, B.S. (1979). Self-care and lifestyles: Ideological and policy implications. In J.A. Fry (Ed.), *Economy, class and social reality: Issues in contemporary Canadian society* (pp. 350-63). Toronto: Butterworths.

Bolaria, B.S. (1991). Environment, work and illness. In B.S. Bolaria (Ed.), *Social issues and contradictions in Canadian society* (pp. 222-246). Toronto: Harcourt Brace Jovanovich.

Brett, G. (1992, March 28). One out of four workers lacks regular job, StatsCan finds. *Toronto Star*, p. C1.

Brown, G., & Crossman, B. (1981, June). Workers' compensation: Tinkering with the system. *Briarpatch*, p. 12-13.

Campbell, J. (1981). Class struggle and the state: Workmen's compensation legislation in Ontario, 1900-1939. Paper presented to the Fourth Conference on Blue-collar Workers and their Communities. Hamilton: McMaster University.

Chawla, R.K. (1990, Winter). Labour force participation: An international comparison. *Perspectives on Labour and Income.*

Clark, B., & Gray, S. (1991). *Double burden: Women's experience with workplace injury and disease in Ontario.* Toronto: Ontario Workers' Health Centre.

Coalition against Bill 162. (1989, May). Bill 162 disability legislation. *Our Times*, 11-12.

De Carlo, N. (1989, May). The right to refuse Bill 208. *Our Times*, 9-11.

DeMatteo, B. (1988, February). Power to kill: Safety law, management rights and workers' health. *Our Times*, 18-21.

Dickinson, H.D. (1991).Work and unemployment as social issues. In B.S. Bolaria (Ed.), *Social issues and contradictions in Canadian society* (pp. 278-299). Toronto: Harcourt Brace Jovanovich.

Digby, C., & Riddell, W.C. (1986). Occupational health and safety in Canada. In W.C. Riddell (Ed.), *Canadian labour relations* (pp. 285-320). Toronto: University of Toronto.

Doern, C.B. (1977). The political economy of regulating occupational health: The Ham and Beaudry reports. *Canadian Public Administration*, 20, (1), 1-33.

Doran, C. (1988). Canadian workers' compensation: Political, medical and health issues. In B.S. Bolaria & H.D. Dickinson (Eds.), *Sociology of Health Care in Canada* (pp. 460-472). Toronto: Harcourt Brace Jovanovich.

Eady, M. (1982). The unemployment of the future. *Canadian Forum*, 62, (717), 18-19.

Economic Council of Canada. (1990). *Good jobs, bad jobs: Employment in the service economy*. Ottawa: Minister of Supply and Services.

Epp, J. (1986). *Achieving health for all: A framework for health promotion*. Ottawa: Health and Welfare Canada.

Guest, D. (1985). *The emergence of social security in Canada* (2nd ed.). Vancouver: University of British Columbia Press.

Ison, T. (1978). *The dimensions of industrial disease*. Kingston: Industrial Relations Centre, Queen's University.

Kalwa, R. (1981, May 15-18). *Health and safety under capitalism*. Paper presented to the Fourth Conference on Blue-collar Workers and their Communities. Hamilton: McMaster University.

King, A., & McCombie, N. (1981). Worker's comp. *This Magazine*, 15, (1), 34-38.

Labour Canada. (1991). *Occupational injuries and their costs in Canada, 1987-1989*. Ottawa: Author.

Lalonde, M. (1974). *A new perspective on the health of Canadians*. Ottawa: Information Canada.

Lanoie, P. (1992). Government intervention in occupational safety: Lessons from the American and Canadian experience. *Canadian Public Policy*, 18, (1), 62-75.

Lester, L. (1992, February 27). Employers to discuss WCB funds. *The Financial Post*, p. 8.

Lewis, G.A. (1986, October). Getting healthy through workers' control: Self organizing around safety issues. *Our Times*, 28-31.

Marsh, L. (1975). *Report on social security for Canada 1943*. Toronto: University of Toronto Press.

McCombie, N. (1982). Who pays for compensation? *Canadian Dimension*, 16, (2), 12-13.

McGilly, F. (1990). *An introduction to Canada's public services: Understanding income and health programs*. Toronto: McClelland & Stewart.

Miller, B.J. (1988, March/April). Unmasking the labour board: Health and safety hazards. *Our Times*, 31-35.

Millis, H.A., & Montgomery, R.E. (1938). *Labor's risks and social insurance*. New York: McGraw-Hill Book Company.

Morton, D. (1990). *Working people: An illustrated history of the Canadian labour movement* (3rd ed.). Toronto: Summerhill Press.

Papp, L. (1992, May 25). Paying for worker pain has everyone feeling hurt. *Toronto Star*, p. A17.

Paterson, C. (1981). W.C.B. investment decisions: Health issues take a back seat. *Leftwords*, 3, (3), 7-8.

Reasons, C.E., Ross, L.L., & Paterson, C. (1981). *Assault on the worker: Occupational health and safety in Canada*. Toronto: Butterworths.

Sentes, R. (1985). The politics of health standards setting. In H.D. Dickinson & B. Russell (Eds.), *The politics of work in the west: Historical and contemporary perspectives* (pp. 162-179). Saskatoon: Social Research Unit, Department of Sociology, University of Saskatchewan.

Shields, J. (1988). The capitalist state and class struggle in the fruit and vegetable industry in British Columbia. In D.A. Hay & G.S. Basran (Eds.), *The political economy of agriculture in western Canada* (pp. 87-106). Toronto and Saskatoon: Garamond Press and Social Research Unit.

Shields, J. (1991). *Part-time employment: A survey of issues and structure of part-time work with special reference to Ontario*. Toronto: Ontario Ministry of Labour.

Statistics Canada. (1992). *Canada Yearbook, 1992*. Ottawa: Supply and Services Canada.

Statistics Canada. (1991). *Work injuries, 1988-1990*. Ottawa: Author.

Tucker, E. (1992). Worker participation in health and safety regulation: Some lessons from Sweden. *Studies in Political Economy: A Socialist Review*, 37, 95-127.

Weils, H. (1992, October). Sexual harassment. *Briarpatch*, 21, 31-32.

Chapter 33

Agricultural Production, Work, and Health

B. Singh Bolaria, University of Saskatchewan

Introduction

During the past few decades there have been tremendous changes in agricultural production processes. Capitalization and mechanization of the agricultural sector have been accompanied by improved methods of cultivation, intensive farming, and increased use of chemicals, all of which have contributed to increased production and efficiency. Agricultural production is also increasingly dependent upon hired, seasonal, and migrant labour (Bolaria, 1992; Coye, 1985). This structural transformation of agricultural production is a mixed blessing. For instance, while the use of chemicals has contributed substantially to an increase in agricultural production, it also poses numerous health risks for the farmers and farm workers, and when some of these chemicals end up in the food chain, the health of the whole population is threatened. While the structural transformation of agricultural production has produced a number of other social and economic contradictions (Basran, 1992; Bolaria, Dickinson, &Wotherspoon, 1991), the focus here is on the health effects of agricultural production and the work environment.

Work Conditions and Health Risks

Agriculture is the third most dangerous industry after mining and construction (Jasso & Mazorra, 1984; Reasons et al., 1981). Numerous studies indicate that farmers, farmworkers, and their families have a high incidence of work-related accidents and fatalities and experience poor health status, which is reflected in such indicators as life expectancy and mortality (Rust, 1990; Coye, 1985; Sakala, 1987; Campbell, 1986; Canadian Centre for Occupational Health and Safety, 1986; Cliff, 1981; Dosman, 1985). A number of factors contribute to this ill health: farm machinery, chemicals, intensification of farm work, ramshackle housing, low wages, nonexistent sanitation facilities, and long hours of arduous labour.

Many of the accidents, fatalities, and health hazards in agriculture are associated with farm machinery. About half of all farm injuries are machinery related (Simpson, 1984). Tractors are most frequently involved in farm injuries and, along with grain augers and power takeoffs, account for many severe and disabling injuries, involving crush and compound fractures and amputations (Simpson, 1984). The intensification of farm work in association with farm machinery has increased the likelihood of being killed on the job (Sandborn, 1986; Ministry of Agriculture, 1985). One area that has received considerable attention is noise-induced hearing loss and speech-hearing difficulty with continuous and prolonged exposure to noise (Dennis, 1969; Pierce et al., 1985; Alberta Agriculture, 1982). While improved mufflers and soundproof cabs alleviate noise hazards to some extent in tractors, much self-propelled farm equipment lack adequately sound-insulated cabs.

Farm machinery and farm work pose other hazards to farmers and farm workers. Farm accidents claim somewhere between 150 to 200 lives in Canada every year (Robertson, 1984). A report of 23 farm fatalities in Alberta revealed that about 65 percent involved machinery, 91 percent of the victims were males, and the majority of these were over the age of 45 years of age. All of these accidents occurred during work, and the majority of the victims were working alone. The victims mostly died due to loss of blood or suffocation after the accidents. Many factors account for these fatalities. As the report states: "Most of the farm deaths involve the victim doing something they already knew was unsafe but due to fatigue, haste, stress, age and poor attitude they did it anyway" (Alberta Agriculture, 1983). There are numerous nonfatal farm accidents leading to severe and permanent injuries and, in some cases, amputation. As discussed later in this article, farm accidents also involve children leading to deaths or serious injuries every year (Alberta Agriculture, 1983; Ontario Ministry of Agriculture, 1985).

In any discussion of the health risks in agricultural production, the chemical industry occupies a central place. There has been a tremendous increase in the use of chemicals in agriculture (Bird & Rapport, 1986). While these chemicals control pests such as insects and weeds, they also pose environmental hazards. As Bird and Rapport (1986, p. 174) state: "some of these pesticides are known to be highly persistent, mobile and bioaccumulative and have already been associated with adverse ecological or human health effects." The human cost of the use of agricultural chemicals has been severe. It is estimated that each year they are responsible for the deaths of 10 000 and the acute poisoning of 400 000 people in the Third World (Rogers et al., 1988, p. 284). These health hazards are not confined to the Third World. Agricultural workers in Canada and the United States face extensive chemical exposure and associated health risks (Matsqui, Abbotsford Community Services, 1982; Stringini, 1982; Stubbs et al., 1984; Barthel, 1981). A survey of 270 farmworkers in 1982 (Matsqui, Abbotsford Community Services) revealed that they are exposed to dangerous pesticides:

1. Eight out of 10 farmworkers regularly suffer from direct contact with pesticides and a majority (55 percent) have been directly sprayed;
2. Eight out of 10 farmworkers have had to work immediately after a spraying;
3. Over 25 percent have had their living quarters sprayed with pesticides;
4. Seven out of 10 farmworkers became physically ill after a direct spraying, yet only 3 percent received medical help provided by their employers;
5. Almost 20 percent frequently breathe pesticide fumes while working.

Many of the workers spend long hours in the fields and therefore have prolonged periods of exposure to pesticides. As many of the pesticides are carcinogenic, farm workers suffer from many ill effects of exposure to spraying. The Matsqui study revealed that 90 percent of the workers had experienced one or more symptoms of pesticide spraying. For instance,

1. Forty-four percent suffered skin rashes;
2. Forty-seven percent suffered itching;
3. Fifty percent reported headaches;
4. Thirty-five percent experienced dizziness;
5. Seventeen percent suffered from gastro-intestinal problems;
6. Almost 60 percent of the children working in the fields experienced the same sorts of symptoms;
7. Almost 50 percent reported various central nervous system disorders;
8. Twenty percent had missed work due to work-related health problems.

The majority of workers did not speak the English language and many of them did not receive information or instructions on the health hazards of pesticides. A vast majority (over 80 percent) ate their lunches in the sprayed field areas. One writer has commented that "the living and working conditions of Canadian farm labourers (especially in B.C.'s

Fraser Valley) bear a closer resemblance to those of Third World peasants than to those of the average Canadian worker (Labonte, 1982-83, p. 6). Also, the pesticide safety regulations are either nonexistent or not enforced. There is continued use of pesticides that have never been adequately tested for safety, and cases of severe pesticide poisoning and death are not uncommon.

A study of 488 farmers in Alberta indicated that 10 percent of them had suffered symptoms of pesticide poisoning during the survey year (Hussain, 1983). The study also reported that within the previous five years, 26 percent of the sample had experienced some poisoning and 3 percent reported chronic health problems related to pesticides. The 10 percent a year pesticide-poisoning amounts to a very large number of farmers at risk (Hussain, 1983; Moore, 1984). It amounts to approximately 5 000 farmers in Alberta (Hussain, 1983) and over 7 000 in Saskatchewan (Moore, 1984).

Studies of farm workers in the United States also pointed to the grim health status of farm workers. Their life expectancy is 20 percent less than the average American and the infant mortality among their children is 60 percent above the national average (United States Congress, 1972). Other evidence from the United States indicates that "farmworkers have an injury rate due to toxic chemicals almost three times as high as injuries of all types for workers in other industries," and "farmworkers lost twice as many hours due to pesticide-related illnesses than hours lost by manufacturing workers due to all causes" (British Columbia Human Rights Commission, 1983, p. 22). Migrant workers in the United States have a life expectancy of only 49 years. Eitzen and Zinn (1989, p. 456) state that "this low rate is a consequence of living in poverty or near poverty and, most significant, the exposure to herbicides and pesticides sprayed on the fields where they work."

Direct exposure to chemicals for farmworkers has quite serious health consequences. For instance, Temik, a pesticide used to control potato bugs, is associated with a higher number of miscarriages for pregnant women and increased rates of stomach cancer (Freudenberg, 1989). Since the use of many chemicals in agricultural production is relatively new, the long-term consequences are only just beginning to appear. The link between pesticides and cancer has received the most attention (Burmeister, 1985; Gallagher et al., 1985; Harding, 1988; Barthel, 1981; Mills, 1984). Other long-term ailments associated with chemicals include birth defects, neurological disorders, reproductive disorders, and sterility (Chase et al., 1973; Epstein, 1979; Freudenberg, 1989; Kahn, 1976; Milvey & Wharton, 1980; Bull, 1982).

In the face of all the ill effects of pesticides, the "agrichem" business continues to flourish and the use of many pesticides continues without having been properly tested and in some cases when they are known to be carcinogenic (Goff & Reasons, 1986; B.C. Human Rights Commission, 1983).

The deplorable working conditions of both the domestic transient farm labourers and the migrant imported workers are well documented (Sanderson, 1974; Labonte, 1980, 1982; Sandborn, 1983, 1986; Canada Department of Manpower and Immigration, 1973; Report of the Special Committee on Visible Minorities in Canadian Society, 1984; Sharma, 1983; Kelly, 1983; B.C. Human Rights Commission, 1983). Workers and their families are often exposed to harmful substances on farms. There is inadequate or nonexistent enforcement of the Health Act Regulations, in addition to physical danger, occupational diseases, pesticides, and a high risk of injury. Also farm workers are not fully and adequately protected by minimum wage legislation, working hours, and overtime wages (Report of the Special Committee on Visible Minorities in Canadian Society, 1984). Both the living and working conditions of farm labour contribute to their ill health. A federal task force report in 1973 on seasonal migrant farmworkers uncovered instances of "child labour, sick, pregnant, and otherwise unfit adults working in the fields; and of entire families working with only the head of the family being paid" (Sanderson, 1974, p. 405). The task force was "shocked, alarmed, and sickened" at the working conditions, wage levels, malnutrition, nonexistent health facilities, and people living in "indescribable squalor" (Canada, Department of Manpower and Immigration, 1973, p. 17; Sanderson, 1974).

The task force uncovered many cases of violation of the Immigration Act, Child Labour Act, human rights, and minimum sanitation standards. The employers, of course, benefit from family labour and are "delighted" to have foreign workers with large families (Canada Department of Manpower and Immigration, 1973).

The working and living conditions of farmworkers in British Columbia are similar to the conditions which minority workers face in Ontario. Farmworkers in British Columbia receive low wages; face exploitation due to labour contracting system, long hours of work, no overtime pay or benefits, unhealthy working conditions, lack of toilet or drinking water facilities on many farms, and crowded and dangerous shacks;, and are exposed to chemicals and pesticides in the field (Sharma, 1983; Canadian Farmworkers' Union, 1980; Labonte, 1980, 1982-83; Kelly, 1983).

The entire family works and "lives" in the fields. Because of poor sanitation and hygiene facilities and poor water supply, farm workers have a very high incidence of infectious diseases and diseases linked to fecal contamination (Arbab & Weidner, 1986). Lack of proper toilet facilities may affect the female workers more seriously than other farm labour. For instance, among women, high rates of urinary infections are often associated with prolonged retention of urine (Jasso & Mazorra, 1984). The need for toilet facilities was highlighted in evidence presented to a tribunal investigating such facilities for field workers. In her statement, a woman worker indicated that: "whenever there is a ditch or woods nearby, we go there. When this does not exist, we just have to wait. Or otherwise a group of us get together and stand around the person and cover him or her up" (Jasso & Mazorra, 1984, p. 90).

In some cases, workers have to pay high rents for "housing accommodations" provided by the farmers. These "accommodations" are usually small, overcrowded, and unhealthy firetraps without in-unit bathrooms or running water (Sharma, 1982, p. 13). A survey of 270 farmworkers in 1982 revealed that a large proportion of the accommodations (about 80 percent) had no proper wash-up facilities and 44 percent had no access at all to shower facilities (Matsqui, Abbotsford Community Services, 1982).

Due to the lack of day-care facilities for the children of mothers who are forced to work to support their families, several incidents of drowning have been reported (Sharma, 1982; Sharma, 1983). The coroner's jury, which, in August 1980, investigated the death of a child who rolled off a bunk and drowned in the water bucket, recommended that immediate steps be taken to establish standards for farm labour housing. The irony is, however, that the existing standards established in 1946 are not being enforced (B.C. Human Rights Commission, 1983).

In addition, since young children are an important source of farm labour, they are subject to occupational injury and health risks. Some U.S. estimates indicate that children 15 years of age or younger suffer 14 to 24 percent of all fatal injuries on farms (Field & Purschwitz, 1987). It is also estimated that persons 19 years of age and younger are involved annually in 300 injury deaths (Rivara, 1985), and that this group also accounts for 29 percent of fatal injuries involving tractors (Karlson & Noren, 1979). Other studies also report that primarily due to their involvement with farm machinery, minors (children) suffer from many severe work-related injuries (Cogbill et al., 1985; Salmi et al., 1989; Swanson et al., 1987). A study of children of migrant agricultural workers in Wisconsin concluded: "Our analysis of preventive medical care, morbidity, and mortality among children of migrant workers supports the view that this group is at substantially greater risk of health problems and early mortality than the general population" (Slesinger, Christenson, & Cautley, 1986, p. 72). A more recent study of minors involved in farm work, covering the period 1986-89 in Washington State, concluded that "farm work is dangerous for young children" (Heyer et al., 1992, p. 557).

Both in British Columbia (Canada) and Washington State (United States), there are a number of examples during the past few years that illustrate continuous health risks and mortality faced by children.

1. In 1988, Binh Thanh Hoang, 9, is left alone in a parked car on a Matsqui, B.C. farm, where his mother is picking raspberries. He is killed when the car rolls down an embankment.

2. In September of that year, Joel Campos, 14, is cutting vines in a hops field in Moxee, Washington. He falls asleep in a furrow and is crushed to death by a truck.

3. Dina Pedro, 7, drowns in an uncovered and unfenced tank of pesticide on a Saanich, B.C. farm.

4. A child under 10 is killed crossing a road to work in a Washington State asparagus field.

5. Gurjit Pejatta, 8, his brother, Sumin, 9, and Boota Bassi, 10, all drown in a pond in Aldergrove, B.C., in 1980. The parents are picking berries at a nearby farm. A few miles further up the Fraser Valley, an infant, Sukhdeep Madhar, rolls off a cot in a farmworker cabin and drowns in a bucket of water.

    (MacQueen, 1990, p. B1).

There has been considerable opposition to covering farm workers under the workers' compensation board (WCB) regulations. The B.C. government in May 1982 had decided to protect farmworkers through such measures as WCB inspection of farms, safety standards, and pesticide control. However, the government reversed its plan in March 1983 to extend WCB regulation regarding health and safety to farm labour. This decision came during a coroner's jury inquest into the pesticide poisoning death of a farmworker. The jury ruled that the death was "preventable homicide" (*Vancouver Sun*, March 18, 1983; Pynn, 1983; Koch, 1983). The extension of the WCB regulation to farmworkers was opposed by the B.C. Federation of Agriculture on the grounds that it would be costly, unrealistic, and impractical (*Victoria Times-Colonist*, March 12, 1983). Failure of legal protection in this case largely affected racial minority workers. Even when these protections are in place, they are inadequately enforced.

As noted above, agricultural workers fare very badly as regards general living conditions — labour compounds; unsanitary, unsafe and overcrowded accommodations — which, combined with long hours of arduous work, tend to produce ill health. Insecure and depressing working conditions; the misery of the material, social, and environmental deprivations; racial subordination; long-distance migrations and uprooting from stable traditional cultures and disruption of stable community ties, all contribute toward psychological distress and mental disorders (Doyal & Pennell, 1979; Eyer, 1984; Kuo & Tsai, 1986).

Farming is among the most stressful occupations in North America (Alberta Agriculture, 1982). The nature of agricultural production, long working hours, the uncertainty of the weather, the high cost of farm machinery and other inputs, high interest rates and uncertain markets all contribute to stress, psychological despair, and social disruptions. The stress of farm life and farming may also be exacerbated by the need for off-farm work to support the farm operation. Dependence on off-farm work has been growing (Bollman & Smith, 1988). The effects of stress may be manifested in such problems as alcohol and drug abuse, family violence, and suicides on farms (Gordon, 1988; Haslett, 1984).

It should be noted that health hazards in the fields vary according to the type of farming. In addition to exposure to various chemicals, farmers and farmworkers have excessive exposure to commercial solvents, sunlight, and heat. Those who work with animals are at risk to bacterial and viral infections (George, 1976). Prairie farmers and farmworkers suffer from serious lung diseases, the most common of which are: farmer's lung, caused by inhalation of mouldy grain dust; grain–dust asthma; and silo filler's lung. Respiratory problems are likely to be higher among farmers and farmworkers who handle wet and mouldy grains or hay (Warren, 1977). These episodes are even higher among those who work with inadequate equipment for drying and storing grains and hay. Small and less profitable farms are more likely to have inadequate equipment. It is also on these farms that wives and other family members who assist in farm work and whose labour is essential to survival of the small farm units, are exposed to health hazards. Therefore, under these circumstances the incidence of respiratory and other symptoms associated with handling of mouldy and wet grains and hay are likely to be higher among the family members (George, 1976).

Chronic back injury is one of the most common occupational diseases among farm workers who work with short hoes. As Waitzkin (1983, p. 15) states, "The short hoe's human toll is crippling back disease for thousands of farmworkers; the main injuries are slipped discs and degenerative arthritis of the spine." Waitzkin (1983, p. 15) further states that "these problems occur in younger workers who do stoop labour, and their physical effects are irreversible. Since migrant workers most often lack educational opportunities and frequently know little English, farm workers' back usually means permanent economic disability." Yet this is a preventable disease. Migrant workers are an easily replaceable work force. A reserve army of migrants is available to replace workers who are crippled by back injuries or who resist the conditions of their work. As Waitzkin (1983, p. 15) states: "powerlessness resulted from lack of organization; individual farmworkers had no alternative to the crippling effects of the short hoe, because resistance meant loss of work."

It is evident from the above discussion that numerous factors contribute to rural environmental degradation and adverse health effects for farmers, farm workers, and their families. Ironically, while the producers and workers are indispensable for the production of fruit, vegetables, and other food commodities that are essential for a nation's health and nutrition, they themselves suffer from a vast range of work-related health risks. This portrayal of the rural environment and way of life is quite contrary to the idyllic image of rural Canada still held by many people.

Summary and Conclusions

This chapter has discussed the linkages between agricultural production, working conditions, and health risks faced by farmers, farmworkers, and their families. Agricultural production processes and working conditions pose numerous health risks for producers and workers. Mechanization of agriculture, farming practices, use of chemicals, market uncertainties, pressures to maintain the "family farm," unsafe and unsanitary living and working conditions for many farmworkers, all contribute to their physical and psychological ill health.

It was noted earlier that after mining and construction, farming in North America is the third most dangerous industry. The extent and severity of occupational illnesses and deaths and health and safety risks in farming raises the question of causes.

Explanations of occupational injury, illnesses, and deaths tend to fall into three broad categories: individual, technical, and labour process (Dickinson & Stobbe, 1988). Individual-level explanations tend to blame the worker and attribute accidents to the individual's carelessness or inability to function in an industrial setting, or to the individual's "accident proneness." Technical explanations tend to focus on such factors as design of machinery and other physical conditions surrounding work, such as lights. The third-level explanations give primacy to class relations at the workplace and the distribution of power and control to determine the production levels, work hours, work content, and other conditions of work

Agricultural wage labour is primarily composed of indigenous transient workers who are often shut out of the other labour market opportunities, recently arrived immigrants, migrants, and often illegal workers. Also, as Martin (1985) notes, agricultural "dirty" work in many countries is performed by "dark-skinned" foreign workers. This labour force in many respects is a marginalized, subordinated, and powerless segment of the working class (Bolaria, 1992). Thus the control of the employer over the workers and the labour process primarily rests on the powerlessness of the workers. Work-related accidents in this context have less to do with the personal background and psychological characteristics of the workers, their "accident proneness," and their inability to adjust and function in a mechanized work setting, than the tasks they perform and the working conditions and the work environment in which they are compelled to work, primarily because of their powerlessness and vulnerability. What about the farmers who are self-employed? In this regard, Denis (1988) argues that individual-level explanations are incomplete and weak and that institutional and structural factors are important in understanding farm hazards. In particular, primacy is given to the social, economic, and market forces that compel farmers to constantly increase production, even at the cost of exposing themselves and their families to hazardous chemicals and work-risks for survival.

In conclusion, it is argued that the greater exploitation of farm labourers and their health status should be understood in the context of the objective vulnerability of this labour force and the agricultural production process. The health, health care, and safety of the workers should be analyzed in the context of class relations at the workplace, where employers basically control the labour process. The survival of the small farmers and the profits of the large farms may depend upon access to a cheap, docile, and vulnerable labour force. Access to offshore workers assures an almost infinite supply of labour. When labour is plentiful and healthy workers are available to replace the weak and the sick, employers are less concerned about the health and safety of the workers. Self-employed farmers also operate under numerous structural constraints imposed primarily by economic and market forces. These forces put pressure on farmers to adopt farming practices that expose them and their families to numerous occupational injuries, illnesses, and death. Thus external structural imperatives exert a greater influence on the work conditions, work environment, farm practices, and health and safety of the farmers and farmworkers and their families than do the personal and psychological attributes, cultural characteristics, and "accident proneness" of individuals.

Study Questions

1. Discuss the health hazards faced by farmers and farm workers because of agricultural production processes.
2. Discuss the specific health problems faced by women and children in agriculture.
3. Discuss the economic and environmental factors that may contribute to the physical and psychological ill health of farmers.
4. Discuss the statement that "chemicals used on the farm affect not only the farmers, farm workers, and their families, but also the rest of the population."
5. It is often argued that there is a basic contradiction between profits and labour costs. Discuss how this contradiction is manifested in the agriculture sector with respect to wage levels, working conditions, and health and safety standards.

Recommended Reading

Basran, G.S., & Hay, D. (Eds.). (1988). *The political economy of agriculture in western Canada*. Toronto and Saskatoon: Garamond Press and Social Research Unit, Department of Sociology, University of Saskatchewan

Bolaria, B.S. (1992). Farm labour, work conditions, and health Risks. In D.A. Hay & G.S. Basran (Eds.), *Rural sociology in Canada* (pp. 228-245). Toronto: Oxford University Press.

Bolaria, B.S., Dickinson, H.D., & Wotherspoon, T. (1988). Rural issues and problems. In B.S. Bolaria (Ed.), *Social issues and contradictions in Canadian society* (pp. 393-416). Toronto: Harcourt Brace Jovanovich.

Denis, W.B. (1988). Causes of health and safety hazards in Canadian agriculture. *International Journal of Health Services*, 18, 419-436.

Dosman, J. (Ed.). (1985). *Health and safety in agriculture*. Saskatoon: University of Saskatchewan (conference proceedings).

Pugh, T. (Ed.). (1987). *Fighting the farm crisis*. Saskatoon: Fifth House.

References

Alberta Agriculture. (1982a). *Safety guide for farming*. Edmonton.

Alberta Agriculture. (1983b). *A manager's guide to farm safety*. Edmonton.

Arbab, D.M., & Weidner, B.L. (1986). Infectious diseases and field water supply and sanitation among migrant farm workers. *American Journal of Public Health*, 76, (6), 694-695.

Barthel, E. (1981). Increased risk of lung cancer in pesticide-exposed male agricultural workers. *Journal of Toxicology and Environmental Health*, 8, 1027-1040.

Basran, G.S. (1992). Changes in agriculture in Canada: Theoretical perspectives. In D. Hay & G.S. Basran (Eds.), *Rural sociology in Canada* (pp. 4-15). Toronto: Oxford University Press.

Bird, P.M., & Rapport, D.J. (1986). *State of the environment report for Canada*. Ottawa: Ministry of Supply and Services.

Bolaria, B.S. (1992). Farm labour, work conditions and health risks. In D. Hay & G.S. Basran (Eds.), *Rural sociology in Canada* (pp. 228-245). Toronto: Oxford University Press.

Bolaria, B.S., Dickinson, H.D., & Wotherspoon, T. (1991). Rural issues and problems. In B.S. Bolaria (Ed.), *Social issues and contradictions in Canadian society* (pp. 393-416). Toronto: Harcourt Brace Jovanovich.

Bollman, R.D., & Smith, P. (1988). Integration of Canadian farm and off-farm markets and off-farm work of farm women, men, and children. In D. Hay & G.S. Basran (Eds.), *The political economy of agriculture in western Canada* (pp. 185-202). Toronto and Saskatoon: Garamond Press and Social Research Unit, Department of Sociology, University of Saskatchewan.

British Columbia Human Rights Commission. (1983, February). *What this country did to us, it did to itself*. Vancouver: B.C. Human Rights Commission on Farmworkers and Domestic Workers.

Bull, D. (1982). *A growing problem: Pesticides and the third world poor*. Oxford: Oxfam.

Burmeister, L.F. (1985). Cancer mortality in Iowa farmers. In J. Dosman (Ed.), *Health and safety in agriculture*. Saskatoon: University of Saskatchewan.

Campbell, I. (1986). Health and safety on the farm. *At the Centre*, 9, (3), 1, 5, 7.

Canada, Department of Manpower and Immigration. (1973). *The seasonal farm labour situation in southwestern Ontario* (mimeographed report).

Canadian Centre for Occupational Health and Safety. (1986). Occupational health and safety in agriculture. *At the Centre*, 9, (3).

Canadian Farmworkers' Union. (1980). *Support British Columbia farmworkers*.

Chase, H.P., Barnett, S. Welch, N., Briese, F., & Krossner, M. (1973). Pesticides and U.S. farm labour families. *Rocky Mountain Medical Journal*, 70, 27-31.

Cliff, K.S. (1981). Agriculture — the occupational hazards. *Public Health*, 95, 15-27.

Cogbill, T.H., Busch, H.M., & Stiers, G.R. (1985). Farm accidents in children. *Pediatrics*, 83, 267-271.

Coye, M.J. (1985, September). The health effect of agricultural production: The health of agricultural workers. *Journal of Public Health Policy*, 349-370.

Dennis, C.A.R. (1969). *A survey of the hearing levels of Saskatchewan farmers*. Regina: Department of Public Health, Occupational Health Branch.

Denis, W.B. (1988). Causes of health and safety hazards in Canadian agriculture. *International Journal of Health Services*, 18, (3), 419-436.

Dickinson, H.D., & Stobbe, M. (1988). Occupational health and safety in Canada. In B.S. Bolaria & H.D. Dickinson (Eds.), *Sociology of health care in Canada* (pp. 426-436). Toronto: Harcourt Brace Jovanovich.

Dosman, J. (Ed.). (1985). *Health and safety in agriculture*. Saskatoon: University of Saskatchewan (conference proceedings).

Doyal, L., & Pennell, I. (1979). *The political economy of health*. London: Pluto Press.

Eitzen, D.S. & Zinn, M.B. (1989). *Social problems* (4th ed.). Boston: Allyn & Bacon.

Epstein, S. (1979). *The politics of cancer*. Garden City: Anchor Books.

Eyer, J. (1984). Capitalism, health and illness. In J.B. McKinlay (Ed.), *Issues in the political economy of health care*. New York: Tavistock Publications.

Freudenberg, N. (1989). The corporate assault on health. In P. Brown (Ed.), *Perspectives in medical sociology* (pp. 104-121). Belmont: Wadsworth.

Field, W.E., & Purschwitz, M.A. (1987). Cost of farm and rural injuries. *Public Health Reports*, 102, (6), 642-644.

Gallagher, R.F., et al. (1985). Cancer in farmers and farm labourers in British Columbia. In J. Dosman (Ed.), *Health and safety in agriculture*. Saskatoon: University of Saskatchewan (conference proceedings).

George, A. (1976, October). *Occupational health hazards to women*. Ottawa: Advisory Council on the Status of Women.

Goff, C.H., & Reasons, C.E. (1986). Organizational crimes against employees, consumers, and the public. In B.D. MacLean (Ed.), *The political economy of crime*. Scarborough: Prentice-Hall.

Gordon, F. (1988). Stress in the farm family: Implications for the rural human service worker. In D. Hay & G.S. Basran (Eds.), *The political economy of agriculture in western Canada* (pp. 143-151). Toronto and Saskatoon: Garamond Press and Social Research Unit, Department of Sociology, University of Saskatchewan.

Harding, J. (1988). Environmental degradation and rising cancer rates: Exploring the links in Canada. In B.S. Bolaria & H.D. Dickinson (Eds.), *Sociology of health care in Canada* (pp. 411-425). Toronto: Harcourt Brace Jovanovich.

Haslett, E.A. (1984). *Structure of Ontario agriculture as related to health and safety*. Toronto: Ontario Ministry of Agriculture, Food and Labour. Task Force on Health and Safety (Background Paper #1).

Heyer, N.J., Franklin, G., Rivara, F.P., Parker, P., & Haug, J.A. (1992). Occupational injuries among minors doing farm work in Washington State: 1986 to 1989. *American Journal of Public Health*, 82, 557-560.

Hussain, M. (1983). *Pesticide safety survey*. Edmonton: Alberta Agriculture.

Jasso, S., & Mazorra, M. (1984). Following the harvest: The health hazards of migrant and seasonal farmworking women. In W. Charkin (Ed.), *Double exposure: Women's health hazards on the job and at home*. New York: Monthly Review Press.

Kahn, E. (1976). Pesticide related illness in California farm workers. *Journal of Occupational Medicine*, 18, 693-696.

Karlson, T., & Noren, J. (1979). Farm tractor fatalities: The failure of voluntary safety standards. *American Journal of Public Health*, 69, 146-149.

Kelly, R. (1983, November). Bitter harvest. *New West Review*.

Koch, T. (1983, March 17). Farm poison death government fault, jury says. *The Vancouver Province*, p. B1.

Kuo, W.H., & Tsai, Y. (1986). Social networking, hardiness and immigrant's mental health. *Journal of Health and Social Behavior*, 27, 133-149.

Labonte, R. (1980, August 25).The plight of the farmworkers. *Vancouver Sun*.

Labonte, R. (1982, June-July). Racism and labour: The struggle of British Columbia's farmworkers. *Canadian Forum*.

Labonte, R. (1982-1983). Of cockroaches and berry blight. *This Magazine*, 15, (6), 4-6.

Labonte, R. (1984). Chemical justice: Dioxin's day in court. *This Magazine*, 17, (6), 4-9.

Martin, P.L. (1985). Migrant labor in agriculture: An international comparison. *International Migration Review*, 19, (1), 135-143.

Matsqui, Abbotsford Community Services. (1982, October). Agricultural pesticide and health survey results. Abbotsford: A project of the Matsqui, Abbotsford Community Services (October).

MacQueen, K. (1990, September 22). Slim pickings. *Vancouver Sun*, p. B1.

Mills, P.K., Newell, G.R., Johnson, D.E. (1984). Testicular cancer associated with employment in agriculture and oil and natural gas extraction. *Lancet*, 1, 207-210.

Milvey, T.H., & Wharton, D. (1980). Epidemiological assessment of occupationally related chemically induced sperm count suppressions. *Journal of Occupational Medicine, 22,* 77-78.

Moore, A. (1984, March 15). Study shows at least 7000 farmers poisoned by pesticides last year. *Commonwealth.*

Ontario Ministry of Agriculture and Food, and Ministry of Labour. (1985). Report of the task force on health and safety in agriculture. Author: Toronto.

Pierce, W.E., et al. (1985). Prevention of hearing loss among animals. In J. Dosman (Ed.), *Health and safety in agriculture.* Saskatoon: University of Saskatchewan.

Pynn, L. (1983, March 11). Exempting farmers from safety rules attacked. *Vancouver Sun.*

Reasons, C.E., Ross, L., & Peterson, C. (1981). *Assault on the workers.* Toronto: Butterworths.

Report of the Special Committee on Visible Minorities in Canadian Society. (1984). *Equality now!* Ottawa: House of Commons.

Rivara, F.P. (1985). Fatal and nonfatal farm injuries to children and adolescents in the United States. *Pediatrics, 76,* 567-573.

Robertson, L. (1984). It's spring: The farm fatality season. *Country Guide, 103,* (5), 20-22.

Rogers, E.M., Burdge, R.J., Horsching, P.F., & Donnemeyer, J.F. (1988). *Social change in rural societies.* Englewood Cliffs: Prentice Hall.

Rust, G.S. (1990, October 10). Health status of migrant farmworkers: A literature review and commentary. *American Journal of Public Health, 80,* 1213-1217.

Sakala, C. (1987). Migrant and seasonal farmworkers in the United States: A review of health hazards, status, and policy. *International Migration Review, 21,* (3), 659-687.

Salmi, L.R., Weiss, H.B., Peterson, P.L., Spengler, R.F., Sattin, R.W., & Anderson, H.A. (1989). Fatal farm injuries among young children. *Pediatrics, 83,* 267-271.

Sandborn, C. (1983). Equality for farmworkers — A question of social conscience. Submission to the legislative caucus of the provincial New Democratic Party.

Sandborn, C. (1986). OHS on the Canadian farm: What is to be done? *At the Centre, 9,* (3), 1-5.

Sanderson, G. (1974). The sweatshop legacy: Still with us in 1974. *The Labour Gazette, 74,* 400-417.

Sharma, H. (1983). Race and class in British Columbia — The case of B.C.'s farmworkers. *South Asian Bulletin, 3,* 53-69.

Sharma, S. (1982). East Indians and the Canadian ethnic mosaic: An overview. *South Asian Bulletin, 1,* 6-18.

Simpson, S.G. (1984). Farm machinery injuries. *The Journal of Trauma, 24,* (2), 150-152.

Slesinger, D.P., Christenson, B.A., & Cautley, E. (1986). Health and mortality of migrant farm children. *Social Science and Medicine, 23,* (1), 65-74.

Stringini, P. (1982). On the political economy of risk: Farmworkers, pesticides, and dollars. *International Journal of Health Services, 12,* (2), 263-292.

Stubbs, H.A., Harris, J., & Spear, R.C. (1984). A proportionate mortality analysis of California agricultural workers, 1978-79. *American Journal of Industrial Medicine, 6,* 305-320.

Swanson, J.A., Sachs, M., Dahlgren, K.A., & Tinguely, S.J. (1987). Accidental farm injuries in children. *American Journal of Diseases in Children, 141,* 1276-1279.

United States Congress. (1972). *Hearings on migratory labor.* Washington: U.S. Government Printing Office.

Waitzkin, H. (1983). *The second sickness; Contradictions of capitalist health care.* New York: The Free Press.

Warren, C.P. (1977). Lung disease in farmers. *Canadian Medical Association Journal, 119,* 391-394.

Part Ten

Current Issues

Part Ten

Introduction

There is an increasing recognition that social conditions and social contradictions foster and contribute to many illnesses in society. Because of the close linkages between medicine and society, any meaningful discussions of health and illness, health-care delivery systems, and policy alternatives cannot be divorced from the consideration of the political, economic, social, and ideological structures in the society. The chapters in this section illustrate this by a number of diverse cases.

One of the primary contradictions in this society is between profits and health. Illness is exploited for a variety of purposes by a number of groups, including profit-making corporations.

Direct investments by American firms in foreign countries have increased from $16 billion in 1950 to $233.4 billion in 1984. These foreign countries -for the most part located in the Third World — offer multinationals a number of advantages including tax shelters, low production costs, cheap labour, and relaxed health and safety standards. Many of the plants do not enforce even the weakest health standards. Not surprisingly, those directly affected are the workers, many of whom are female. Subjected to toxins that in some cases are banned in advanced countries, these workers are under constant assault by their environment.

Industrial pollution, however, knows no political or national boundaries. Both capitalist and socialist countries are experiencing alarming rates of environmental deterioration. In the case of Mexico, toxins are affecting American border towns and cities. Spills and leakages damage huge areas of land and water, and chemicals banned in the States or Canada, for example, can make their way home in the form of treated foodstuffs such as bananas and coffee. Multinational production, as a consequence, stands for far more than huge profits.

Chapter 34, by Lexchin, is based on the primary thesis that the driving force behind the pharmaceutical industry is profits; ethical considerations are secondary. Lexchin notes that because of foreign domination, opportunities for manufacturing, exporting, and research in the Canadian pharmaceutical industry are severely constrained. However, the pharmaceutical industry is one of the most profitable in Canada. Pharmaceutical companies have been able to achieve this position by limiting price competition and replacing it with product competition. Lexchin argues that product competition also forms a key element in the orientation of many of the research activities of this industry. Development of new drugs is guided by the potential for profit rather than health. Pharmaceutical companies exercise a major influence over prescription practices of physicians and "stocking practices" of pharmacists, which affect their sales and profits.

Weston and Jeffery in Chapter 35 discuss the influence of institutions and social forces external to medicine in the perception and definition of and reaction to AIDS. The authors posit that the social issues override the medical issues of disease, with the result that AIDS is seen less as an illness or medical condition than a sensationalized social phenomenon. The authors discuss AIDS in the context of Western society's views of sexuality and of sickness, and the role which religious institutions, the state, and medicine play in the control of deviant behaviour. Several factors have shaped public perceptions and reactions to AIDS, including marginality of the groups considered at risk, the rise of the political right, and the fact that currently science has no cure for AIDS.

Ethics in health care has historically attracted attention from scholars, health professionals, and the public. In recent years, however, new ethical issues have arisen as traditional patterns of health care are challenged and as technology makes possible new procedures.

Storch, in Chapter 36, discusses some of these health-care ethics in relation to both "spectacular" and "non-spectacular" issues — abortion, euthanasia, and new reproductive technologies being examples of the former, and patient confidentiality and patient education examples of the latter. The paper examines, from a Canadian perspective, clinical treatment, focussing on beginning and ending of life (abortion, euthanasia), ethics in day-to-day health-care delivery, and broader issues of health-care delivery. Storch summarizes the paper with a discussion of emerging structures and processes that help to address problems of ethics in Canadian health care.

Individual lifestyles and consumption patterns are now widely invoked as explanations of the present increase in many chronic and degenerative diseases. As these explanations and the attendant solutions are being given wide publicity through the mass media and professional journals and are increasingly gaining acceptance, they are bound to have far-reaching consequences in the provision of health services and health-related policy issues.

Change of individual behaviour and promotion of self-care prevention through health education are important parts of the strategy to reduce health-care costs. The burden of health care crises may be borne by individuals to the extent that they accept the proposition that illnesses that are the result of environmentally induced conditions can be solved individually by self-care and "wise living."

Chapter 34

Profits First:

The Pharmaceutical Industry

in Canada

Joel Lexchin, University of Toronto

Introduction

The pharmaceutical industry is no different from any other enterprise in a capitalist economy: the primary motivation for making drugs is profit. Although the *Principles and Code of Marketing Practice* of the Pharmaceutical Manufacturers Association of Canada (PMAC)[1] states that "the calling of a pharmaceutical manufacturer is one dedicated to a most important public service, and such public service shall be the first and ruling consideration in all dealings" (1972, p. 3), the practical ethics of the industry are summed up in a quote from W.M. Garton, president of PMAC: "The pharmaceutical industry has never claimed to be motivated by altruism, but rather by profit for survival" (1980).

The incompatability between public service and private profit becomes evident when the stated ethics of the industry clash with the realities of turning a profit. In 1975, medical reports began appearing which warned that sudden withdrawal of a drug called propranolol, marketed by Ayerst Laboratories as Inderal and used for treating high blood pressure and angina (heart pain), could lead to heart attacks in some cases. Warnings to that effect appeared in advertisements in American medical journals, but not in Canadian journals.[2] When asked about this discrepancy by a reporter for *The Globe and Mail*, a representative of Ayerst said, "This is of no concern to the consuming public. . . . We're getting into more complex drugs. We can't inform the public on them all" (1975, p. F5). At that time, Inderal was the twelfth most frequently prescribed drug in Canada.

Another, more recent, example of how drug companies put profit above health involved Eli Lilly's anti-arthritis drug benoxaprofen. In 1980, this drug was marketed in Britain under the trade name Opren.[3] Lilly organized an aggressive promotional pro- gram for Opren and very quickly the drug was enjoying large sales. However, shortly after the drug appeared on the shelves of British pharmacies, Lilly's British subsidiary informed British health officials of the first of eight deaths resulting from suspected adverse reaction to Opren that occurred between May 1, 1981 and January 1982. In February 1982, nine months after the first known British death, benoxaprofen was evaluated by the Canadian Health Protection Branch (HPB) as safe for use in Canada.[4] In its submission to the HPB, Lilly did not mention the eight deaths in Britain connected to benoxaprofen and omitted information about other studies indicating potential prob- lems with the drug. Lilly officials did not give any of this critical information about their product to the HPB until just before reports of the deaths in Britain were going to appear in the *British Medical Journal*.

Foreign Domination

According to the Statistics Canada, there were 137 pharmaceutical companies operat- ing in Canada at the end of 1986 (1988, p. 1). Although about 60 percent of all these enterprises are Canadian owned, the Report of the Commission of Inquiry on the Pharmaceutical Industry (*Eastman Report*) calculated that domestically controlled firms accounted for less than 16 percent of the value of factory shipments of pharmaceuti- cals and medicines for human use (1985, p. 54). By 1987, factory-gate sales of human medicines were running at about $3.1 billion (Breton, 1990, p. 187). This foreign domination of the Canadian industry is further illustrated by examining the makeup of the top 25 companies operating in this country. Only two of these companies were Canadian owned and the largest of these, Novopharm, ranked 14th in terms of sales.[5]

The Canadian pharmaceutical industry is one of the most heavily foreign- dominated in the world. According to a chart in the *Eastman Report* (1985, p. 248), out of the 25 countries listed, Canada ranked 21st in terms of domestic control of the market. This high degree of foreign control allows the multinationals to manipulate their profit levels in Canada as will be seen in the next section. It also has serious consequences for pharmaceutical manufacturing in this country. Information from the Bureau of Policy Coordination, a section of the Department of Consumer and Corporate Affairs, shows that between 1967 and 1981, Canada's contribution to the world output of pharmaceuti- cals fell from 2.6 to 1.6 percent of the total (1982, p. 5). Pharmaceutical manufacturing in Canada has always been minimal. Even in the late 1960s, 85 percent of manufacturing was confined to the conversion of imported material into final-dosage form. The reason why manufacturing has declined even further is that the multinationals are finding that they can generate greater profits by consolidating production in other countries. An analysis of import and export figures confirms that the multinationals are centralizing their production. Between 1968 and 1977, the country that had the largest relative gain in exports to Canada was Puerto Rico. The rise in imports from Puerto Rico was the result of U.S. companies moving their manufacturing operations there to take advantage of tax concessions. Gordon and Fowler have found that "for Canada, importing fine chemicals had been the rule, but what took place during the seventies was the massive transfer abroad of the secondary stages of drug manufacture, including the production of the end product" (1981, p. 50).

The ability of Canadian branch plants to export drugs is also limited by foreign control. With most patents on drugs foreign-owned,[6] subsidiary companies of the parent patentees control the market within their own jurisdictions. Export activity has to be confined to world areas where patents are not taken out; areas that are commercially insignificant. Having a successful Canadian operation takes second place to achieving an optimal overall international performance. This situation leads to the finding by the Department of Industry, Trade and Commerce that Canadian subsidiaries are usually "not encouraged or permitted by the head office to assume responsibility for exports of their products" (1980, p. 5).

A study by Burstall, Dunning, and Lake for the Organization for Economic Co-operation and Development has concluded that in countries where the industry is dominated by foreign multinational companies, the prospects of developing a viable indigenous pharmaceutical sector, actively engaged in international operations, are very limited (1981, p. 100).

Research and development in Canada is also severely constrained because of foreign domination. Up until 1988, multinational subsidiaries operating in Canada had traditionally spent about 3.5 percent of sales on research and development (Commission of Inquiry on the Pharmaceutical Industry,1985, p. 230; Statistics Canada, 1989, p. 62). Since the passage of Bill C-22 in December 1987, R & D expenditures in Canada have been growing (see the section on Public Policy and the Pharmaceutical Industry for more information on compulsory licensing and Bill C-22) and by 1990, R & D represented 8.8 percent of Canadian sales (Patented Medicine Prices Review Board, 1991, p. 20). However, Canadian concerns still have little influence on the research decisions of the multinational drug companies as Canada represents only about 1.5 percent of the world pharmaceutical market. The major incentive to do research and development lies in the profits to be derived from selling pharmaceuticals in the major world markets: the United States, Western Europe, and Japan, which represent 28, 21, and 15 percent of world sales respectively (World Health Organization, 1988, p. 9). Furthermore, only about a quarter of the research done in this country is basic research, that is, the actual discovery of new drugs. The bulk of the research dollar goes into testing new drugs to see how well they work and how safe they are. This type of research is obviously important, but it is basic research that is necessary to keep scientists in Canada and it is basic research that is going to produce major new treatments. The reason for the relative lack of basic research in Canada is simple: multinationals concentrate these facilities almost exclusively in their home countries. Taylor quotes Donald Davies, chairman of Ayerst McKenna and Harrison: "Virtually all companies do most of their research in their home country . . . German companies do the bulk of their research in Germany, and French companies do their work in France. That's just the way it is" (1983, p. B1). The OECD study by Burstall and co-workers (1981, p. 213) and the *Eastman Report* (1985, p. 423) both confirmed the truth of Davies' statement.

Profits in the Pharmaceutical Industry

The Canadian subsidiaries of multinational drug companies, and the industry in general, have been extremely profitable. A 1983 report by the investment firm of Walwyn Stodgell Cochrane Murray Ltd. of Toronto called the pharmaceutical industry "a particularly attractive area for long-term investment. The field is characterized by high profitability and consistent growth. Favourable demographics assure that this growth will continue well into the foreseeable future" (1983, p. 142). This opinion is reinforced by Kenneth R. Kulju, senior health-care analyst with Fahnestock and Co. Inc. in New York, who considers pharmaceutical stocks to be the premier investment group in the market (Livingston, 1988, p. 61). Examining Table 1 shows the accuracy of this statement.

Over the ten-year period 1977-1986, pharmaceutical firms were over 173 percent more profitable than manufacturing companies in general. The Eastman Report concluded that profit levels in Canada were generally higher than in most other well-developed countries in the world (1985, p. 277).

As robust as these profits seem, it is quite likely that they are an underestimate of the industry's true profit picture. The 1964 *Report of the Royal Commission on Health Services* said that "the earnings of the Canadian drug industry are not a satisfactory test of the overall pricing policies of the industry because they are understated" (1964, p. 679). This statement recognizes that multinational firms tend to charge the most advantageous "cost" of raw materials supplied by their plants in other countries, so as to have lower profits in high-tax countries than in low-tax countries. Gordon and Fowler provide evidence to back up this contention (1981, pp. 46,72,73). They concluded that the terms under which resale products (finished products that are imported into Canada for sale), raw materials and business services were transferred from foreign parents to Canadian

Table I   Rate of Return on Capital Employed, Before Taxes, 1970-1982

Year	Pharmaceutical Manufacturing (%)	All Manufacturing (%)	Rank of Pharmaceutical Industry out of 87 Manufacturing Industries
1970	20.9	8.2	3
1971	23.8	9.5	2
1972	23.8	10.8	3
1973	22.3	15.2	11
1974	25.0	17.3	8
1975	22.6	13.4	10
1976	19.4	11.7	13
1977	18.7	10.8	13
1978	20.4	12.8	12
1979	24.9	16.2	10
1980	27.1	14.7	4
1981	27.8	11.9	1
1982 (prelim)	26.1	3.3	2
Average	23.3	12.0	7

Source: Statistics Canada. *Corporate Financial Statistics — Detailed Income and Retained Earnings Statistics for 182 Industries*. Ottawa: various years.

subsidiaries were designed to transfer profits out of the Canadian subsidiaries. In 1976, the cost to Canadian subsidiaries for resale products was 73.4 percent of sales. This figure, which is more than twice the production cost in the United States on these products, provides the parent companies with substantial profits.[7]

In 1980, the Department of National Revenue launched an industry-wide audit of the international transactions of the pharmaceutical industry. The results of this audit were cited in a study by the Department of Consumer and Corporate Affairs. A sampling of fourteen major drugs in Canada, covering the period 1977 to 1979, revealed that prices charged by one subsidiary to another subsidiary of the same company were more than three times higher than the prices paid for the same drugs when the transaction was between two independent companies (1983, p. 16). Findings of this sort led a representative of the department to comment in *The Globe and Mail* that "profits were not being reported in Canada but somewhere else" (1980, p. B1). Leslie Dan, president of Novopharm, believed that because of the government audit, $20 to $25 million in additional tax reassessments were filed and promptly paid by several companies in order to avoid court action (1982, pp. 64-5).

Looking at the figures in Table 1 and all the evidence just presented suggesting that these figures are an understatement of the industry's true profits, it would seems difficult to deny that there are huge profits to be derived from manufacturing pharmaceuticals. But the PMAC repeatedly claims that the high profits are an accounting illusion created by the standard accounting practice of treating research and development expenditures as expenses against current income rather than capitalizing these outlays as an investment item (1975, p.18). However, as Gary Gereffi, professor of sociology at Duke University, makes clear, the accounting explanation of high profitability is inadequate for several reasons (1983, p. 192). First, the accounting bias is not just confined to the pharmaceutical industry but is present in all "discovery-intensive" industries such as oil and gas and in industries with high levels of research and development expenditures. Under certain circumstances the accounting rate of return could actually understate rather than overstate the "real" or economic rate of return. Second, as we have just seen, under any method of calculating profitability, the declared profits of the industry in Canada are likely to be artificially depressed. Finally, by allowing pharmaceutical companies to treat research and development costs as a current accounting expense, the government, in effect, is granting them an indirect fiscal subsidy to encourage their risk-taking efforts. This accounting method thus serves to raise the drug firm's profitability in fact as well as on paper. Temin showed that even after "correcting" profits by treating research and development expenditures as an investment, the drug industry was still one of the most profitable industries around (1979, p. 445).

The other major argument that the pharmaceutical companies use to counter charges of excessive profits is to maintain that these profits are necessary because theirs is an inherently high-risk industry. A fairly typical example of this type of defence came from a president of the PMAC, Judy Erola: "High risk, high profit. It has to be. There's just no question that an industry as risky as this one has to have a high return"[8] (Gammal, 1991). In a study by Orr, 71 Canadian manufacturing industries were ranked on the basis of risk. The drug industry was 67th, showing itself to be almost the lowest risk industry in Canada (1974, pp. 39-49). The Special House of Commons Committee on the price of drugs concluded:

> [A] review of the evidence before this Committee seems to indicate that, in comparison to manufacturing in general, the effects of losses on the pharmaceutical firms as a group does not indicate the presence of greater risk. In fact . . . the pharmaceutical industry in Canada has been increasingly less risky as compared with manufacturing in general. (1967, p. 71)

Competition in the Pharmaceutical Industry

One of the major reasons that the pharmaceutical industry has been able to sustain such high profit levels is the absence of price competition for most products. Figures in the

Table 2   Effect of Competition on Drug Prices

ONTARIO 1985

No. of suppliers of drug	2	3	4	5	6	7	8	10
Price of least expensive brand as a percent of most expensive brand	81.3	71.6	60.4	55.2	42.3	26.1	36.3	27.5

Source: Calculated from: *Ontario Drug Benefit Formulary*, January, 1985.

MANITOBA 1985

No. of suppliers of drug	2	3	4	5	6
Price of least expensive brand as a percent of most expensive brand	73.5	49.2	48.0	29.4	17.4

Source: Calculated from: *Manitoba Drug Standards and Therapeutics Formulary*, January 1985.

Eastman Report show that, on average, when there is more than one firm selling a drug that the ensuing competition results in a halving of the cost of the drug.[9] Looking at Table 2, which examines the effect of competition in Ontario and Manitoba, we see that the greater the number of companies making a drug the greater the price differential between the lowest and highest cost versions of that drug.

However, for most drugs on the Canadian market there is no competition. Of 1 525 drug preparations[10] listed in the January 1988 *Ontario Drug Benefit Formulary*, only 411 were available from more than one manufacturer.

In place of price competition, the industry has given us product competition. In product competition, drugs are promoted not on the basis of being less expensive than other equivalent products, but on the grounds that they are superior in their action, whether or not that is in fact the case. Companies identify successful drugs sold by their competitor and then expend large quantities of money in an attempt to invent new drugs that circumvent existing patents and thereby secure their own product for which they can obtain a patent.

Product competition is a formidable entry barrier into therapeutic classes, especially for small companies.[11] In order to develop a new patentable product, a company must be able to expend substantial capital, first on research and later on marketing. Smaller companies lack the necessary funding and therefore are denied entry into the market. The strength of the entry barrier into the pharmaceutical manufacturing industry was illustrated in Orr's (1974) study of 71 Canadian manufacturing industries. The entry barrier was measured against the following five characteristics: empirically observed ability to meet capital requirements, advertising intensity, research and development intensity, risk, and level of concentration within the industry. Of the 71 industries, the pharmaceutical industry had the 12th highest entry barrier.

The net result, has been a high level of concentration within therapeutic classes. Among the large firms, a pattern of specialization has emerged that tends to break the companies into smaller, rather exclusive groups. Each group shares a therapeutic class such as antibiotics or steroids. The PMAC tries to hide this type of concentration by talking about overall industry concentration statistics instead. The top four drug manufacturers, all foreign controlled, accounted for less than 25 percent of total pharmaceutical industry shipments in 1982. A PMAC-sponsored study by J.J. Friedman & Associates weighed these figures against the comparable figure of 50 percent for all Canadian manufacturing industries and proclaimed that "drug manufacturing is relatively unconcentrated" (1981, pp. 60-1). However, these statistics ignore the relatively high degree of concentration in therapeutic classes. The *Eastman Report* listed sales in 14 therapeutic classes in 1984. In 11 of these 14, four companies accounted for over 50 percent of sales[12] (1985, p. 131).

Research in the Pharmaceutical Industry

The multinational pharmaceutical companies are also able to maintain high profit levels by virtue of targeting their research efforts in certain directions. In an article in the *New England Journal of Medicine*, VanWoert stated that a representative of the United States Pharmaceutical Manufacturers Association confirmed that, in general, drug companies do not undertake research on relatively uncommon diseases, because drugs for them would generate insufficient profits (1978, p. 904). These same sentiments were echoed in 1980 by Joseph Williams, president of Warner Lambert, who was quoted by Gray as saying that "Our [Warner Lambert's] focus is to develop major drugs for major markets" (1981, p. 791).

Pharmaceutical companies rarely do research on drugs that do not have the potential to generate large sales and ultimately large profits. One of the major factors that go into determining the profit potential of a drug is whether or not it is patentable. If a drug can be patented, then the company has a monopoly on its sales until the patent expires — 20 years in major markets such as the United Kingdom, the United States, and West Germany.[13]

One example of how patentability affected the development of useful drugs is lithium, a medication that may be very beneficial in manic-depressive disorders. Reports of lithium's effectiveness began appearing as long ago as 1949. But lithium, which is a naturally occurring element, cannot be patented. Gershon and Shopsin reported that only when it was found that lithium could be compounded into a patentable slow-release form did the drug companies start researching and manufacturing it (1974).

In testimony before the Special House of Commons Committee, the province of Alberta severely criticized the effect of patents on applied research.

> Hence patents have not only induced a distortion between basic and applied research, but in making the latter budgets relatively too large have induced wasteful duplication of effort and the misdirection of effort toward rivalry-oriented molecular manipulation (1967, p. 2444).

In an industry where product, not price, competition is the chief form of rivalry, it is essential to keep churning out new products. Pierre Garai, an advertising executive and a staunch supporter of the pharmaceutical industry and the free enterprise system in general, recognized this reality.

> No manufacturer of drugs can afford to restrict his production to genuinely significant pharmaceutical innovations. There simply aren't enough of these around in any given fiscal year or, for that matter, any dozen fiscal years. It should therefore surprise no one that we find slight modifications of existing products marketed by the bushel, a veritable blizzard of parity products slugging it out as each company strives to extend its share of the market, endless polypharmaceutical combinations of dubious merit, and a steady outpouring of new chemical entities whose advantages, to say the least, remain to be established. (1964, p. 194)

Mr. Garai was writing over 25 years ago, but the situation is little different today. From the beginning of 1988 to the end of 1990, only 8 of the 177 new drugs (4.5 percent) introduced onto the Canadian market were breakthrough products or represented substantial improvements over existing drugs (Patented Medicine Prices Review Board, 1991, p. 13).

In more concrete terms, we can look at the plethora of anti-inflammatory (anti-arthritis) drugs currently available in Canada. There are over a dozen arthritis medications on the market. For a small minority of patients, this kind of choice is beneficial because for them only one particular anti-inflammatory will work; but in the vast majority of cases there is no clinical difference between any of the anti-inflammatories. The reasons that the Canadian market is flooded with these products, and new ones are regularly being introduced, is because they are drugs with huge markets. In 1988, this class of drugs generated almost $190 million in sales, with a growth rate of 13 percent per annum. As the population ages, the market for these products will probably expand even more rapidly (Miller, 1990). We are now witnessing the same trend when it comes to drugs for ulcer treatment. First onto the market was cimetidine in 1977, then ranitidine, and in quick succession famotidine and nizatidine. Once again, these newer products offer few, if any, advantages over the original (Anonymous, 1988), but their makers are hoping to cash in on the hundreds of millions of dollars of Canadian sales.

In terms of research it is clear that the pharmaceutical industry puts its money where the dollars are, not necessarily where the health need is.

The Pharmaceutical Industry and the Medical Profession

Doctors, their associations, and their journals are all prime objects of attention for the drug companies. Doctors are the ones who prescribe, and it is these prescriptions that translate into sales for the pharmaceutical houses. Nearly every doctor engaged in clinical medicine will prescribe, but a simple willingness to prescribe is not enough for the drug companies. In order to increase sales, and profits, the industry wants, and needs, more from doctors. Prominent among the strategies it uses for expanding sales and profits is to encourage the medical profession to look first to drug therapy for medical problems. It tries to present an image that will make the medical profession sympathetic towards the claims that the industry makes for its products; and that will take the industry's side against legislation that the industry sees as hostile to its interests. In short, the pharmaceutical industry needs a medical profession as an ally; a medical profession that sees the industry's goals as being harmonious with its own.

In order to achieve this alliance, the industry literally wines and dines doctors: evening seminars are run by drug companies accompanied by a free bar and a free meal. Doctors, from the moment they enter medical school, are provided with a veritable flood of free gifts from the industry — pens, notebooks, textbooks, rulers, calendars. Drug companies underwrite the cost of medical meetings, thereby limiting physicians' out-of-pocket expenses. Detailers, company representatives paid to go from office to office, are trained to be deferential to doctors and will arrange to get doctors free samples of almost any product. All of these activities are sponsored by individual companies, and although the gifts almost always bear the name of one of the company's products, the aim of all this largesse is not solely to sell a particular drug. The companies, and by extension the industry as a whole, are after the good will of the doctors. They want to establish a positive view of the industry in doctors' minds to build, and maintain, the needed alliance with the medical profession.

While it is eminently obvious why the drug industry wants an alliance with physicians, it is less clear why doctors should be willing to enter into such an alliance. The various gifts that doctors receive from the industry are certainly one factor, but probably a very minor one. It may be possible to buy the favour of some doctors, but not the vast majority. More important is the industry's support for various projects backed by physicians such as the organ-donation program and the research funding that comes from the drug companies, but these activities directly impact on only a relatively small number of doctors. There are, however, interactions with the drug companies that affect, and are appreciated by the majority of doctors. Drug-company funding of continuing medical education is one, and personal visits from detailers are another (Woods, 1986). The latter activity represents an expenditure of 9.2 percent of the sales dollar or about $2 500 per physician per year (Commission of Inquiry on the Pharmaceutical Industry, 1985, p. 223) and overall by 1985 pharmaceutical companies were spending $285 million annually promoting their products (Sutter, 1988).

The reason for the advertising is, of course, the same as in any industry — to sell the product and increase profits. The companies would not spend so lavishly on promotion unless it was working, and it does. The more intensively a product is advertised in journals, the greater its market share (Montgomery & Silk, 1972; Leffler, 1981; Krupka & Vener, 1985). Numerous studies have all shown that a substantial percentage of Canadian physicians rely heavily on company-sponsored sources of drug information (Fassold & Gowdey, 1968; Hall & Parker, 1976; Dunn et al., 1982; Angus Reid Group, 1991). The more physicians remember a journal ad, the more likely they are to prescribe the product (Walton, 1980; Healthcare Communications Inc., 1989). Avorn and co-workers (1982) have demonstrated that even physicians who believe that drug advertising plays only a minor role in their use of drugs may be unknowingly influenced by promotion: a fact that they attribute to the attractiveness of advertising displays and their ubiquitousness.

There is a serious problem with relying on commercial sources, that is industry sources, for information about drugs. In an article on pharmaceutical promotion Lexchin (1989) found that all of the studies done on the relationship between advertising and prescribing have reached the same conclusion. The more doctors rely on commercial sources for their information, the less rational they are as prescribers: they are more likely to prescribe the wrong drug in the wrong formulation for the wrong reason in an incorrect dosage for an inappropriate length of time. Lexchin (1987) links heavy promotion of antibiotics, ulcer medications, and antihypertensives with widespread irrational use of these drugs. In a 1974 appearance before the Canadian House of Commons standing committee on health, welfare, and social affairs, the head of the Health Protection Branch charged that: "Much of the problem of drug over-use and the resultant problem of adverse reactions relate to the aggressive marketing tactics of the drug industry" (Canada, House of Commons, 1974, pp. 7,25).

The relationship between the medical profession and the pharmaceutical industry has also had its effect in other areas. The Canadian Medical Association (CMA) and its *Journal* have consistently supported the PMAC in its battles over generic substitution and drug patents. The CMA's 1966 brief to the parliamentary committee considering compulsory licensing acknowledged that information had been provided by the PMAC, while the CMA's 1984 submission to the Eastman Commission questioned the quality of generic products; suggested that compulsory licensing may cause a downturn in research and development in the near future; and posed the possibility of increasing the royalty rate for compulsory licences. All of these positions reflected PMAC policy (Lexchin, 1988).

Similar to the CMA, the *Canadian Medical Association Journal (CMAJ)* has historically promoted the interests of the multinational pharmaceutical industry. The *Journal*'s reaction to the *Eastman Report*, which reported substantial savings as a result of compulsory licensing, was to dismiss it with the statement that it "should be taken with a grain of salt" (Woods, 1985). Editorials in the *CMAJ* have long defended advertising by pharmaceutical manufacturers (Morgan, 1984; Squires, 1987).

The Pharmaceutical Industry and the Pharmacists

Pharmacists are also important to the profits of the drug industry. If more than one company makes a drug, then when pharmacists are presented with a prescription they are free to dispense any company's brand of that drug, regardless of which particular trade name the doctor has written on the prescription.[14] The only time pharmacists cannot substitute is if the doctor has written "no substitution" on the prescription. However, just because pharmacists have the power to substitute does not mean that they are going to do so.[15] Pharmacists generally make their decision on which brand to dispense depending on which products they have in stock and which products yield the greatest profit margin. If pharmacists do not choose a company's brand, then obviously sales for that company are going to suffer. Therefore it is in the interests of companies to encourage pharmacists to stock their products and to ensure that the pharmacist gets a good profit margin on the drug.

There have been reports in British Columbia and Alberta that pharmaceutical companies have been offering inducements to pharmacists, such as free trips to Paris, silver ingots, and television sets to purchase their products. This practice is not confined to the multinational companies, but is also used by Canadian owned firms. In a *Vancouver Sun* story Jack Kay, a vice president of Apotex, the second-largest Canadian-owned company, admitted that Apotex had done the same thing. Kay went on to say that the practice of offering inducements to pharmacists was going on across Canada. Gordon Postlewaite, director of professional relations for the Pharmaceutical Manufacturers Association of Canada, also quoted in the same article, side-stepped the issue by claiming that "as an association we cannot require that our members do anything with respect to prices" (Kieran & Fitterman, 1986, pp. A-1, A-2).

Cockerill and Williams (1990) surveyed Ontario pharmacists regarding their relationships with the pharmaceutical industry for the Pharmaceutical Inquiry of Ontario. They found that, on average, in the year preceeding the survey, pharmacists were offered free goods or rebates five times, free meals twice, and gifts or bonuses once. Pharmaceutical company representatives offered conference fees, travel expenses, and computer equipment less than once a year. Only half of the pharmacists agreed that there was a potential conflict of interest in accepting benefits from pharmaceutical companies.

To encourage pharmacists to dispense their brand of a drug companies engage in what is called "discount pricing" or "discount competition." Under a provincial drug plan, drug "A" will be listed in the provincial formulary[16] as selling for, say $10 per 100 pills. That figure is the amount that the pharmacist is supposed to have paid the drug company for 100 pills, and that is the amount the pharmacist will be reimbursed by the government if the pharmacist dispenses the 100 pills to someone covered by the province's drug program. The pharmacist's profit theoretically derives from the dispensing fee.[17]

Under discount pricing, the drug company will sell its product for, say, $2 per 100 instead of the listed price of $10. The government still pays the pharmacist $10 — the pharmacist pockets the extra $8.00 as pure profit.[18] The drug companies are willing to discount their drugs because the bigger the pharmacists' profit margin, the more likely they are to dispense that particular company's brand of drug "A," thereby increasing the company's market share. In fact, it is even in the interests of the drug companies to inflate the prices for their products listed in the provincial formularies because the larger the profit margin for the pharmacist, the greater the incentive to use the company's brand. As was the case with inducements, discount pricing is not confined to the multinationals, but is also practised by the generic companies. A 1983 news story by Peter Calamai estimated that discount pricing was costing provincial drug plans across Canada $40 to $60 million annually (1983, pp. 1-2). Many provinces are now reimbursing pharmacists for their actual acquisition costs, thereby minimizing the potential for discount pricing under provincial drug plans. For an analysis of the Ontario system see Gorecki (1990). However, discount pricing is still possible when either third-party insurers are paying the cost of prescriptions or when patients pay out of pocket. Especially in the latter case, it is impossible for the payor to know what the actual acquisition cost was.

While the interactions between the pharmaceutical industry and pharmacists do not have negative effects on people's health, they do have profound negative effects on the cost of drugs.

Public Policy and the Pharmaceutical Industry

Both federal and provincial governments have been involved with the pharmaceutical industry through efforts to control the costs of drugs. The industry is generally quite accepting of moves to cover drug costs through insurance schemes, since the result is more people filling prescriptions and therefore larger sales. However, the response to measures aimed at lowering overall costs has been much different for obvious reasons. W.M. Garton, the 1978 president of the PMAC, voiced the general reaction of the multinationals to government plans for price reduction:

> Such well-intentioned policies presented disincentives to the further extension of an industry oriented towards innovation, investigation and development in Canada. . . . It is an unfortunate observation that many were, and continue to be based as much on emotional or political factors as on a careful consideration of objective evidence and we have consequently witnessed the "stretching of the skin of science to fit the drum of political necessity" (1978, p. 7).

In 1962, Alberta was the first province to allow a pharmacist to substitute a generic or name brand equivalent for the drug named in the prescription. The Swiss multinational CIBA unsuccessfully challenged the legislation in the courts. When Manitoba allowed pharmacists to substitute and stipulated that the substitute could not be sold at a price higher than that of the lowest-priced equivalent drug, Dr. W. Wigle, the president of the PMAC, made a thinly veiled threat that the drug companies might pull out of Manitoba (Harper, 1972, p. 74). A similar warning aimed at the Ontario government came from the senior vice-president for pharmaceuticals at Boehringer Ingelheim (Canada) in 1989. Commenting on Ontario's moves to control drug costs, Sheldon Burkle said that the Ministry of Health was "preventing ethical, innovative, research-based pharmaceutical manufacturers from capturing the sales and profits needed to make investments back into the province" (Anonymous, 1989).

In 1969, the federal government amended the Patent Act to allow for compulsory licensing to import drugs still under patent.[18] This action came after three major federal reports from the Restrictive Trade Practices Commission (1963), the Royal Commission on Health Services (1964), and the Special Committee on Drug Costs and Prices (1967) had all concluded that Canadian drug prices were among the highest in the world.

The PMAC mounted a campaign against compulsory licensing estimated by Lang to have cost $200 000 to $250 000 annually (Lang, 1974, p. 59). While the Special Commons Committee was meeting, the PMAC had a representative at all the meetings of the committee to provide information to the Conservative members of the committee. After the committee reported, Dr. Wigle threatened that if this recommendation was acted upon the large companies operating in Canada would close down their plants (1967, p. 1361).

After the legislation allowing compulsory licensing passed in March 1969, American Home Products Ltd. immediately challenged the bill in court. When the case reached the Ontario Court of Appeals in March 1970, it was dismissed within fifteen minutes. By 1971, of the 60 licences issued, there had been 43 appeals before the courts.

The *Eastman Report* calculated that compulsory licensing to import saved $211 million for Canadians out of a total 1983 drug bill of $1.6 billion, without affecting the profitability of the multinational drug companies or their willingness to invest in Canada (1985). However, the industry continued its vigorous lobbying efforts against compulsory licensing and with the election of Brian Mulroney and the Conservatives in 1984 it found an ally. The Conservatives wanted a free trade deal with the U.S. and the multinationals were able to get the American government to apply pressure in their favour (Sawatsky & Cashore, 1986).

At the end of June 1986, the new Consumer and Corporate Affairs Minister, Michel Cote, unveiled his proposed legislation which weakened the role of the generic companies and gave generous concessions to the multinationals. But, the bill would have extended patent protection against generic competition only if the drug was manufactured in Canada within two years by the patent holder. The Patented Medicine Prices Review Board, to be created under the new legislation, would have had the power to allow generic competition against all products of a manufacturer that was found to be overcharging on a drug protected from generic competition. These provisions were unacceptable to the U.S. drug multinationals and the U.S. trade negotiators. Over the summer of 1986, Harvie Andre took over the portfolio of Consumer and Corporate Affairs and when Andre introduced the new bill in November 1986, the manufacturing requirement was gone and the powers of the board were drastically reduced.

It was this version of the legislation, Bill C-22, with some minor modifications, that was finally passed in December 1987. According to Jon Johnson, president of Government Policy Consultants, the PMAC lobby around this bill cost "tens of millions of dollars" (1991). The bill effectively prohibits generic competition for seven to ten years on all drugs introduced after June 1986. Bill C-22 is subject to a cabinet review in the winter of 1991-92 and a full parliamentary review in 1996. The multinational drug companies have already announced that their goal in these reviews will be to eliminate compulsory licensing altogether (Gherson, 1991).[19]

Although the preceeding discussion would seem to indicate that the multinational companies and the federal government often relate to each other in an adversarial fashion, that is, in fact, far from being the case. There is a close working relationship between the Health Protection Branch, which is responsible for regulating drug safety, quality and efficacy, and the PMAC. These two groups interact primarily through a system of liaison committees that allows the PMAC to participate in the early stages of drug-policy formation. Other groups, such as workers and consumers, are excluded from such discussions. One substantial indication of this relationship is that the HPB has virtually ceded responsibility for enforcement of regulations to the PMAC in the area of pharmaceutical promotion. Lexchin (1990) has argued that it is this form of interaction between the industry and the HPB that is largely responsible for the deficiencies in Canada's drug laws and regulations. His solution is to open up the process of policy making to a wide range of interested parties ranging from consumer groups, to women's health groups, to professional associations.

Summary and Conclusion

The thesis of this chapter has been that the driving force behind the pharmaceutical industry is the profit motive; ethical considerations are secondary.

The Canadian pharmaceutical industry is heavily foreign dominated and as a result the opportunites for manufacturing, exporting, and research are severely constrained. Over the years, the pharmaceutical industries have been much more profitable than Canadian manufacturing industries in general. None of the rationales that the industry uses to justify this level of profit has any basis in fact. The companies have been able to achieve this position primarily by limiting price competition and replacing it with product competition.

Product competition also forms a key element in the orientation of much of the research carried out by the industry. Instead of trying to develop drugs that have the greatest health potential, the companies generally direct their research efforts towards developing drugs with the greatest profit potential. The central goal of this research strategy is for firms to identify highly profitable drugs produced by competitors and then to develop their own version of these products. The end result is a proliferation of virtually identical drugs, none of which is superior to the other in any significant way.

The medical profession, at all levels, is constantly courted by the pharmaceutical companies. Doctors receive endless little gifts, the cost of their conferences are underwritten, and hundreds of millions of dollars are spent on pharmaceutical promotion directed at them. The ultimate goal of all of this attention is to persuade physicians to prescribe in a manner so as to increase the sales and profits of the drug companies. Unfortunately, those doctors who are so influenced are also the ones who are the least correct prescribers and the health of their patients suffers accordingly. The relationship between organized medicine and the pharmaceutical industry has meant that the Canadian Medical Association and its *Journal* have consistently taken policy decisions supporting the multinational pharmaceutical industry over issues of generic prescribing and patents.

The companies, both the multinationals and the Canadian owned ones, have complex economic relations with the pharmacists. Inducements are offered to pharmacists to stock certain brands of drugs and officially listed prices are undercut in order to allow pharmacists to increase their profit margins. While these measures do not affect health, they do increase the cost of drugs to the consumer.

Provincial and federal governments have attempted to control drug prices by fostering price competition among companies and have introduced programs to ease the burden of drug costs to various segments of the population. Where the drug companies have viewed government action as a threat to their profits, the response has usually been to predict a decline in the quality of drugs and the ultimate demise of the Canadian pharmaceutical industry. Although at times the industry and the federal government have been at odds, there is a close working relationship between the Health Protection Branch and the PMAC when it comes to formulation of drug policy. This interaction, which virtually excludes all other interested parties, may be largely responsible for the deficiencies in Canada's drug laws and regulations.

Notes

1. The Pharmaceutical Manufacturers' Association of Canada currently has 67 member companies, including all the large multinationals operating in Canada. Fewer than half a dozen of its members are Canadian-owned companies. The Canadian Drug Manufacturers' Association represents 18 Canadian-owned companies, the largest of which are Apotex and Novopharm.
2. Since then, such warnings have also been included in advertisements in Canadian medical journals.
3. In Canada and the United States, the drug was called Oraflex.
4. The Health Protection Branch is the division of the Department of National Health and Welfare charged with monitoring the safety and efficacy of prescription drugs. Before the HPB allows a drug to enter the Canadian market, the manufacturer has to present evidence that the product is both safe and effective for human use.
5. Breton gives Novopharm's 1987 sales at $67 734 000. The leading company that year was Glaxo with sales of $163 668 000 (1990, p. 187).
6. In the mid-1960s, the Royal Commission on Health found that of 395 patents on fourteen "important pharmaceutical products" only nine, or less than 3 percent, were held by genuine Canadian firms (1964, p. 656).
7. In 1976, resale products accounted for almost 20 percent of sales in Canada.
8. Currently, industry spokespeople quote a figure of $200 to $250 million as the cost of developing and marketing a new drug. However, a preliminary report by the United States office of Technology Assessment suggests that that figure is an arbitrary number with no intrinsic meaning (Anonymous, 1991, p. 20).
9. One of the studies done for the *Eastman Report* examined the actual savings that competition produced in a sample of 32 multiple-source drugs. The 1983 sales of these drugs amounted to $216 million. Without competition, the cost would have been $426.6 million (1985, p. 315).

10. This figure includes different dosage forms of the same drug and different formulations of the same drug; for instance, a drug may be marketed as pills, capsules, solutions, creams, or ointments.

11. A "therapeutic class" consists of drugs used in the treatment of a particular problem or disease, such as arthritis or ulcers. All drugs may be placed into one or more therapeutic classes, depending on how many uses the drug has.

12. The *Eastman Report* also evaluated submarket concentration in alternative ways and the figures produced from these assessments showed a lower level of concentration than the ones obtained by an analysis of therapeutic classes (1985, pp. 135-142). While all of these methods have their limitations, they all showed that submarket concentration was higher than overall industry concentration.

13. The situation in Canada is somewhat different owing to the existence of compulsory licensing to import. Between 1969 and 1987, a company wishing to import a drug that was still under patent protection in Canada could apply to the Commissioner of Patents in Ottawa for a licence to import the drug. The licence was almost always granted whether or not the patent holding company agreed, hence the term compulsory licensing. In return for losing its monopoly, the patentee received a royalty of 4 percent of sales from the company granted the licence. (The companies taking out compulsory licences are often collectively referred to as "generic firms" and their products, whether or not they have their own trade names, are called "generic drugs.") Therefore, in Canada, the monopoly period during this eighteen-year period was as short as four years. Since the passage of Bill C-22 in December 1987, new drugs are now protected against compulsory licensing for seven to ten years.

14. The trade name of a drug is the name that a company has given to its particular version of that drug. Drugs also have a true scientific name called the "chemical name" and a generic name that is an abbreviated scientific name and can be used in prescribing, naming, and identifying the drug. For example, Miltown is Horner's trade name for a tranquillizer. The generic name is "meprobamate" and the chemical name is "2-methyl-2-propyl-1,3-propanedioldicarbamate." Besides prescribing by the trade name, doctors may also prescribe by the generic name. If they do, then pharmacists are again free to pick any company's product.

15. In Saskatchewan, for certain multiple-source high-volume drugs, pharmacists must dispense a particular brand unless the physician has written "no substitution" on the prescription.

16. A provincial formulary is a listing of all the drugs covered under the provincial drug plan. All provinces publish a formulary except Alberta, British Columbia, and Prince Edward Island. Ontario's formulary is widely used in British Columbia. For more information about the provincial drug plans see Anderson (1990).

17. The dispensing or professional fee is the amount that pharmacists charge for their professional services.

18. Compulsory licensing to manufacture had been around since 1923. Under this provision of the Patent Act, companies wishing to manufacture in Canada a drug still under patent here could get a licence to do so. There were very few licences of this type issued, primarily because of the cost of setting up a plant to manufacture a drug just for the small Canadian market.

19. In 1993, rather than conducting a cabinet review of Bill C-22, the federal government passed Bill C-91, which abolished compulsory licencing.

Study Questions

1. How would you account for the foreign domination of the Canadian pharmaceutical industry?

2. Besides controlling drug costs by increasing competition, what other methods could be used?

3. If the profit motive for researching new drugs were removed, how do you think that would affect the development of drugs?

Would companies bother to invest money in research and development?

4. Speculate on how the involvement of the medical profession with the pharmaceutical industry may have affected physicians' ability to be objective about the benefits of pharmaceuticals.

5. Consider the mechanism and implications of opening up the drug policy process to groups outside of the drug companies and the Health Protection Branch.

Recommended Reading

Inquiry on the Pharmaceutical Industry. (1985). *Report*. Ottawa: Minister of Supply and Services Canada.

Gordon, M., & Fowler, D. (1981). *The drug industry: A case study in foreign control*. Toronto: James Lorimer.

Lang, R.W. (1974). *The politics of drugs*. Westmead: Saxon House.

Lexchin, J. (1984). *The real pushers: A critical analysis of the Canadian drug industry*. Vancouver: New Star Books.

Lexchin, J. (1988). The medical profession and the pharmaceutical industry: An unhealthy alliance. *International Journal of Health Services*, 18, 603-16.

Lexchin, J. (1990). Drug makers and drug regulators: Too close for comfort. A study of the Canadian situation. *Social Science and Medicine*, 31, 1257-63.

Patented Medicine Prices Review Board. (1991). *Third annual report*. Ottawa: Supply and Services Canada.

Pharmaceutical Inquiry of Ontario. (1990). *Prescriptions for health*. Toronto: Author.

References

Anderson, L.J. (1990). *Provincial and territorial drug reimbursement programs: Descriptive summary*. Ottawa: Health and Welfare Canada.

Angus Reid Group. (1991). *Credibility and the marketing mix*. Toronto: Author.

Anonymous. (1988). Nizatidine (Axid). *The Medical Letter*, 30, 77-8.

Anonymous. (1989, October 2). Mixed Messages. *Ontario Medicine*, 24.

Anonymous. (1991, May 8/10). US OTA queries industry R & D cost data. *Scrip*, No. 1614.

Avorn, J., Chen, M., &Hartley, R. (1982). Scientific versus commercial sources of influence on the prescribing behavior of physicians. *American Journal of Medicine*, 73, 4-8.

Bell, P. (1975, June 12). Ayerst man disagrees with FDA warning. *Globe and Mail*, p. F2.

Breton, G. (1990). *Une appréciation de la position stratégique des entreprises pharmaceutiques québécoises*. Montreal: Cetai.

Bureau of Policy Coordination. (1982, September). *A policy analysis of the compulsory licensing of pharmaceutical patents in Canada*. Ottawa: Department of Consumer and Corporate Affairs.

Burstall, M.L., Dunning, J.H. & Lake, A. (1981). *Multinational enterprises, governments and technology: Pharmaceutical industry*. Paris: Organisation for Economic Co-operation and Development.

Calamai, P. (1983, October 21). Hidden drug profits total $50 million a year. *The Sault Star*, p. A1-2.

Canada, House of Commons. (1974, April 4). *Minutes of proceedings and evidence of the Standing Committee on health, welfare and social affairs*. Ottawa: Queen's Printer, Issue No. 6.

Canada, House of Commons. (1967). *Second (final) report of the Special Committee of the House of Commons on drug costs and prices*. Ottawa: Queen's Printer.

Canada, House of Commons, Special Committee on Drug Costs and Prices. (1967). *Minutes of proceedings and evidence, No. 33*. Ottawa: Queen's Printer.

Cockerill, R., & Williams, P. (1990). Report on the 1989 survey of the dispensing practices and attitudes toward prescription drugs of Ontario pharmacists. In Pharmaceutical Inquiry of Ontario, *Prescriptions for Health, Appendix 2*. Toronto.

Commission of Inquiry on the Pharmaceutical Industry. (1985). *Report*. Ottawa: Minister of Supply and Services.

Consumer and Corporate Affairs Canada. (1983). *Compulsory licensing of pharmaceuticals: A review of Section 41 of the Patent Act*. Ottawa: Author.

Dan, L.L. (1982, Autumn). The drug industry in Canada: A position analysis. *Business Quarterly*, 47, 62-71.

Department of Industry, Trade and Commerce. (1980). *The health care products industry in Canada*. Ottawa: Author.

Dunn, E., Williams, J.I., Bryans, A.M., et al. (1982). Continuing medical education in Ontario: A primary care perspective. *Canadian Family Physician*, 28, 1327-33.

Fassold, R.W., & Gowdey, C.W. (1968). A survey of physicians' reactions to drug promotion. *Canadian Medical Association Journal*, 98, 701-5.

Friedman, J.J. & Associates. (1981). *Pharmaceutical prices in Canada: Guiding principles for government policy*. Ottawa: Pharmaceutical Manufacturers Association of Canada.

Gammal, P. (1991, March 4). Encounter: Judy Erola. *Financial Times of Canada*, p. 35.

Garai, P.R. (1964). Advertising and promotion of drugs. In P. Talalay (Ed.). *Drugs in our society* (pp. 189-202). Baltimore: Johns Hopkins Press.

Garton, W.M. (1978, January). The pharmaceutical sector in Canada — Its environment and performance. *Drug Merchandising*, 111, 6-7.

Garton, W.M. (1980, May 26). *Personal communication*.

Gereffi, G. (1983). *The pharmaceutical industry and dependency in the Third World*. Princeton: Princeton University Press.

Gershon, S., & Shopsin, B. (1973). *Lithium: Its role in psychiatric research and treatment*. New York: Plenum Press.

Gherson, G. (1991, April 15). Drug wars: The $4-billion battle begins. *Financial Times of Canada*, p. 1.

Gordon, M., & Fowler, D. (1981). *The drug industry: A case study in foreign control*. Toronto: James Lorimer & Company.

Gorecki, P.K. (1990). Getting it right: An evaluation of alternative systems of the organization on the Ontario prescription drugs distribution system. In Pharmaceutical Inquiry of Ontario, *Prescriptions for Health, Appendix 3*. Toronto.

Gray, C. (1981). The pharmaceutical industry: Promoting research in the 80's. *Canadian Medical Association Journal*, 124, 787-92.

Hall, K.W., & Parker, W.A. (1976). Physician's view of the pharmacist's professional role. *Canadian Pharmaceutical Journal*, 109, 311-314.

Harper, D. (1972, September). No threat made by Dr. Wigle. *Drug Merchandising*, 53, 56, 74.

Healthcare Communications Inc. (1989). *The effect of journal advertising on market shares of new prescriptions*. New York: The Association of Independent Medical Publications, Inc.

Johnson, J. (1991, June 12). *Annual general meeting, Canadian Drug Manufacturers Association*.

Kieran, B., & Fitterman, L. (1986, March 18). Probe set in gifts to druggists. *Vancouver Sun*, p. A1

Krupka, L., & Vener, A. (1985). Prescription drug advertising: Trends and implications. *Social Science and Medicine*, 20, 191-7.

Lang, R.W. (1974). *The politics of drugs*. Westmead: Saxon House.

Leffler, K. (1981). Persuasion or information? The economics of prescription drug advertisement. *Journal of Law and Economics*, 24, 45-74.

Lexchin, J. (1984). *The real pushers: A critical analysis of the Canadian drug industry*. Vancouver: New Star Books.

Lexchin, J. (1987). Pharmaceutical promotion in Canada: Convince them or confuse them. *International Journal of Health Services*, 17, 77-89.

Lexchin, J. (1988). The medical profession and the pharmaceutical industry: An unhealthy alliance. *International Journal of Health Services*, 18, 603-16.

Lexchin, J. (1989). Doctors and detailers: Therapeutic education or pharmaceutical promotion? *International Journal of Health Services*, 19, 663-79.

Lexchin, J. (1990). Drug makers and drug regulators: Too close for comfort. A study of the Canadian situation. *Social Science and Medicine*, 31, 1257-63.

Livingston, M. (1988, January). Pharmaceutical stocks: Prescription for financial health. *Physician's Management Manuals*, 57-61.

Miller, E. (1990). Director of market planning, Upjohn. *Non-hormonal antiarthritics, drug store and hospital purchases, 1989 monthly dollar volume (in 000s)*. (mimeographed).

Montgomery, D., & Silk, A. (1972). Estimating dynamic effects of market communications expenditures. *Management Science*, 18, B485-B501.

Morgan, P.P. (1984). Pharmaceutical advertising in medical journals. *Canadian Medical Association Journal*, 130, 1412.

Orr, D. (1974). An index of entry barriers and its application to the market structure performance relationship. *Journal of Industrial Economics*, 23, 39-49.

Parboosingh, J., Lockyer, J., McDougall, G., & Chugh, U. (1984). How physicians make changes in their clinical practice: A study of physicians' perception of factors that facilitate this process. *Annal of the Royal College of Physicians and Surgeons of Canada*, 17, 429-435.

Patented Medicine Prices Review Board. (1991). *Third annual report*. Ottawa: Supply and Services.

Pharmaceutical Manufacturers Association of Canada. (1972). *Principles and code of marketing practice*. Ottawa: Author.

Pharmaceutical Manufacturers Association of Canada. (1975). *The performance of the Canadian pharmaceutical manufacturing industry*. Ottawa: Author.

Restrictive Trade Practices Commission. (1963). *Report concerning the manufacture, distribution and sale of drugs*. Ottawa: Queen's Printer.

Royal Commission on Health Services. (1964). *Report*. Ottawa: Queen's Printer.

Sawatsky, J., & Cashore, H. (1986, August/ September). Inside dope: The multi-million-dollar sellout of Canada's generic drug industry. *This Magazine*, 20, 4-12.

Squires, B.P. (1987). In whose service? *Canadian Medical Association Journal*, 137, 983.

Sutter S. (1988, February 15). Drug makers prescribe tough advertising ethics. *Marketing*, p. 2.

Statistics Canada. (1988). *Chemical and chemical products industries*. Ottawa: Supply and Services.

Statistics Canada. (1989). *Industrial research and development statistics 1987*. Ottawa: Supply and Services.

Taylor, P. (1983, July 16). Generics a bitter pill for big drug firms. *Globe and Mail*, p. B1.

Temin, P. (1979). Technology, regulation, and market structure in the Modern pharmaceutical industry. *Bell Journal of Economics*, 10, 429-46.

VanWoert, M.H. (1978). Profitable and non-profitable drugs. *New England Journal of Medicine*, 298, 903-5.

Walton, H. (1980, June). Ad recognition and prescribing by physicians. *Journal of Advertising Research*, 20, 39-48.

Walwyn Stodgell Cochran Murray Ltd. (1983, May 10). For pill, like to try one from the UK? *Investor's Digest*, 142.

Westell, D. (1980, May 5). Pharmaceutical industry picked for audit by National Revenue. *Globe and Mail*, p. B1.

Wigle, W.W. (1967). A pharmaceutical industry in Canada? *Canadian Medical Association Journal*, 97, 1361.

Woods, D. (1985). The Eastman prescription: A dispensable package. *Canadian Medical Association Journal*, 133, 7.

Woods, D. (1988). PMAC to spend almost $1 million annually to reach 'stakeholders'. *Canadian Medical Association Journal*, 134, 1387-9.

World Health Organization. (1988). *The world drug situation*. Geneva: Author.

Chapter 35

AIDS: The Politicizing of a Public Health Issue

Marianne Weston and Bonnie Jeffery, University of Regina

Introduction

Because of the incompleteness of medical science's current understanding of the disease and because there are ethical and political implications yet to become apparent and to be addressed, the present chapter can deal only superficially with the issues associated with AIDS. By the time the article appears in print, cures for the disease may be closer, preventive measures better understood, and different issues associated with the disease may have emerged. Nonetheless, Conrad and Schneider's (1980) concept of "medicalization of deviance" provides a useful theoretical framework in which to analyze some of the reasons for the present definitions and meanings associated with AIDS. A cursory examination of popular journalism that has dealt with AIDS would lead us to conclude that the disease has often been associated with "badness" rather than "sickness" labels. The professional literature dealing with AIDS is also replete with sometimes subtle, sometimes not so subtle, designations of "badness." This chapter will examine some of the non-medical factors that have contributed to AIDS being defined in a negative sense.

AIDS Is an Illness

There is a great deal of fear, uncertainty, and mythology surrounding AIDS. It is important that any discussion of AIDS firmly establish it as a disease prior to an examination of the processes that have influenced its meaning.

AIDS is a widely used acronym standing for an infectious disease called acquired immune deficiency syndrome. The disease was named in 1982, although Mass (1985, p. 56) indicates that the first case of AIDS came to the attention of the United States Department of Health and Human Services for Disease Control Centers (CDC) in late 1979. By 1981, as an increasing number of cases were reported, it was clear to U.S. public-health authorities that something more than individual cases of an unknown disease was occurring. According to Parent (1985, p. 22), the first case of AIDS in Canada was reported in February of 1982.

AIDS is caused by a retrovirus known as lymphadenopathy-associated virus (LAV) or human T-cell lymphotropic virus type III (HTLV-III). LAV was discovered by the French scientist Luc Montagnier in 1983; one year later, the American scientist Robert Gallo discovered HTLV-III. In September 1986, the *Canada Disease Weekly Report* (CDWR) (Sept. 13, 1986, p. 169) adopted the International Committee on Taxonomy of Viruses' terminology of "human immunodeficiency virus" (HIV).

Many of those who have been identified as carrying the virus do not have AIDS. For example, in Canada it has been estimated that "50 000 Canadians are now infected with HIV. By 1993 more than 7 000 people with HIV infection in Canada will have progressed to AIDS" (Health and Welfare Canada, 1991).

AIDS itself is a breakdown in the body's immune system. Those who have developed what clinicians refer to as "frank" or "full-blown" AIDS become vulnerable to a number of serious and frequently fatal opportunistic diseases and malignancies. Two of the most frequent of these diseases are a protozoan infection of the lungs call Pneumocystis cerinii pneumonia (PCP) and Kaposi's sarcoma (KS). PCP, KS, and many of the other opportunistic infections to which AIDS predisposes the body are relatively infrequent in persons who have healthy immune systems.

The issue of defining who has AIDS, as opposed to those who are HIV infected, is one that has evolved throughout the late 1980s. The most current definition for AIDS case reporting is being proposed for use in the United States. This revision of the 1987 definition has been expanded to include all HIV-infected persons who fall within specific clinical indicators. According the United States Department of Health and Human Service's Centres for Disease Control:

The CD4+, or T-helper, lympocyte is the primary target cell for HIV infection, and a decrease in the number of these cells correlates with the risk and severity of HIV-related illnesses. CDC is revising the classification system for HIV infection to emphasize the clinical importance of the CD4+ lymphocyte count in the categorization of HIV-related clinical conditions.[1] (United States Department of Health and Human Services, 1991).

Essentially, this expanded case definition of AIDS includes those who have symptoms of HIV-related illnesses in conjunction with a CD4 + cell count of less than 200/mm. In other words, those who have been identified as HIV infected (possibly with a less severe manifestation of the virus) will be reported as having AIDS if they also have this AIDS-indicator cell count.

This expanded AIDS surveillance case definition also proposes to include several gynecological conditions that have been reported in HIV-infected women.

> . . . these conditions are also commonly diagnosed in women without HIV infection and are neither specific for nor highly predictive of severe HIV-related immunosuppression. The proposed expansion of the AIDS surveillance case definition will comprehensively represent HIV-infected women with severe immunodeficiency. (United States Department of Health and Human Services, November 15, 1991)

Incidence and Trends of AIDS

In order to discuss some of the statistics related to current incidence and projected trends of AIDS, we must first examine how the disease is defined for the purpose of official reporting. Canada has adopted the CDC case definition that was first published in September 1982 and revised in 1987. This revision added "most severe non-infectious, non-cancerous HIV associated conditions that are categorized in the CDC clinical classification systems for HIV infection among adults and children" (CDC, 1987).

In Canada, AIDS was included for the first time in January 1986, on the list of notifiable diseases compiled by Statistics Canada. As of July 14, 1986 the National AIDS Centre surveillance program in Canada had received report of 638 cases of AIDS. By January 1, 1992 the *Canada Communicable Disease Report* (CCDR) had received reports of 5 647 cases meeting the surveillance case definition for AIDS (revised, September 1, 1987). These included 5 583 adults (5 294 males, 289 females) and 64 paediatric cases. A total of 3 432 deaths had been reported (March 14, 1992). Based on reported cases the risk factors for exposure to HIV are as follows:

Homosexual/bisexual activity only	78%	Heterosexual activity	
Injection drug use only	2%	– origin in pattern II country*	4%
Both of the above	4%	– sexual contact with person as risk	4%
Recipient of blood or blood products	5%	No identified risk factor	4%
		(CCDR, March 13, 1992)	

* defined by WHO as countries with a high rate of HIV infection where the predominant means of transmission is heterosexual contact

Global reporting of AIDS throughout the World Health Organization (WHO) began in August 1985. Seventy-seven countries were reporting, with the U.S. data accounting for about three-quarters of all cases. As of November 1986, 34 448 cases of AIDS had been reported to the WHO Global Control Programme (CDWR, January 10, 1987). By November 1990 there were a total of 158 countries who had reported 307 379 cases of AIDS to the World Health Organization (WHO, 1990). Current information from WHO estimates that worldwide a total of 5 to 6 million men and 3 to 4 million women have been infected with HIV. Of these 8 to 10 million infected adults, over 1 million have progressed to AIDS. A similar number have developed less severe illnesses related to infection. HIV-infected mothers have borne approximately 1 million infected children, over half of whom have developed AIDS and died. As well, there are almost 2 million uninfected children who are already or are potentially AIDS orphans (CCDR, January 17, 1992). These figures emphasize the severity of the worldwide situation:

> World AIDS day was commemorated for the fourth consecutive year on December 1, 1991, at a time when awareness of the pandemic of acquired immunodeficiency syndrome (AIDS) as a major global threat to the health, development and stability of innumerable communities around the world was greater than ever. As the AIDS pandemic enters its second decade, its dimensions have become clearer, even though precise estimates and long-term projections of its ultimate course cannot be made with absolute assurance. (CCDR, January 17, 1992, p. 1)

It is important to note that there is no known cure for AIDS, nor is there a vaccine that will prevent transmission of the virus. Medical science has not yet discovered why some persons who carry the virus develop AIDS and others do not. As discussed later, this fact undoubtedly influences the more tenuous hold that the medical profession has on the definition of the illness. Because its knowledge and technology have not yet developed a cure for those with the disease, in the case of AIDS, the medical profession has been denied the power and control it has with regard to other diseases.

Historical Context of Sexuality and Sickness

In order to further our understanding of the various meanings that have been associated with AIDS, we must examine historical definitions of both sexuality and illness. Although AIDS is known to be transmitted in non-sexual ways, it is its sexual transmission that has most greatly influenced its meaning in Canada and the United States. The connection between AIDS and sexuality is firmly and inextricably reinforced through public reporting of aspects of the illness.

Conrad and Schneider (1980, p. 27) have defined three major paradigms that have influenced deviance and therefore sickness and sexual behaviour designations throughout history. These models trace the definitions of unacceptable behaviour from deviance as sin, to deviance as crime, to deviance as sickness. These historical changes are very closely related to the influence of the Church, the state, and medicine as a profession.

Not only have the definitions of deviant sexual behaviour and sickness changed over time, but the agents of social control that have been brought to bear on these deviant states and practices have also changed. It is critical, then, to discuss the relationship between the dominant view of sexuality and the views of the disease called AIDS. Furthermore, we must examine how these views, represented by various interest groups, have affected each other within this decade to change our labels for both sickness and sexuality.

Historically, every culture has had its own definitions of approved versus deviant sexual behaviour. What is considered deviant sexual behaviour has varied among cultures at similar points in history as well as within cultures over time. Anthropological and historical studies would seem to indicate that there are few sexual practices that have been historically and universally taboo.

Just as our definitions of what is acceptable or unacceptable sexual behaviour have changed, so too have the labels assigned to such behaviour. Prior to the nineteenth century, approved sexual practices were defined and controlled by the Church. Words such as "good" and "evil" or "virtue" and "vice" were used to distinguish behaviour that was considered to be good or acceptable. Underlying these words was the fundamental notion of deviant sexual behaviour being defined as sin. When the definitions of acceptable or approved sexual behaviour came to be legitimized through the state, the enforcement of such behaviours was achieved through the criminal justice system. Consequently, certain sexual behaviours or practices that previously had been defined as "sinful" were now defined as "criminal."

The development of the post-industrial society resulted in an increasing reliance on and faith in scientific discovery and knowledge. Science had been added to the list of agents of social control and biologists began to define "degenerative" or "maladaptive" sex as opposed to species-enhancing or adaptive sex. Psychologists also began to label certain sexual practices as "abnormal" or "pathological" and more recently, as neurotic, immature, or aberrant. The medical profession became the watchdog of scientific standards, and at the beginning of the twentieth century began to attain increasing control over definitions of acceptable sexual behaviour. Gagnon (1977, p. 26) notes that the transition from religion to the state and then to the medical profession as primary agent of social control has coincided with the move from collective or societal to personal justifications for various sexual behaviours.

Until recent times, we have had collective justifications for sexual conduct even though the source (i.e., Church, state, medical profession) of the collective justification has changed. Since the 1950s, a far more individualistic perspective on sexuality has developed. The collective definition for appropriate sexual behaviour has less appeal today because it has come to conflict with the sexual activity of the majority. Sexual practices are now defined in terms of individual preference, and popular views on sex see it as joy, play, intimacy, and recreation. This shift in the way we define or justify our sex practices has also changed the way we perceive the purpose of sex. The current trend toward individual rather than collective decisions about the purpose of sex has meant that the agents of social control have not been able to cast their net as widely. As sex has come to have more individual purposes, various sexual practices have come to be defined as "conventional" and "unconventional," or "satisfying" and "unsatisfying." These terms are much less loaded than words like "immoral," "criminal," or "pathological." When freed from the constraints of collective definitions, violations of the sexual norms are either not considered very important or, at the very least, are seen as an individual and private decision. Katchadourian and Lunde (1975, p. 9) also support this idea and note that society now distinguishes between public and private sexual behaviour. Those behaviours or practices conducted in private between consenting adults are considered beyond the scope of societal regulation. The ability of a collective view of sexuality to be imposed on individual behaviour and choices has been diminished, except in times of crisis. While it may be too early to judge, there are signs that AIDS has become the crisis which may precipitate a move back to a collective rather than an individual definition of acceptable sexual behaviour. One wonders whether the widespread fear of AIDS will allow the Church, state, and/or the medical profession to re-impose control over the definition of acceptable sexual behaviour.

Historically, disease or illness has been conceptualized as a symptom of sin and as a punishment for moral corruption. Sontag, for example, notes:

> With the advent of Christianity which imposed more moralized notions of disease, as of everything else, a closer fit between disease and "victim" gradually evolved. The idea of disease as punishment yielded the idea that a disease could be particularly appropriate and just punishment. (1978, p. 47)

Various cultures and historical periods have denied specific diseases and illnesses differently, and our culture's views and labels have changed over time.

Several writers have discussed the increasing medicalization of society and the implications of this trend. Some, such as Illich, see the increasing involvement of the medical profession in all aspects of life as a negative trend:

During the last generation the medical monopoly over health care has expanded without checks and has encroached on our liberty with regard to our own bodies. Society has transferred to physicians the exclusive rights to determine what constitutes sickness, who is or might become sick, and what shall be done to such people. Deviance is now "legitimate" only when it merits and ultimately justifies medical interpretation and intervention. (1976, pp. 13-14)

Conrad and Schneider (1980, pp. 246-247), when discussing the "medicalization of deviance," point out some of the positive aspects that can be the result of the growing medical involvement in the definition and control of human conditions and social problems. They argue that the medicalizing of social problems such as alcoholism and juvenile delinquency removes both the burden of responsibility and the stigma attached to the condition from the individual. The condition or social problem is depoliticized and thus exempt from punitive consequences.

Talcott Parsons (1951) has pointed out that the labelling of someone as ill serves to conditionally legitimate the condition, thus exempting the individual from normal responsibilities to whatever extent may be necessary in order to get well. Society does not hold individuals responsible for their illnesses, although they are expected to want to get well and to co-operate with a physician to that end. Medicine both defines the sick role and acts as the agent of social control limiting certain behaviours of the individual. An overriding theme in the medicalization of behaviours or conditions is one of humanitarian concern. While it is difficult to object to the notion of caring for others, the humanitarian concerns can promote the view of individuals being "victims." Moreover, the assumption that a medical definition is always neutral and objective ignores the reality of the power that society has granted to the medical profession.

Some authors have questioned the idea that those who are ill are not punished or are exempt from moral judgements. Zola, for example, writes:

Most analysts have tried to make a distinction between illness and crime on the issue of personal responsibility. The criminal is thought to be responsible and therefore accountable (or punishable) for his act, while the sick person is not. While the distinction does exist it seems to be more a quantitative one rather than a qualitative one, with moral judgements but a pinprick below the surface. (1972, p. 490)

Conrad and Schneider also argue that social judgements are very much connected to moral judgements because "they are related directly and intimately to the moral order of society" (1980, p. 35).

While there is a great deal of evidence that the medical profession has been successful in increasing its domain and in destigmatizing those conditions it defines as illnesses, this does not hold true when we examine the reactions to AIDS. In the public mind, sexually transmitted diseases, and AIDS in particular, continue to have associations of immorality. Thus the majority of those with AIDS bear a double burden. They face the future with the grim knowledge that medical science has yet to discover a cure for their illness. They also face the reactions of others, both those in their social circle and the general public, who have come to identify the disease with homosexuality. Until the development of what have been considered "innocent" AIDS cases, that is, those not resulting from homosexual contact, many viewed AIDS as punishment for homosexual behaviour. The medical profession's control over the meanings of illness and deviance becomes tentative, especially when sexuality comes face to face with germs.

Homosexuality in the Western world prior to the twentieth century was viewed as sinful. With the gradual relinquishment of the Church's power to the state, it became defined as a criminal activity. Later, through what Illich (1976, p. 47) calls the increasing "medicalization of life," behaviours and events such as childbirth and menopause, which had previously been defined as normal, became defined as sickness. Homosexuality also came to be defined as an illness, to be subjected to cure rather than punishment. The medicalizing of homosexuality and the accompanying belief that it was an illness to be cured provided the basis for the decriminalization of homosexual relations. During the 1970s, the homosexual community increased its organizing and lobbying efforts to both decriminalize and demedicalize homosexuality. This led to both its removal from the Criminal Code of Canada and from the American Psychiatric Association's DSM classification in the same decade.[2]

With the advent of AIDS, however, it can be argued that many of these more progressive attitudes are being undermined. In the Western world, AIDS has been very clearly defined as a "homosexual" disease. In fact, it has been referred to as the "homosexual plague." This understanding of the disease grew out of the fat that the first cases of AIDS recognized in the United States were among homosexual men. In fact, although it was never officially termed thus, AIDS was known in the beginning as GRID (gay-related immune deficiency). The emphasis of the American scientists on the epidemiology rather than virology is undoubtedly a significant factor in the disease's association with a lifestyle rather than a micro-organism. Clearly, gay men are not the only victims of the disease, but in both statistical and political terms they are the most significant. As Altman points out: "Among gay men AIDS has become an omnipresent nightmare . . . AIDS haunts us both asleep and awake, and it changes not just our behaviour but our very conceptions of who we are and our belief in ourselves" (1986, p. 39).

Homophobia has surfaced more publicly as the fear about AIDS increases. What we are witnessing is the blaming of homosexuality for a disease. Rather than viewing the illness as primarily a medical condition, public views and reactions have spilled over into the area of sexuality, and allowed the opportunity for a variety of interest groups to launch anti-gay campaigns.

The Marginality of the Risk Groups

Initially, the way society responded to AIDS, the allocation of research dollars and the treatment AIDS patients received were influenced by perceptions that the disease affected those who were marginalized. Those primarily affected were seen as members of unpopular, even mistrusted groups, who often lacked both resources and power. During the 1980s, the popular media began to talk of the "innocent" victims of the disease (hemophiliacs, babies, those who received blood transfusions, and heterosexual partners of AIDS carriers). This promoted the false impression that there were other groups who were "guilty."

The marginality of homosexuals, who were and still are the most prominent risk group, is best exemplified by the fact that many of them were to some degree in violation of the law or at least are not afforded equal protection under the law. In the United States, homosexuality is still illegal in many states. In all but four provinces in Canada, homosexuals are not protected under human rights legislation and thus can be fired from jobs or denied employment or housing on the grounds of their sexual orientation.

Drug users may be the most marginal of all of the groups at risk. They are perhaps the poorest, are clearly engaged in illegal activity, are unorganized and have no power as an identifiable group. Society has little understanding of the factors and culture that underlie drug use, and attempts to reach users and change the practice of needle sharing may prove to be difficult. Drug users have received the least attention as a risk group. Their numbers were likely underestimated since those who both engage in homosexual practices and are intravenous drug users are classified in the homosexual or bisexual category only.

The immigrant populations once mentioned in Canada's health pamphlets and who once formed a risk group in both Canada and the United States were also clearly marginal. The Haitian community in both countries tended to be poor, lacked access to the media, and did not speak English well; furthermore, some of its members were living in the country illegally. Despite their marginal status in North America, Haitians did have status as a nationality. Thus, in part because of increasing pressure from Haitian government officials, both the United States and Canada removed Haitians from their risk group classification in 1985. A second factor which no doubt influenced this action was medical science's inability to find a scientific basis for the classification. Since they could not determine why Haitians were at risk, the medical profession's authority to control and define the disease was clearly capable of being undermined.

It has been claimed that Haitians were the only group classified on the basis of who they were rather than what they practised. While this is to some extent valid, most of the medical literature and certainly the popular media constantly referred to risk groups as homosexual men, bisexual men, drug users, and hemophiliacs. These were clearly words that identify *groups*, not practices. The Centers for Disease Control in the United States continue to use terms associated with groups, although in Canada the Laboratory Centre for Disease Control talk of homosexual/bisexual practices.

If the medical profession had been focussed on minimizing the further stigmatization of already marginal groups, practices and situations which facilitate transmission would have been emphasized, rather than particular group identities.

Haitians, unlike the other groups at risk, protested their classification and despite the fact of being a low-status marginal group in the United States and Canada, their status as a nationality lent a certain power to their claim.

Altman (1986, p. 74) points out, however, that their removal from the "at risk" list has done nothing to alleviate the discrimination against them, and it is difficult for Haitians to either obtain or retain jobs or housing. As late as 1986 their high-risk status often remained subtly alluded to, as in Canada's AIDS pamphlet (1986), which stated: "AIDS has also occurred among recent immigrants from some areas in the Caribbean and Central Africa where AIDS is widespread."

With the appearance of AIDS in the heterosexual community, a new group, prostitutes, began to be scapegoated for its spread. Western society has had a history of scapegoating prostitutes for both social problems like family breakdown and diseases such as venereal disease. As Adams (1986, p. 27) points out: "In 1918 and 1920, 18 000 American prostitutes were rounded up and committed to prison hospitals to protect the health of American troops (who presumably were incapable of protecting themselves.)"

The length to which American and Canadian society will go to quarantine (incarcerate) prostitutes remains to be documented, but already one prostitute who carries the virus has been arrested in Canada. Further evidence of scapegoating is that public-health and other authorities, as well as the media, seem almost singularly concerned with prostitutes' transmittal of the disease rather than worrying about how to protect them from the risk of receipt of the virus from bisexual men. As Adams (1986, p. 27) states, prostitutes "are more often seen as receptacles of and transmitters of the virus" rather than being recognized as persons at risk of contracting the disease.

Marginality is clearly linked to lack of resources and power, although this varies among different groups. As Altman states: "One of the reasons that the perception of AIDS has been so closely linked to gay men is that no other affected group has comparable political will and resources to deal with the issue" (1986, p. 39).

Drug users have no resources to deal with the issue and if they did, the illegality of their activities and their very addiction would make them unlikely to organize. The Haitian community also lacks resources, and in any case, in the past tended to use whatever resources and status they had to deny that they were at risk. Prostitutes, by the nature of their profession, also find it difficult to organize and to be perceived as a credible voice. However, in the last few years some steps have been made in this direction in order to argue for the removal of prostitution from the Criminal Code of Canada. Ironically, their failure to effect Criminal Code changes may make it even more difficult for them to congregate in order to discuss issues affecting them, and thus their risk of contracting the AIDS virus may be increased.

In relative terms, the gay community is the least marginal. It has large numbers in some locales, it has the skills and resources, and it has organization upon which to build. As Altman (1986, p. 39) suggests, however, the need and competence with which the gay community has organized itself against the disease only serves to reinforce the perception of AIDS as connected with homosexuality. Other factors, such as the early detection of AIDS in only homosexual men, the U.S. concentration on the epidemiology of the disease, the tendency of the media and the New Right to promote the association of the disease with homosexuals by referring to it as "the gay plague," the homophobia in general of Western society, the large proportion of cases among homosexual or bisexual men, and the historical context within which the disease occurred all served to further label the disease as primarily a "gay" issue. Not until less marginal members of the general population, which included children, hemophiliacs, recipients of blood transfusions, and the partners of bisexual men and drug users began to contract the virus did it become recognized as a general public-health issue.

For example, it was not until the fall of 1990 that the Canadian government began to focus on the effects of AIDS on women, producing a widely distributed discussion paper. This discussion paper stated that "a comprehensive prevention strategy which effectively addresses all populations whose behaviours place them at risk of infection is necessary, and the prevention for women will be a key part of the strategy" (1990, p. i).

The New Right

AIDS came to the public's attention at the same time as the New Right was gaining increasing political power. Control of sexuality has always been a dominant theme of the right, which believes that medical technology (birth control and cures for syphilis and gonorrhea) has served to free our sexuality from the moral agents of social control. They blame sexual liberation for massive social problems such as family breakdown, teen pregnancies, and disease; and thus advocate for a return to traditional values (i.e., sex for procreation and only within marriage) and punitive social controls to enforce these values.

While at times the New Right's agenda has seemed badly out of step, it cannot be dismissed. From time to time, it has had the power to appeal to the latent guilt that even the most liberal carry, which is predicated on the historical meanings we have attached to both sexuality and disease.

The New Right, because homosexuality violates its value system, promotes homophobia, playing on the general population's suspicions of those who are different. The spokespersons of the movement, already associating homosexuality with numerous signs of social decay, were quick to seize upon the appearance of AIDS as further proof of their position. They have resurrected the language and meanings associated with religion as the agent of social control, and directed it at homosexuals. In so doing they have added to the public's tendency to associate the disease with gayness rather than with health practices.

Examples of the New Right's determination to combine religious and medical meanings to provoke hatred of homosexuals abound. Both Altman (1986) and Patton (1985) cite numerous American examples. For example, Altman quotes a Nevada minister as saying: "I think we should do what the Bible says and cut their [homosexuals'] throats" (1986, p. 68). As an example of the strength of morality even among some professionals themselves, Altman quotes from an article by Dr. James Fletcher in the *Southern Medical Journal*:

> A logical conclusion is that AIDS is a self-inflicted disorder for the majority of those who suffer from it. For again, without placing reproach upon certain Haitians or hemophiliacs, we see homosexual men reaping not only expected consequences of sexual promiscuity, suffering even as promiscuous heterosexuals the usual venereal diseases, but other consequences as well.
>
> Perhaps, then, homosexuality is not "alternative" behaviour at all, but as the ancient wisdom of the Bible states, most certainly pathologic. Indeed from an empirical medical perspective alone, current scientific observation seems to require the conclusion that homosexuality is a pathologic condition (1986, p. 66).

In Canada in 1987, the *Regina Leader Post* allowed Reverend John Bergen regular paid advertising which promoted hatred of homosexuality and linked this lifestyle to AIDS. The New Right took its campaign door-to-door and for the first time in many years specifically anti-homosexual literature was being distributed to households in a major Saskatchewan city. REAL Women of Canada distributed a pamphlet targeting homosexuals as promoters of AIDS that stated:

> The new findings on AIDS have destroyed the idea that the "gay rights" movement doesn't injur [sic] anyone, and that what they do is their "own business." Homosexuals are a medical threat to their own sex, to those who require blood transfusions, to the promiscuous and their unknowing spouses.

The effect of the New Right's rhetoric has been to burden the disease with even more symbolic baggage to ensure it is firmly anchored as a homosexual rather than as a health issue.

Their appeals have also served to fuel both fears and hatred at a time when political will, the ability to be non-judgmental in the development of public-education programs, and rationality are needed. The urgency of the need for programs is underscored by the World Health Organization which projects the number of HIV-infected people will at best triple and at worst quadruple in eight year's time in the absence of a vaccine or aggressive national programs that do not shrink from the public health challenge of AIDS prevention (CCDR, January 17, 1992).

The public's reaction to the need for education on this health issue, as distinct from their reaction to the need for education to combat the issue of teen pregnancy, has been ironic in light of the right-wing conservative agenda. While on the one hand, there are numerous examples of the power of the right to blame the victims of the disease and to label it as punishment for immorality and promiscuousness, on the other hand, the disease and the nature of its prevention is wresting away the control that the right previously exercised to deny young people access to birth control and explicit information on sexuality.

While the fight continues, it would appear that explicit discussion of sexual practices and information on condoms will be mandated in school programs by many provinces. Those concerned about teen pregnancy have fought for many years to have schools provide information on birth control methods, but success has been minimal. It now appears that AIDS is providing the impetus for dissemination of this information, and education will go beyond the classroom to widespread media campaigns, although this has been slow to happen in Canada.

Making available to the general public reliable information on AIDS prevention is, at face value, a positive step. Although by denying our young people access to information, we have exposed them to unwanted pregnancies, those who have the power in most provinces are not willing to similarly deny specific information about sex, drug use, and alternative lifestyles to those engaged in sex outside of marriage, when the consequences may entail death.

Just how positive this move is will likely be measured by the extent to which "safer sex" education can be integrated into a broader program of education on sexuality. Standing alone, this education runs the risk of entrenching fear and hatred of homosexuality and of promoting anti-sex attitudes. To the extent that sex becomes increasingly associated with death, it may in the end support the New Right's ethics after all.

Summary and Conclusions

Previous sections of this chapter have discussed some of the reasons for the medical profession's inability to bring the definition of AIDS firmly under its control. What, then, are the implications? Medicalizing a social problem such as alcoholism works to hold the moralists and the state at bay. Defining alcoholism as an illness removes blame from individuals and means that treatment and rehabilitation rather than jail or damnation are the preferred ways of controlling alcoholic behaviour. There is, however, no effective treatment or cure for AIDS. The blaming of specific marginal groups for the spread of AIDS supports the view that the "medicalization of deviance" has not occurred with this disease.

Since the late 1980s AIDS has received increased public attention. This has made it somewhat easier to follow the power struggle for control over the meaning of AIDS, although the media themselves play a major role by controlling information. It is clear that moral leaders, the state, and the medical profession are all vying for position with regard to control of the disease and its meanings. At present, morality seems to have the upper hand, probably because frightened societies tend to seek scapegoats onto which to project their anxieties. In *AIDS and Its Metaphors*, Susan Sontag notes:

> . . . AIDS is understood in a premodern way, as a disease incurred by people both as individuals and as members of "risk groups: — that neutral-sounding, bureaucratic category which also revives the archaic idea of a tainted community that illness has judged.

Scapegoats are almost always marginal groups of one kind or another. In this case it is the gay male community that has been blamed for propagating the epidemic, despite the fact that in many African countries males and females are equally affected.

Fear of the disease will continue in the face of the expanding number of cases and the lack of a cure. Both of these will work against the dominance of the medical profession's perspectives and its ability to give the humanitarian protection of the sick role.

Of course, we all need to be concerned about AIDS, but we can react to disease on the basis of scientific and medical facts, or we can react with fears that create community and social tensions and that ultimately compound the effects of the disease itself. Because the meaning of and, therefore, our reactions to AIDS are not firmly established, moral leaders, the state, and the medical profession will all continue to interact to define the general public's view of the disease.

Not only will the dominant agents of social control vie amongst themselves for power, but also within themselves. The law (state) usually operates in one of two ways. The first is to protect the sick from discrimination, thereby entrenching the sick role. If the state decides to protect those with AIDS rather than holding them responsible for the disease, we will likely see more anti-discrimination laws enacted[3] as well as court interpretations of human rights codes and the Canadian Charter of Rights to include protection to those with AIDS.

If, on the other hand, the state chooses to ignore individuals rights in favour of protecting the public's health, we will see a number of punitive measures such as antibody testing as a marriage requirement, exclusion of HIV-positive children and teachers from schools, jailing of prostitutes who have tested HIV-positive and, as authors such as Hancock and Carim (1986) have suggested, quarantine. These authors quote Ben Schatz, the lawyer who heads the National Gay Rights Advocates in the United States, and who posits the extreme case:

> I wouldn't rule out the possibility of concentration camps for gays in America. One would like to think that such things would not be possible because this is the 20th century but, on the other hand, the most gross violations of human rights have occurred in the 20th century. The fact is that once fear gets hold of people, it's very hard to shake it. (1986, p. 185)

The physician as official designator of the sick role can also take on one of two functions. The first is a gatekeeping function that usually works to exempt the sick from school or jobs without penalty. Because AIDS victims are the subject of such widespread discrimination due to fear and misunderstandings, this role is presently being exercised to allow inclusion rather than exclusion. For example, Saskatchewan's *Guidelines for Schools and Day Care Services* states:

> Infection with AIDS should not prevent a person from being employed or working in a school except as determined by the personal physician and MHO (Medical Health Officer) in consultation with the individual. In cases where employment is a health risk to the school population as determined by the personal physician and MHO, the MHO will advise the Director of Education (p. 4).

While the physician's function is often to protect the sick, she or he can also become an agent of society rather than of sick individuals. This is the more likely role in times of fear. If AIDS becomes defined as a public-health problem requiring radical intervention, the physician will undoubtedly become the agent of the state, determining who should be segregated from the rest of society and the nature of the segregation environment.

Present overtones of sexual morality and judgement mask the fact that AIDS is an illness and work against the ability of major institutions to offer the protection of the sick role. These overtones also work against useful prevention strategies and tend to promote control strategies. It is essential in preventing the transmission of the HIV virus that sexual practices be altered. According to Health and Welfare Canada:

> AIDS is essentially a sexually transmitted disease (STD), which like other STDs can also be transmitted through blood and perinatally. Its control, therefore, poses the challenge of informing, educating and supporting sexually active people to protect themselves from HIV infection — either by remaining in mutually faithful relationships with other people, or by practising "safe sex," that is, sex not involving oral, vaginal, or anal intercourse, or sexual intercourse that is consistently and properly "protected" with a condom. No matter how culturally or politically difficult it may be to carry out such education and provide necessary support services, such as condom supply and efficient treatment of other STDs (which if untreated facilitate the transmission of HIV) it cannot be put off (January 17, 1992, p. 4).

Those who are well deserve education; those who are sick deserve protection. AIDS offers us the chance to measure the degree to which we are an "enlightened" humanitarian society. One cannot truly capture the personal experiences and suffering of those who are ill with AIDS, nor of those who have lost family members or friends. The disease will ultimately heighten the vulnerability of those at risk and those suffering from the disease, or else it will cause more firmly entrenched civil rights protections for them. Those with power will decide.

Notes

1. The retrovirus that is believed to be the cause of AIDS has been known by a variety of names. It is referred to in the literature as LAV (lymphadenophathy-associated virus) and HTLV-III (human T-cell lymphotropic virus type III) and LAV/HTLV-III (a combined abbreviation). The *Canada Diseases Weekly Report*, in its September 13, 1986 publication, reports that the Executive Committee of the International Committee on Taxonomy of Viruses endorsed the term "human immunodeficiency virus" or HIV and recommended that it be used to replace the other designations. The name HIV is now used by the *Canada Diseases Weekly Report* and in all World Health Organization's publications and documents.

2. The Diagnostic and Statistical Manual of Mental Disorders (DSM) is the official classification of psychiatric disorders of the American Psychiatric Association. In DSM-I (1952), homosexuality was defined as a form of sexual deviation under the category of "Sociopathic Personality Disturbance." DSM-II (1968), still defines homosexuality as a sexual deviation but it was changed to fall within the general category of "Personality Disorders and Certain Other Non-Psychotic Mental Disorders." The DSM-III (1980) was changed as a result of a referendum of APA in 1974, and homosexuality became defined as "Homosexual-Conflict Disorder" (Conrad & Schneider, 1980, pp. 193, 208-209).

3. According to Leonard (1985, p. 30), Los Angeles and West Hollywood, California have enacted local ordinances expressly prohibiting discrimination in employing persons with AIDS unless the employer can show that absence of AIDS is a bona fide occupational qualification.

Study Questions

1. To what extent does the media's discussion of AIDS contribute to the stigmatizing of those who have the disease?
2. Are there other health issues that the medical profession has been less than successful in bringing under its control? What are some of the reasons for its lack of success?
3. Are there any examples you know of AIDS, or AIDS antibody tests being used to discriminate against risk groups or sick individuals?
4. Do you think that insurance companies have the right to deny coverage go those with sero-positive blood or those who are homosexual? What factors are likely to motivate their decision?
5. What are some of the potential implications of applying the Charter of Rights to those who are afflicted with AIDS?

Recommended Reading

Altman, D. (1986). *AIDS in the mind of America*. New York: Anchor Press/Doubleday.

AMA Management Briefing. (1985). *AIDS: The workplace issues*. New York: AMA Membership Publications Division.

Bayer, R. (1989). *Private acts, social consequences*. New York: The Free Press.

Conrad, P., & Schneider, J.W. (1980). *Deviance and medicalization: From badness to sickness*. St. Louis: C.V. Mosby.

Patton, C. (1985). *Sex and germs*. Boston: South End Press.

Sontag, S. (1989). *AIDS and its metaphors*. Markham: Penguin Books.

References

Adams, M.L. (1986, September). Politics, women and AIDS. *Horizons*, 4, (9), 21-23.

Altman, D. (1986). *AIDS in the mind of America*. New York: Anchor Press/Doubleday.

Conrad, P., & Schneider, J.W. (1980). *Deviance and medicalization: From badness to sickness*. St. Louis: C.V. Mosby.

Gagnon, J.H. (1977). *Human sexualities*. Glenview: Scott, Foresman and Co.

Hancock, G., & Carim, E. (1986). AIDS: *The deadly epidemic*. London: Victor Gollancz.

Health and Welfare. (1986). *AIDS in Canada: What you should know*. (Cat. no. H46-121). Ottawa: Author

Health and Welfare. (1986, September 13). *Canada diseases weekly report*, 12, (37). Ottawa: Author.

Health and Welfare. (1987, January 10). *Canada diseases weekly report*, 13, (1). Ottawa: Author.

Health and Welfare. (1990, September 5). *Women and AIDS: An issue for Canada in the nineties*. (A discussion paper). Ottawa: Federal Centre for AIDS, Bureau of Information and Education Services, Health and Welfare.

Health and Welfare. (1991, February). *AIDS in the 1990s: The new facts of life*. (pamphlet). Ottawa: Author.

Health and Welfare. (1992, January 17). *Canada communicable disease report*, 18, (1). Ottawa: Author.

Health and Welfare. (1992, March 13). *Canada communicable disease report*, 18, (5). Ottawa: Author.

Illich, I. (1976). *Limits to medicine: Medical nemesis, the expropriation of health*. Toronto: McClelland & Stewart.

Katchadourian, H.A., & Lunde, D.T. (1975). *Fundamentals of human sexuality*. Holt, Rinehart & Winston.

Leonard, A.S. (1985). The legal issues. In *AIDS: The workplace issues* (pp. 28-46). New York: AMA Membership Publications Division.

Mass, L. (1985). Medical answers about AIDS. In *AIDS: The workplace issues* (pp. 55-76). New York: AMA Membership Publications Division.

New human retroviruses: One causes AIDS. (1986, April). *Nature*, 320, (3), 325.

Parent, G. (1985). *The AIDS phenomenon: A medical mystery*. Toronto: Toronto Sun Publishing Corporation.

Parsons, T. (1951). *The social system*. New York: Free Press.

Patton, C. (1985). *Sex and germs*. Boston: South End Press.

REAL Women of Canada. (no date). *Laws protecting homosexuals on "sexual orientation" legislation*. Toronto: Author.

Saskatchewan Advisory Committee on AIDS. (no date). *Information on AIDS: Guidelines for schools and day care services.* (pamphlet).

Sontag, S. (1978). *Illness as metaphor.* Markham: Penguin Books.

Sontag, S. (1989). *AIDS and its metaphors.* Markham: Penguin Books.

United States. Department of Health and Human Services, Centers for Disease Control. (1987). *Morbidity and mortality weekly report*, 36, 1-15S.

United States. Department of Health and Human Services, Centers for Disease Control. (1991, November 15). *1992 revised classification system for HIV infection and expanded AIDS surveillance case definition for adolescents and adults.* (Draft).

World Health Organization. (1990). *Weekly epidemiology record*, 65, (49).

Zola, I.K. (1972, November). Medicine as an institution of social control. *The Sociological Review*, 487-504.

Chapter 36

Ethics in Health Care
in Canada

Janet Storch, University of Calgary

Introduction

There is little doubt that ethics in health care has attracted widespread attention from academic scholars, practising health professionals, and from the public. Although attention to ethical issues has always been part of the education and practice of health professionals, these issues have become increasingly problematic (Oleson, 1989). The conception of the sick role and its demands as described by Talcott Parsons (1951) has influenced scholarly thinking and professional and lay practice for several decades. But these traditional patterns of health-care practice and socially defined ways of seeking and responding to care are being seriously challenged.

In addition, advances in medical technology and increasing levels of complexity in the delivery of health services have given rise to profound questions about the limits to treatment; the ability to ensure equitable access to care and treatment; the appropriate scope of health care itself (i.e., what types of services reasonably fall under the umbrella of health care); the appropriate approach to the new reproductive technologies, genetic engineering and genetic counselling, organ transplants, and behaviour modification; and the degree of respect for the autonomy of individuals in health care. All these issues involve personal and professional values, as well as relationships in health-care settings and in society. All, therefore, are questions involving ethics of and ethics in health care.

Some of these questions relate to the spectacular and long-standing ethical "life and death" issues of health care, such as abortion and euthanasia. Other questions are about everyday occurrences in health care, such as ensuring patients receive information and understand the treatment to which they are consenting; ensuring patient privacy is respected; and ensuring that confidentiality is maintained. These latter concerns are not spectacular issues in health care, but they are the situations in which violations of ethical conduct frequently occur, either due to inattention, lack of awareness, or traditional paternalistic practices.

In this chapter health-care ethics will be discussed, including reference to both the "spectacular" and "non-spectacular issues" involved. Care will be taken to identify Canadian initiatives in addressing many of these important issues. Beginning with aspects of clinical treatment (with a particular focus on ethical issues at the beginning and end of life), attention will next focus on the ethics involved in day-to-day health-care delivery, and on broader issues of health-care delivery, such as questions involving resource allocation. Finally, emerging structures and processes to address problems of ethics in health care will be discussed.

Clinical Issues

In the realm of clinical practice, two issues that have commanded attention over time have been abortion and euthanasia. Religious bodies have taken positions on these issues, professional codes of ethics since time immemorial have addressed these issues, and the public has debated these issues often in the forum of the court. Much discussion in and out of the courts has focussed on problems of definition, for example, refinements of the stage of fetal development, differentiation between active and passive euthanasia, and other debatable definitions. In Canada, in January 1988, the section on abortion was struck from the Criminal Code of Canada by a decision of the Supreme Court of Canada in R v. Morgentaler, thereby eliminating abortion from a criminal action in the law (LRC, 1989), and in 1989 a new section was proposed that has not yet been enacted. In Canada, euthanasia is not a legally accepted practice, and the Law Reform Commission of Canada (1983) recommended against decriminalizing voluntary active euthanasia in any form. However, despite the relatively clear legal status of these processes, the frequency with which both these issues involving the sanctity and the quality of human life resurface, implies that they are far from settled issues from a social and moral perspective. Further, the substance of these debates often takes on a different focus, either as newer technologies develop, or as more radical ways of thinking permeate health care.

Euthanasia or Cessation of Treatment?

In the debate about euthanasia, distinctions between passive and active euthanasia still prevail. Passive euthanasia has been commonly defined as withholding treatment to allow someone to die; active euthanasia as deliberately bringing about the early death of another with the intent of assisting that other to have a good, usually less painful death. While these general understandings still prevail, the delineation of when treatment might sensibly be discontinued has become even less distinct with technological advances in medical care. Even the definition of death has become problematic with the introduction of respirators and cardiac stimulators, since cessation of respiration and heartbeat can no longer be distinguished from mechanical stimulation. The Harvard Criteria for the Determination of Death, developed in the United States in 1968 (Ufford, 1980), were advanced as one way to deal with the increasing medical uncertainty of the determination and pronouncement of death. In that same year, the Canadian Medical Association (1968) adopted criteria similar to the Harvard definition and criteria. In 1981, the Law Reform Commission of Canada developed a document on the criteria for determination of death, which eventually led to subsequent modification of legislation to accommodate the new criteria, with the hope that some of the concerns surrounding the determination of death from a medical and legal perspective would be alleviated.

Increasingly problematic in Canada is a section of the the Criminal Code which states that "everyone who undertakes to do an act is under a legal duty to do so if an omission to do the act may be dangerous to life" (Pocket Criminal Code, 1989, p.128). Because this section seems to compel physicians to treat, several hospitals began the development of "Do Not Resuscitate" policies in an attempt to protect patients from further loss of dignity by the prolongation of life for legal reasons only, and to protect health professionals from legal liability should they determine that further treatment by resuscitation would be medically useless. This action eventually led to agreement by four major professional bodies in Canada (the Canadian Medical Association, the Canadian Hospital Association, the Canadian Nurses' Association, and the Canadian Bar Association) to a common Canadian guideline. In 1983, the Law Reform Commission of Canada recommended that nothing in the various sections of the Criminal Code should be interpreted as requiring a physician "to continue to administer to or undertake medical treatment against the clearly expressed wishes of the person for whom the treatment is intended" or "to continue to administer or to undertake medical treatment, when such treatment is medically useless and is not in the best interests of the person for whom it is intended, except in accordance with the clearly expressed wishes of this person for whom it is intended" (LRC, 1983, p. 32). The commission also addressed the problem of pain relief in palliative care by recommending that nothing in the Criminal Code should be "interpreted as preventing a physician from undertaking or obliging him to cease administering appropriate palliative care intended to eliminate or to relieve the suffering of a person, for the sole reason that such care or measures are likely to shorten the life expectancy of this person" (LRC, 1983, p. 35).

Yet the problems of stopping treatment continue to manifest themselves in different clinical areas. At one time, the terms "ordinary" and "extraordinary" care had meaning, with the Catholic Church declaring that extraordinary care was not required, thereby sanctioning withholding or withdrawing such treatments. In 1957, the Pope expressed the view that a physician was morally obliged to use only ordinary means to preserve life and health, that is, means that do not involve serious inconvenience for the patient. Ordinary care was taken to involve those treatments that would be considered standard medical care, while extraordinary treatment referred to procedures that were heroic and not within the current standard of care and treatment for a particular condition. But those distinctions have become blurred, as is apparent in the debate about the ethics of withholding food and fluids. At what point would administration of food and fluids be extraordinary? — if administered by nasogastric tube? by gastrostomy? parenteral nutrition? When might individuals in a persistent vegetative state (those unable to perform basic functions unaided and who have no apparent ability to relate to their environment), sustained only by tube feedings, be allowed to die (starve to death or dehydrate) by withholding that which keeps them alive? The United States court cases involving two young women in a persistent vegetative state have had a significant effect upon sensitivity to this issue. Karen Quinlan was sustained by a respirator that was eventually removed with court permission, but she continued to breathe for several years following. Nancy Cruzan was sustained by tube feedings and, after a bitter struggle, her parents received permission to discontinue tube feedings. She died five days later (Colby, 1990; Allsopp, 1992). In Canada, in November, 1991 the Quebec case of Nancy B., a young paralyzed woman seeking an injunction to turn off her respirator became newsworthy, raising again a fervoured debate about whether acceding to her wishes constituted euthanasia or whether it was clearly a case of responding to her expressed wishes. The anxiety created by the release of a book by Derek Humphrey (1991) entitled *The Final Exit*, which describes ways to commit suicide and was intended for patients who are facing a prolonged and painful dying, is adequate testimony to the unsettling nature of this issue of dying in or out of the health-care system. Choosing to die challenges Parson's sick-role concept by the patient's choice not to get well and by removing the authority for decision-making from the physician. As Ivan Illich (1975) noted, physicians have played the role of umpire in the game of life, determining when patients are free to leave the game. Choosing to die, in a society where life can be extended, also challenges Western societal values about the sanctity of life.

Quality of Life

A critical value conflict relates to the elusive nature of quality of life and to the centrality of patient autonomy. The most troublesome aspect of quality of life lies in its ambiguity and in determining who can adequately make a quality of life assessment (Molzahn, 1990). In many instances, health professionals may take a position that a particular patient's quality of life is poor, leading to a conclusion that death is preferable. But perceptions of quality of life can be highly individual. If one has been disabled since birth, that individual's assessment of a life worth living is likely to deviate markedly from an assessment by an individual formerly robust and healthy, but now incapacitated. Implementation of poorly defined quality of life assessments also have the potential to be most detrimental to the elderly, a group already devalued in Western society, by providing an excuse to treat less extensively, or to shorten life by withholding treatment.

This same concern about quality of life assessment is at the heart of the debate about sustaining the life of very low birth weight babies (whose assessment counts? the parents? the physicians?), and it has crept into the substance of the abortion controversy, as for example, when a woman believes that she would be unable to provide a good quality of life for her child. In a different manner, quality of life has been used as the impetus for the development of newer ways in which previously infertile individuals and others desiring offspring can conceive children. In this case, the argument is in favour of broadening the definition of health care to include services that enhance reproductive capacity because, from the perspective of some, having children is seen to be important to health, happiness, and quality of life.

New Reproductive Technologies

The drive to procreate has lead to the development of techniques to assist infertile couples and, more recently, single women to conceive offspring. As enhanced capacity to diagnose causes of infertility expanded, new solutions were developed to counter-act reproductive disorders (CMA, 1991). Each "solution" has added new ethical dimensions to the already existing plethora of ethical issues surrounding reproduction. For example, the development of drugs to increase fertility has often led to the production of multiple fetuses. Frequently, there is a need to reduce the number of fetuses to preserve the life of other fetuses or simply to reduce the number of viable children produced. Also, Artificial Insemination by Donor (AID) and Artificial Insemination by Homolgous Donor (AIH) procedures have lead to numerous legal and ethical dilemmas concerning confidentiality of donors versus the child's right/need to know its parentage; the value bias in selection of donors versus the need to choose healthy knowledgeable donors (the argument for excessive use of medical students); the risk factors in freezing human sperm versus the need to have suitable sperm available for the procedure; and the need for regulation of the frequency of one donor's sperm to prevent future sibling intermarriage with potential genetic weakness. The development of In Vitro Fertilization (IVF) not only renewed the ethical concern about fetal safety due to medical intervention, but also raised moral issues surrounding the destruction of unused fertilized ova; regulation of the multiple possibilities of parentage of the child; and the efficacy of the technique itself, given the physical and mental pain experienced by the woman when the success rate remains so minimal. The development of AID, AIH, and IVF procedures has also led to questioning of the social and ethical acceptability of surrogate motherhood.

Because of these remarkable developments in reproductive technology, health professionals, patients, and the public are experiencing considerable uncertainty in a largely uncharted area of ethics. Some physicians and health professionals have decided to simply accept these new developments as scientific progress while others debate the morality of the issues at stake. This stance would not be typical of most health professionals who agonize over the decisions to be made and seek to find ways to arrive at acceptable solutions to the ethical dilemmas involved. Because of the manifold questions of ethics raised by these new reproductive technologies (NRTs), the federal government in Canada established a Royal Commission on New Reproductive Technologies in 1990 to examine and make recommendations on these issues. Given the hugeness of its task, the commission required an extension to its deadlines.

Organ Donation

Organ donation for organ transplantation, another relatively recent medical advance, continues to raise numerous ethical concerns. Among these are the ethics of attaching human beings declared dead to a ventilator for the purposes of sustaining their organs and tissues in a state suitable for transplant; the ethics of buying and selling organs for transplant; the ethics of consent to transplant without full knowledge of long term consequences of the procedure itself or the effects of drugs necessary for transplant procedures; and the ethics of parents giving consent for their children to be used for the purposes of bone marrow transplant to sustain the life of a sibling. A related concern is the ethics surrounding the harvesting of organs from anencephalic infants. The status of the personhood of the infant, the criteria for determining death when there is not a functioning brain, and the justification for rationalizing the use of one infant for the good of another, are all extremely volatile ethical issues. More recently, the chance of therapeutic benefit for patients suffering from Parkinson's disease through implantation of fetal tissue has raised specific concerns about the potential for couples to choose conception for the sole purpose of producing fetal tissue through an early abortion. At least two major concerns surface in this experimentation verging on innovative therapy: a concern for the sanctity of human life and a concern about the "slippery slope" phenomenon (e.g., that many women might conceive and deliberately abort to provide homologous tissue for a relative with Parkinson's disease) (Vawter & Gervais, 1991).

The significance and the complexity of these clinical issues cannot be over-emphasized. Many of these issues challenge the most precious values of Canadian society. And as Canada becomes increasingly multicultural, the task of arriving at shared social and ethical values becomes an enormous challenge. What is morally right and what is morally wrong have never been more clouded.

Everday Issues of Care

In this section, the ethical behaviour of caregivers will be discussed, including the impact of the patient rights movement on turning the attention of health professionals to ethical issues, such as respect for patient autonomy, and issues of balancing benefits with harms. These issues necessarily involve consideration of the patient's rights versus the health professional's rights, as for example, in the treatment of patients with the disease of autoimmune deficiency syndrome (AIDS).

Issues of Autonomy

By law, an individual of sound mind has the right to determine what shall happen with his or her body. In medical care, this is the doctrine of informed consent by which physicians and other health professionals are required to obtain the patient's consent before proceeding with a diagnostic procedure or with treatment. Although the law is fairly straightforward on this issue, the mechanics of ensuring there is proper consent to treatment are enormous and have very little to do with the "consent form," which is too often viewed as an end in itself rather than as a means to an end.

To be informed, a patient must be given information about a particular procedure in such a way that it is understandable and meaningful. The person being diagnosed or treated must also be able to weigh the advantages and disadvantages of having the procedure and must be able to arrive at his or her own conclusions about whether to proceed or not to proceed to be diagnosed or treated. The legal standard of consent to treatment in Canada is demanding. According to the Supreme Court of Canada case of Riebl v. Hughes in 1980, the physician must understand the patient well enough to know what risks the patient would consider relevant to the decision as well as be able to provide sufficient information about the range of medical risks involved in the proce-dure (Storch, 1982).

It is one thing to give information and another to present it in such a way that it is meaningful and comprehensible. Beauchamp and Childress (1989) describe the process of consent from an ethical perspective as involving the individual with a capacity (competence) to decide and to be fully able to receive and understand information about the treatment. In practice, there is wide room for violation in consent process. Hospitals and clinics (where most invasive treatments are carried out) are busy places, not well attuned to allowing time for patients to hear, to consider, or to understand. Patients are usually in a vulnerable position, by reason of their illness, their fear, and their discomfort in a foreign environment. They are, therefore, not always able to hear or to assimilate information provided, and few patients feel confident enough to disagree with a recommended diagnosis or treatment, particularly in a situation requiring prompt action on the part of the health professional. Further, the continued knowledge gap or the intimidation of the authority of the physician often prevents patients from questioning or admitting to limited comprehension of the information. Nurses are among the health professionals who find themselves in situations where the patient's inadequate understanding about a procedure is evident. Because patients are frequently less intimidated by nurses, and because nurses are with the patient on a more constant basis than physicians, patients are more inclined to share their concerns and their doubts with nurses. Nurses are then left with a choice of re-explaining the procedure (considered in some settings to be an inappropriate and perhaps an illegal action for the nurse), or calling a physician back to the unit to explain the procedure to the patient again. Given the fast pace of activity in most health-care settings and the hierarchial system of hospitals, neither of these choices are particularly easy ones for the nurse to make or to execute.

Doing Good and Minimizing Harms

Violations of patient autonomy can also occur because the patient may be labelled incompetent when she or he is not. Until recently, the habit of proceeding with a recommended treatment over the patient's wishes was often justified on the grounds of the patient's incompetency to make key decisions. Assessment of competency is complex and often overlooked is the fact that individuals may be competent to make decisions in one area of life, but not in other areas. The fact that a family member may serve as trustee or have power of attorney over a patient's financial affairs does not automatically mean this same patient is unable to make decisions about his or her care and treatment. Partly due to oversight, and partly due to uncertainty in difficult cases, overriding patient wishes where an individual has been deemed to be incompetent in financial or property matters is far more common that one would assume. Assessment of competency must include attention both to cognition and to psychological well-being (Freedman, Stuss, & Gordon, 1991).

In all health-care settings, competency is an important issue, but it has become most critical in cases where patients are refusing treatment, or where there could be potential abuse of individuals socially and physically disadvantaged. In acute-care settings, competency to make decisions about care and treatment generally focusses around a limited set of critical events. In rehabilitation settings, assessment of the degree of competency to consent to treatment can become a daily issue. Physiotherapists and occupational therapists frequently struggle with assessment of competency and may determine that there is a need to overrule a patient's immediate wishes for that patient's longer-term gain. A common example of this practice occurs in the care and treatment of individuals who have recently sustained serious motor vehicle injury. If the injuries are likely to be permanently handicapping, such as in cases where permanent paralysis is likely, patients may request that no further treatment or rehabilitation be provided. Therapists may ignore these wishes, justifying their paternalistic actions on the patient's depression, a normal occurrence following severe injury. The balancing of harms and benefits is difficult for most caregivers in rehabilitation settings, as it is for those providing care for residents in long-term care (Haas, Caplan, & Callahan, 1988). When does the overriding of wishes become a violation, and when is it appropriate beneficent paternalism?

Similar dilemmas arise in the care and treatment of children. Each province in Canada has slightly different legislation governing the age at which children can consent to treatment. But the legal and moral standard of consent remains that the person be able to comprehend the nature of the treatment and the risks and benefits involved. Again, children are frequently ignored in decision making about their care even when they have the capacity to make choices.

One of the ethical dilemmas of health care causing a re-evaluation of the health professional's duty to the patient is the advent of the disease of AIDS. Codes of ethics have traditionally contained a clause upholding the professional's primary duty to be to the patient. With the spread of AIDS, the risk of providing care is perceived to involve substantial risk to the caregiver despite evidence to the contrary (Inions, 1989). Some have cautioned that separation of the issue of risk from the issue of prejudice is critical to determining the obligation of the health professional (Fowler, 1988). Fowler has noted that the duty of care is conditioned by both the risk of harm to the patient and the risk of harm to the professional with an ideal of service informing one's practice as impartial, courageous, and compassionate. Although the issue of risk to the professional is not new (having surfaced in almost every life-threatening epidemic and in other disease such as leprosy), the panic surrounding AIDS is somewhat new and likely indicative of an attitude by some health professionals in this decade becoming more sensitized to their individual rights and less concerned about their duty of beneficence.

Approaches to Ethical Decision Making

To address the concerns about finding the appropriate, morally justifiable balance between providing benefit to the patient while attempting to minimize the potential harms, a number of mechanisms have been developed. Most of these involve ways of providing for decision making in as objective and systematic a manner as possible. In some cases, these approaches take the form of proxy decision makers for the patient, in others the process involved is one of substituted judgement, whereby an individual attempts to decide about care and treatment as if he or she were the patient. This judgement involves taking into account the patient's values and expressed wishes and attempting to make decisions in keeping with those expressions.

One emerging approach to substitute decision making in Canada is evident in the renewed attention to the provision of "living wills" — essentially a statement about the individual's wishes when dying (Alberta, 1991). The individual specifies to what extent he or she wishes to be treated by "heroic" measures in order to sustain life, or to what extent the individual wishes to be allowed to die free of medical treatment, except for supportive care and comfort measures. Problems arise if the "will" is too broad and too general to enable the health professional to understand what the patient had intended. To that end, some physicians have been involved in developing more detailed "will" protocols which would indicate the measures the patient wished to decline (Kelly, Elphick, Mepham, & Molloy, 1989). Given that the "living will" is intended to serve as a means of better communication between the physician/health professional and the patient, the intrusion of lawyers into this arena is considered somewhat worrisome. As with the document of consent to treatment, the living will must be understood as a means of written communication between the patient and the health-care team. Otherwise, the purpose of the document becomes distorted and only adds to difficult communication in health care, with increased potential for harm to the patient.

Another means to enhance decision making to benefit the patient is the mechanism of the ethics committee. Ethics committees have been defined as "any committee that is primarily involved in ethical issues regarding patient care." A survey completed in 1989 indicated a substantial growth in the number of ethics committees in hospitals in Canada, with the majority of committees involved in a consultation function to consider difficult ethical dilemmas arising in patient care (Storch, Griener, Marshall, & Olineck, 1990; Storch, & Griener, 1992). These committees are also involved in the development of policy addressing ethical problems, and the education of hospital staff on ethical issues.

Codes of ethics have served as a long-standing mechanism to improve decision making in health care on matters of ethical concern. Most health professionals have such codes, and most codes have been subject to substantial revision during the past decade to be relevant to the broadening field of health care ethics. While codes cannot address all issues, nor provide complete guidance necessary to address the complexity of issues, they do serve a noteworthy role in providing a standard for ethical behaviour, and in facilitating greater sensitivity to ethical issues. One recently revised code of ethics divides ethical problems in health care into three main areas: ethical violations, ethical dilemmas, and ethical distress (Canadian Nurses' Association, 1991). Each type of problem is seen to require a different form of guidance and direction for appropriate personal and professional behaviour.

Many hospitals and health agencies have also developed statements of philosophy towards patient care to provide an additional form of guidance for the behavior of health professionals. This type of guidance is most apparent in the religious hospitals, where statements of philosophy of care are seen to emphasize the uniqueness of the religious hospitals. The *Health Care Ethics Guide* of the Catholic Healthcare Association of Canada (1991) is one example of a collective statement designed to identify the orientation of the Catholic health facility.

Justice and the Allocation of Health Resources

There is little question that the health-care system has grown to become a major medical establishment (Relman, 1980). There is also little question that the growth in size and complexity of health systems in the Western world presents significant problems for economic viability. From a language of health management that focussed primarily on expansion of services with no limits to the possibilities for medical advance, a new language of down-sizing (otherwise known as right-sizing) and examining the appropriate limits of medicine is gradually becoming the norm (Callahan, 1990).

The immensity of economic needs to sustain the current system in Canada has paved the way for profound debate about sensible approaches to the provision of health services, to numerous government studies of provincial systems of care, and to suggestions of reducing benefits in Canadian medicare with convenient charges of patient abuse to justify removal of services (Evans, Barer, & Hertzman, 1991). One set of voices reminding the health establishment that we are responsible for encouraging patient use of the system and that we ourselves have accepted few limits to our modes of practice (Jecker, 1991), is not often heard or acknowledged.

Beginning in the mid-1940s, Canadians gradually developed the framework for a Canadian health-care system based upon values of equity. The belief that all persons should have access to required medical care and hospital services was enshrined in the legislation introducing hospital insurance and medical care in Canada in 1957 and 1967 respectively. The right to health care was further emphasized in the Canada Health Act of 1984 amidst bitter disputes about the physician's right to independence versus the citizen's rights to access to care (Taylor, 1987).

Within the economic climate of Canada during the 1990s, one force preserving Canadian medicare might be the admiration some Americans exhibit towards Canada's health-care system. Yet, despite its relative equity, the just allocation of health-care resources is subject to serious challenge.

Decisions about the allocation of health-care resources occur at different levels of government. At a national level, the federal government has limited authority to direct health priorities in a direct way, but has been highly successful in influencing provincial agendas, at least until the late 1980s. With the reduction of Established Program Funding (EPF) to the provinces, this influence is likely to diminish to a substantial degree with some concern about the continued viability of a national health insurance system with common parameters. Nevertheless, the federal government has continued its attempts to influence health care by developing numerous documents, for example, those emphasizing health promotion, and encouraging greater attention to lifestyle and the environmental factors that affect health.

Provincial governments determine programs and funding mechanisms, with many health ministries now developing complex formulas for funding, largely based on acuity of care. While lip service and some funding is available for home-care services, the majority of health-care resources continue to be concentrated on high-tech care with continued funding of transplant programs and cardiac surgeries, and substantial attention to treatment of cancers and other life-threatening illnesses. This focus often leaves few resources for simple techniques that serve a preventive function, such as in hypertension, prenatal care, and other preventive modalities, or for ongoing care for chronic conditions.

Summary and Conclusions

Although some ethical issues tend to continually "catch the headlines" in health care, taking ethics in health care seriously often results in seeing problems where we previously saw none. Thus, even some of the more mundane issues of health care, such as those involving greater attention to patient autonomy and patient choice have become serious concerns. Attention to these issues, in turn, has lead to a re-examination of the proper relationships between thephysician/health professional and the patient.

The more spectacular ethical issues in health care continue to be unsettled as beliefs about sanctity of life, quality of life, and appropriate medical interventions elicit polarized value positions. The less spectacular issues in health care remain troublesome as the needs of health professionals, health institutions, government funding formulas, and patients often are in conflict.

Attention to improved ethical decision making by all those involved in health care has never been greater. Improving existing means of ethics education for health professionals, existing ethics committees, and existing guidelines for ethical decision making while developing new and better ways to monitor and correct ethical violations, to resolve ethical dilemmas, and to relieve ethical distress should command the commitment of all health professionals, the public, government officials, and politicians.

Study Questions

1. How does the vocabulary of "ordinary" and "extraordinary" care become problematic in making decisions about treatment at the end of life?
2. To what extent is quality of life a value judgment? Is quality of life measurable?
3. Is Talcott Parson's "sick role" congruent with the principles of consent to treatment? If not, where are the incongruencies?
4. What sociological impediments might be inherent in the structure and function of ethics committees?
5. Is equity possible in Canadian health care? Is it desirable? Why or why not?

Recommended Reading

Callahan, D. (1990). *What kind of life: The limits to medical progress*. Toronto: Simon & Schuster.

Canadian Medical Association. (1991). *New reproductive technologies*. Ottawa: Canadian Medical Association.

Jecker, N.S. (1991). Knowing when to stop: The limits of medicine. *Hastings Center Report*, 21, (3), 35-38.

Law Reform Commission. (1989). *Crimes against the foetus*. Working Paper 58. Ottawa: Author.

Dougherty, C.J. (1991). Setting health care priorities: Oregon's next steps. *Hastings Center Report*, 21, (3), 1-16.

Storch, J.L. (1982). *Patients' rights: Ethical and legal issues in health care and in nursing*. Toronto: McGraw-Hill.

References

Alberta Law Reform Institute. (1991). *Advance directives and substitute decision-making in personal health care*. Edmonton: Author.

Allsopp, E. (1992). From Quinlan to Cruzan: Patterns in the fabric of US "Right-to-Die" case law. *Humane Medicine*, 8, (2), 122-131.

Beauchamp, T.L., & Childress, J.F. (1980). *Principles of biomedical ethics* (3rd ed.). New York: Oxford University Press.

Callahan, D. (1990). *What kind of life: The limits to medical progress*. Toronto: Simon & Schuster.

Canadian Medical Association Statement on Death. (1968, December 28). *Canadian Medical Association Journal*, 99, 1266-1267.

Canadian Medical Association. (1991). *New human reproductive technologies*. Ottawa: Author.

Canadian Nurses' Association. (1991). *Code of ethics for nursing*. Ottawa: Author.

Catholic Health Association. (1991). *Health care ethics guide*. Ottawa: Author.

Do Not Resuscitate Policy. (1981, October 15). *Canadian Medical Association*, 125, 835.

Fowler Marsh, D.M. (1988). AIDS and refusal to provide care. *Heart and Lung*, 17, (2), 15-18.

Freedman, M., Stuss, D.T., & Gordon, M. (1991). Assessment of competency: The role of neurobehavioral deficits. *Annals of Internal Medicine*, 115, 203-208.

Humphrey, D. (1991). *Final exit*. Eugene: The Hemlock Society.

Illich, I. (1975). *Medical nemesis: The expropriation of health*. London: Calder & Boyars.

Inions, N. (1989). The right of physicians to refuse versus the obligation of physicians to treat AIDS patients. *Healthcare Management Forum*, 2, (2), 24-30.

Jecker, N.S. (1991). Knowing when to stop: The limits of medicine. *Hastings Centre Report*, 21, (3), 5-8.

Kearney, W., Vawter, D.E., & Gervais, K.G. (1991). Fetal tissue research and the misread compromise. *Hastings Centre Report*, 21, (5), 7-12.

Kelly, J.L., Elphick, G., Mepham, V., & Molloy, D.W. (1989). *Let me decide*. Hamilton: Hamilton Civic Hospitals.

Law Reform Commission of Canada. (1981). *Criteria for the determination of death*. Report Number 15. Ottawa: Author.

Law Reform Commission of Canada. (1983). *Euthanasia, aiding suicide and cessation of treatment*. Report Number 20. Ottawa: Author.

Law Reform Commission of Canada. (1989). *Crimes against the foetus*. Working Paper 58. Ottawa: Author.

Oleson, V.L. (1989). Caregiving, ethical and informal: Emerging challenges in the sociology of health and illness. *Journal of Health and Social Behavior*, 30, 1-10.

Parsons, T. (1951). *The social system*. New York: The Free Press.

Relman, A.S. (1980). The new medical industrial complex. *New England Journal of Medicine*, 303, (17), 963-970.

Rodrigues, G.P. (1989). *Pocket criminal code*. Toronto: Carswell.

Storch, J.L., Griener, G.G., Marshal, D., & Olineck, B.A. (1990). Ethics committees in Canadian hospitals: Report of the 1989 survey. *Healthcare Management Forum*, 3, (4), 3-8.

Taylor, M.G. (1987). *Health insurance and Canadian public policy*. Montreal: McGill-Queen's University Press.

Ufford, M.R. (1980). Brain death/termination of heroic efforts to save life — Who decides? *Specialty Law Digest*, 10, 5-39.

Part Eleven

Sociology, Health, Illness, and the Health-Care System

Chapter 37

Sociology, Health, Illness, and the Health-Care System: Current Issues and Future Prospects

Harley D. Dickinson and B. Singh Bolaria,
University of Saskatchewan

Introduction

When medicare was established in the post–World War II period it was widely hoped that it would eliminate the financial barriers to the receipt of necessary hospital and medical care services faced by many low income people and by so doing contribute to an improvement in the overall health status of the population. To an extent this happened. Of course, the elimination of financial barriers to the use of hospital and medical care services resulted in increased utilization rates and consequently increased health care costs. Indeed, it is estimated that total health expenditures in Canada in 1991 were $66.7 billion, up from $12.3 billion in 1975 (Health Information Division, 1993).

This level of expenditure has led many to claim that health care costs in Canada are unsustainable and that they must be reduced. The hoped for improvement in health status that ushered in medicare, although it may have occurred, has also resulted in the rise to prominence of a range of chronic and degenerative health problems for which our existing hospital-centred and medically dominated health care system is inadequate. It has also been demonstrated that although financial barriers to health care services are one factor that impede access to necessary services, there are other social, cultural, and hidden economic costs that result in continued inequities, both in access to health care services and in health status. Concerns about rising costs and inefficient and ineffective expenditures of health care dollars are also fueled by demographic projections which show an increasing percentage of elderly people, typically high users of health care resources.

Thus, despite the many successes of the Canadian health care system, there are also a number of problem areas and concerns that policy makers are currently attempting to address. To this end, a health promotion framework has been proposed as the means to reform the nature and organization of health care in Canada (Lalonde, 1974; Epp, 1986).

Although there is disagreement over what health promotion means in practical terms, there is general agreement concerning the broad category of factors that influence health status, the distribution of injury and illness, and the need for health care services. These were identified by Lalonde (1974) as human genetics, lifestyles, the environment, and the health care system. Changes in these areas are thought to have consequences, both intended and unintended, for health and illness status and for utilization patterns and costs of health care services.

One development in the area of genetics that is thought by many to have profound medical and social consequences is the Human Genome Project, which has as its general objective the identification and location, or mapping, of all the genes in the human genome. This project, which began in the United States in the late 1980s, was originally sponsored by the National Institutes of Health and the Department of Energy (Kevles, 1993, p. 22). Since that time it has become a massive international collaborative effort, involving many nations, including Canada. The genes being mapped first are those associated with various abnormalities. It is thought to be only a matter of time, however, before the entire genetic make-up of human beings is known and mapped.

Related to the Human Genome Project are the new reproductive technologies. Whereas the new genetics is intended to produce knowledge about the nature and quality of the human embryo, the new reproductive technologies are concerned with the creation of human embryos. As Burstyn (1993, p. 64) points out, the new reproductive techniques are "handmaids to the genetic technologies, for without them the human embryo would not be open to judgement and available for genetic manipulation."

Despite the real promise of these two bodies of knowledge and associated technologies coming together to bring babies to the childless and to prevent much unnecessary suffering as a result of the identification of genetic defects and their prevention through therapeutic abortion or other techniques, many see a darker side to this new frontier of human knowledge. Specifically, concerns have been expressed over the possibility that the new reproductive technologies and the new genetics might give rise to a neo-eugenics movement.

The original eugenics movement developed in the nineteenth century as an effort to apply the principles of plant and animal breeding to human populations. Eugenicists thought that various aspects of modern social life and government policy were contributing to the social and racial degeneration of society by encouraging the breeding of socially undesirable elements and discouraging the breeding among those with socially desirable characteristics. Eugenicists proposed to correct this "problem," either by encouraging those with desirable qualities, usually the white middle and upper classes, to bear more children, and/or by discouraging or preventing those who were deemed to be dysgenic from bearing or raising children. These interrelated objectives are known as positive and negative eugenics.

Negative eugenics was predominant. In its most brutal manifestation, it took the form of genocide and other attempts to exterminate problem populations in Nazi Germany. Although the Nazi atrocities in the name of eugenics and science are often explained away as an historical aberration that could not happen again, eugenical policies involving compulsory sterilization, especially of those considered mentally ill and "feebleminded," were enacted throughout much of the Western World, including some Canadian provinces (McLaren, 1990). It is increasingly being argued that although the brutality of the Nazi application of genetic and medical science to its populations was exceptional in its magnitude, it was not absolutely aberrant, but rather an extreme example of the application of normal science. If this is so, critics warn, it could happen again.

In the past, programs of positive eugenics were much more limited than those of negative eugenics, largely due to lack of knowledge and technical ability. The promise and threat of the new genetics, in combination with the new reproductive technologies, is that it is now possible to selectively produce embryos through such technologies as pharmaceutically induced ovulation, sperm and egg manipulation, surgical insemination, Petri dish insemination, embryo transfer, embryo banking, and so on (Burstyn, 1993, p. 64). Critics warn that these new technologies have the potential of enabling a new eugenics movement that has the could be more effective in achieving its goals of social development and racial purity than was previously possible.

Even if one doesn't share concerns about the possibility of a new eugenics movement, a host of ethical, social, and legal issues arise given the potential of these new technologies to enable human reproduction in ways that historically have never been possible. The institutions of society have not been developed and they currently may not be equipped to solve the problems that this new knowledge and these new technologies may potentially generate. The magnitude of the potential consequences of the further development and application of this knowledge has resulted in the striking of a Canadian Royal Commission on the New Reproductive Technologies, which has been surrounded in conflict and controversy since its inception. The long-awaited release of its report is expected to intensify debate and struggle. It is clear that this is an area that requires further study.

Individuals' lifestyles are also seen as important factors in increasing or decreasing health risks and presumably health status. The decisions individuals make concerning diet, exercise, sexual behaviour, drinking habits, tobacco use, and so on are all seen to be important factors affecting one's health. Considerable resources have been directed toward trying to persuade people to maximize healthy choices and minimize unhealthy choices. We have all been exposed to a barrage of information on safe sex, drinking and driving, smoking, exercise, diet, and a multitude of other behaviours thought to have health consequences. At the same time as the government and various voluntary agencies are trying to get us to make healthy choices, of course, we are bombarded by another set of messages from commercial interests intent on persuading us to consume a plethora of dangerous and potentially health-and environment-destroying products, such as automobiles, high-fat fast foods, alcohol, and tobacco to name a few. It has been suggested that these economically motivated "manufacturers of illness" are largely responsible for many of the unhealthy habits that are the object of recent health promotion campaigns (McKinlay, 1981).

Although there is a certain self-evident truth to the claims of the purveyors of healthy lifestyles, it has been pointed out by many that such an approach to the issues of health and illness tends to individualize the problems and the solutions. Many are unable to choose healthy lifestyles because of the social, economic, and political structures that constrain their opportunities and give shape to their conditions of existence. Without recognition of this fact, entreaties to choose healthy lifestyles apparently fall on deaf ears. This often results in the assessment of people who persist in unhealthy lifestyles as stupid, self destructive, or both. Whatever the explanation, such people are seen to be personally responsible for their poor health.

Victim blaming of this sort is also often used as a rationale for rationing access to publicly financed health care services; that is, if individuals insist on living unhealthy lives, they should not expect taxpayers to pick up the bill for resultant health care services. In the context of vigorous efforts to reduce health care costs, attacks like these on the principle of universality may gain increased support and endorsement. Research into public attitudes concerning such issues will be both timely and important.

The issue of lifestyles, as we have suggested above, must be placed in the context of both the social and physical environments within which individuals live their lives. This is one of the primary insights of sociology. An important, and arguably the most important aspect of the social environment, is the economy, including the nature and organization of work. Research into the effects of changes to the forms of employment and new technologies for worker health and safety are issues requiring additional study.

On the other hand, in these times of globalization and capital restructuring the health effects of unemployment and underemployment are increasingly important. Also relevant to the economic component of the social environment is the issue of the manufacture and marketing or distribution of various products. This point is clearly made in relation to recent revelations about the distribution and use of blood tainted with the HIV virus.

The relationship between social environment, the physical environment, and health also promises to be an area of increasing importance. It appears that current economic and military practices have the potential to result in ecological disasters of unprecedented proportions. The disposal of nuclear wastes, clear-cut logging, oil spills, and other forms of environmental pollution may have profound consequences for human morbidity and mortality patterns. Indeed, some are predicting that unless there are major changes to the ways we use and abuse the physical environment, it may become incapable of sustaining life as we know it.

Another area of research for medical sociologists and an area of social life that is seen as directly affecting health is the nature and organization of the health care system. Although it may well be the case that health care professionals are at least partly motivated by altruism and a genuine desire to help others, they are also at least partly motivated by self interests and professional concerns, including the terms and conditions of their work and the form and level of their remuneration.

It is becoming increasingly clear that a potential conflict of interests exists between health care service providers and consumers. A growing patients'/consumers' rights movement that is willing and able to develop effective advocacy organizations and to use various legal channels to pursue their interests is resulting in substantial and significant changes in relations between health care providers and health care consumers. Increased numbers of malpractice suits and widespread concerns about sexual misconduct are indicative of some of these changes.

The dominating issue facing the existing health care system is restructuring and downsizing. The health promotion policy framework being developed and applied across the country has as an explicit objective — the reduction of costs and the reallocation of health care resources. What this will ultimately mean for the health care system is unknown at this time, although there is mounting pressure from several sources for the abandonment of the principle of universality.

Moves in that direction have already been taken in a number of provinces in the form of caps or restrictions placed on the number and types of health care services that individuals can receive under medicare. This, of course, is a form of rationing of health care services. Those who can afford private insurance, or who can pay directly for health care services can and will. Those most negatively affected by the erosion of universality are the poor. As we have seen, poverty and ill health go hand in hand. Consequently, rationing health care services as a means to cut costs has the effect of reducing access to necessary services for those with the greatest need.

Moves to ration health care services as a means of managing the fiscal crisis of the state are also related to various efforts to privatize the provision of health care. Proponents of privatization were very vocal in the 1980s, claiming that government operated and financed services of any kind were inherently inefficient compared to those owned and operated on a private, for-profit basis. There is no evidence that this is true. In fact, the evidence with regard to health care appears to show the opposite. As a result, there has been an apparent reduction in the decibel level of the calls for privatization. This hush is also related to the fact that public opinion polls show that medicare is still one of the most popular government programs. Indeed, for many Canadians medicare, and the principles upon which it is founded, are seen as definitive of Canadian national identity — something that distinguishes us from and makes us better than Americans.

Given the emotional and political support for medicare among Canadians, politicians and policy makers are somewhat hesitant to be seen as threatening its vitality or existence. Consequently, few are willing to openly recommend the dismantling of our medical care insurance system. Indeed, most proposals for change are presented as improvements to that which exists or reforms necessitated by fiscal exigencies. Despite the stated intentions, the consequences in many cases are the same — an erosion of the health care system as we know it. Whether the new system that emerges in the wake of the reform efforts currently underway will be better or worse than that which we have remains to be seen. Research into these issues at this time promises to be influential and important.

Sociologists should also undertake research into the relationships between the health care system, current reform, restructuring efforts, and the broader society. We have been told so often, by so many people, that government deficits and mounting debts have created a situation that requires drastic cost cutting and sacrifice by us all, that many accept these as self-evident truths. It is worthwhile to critically examine these "truths." The fact that $67 billion per year is spent on health care, although staggering, is not proof in itself that too much is being spent, or that costs are rising out of control. There is no way that one can determine if too much or too little is being spent simply by looking at absolute dollar amounts. Those decisions are moral and political in nature; they are not purely technical or accounting decisions. Thus, to say that too much is being spent on health care means that one thinks those funds should be spent on something else. Although some people will support the idea that too much is being spent on health care for ideological reasons, that is, because they think it is the right thing to do, often the principle proponents of an idea have real political or economic interests at stake.

With reference to the idea that too much is being spent on health care and that privatization will solve the fiscal crisis, for example, it is readily apparent that there are many political and/or economic advantages for the main advocates of that policy, including private insurance companies, the pharmaceutical industry, other health sector businesses, pro-business political parties and governments, and many doctors. Similarly, it is apparent that there are few benefits for most health care consumers.

Whether defenders of medicare and the principles upon which it stands can successfully organize and mobilize to protect and extend the availability of effective and appropriate health care services remains to be seen. Success in this regard will depend in part on the availability of information and knowledge. The creation and dissemination of such information falls within the domain of sociology.

In an effort to protect something that is generally good and widely popular, we should not be blinded to the shortcomings of medicare and some of its features. We know, for example, that the fee-for-service remuneration system for physician services produces a built in tendency for over servicing. This is because physician incomes are directly related to the number of services provided. This clearly has the potential to encourage unnecessary physician-generated utilization patterns. Research and experimentation with alternative forms of remuneration is warranted and promises to improve the efficiency of our health care system without threatening the principles of universality and accessibility.

The concern has also been expressed that the nature and organization of modern medicine itself contributes to ill health. The issue of iatrogeic, or physician-created illness and injury is a sensitive, but important, topic for investigation (Illich, 1976; Roemer & Schwartz, 1979). Stories about unnecessary surgery and health-threatening drug prescription patterns suggest additional areas for rigorous research.

As has been seen throughout this book, and as we have tried to summarize in this short chapter, sociology can make contributions to our understanding of the nature and social distribution of health, illness, injury, and death, as well as to our understanding of both the internal and external forces shaping the nature and effects of our health care system. Although there may be a number of specific objectives underpinning any individual piece of research or analysis, the ultimate goal is to contribute to the improvement of the health status of the population and to improve the efficiency and effectiveness of our health care system.

The achievement of these goals often entails challenging powerful vested interests and established patterns of thinking and practice. This fact places limits on the pace and extent of reform efforts. Just as socio-economic structures are implicated in morbidity and mortality patterns and are powerful influences on the form and content of the health care system, so too do those same forces influence the extent and effectiveness of reform. It is now apparent, for example, that inequalities of health status cannot be eliminated simply by removing inequalities in access to health care services. So long as class, gender, racial, and other structural forms of inequality persist, there will continue to be inequalities in health status. It is in this sense that health and illness are political, economic, moral, and cultural phenomena, as well as medical problems. By theorizing and analyzing the linkages between the biological base of the human species, lifestyles, the social and physical environments, and the health care system, medical sociologists can make important contributions to both health care and sociology.

References

Burstyn, V. (1993, June). Breeding discontent. *Saturday Night*, 15-17, 62-67.

Health Information Division. (1993). *Health expenditures in Canada, summary report, 1987-1991*. Ottawa: Health and Welfare Canada.

Illich, I. (1976). *The limits to medicine: Medical nemesis, the expropriation of health*. Toronto: McClelland & Stewart.

Kevles, D.J. (1993, Spring). Is the past prologue? Eugenics and the human genome project. *Contention*, 2, (3), 21-37.

McKinlay, J.B. (1981). A case for refocusing upstream: The political economy of illness. In P. Conrad & R. Kerns (Eds.), *The sociology of health and illness: Critical perspectives* (pp. 613-33). New York: St. Martin's Press.

McLaren, A. (1990). *Our own master race: Eugenics in Canada, 1885-1945*. Toronto: McClelland & Stewart.

Roemer, M.I., & Schwartz, J.L. (1979, December). Doctor slow-down: Effects on the population of Los Angeles County. *Social Science and Medicine*, 13C, (4), 213-18.

Reader Reply Card

We are interested in your reaction to *Health, Illness, and Health Care in Canada*, 2/e by B. Singh Bolaria and Harley D. Dickinson. You can help us to improve this book in future editions by completing this questionnaire.

1. What was your reason for using this book?

   ☐ university course   ☐ college course   ☐ continuing education course

   ☐ professional   ☐ personal   ☐ other_____
       development   interest   _____

2. If you are a student, please identify your school and the course in which you used this book.

3. Which chapters or parts of this book did you use? Which did you omit?

4. What did you like best about this book?

5. What did you like least about this book?

6. Please identify any topics you think should be added to future editions.

7. Please add any comments or suggestions.

8. May we contact you for further information?

   Name _____

   Address: _____

   _____

   Phone: _____

(fold here and tape shut)

MAIL ⮞ POSTE
Canada Post Corporation / Société canadienne des postes

Postage paid
If mailed in Canada

Port payé
si posté au Canada

Business Reply

Réponse d'affaires

0116870399   01

0116870399-M8Z4X6-BR01

Heather McWhinney
Publisher, College Division
HARCOURT BRACE & COMPANY, CANADA
55 HORNER AVENUE
TORONTO, ONTARIO
M8Z 9Z9